Contents

In addition to those situated in the main cities, restaurants renowned for their excellent cuisine will be found in the towns printed in light type in the list above.

Dear Reader

With the aim of giving the maximum amount of information in a limited number of pages Michelin has adopted a system of symbols which is renowned the world over.
Failing this system the present publication would run to six volumes.
Judge for yourselves by comparing the descriptive text below with the equivalent extract from the Guide in symbol form.

La Résidence (Paul), 21 32 43, Fax 21 32 49, lake, « Flowered garden », – BX **a**
March-November – **Meals** *(closed Sunday)* 350/650 – 75 – **25 rm** 500/800.
Spec. Goujonnettes de sole, Poulet aux écrevisses, Profiteroles.
Wines. Vouvray, Bourgueil.

This demonstration clearly shows that each entry contains a great deal of information. The symbols are easily learnt and to know them will enable you to understand the Guide and to choose those establishments that you require.

A very comfortable hotel where you will enjoy a pleasant stay and be tempted to prolong your visit.
The excellence of the cuisine, which is personally supervised by the proprietor Mr Paul, is worth a detour on your journey.
The hotel is in a quiet secluded setting, away from built-up areas.
To reserve phone 21 32 43 ; the Fax number is 21 32 49.
The hotel affords a fine view of the lake ; in good weather it is possible to eat out of doors. The hotel is enhanced by an attractive flowered garden and has an indoor swimming pool and a private tennis court.
Smoking is not allowed in certain areas of the hotel.
Direct dialling telephone in room.
Parking facilities, under cover, are available to hotel guests.
The hotel accepts payment by American Express, Eurocard and Japan Credit Bureau credit cards.
Letters giving the location of the hotel on the town plan : BX **a**.
The hotel is open from March to November but the restaurant closes every Sunday.
The set meal prices range from 350 F for the lowest to 650 F for the highest.
The cost of continental breakfast served in the bedroom is 75 F.
25 bedroomed hotel. The charges vary from 500 F for a single to 800 F for the best double or twin bedded room.
Included for the gourmet are some culinary specialities, recommended by the hotelier : Strips of deep-fried sole fillets, Chicken with crayfish, Choux pastry balls filled with ice cream and covered with chocolate sauce. In addition to the best quality wines you will find many of the local wines worth sampling : Vouvray, Bourgueil.

This revised edition from
Michelin Tyre Company's Tourism Department
offers you a selection of
hotels and restaurants in the main European cities.
The latter have been chosen for
their business or tourist interest.

In addition the guide indicates establishments,
located in other towns,
renowned for the excellence of their cuisine.

We hope that the guide will help you
with your choice of hotel or restaurant
and prove useful for your sightseeing.
Have an enjoyable stay.

Hotels, Restaurants

Categories, standard of comfort

🏨🏨🏨🏨🏨	XXXXX	*Luxury in the traditional style*
🏨🏨🏨🏨	XXXX	*Top class comfort*
🏨🏨🏨	XXX	*Very comfortable*
🏨🏨	XX	*Comfortable*
🏨	X	*Quite comfortable*
M		*In its class, hotel with modern amenities*

Atmosphere and setting

🏨🏨🏨🏨🏨 ... 🏨	*Pleasant hotels*
XXXXX ... X	*Pleasant restaurants*
« Park »	*Particularly attractive feature*
🐦	*Very quiet or quiet secluded hotel*
🐦	*Quiet hotel*
< sea, ✳	*Exceptional view, Panoramic view*
<	*Interesting or extensive view*

Cuisine

✿✿✿	*Exceptional cuisine in the country, worth a special journey*
✿✿	*Excellent cooking : worth a detour*
✿	*A very good restaurant in its category*
Meals	*Other recommended carefully prepared meals*

Hotel facilities

30 rm	*Number of rooms*
	Lift (elevator) – Television in room
	Non-smoking areas
	Air conditioning
	Telephone in room: direct dialling for outside calls
	Telephone in room: outside calls connected by operator
	Tennis court(s) – Outdoor or indoor swimming pool
	Sauna – Exercise room
	Garden – Beach with bathing facilities
	Meals served in garden or on terrace
P	*Garage – Car park*
	Bedrooms accessible to disabled people
150	*Equipped conference room : maximum capacity*
	Dogs are not allowed
without rest.	*The hotel has no restaurant*

Prices

These prices are given in the currency of the country in question. Valid for 1996 the rates shown should only vary if the cost of living changes to any great extent.

Meals

Meals 130/260	*Set meal prices*
Meals a la carte 160/290	*"a la carte" meal prices*
b.i.	*House wine included*
	Table wine available by the carafe

Hotels

30 rm 305/500	*Lowest price for a comfortable single and highest price for the best double room.*
30 rm 345/580	*Price includes breakfast*

Breakfast

55	*Price of breakfast*

Credit cards

AE GB JCB VISA	*Credit cards accepted*

Service and Taxes

Except in Finland, Greece and Spain, prices shown are inclusive, that is to say service and V.A.T. included. In the U.K. and Ireland, s = service only included, t = V.A.T. only included. In Italy, when not included, a percentage for service is shown after the meal prices, eg. (16 %).

Town Plans

Main conventional signs

Tourist Information Centre
Hotel, restaurant – Reference letter on the town plan
Place of interest and its main entrance } *Reference letter on*
Interesting church or chapel } *the town plan*
Thiers (R.) *Shopping street – Public car park*
Tram
Underground station
One-way street
Church or chapel
Poste restante, telegraph – Telephone
Public buildings located by letters:
POL T M *Police (in large towns police headquaters) – Theatre – Museum*
Coach station – Airport – Hospital – Covered market
Ruins – Monument, statue – Fountain
Garden, park, wood – Cemetery, Jewish cemetery
Outdoor or indoor swimming pool – Racecourse – Golf course
Cable-car – Funicular
Sports ground, stadium – View – Panorama

Names shown on the street plans are in the language of the country to conform to local signposting.

Sights

★★★ *Worth a journey*
★★ *Worth a detour*
★ *Interesting*

Avec cette nouvelle édition,
les Services de Tourisme du Pneu Michelin
vous proposent une sélection
d'hôtels et restaurants
des principales villes d'Europe,
choisies en raison de leur vocation
internationale
sur le plan des affaires et du tourisme.

Vous y trouverez également les grandes tables
situées hors de ces grandes villes.

Nous vous souhaitons d'agréables séjours
et espérons que ce guide vous aidera
utilement
pour le choix d'un hôtel,
d'une bonne table
et pour la visite des principales curiosités.

Hôtels, Restaurants

Classe et confort

		Grand luxe et tradition
		Grand confort
		Très confortable
		Bon confort
		Assez confortable
M		*Dans sa catégorie, hôtel d'équipement moderne*

L'agrément

...	*Hôtels agréables*
...	*Restaurants agréables*
« Park »	*Élément particulièrement agréable*
	Hôtel très tranquille, ou isolé et tranquille
	Hôtel tranquille
sea,	*Vue exceptionnelle, panorama*
	Vue intéressante ou étendue

La table

	Une des meilleures tables du pays, vaut le voyage
	Table excellente, mérite un détour
	Une très bonne table dans sa catégorie
Meals	*Autre table soignée*

L'installation

30 rm	*Nombre de chambres*
	Ascenseur – Télévision dans la chambre
	Non-fumeurs
	Air conditionné
	Téléphone dans la chambre direct avec l'extérieur
	Téléphone dans la chambre relié par standard
	Tennis – Piscine : de plein air ou couverte
	Sauna – Salle de remise en forme
	Jardin – Plage aménagée
	Repas servis au jardin ou en terrasse
	Garage – Parc à voitures
	Chambres accessibles aux handicapés physiques
150	*Salles de conférences : capacité maximum*
	Accès interdit aux chiens
without rest.	*L'hôtel n'a pas de restaurant*

Les prix

Les prix sont indiqués dans la monnaie du pays. Établis pour l'année 1996, ils ne doivent être modifiés que si le coût de la vie subit des variations importantes.

Au restaurant

Meals 130/260	*Prix des repas à prix fixes*
Meals à la carte 160/290	*Prix des repas à la carte*
b.i.	*Boisson comprise*
	Vin de table en carafe

A l'hôtel

30 rm 305/500	*Prix minimum pour une chambre d'une personne et maximum pour la plus belle chambre occupée par deux personnes*
30 rm 345/580	*Prix des chambres petit déjeuner compris*

Petit déjeuner

55	*Prix du petit déjeuner*

Cartes de crédit

AE GB JCB VISA	*Cartes de crédit acceptées*

Service et taxes

A l'exception de la Finlande, de la Grèce et de l'Espagne, les prix indiqués sont nets. Au Royaume Uni et en Irlande, **s** *= service compris,* **t** *= T.V.A. comprise. En Italie, le service est parfois compté en supplément aux prix des repas. Ex. : (16 %).*

Les Plans

Principaux signes conventionnels

Information touristique

Hôtel, restaurant – Lettre les repérant sur le plan

Monument intéressant et entrée principale } *Lettre les repérant sur le plan*

Église ou chapelle intéressante

Thiers (R.) *Rue commerçante – Parc de stationnement public*

Tramway

Station de métro

Sens unique

Église ou chapelle

Poste restante, télégraphe – Téléphone

Édifices publics repérés par des lettres :

POL T M *Police (dans les grandes villes commissariat central) – Théâtre – Musée*

Gare routière – Aéroport – Hôpital – Marché couvert

Ruines – Monument, statue – Fontaine

Jardin, parc, bois – Cimetière, Cimetière israélite

Piscine de plein air, couverte – Hippodrome – Golf

Téléphérique – Funiculaire

Stade – Vue – Panorama

Les indications portées sur les plans sont dans la langue du pays, en conformité avec la dénomination locale.

Les curiosités

★★★ *Vaut le voyage*

★★ *Mérite un détour*

★ *Intéressante*

Mit dieser Neuauflage
präsentieren Ihnen die Michelin-Touristikabteilungen
eine Auswahl von Hotels und Restaurants
in europäischen Hauptstädten
von internationaler Bedeutung
für Geschäftsreisende und Touristen.

Besonders gute Restaurants in der näheren Umgebung
dieser Städte wurden ebenfalls aufgenommen.

Wir wünschen einen angenehmen Aufenthalt
und hoffen, daß Ihnen dieser Führer
bei der Wahl eines Hotels, eines Restaurants
und beim Besuch der Hauptsehenswürdigkeiten
gute Dienste leisten wird.

Hotels, Restaurants

Klasseneinteilung und Komfort

	XXXXX	*Großer Luxus und Tradition*
	XXXX	*Großer Komfort*
	XXX	*Sehr komfortabel*
	XX	*Mit gutem Komfort*
	X	*Mit Standard-Komfort*
M		*Moderne Einrichtung*

Annehmlichkeiten

...	*Angenehme Hotels*
XXXXX ... X	*Angenehme Restaurants*
« Park »	*Besondere Annehmlichkeit*
	Sehr ruhiges oder abgelegenes und ruhiges Hotel
	Ruhiges Hotel
sea,	*Reizvolle Aussicht, Rundblick*
	Interessante oder weite Sicht

Küche

✿✿✿	*Eine der besten Küchen des Landes : eine Reise wert*
✿✿	*Eine hervorragende Küche : verdient einen Umweg*
✿	*Eine sehr gute Küche : verdient Ihre besondere Beachtung*
Meals	*Andere sorgfältig zubereitete Mahlzeiten*

Einrichtung

30 rm	*Anzahl der Zimmer*
	Fahrstuhl – Fernsehen im Zimmer
	Nichtraucher – Klimaanlage
	Zimmertelefon mit direkter Außenverbindung
	Zimmertelefon mit Außenverbindung über Telefonzentrale
	Tennis – Freibad – Hallenbad
	Sauna – Fitneß Center
	Garten – Strandbad
	Garten-, Terrassenrestaurant
	Garage – Parkplatz
	Für Körperbehinderte leicht zugängliche Zimmer
150	*Konferenzräume mit Höchstkapazität*
	Das Mitführen von Hunden ist unerwünscht
without rest.	*Hotel ohne Restaurant*

Die Preise

Die Preise sind in der jeweiligen Landeswährung angegeben. Sie gelten für das Jahr 1996 und können nur geändert werden, wenn die Lebenshaltungskosten starke Veränderungen erfahren.

Im Restaurant

Meals 130/260	*Feste Menupreise*
Meals à la carte 160/290	*Mahlzeiten "a la carte"*
b.i.	*Getränke inbegriffen*
	Preiswerter Tischwein in Karaffen

Im Hotel

30 rm 305/500	*Mindestpreis für ein Einzelzimmer und Höchstpreis für das schönste Doppelzimmer für zwei Personen.*
30 rm 345/580	*Zimmerpreis inkl. Frühstück*

Frühstück

55	*Preis des Frühstücks*

Kreditkarten

AE GB JCB VISA	*Akzeptierte Kreditkarten*

Bedienungsgeld und Gebühren

Mit Ausnahme von Finnland, Griechenland und Spanien sind die angegebenen Preise Inklusivpreise. In den Kapiteln über Großbritannien und Irland bedeutet s = Bedienungsgeld inbegriffen, t = MWSt inbegriffen. In Italien wird für die Bedienung gelegentlich ein Zuschlag zum Preis der Mahlzeit erhoben, zB (16 %).

Stadtpläne

Erklärung der wichtigsten Zeichen

Informationsstelle

a — *Hotel, Restaurant – Referenzbuchstabe auf dem Plan*

Sehenswertes Gebäude mit Haupteingang } *Referenzbuchstabe auf dem Plan*

B — *Sehenswerte Kirche oder Kapelle* } *Referenzbuchstabe auf dem Plan*

Thiers (R.) — *Einkaufsstraße – Öffentlicher Parkplatz, Parkhaus*

Straßenbahn

U-Bahnstation

Einbahnstraße

Kirche oder Kapelle

Postlagernde Sendungen, Telegraph – Telefon

Öffentliche Gebäude, durch Buchstaben gekennzeichnet :

POL T M — *Polizei (in größeren Städten Polizeipräsidium) – Theater – Museum*

Autobusbahnhof – Flughafen

Krankenhaus – Markthalle

Ruine – Denkmal, Statue – Brunnen

Garten, Park, Wald – Friedhof, Jüd. Friedhof

Freibad – Hallenbad – Pferderennbahn –

18 — *Golfplatz und Lochzahl*

Seilschwebebahn – Standseilbahn

Sportplatz – Aussicht – Rundblick

Die Angaben auf den Stadtplänen erfolgen, übereinstimmend mit der örtlichen Beschilderung, in der Landessprache.

Sehenswürdigkeiten

★★★ *Eine Reise wert*

★★ *Verdient einen Umweg*

★ *Sehenswert*

この改訂版ガイドブックはミシュラン・タイヤ社観光部がおとどけするものです。

ビジネスに、観光に、国際的な拠点ヨーロッパ主要都市が誇る自慢のホテルとレストランを、そして郊外にたたずむ名うてのレストランをあわせて、御紹介いたします。

このガイドブックが、より快適なホテル、味わい深いレストランやあこがれの地と出逢うきっかけとなり、皆さまの旅をより素晴らしいものにするお手伝いができれば幸いです。

ホテル　レストラン

等級と快適さ

🏨🏨🏨🏨🏨 XXXXX	豪華で伝統的様式
🏨🏨🏨🏨 XXXX	トップクラス
🏨🏨🏨 XXX	たいへん快適
🏨🏨 XX	快適
🏨 X	割に快適
M	等級内での近代的設備のホテル

居心地

🏨🏨🏨🏨🏨 ... 🏨	居心地よいホテル
XXXXX ... X	居心地よいレストラン
« Park »	特に魅力的な特徴
🐦	大変静かなホテルまたは人里離れた静かなホテル
🐦	静かなホテル
≤ sea ✳	見晴らしがよい展望(例：海)、パノラマ
≤	素晴らしい風景

料理

✿✿✿	最上の料理、出かける価値あり
✿✿	素晴らしい料理、寄り道の価値あり
✿	等級内では大変おいしい料理
Meals	その他の心のこもった料理

設備

30 rm	ルームナンバー
	エレベーター、室内テレビ
	非喫煙室
	空調設備
	室内に電話あり、外線直通
	室内に電話あり、外線は交換台経由
	テニスコート。屋外プール。屋内プール。
	サウナ。トレーニングルーム。
	くつろげる庭。整備された海水浴場
	食事が庭またはテラスでできる。
	駐車場、パーキング。
	体の不自由な方のための設備あり
	会議又は研修会の出来るホテル
	犬の連れ込みおことわり
without rest.	レストランの無いホテル

料金

料金は1996年のその国の貨幣単位で示してありますが、物価の変動などで変わる場合もあります。

レストラン

Meals 130/260 **Meals** à la carte 160/290	**定食、ア・ラ・カルトそれぞれの最低料金と最高料金。**
b.i.	**飲物付**
	デカンター入りテーブルワイン有ります。

ホテル

30 rm 305/500	**一人部屋の最低料金と二人部屋の最高料金。**
30 rm 345/580	**朝食代は含まれています**

朝食

55	**朝食代**

クレジット・カード

クレジット・カード使用可

サービス料と税金

フィンランド、ギリシャ、スペイン以外の国に関しては正価料金。英国及びアイルランドでは、s.：サービス料込み、t.：付加価値税込み、を意味する。イタリアでは、サービス料が料金に加算されることがある。例：（16%）

地図

主な記号

	ツーリストインフォメーション	
□ ⓐ ● ● a	ホテル・レストラン — 地図上での目印番号	
	興味深い歴史的建造物と、その中央入口	地図上での目印番号
B	興味深い教会または聖堂	地図上での目印番号
Thiers (R.) P	商店街　公共駐車場	
	路面電車	
	地下鉄駅	
→ ►	一方通行路	
	教会または聖堂 —局留郵便、電報 —電話	
	公共建造物、記号は下記の通り	
POL T M	警察（大都市では、中央警察書） —劇場 — 美術観、博物館	
	長距離バス発着所 — 空港 — 病院 — 屋内市場	
∴ ■ ◎	遺跡 — 歴史的建造物、像 — 泉	
	庭園、公園、森林 — 墓地 — ユダヤ教の墓地	
9	屋外プール、屋内プール — 競馬場 — ゴルフ場	
	ロープウェイ — ケーブルカー	
	スタジアム — 風景 — パノラマ	

地図上の名称は、地方の標識に合わせてその国の言葉で表記されています。

名所

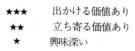

★★★ 出かける価値あり

★★ 立ち寄る価値あり

★ 興味深い

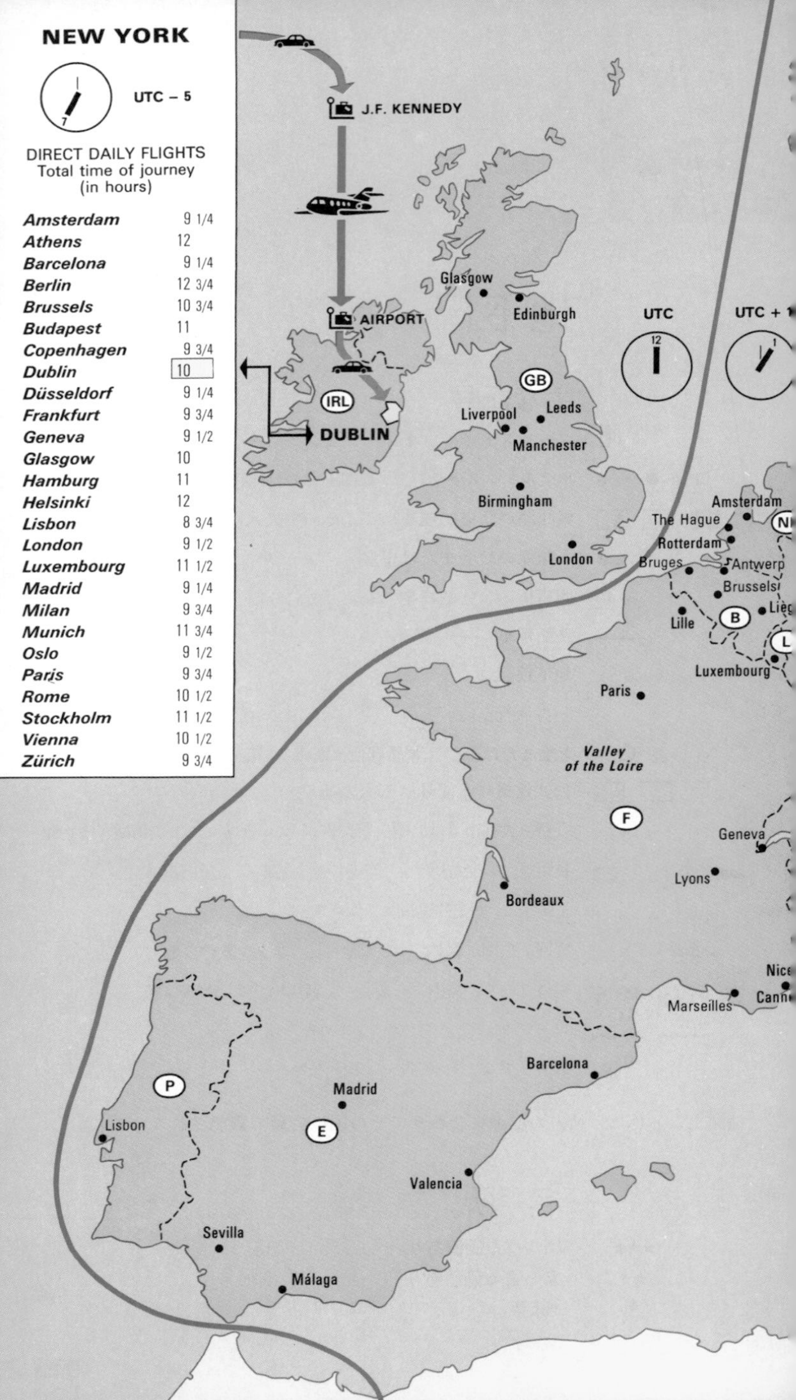

NEW YORK

UTC – 5

DIRECT DAILY FLIGHTS
Total time of journey
(in hours)

Amsterdam	9 1/4
Athens	12
Barcelona	9 1/4
Berlin	12 3/4
Brussels	10 3/4
Budapest	11
Copenhagen	9 3/4
Dublin	10
Düsseldorf	9 1/4
Frankfurt	9 3/4
Geneva	9 1/2
Glasgow	10
Hamburg	11
Helsinki	12
Lisbon	8 3/4
London	9 1/2
Luxembourg	11 1/2
Madrid	9 1/4
Milan	9 3/4
Munich	11 3/4
Oslo	9 1/2
Paris	9 3/4
Rome	10 1/2
Stockholm	11 1/2
Vienna	10 1/2
Zürich	9 3/4

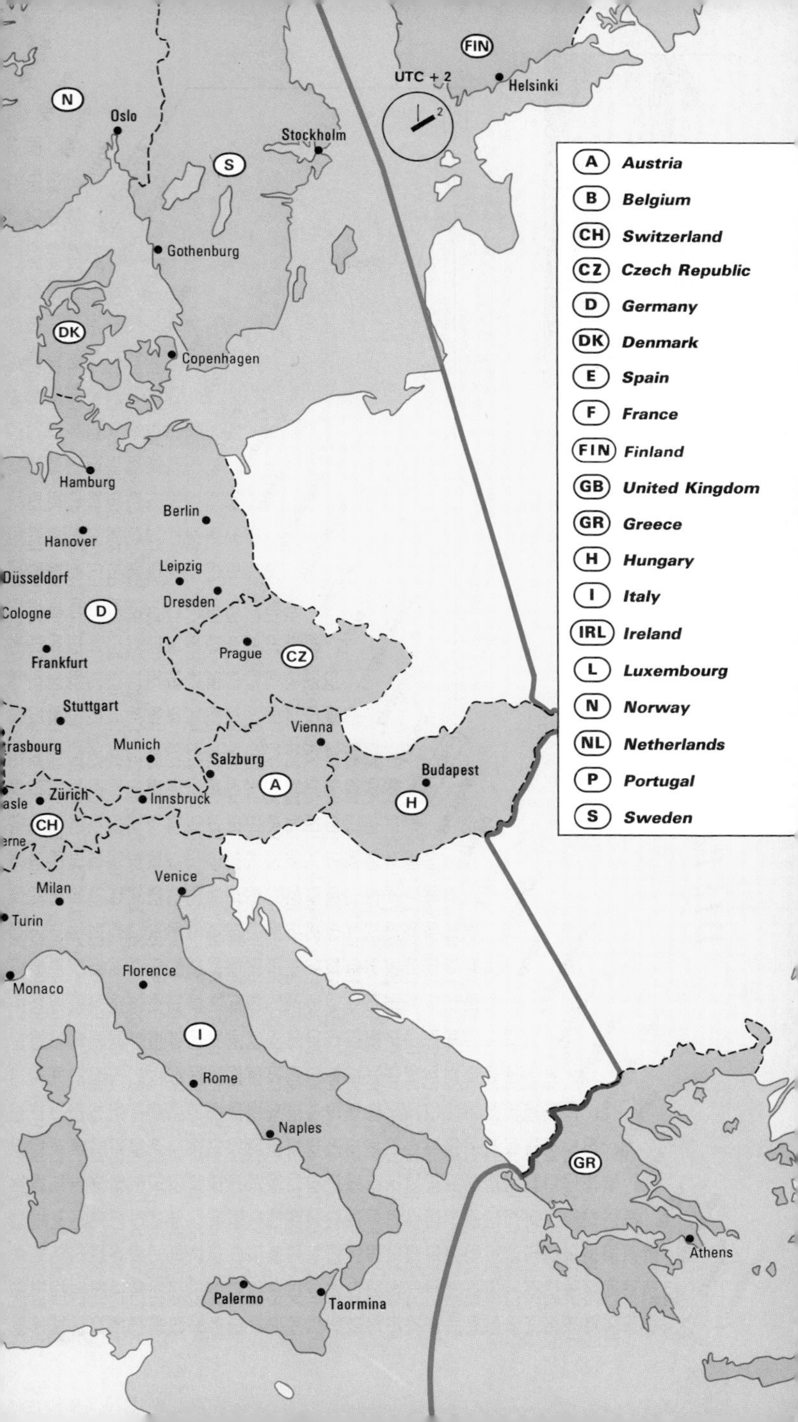
FIN
UTC + 2
2
Helsinki
N
Oslo
Stockholm
S
Gothenburg
DK
Copenhagen
Hamburg
Berlin
Hanover
Leipzig
Düsseldorf
Dresden
Cologne
D
Prague
CZ
Frankfurt
Stuttgart
Vienna
rasbourg
Munich
Salzburg
Budapest
A
asle
Zürich
Innsbruck
H
CH
rne
Venice
Milan
Turin
Monaco
Florence
I
Rome
Naples
GR
Athens
Palermo
Taormina
A Austria
B Belgium
CH Switzerland
CZ Czech Republic
D Germany
DK Denmark
E Spain
F France
FIN Finland
GB United Kingdom
GR Greece
H Hungary
I Italy
IRL Ireland
L Luxembourg
N Norway
NL Netherlands
P Portugal
S Sweden

DISTANCES BY ROAD

(in kilometres)

	Amsterdam	Athens	Barcelona	Berlin	Berne	Bordeaux	Brussels	Budapest	Cologne	Copenhagen	Dublin	Edinburgh	Frankfurt	Geneva	Hamburg	Helsinki	Lisbon	London	Luxembourg	Lyons	Madrid	Manchester	Marseilles	Milan	Munich	Nice	Oslo	Paris	Prague	Rome	Stockholm	Strasbourg	Stuttgart	Venice	Vienna
Athens	2837																																		
Barcelona	1565	3091																																	
Berlin	665	2584	1864																																
Berne	840	3316	926	914																															
Bordeaux	1080	3240	569	1630	847																														
Brussels	207	2793	1360	775	639	893																													
Budapest	1394	1510	1352	883	1873	2041	1350																												
Cologne	256	2579	1362	566	588	1068	211	1136																											
Copenhagen	778	2938	2097	392	1222	1797	897	1293	732																										
Dublin	953	3587	1921	1528	1365	1460	795	2144	1013	1669																									
Edinburgh	1097	3823	2065	1672	1509	1604	938	2380	1157	469	378																								
Frankfurt	440	2396	1330	538	429	1150	399	953	189	799	1201	1345																							
Geneva	915	2446	762	1074	164	683	711	1308	748	1381	1334	1478	588																						
Hamburg	464	2780	1783	284	913	1483	583	1198	418	321	1364	1508	489	1072																					
Helsinki	1205	2540	2389	505	1883	2182	1317	1630	1110	795	2154	2390	1101	1656	776																				
Lisbon	2276	4320	1237	2826	2147	1193	2088	3182	2263	2992	2655	2799	2345	1984	2678	3423																			
London	479	3253	1448	1055	891	986	321	1810	539	1195	468	642	727	860	881	1820	2182																		
Luxembourg	384	2637	1156	768	435	931	214	1165	193	927	1002	1146	237	506	613	1303	2127	528																	
Lyons	932	2560	635	1231	314	536	728	1421	730	1465	1339	1483	697	151	1151	1758	1857	865	523																
Madrid	1772	3761	616	2323	1527	689	1584	2622	1760	2489	2151	2295	1842	1364	2175	2913	621	1678	1622	1236															
Manchester	818	3478	1787	1394	1230	1325	660	2035	878	1534	212	351	1066	1199	1220	2045	2521	333	867	1205	2017														
Marseilles	1245	2622	504	1544	606	653	1041	1483	1043	1778	1652	1796	1010	443	1464	2070	1726	1178	836	315	1105	1517													
Milan	1085	2128	980	1033	314	1129	885	990	833	1424	1610	1754	674	316	1115	1575	2201	1136	679	458	1581	1475	507												
Munich	831	2063	1377	586	434	1408	730	678	580	947	1550	1694	398	594	788	1120	2599	1076	514	744	1979	1415	999	496											
Nice	1404	2434	662	1347	524	812	1199	1296	1148	1739	1810	1954	988	457	1430	1890	1884	1336	994	474	1263	1675	190	319	811										
Oslo	1046	3521	2366	970	1502	2066	1166	1876	1000	556	998	727	1079	1662	592	690	3262	1460	1196	1733	2758	768	2048	1705	1525	2019									
Paris	497	2913	1043	1047	552	581	309	1470	484	1213	876	1020	577	501	899	1605	1777	402	357	461	1274	741	776	845	834	932	1481								
Prague	848	2110	1710	344	761	1604	871	535	655	739	1673	1817	502	920	630	1095	2800	1199	729	1077	2311	1538	1392	871	384	1185	1317	1030							
Rome	1653	2389	1350	1476	882	1500	1453	1251	1401	1837	2178	2322	1242	870	1678	2041	2572	1704	1247	965	1951	2043	878	564	886	690	2415	1399	1274						
Stockholm	1386	3568	2706	1001	1830	2405	1505	1923	1340	586	2286	965	1407	1990	929	165	3601	1800	1536	2073	3098	2151	2388	2032	1556	2347	534	1822	1347	2445					
Strasbourg	595	2438	1129	747	243	1064	426	1053	348	1007	1206	1350	214	402	698	1286	2260	732	221	496	1730	1071	811	488	361	802	1288	490	600	1056	1616				
Stuttgart	600	2302	1229	630	286	1194	516	917	348	968	1336	1480	189	445	658	1166	2390	862	300	595	1830	1201	890	477	220	791	1248	620	477	1045	1576	152			
Venice	1245	1878	1234	1044	567	1384	1138	740	993	1405	1863	2007	856	578	1246	1615	2456	1389	932	720	1835	1728	762	269	454	574	1983	1107	819	523	2013	743	636		
Vienna	1146	1862	1787	635	865	1805	1105	243	895	1030	1907	2051	713	1024	921	924	3009	1433	929	1174	2388	1772	1315	822	394	1127	1608	1231	291	1076	1638	762	617	570	
Zurich	803	2417	1048	832	126	955	629	989	551	1169	1355	1499	392	286	860	1388	2269	881	424	436	1649	1220	730	280	313	594	1450	594	678	848	1777	208	204	533	758

Helsinki – Strasbourg: 1286

AIR LINKS (in hours)

31/2 not daily

	Amsterdam	Athens	Barcelona	Berlin	Berne	Bordeaux	Brussels	Budapest	Cologne	Copenhagen	Dublin	Edinburgh	Frankfurt	Geneva	Hamburg	Helsinki	Lisbon	London	Luxembourg	Lyons	Madrid	Manchester	Marseilles	Milan	Munich	Nice	Oslo	Paris	Prague	Rome	Stockholm	Strasbourg	Stuttgart	Venice	Vienna
Athens	5																																		
Barcelona	33/4	41/2																																	
Berlin	3	8	53/4																																
Berne	31/4																																		
Bordeaux	23/4	9		81/2																															
Brussels	21/2	5	33/4	41/4	31/2	51/2																													
Budapest	4	33/4		31/2			4																												
Cologne		6	51/4	23/4		71/4		33/4																											
Copenhagen	3	5	41/2	4		6	31/4	33/4	41/4																										
Dublin	31/4	8	61/2	51/2		53/4	31/4		51/2	4																									
Edinburgh	33/4	81/2	61/4	6		51/2	43/4		51/4	51/2	23/4																								
Frankfurt	23/4	41/2	33/4	23/4		61/4	23/4	31/2	21/2	31/4	33/4	53/4																							
Geneva	3	41/2	3	41/2	31/2	3	3		41/2	33/4	4	51/2	3																						
Hamburg	23/4	61/2	51/2	21/2		53/4	3	4	23/4	21/2	51/2	61/4	23/4	43/4																					
Helsinki	51/4	91/2	71/2	5		91/4	41/2	41/2	6	31/4	73/4	83/4	41/4	6	33/4																				
Lisbon	41/2	91/2	31/4	71/2			41/2		71/2	51/2	63/4	71/4	43/4	31/4	61/4	8																			
London	23/4	53/4	41/4	7	33/4	33/4	31/4	5	31/2	4	31/4	31/2	31/2	31/2	33/4	51/4	43/4																		
Luxembourg	21/2	61/2	63/4	43/4		61/4	21/4		41/2	43/4	51/2		21/2	4	43/4	53/4	63/4	31/4																	
Lyons	31/2	71/4	3	4		3	31/4		5	4	6	6	31/4		51/2	8	41/4	4																	
Madrid	3	61/4	23/4	61/4		3	4	5	51/2	43/4	4	6	41/4	31/2	6	73/4	23/4	41/4	6	43/4															
Manchester	3	71/4	6	51/2		53/4	3		51/2	33/4	23/4	3	33/4	4	5	71/2	43/4	31/4	53/4	6	41/4														
Marseilles	41/2	53/4	23/4	71/4		23/4	31/2		61/2	51/4	61/4	61/4	41/2	21/2	61/2	83/4	4	4	6	23/4	31/4	53/4													
Milan	3	33/4	31/4	5		51/4	31/4	33/4	41/4	33/4	51/4	61/4	3	21/2	43/4	61/4	51/4	4	43/4	3	33/4	4	3												
Munich	31/4	41/4	33/4	3	21/2	6	3	31/4	23/4	31/4	41/4	61/4	23/4	31/2	3	41/2	61/2	4	41/4	51/4	51/2	51/2	8	23/4											
Nice	31/4	63/4	23/4	61/4		3	3		51/4	4	51/2	61/2	31/4	21/2	51/2	7	4	4	4	23/4	31/4	4	21/4	23/4	3										
Oslo	3	83/4	61/4	41/2		71/4	43/4		63/4	31/2	6	71/2	31/2	51/4	23/4	4	71/4	3	6	53/4	61/2	51/4	7	51/4	5	53/4									
Paris	2	5	31/2	43/4	3	3	23/4	41/4	3	33/4	33/4	5	31/4	3	31/2	5	41/2	31/2	23/4	3	33/4	31/4	3	31/4	31/2	31/4	4								
Prague	31/2	41/2	41/4	3			31/2	31/4	31/2	33/4			3	33/4	33/4	4		41/2	33/4		43/4	51/2		41/4	3			33/4							
Rome	3	33/4	31/2	51/4		81/4	4	4	53/4	41/2	41/4	63/4	33/4	31/2	53/4	71/4	43/4	43/4	33/4	5	41/4	5	3	3	31/2	23/4	61/2	41/4	41/4						
Stockholm	4	61/4	73/4	5		63/4	51/4	61/4	61/2	31/4	7	71/4	4	6	31/2	23/4	91/4	5	63/4	61/2	7	6	73/4	6	53/4	6	23/4	43/4	41/4	7					
Strasbourg	21/2	71/4	63/4			41/2	21/2			53/4	61/2	53/4		23/4		81/4	61/2	41/2		31/4	7	43/4	33/4	23/4		23/4	63/4	3		43/4	81/2				
Stuttgart	33/4	8	33/4	3		8	33/4	31/2	21/2	31/4	51/2	63/4	21/2	33/4	3	61/4	43/4	33/4	41/4	5	41/4	5	61/4	23/4	21/2	23/4	5	31/4	3	51/2	51/2				
Venice	51/2	61/4	53/4	5			43/4		51/4	53/4	61/4		3	43/4	5	71/4	7	41/4	5	5	51/4	61/2	43/4	21/2	3	31/4	6	31/2		3	61/2		5		
Vienna	31/2	4	4	5	31/4	6	31/2	23/4	41/2	31/4	53/4	61/4	3	31/4	43/4	6	61/2	41/2	43/4	51/2	43/4	53/4	6	3	23/4	31/4	5	33/4	3	31/2	41/4		3	31/4	
Zurich	3	41/2	31/4	31/4	31/4	6	3	31/2	23/4	31/2	53/4	51/2	23/4	21/2	3	53/4	41/2	33/4	21/2	31/4	33/4	33/4	5	21/2	21/2	23/4	5	31/4	33/4	31/2	41/2	21/2	21/2	33/4	3

Hamburg – Oslo: 23/4

HAMBURG
FUHLSBÜTTEL
FORNEBU
OSLO

Austria

Österreich

VIENNA
INNSBRUCK - SALZBURG

PRACTICAL INFORMATION

LOCAL CURRENCY

Austrian Schilling; 100 ATS = 9.91 USD ($) (Jan. 96)

TOURIST INFORMATION

In Vienna: Österreich-Information, 1040 Wien, Margaretenstr. 1, ✆ (01) 5 87 20 00, Fax 588 66 20
Niederösterreich-Information, 1014 Wien, Heidenschuß 2, ✆ (01) 5 33 31 14, Fax 533 100 60 60

AIRLINES

AUSTRIAN SWISSAIR: 1010 Wien, Kärtner Ring 18, ✆ (01) 5 05 57 57, Fax 505 14 34
AIR FRANCE: 1010 Wien, Kärntner Str. 49, ✆ (01) 5 14 18 18, Fax 513 94 26
BRITISH AIRWAYS: 1010 Wien, Kärntner Ring 10, ✆ (01) 505 76 91, Fax 504 20 84
DEUTSCHE LUFTHANSA: 1060 Wien, Maria Hilfer Str. 123, ✆ (01) 5 99 11 99, Fax 599 11 90
JAPAN AIRLINES: 1010 Wien, Kärntner Str. 11, ✆ (01) 512 75 22, Fax 512 75 54

FOREIGN EXCHANGE

Hotels, restaurants and shops do not always accept foreign currencies and it is wise, therefore, to change money and cheques at the banks and exchange offices which are found in the larger stations, airports and at the frontier.

SHOPPING and BANK HOURS

Shops are open from 9am to 6pm, but often close for a lunch break. They are closed Saturday afternoon, Sunday and Bank Holidays (except the shops in railway stations).
Branch offices of banks are open from Monday to Friday between 8am and 12.30pm (in Salzburg 12am) and from 1.30pm to 3pm (in Salzburg 2pm to 4.30pm), Thursday to 5.30pm (only in Vienna).
In the index of street names those printed in red are where the principal shops are found.

BREAKDOWN SERVICE

ÖAMTC: See addresses in the text of each city.
ARBÖ: in Vienna: Mariahilfer Str. 180, ✆ (01) 8 91 21
in Salzburg: Münchner Bundesstr. 9, ✆ (0662) 43 83 81, in Innsbruck: Stadlweg 7, ✆ (0512) 34 51 23
In Austria the ÖAMTC (emergency number ✆ 120) and the ARBÖ (emergency number ✆ 123) make a special point of assisting foreign motorists. They have motor patrols covering main roads.

TIPPING

Service is generally included in hotel and restaurant bills. But in Austria, it is usual to give more than the expected tip in hotels, restaurants and cafés. Taxi-drivers, porters, barbers and theatre attendants also expect tips.

SPEED LIMITS

The speed limit in built up areas (indicated by place name signs at the beginning and end of such areas) is 50 km/h - 31 mph; on motorways 130 km/h - 80 mph and on all other roads 100 km/h - 62 mph.

SEAT BELTS

The wearing of seat belts in Austria is compulsory for drivers and all passengers.

Vienna

(WIEN) Austria 987 ㊵, 426 ⑫ - pop. 1 640 000 - alt. 156 m. - ☎ 01.

HOFBURG★★★ FGY

Imperial Palace of the Habsburgs (Kaiserpalast der Habsburger) : Swiss Court - Royal Chapel - Amalienhof - Stallburg - Leopold Wing - Ballhausplatz - Imperial Chancellery - Spanish Riding School - Neue Burg - Josefsplatz - Michaelerplatz - In der Burg - Capuchins Crypt - Church of the Augustinians. Art Collections : Imperial Treasury★★★ - Imperial Apartments★★ - Austrian National Library (Great Hall★ - Frescoes★★) - Collection of Court Porcelain and Silver★★ - Collection of Arms and Armour★★ - Collection of Old Musical Instruments★ - Albertina (Dürer Collection★) - Museum of Ephesian Sculpture (Reliefs of Ephesus★★).

BUILDINGS AND MONUMENTS

St Stephen's Cathedral★★★ (Stephansdom) GY - Schönbrunn★★★ (Apartments★★★, Park★★, Gloriette★★, Coach Room★★) AS - Upper and Lower Belvedere★★ (Oberes und Unteres Belvedere) (Terraced Gardens and Art Collections★) HZ and DV - Opera★ (Staatsoper)★ GY - Church of St Charles★★ (Karlskirche) GZ - Church of St Michael (Michaeler Kirche) GY - Church of the Minor Friars (Minoritenkirche) FY - Church of the Teutonic Order (Deutschordenskirche) (Altarpiece★, Treasure★) GY **E** - Church of the Jesuits (Jesuitenkirche) HY **H** - Church of Our Lady of the River Bank (Maria am Gestade) GX - Church of the Faithful Virgin (Maria Treu) AR - Mozart Memorial (Mozart-Gedenkstätte) GY **F** - Dreimäderlhaus FX **W** - Pavilion Otto Wagner★ GZ **Q** - Pavilion of the Secession★ GZ **S**.

STREETS, SQUARES, PARKS

The Tour of the Ring★ - The Old Town (Altstadt)★ - Kärntner Straße GY - Graben (Plague Column) GY - Am Hof (Column to the Virgin) GY - Herrengasse★ GY - Maria-Theresien-Platz FY - Prater★ (Giant Wheel, ≤★) BR - Oberlaapark★ BS - Donner Fountain (Donnerbrunnen)★ GY **Y** - Heldenplatz FY - Burggarten GY - Volksgarten FY - Rathausplatz FY.

IMPORTANT MUSEUMS (Hofburg and Belvedere see above)

Museum of Fine Arts★★★ (Kunsthistorisches Museum) FY - Historical Museum of the City of Vienna★★ (Historisches Museum der Stadt Wien) GZ **M6** - Austrian Folklore Museum★★ (Österreichisches Museum für Volkskunde) AR **M7** - Gallery of Painting and Fine Arts★ (Gemäldegalerie der Akademie der Bildenden Künste) GZ **M9** - Natural History Museum★ (Naturhistorisches Museum) FY **M1** - Birthplace of Schubert (Schubert-Museum) BR **M16** - Austrian Museum of Applied Arts★ (Österreichisches Museum für angewandte Kunst) HY **M10** - Clock Museum (Uhrenmuseum der Stadt Wien) GY **M3**.

EXCURSIONS

Danube Tower★★ (Donauturm) BR - Leopoldsberg ≤★★ AR - Kahlenberg ≤★ AR - Klosterneuburg Abbey (Stift Klosterneuburg) (Altarpiece by Nicolas of Verdun★) AR - Grinzing★ AR - Baden★ AS - Vienna Woods★ (Wienerwald) AS.

18 Freudenau 65a, ☎ 2 18 95 64 9 At Wienerberg ☎ 661 23 70 00, Fax 661 23 77 89

✈ Wien-Schwechat by ③, ☎ 711 10 and 711 10 22 31, Air Terminal, at Stadtpark (HY) ☎ 72 35 34

☎ 58 00 29 89.

Exhibition Centre, Messeplatz 1, ☎ 727 20.

ℹ Tourist-information, ✉ A-1010, Kärtner Str. 38, ☎ 513 88 92 - ÖAMTC, ✉ A-1010, Schubertring 1, ☎ 71 19 90, Fax 7 13 18 07.

Budapest 208 ④ - München 435 ⑦ - Praha 292 ① - Salzburg 292 ⑦ - Zagreb 362 ⑥.

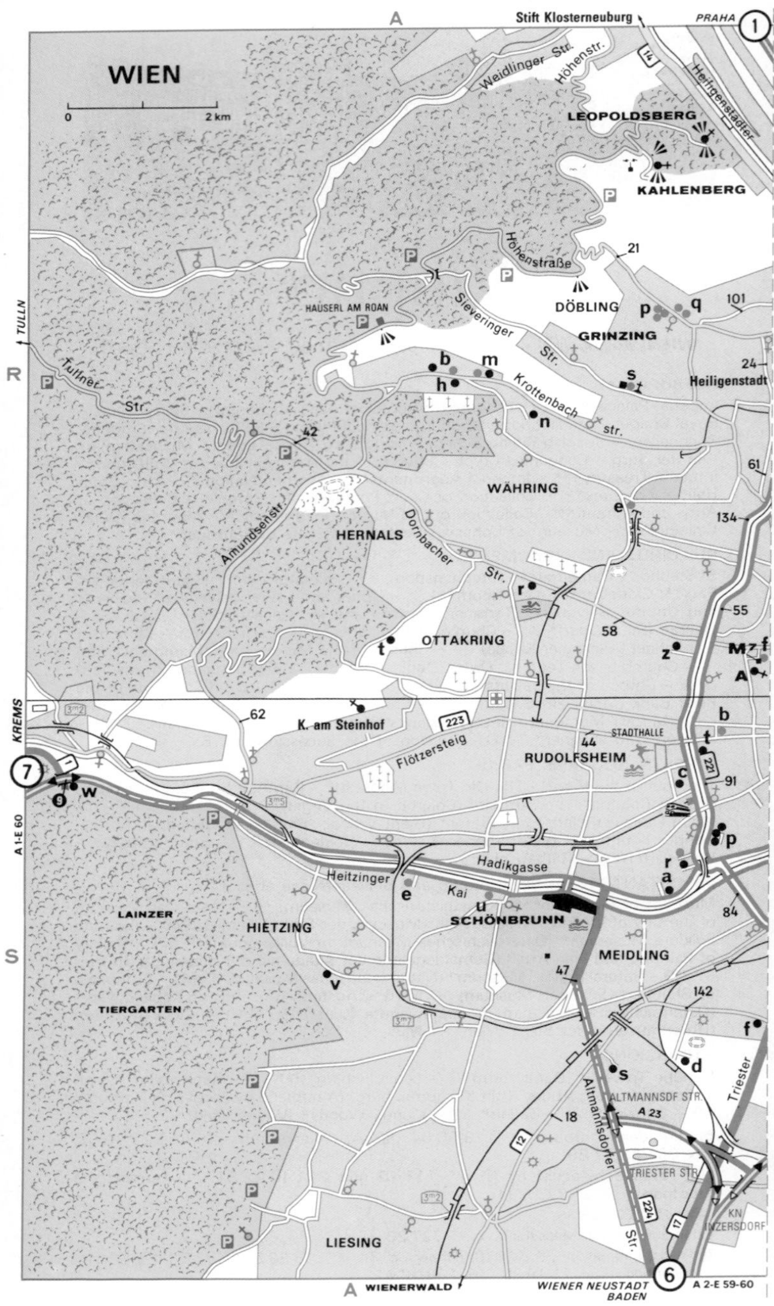
WIEN
0
2 km
A
Stift Klosterneuburg
PRAHA
1
Weidlinger Str.
Höhenstr.
Heiligenstädter
LEOPOLDSBERG
KAHLENBERG
Höhenstraße
21
DÖBLING
GRINZING
101
HAUSERL AM ROAN
Sieveringer Str.
Krottenbach str.
24
Heiligenstadt
TULLN
R
Tullner Str.
42
61
WÄHRING
134
HERNALS
Amundsenstr.
Dornbacher Str.
55
58
OTTAKRING
62
K. am Steinhof
223
Flötzersteig
44
STADTHALLE
RUDOLFSHEIM
221
91
KREMS
7
A 1-E 60
Hadikgasse
Heitzinger Kai
SCHÖNBRUNN
84
LAINZER
HIETZING
MEIDLING
S
TIERGARTEN
47
142
Triester
Altmannsdorfer Str.
ALTMANNSDF STR.
A 23
18
12
TRIESTER STR.
224
17
KN INZERSDORF
LIESING
6
A
WIENERWALD
WIENER NEUSTADT
BADEN
A 2-E 59-60

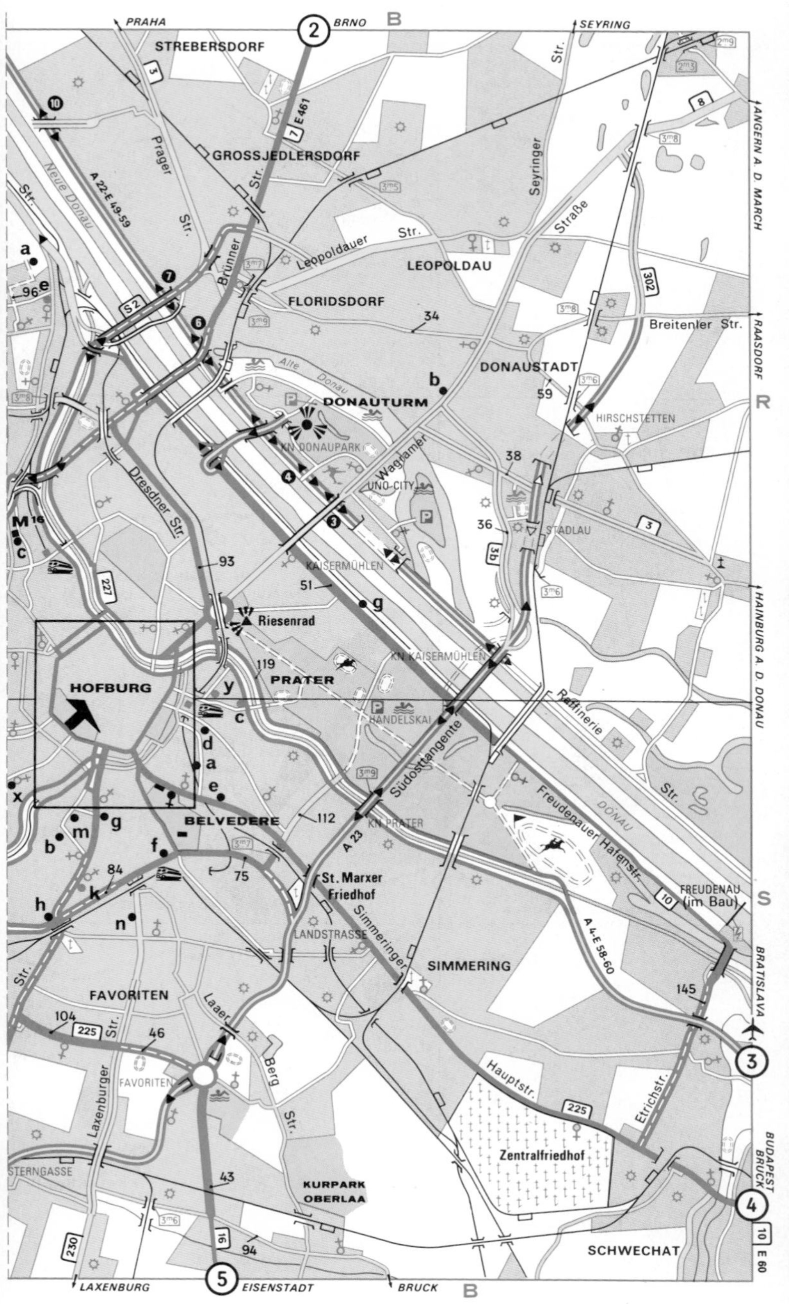
PRAHA
BRNO
SEYRING
STREBERSDORF
GROSSJEDLERSDORF
LEOPOLDAU
FLORIDSDORF
DONAUSTADT
DONAUTURM
HIRSCHSTETTEN
KN DONAUPARK
UNO-CITY
STADLAU
KAISERMÜHLEN
Riesenrad
KN KAISERMÜHLEN
HOFBURG
PRATER
HANDELSKAI
Südosttangente
BELVEDERE
KN PRATER
St. Marxer Friedhof
FREUDENAU (im Bau)
LANDSTRASSE
SIMMERING
FAVORITEN
Zentralfriedhof
STERNGASSE
KURPARK OBERLAA
SCHWECHAT
LAXENBURG
EISENSTADT
BRUCK
ANGERN A. D. MARCH
RAASDORF
HAINBURG A. D. DONAU
BRATISLAVA
BUDAPEST BRUCK
Neue Donau
Alte Donau
DONAU
Prager Str.
Brünner Str.
Leopoldauer Str.
Seyringer Straße
Breitenler Str.
Wagramer
Dresdner Str.
Raffinerie Str.
Freudenauer Hafenstr.
Simmeringer Hauptstr.
Laaer Berg Str.
Laxenburger Str.
Etrichstr.
A 22-E 49-59
A 23
A 4-E 58-60
E 461
E 60

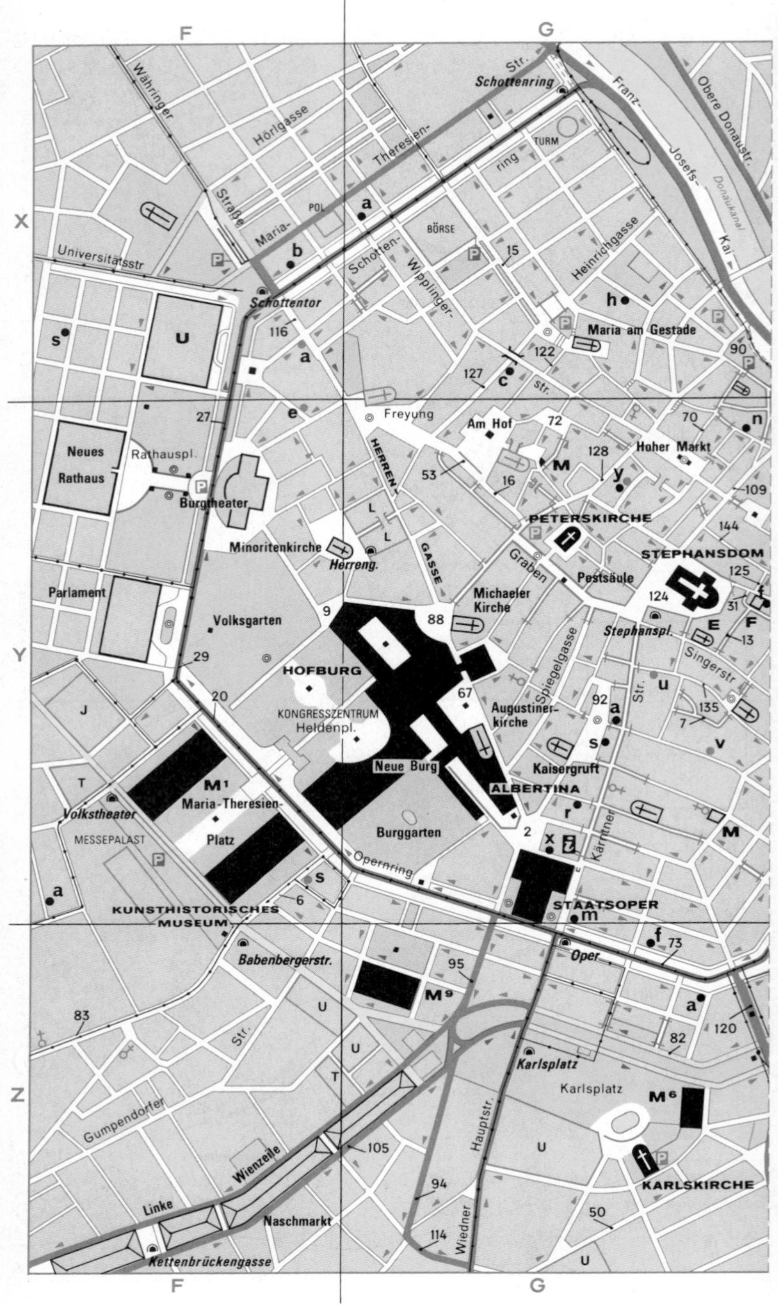
F
G
X
Y
Z
Währinger
Straße
Universitätsstr
Hörlgasse
Maria-
Theresien-
Str.
Schottenring
Schottentor
Franz-
Josefs-
Kai
Obere Donaustr.
Donaukanal
TURM
ring
POL
BÖRSE
Schotten-
Wipplinger-
Heinrichgasse
Maria am Gestade
str.
Freyung
Am Hof
Hoher Markt
HERREN-
GASSE
Neues
Rathaus
Rathauspl.
Burgtheater
Minoritenkirche
Herreng.
PETERSKIRCHE
STEPHANSDOM
Graben
Pestsäule
Stephanspl.
Singerstr.
Parlament
Volksgarten
HOFBURG
KONGRESSZENTRUM
Heldenpl.
Michaeler
Kirche
Spiegelgasse
Augustiner-
kirche
Kaisergruft
Neue Burg
ALBERTINA
Kärntner
Str.
Volkstheater
MESSEPALAST
Maria-Theresien-
Platz
Burggarten
Opernring
STAATSOPER
KUNSTHISTORISCHES
MUSEUM
Babenbergerstr.
Oper
Gumpendorfer
Str.
Karlsplatz
Hauptstr.
Wiedner
KARLSKIRCHE
Linke
Wienzeile
Naschmarkt
Kettenbrückengasse

WIEN

Street	Grid	No.
Babenbergerstr	FY	6
Graben	GY	
Kärntner Straße	GY	
Landstraßer Hauptstr	HY	76
Mariahilfer Str.	FZ	83
Rotenturmstraße	GY	109
Stephansplatz	GY	124
Tuchlauben	GY	128
Wollzeile	GY	144

Street	Grid	No.
Albertinaplatz	GY	2
Ballgasse	GY	7
Ballhausplatz	FY	9
Bäckerstr	HY	10
Blutgasse	GY	13
Börsegasse	GX	15
Bognergasse	GY	16
Breitenfurter Str.	AS	18
Burgring	FY	20
Cobenzlgasse	AR	21
Döblinger Hauptstr.	AR	24
Dr. Karl-Lueger-Platz	HY	26
Dr. Karl-Lueger-Ring	FY	27
Dr. Renner-Ring	FY	29
Domgasse	GY	31
Dominikanerbastei	HY	32
Donaufelder Str.	BR	34
Donaustadtstr.	BR	36
Erzherzog-Karl-Str.	BR	38
Essiggasse	HY	40
Exelbergstr.	AR	42
Favoritenstr.	BS	43
Gablenzgasse	AS	44
Grenzackerstr.	BS	46
Grünbergstr.	AS	47
Gußhausstr	GZ	50
Handelskai	BR	51
Heidenschuß	GY	53
Heiligenkreuzerhof	HY	54
Hernalser Gürtel	AR	55
Hernalser Hauptstr.	AR	58
Hirschstettner Str.	BR	59
Hohe Warte	AR	61
Huttelbergstr.	AS	62
Invalidenstr	HY	63
Josefsplatz	GY	67
Judengasse	GY	70
Judenplatz	GY	72
Kärntner Ring	GZ	73
Landstraßer Gürtel	BS	75
Leopoldsgasse	HX	79
Lothringerstr	GZ	82
Margareten Gürtel	ABS	84
Marienbrücke	HX	85
Marxergasse	HY	86
Michaelerplatz	GY	88
Morzinplatz	GX	90
Neubau Gürtel	AR	91
Neuer Markt	GY	92
Nordbahnstr.	BR	93
Oberlaaer Str.	BS	94
Operngasse	GZ	95
Pfarrplatz	BR	96
Postgasse	HY	97
Prinz-Eugen-Str.	HZ	99
Probusgasse	AR	101
Raxstr.	BS	104
Rechte Wienzeile	GZ	105
Rennweg	HZ	107
Rosenbursenstr	HY	108
Schlachthausgasse	BS	112
Schleifmühlgasse	GZ	114
Schönlaterngasse	HY	115
Schottengasse	FX	116
Schubertring	HY	118
Schüttelstr.	BR	119
Schwarzenbergplatz	GZ	120
Schwedenbrücke	HX	121
Schwertgasse	GX	122
Sonnenfelsgasse	HY	123
Strobelgasse	GY	125
Tiefer Graben	GX	127
Vordere Zollamtsstr.	HY	132
Währinger Gürtel	AR	134
Weihburggasse	GY	135
Weiskirchnerstr	HY	137
Wienerbergstr.	AS	142
Zinnergasse	BS	145

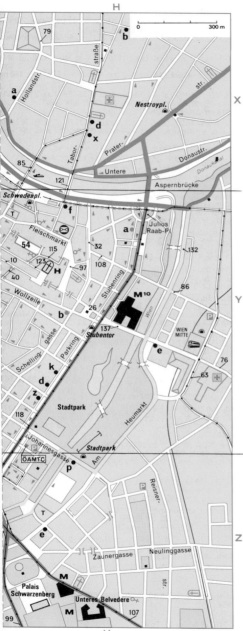

North is at the top on all town plans.

Town Centre, city districts (Stadtbezirke) 1 - 9 :

Imperial (converted 19C palace), Kärntner Ring 16, ✉ A-1015, ☎ 50 11 00, Telex 112630, Fax 50110410 - rm TV - 130. AE E VISA JCB. rest GZ **a**
Imperial (booking essential) *(dinner only)* **Meals** à la carte 530/890 - ***Café Imperial*** **Meals** à la carte 290/530 - **128 rm** 4370/9600 - 22 suites.

Bristol, Kärntner Ring 1, ✉ A-1015, ☎ 51 51 60, Fax 51516550 - rm TV - 180. AE E VISA JCB. rest GYZ **m**
Meals (see also ***Korso*** below) - ***Rôtisserie Sirk :*** **Meals** 380 and à la carte 470/770 - **146 rm** 3500/5900 - 10 suites.

Plaza Wien, Schottenring 11, ✉ A-1010, ☎ 31 39 00, Telex 135859, Fax 31390160, Massage, - rm TV - 150. AE E VISA JCB GX **a**
Meals (see ***La Scala*** below) - **218 rm** 2850/4250 - 36 suites.

Sacher, Philharmonikerstr. 4, ✉ A-1010, ☎ 5 14 56, Telex 112520, Fax 51457810, « Collection of valuable furniture and paintings » - rm TV. AE E VISA JCB. rest GY **x**
Meals 450 (lunch) and à la carte 560/760 - **116 rm** 2150/5900 - 3 suites.

ANA Grand Hotel, Kärtner Ring 9, ✉ A-1010, ☎ 51 58 00, Telex 115760, Fax 5151313 - rm TV - 300. AE E VISA JCB. rest GZ **f**
Le ciel : **Meals** à la carte 510/660 - ***Unkai*** (Japanese cuisine) **Meals** 220 (lunch) and 490/1000 - **205 rm** 3500/7500 - 11 suites.

Hotel im Palais Schwarzenberg, Schwarzenbergplatz 9, ✉ A-1030, ☎ 7 98 45 15, Telex 136124, Fax 7894714, « Converted 1727 baroque palace, park », - TV - 200. AE E VISA JCB. rest HZ
Meals 390 (lunch) and à la carte 510/810 - **38 rm** 2570/7650.

Vienna Hilton, Landstraßer Hauptstr. 2 (near Stadtpark), ✉ A-1030, ☎ 71 70 00, Telex 136799, Fax 7130691 - rm TV - 660. AE E VISA JCB. rest HY **e**
Meals 360 (buffet lunch) and à la carte 400/550 - **600 rm** 3460/7920 - 25 suites.

Vienna Marriott Hotel, Parkring 12a, ✉ A-1010, ☎ 51 51 80, Fax 515186722, Massage, - rm TV - 600. AE E VISA JCB. rest HY **d**
Meals à la carte 380/600 - **310 rm** 3750/5400 - 7 suites.

Intercontinental, Johannesgasse 28, ✉ A-1037, ☎ 71 12 20, Telex 131235, Fax 7134489, - rm TV - 1200. AE E VISA JCB. rest HZ **p**
Vier Jahreszeiten (closed Saturday and Sunday, 2 to 23 January and 2 weeks July) **Meals** à la carte 470/750 - ***Brasserie :*** **Meals** à la carte 280/540 - **460 rm** 2770/4320 - 62 suites.

Penta Renaissance Hotel (former imperial riding school with modern hotel wing), Ungargasse 60, ✉ A-1030, ☎ 71 17 50, Telex 112529, Fax 7117590, Massage, - rm TV - 500. AE E VISA JCB BS **a**
Meals 390 (buffet lunch) and à la carte 310/530 - **342 rm** 2100/4000.

Scandic Crown Hotel, Handelskai 269, ✉ A-1020, ☎ 7 27 77, Telex 133318, Fax 72777199, (heated), - rm TV - 300. AE E VISA JCB. BR **g**
Meals 325 (buffet lunch) and à la carte 325/615 - **367 rm** 1575/4200.

Radisson SAS-Palais-Hotel, Parkring 16, ✉ A-1010, ☎ 51 51 70, Telex 136127, Fax 5122216, - rm TV - 300. AE E VISA JCB HY **z**
Meals *(closed Saturday, Sunday and Bank Holidays)* 340 (buffet lunch) and à la carte 455/655 - **245 rm** 2560/5020 - 34 suites.

Hotel de France, Schottenring 3, ✉ A-1010, ☎ 31 36 80, Telex 114360, Fax 3195969, - rm TV - 120. AE E VISA JCB FX **b**
Meals *(closed Saturday)* 290/590 (buffet lunch) and à la carte 390/610 - **216 rm** 1805/3700 - 10 suites.

Wimberger, Neubaugürtel 34, ✉ A-1070, ☎ 52 16 50, Fax 52165810, - rm TV - 700. AE E VISA. rest AS **t**
Meals 260 (buffet lunch) and à la carte 315/590 - **225 rm** 1700/3630.

Biedermeier, Landstraßer Hauptstr. 28 (at Sünnhof), ✉ A-1030, ☎ 71 67 10, Telex 111039, Fax 71671503, - TV - 100. AE E VISA JCB BS **d**
Meals à la carte 323/535 - **203 rm** 1900/2400 - 11 suites.

Ambassador, Neuer Markt 5, ✉ A-1015, ☎ 5 14 66, Fax 5132999 - TV. AE E VISA JCB GY **s**
Meals à la carte 350/690 - **106 rm** 1650/4500.

City-Central without rest, Taborstr. 8a, ✉ A-1020, ☎ 21 10 50, Fax 21105140 - TV. AE E VISA HX **x**
58 rm 1580/2180.

Nestroy without rest, Rotensterngasse 12, ✉ A-1020, ☎ 21 14 00, Fax 211407, - TV - 60. AE E VISA HX **b**
62 rm 1650/2300 - 7 suites.

Europa, Neuer Markt 3, ✉ A-1015, ☎ 51 59 40, Telex 112292, Fax 5138138 - TV - 60. AE E VISA JCB. rest GY **a**
Meals à la carte 380/590 - **102 rm** 1600/2650.

Arkadenhof without rest, Viriotgasse 5, ✉ A-1090, ☎ 3 10 08 37, Fax 3107686 – 30. AE ① E VISA JCB BR **c**
45 rm 1380/1880 – 10 suites.

K. u. K. Hotel Maria Theresia without rest, Kirchberggasse 6 - 8, ✉ A-1070, ☎ 5 21 23, Telex 111530, Fax 5212370 – rm – 40. AE ① E VISA JCB FY **a**
123 rm 1640/2600.

Pannonia, Matrosengasse 6, ✉ A-1060, ☎ 59 90 10, Telex 132940, Fax 5976900 – rm – 70. AE ① E VISA JCB AS **p**
Meals à la carte 300/530 – **211 rm** 1500/2400 – 6 suites.

Kummer, Mariahilfer Str. 71a, ✉ A-1060, ☎ 58 88 95, Telex 111417, Fax 5878133 – rm. AE ① E VISA JCB BS **x**
Meals à la carte 280/400 – **100 rm** 1450/2200.

Sofitel Hotel Belvedere, Am Heumarkt 35-37, ✉ A-1030, ☎ 71 61 60, Telex 111822, Fax 71616844 – rm – 30. AE ① E VISA JCB. rest HZ **e**
Meals à la carte 220/425 – **211 rm** 1920/2360.

President, Wallgasse 23, ✉ A-1060, ☎ 5 99 90, Fax 5967646, – – 50. AE ① E VISA AS **p**
Meals *(closed Sunday)* à la carte 240/460 – **77 rm** 1350/2350.

Stefanie, Taborstr. 12, ✉ A-1020, ☎ 21 15 00, Telex 134589, Fax 21150160, – – 90. AE ① E VISA JCB HX **d**
Meals à la carte 320/430 – **131 rm** 1480/2440.

Alba Palace, Margaretenstr. 92, ✉ A-1050, ☎ 54 68 60, Telex 114321, Fax 5468686, – – 100. AE ① E VISA JCB BS **b**
Meals à la carte 300/480 – **117 rm** 1390/2600.

Amadeus without rest, Wildpretmarkt 5, ✉ A-1010, ☎ 5 33 87 38, Fax 533873838 – . AE ① E VISA GY **y**
closed 22 to 27 December – **30 rm** 1090/1950.

Alba-Accadia, Margaretenstr. 53, ✉ A-1050, ☎ 58 85 00, Telex 113264, Fax 58850899, , – – 60. AE ① E VISA JCB BS **m**
Meals à la carte 300/480 – **104 rm** 1390/2600.

Astoria (19C period house with typical interior), Führichgasse 1, ✉ A-1015, ☎ 51 57 70, Fax 5157782 – . AE ① E VISA JCB GY **r**
Meals *(closed July - August and Saturday - Sunday)* à la carte 370/580 – **108 rm** 1700/2700.

Tigra without rest, Tiefer Graben 14 - 18, ✉ A-1010, ☎ 53 39 64 10, Telex 114651, Fax 5339645 – rm . AE ① E VISA GX **c**
55 rm 1280/1850.

Rathauspark without rest, Rathausstr. 17, ✉ A-1010, ☎ 40 41 20, Fax 40412761 – – 20. AE ① E VISA JCB FX **s**
117 rm 1340/2400.

K u. K Palais Hotel without rest, Rudolfsplatz 11, ✉ A-1010, ☎ 5 33 13 53, Telex 134049, Fax 533135370 – rm – 40. AE ① E VISA JCB GX **h**
66 rm 1460/2240.

Am Parkring, Parkring 12, ✉ A-1015, ☎ 51 48 00, Fax 5148040, ← – . AE ① E VISA JCB. HY **k**
Meals *(closed Sunday and Monday dinner)* à la carte 350/500 – **65 rm** 1640/2600 – 3 suites.

Erzherzog Rainer without rest, Wiedner Hauptstr. 27, ✉ A-1040, ☎ 50 11 10, Fax 50111350 – rest – 50. AE ① E VISA BS **g**
84 rm 1360/2340.

Capricorno without rest, Schwedenplatz 3, ✉ A-1010, ☎ 53 33 10 40, Fax 53376714 – . AE E VISA HY **f**
46 rm 1280/2230.

Mercure without rest, Hollandstr. 3, ✉ A-1020, ☎ 21 31 30, Fax 21313230 – rm . AE ① E VISA JCB HX **a**
63 rm 1600/2110.

Mercure, Fleischmarkt 1a, ✉ A-1010, ☎ 53 46 00, Fax 53460234 – rm . AE ① E VISA JCB GY **n**
Meals à la carte 305/485 – **154 rm** 1630/2650.

König von Ungarn, Schulerstr. 10, ✉ A-1010, ☎ 5 15 84, Fax 515848 – rm . AE ① E VISA GY **f**
Meals à la carte 350/640 – **33 rm** 1800/2100.

Prinz Eugen without rest, Wiedner Gürtel 14, ✉ A-1040, ☎ 5 05 17 41, Telex 132483, Fax 505174119 – . AE ① E VISA JCB BS **f**
109 rm 1495/3000.

Artis, Rennweg 51, ✉ A-1030, ☎ 7 13 25 21, Telex 131797, Fax 7145930 – – 60. AE ① E VISA JCB BS **e**
Meals *(closed Sunday)* à la carte 240/420 – **168 rm** 1200/1880.

Ibis, Mariahilfer Gürtel 22, ✉ A-1060, ☎ 5 99 98, Telex 133833, Fax 5979090 – rm – 120. AE ① E VISA AS **p**
Meals à la carte 230/330 – **341 rm** 1110/1325.

XXXX ✿ **Korso** - Hotel Bristol, **Kärntner Ring 1**, ✉ A-1015, ☎ 51 51 65 46, Fax 51516550 – ▤. AE ⓓ E VISA JCB. ✗ GYZ n
closed Saturday lunch and 3 weeks August – **Meals** 380 (lunch) and à la carte 470/855
Spec. Hausgemachte Zitronennudeln mit Kaviar, Zander in Kartoffelkruste mit Kürbiskernöl Sabayon, Rebhuhn mit Polenta und Champagnerkraut.

XXXX ✿✿ **Steirereck,** Rasumofskygasse 2 / Ecke Weißgerberlände, ✉ A-1030, ☎ 7 13 31 68 Fax 71351682 – ✗ AE E VISA BS e
closed Saturday, Sunday an Bank Holidays – **Meals** (booking essential) 395 (lunch) and a la carte 620/810.
Spec. Gäseleber - Cox Orange, Kaninchen mit Kapern und Salatgurken, Geeister Eierlikör-Spitz

XXXX ✿ **La Scala** - Hotel Plaza Wien, **Schottenring 11**, ✉ A-1010, ☎ 31 39 01 50, Fax 3139016 – ▤. AE ⓓ E VISA JCB. ✗ GX a
closed Sunday dinner, Sunday and Bank Holidays – **Meals** 275 (lunch) and à la carte 350/745
Spec. Gerandelte Teigtascherln mit Kalbsmilcher und Petersilie, Gebratenes Zanderfilet auf grünen Linsen in Veltliner, Marinierte Beeren im Blätterkrokant.

XXXX ✿ **Drei Husaren**, Weihburggasse 4, ✉ A-1010, ☎ 51 21 09 20, Fax 512109218 – AE ⓓ E VISA JCB GY u
closed mid July - mid August – **Meals** 390 (lunch) and à la carte 610/850
Spec. Hechtnockerln mit Hummersauce und grünem Spargel, Glasierte Brust vom Freilandhuhn mit gefüllten Rahmmorcheln, Lammsattel mit Thymiankruste.

XXX ✿ **Gottfried**, Untere Viaduktgasse 45/Marxergasse, ✉ A-1030, ☎ 7 13 82 56, Fax 7138257 – AE VISA BRS y
closed Saturday lunch, Sunday and Bank Holidays – **Meals** *(booking essential)* (outstanding wine list) 380/890 and à la carte 460/650
Spec. Zander auf der Haut gebraten mit Kürbis und Kümmel, Gepökelte Taube "knusperig" mit Trüffeltascherl, Grießknödel mit kandierten Orangensschalen, schwarze Ribieselsauce.

XXX **Grotta Azzurra** (Italian rest.), Babenberger Str. 5, ✉ A-1010, ☎ 58 61 04 40, Fax 586104415 – AE ⓓ E VISA JCB FY s
closed Sunday, mid July - mid August and 24 to 27 December – **Meals** 270 (lunch) and à la carte 3905/580.

XXX **Kupferdachl**, Schottengasse 7 (entrance Mölker Bastei), ✉ A-1010, ☎ 5 33 93 81, Fax 53393814 – AE ⓓ E VISA FX a
closed Christmas – **Meals** à la carte 330/530.

XXX **Steirer Stub'n**, Wiedner Hauptstr. 111, ✉ A-1050, ☎ 5 44 43 49, Fax 5440888 – AE ⓓ E VISA BS k
closed Sunday – **Meals** *(booking essential)* à la carte 340/490.

XX **Plachutta**, Wollzeile 38, ✉ A-1010, ☎ 5 12 15 77, Fax 512157720, 🏠 – ▤. E VISA HY b
closed 24 July to 6 August – **Meals** 250/380 and à la carte 320/550.

XX Schubertstüberln, Schreyvogelgasse 4, ✉ A-1010, ☎ 5 33 71 87, Fax 5353546, 🏠 FXY e

XX **Steinerne Eule**, Halbgasse 30, ✉ A-1070, ☎ 5 23 72 68, Fax 5233818, 🏠 – AE ⓓ E VISA AS b
closed Sunday and Monday – **Meals** 315 and à la carte 330/575.

XX Selina, Laudongasse 13, ✉ A-1080, ☎ 4 05 64 04, Fax 4080459 – AR f

XX **Zum Kuckuck**, Himmelpfortgasse 15, ✉ A-1010, ☎ 5 12 84 70, Fax 5233818 – AE ⓓ E VISA GY v
closed Saturday and Sunday – **Meals** à la carte 360/600.

XX **Salut**, Wildpretmarkt 3, ✉ A-1010, ☎ 5 33 13 22 – AE ⓓ E VISA GY y
closed Sunday and Bank Holidays – **Meals** 220/600 and à la carte 445/580.

X **Hedrich**, Stubenring 2, ✉ A-1010, ☎ 5 12 95 88 – HY a
closed Friday - Sunday, Bank Holidays and August – **Meals** à la carte 250/495.

City districts (Stadtbezirke) 10 - 15 :

🏨 **Holiday Inn**, Tviester Str. 72, ✉ A-1100, ☎ 6 05 30, Fax 60530580, ≤ – 🛗 ✗ rm ▤ TV ☎ ♿ 🚗 – 🏛 260. AE ⓓ E VISA JCB AS f
Meals à la carte 290/480 – **176 rm** ☕ 1730/3030 – 4 suites.

🏨 **Wien Renaissance Hotel**, Ullmannstr. 71, ✉ A-1150, ☎ 8 50 40, Telex 112206, Fax 8504100, ≘s, 🏊 – 🛗 ✗ rm ▤ TV ☎ 🚗 – 🏛 200. AE ⓓ E VISA JCB. ✗ rest AS a
– ***Orangerie :*** **Meals** a la carte 360/675 – ***Allegro :*** **Meals** 360 (buffet only) – **309 rm** ☕ 1700/3190 – 3 suites.

🏨 **Bosei** 🐎, Gutheil-Schoder-Gasse 9, ✉ A-1100, ☎ 66 10 60, Fax 66106-99 – 🛗 ✗ rm TV ☎ Ⓟ – 🏛 240. AE ⓓ E VISA AS d
Meals à la carte 270/420 – **190 rm** ☕ 1250/2400 – 8 suites.

🏨 **Wiener Gartenhotel Altmannsdorf** 🐎, Hoffingergasse 26, ✉ A-1120, ☎ 8 04 75 27, Fax 804752751, 🏠, Park, ≘s – 🛗 ✗ rm TV ☎ 🚗 – 🏛 140. AE ⓓ E VISA AS s
Meals à la carte 290/450 – **92 rm** ☕ 1300/1850.

🏨 **Trend Hotel Favorita**, Laxenburger Str. 8-10, ✉ A-1100, ☎ 60 14 60, Fax 60146720, ≘s – 🛗 TV ☎ 🚗 – 🏛 200. AE ⓓ E VISA. ✗ rest BS n
Meals à la carte 230/570 – **161 rm** ☕ 1320/1700 – 4 suites.

Austrotel, Felberstr. 4, A-1150, 98 11 10, Fax 98111930, - rm - 250. AE E VISA AS **c**
Meals à la carte 250/410 - **250 rm** 1760/3900.

Amarante, Matzleinsdorferplatz 1, A-1050, 5 44 27 43, Fax 544274380 - . AE E VISA BS **h**
Meals à la carte 310/450 - **43 rm** 950/1650.

Reither without rest, Graumanngasse 16, A-1150, 8 93 68 41, Fax 8936835, , - . AE E VISA AS **r**
closed 22 to 27 December - **50 rm** 1100/2240.

Arabella - Hotel Jagdschloß without rest, Jagdschloßgasse 79, A-1130, 8 04 35 08, Fax 8043500, (heated), - AS **v**
closed January - February - **48 rm** 820/1800.

Villa Hans Moser, Auhofstr. 76, A-1130, 87 74 74 70, Fax 8776050, - rest. AE E VISA. AS **e**
closed Sunday - **Meals** (dinner only) 350 and a la carte 400/800.

Altwienerhof with rm, Herklotzgasse 6, A-1150, 8 92 60 00, Fax 89260008, « Winter garden, courtyard-terrace » - . AE E VISA AS **r**
closed 1 to 24 January - **Meals** *(closed Saturday lunch and Sunday)* (outstanding wine list) 333 (lunch) and à la carte 480/695 - **23 rm** 580/1800
Spec. Pfefferkugel von der Gänseleber, Champignontorte, Fasanenbrust poêliert mit Gänselebersauce.

Hietzinger Bräu, Auhofstr. 1, A-1130, 87 77 08 70, Fax 877708722 - E VISA AS **u**
closed mid July - mid August - **Meals** *(mainly boiled beef dishes)* a la carte 355/545.

City districts (Stadtbezirke) 16 - 19 :

Clima Villenhotel, Nussberggasse 2c, A-1190, 37 15 16 (Hotel) 37 16 61 (Rest.), Telex 115670, Fax 371392, « Rest. Bockkeller, vaulted cellar with Tyrolian farmhouse furniture », , , , - - 60. AE E VISA BR **a**
Meals *(closed Sunday)* à la carte 363/633 - **30 rm** 1750/2500.

Landhaus Fuhrgassl-Huber without rest, Rathstr. 24, A-1190, 4 40 30 33, Fax 4402714, « Country house atmosphere », - . E VISA AR **m**
closed February - **22 rm** 960/1470.

Schloß Wilhelminenberg, Savoyenstr. 2, A-1160, 45 85 03, Fax 454876, « Terrace with Vienna, Park » - - 350. AE E VISA AR **t**
Meals à la carte 330/430 - **90 rm** 995/1510.

Maté (with guesthouse), Ottakringer Str. 34, A-1170, 4 04 55, Telex 115485, Fax 40455888, , - rm . AE E VISA AR **z**
Meals à la carte 250/490 - **172 rm** 1420/2350.

Gartenhotel Glanzing without rest, Glanzinggasse 23, A-1190, 47 04 27 20, Fax 470427214, - . AE E VISA AR **n**
18 rm 1180/2200.

Jäger without rest, Hernalser Hauptstr. 187, A-1170, 48 66 62 00, Fax 48666208 - . E VISA AR **r**
18 rm 950/1600.

Celtes without rest, Celtesgasse 1a, A-1190, 4 40 41 51, Fax 4404152116 - . AE E VISA JCB AR **b**
16 rm 850/1400.

Schild without rest, Neustift am Walde 97, A-1190, 44 04 04 40, Fax 4404000, - . AE E VISA AR **h**
33 rm 780/1420.

Plachutta, Heiligenstädter Str. 179, A-1190, 37 41 25, Fax 37412520 - E VISA BR **e**
closed August - **Meals** à la carte 370/525.

Eckel, Sieveringer Str. 46, A-1190, 32 32 18/9 63 20 32 18, Fax 326660/963206660, - AE VISA AR **s**
closed Sunday, Monday, Bank Holidays, 11 to 25 August and 23 December - 20 January - **Meals** à la carte 305/685.

Sailer, Gersthofer Str. 14, A-1180, 47 92 12 12, Fax 47921214, - E AR **e**
closed Sunday and Bank Holidays dinner - **Meals** 200/450 and à la carte 380/550.

City district (Stadtbezirk) 22 :

Trend Hotel Donauzentrum, Wagramer Str. 83, A-1220, 20 35 54 50, Telex 113785, Fax 2035545183, - rm - 60. AE E VISA BR **b**
Meals à la carte 210/380 - **137 rm** 1320/2200.

Heurigen and Buschen-Schänken (wine gardens) - (mostly self-service, hot and cold dishes from buffet, prices according to weight of chosen meals, therefore not shown below. Buschen-Schänken sell their own wines only) :

Kirchenstöckl, Cobenzlgasse 3, A-1190, 3 20 66 62, Fax 320571322, - AR **p**
(dinner only).

Oppolzer, Himmelstr. 22, A-1190, 3 20 24 16, Fax 32024616, « Garden » - AR **p**
closed Sunday, Bank Holidays and Christmas - **Meals** (dinner only) à la carte 170/310.

Altes Preßhaus, Cobenzlgasse 15, ✉ A-1190, ℘ 32 23 93, Fax 32234285, « Old vaulted wine cellar » – AE ⓓ E VISA JCB — AR p
Meals (dinner only) à la carte 225/450.

Wolff, Rathstr. 44, ✉ A-1190, ℘ 4 40 23 35, Fax 4401403, « Terraced garden » — AR n
Meals (buffet only).

Fuhrgassl Huber, Neustift am Walde 68, ✉ A-1190, ℘ 4 40 14 05, Fax 4402730, (wine garden with Viennese Schrammelmusik), « Courtyard-terrace » – E VISA — AR b
closed February – **Meals** (buffet).

Grinzinger Hauermandl, Cobenzlgasse 20, ✉ A-1190, ℘ 32 30 27, Fax 320571322, (dinner only). — AR c

Grinzinger Weinbottich, Cobenzlgasse 28, ✉ A-1190, ℘ 3 20 42 37, Fax 32071322, « Shady garden » — AR o
(dinner only).

at Auhof motorway station W : 8 km :

Novotel Wien-West, Wientalstraße/Am Auhof, ✉ A-1140, ℘ (01) 97 92 54 20, Telex 135584, Fax 9794140, (heated), – rm rest TV ☎ & P – 250. AE ⓓ E VISA — AS w
Meals à la carte 190/370 – **115 rm** 1155/1410.

at Perchtoldsdorf **A-2380** SW : 13 km by B12 and Breitenfurter Str. AS :

XXX ✿ **Jahreszeiten**, Hochstr. 17, ℘ (01) 8 65 31 29, Fax 865312973 – . AE ⓓ E VISA
closed Saturday lunch, Sunday dinner, Monday and Bank Holidays, 29 July - 18 August – **Meals** 330 (lunch) and à la carte 540/660
Spec. Hausgebeizter Lachs auf Trüffelnudeln, Saibling auf Linsensalat mit Polenta, Zitronensoufflé mit frischem Fruchtmark.

at Vösendorf **A-2334** S : 11 km by ⑥ or A 2 AS :

Novotel Wien-Süd, Nordring 4 (Shopping City Süd), ℘ (01) 6 92 60 10, Telex 134793, Fax 694859, (heated) – rm rest TV ☎ & P – 250. AE ⓓ E VISA
Meals à la carte 220/390 – **102 rm** 1150/1410.

at Groß-Enzersdorf **A-2301** E : 16 km, by B 3 BR :

Am Sachsengang, Schloßhofer Str. 60 (B 3), ℘ (02249) 2 90 10, Fax 2905, « Terrace », Massage, – rm TV ☎ P – 300. AE ⓓ E VISA
closed 23 to 27 December – ***Taverne*** **Meals** 280 and à la carte 350/595 – **106 rm** 860/1600.

When travelling through Europe
use the MICHELIN red-cover map series, nos 980 to 991

INNSBRUCK

6020 Austria – pop. 120 000 – alt. 580 m – Wintersport : 580/2300 m 3 7 – ☎ 0512.

See : Maria-Theresien-Strasse ★ CZ ≤ ★★ on the Nordkette, Belfry (Stadtturm) CZ **B** ✻ ★ over the city – Little Golden Roof (Goldenes Dachl) ★ CZ – Helblinghaus ★ CZ – Hofburg ★ CZ – Hofkirche CZ (Maximilian's Mausoleum ★, Silver Chapel ★★) – Tyrol Museum of Popular Art (Tiroler Volkskunstmuseum) ★★ CDZ – "Ferdinandeum" Tyrol Museum (Tiroler Landesmuseum "Ferdinandeum") ★ DZ**M2** – Wilten Basilica ★ AY.

Envir. : Hafelekar ✻ ★★ – Upland Tour (Mittelgebirge) ★★ (Hall in Tirol ★, Volders ★, Igls ★, Elbögen road ★★) – The Stubaital ★.

9 Innsbruck-Igls, Lans (05222)7 71 65 ; 18 Innsbruck-Igls, Rinn (05223)81 77.

Innsbruck Information, Burggraben 3, ℘ 53 56, Fax 535643.

ÖAMTC, Andechsstr. 81, ℘ 3 32 01 20, Fax 491612.

Wien 733 – München 140 – Salzburg 164.

Plans on following pages

Europa-Tyrol, Südtiroler Platz 2, ℘ 59 31, Fax 587800, – rm TV ☎ – 250. AE ⓓ E VISA JCB. rest — DZ a
Meals à la carte 340/545 – **122 rm** 1800/3300 – 6 suites.

Scandic Crown Hotel, Salurner Str. 15, ℘ 5 93 50, Telex 534267, Fax 5935220, – rm TV ☎ – 300. AE ⓓ E VISA JCB — CDZ b
Guggeryllis : **Meals** à la carte 300/510 – **176 rm** 1600/2700 – 4 suites.

Goldener Adler, Herzog-Friedrich-Str. 6, ℘ 58 63 34, Fax 584409, « 14C Tyrolian inn » – TV ☎. AE ⓓ E VISA — CZ c
Meals à la carte 315/580 – **37 rm** 1080/1600.

Central, Gilmstr. 5, ℘ 59 20, Telex 533824, Fax 580310, – TV ☎ – 30. AE ⓓ E VISA — DZ d
Meals à la carte 195/408 – **87 rm** 1050/2100.

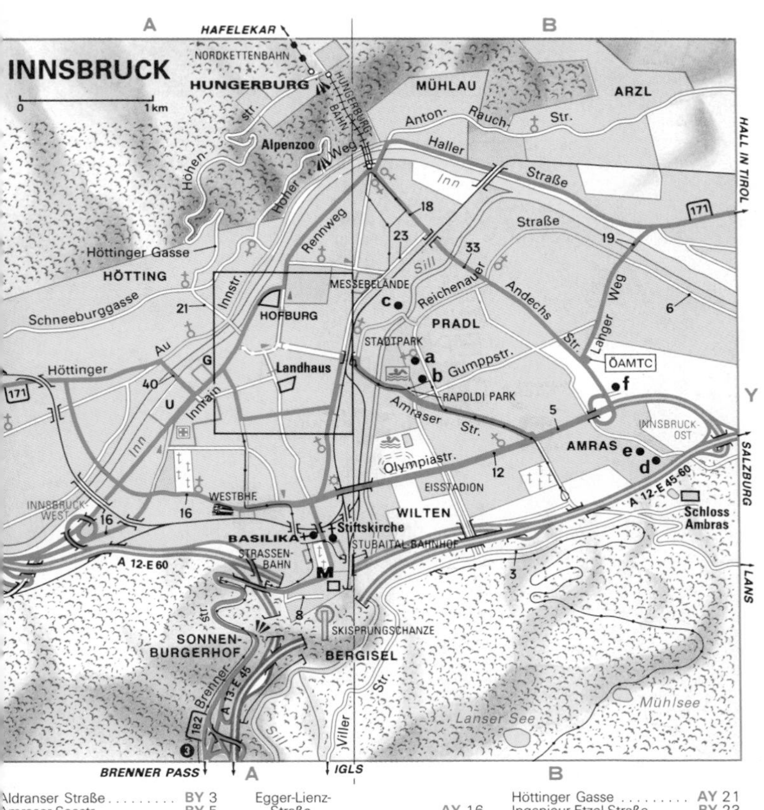

ldranser Straße	BY 3	Egger-Lienz-Straße	AY 16	Höttinger Gasse	AY 21
mraser-Seestr.	BY 5	Erzherzog-Eugen-Straße	BY 18	Ingenieur-Etzel-Straße	BY 23
rchenweg	BY 6	Grenobler Brücke	BY 19	Prinz-Eugen-Straße	BY 33
ergiselweg	AY 8			Universitäts-Brücke	AY 40
urgenland-Straße	BY 12				

Maria Theresia without rest, Maria Theresienstr. 31, ✆ 59 33, Telex 533300, Fax 575619 – AE ① E VISA JCB CZ **g**
103 rm 1300/2200.

Romantik Hotel Schwarzer Adler, Kaiserjägerstr. 2, ✆ 58 71 09, Fax 561697 – rm – 40. AE ① E VISA DZ **e**
Meals *(closed Sunday and Bank Holidays)* à la carte 315/500 – **26 rm** 1100/2300.

Alpotel Tirol, Innrain 13, ✆ 57 79 31, Fax 57793115, – 50. AE ① E VISA CZ **f**
Meals *(closed Saturday lunch, Sunday and Bank Holidays)* à la carte 270/540 – **73 rm** 1020/1760.

Sailer, Adamsgasse 6, ✆ 53 63, Fax 53637 – – 300. AE ① E VISA JCB
Meals à la carte 230/480 – **86 rm** 1000/1800. DZ **h**

Grauer Bär, Universitätsstr. 7, ✆ 5 92 40, Fax 574535 – rm – 100. AE ① E VISA DZ **k**
Meals à la carte 265/465 – **96 rm** 930/1900.

Sporthotel Penz, Fürstenweg 183, ✆ 2 25 14, Fax 22514124 – – 50. AE E VISA. by Fürstenweg AY
Meals à la carte 175/350 – **60 rm** 680/1450.

Maximilian without rest, Marktgraben 7, ✆ 5 9967, Fax 577450 – . AE ① E VISA
40 rm 750/1600. CZ **a**

Innsbruck, Innrain 3, ✆ 5 98 68, Fax 572280, – . AE ① E VISA
Meals (dinner only)(residents only) – **91 rm** 1100/1800. CZ **e**

INNSBRUCK

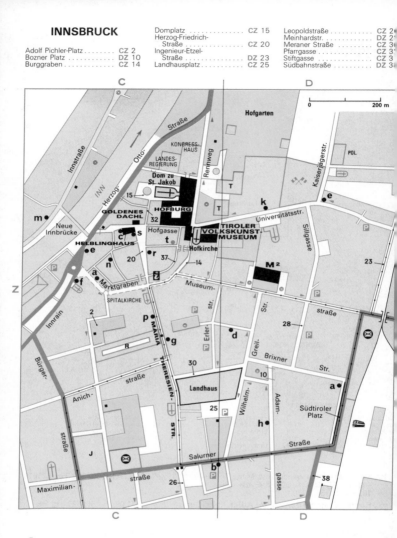

Tourotel Breinössl, Maria Theresien Str. 12, ✆ 58 41 65, Fax 58416524, beer garden – 🛗 rm TV ☎ P – 40. AE ⓓ E VISA — CZ **p**
Meals à la carte 190/300 – **41 rm** ☐ 950/1440.

Weißes Rößl, Kiebachgasse 8, ✆ 58 30 57, Fax 5830575, – 🛗 TV ☎. AE ⓓ E VISA — CZ **n**
closed 2 weeks April and November – **Meals** *(closed Sunday and Bank Holidays)* à la carte 160/400 – **13 rm** ☐ 850/1500.

Weisses Kreuz, Herzog-Friedrich-Str.31, ✆ 5 94 79, Fax 5947990, « 15C Tyrolian inn » – TV ☎. AE E VISA — CZ **r**
Meals à la carte 205/405 – **39 rm** ☐ 710/1380.

Mondschein without rest, Mariahilfstr. 6, ✆ 2 27 84, Fax 2278490 – 🛗 TV ☎. AE ⓓ E VISA — CZ **m**
closed mid November to Christmas – **35 rm** ☐ 700/1400.

Altstadtstüberl, Riesengasse 11, ✆ 58 23 47, Fax 583495 – AE ⓓ E VISA JCB — CZ **t**
closed Sunday and Bank Holidays, 20 May to 10 June – **Meals** à la carte 310/450.

at Innsbruck-Amras

Austrotel Innsbruck, Bernhard Höfel Str. 16, ℘ 3 44 33 30, Telex 533292, Fax 344428, - 200. BY f
Meals à la carte 180/430 - **137 rm** 1380/2060.

Kapeller, Phillipine-Welser-Str. 96, ℘ 34 31 06, Fax 34310668 - - 50. rest BY e
Meals *(closed Monday lunch, Sunday and Bank Holidays, 2 weeks January and 3 weeks July)* à la carte 275/520 - **36 rm** 700/1650.

Bierwirt, Bichlweg 2, ℘ 34 21 43, Fax 3425475, « Cosy lounge », - - 80.
Meals *(closed Sunday)* à la carte 185/415 - **47 rm** 600/1060.

at Innsbruck-Pradl

Alpinpark, Pradler Str. 28, ℘ 34 86 00, Telex 533509, Fax 364172, - - 40. BY a
Meals à la carte 210/500 - **87 rm** 890/1500.

Leipzigerhof, Defreggerstr. 13, ℘ 34 35 25, Fax 394357 - rm . rest
Meals *(closed Sunday)* à la carte 195/400 - **55 rm** 750/1350. BY b

at Igls S : 4 km by Viller Str. AB :

Schlosshotel, Viller Steig 2, ✉ 6080, ℘ (0512) 37 72 17, Fax 378679, , - - 20. rest
closed 15 October - 21 December - **Meals** à la carte 550/1030 - **20 rm** 2150/4000 - 5 suites.

Sporthotel Igls, Hilber Str. 17, ✉ 6080, ℘ (051) 237 72 41, Fax 378679, , Massage, , , , - - 50. rest
closed 15 October - 21 December - **Meals** à la carte 345/650 - **80 rm** 1370/2740 - 6 suites.

Batzenhäusl, Lanserstr. 12, ✉ 6080, ℘ (0512) 3 86 18, Fax 386187, , , - . rest
closed 20 October to 15 December - **Meals** 190/350 and à la carte - **33 rm** 950/1900 - 3 suites.

Römerhof, Römerstr. 62, ✉ 6080, ℘ (0512) 37 89 02, Fax 37890220, , - - 15. rm
Meals *(closed Monday)* (weekdays dinner only) à la carte 260/430 - **18 rm** 750/1500.

at Lans SE : 6km by Aldranser Str. BY :

Wilder Mann with rm, Römerstr. 12, ✉ 6072, ℘ (0512) 37 96 96, Fax 379139, - - 40.
Meals à la carte 260/525 - **14 rm** 830/1660.

SALZBURG 5020. Austria 987 ㊳, 426 K 5, 413 W 23 - pop. 140 000 - alt. 425 m - 0662.

See : ≤ ★★ over the town (from the Mönchsberg) X and ≤★★ (from Hettwer Bastei) Y - Hohensalzburg ★★ X, Z : ≤★★ (from the Kuenburg Bastion), ★★ (from the Reck Tower), Museum (Burgmuseum)★ - St. Peter's Churchyard (Petersfriedhof)★★ Z - St. Peter's Church (Stiftskirche St. Peter)★★ Z - Residenz★★ Z - Natural History Museum (Haus der Natur)★★ Y **M2** - Franciscan's Church (Franziskanerkirche)★ Z **A** - Getreidegasse★ Y - Mirabell Gardens (Mirabellgarten)★ V (Grand Staircase ★★ of the castle) - Baroquemuseum ★ V **M 3** - Dom★ Z.

Envir. : Road to the Gaisberg (Gaisbergstraße)★★ (≤★) by ① - Untersberg★ by ② : 10 km (with) - Castle Hellbrunn (Schloß Hellbrunn) ★ by Nonntaler Hauptstraße X.

9 Salzburg-Wals, Schloß Klessheim, ℘ 85 08 51 ; 9 Hof (① : 20 km), ℘ (06229) 23 90 ; 18 St. Lorenz (① : 29 km), ℘ (06232) 38 35.

Innsbrucker Bundesstr. 95 (by ③), ℘ 85 12 23 - City Air Terminal, Südtiroler Platz (Autobus Station) V.

℘ 71 54 14 22.

Exhibition Centre (Messegelände), Linke Glanzeile 65, ℘ 3 45 66.

Tourist Information, Mozartplatz 5, ℘ 84 75 68, Fax 8898732.

ÖAMTC, Alpenstr. 102 (by ②), ℘ 2 05 01, Fax 2050145.

Wien 292 ① - Innsbruck 164 ③ - München 140 ③.

Plans on following pages

Österreichischer Hof, Schwarzstr. 5, ℘ 8 89 77, Telex 633590, Fax 8897714, « Salzach-side setting, terrace with ≤ old town and castle » - rm - 70. Y b
***Zirbelzimmer* : Meals** à la carte 460/710 - ***Salzach-Grill* : Meals** à la carte 250/500 - **120 rm** 2200/5900 - 7 suites.

Salzburg Sheraton Hotel, Auerspergstr. 4, ℘ 88 99 90, Telex 632518, Fax 881776, « Terrace in spa gardens », entrance to the spa facilities - rm - 120. rest V s
***Mirabell* - *Bistro* : 144 rm** - 9 suites.

Altstadt Radisson SAS, Judengasse 15, ✆ 8 48 57 10, Fax 8485716, « Modernised 14C nobleman's house, antique furnishings » – |♦| ⇔ rm TV ☎ – 🔔 35. AE ⓓ E VISA. ✗ rest Y s
Meals à la carte 380/530 – **60 rm** ☐ 1750/6400 – 16 suites.

Bristol, Makartplatz 4, ✆ 87 35 57, Telex 633337, Fax 8735576 – |♦| ⇔ rm ▤ TV ☎ – 🔔 60. AE E VISA JCB. ✗ rest Y a
closed early January - end March – **Meals** *(closed Sunday except Festival)* à la carte 300/560 – **70 rm** ☐ 2800/5200 – 9 suites.

Holiday Inn Crowne Plaza - Pitter, Rainerstr. 6, ✆ 8 89 78, Telex 633532, Fax 878893, ⛲, ⚲, ≘ – |♦| ⇔ rm ▤ TV ☎ – 🔔 160. AE ⓓ E VISA JCB. ✗ rest V n
Rainerstube *(dinner only)* **Meals** à la carte 380/510 – ***Auersberg :*** **Meals** à la carte 260/470 – **186 rm** ☐ 1900/4400 – 6 suites.

Ramada Hotel Salzburg, Fanny-von-Lehnert-Str. 7, ✆ 4 68 80, Telex 632695, Fax 4688298, ⛲, Massage, ⚲, ≘, ▭ – |♦| ⇔ rm ▤ TV ☎ ♿ ⇔ – 🔔 810. AE ⓓ E VISA JCB. ✗ rest by Kaiserschützenstraße V
Meals à la carte 260/380 – **257 rm** ☐ 2130/2330.

SALZBURG

Auerspergstraße	V 3
Bürglsteinstraße	X 5
Erzabt-Klotz-Str.	X 9
Gstättengasse	X 12
Kaiserschützenstr.	V 20
Nonntaler Hauptstr.	X 29
Späthgasse	X 37

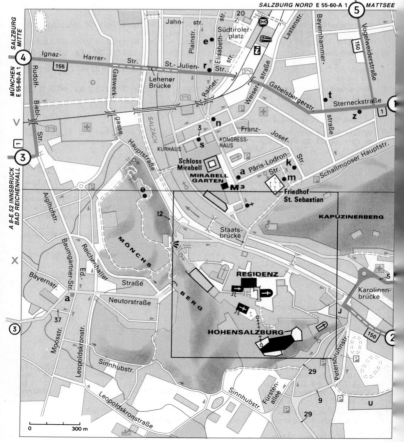

Goldener Hirsch, Getreidegasse 37, ✆ 84 85 11, Telex 632967, Fax 843349, « 15C nobleman's house, tastefully furnished » – 🛗 ⇆ rm ▤ TV ☎ – 🔬 30. AE ⓓ E VISA JCB Y **e**
Meals à la carte 400/650 – **71 rm** ☐ 2450/3850 – 3 suites.

Schloß Mönchstein 🔇, Mönchsberg Park 26, ✆ 8 48 55 50, Fax 848559, ≤ Salzburg and surroundings, ⛱, « Small castle with elegant, stylish furnishings, wedding chapel, park », 🌳, 🎾 – 🛗 TV ☎ 🚗 🅿 – 🔬 30. AE ⓓ E JCB. ✂ rest X **e**
Meals à la carte 460/800 – **17 rm** ☐ 2200/6200.

Rosenberger, Bessarabierstr. 94, ✆ 4 35 54 60, Fax 43951095, 🏊 – 🛗 ⇆ rm TV ☎ ♿ 🚗 🅿 – 🔬 360. AE ⓓ E VISA by ④
Meals à la carte 210/350 🌡 – **120 rm** ☐ 1290/1900.

Dorint-Hotel, Sterneckstr. 20, ✆ 88 20 31, Telex 631075, Fax 8820319, 🏊 – 🛗 ▤ rest TV ☎ ♿ 🚗 – 🔬 150. AE ⓓ E VISA. ✂ rest V **z**
Meals à la carte 220/420 – **140 rm** ☐ 1400/1900.

Austrotel, Mirabellplatz 8, ✆ 88 16 88, Telex 632361, Fax 881687 – 🛗 ⇆ rm TV ☎ – 🔬 25. AE ⓓ E VISA JCB V **a**
Meals *(closed Saturday - Sunday)* à la carte 290/415 – **74 rm** ☐ 1700/2600.

Mercure, Bayerhamerstr. 14, ✆ 8 81 43 80, Fax 871111411, ⛱ – 🛗 ⇆ rm TV ☎ ♿ 🚗 🅿 – 🔬 90. AE ⓓ E VISA JCB V **t**
Meals à la carte 260/360 – **121 rm** ☐ 1400/2100.

Novotel Salzburg City, Franz-Josef-Str. 26, ✆ 88 20 41, Telex 632886, Fax 874240, 🏊 – 🛗 ⇆ rm TV ☎ ♿ 🚗 🅿 – 🔬 110. AE ⓓ E VISA V **k**
Meals (dinner only) à la carte 230/300 – **140 rm** ☐ 1360/2250.

Zum Hirschen without rest, St.-Julien-Str. 21, ✆ 88 90 30, Fax 8890358, ⛱, Massage, 🏊 – 🛗 TV ☎ 🅿. AE ⓓ E VISA V **r**
64 rm ☐ 790/1700 – 5 suites.

Kasererbräu without rest, Kaigasse 33, 84 24 06, Fax 84244551, – TV . AE E VISA JCB Z n
closed February – **54 rm** 1120/2640.

Kasererhof without rest, Alpenstr. 6, 6 39 65, Telex 633477, Fax 6396550, – TV P. AE E VISA JCB by ②
closed February **54 rm** 1160/3560.

Wolf-Dietrich, Wolf-Dietrich-Str. 7, 87 12 75, Fax 882320, – TV . AE VISA JCB V m
closed early February - end March – **Meals** *(closed Sunday)* (dinner only) à la carte 210/360 – **29 rm** 920/2175.

Hohenstauffen without rest, Elisabethstr. 19, 8 77 66 90, Fax 87219351 – TV . AE E VISA JCB V e
27 rm 800/1990.

Fuggerhof without rest, Eberhard-Fugger-Str. 9, 6 41 29 00, Fax 6412904, ≤, – TV P. by Bürglsteinstr. X
closed 20 December - 26 January – **20 rm** 980/2400.

Gablerbräu, Linzer Gasse 9, 8 89 65, Telex 631067, Fax 8896555, – – 25. AE E VISA JCB Y d
Meals à la carte 180/430 – **52 rm** 1070/1740.

Elefant, Sigmund-Haffner-Gasse 4, 84 33 97, Fax 84010928 – TV Y f
36 rm.

K u. K Restaurant am Waagplatz, Waagplatz 2 (1st floor), 84 21 56, Fax 84215633, , « Medieval dinner with period performance in the Freysauff-Keller (by arrangement) » – AE E VISA Z h
closed Sunday January to Easter – **Meals** (booking essential) a la carte 260/540.

Riedenburg, Neutorstr. 31, 83 08 15, Fax 5217743, – P. AE E VISA X a
closed Monday lunch, Sunday and 2 weeks June – **Meals** à la carte 365/510.

Zum Mohren, Judengasse 9, 84 23 87, Fax 50179 – AE E VISA Y g
closed Sunday, Bank Holidays and mid June - mid July – **Meals** (booking essential) à la carte 220/410.

at Salzburg-Aigen **5026** by Bürglsteinstr. X :

Doktorwirt, Glaser Str. 9, 62 29 73, Fax 62171724, , , (heated), – TV P – 25. AE E VISA JCB. rest
closed 10 to 26 February and end October - end November – **Meals** *(closed Monday)* à la carte 200/400 – **39 rm** 850/1950.

Gasthof Schloß Aigen, Schwarzenbergpromenade 37, 62 12 84, Fax 621284, – P. AE E VISA
closed Thursday lunch, Wednesday, early January - early February and 2 to 8 September – **Meals** à la carte 310/520.

at Salzburg-Liefering **5020** by ④ :

✿ **Brandstätter**, Münchner Bundesstr. 69, 43 45 35, Fax 43453590, , , , – TV P – 40. rest
closed 22 to 27 December – **Meals** *(closed 2 to 16 January)* (booking essential) à la carte 290/520 – **34 rm** 780/2300
Spec. Haussulz mit steirischem Kürbiskernöl, Kalbssalonbeuscherl mit Semmelknödel, Rehrückenmedaillons mit Eierschwammerln und Serviettenknödel.

at Salzburg-Maria Plain **5101** by Plainstr. V :

Maria Plain (17C inn), Plainbergweg 41, 5 07 01, Fax 5070119, « Garden with ≤ » – TV P – 40. AE
closed 1 week July – **Meals** *(closed Tuesday - Wednesday, except Festival)* à la carte 260/380 – **27 rm** 748/1200 – 5 suites.

at Salzburg-Nonntal **5020**

Purzelbaum (Bistro-rest.), Zugallistr. 7, 84 88 43, Fax 5217743, – AE E VISA. Z e
closed Monday lunch, Sunday and 2 weeks July – **Meals** (booking essential for dinner) à la carte 420/550.

at Salzburg-Parsch **5020** by Bürglsteinstr. X :

Villa Pace, Sonnleitenweg 9, 6 41 50 10, Fax 6415015, ≤ town and Hohensalzburg, , , (heated), – rm TV P. AE E VISA JCB. rest
closed November - February – **Meals** *(closed Monday lunch and Sunday, except Festival)* (booking essential) à la carte 430/570 – **15 rm** 2450/7100 – 5 suites.

on the Heuberg NE : 3 km by ① – alt. 565 m

Schöne Aussicht, Heuberg 3, ✉ A-5023 Salzburg, (0662) 64 06 08, Fax 6406082, « Garden with ≤ Salzburg and Alps », , , , – TV P – 30. AE E VISA
closed November - March – **Meals** *(April, October and Sunday dinner only)* a la carte 265/480 – **28 rm** 830/2200.

on the Gaisberg by ① :

Kobenzl, Gaisberg 11, alt. 750 m, A-5020 Salzburg, (0662) 64 15 10, Telex 633833, Fax 642238, « Beautiful panoramic location with < Salzburg and Alps », Massage, – 40. AE E VISA. rest
closed mid November - mid March – **Meals** à la carte 320/600 – **38 rm** 1650/3300 – 5 suites.

Romantik-Hotel Gersberg Alm, Gersberg 37, alt. 800 m, A-5023 Salzburg-Gnigl, (0662) 64 12 57, Fax 64125780, – 55. AE E VISA
closed 5 to 18 February – **Meals** à la carte 300/470 – **40 rm** 1230/2900.

near Airport by ③ :

Radisson-Center-Hotel, Innsbrucker Bundesstr. 4, A-5073 Salzburg-Wals, (0662) 8 58 10, Fax 85814000 – rm – 90. AE E VISA JCB
Meals à la carte 290/520 – **152 rm** 1050/2300.

Airporthotel, Loigstr. 20a, A-5020 Salzburg-Loig, (0662) 85 00 20, Telex 633634, Fax 85002044, – rm – 25. AE E VISA JCB
Meals (residents only) (dinner only) – **32 rm** 1200/1960.

at Anif **5081** ② : 7 km – 06246 :

Friesacher, 89 77, Fax 897749, – 25
closed 2 to 22 January – **Meals** *(closed Wednesday)* à la carte 180/410 – **52 rm** 720/1610.

Point Hotel, Berchtesgadener Str. 364, 74 25 60, Fax 74256443, Massage, (heated), (indoor) – – 100. AE E VISA. rest
Meals à la carte 210/420 – **62 rm** 1430/2254.

at Elixhausen **5161** N : 8 km by ⑤ :

Romantik-Hotel Gmachl, Dorfstr. 14, (0662) 48 02 12, Fax 4802 1272, (indoor court), (indoor) – – 40. AE E VISA
closed 1 - 14 July **Meals** *(closed Sunday dinner, Monday lunch)* à la carte 270/470 – **56 rm** 1050/2150 – 3 suites.

at Hof **5322** ① : 20 km :

Schloß Fuschl (former 15C hunting seat with 3 guesthouses), (06229) 2 25 30, Telex 633454, Fax 2253531, <, Massage, – – 100. AE E VISA. rest
Meals à la carte 450/800 – **84 rm** 2800/5900 – 12 suites.

Jagdhof am Fuschlsee (former 18C farmhouse with guesthouse), (06229) 2 37 20, Telex 633454, Fax 2372413, <, – – 90. AE E VISA. rest
Meals à la carte 220/400 – **54 rm** 950/1800.

at Fuschl am See **5330** ① : 26 km :

Parkhotel Waldhof, Seepromenade, (06226) 2 64, Fax 644, <, Massage, – – 60. rest
closed 3 weeks March - April and November - 15 December – **Meals** (booking essential) à la carte 280/500 – **75 rm** 955/2460.

at Mondsee ① : 28 km (by motorway A 1) – 06232 :

Seehof, (SE : 7 km), A-5311 Loibichl, (06232) 50 31, Fax 503151, <, « Garden-terrace », Massage, – rest – 15
closed mid September - mid May – **Meals** à la carte 370/515 – **35 rm** 3600/5560 – 4 suites.

XXX ✿ **Landhaus Eschlböck-Plomberg** with rm, (S : 5 km), A-5310 St. Lorenz-Plomberg, (06232) 35 72, Fax 316620, <, boat landing place – rest . AE E VISA
Meals *(closed September - May Tuesday and Wednesday)* (booking essential) à la carte 400/700 – **12 rm** 1000/3050
Spec. Eierschwammerlgulyás mit Briocheknöderl (June - August), Fische aus dem Mondsee mit Trüffelbutter, Medaillons vom Reh mit Pilzen (August - April).

Benelux

Belgium
BRUSSELS – ANTWERP – BRUGES – LIÈGE

Grand Duchy of Luxembourg
LUXEMBOURG

Netherlands
AMSTERDAM – The HAGUE – ROTTERDAM

PRACTICAL INFORMATION

LOCAL CURRENCY

Belgian Franc: 100 BEF = 3.40 USD ($) (Jan. 96) can also be used in Luxembourg

Dutch Florin: 100 NLG = 62.23 USD ($) (Jan. 96)

TOURIST INFORMATION

Telephone numbers and addresses of Tourist Offices are given in the text of each city under ℹ.

AIRLINES

SABENA : rue Marché-aux-Herbes 110, 1000 Bruxelles, ✆ (02) 723 89 40, 70, Grand-Rue, L-1660 Luxembourg, ✆ 22 12 12, Weteringschans 26, 1017 SG Amsterdam, ✆ (020) 626 29 66.

LUXAIR : Luxembourg Airport, L-2987 Luxembourg, ✆ 4 79 81.

KLM : avenue Marnix 28, 1050 Bruxelles, ✆ (02) 507 70 70, 1, Airport Findel, Air terminal (office 327), L-1110 Luxembourg, ✆ 42 48 42, Amsterdamseweg 55, 1182 GP Amsterdam, ✆ (020) 649 91 23.

FOREIGN EXCHANGE

In Belgium, banks close at 4.30pm and weekends;

in the Netherlands, banks close at 5.00pm and weekends, Schiphol Airport exchange offices open daily from 6.30am to 11.30pm.

TRANSPORT

Taxis: may be hailed in the street, at taxi ranks or called by telephone.
Bus, tramway: practical for long and short distances and good for sightseeing.

Brussels has a **Métro** (subway) network. In each station complete information and plans will be found.

POSTAL SERVICES

Post offices open Monday to Friday from 9am to 5pm in Benelux.

SHOPPING

Shops and boutiques are generally open from 9am to 7pm in Belgium and Luxembourg, and from 9am to 6pm in the Netherlands. The main shopping areas are:

in Brussels: Rue Neuve, Porte de Namur, Avenue Louise - Also Brussels antique market on Saturday from 9am to 3pm, and Sunday from 9am to 1pm (around place du Grand-Sablon) - Flower and Bird market (Grand-Place) on Sunday morning.

in Luxembourg: Grand'Rue and around Place d'Armes - Station Quarter.

in Amsterdam: Kalverstraat, Leidsestraat, Nieuwendijk, P.C. Hoofstraat and Utrechtsestraat. Second-hand goods and antiques. Amsterdam Flea Market (near Waterlooplein).

BREAKDOWN SERVICE

24 hour assistance:

Belgium: TCB, Brussels ✆ (02) 233 22 11 – VTB-VAB, Antwerp ✆ (0 3) 253 63 63 – RACB, Brussels ✆ (0 2) 287 09 00.

Luxembourg: ACL ✆ 45 00 45.

Netherlands: ANWB, The Hague ✆ (0 70) 314 71 47.

TIPPING

In Benelux, prices include service and taxes.

SPEED LIMITS – SEAT BELTS

In Belgium and Luxembourg, the maximum speed limits are 120 km/h-74 mph on motorways and dual carriageways, 90 km/h-56 mph on all other roads and 50 km/h-31 mph in built-up areas. In the Netherlands, 100/120 km/h-62/74 mph on motorways and "autowegen", 80 km/h-50 mph on other roads and 50 km/h-31 mph in built-up areas. In each country, the wearing of seat belts is compulsory for driver and passengers.

Brussels

(BRUXELLES - BRUSSEL) 1000 Région de Bruxelles-Capitale - Brussels Hoofdstedelijk Gewest 213 ⑱ and 409 G 3 - ⑫ S - Pop. 667 825 - ☎ 0 2.

See : Atomium★ (Heysel) - National basilica of Koekelberg★ - Place Royale★ KZ - Market Square★★★ (Grand-Place) JY - Monnaie Theatre★ JY - St-Hubert Arcades★★ JY - Erasmus House★★ (Anderlecht) - Gauchie House★ (Etterbeek HS **W** - Castle and park★★ (Gaasbeek, SW : 12 km) - Royal Plant Houses★★ (Laeken) - Horta Museum★★ (St-Gilles) EFU **M10** - Van Buuren House★ (Uccle) EFV **M13** - Old England★ KZ **B** - Sts-Michaels and Gudule Cathedral★★ KY - Church of N.-D. de la Chapelle★ JZ - Church of N.-D. du Sablon★ JZ - Cambre Abbey★★ (Ixelles) FGV - Church of Sts-Pierre and Guidon★ (Anderlecht) - Royal Museums of Belgian Fine Arts★★★ KZ - Florist De Backer★ KY **F1** - Grand et Petit Sablon★★ JZ - Rue des Bouchers★ JY - Manneken Pis★★ JZ.

Museums : Ancien Art★★★ KZ- Royal Museum of Art and History★★★ HS **M7** - Modern Art★★ KZ **M1** - Belgian Centre of Comic Strips★★ KY **M5** - Autoworld★★ HS **M23** - Natural Science (Royal Institute)★★ GS **M9** - Musical Instruments★★ JZ **M2** - Meunier★ (Ixelles) FV **M12** - Ixelles Municipal Museum★★ FGT **M11** - Charlier★ FR **M21** - Bibliotheca Wittockiana★ (Woluwé-St-Pierre).

18 9 at Tervuren SE : 14 km, Château de Ravenstein ☎ (0 2) 767 58 01, Fax (0 2) 767 28 41 - 18 at Melsbroek NE : 14 km, Steenwagenstraat 11 ☎ (0 2) 751 82 05, Fax (0 2) 751 84 25 - 18 at Anderlecht, Sports Area of la Pede, r. Scholle 1 ☎ (0 2) 521 16 87, Fax (0 2) 521 51 56 - 9 at Watermael-Boitsfort, chaussée de la Hulpe 53a ☎ (0 2) 672 22 22, Fax (0 2) 675 34 81 - 9 at Overijse SE : 16 km, Gemslaan 55 ☎ (0 2) 687 50 30, Fax (0 2) 687 37 68 - 9 at Itterbeek W : 8 km, J.M. van Lierdelaan 28 b ☎ (0 2) 567 00 38, Fax (0 2) 567 02 23 - 18 at Kampenhout NE : 20 km, Wildersedreef 56 ☎ (016) 65 12 16, Fax (0 16) 65 16 80 - 9 at Duisburg E : 18 km, Hertswegenstraat 39 ☎ (0 2) 767 97 52.

✈ Sabena office, r. Marché-aux-Herbes 110, ✉ 1000, ☎ 723 89 40, direct railwayline ☎ 753 21 11. - 🚘 ☎ 203 36 40 and 203 28 80.

ℹ (closed Sundays in Summer) Town Hall (Hôtel de Ville), Grand'Place, ✉ 1000 ☎ 513 89 40, Fax 514 45 38 - Office de Promotion du Tourisme (O.P.T.) r. Marché-aux-Herbes 61, ✉ 1000, ☎ 504 02 22, Fax 513 69 50 - Vlaams Commissariaat-Generaal voor Toerisme (V.C.G.T.), Grasmarkt 61, ✉ 1000, ☎ 504 03 00, Fax 513 88 03.

Paris 308 - Amsterdam 204 - Düsseldorf 222 - Lille 116 - Luxembourg 219.

BRUXELLES BRUSSEL

Louise (Galerie) .... FS 161
Midi (Bd du) .... ES

Baudouin (Bd) .... EQ 16
Bienfaiteurs (Pl. des) .... GQ 21
Brabançonne (Av. de la) . GR 28
Edouard de Thibault (Av.). HS 72
Europe (Bd de l') .... ES 89
Frans Courtens (Av.) .... HQ 102
Frère-Orban (Sq.) .... FR 104

Froissart (R.) .... GS 106
Gén. Eisenhower (Av.) ... GQ 108
Hal (Porte de) .... ES 114
Henri Jaspar (Av.) ...... ES 117
Herbert Hoover (Av.) .... HR 118
Industrie (Quai de l') .... ER 126
Jan Stobbaerts (Av.) .... GQ 133

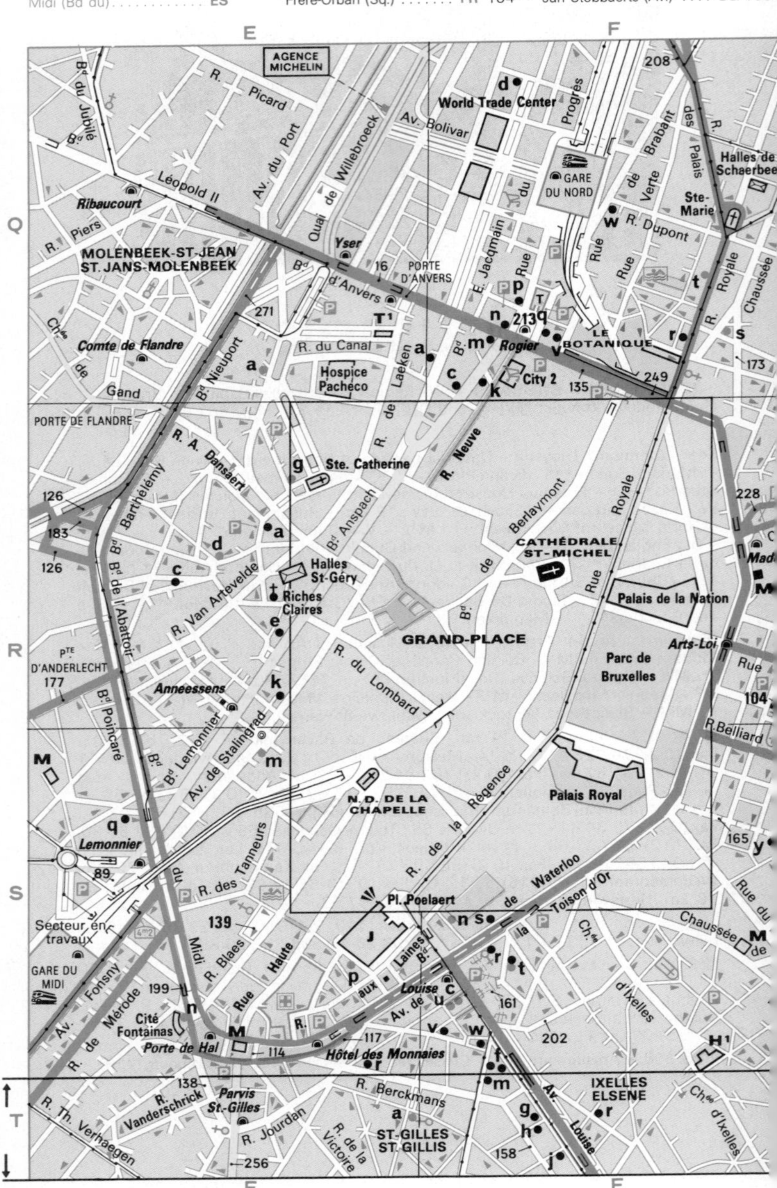

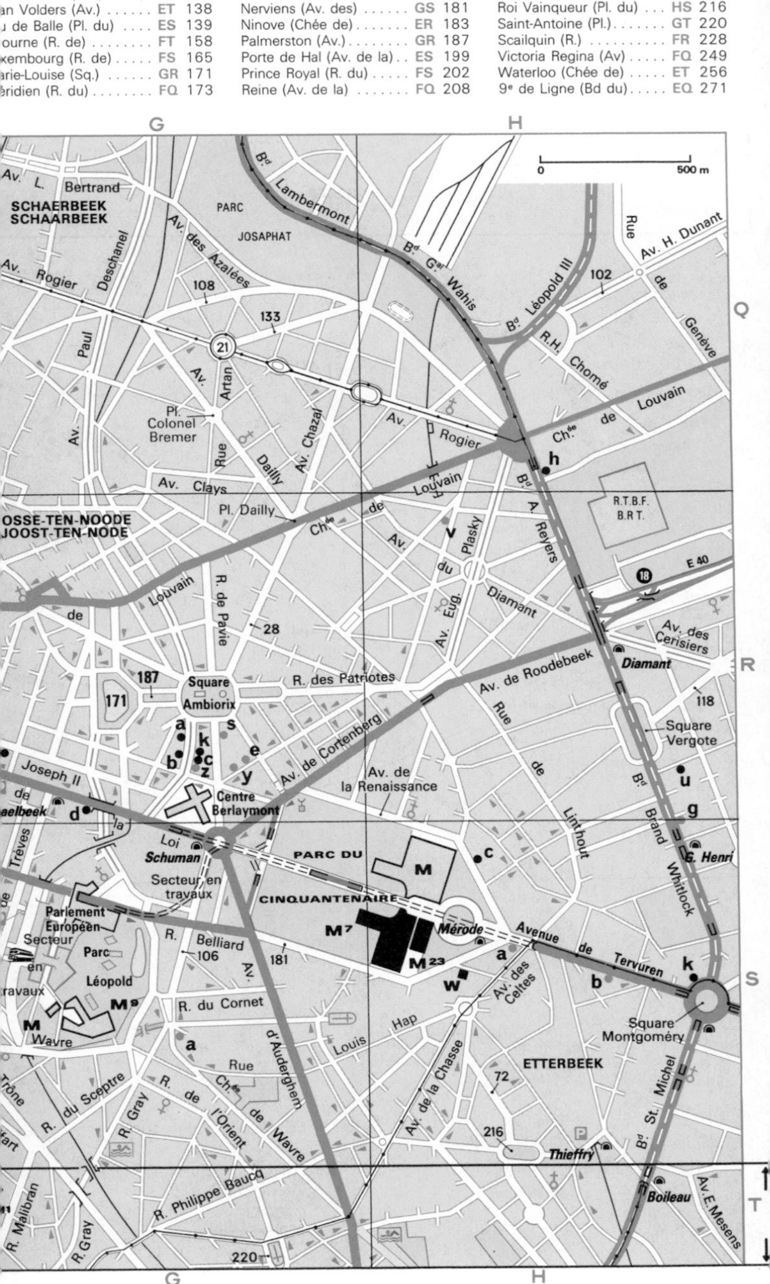

G
H
0
500 m
Q
R
S
T
SCHAERBEEK
SCHAARBEEK
PARC
JOSAPHAT
Av. L. Bertrand
Av. des Azalées
Bd Lambermont
Bd Gal Wahis
Bd Léopold III
Rue de Genève
Av. H. Dunant
R.H. Chomé
Chée de Louvain
Av. Rogier
Deschanel
Paul
Av.
Av. Artan
Rue Artan
Pl. Colonel Bremer
Av. Chazal
Dailly
Av. Clays
Pl. Dailly
OSSE-TEN-NOODE
JOOST-TEN-NODE
Bd A. Reyers
R.T.B.F.
B.R.T.
E 40
Av. Plasky
Av. du Diamant
Av. Eug.
R. de Pavie
Av. des Cerisiers
Diamant
Av. de Roodebeek
R. des Patriotes
Square Ambiorix
Av. de Cortenberg
Av. de la Renaissance
Rue de Linthout
Square Vergote
Bd Brand Whitlock
Joseph II
Centre Berlaymont
Loi
Schuman
Secteur en travaux
PARC DU
CINQUANTENAIRE
M
M7
M23
Mérode
G. Henri
Parlement Européen
Secteur en travaux
Parc Léopold
M9
R. Belliard
Av. d'Auderghem
Avenue de Tervuren
Av. des Celtes
Square Montgoméry
Bd St. Michel
ETTERBEEK
R. du Cornet
Wavre
Louis Hap
Rue
Chée de Wavre
Av. de la Chasse
R. de l'Orient
R. du Sceptre
R. Gray
R. Philippe Baucq
R. Malibran
Thieffry
Boileau
Av. E. Mesens
Trèves
Trône

BRUXELLES
BRUSSEL

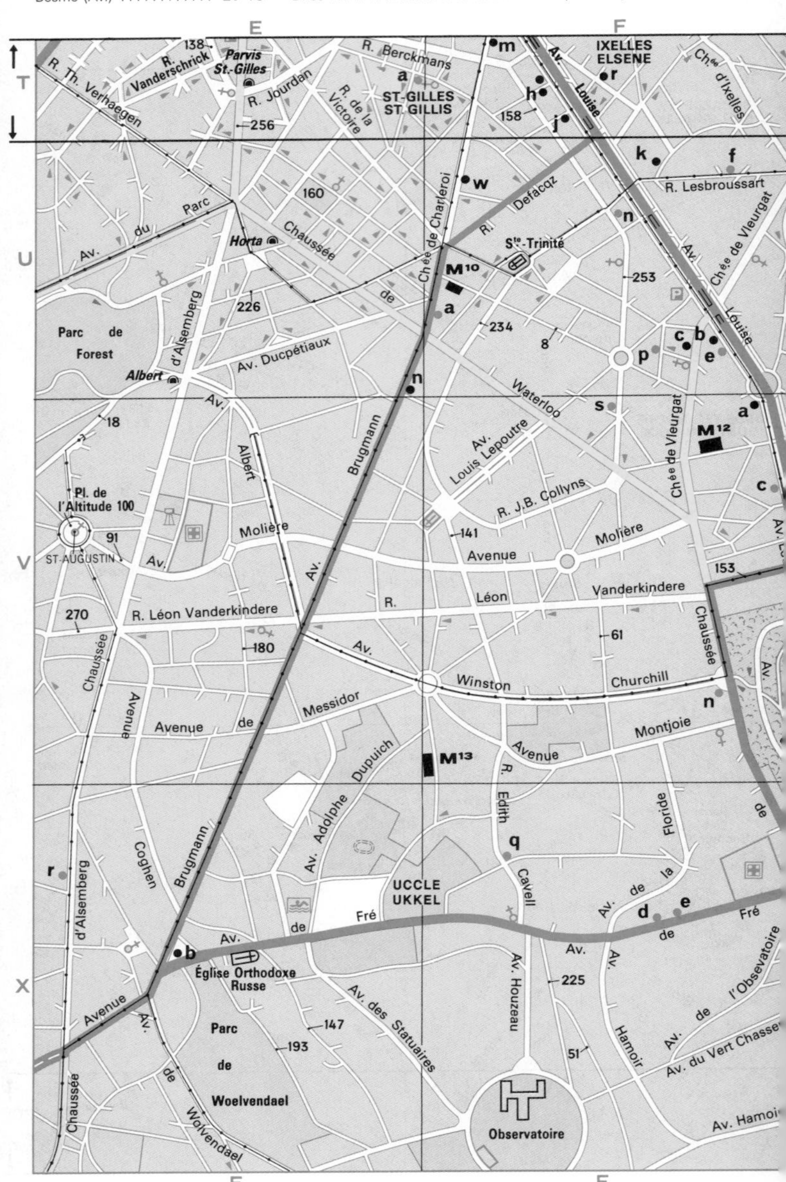

alides (Bd des) .... HV 127	Louis Morichar (Pl.) ..... EU 160	Savoie (R. de) .... EU 226
an Volders (Av.) ...... ET 138	Mutualité (R. de la) ..... EV 180	Tabellion (R. de) .... FU 234
s Stallaert (R.) .... FV 141	Nouvelle (Av.) .... GU 184	Washington (R.) .... FU 253
iette Wytsman (R.) .... GU 145	Paul Stroobant (Av.) ..... EX 193	Waterloo (Chée de) ..... ET 256
nerdelle (Av.) .... EX 147	Saint-Antoine (Pl.) .... GT 220	2e Rég. de Lanciers
grand (Av.) .... FV 153	Saisons (Av. des) .... GV 223	(Av. du) .... GHU 265
ourne (R. de) .... FT 158	Saturne (Av. de) .... FX 225	7 Bonniers (Av. des) .... EV 270

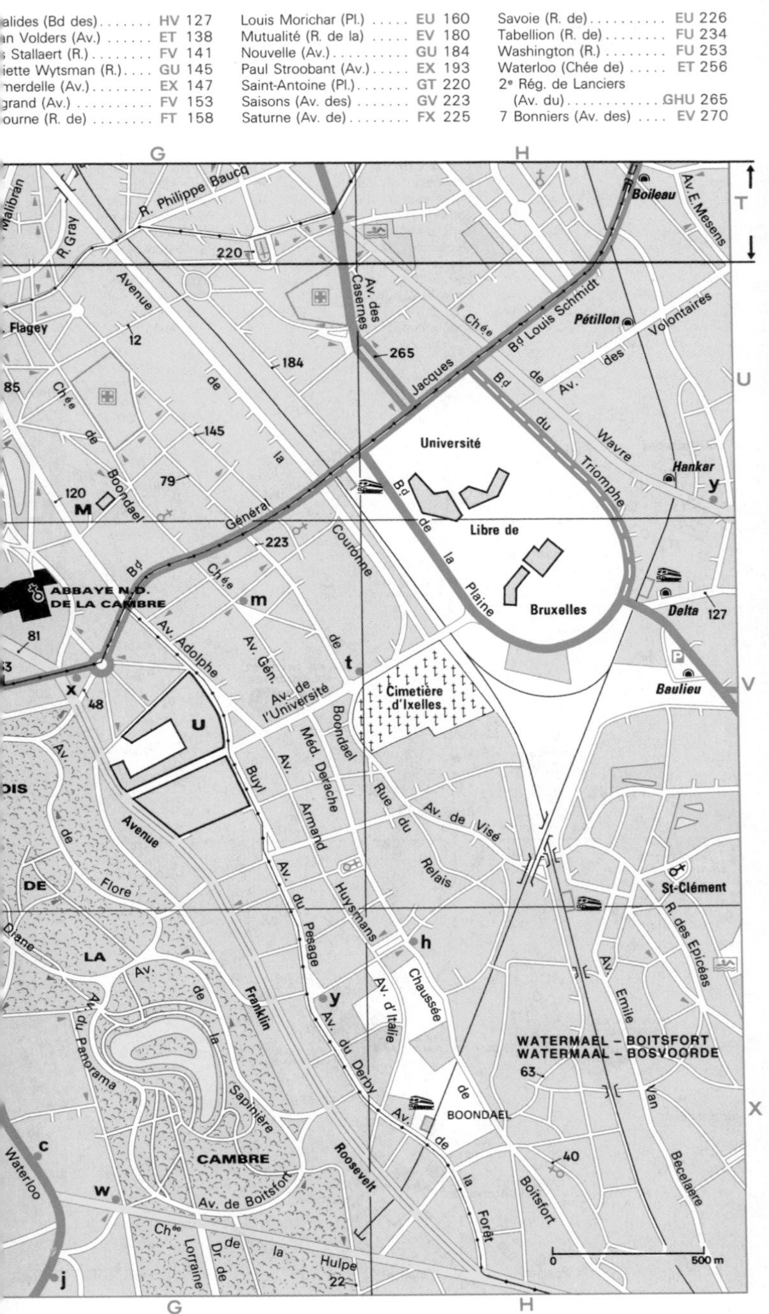

BRUXELLES BRUSSEL

Adolphe Max (Bd) . . . . . JY 3
Anspach (Bd) . . . . JY
Beurre (Rue au) . . . . JY 19
Etuve (R. de l') . . . . JZ 88
Fripiers (R. des) . . . . JY 105
Grand Sablon (Pl. du) . . . KZ 112
Ixelles (Chée d') . . . . KZ 129
Marché-aux-Herbes (R. du) . . . . JY 168
Marché-aux-Poulets (R. du) . . . . JY 169
Midi (R. du) . . . . JYZ
Neuve (Rue) . . . . JY
Reine (Galerie de la) . . . . JY 210
Roi (Galerie du) . . . . KY 214
Toison d'Or (Av. de la) . . KZ 238

Albertine (Pl. de l') . . . . . KZ 4
Assaut (R. d') . . . . KY 10
Baudet (R.) . . . . KZ 15
Bortier (Galerie) . . . . JZ 23
Bouchers (Petite rue des) . JY 24
Bouchers (R. des) . . . . JY 25
Bourse (Pl. de la) . . . . JY 27
Briques (Quai aux) . . . . . . JY 29
Chêne (R. du) . . . . JZ 39
Colonies (R. des) . . . . KY 43
Comédiens (R. des) . . . . . KY 45
Commerce (R. du) . . . . . . KZ 46
Croix-de-Fer (R. de la) . . . . KY 52
Duquesnoy (Rue) . . . . . . JYZ 66
Ernest Allard (R.) . . . . JZ 87
Europe (Carr. de l') . . . . . KY 90
Fossé-aux-Loups (R. du) . . . . JKY 99
Impératrice (Bd de l') . . . . KY 124

Joseph Lebeau (R.) . . . . . JZ 142
Laeken (R. de) . . . . JY 151
Louvain (R. de) . . . . KY 163
Mercier (R. du Card.) . . . . KY 172
Montagne (Rue de la) . . . KY 178
Musée (Pl. du) . . . . KZ 179
Nord (Passage du) . . . . . . JY 182
Petit Sablon (Sq. du) . . . . KZ 195
Presse (R. de la) . . . . KY 201
Princes (Galeries des) . . . JY 205
Ravenstein (R.) . . . . KZ 207
Rollebeek (R. de) . . . . JZ 217
Ruysbroeck (R. de) . . . . . . KZ 219
Ste-Catherine (Pl.) . . . . JY 221
Sainte-Gudule (Pl.) . . . . . . KY 222
Trône (R. du) . . . . KZ 241
Ursulines (R. des) . . . . JZ 243
Waterloo (Bd de) . . . . KZ 255
6 Jeunes Hommes (R. des) . . . . KZ 268

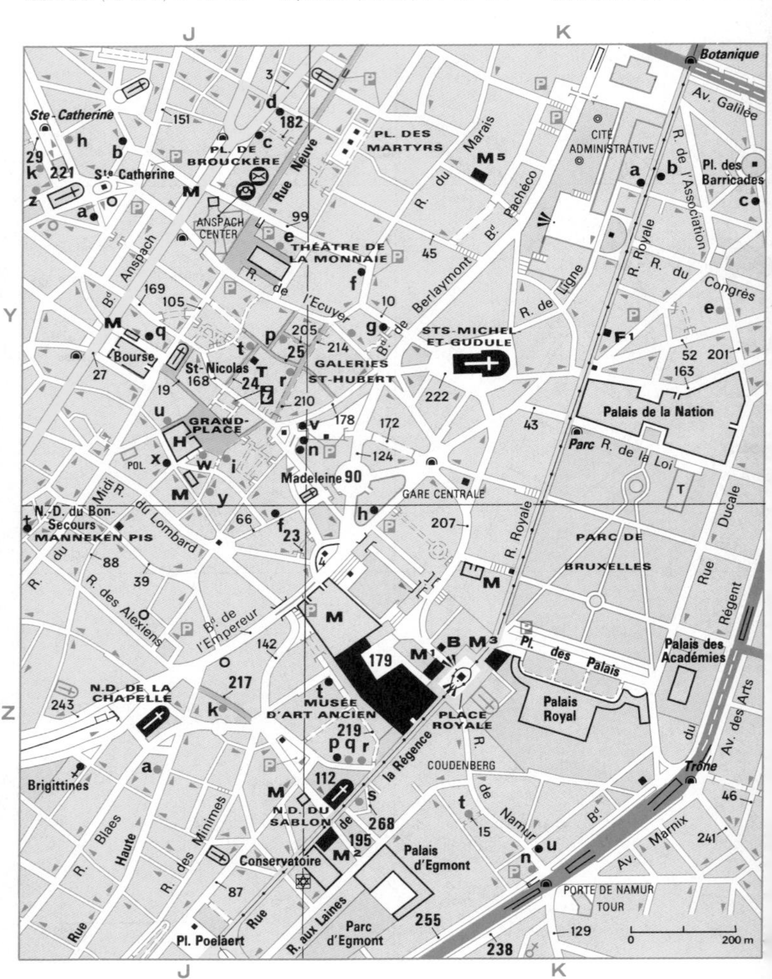

BRUXELLES (BRUSSEL)

Radisson SAS, r. Fossé-aux-Loups 47, ✉ 1000, ℘ 219 28 28, Telex 22202, Fax 219 62 62, « Patio with remains of 12C City enclosure wall », ⚒, ≘s - |♣| ⇆ ▤ TV ☎ ♿ ⇔ - 🏛 25-380. AE ⓓ E VISA. ✻ rest KY f
Meals see rest *Sea Grill* below - *Atrium* *Lunch 975* - a la carte 900/1300 - ☐ 550 - **275 rm** 13000/14000, 6 suites.

Métropole, pl. de Brouckère 31, ✉ 1000, ℘ 217 23 00, Telex 21234, Fax 218 02 20, « Late 19C hall and lounges », ⚒, ≘s - |♣| ⇆ ▤ rest TV ☎ - 🏛 25-500. AE ⓓ E VISA JCB
Meals see rest *L'Alban Chambon* below - **308 rm** ☐ 6850/11400, 5 suites. JY c

Astoria, r. Royale 103, ✉ 1000, ℘ 217 62 90, Telex 25040, Fax 217 11 50, « Hall, lounges and restaurant with early 20C decor » - |♣| ⇆ ▤ TV ☎ Ⓟ - 🏛 25-320. AE ⓓ E VISA. ✻
Meals *Le Palais Royal* *(closed Saturday lunch and Sunday dinner)* *Lunch 1550* - a la carte 1800/2500 - ☐ 850 - **107 rm** 8000, 12 suites. KY b

Jolly Atlanta, bd A. Max 7, ✉ 1000, ℘ 217 01 20, Telex 21475, Fax 217 37 58 - |♣| ⇆ ▤ rest TV ☎ ⇔ - 🏛 25-50. AE ⓓ E VISA. ✻ rest JY d
Meals *(closed Saturday, Sunday and July-August)* *Lunch 950* - a la carte approx. 1700 - **234 rm** ☐ 6000/8950, 6 suites.

Bedford, r. Midi 135, ✉ 1000, ℘ 512 78 40, Telex 24059, Fax 514 17 59 - |♣| ⇆ ▤ TV ☎ ⇔ - 🏛 50-200. AE ⓓ E VISA. ✻ ER k
Meals *Lunch 1050* - 1050 - **294 rm** ☐ 7300, 1 suite.

Président Centre without rest, r. Royale 160, ✉ 1000, ℘ 219 00 65, Telex 26784, Fax 218 09 10 - |♣| ⇆ ▤ TV ☎ ⇔. AE ⓓ E VISA JCB. ✻ KY a
73 rm ☐ 4900/5900.

Embassy without rest, bd Anspach 159, ✉ 1000, ℘ 512 81 00, Fax 514 30 97, ≘s - |♣| ⇆ TV ☎ - 🏛 25-60. AE E VISA. ✻ ER e
54 rm ☐ 5500/6500.

Arenberg, r. Assaut 15, ✉ 1000, ℘ 511 07 70, Fax 514 19 76 - |♣| ⇆ ▤ rest TV ☎ - 🏛 25-90. AE ⓓ E VISA JCB. ✻ KY g
Meals (dinner only) a la carte approx. 1200 - **155 rm** ☐ 3000/6800.

Chambord without rest, r. Namur 82, ✉ 1000, ℘ 513 41 19, Fax 514 08 47 - |♣| TV ☎. AE ⓓ E VISA KZ u
69 rm ☐ 1995/4995.

George V ⛲ without rest, r. 't Kint 23, ✉ 1000, ℘ 513 50 93, Fax 513 44 93 - |♣| ☎ Ⓟ. E VISA
17 rm ☐ 2400. ER c

Queen Anne without rest, bd E. Jacqmain 110, ✉ 1000, ℘ 217 16 00, Telex 22676, Fax 217 18 38 - |♣| TV ☎. AE ⓓ E VISA EFQ a
60 rm ☐ 3250/3750.

Sabina without rest, r. Nord 78, ✉ 1000, ℘ 218 26 37, Fax 219 32 39 - |♣| TV ☎. AE ⓓ E VISA JCB KY c
23 rm ☐ 1800/2200.

XXXX ✿ **Sea Grill** - (at Radisson SAS H.), r. Fossé-aux-Loups 47, ✉ 1000, ℘ 217 92 25, Telex 22202, Fax 219 62 62, Seafood - ▤ Ⓟ. AE ⓓ E VISA. ✻ KY f
closed Saturday lunch, Sunday, Bank Holidays, 7 to 14 April and 21 July-18 August - **Meals** 1650/2400, a la carte 2050/2600
Spec. St-Jacques à la vapeur, crème de cresson (15 September-15 April), Manchons de crabe royal tièdis au beurre de persil plat, Homard à la presse.

XXX ✿✿✿ **Comme Chez Soi** (Wynants), pl. Rouppe 23, ✉ 1000, ℘ 512 29 21, Fax 511 80 52, « Belle Epoque atmosphere with Horta decor » - ▤ Ⓟ. AE ⓓ E VISA ES m
closed Sunday, Monday, 30 June-29 July and Christmas-New Year - **Meals** (booking essential) 1975/4750, a la carte 2500/3400
Spec. Filets de sole, mousseline aux crevettes grises et Riesling, Escalopes de foie de canard en maraîchère du soleil, Écrin de pêches vanillées à l'eau de Villée et à la badiane (21 June-21 September).

XXX **L'Alban Chambon** - (at Métropole H.), pl. de Brouckère 21, ✉ 1000, ℘ 217 76 50, Fax 218 02 20, « Late 19C atmosphere » - ▤. AE ⓓ E VISA JCB. ✻ JY c
closed Saturday, Sunday and Bank Holidays - **Meals** *Lunch 1350 b.i.* - 1350 b.i./2600 b.i.

XX **Astrid "Chez Pierrot",** r. Presse 21, ✉ 1000, ℘ 217 38 31, Fax 217 38 31 - AE ⓓ E VISA JCB
closed Sunday, Easter week and 15 July-15 August - **Meals** *Lunch 895* - 895/1600. KY e

XX **Roma,** r. Princes 12, ✉ 1000, ℘ 219 01 94, Fax 218 34 30, Partly Italian cuisine - ▤. AE ⓓ E VISA. ✻ JY e
closed Saturday lunch, Sunday, Bank Holidays and mid July-mid August - **Meals** *Lunch 990* - a la carte 1100/2100.

XX **J and B,** r. Baudet 5, ✉ 1000, ℘ 512 04 84, Fax 511 79 30 - ▤. AE ⓓ E VISA JCB KZ t
closed Saturday lunch, Sunday, Bank Holidays and 21 July-15 August - **Meals** *Lunch 725* - 995/1425.

XX **Bernard** 1st floor, r. Namur 93, ✉ 1000, ℘ 512 88 21, Fax 502 21 77 - ▤. AE ⓓ E VISA JCB
closed Sunday, Monday and July - **Meals** 1200/1500 b.i. KZ n

X **In 't Spinnekopke,** pl. du Jardin aux Fleurs 1, ✉ 1000, ℘ 511 86 95, Fax 513 24 97, 🏕, Partly regional cuisine, open until 11 p.m., « Typical ancient Brussels pub » - AE ⓓ E VISA
closed Saturday lunch, Sunday and Bank Holidays - **Meals** a la carte 800/1350. ER d

Quartier de l'Europe

Europa, r. Loi 107, ✉ 1040, ☎ 230 13 33, Telex 26310, Fax 230 01 20, - - - - GR d
Meals *Les Continents* Lunch 1050 - a la carte 1850/2150 - 750 - **236 rm** 7900/8500, 4 suites.

Dorint Brussels, bd Charlemange 11, ✉ 1000, ☎ 231 09 09, Fax 230 33 71, - - 25-125. AE E VISA. GR c
Meals Lunch 950 - 800/1250 - 600 - **210 rm** 7500, 2 suites.

Eurovillage, bd Charlemagne 80, ✉ 1000, ☎ 230 85 55, Fax 230 56 35, - - 80-120. AE E VISA GR a
Meals *(closed 1 to 25 August and lunch Saturday and Sunday)* Lunch 650 - 870/1600 - 500 - **80 rm** 5250/6000.

Euroflat without rest, bd Charlemagne 50, ✉ 1000, ☎ 230 00 10, Telex 21120, Fax 230 36 83, - - 30. AE E VISA GR b
121 rm 5700/7300, 12 suites.

City Garden without rest, r. Joseph II 59, ✉ 1000, ☎ 282 82 82, Fax 230 64 37 - . AE E VISA. GR f
96 rm 4100/6000.

New Charlemagne without rest, bd Charlemagne 25, ✉ 1000, ☎ 230 21 35, Telex 22772, Fax 230 25 10 - - 30-60. AE E VISA GR k
495 - **66 rm** 3200/4900.

Le Jardin d'Espagne, r. Archimède 65, ✉ 1000, ☎ 736 34 49, Fax 735 17 45, , Partly Spanish cuisine - AE E VISA GR s
closed Saturday lunch, Sunday and Bank Holidays - **Meals** Lunch 580 - 800/950.

Pappa e Citti, r. Franklin 18, ✉ 1000, ☎ 732 61 10, Fax 732 57 40, , Italian cuisine - AE E VISA JCB. GR e
closed Saturday, Sunday, Bank Holidays, 2 August-4 September and 23 December-5 January - **Meals** Lunch 550 - a la carte 1250/1600.

L'Atelier, r. Franklin 28, ✉ 1000, ☎ 734 91 40, Fax 735 35 98, , Buffets - AE E VISA GR y
closed Bank Holidays, weekends, 5 August-3 September and 24 December-6 January - **Meals** Lunch 770 - a la carte approx. 1200.

Takesushi, bd Charlemagne 21, ✉ 1000, ☎ 230 56 27, , Japanese cuisine - AE E VISA GR z
closed Saturday and 2 weeks August - **Meals** Lunch 450 - 780/1950.

Quartier Grand'Place (Ilot Sacré)

Royal Windsor, r. Duquesnoy 5, ✉ 1000, ☎ 505 55 55, Telex 62905, Fax 505 55 00, - - 25-250. AE E VISA JYZ f
Meals see rest **Les 4 Saisons** below - 750 - **255 rm** 9750/10250, 11 suites.

Amigo, r. Amigo 1, ✉ 1000, ☎ 547 47 47, Telex 21618, Fax 513 52 77, « Collection of works of art » - rm - 25-150. AE E VISA JCB. rest JY x
Meals Lunch 1460 b.i. - 1460 b.i./3020 - **200 rm** 6200/9000, 7 suites.

Le Méridien M, Carrefour de l'Europe 3, ✉ 1000, ☎ 548 42 11, Telex 21787, Fax 548 40 80, - - 25-200. AE E VISA. rm KZ h
Meals *L'Epicerie* (open until 11 p.m.) Lunch 1090 - a la carte 1200/1600 - **212 rm** 10000/12000, 12 suites.

Carrefour de l'Europe without rest, r. Marché-aux-Herbes 110, ✉ 1000, ☎ 504 94 00, Telex 22050, Fax 504 95 00 - - 50-100. AE E VISA. JKY n
60 rm 8300/9300, 5 suites.

Novotel off Grand'Place, r. Marché-aux-Herbes 120, ✉ 1000, ☎ 514 33 33, Telex 20377, Fax 511 77 23 - rest - 25. AE E VISA JCB JKY n
Meals Lunch 550 - a la carte 900/1200 - 480 - **136 rm** 5400.

Matignon, r. Bourse 10, ✉ 1000, ☎ 511 08 88 and 511 09 09 (rest), Fax 513 69 27 - . AE E VISA. rest JY q
Meals *(closed Monday and 15 January-25 February)* (open until 11 p.m.) a la carte approx. 900 - **21 rm** 2500/3100.

Ibis Grand'Place without rest, r. Marché-aux-Herbes 100, ✉ 1000, ☎ 514 40 40, Fax 514 50 67 - - 25-130. AE E VISA JCB JKY v
172 rm 4100/4400.

La Maison du Cygne, Grand'Place 9, ✉ 1000, ☎ 511 82 44, Fax 514 31 48, « Former 17C guildhouse » - . AE E VISA JCB. JY w
closed Saturday lunch, Sunday, first 3 weeks August and late December - **Meals** Lunch 1300 - a la carte 1350/2000.

✿ **Les 4 Saisons** - (at Royal Windsor H.), 1st floor, r. Homme Chrétien 2, ✉ 1000, ☎ 505 55 55, Telex 62905, Fax 505 55 00 - . AE E VISA JYZ f
closed Saturday lunch and 20 July-17 August - **Meals** Lunch 1490 - 1690/2290, a la carte 1900/2600
Spec. Terrine de foie d'oie au naturel, Sole pochée à la crème d'écrevisses et duxelles, Filet d'agneau gratiné au fromage de brebis et salpicon d'abats au jus.

XX **La Tête d'Or,** r. Tête d'Or 9, ✉ 1000, ☎ 511 02 01, Fax 502 44 91, « Ancient Brussels residence » – AE ⓓ E VISA JY u
closed Saturday lunch and Sunday – **Meals** a la carte 1100/1800.

XX **Aux Armes de Bruxelles,** r. Bouchers 13, ✉ 1000, ☎ 511 55 98, Fax 514 33 81, Brussels atmosphere, open until 11 p.m. – ▤. AE ⓓ E VISA JCB JY t
closed Monday and 11 June-9 July – **Meals** *Lunch 495* – 995/1695.

X **L'Ogenblik,** Galerie des Princes 1, ✉ 1000, ☎ 511 61 51, Fax 513 41 58, Open until midnight, « Ancient pub interior" – AE ⓓ E VISA JY p
closed Sunday – **Meals** a la carte 1600/2150.

X **La Roue d'Or,** r. Chapeliers 26, ✉ 1000, ☎ 514 25 54, Fax 512 30 81, Open until midnight, « Typical ancient Brussels pub » – AE ⓓ E VISA JY y
closed 20 July-19 August – **Meals** *Lunch 325* – a la carte approx. 1300.

X **Taverne du Passage,** Galerie de la Reine 30, ✉ 1000, ☎ 512 37 32, Fax 511 08 82, 🏠, Brussels atmosphere, open until midnight – AE ⓓ E VISA JY r
closed Wednesday and Thursday in June and July – **Meals** a la carte 1000/1400.

X **'t Kelderke,** Grand'Place 15, ✉ 1000, ☎ 513 73 44, Fax 512 30 81, Brussels atmosphere, open until 2 a.m., « Pub in a vaulted cellar » – AE ⓓ E VISA JY i
Meals *Lunch 275* – a la carte 800/1300.

Quartier Ste-Catherine (Marché-aux-Poissons)

Astrid Ⓜ without rest, pl. du Samedi 11, ✉ 1000, ☎ 219 31 19, Fax 219 31 70 – |‡| TV ☎ ♿ 🚗 – 🏛 25-100. AE ⓓ E VISA JY b
100 rm ☕ 4000/4500.

Atlas without rest, r. Vieux Marché-aux-Grains 30, ✉ 1000, ☎ 502 60 06, Fax 502 69 35 – |‡| TV ☎ 🚗 – 🏛 40. AE ⓓ E VISA ER a
83 rm ☕ 3950/4700, 5 suites.

Ibis Sainte-Catherine without rest, r. Joseph Plateau 2, ✉ 1000, ☎ 513 76 20, Fax 514 22 14 – |‡| ⚡ TV ☎ – 🏛 25-80. AE ⓓ E VISA JCB JY a
235 rm ☕ 3200/3450.

XX **La Sirène d'Or,** pl. Ste-Catherine 1a, ✉ 1000, ☎ 513 51 98, Fax 502 13 05, Seafood – ▤. AE ⓓ E VISA ER g
closed Sunday, Monday, 3 weeks July and 24 December-2 January – **Meals** *Lunch 950* – 1500.

XX **François,** quai aux Briques 2, ✉ 1000, ☎ 511 60 89, Fax 512 06 67, 🏠, Oyster bar, seafood – ▤. AE ⓓ E VISA JY k
closed Monday – **Meals** *Lunch 995* – a la carte 1650/2150.

XX **La Truite d'Argent and H. Welcome** with rm, quai au Bois-à-Brûler 23, ✉ 1000, ☎ 219 95 46, Fax 217 18 87, 🏠 – ▤ rest TV ☎. AE ⓓ E VISA JY h
Meals (Seafood) *(closed Saturday lunch, Sunday, 29 July-18 August and 1 to 16 January)* *Lunch 980* – a la carte approx. 1300 – ☕ 250 – **6 rm** 2200/3000.

XX **La Belle Maraîchère,** pl. Ste-Catherine 11, ✉ 1000, ☎ 512 97 59, Fax 513 76 91, Seafood – ▤ Ⓟ. AE ⓓ E VISA JY z
closed Wednesday and Thursday – **Meals** *Lunch 950* – 950/1700.

X **Le Loup-Galant,** quai aux Barques 4, ✉ 1000, ☎ 219 99 98, 🏠 – AE ⓓ E VISA EQ a
closed Saturday lunch, Sunday, Bank Holidays, 1 week Easter, 1 to 15 August and 24 to 31 December – **Meals** *Lunch 450* – 1000 b.i./1390.

Quartier des Sablons

Jolly du Grand Sablon Ⓜ, r. Bodenbroek 2, ✉ 1000, ☎ 512 88 00, Telex 20397, Fax 512 67 66 – |‡| ⚡ ▤ TV ☎ 🚗 – 🏛 25-100. AE ⓓ E VISA JCB. ✂ rest KZ p
Meals a la carte 1350/1950 – **196 rm** ☕ 7800/10200, 5 suites.

Alfa Sablon Ⓜ without rest, r. Paille 4, ✉ 1000, ☎ 513 60 40, Telex 21248, Fax 511 81 41, ≘s – |‡| ⚡ ▤ TV ☎. AE ⓓ E VISA. ✂ KZ t
28 rm ☕ 4800/6600, 4 suites.

XXX ✿✿ **L'Écailler du Palais Royal** (Basso), r. Bodenbroek 18, ✉ 1000, ☎ 512 87 51, Fax 511 99 50, Seafood – ▤. AE ⓓ E VISA JCB KZ r
closed Sunday, Bank Holidays, 5 to 13 April and August – **Meals** a la carte 2700/3000
Spec. St-Jacques meunières à la crème de cèpes, Blanc de turbot en croustillant de sésame, coulis de persil aux petits légumes, Pot-au-feu de homard et lotte à l'infusion de céleri.

XX **Castello Banfi,** r. Bodenbroek 12, ✉ 1000, ☎ 512 87 94, Fax 512 87 94, Partly Italian cuisine – ▤. AE ⓓ E VISA KZ q
closed Sunday dinner, Monday, 1 week Easter, last 3 weeks August and late December – **Meals** *Lunch 950* – 1595.

XX **En Provence "Chez Marius",** pl. du Petit Sablon 1, ✉ 1000, ☎ 511 12 08, Fax 512 27 89 – AE ⓓ E VISA JZ s
closed Sunday, Bank Holidays and 15 July-15 August – **Meals** *Lunch 850* – 1100/2000.

X **La Clef des Champs,** r. Rollebeek 23, ✉ 1000, ☎ 512 11 93, Fax 513 89 49, 🏠 – ▤. AE ⓓ E VISA JZ k
closed Sunday and Monday – **Meals** 990/1250.

Quartier Palais de Justice

Hilton International, bd de Waterloo 38, ✉ 1000, ☎ 504 11 11, Telex 22744, Fax 504 21 11, ≤ – |‡| ⇔ ▤ TV ☎ ♿ ⇔ – 🏛 45-600. AE ◑ E VISA JCB FS **s**
Meals see rest ***Maison du Bœuf*** below – ***Café d'Egmont*** *Lunch 1040* - a la carte 1100/1400 – ☕ 650 – **441 rm** 8800/13700, 7 suites.

XXXX ✿ **Maison du Bœuf** - (at Hilton H.), 1st floor, bd de Waterloo 38, ✉ 1000, ☎ 504 11 11, Telex 22744, Fax 504 21 11, ≤ – ▤ P. AE ◑ E VISA JCB. ✂ FS **s**
Meals *Lunch 1590* – 1690/2690, a la carte 2500/2750
Spec. Bar de ligne rôti en écailles au thym frais, Train de côtes de bœuf américain rôti en croûte de sel, Tartare de la Maison du Bœuf.

X **L'anecdote,** r. Grand Cerf 16, ✉ 1000, ☎ 511 72 42, Fax 512 17 35 – AE ◑ E VISA FS **n**
closed Sunday, Bank Holidays and 21 July-15 August – **Meals** *Lunch 690* – 690.

X **Les Larmes du Tigre,** r. Wynants 21, ✉ 1000, ☎ 512 18 77, Fax 502 10 03, 🍽, Thaï cuisine – AE ◑ E VISA ES **p**
closed Saturday lunch – **Meals** *Lunch 395* – a la carte 900/1200.

X **Casa Manolo,** r. Haute 165, ✉ 1000, ☎ 513 21 68, Fax 513 35 24, Partly Spanish cuisine, open until midnight – AE ◑ E VISA JCB JZ **a**
closed Wednesday – **Meals** *Lunch 750* – 950 b.i./1300 b.i.

Quartier Léopold (see also at Ixelles)

Renaissance M, r. Parnasse 19, ✉ 1050, ☎ 505 29 29, Fax 505 22 76, 🏋, ≤, 🏊, ⇔ – |‡| ⇔ ▤ TV ☎ ♿ ⇔ – 🏛 25-360. AE ◑ E VISA JCB. ✂ GS **e**
Meals (partly Asian cuisine) *Lunch 790* – a la carte 1100/1500 – ☕ 650 – **238 rm** 8000/9000, 19 suites.

Quartier Louise (see also at Ixelles and at St-Gilles)

Conrad 🐦, av. Louise 71, ✉ 1050, ☎ 542 42 42, Fax 542 42 00, 🍽, « Hotel complex around an early 20C mansion » – |‡| ⇔ ▤ TV ☎ ♿ ⇔ – 🏛 25-750. AE ◑ E VISA JCB FS **f**
Meals see rest ***La Maison de Maître*** below – ***Café Wiltcher's*** *Lunch 1050* - a la carte approx. 1000 – ☕ 900 – **254 rm** 12000/18000, 15 suites.

Bristol Stéphanie M, av. Louise 91, ✉ 1050, ☎ 539 02 40, Telex 25558, Fax 538 03 07, 🏋, ≤, 🏊 – |‡| ⇔ ▤ TV ☎ ⇔ – 🏛 70-215. AE ◑ E VISA JCB. ✂ rest FT **g**
Meals ***L'Avenue Louise*** *(closed Saturday, Sunday, 29 July-18 August and 23 December-1 January) Lunch 895* - 800/1195 – ☕ 540 – **140 rm** 7950/9950, 2 suites.

Mayfair, av. Louise 381, ✉ 1050, ☎ 649 98 00, Telex 24821, Fax 649 22 49 – |‡| ⇔ ▤ TV ☎ ⇔ – 🏛 30-60. AE ◑ E VISA JCB. ✂ FV **a**
Meals see rest ***Taishin*** below – ***Louis XVI*** *(closed Saturday) Lunch 380* - a la carte 900/1500 – ☕ 580 – **97 rm** 5900/8200, 2 suites.

Clubhouse without rest, r. Blanche 4, ✉ 1000, ☎ 537 92 10, Fax 537 00 18 – |‡| ⇔ TV ☎ ⇔ – 🏛 30. AE ◑ E VISA JCB. ✂ FT **h**
80 rm ☕ 5100/6600, 1 suite.

Brussels without rest, av. Louise 315, ✉ 1050, ☎ 640 24 15, Fax 647 34 63 – |‡| TV ☎ ⇔. AE ◑ E VISA FU **b**
36 rm ☕ 4800/5300, 10 suites.

L'Agenda without rest, r. Florence 6, ✉ 1000, ☎ 539 00 31, Fax 539 00 63 – |‡| TV ☎ ⇔. AE ◑ E VISA JCB FT **j**
☕ 300 – **38 rm** 3300/3600.

XXXX ✿ **La Maison de Maître** - (at Conrad H.), av. Louise 71, ✉ 1050, ☎ 542 47 16, Fax 542 42 00 – ▤ P. AE ◑ E VISA FS **f**
closed Saturday lunch, Sunday, Bank Holidays, 8 to 14 April and 22 July-18 August – **Meals** *Lunch 1350* – 1550/2550, a la carte 2450/3000
Spec. Carpaccio de langoustines et crème au caviar, Bar de ligne en croûte de sel, beurre nantais à la citronelle, Ris de veau cloûté de truffes, sauce périgueux.

XX **La Porte des Indes,** av. Louise 455, ✉ 1050, ☎ 647 86 51, Fax 640 30 59, Indian cuisine, « Exotic decor » – ▤. AE ◑ E VISA FV **c**
closed Sunday lunch – **Meals** *Lunch 850* – a la carte 1150/1950.

XX **Taishin** - (at Mayfair H.), av. Louise 381, ✉ 1050, ☎ 647 84 04, Telex 24821, Fax 649 22 49, Japanese cuisine, open until 11 p.m. – ▤ P. AE ◑ E VISA JCB. ✂ FV **a**
closed Sunday – **Meals** *Lunch 450* – 450/2500.

XX **Tagawa,** av. Louise 279, ✉ 1050, ☎ 640 50 95, Fax 648 41 36, Japanese cuisine – ▤ P. AE ◑ E VISA JCB. ✂ FU **e**
closed Saturday lunch, Sunday, Bank Holidays and 1 to 3 January – **Meals** *Lunch 390* – a la carte 1200/1900.

Quartier Bois de la Cambre

XXXXX ✿✿ **Villa Lorraine** (Van de Casserie), av. du Vivier d'Oie 75, ✉ 1000, ☎ 374 31 63, Fax 372 01 95, 🍽 – P. AE ◑ E VISA JCB GX **w**
closed Sunday and 3 weeks July – **Meals** *Lunch 1750* – 3000, a la carte 2850/3250
Spec. Fricassée de homard et huîtres au Riesling (September-April), Barbue à la bière blanche et chicons braisés, Selle de chevreuil aux raisins et épices.

XXX ✿ **La Truffe Noire,** bd de la Cambre 12, ✉ 1000, ✆ 640 44 22, Fax 647 97 04, « Elegant interior » – AE ⓓ E VISA GV **x**
closed Saturday lunch, Sunday, 1 week Easter, first 2 weeks August and late December – **Meals** *Lunch 1450* – 2100/3475, a la carte 2800/3200
Spec. Carpaccio aux truffes, Truffe blanche (October-late December), St-Pierre aux poireaux et truffes.

Quartier Botanique, Gare du Nord (see also at St-Josse-ten-Noode)

Sheraton Towers, pl. Rogier 3, ✉ 1210, ✆ 224 31 11, Telex 26887, Fax 224 34 56, – – 25-600. AE ⓓ E VISA. rest FQ **n**
Meals see rest ***Les Comtes de Flandre*** below – ***Le Pavillon*** (open until 11 p.m.) *Lunch 1050* - a la carte 1050/1600 – 720 – **481 rm** 9900, 44 suites.

President World Trade Center, bd E. Jacqmain 180, ✉ 1000, ✆ 203 20 20, Telex 21066, Fax 203 24 40, – rest – 25-500. AE ⓓ E VISA JCB FQ **d**
Meals *(closed Saturday) Lunch 1290* – a la carte 1700/2400 – **290 rm** 7500/8000, 12 suites.

Le Dome with annex Le Dome II M, bd du Jardin Botanique 12, ✉ 1000, ✆ 218 06 80, Telex 61317, Fax 218 41 12, – rest – 25-100. AE ⓓ E VISA FQ **m**
Meals *(closed Sunday) Lunch 650* – a la carte 900/1350 – **125 rm** 6400/7800.

Président Nord without rest, bd A. Max 107, ✉ 1000, ✆ 219 00 60, Telex 61417, Fax 218 12 69 – . AE ⓓ E VISA JCB. FQ **k**
63 rm 4900/6900.

XXX **Les Comtes de Flandre** - (at Sheraton Towers H.), pl. Rogier 3, ✉ 1210, ✆ 224 31 11, Telex 26887, Fax 224 34 56 – . AE ⓓ E VISA. FQ **n**
closed Saturday, Sunday and August – **Meals** *Lunch 1200* – a la carte 1700/2350.

Quartier Atomium (Centenaire - Trade Mart - Laeken)

XX **Ming Dynasty,** av. de l'Esplanade BP 9, ✉ 1020, ✆ 475 23 45, Fax 475 23 50, Chinese cuisine, open until 11 p.m. – . AE ⓓ E VISA
closed Saturday lunch, Sunday and last 2 weeks July-first 2 weeks August – **Meals** *Lunch 750* – a la carte approx. 1100.

XX **Le Centenaire,** av. J. Sobieski 84, ✉ 1020, ✆ 478 66 23, Fax 478 66 23 – AE ⓓ E VISA
closed Sunday, Monday, July and Christmas-New Year – **Meals** a la carte approx. 1300.

XX ✿ **Les Baguettes Impériales** (Mme Ma), av. J. Sobieski 70, ✉ 1020, ✆ 479 67 32, Fax 479 67 32, , Partly Vietnamese cuisine, « Terrace » – AE ⓓ E VISA.
closed Tuesday, Sunday dinner, 2 weeks Easter and August – **Meals** a la carte 2050/2400
Spec. Mï au homard, Crêpes croustillantes à la vietnamienne au homard, Pigeonneau farci aux nids d'hirondelle.

XX **Lychee,** r. De Wand 118, ✉ 1020, ✆ 268 19 14, Fax 268 19 14, Chinese cuisine, open until 11 p.m. – . AE ⓓ E VISA
closed 15 July-15 August – **Meals** *Lunch 325* – a la carte approx. 850.

X **Adrienne Atomium,** Square Atomium, ✉ 1020, ✆ 478 30 00, Fax (0 10) 68 80 41, town, Buffets – AE ⓓ E VISA
closed Sunday, Bank Holidays, 3 weeks August and 1 week December – **Meals** 800/840.

ANDERLECHT

Le Prince de Liège, chaussée de Ninove 664, ✉ 1070, ✆ 522 16 00, Fax 520 81 85 – – 25. AE ⓓ E VISA
Meals *(closed Sunday dinner and 11 July-9 August) Lunch 535* – 800/1365 – **32 rm** 1950/2950.

Ustel, Square de l'Aviation 6, ✉ 1070, ✆ 520 60 53, Fax 520 33 28 – – 30. AE E VISA ES **q**
Meals *(closed Saturday lunch and Sunday) Lunch 325* – 845 – **64 rm** 3600/4300.

XXX **Saint-Guidon** 2nd floor, av. Théo Verbeeck 2 (in the Constant Vanden Stock stadium), ✉ 1070, ✆ 520 55 36, Fax 523 38 27 – – 25-500. ⓓ E VISA JCB.
closed Saturday, Sunday, Bank Holidays, first league match days, July and Christmas-New Year – **Meals** (lunch only) *Lunch 995* – a la carte 1550/2100.

XX **La Réserve,** chaussée de Ninove 675, ✉ 1070, ✆ 411 26 53, Fax 411 66 67, – AE ⓓ E VISA
closed Monday, Tuesday and Saturday lunch – **Meals** *Lunch 975* – 975/2175.

XX **Alain Cornelis,** av. Paul Janson 82, ✉ 1070, ✆ 525 02 83, Fax 525 02 83, – AE ⓓ E VISA
closed Saturday lunch, Sunday, Bank Holidays, mid July-mid August and Christmas-New Year – **Meals** *Lunch 860* – a la carte 1400/1750.

XX **La Brouette,** bd Prince de Liège 61, ✉ 1070, ✆ 522 51 69, Fax 522 51 69 – AE ⓓ E VISA
closed Saturday lunch, Sunday dinner, Monday and mid July-mid August – **Meals** *Lunch 800* – 950/1600.

X **La Paix** r. Ropsy-Chaudron 49 (opposite the slaughterhouse), ✉ 1070, ✆ 523 09 58, Fax 520 10 39, Pub rest – AE E VISA
closed Saturday, Sunday and last 3 weeks July – **Meals** (lunch only except Friday) a la carte 1050/1350.

AUDERGHEM (OUDERGEM)

XX ✿ **La Grignotière** (Chanson), chaussée de Wavre 2041, ✉ 1160, ☎ 672 81 85, Fax 672 81 85 – AE E VISA
closed Sunday, Monday, Bank Holidays and August – **Meals** 1300/1900
Spec. Jeune morue, vapeur aux tomates et basilic, Croustillant aux amandes de pigeonneau et foie d'oie, Langoustines et émincé d'asperges sautées minute.

XX **L'Abbaye de Rouge Cloître,** r. Rouge Cloître 8, ✉ 1160, ☎ 672 45 25, Fax 660 12 01, ☂, « On the edge of a forest » – P – 25-55. AE ⓓ E VISA
closed Saturday, Sunday dinner and 20 December-6 January – **Meals** *Lunch 750* – a la carte 1200/1950.

XX **New Asia,** chaussée de Wavre 1240, ✉ 1160, ☎ 660 62 06, Fax 675 29 72, ☂, Chinese cuisine, « Terrace » – ▤. AE ⓓ E VISA. ✻ HU y
closed Monday except Bank Holidays – **Meals** *Lunch 290* – 480/680.

ETTERBEEK

X ✿ **Stirwen** (Troubat), chaussée St-Pierre 15, ✉ 1040, ☎ 640 85 41, Fax 648 43 08 – AE ⓓ E VISA GS a
closed Saturday lunch, Sunday, 2 weeks August and 22 December-5 January – **Meals** *Lunch 950* – a la carte 1650/2100
Spec. Tête de veau ravigotte, Joue de bœuf braisé à la bourguignonne, Désossé de pieds de porc à la Ste-Menehould.

Quartier Cinquantenaire (Montgomery)

Park without rest, av. de l'Yser 21, ✉ 1040, ☎ 735 74 00, Fax 735 19 67, ≘s, – |‡| ⇔ TV ☎ – 25. AE ⓓ E VISA JCB – **51 rm** ☐ 5800/7100. HS c

XX **La Fontaine de Jade,** av. de Tervuren 5, ✉ 1040, ☎ 736 32 10, Fax 732 46 86, Chinese cuisine, open until 11 p.m. – ▤. AE ⓓ E VISA HS a
closed Tuesday – **Meals** *Lunch 680* – 950 b.i./1400.

XX **Le Serpolet,** av. de Tervuren 59, ✉ 1040, ☎ 736 17 01, Fax 736 67 85, ☂ – AE ⓓ E VISA
closed Saturday lunch and dinner Sunday and Monday – **Meals** 995/1650. HS b

EVERE

Belson without rest, chaussée de Louvain 805, ✉ 1140, ☎ 705 20 30, Telex 64921, Fax 705 20 43 – |‡| ⇔ ▤ TV ☎ ⇔ – 25. AE ⓓ E VISA JCB. ✻
☐ 595 – **137 rm** 2950/8200, 3 suites.

Mercure, av. J. Bordet 74, ✉ 1140, ☎ 726 73 35, Telex 65460, Fax 726 82 95, ☂ – |‡| ⇔ TV ☎ ♿ ⇔ – 25-60. AE ⓓ E VISA JCB
Meals *(closed Saturday and Sunday lunch)* a la carte approx. 1200 – **113 rm** ☐ 3950/5750, 7 suites.

Evergreen without rest, av. V. Day 1, ✉ 1140, ☎ 726 70 15 – TV ☎ – 40. AE ⓓ E VISA JCB – **19 rm** ☐ 2850/3350.

FOREST (VORST)

De Fierlant without rest, r. De Fierlant 67, ✉ 1060, ☎ 538 60 70, Fax 538 91 99 – |‡| TV ☎. AE ⓓ E VISA – **40 rm** ☐ 2300.

XX **Les Jardins de l'Abbaye,** pl. Saint-Denis 9, ✉ 1190, ☎ 332 11 59, Fax 332 17 52, ≤, ☂ – ▤ P. AE ⓓ E VISA
closed Sunday dinner, Monday and Tuesday dinner – **Meals** *Lunch 850* – a la carte approx. 1100.

GANSHOREN

XXXX ✿✿✿ **Bruneau,** av. Broustin 75, ✉ 1083, ☎ 427 69 78, Fax 425 97 26, ☂, « Terrace » – ▤. AE ⓓ E VISA
closed holiday Thursdays, Tuesday dinner, Wednesday, 15 May-5 June and 24 December-3 January – **Meals** *Lunch 1870* – 2750/3750, a la carte 2500/4000
Spec. Rosace de homard aux truffes (15 December-15 February and 15 July-15 October), Filet de bar de ligne "dos bleu" tartiné au caviar, Rognon de veau en croûte de sel aux échalotes confites.

XXX ✿✿ **Claude Dupont,** av. Vital Riethuisen 46, ✉ 1083, ☎ 426 00 00, Fax 426 65 40 – AE ⓓ E VISA
closed Monday, Tuesday and early July-early August – **Meals** *Lunch 1750* – 2150/3200, a la carte 2150/2700
Spec. St-Jacques à la purée de persil plat et beurre blanc (October-April), Fricassée de homard et de sole au fumet de corail, Selle de chevreuil rôti au thym, poivrade à l'ancienne (October-December).

XXX **San Daniele,** av. Charles-Quint 6, ✉ 1083, ☎ 426 79 23, Fax 426 92 14, Italian cuisine – ▤. AE ⓓ E VISA JCB
closed Sunday, Monday dinner and 15 July-15 August **Meals** – a la carte 1500/2000.

XX **Cambrils** 1st floor, av. Charles-Quint 365, ✉ 1083, ☎ 465 35 82, Fax 465 76 63, ☂ – ▤. AE E VISA – *closed dinner Monday and Thursday, Sunday and 15 July-15 August* – **Meals** *Lunch 595* – 1000/1280.

IXELLES (ELSENE)

XX **Charles-Joseph,** r. E. Solvay 9, ⊠ 1050, ℘ 513 43 90 - AE ① E VISA. ✻ FS x
closed Saturday lunch, Sunday and mid July-mid August - **Meals** *Lunch 850* - a la carte 950/1850.

XX **Le Yen,** r. Lesbroussart 49, ⊠ 1050, ℘ 649 07 47, 余, Vietnamese cuisine, open until 11 p.m. - AE ① E VISA FU f
closed Sunday - **Meals** *Lunch 320* - a la carte 800/1100.

Quartier Boondael (University)

XXX **Le Couvert d'Argent,** pl. Marie-José 9, ⊠ 1050, ℘ 648 45 45, Fax 648 22 28, 余, « Elegant pavilion in garden » - Ⓟ. AE ① E VISA JCB GX y
closed Sunday and Monday - **Meals** *Lunch 1200* - 1200/2200.

XXX **L'aub. de Boendael,** square du Vieux Tilleul 12, ⊠ 1050, ℘ 672 70 55, Fax 660 75 82, 余, Grill rest, Rustic - ▤ Ⓟ. AE ① E VISA HX h
closed Saturday, Sunday, 27 July-18 August and 21 December-19 January - **Meals** *Lunch 1375 b.i.* - a la carte 1400/2000.

X **La Brasserie Marebœuf,** av. de la Couronne 445, ⊠ 1050, ℘ 648 99 06, Fax 648 38 30, Open until midnight - ▤. AE ① E VISA GHV t
closed Sunday - **Meals** *Lunch 550* - a la carte 1100/1500.

X **La Pagode d'Or,** chaussée de Boondael 332, ⊠ 1050, ℘ 649 06 56, Fax 646 54 75, 余, Vietnamese cuisine, open until 11 p.m. - AE ① E VISA JCB. ✻ GV m
closed Monday - **Meals** *Lunch 350* - 890/1350.

Quartier Bascule

🏨 **Capital** Ⓜ, chaussée de Vleurgat 191, ⊠ 1050, ℘ 646 64 20, Fax 646 33 14, 余 - |‡| ⇔ ▤ rest TV ☎ 🚗 - 🔔 25. AE ① E VISA JCB. ✻ rm FU c
Meals *Lunch 420* - a la carte 800/1200 - **62 rm** ☐ 2800/3900.

XXX **La Mosaïque,** r. Forestière 23, ⊠ 1050, ℘ 649 02 35, Fax 647 11 49, 余 - Ⓟ. AE ① E VISA FU p
closed Saturday lunch, Sunday, Bank Holidays, 8 to 14 April, 28 July-18 August and 22 to 29 December - **Meals** *Lunch 1200 b.i.* - 1300/1600.

XX **Maison Félix** 1st floor, r. Washington 149 (square Henri Michaux), ⊠ 1050, ℘ 345 66 93, Fax 344 92 85 - AE ① E VISA FV s
closed Sunday, Monday and last 2 weeks July - **Meals** *Lunch 1290* - 1500/1900.

Quartier Léopold (see also at Bruxelles)

🏨 **Leopold,** r. Luxembourg 35, ⊠ 1050, ℘ 511 18 28, Fax 514 19 39, 余, ≘s - |‡| ▤ TV ☎ - 🔔 25-60. AE ① E VISA FS y
Meals *(closed Saturday lunch and Sunday) Lunch 1100* - a la carte 1500/2000 - **85 rm** ☐ 4150/4950, 1 suite.

Quartier Louise (see also at Bruxelles and at St-Gilles)

🏨 **Sofitel** without rest, av. de la Toison d'Or 40, ⊠ 1050, ℘ 514 22 00, Fax 514 57 44 - |‡| ⇔ ▤ TV ☎ - 🔔 25-120. AE ① E VISA JCB FS r
☐ 700 - **171 rm** 8500/9500.

🏨 **Cadettt** Ⓜ, r. Paul Spaak 15, ⊠ 1000, ℘ 645 61 11, Telex 20819, Fax 646 63 44, 余, Fō, ≘s, 🛏 - |‡| ⇔ ▤ TV ☎ ♿ 🚗 - 🔔 25-40. AE ① E VISA JCB FU k
Meals (open until 11 p.m.) *Lunch 500* - a la carte 850/1200 - ☐ 500 - **128 rm** 5100.

🏨 **Argus** without rest, r. Capitaine Crespel 6, ⊠ 1050, ℘ 514 07 70, Fax 514 12 22 - |‡| TV ☎. AE ① E VISA FS t
41 rm ☐ 3200/3500.

🏨 **Beau-Site** without rest, r. Longue Haie 76, ⊠ 1000, ℘ 640 88 89, Fax 640 16 11 - |‡| TV ☎. AE ① E VISA FT r
38 rm ☐ 2500/3200.

XX **Les Perles de Pluie,** r. Livourne 148, ⊠ 1000, ℘ 649 67 23, Fax 644 07 60, Thaï cuisine, open until 11 p.m. - AE ① E VISA FU n
closed Monday, Saturday lunch and 22 July-5 August - **Meals** *Lunch 420* - 850/1250.

X **Shogun,** r. Capitaine Crespel 10, ⊠ 1050, ℘ 512 83 19, Fax 512 83 19, 余, Japanese cuisine, teppan-yaki, open until 11 p.m. - AE ① E VISA JCB FS t
closed Saturday lunch and Sunday - **Meals** *Lunch 400* - 1300/2000.

JETTE

🏨 **Eurocap,** chaussée de Dieleghem 114, ⊠ 1090, ℘ 478 03 10, Fax 478 43 16 - |‡| TV ☎ 🚗. AE ① E VISA JCB
Meals *(closed Saturday lunch and Sunday dinner)* 895/1295 - **24 rm** ☐ 2650/3150.

XX **Le Sermon,** av. Jacques Sermon 91, ⊠ 1090, ℘ 426 89 35, Fax 426 70 90 - AE E VISA
closed Sunday, Monday, week before Easter and last 3 weeks August - **Meals** *Lunch 1950 b.i.* - a la carte 1700/2800.

MOLENBEEK-ST-JEAN (SINT-JANS-MOLENBEEK)

XXX **Le Béarnais,** bd Louis Mettewie 318, ✉ 1080, ☎ 411 51 51, Fax 410 70 81 – ▤. AE ⓓ E VISA
closed 22 July-8 August – **Meals** *Lunch 1090* – a la carte 1800/2200.

ST-GILLES (SINT-GILLIS)

Forum, av. du Haut Pont 2, ✉ 1060, ☎ 343 01 00, Fax 347 00 54 – |‡| TV ☎ – 25-100. AE ⓓ E VISA JCB EUV r
Meals (Italian cuisine) *(closed Saturday and Sunday lunch) Lunch 480* – a la carte approx. 1100 – **77 rm** ☐ 3700/3950.

XX **Inada,** r. Source 73, ✉ 1060, ☎ 538 01 13, Fax 538 01 13 – AE ⓓ E VISA ET a
closed Saturday lunch, Sunday, Bank Holidays and 16 July-early September – **Meals** *Lunch 720* – a la carte 1400/2000.

XX **Le Forcado,** chaussée de Charleroi 192, ✉ 1060, ☎ 537 92 20, Fax 537 92 20, Portuguese cuisine – ▤. AE ⓓ E VISA EFU a
closed Sunday, Bank Holidays, carnival week and August – **Meals** a la carte approx. 1300.

X **La Mamounia,** av. Porte de Hal 9, ✉ 1060, ☎ 537 73 22, Fax 539 39 59, Moroccan cuisine open until 11 p.m. – AE ⓓ E VISA JCB ES r
closed Monday except Bank Holidays and 15 July-15 August – **Meals** *Lunch 495* – a la carte approx. 1100.

Quartier Louise (see also at Bruxelles and at Ixelles)

Holiday Inn City Centre, chaussée de Charleroi 38, ✉ 1060, ☎ 533 66 66, Fax 538 90 14 – |‡| ▤ TV ☎ – 25-250. AE ⓓ E VISA FT m
Meals *Lunch 890* – a la carte 1200/1750 – ☐ 600 – **201 rm** 6950/7950.

Manos Stephanie without rest, chaussée de Charleroi 28, ✉ 1060, ☎ 539 02 50, Fax 537 57 29, « Mansion with particular atmosphere » – |‡| TV ☎. AE ⓓ E VISA JCB
50 rm ☐ 6450/7850. FS

Manos without rest, chaussée de Charleroi 102, ✉ 1060, ☎ 537 96 82, Fax 539 36 55 – |‡| TV ☎ P. AE ⓓ E VISA JCB FU w
☐ 450 – **38 rm** 3650/4400.

Delta, chaussée de Charleroi 17, ✉ 1060, ☎ 539 01 60, Fax 537 90 11 – |‡| ▤ rm TV ☎ – 25-100. AE ⓓ E VISA JCB. FS w
Meals *Lunch 445* – a la carte 800/1200 – **246 rm** ☐ 5500/6500.

Cascade M without rest, r. Berckmans 128, ✉ 1060, ☎ 538 88 30, Fax 538 92 79 – |‡| ▤ TV ☎ – 25. AE ⓓ E VISA. ES r
80 rm ☐ 4800/5900.

Diplomat without rest, r. Jean Stas 32, ✉ 1060, ☎ 537 42 50, Fax 539 33 79 – |‡| TV ☎. AE ⓓ E VISA JCB. FS v
68 rm ☐ 5500/6500.

XX **I Trulli,** r. Jourdan 18, ✉ 1060, ☎ 538 98 20, Fax 537 79 30, Partly Italian cuisine, open until midnight – AE ⓓ E VISA JCB FS c
closed Sunday, 11 to 31 July and 23 December-4 January – **Meals** *Lunch 445* – a la carte 1350/2000.

ST-JOSSE-TEN-NOODE (SINT-JOOST-TEN-NODE)

Quartier Botanique (see also at Bruxelles)

Royal Crown, r. Royale 250, ✉ 1210, ☎ 220 66 11, Fax 217 84 44, – |‡| ▤ TV ☎ – 40-350. AE ⓓ E VISA JCB FQ r
Meals *Hugo's (closed Saturday, Sunday and 13 July-18 August) Lunch 1250* - a la carte 1600/1950 – ☐ 650 – **303 rm** 7000, 6 suites.

Palace, r. Gineste 3, ✉ 1210, ☎ 203 62 00, Fax 203 55 55 – |‡| TV ☎ – 25-500. AE ⓓ E VISA JCB. FQ v
Meals *Le Temps Présent Lunch 480* - a la carte 800/1400 – **359 rm** ☐ 6300/7300, 1 suite.

New Siru, pl. Rogier 1, ✉ 1210, ☎ 203 35 80, Telex 21722, Fax 203 33 03, « Each room decorated by a contemporary Belgian artist » – |‡| ▤ rest TV ☎ P – 25-80. AE ⓓ E VISA JCB FQ p
Meals (Pub rest, open until 11.30 p.m.) *(closed Sunday and Bank Holidays)* 795 – **101 rm** ☐ 3200/5900.

Eurocity Botanique without rest, r. Brabant 80, ✉ 1210, ☎ 223 07 07, Fax 223 03 24 – |‡| TV ☎ P. AE ⓓ E VISA JCB FQ w
70 rm ☐ 3500/3900.

Albert Premier without rest, pl. Rogier 20, ✉ 1210, ☎ 203 31 25, Telex 27111, Fax 203 43 31 – |‡| TV ☎ – 25-60. AE ⓓ E VISA FQ q
285 rm ☐ 3000/5000.

XX **De Ultieme Hallucinatie,** r. Royale 316, ✉ 1210, ☎ 217 06 14, Fax 217 72 40, « Art Nouveau interior » – P. AE ⓓ E VISA. FQ t
closed Saturday lunch, Sunday and 20 July-18 August – **Meals** *Lunch 950* – 1450/2750 b.i.

X **Les Dames Tartine,** chaussée de Haecht 58, ✉ 1210, ☎ 218 45 49, Fax 218 45 49 – AE ⓓ E VISA. FQ s
closed Saturday lunch, Sunday and Monday – **Meals** *Lunch 750* – a la carte approx. 1300.

SCHAERBEEK (SCHAARBEEK)

Quartier Meiser

Lambermont without rest, bd Lambermont 322, ✉ 1030, ✆ 242 55 95, Fax 215 36 13 – 🛗 TV ☎ 🚗. AE ⓓ E VISA
42 rm ☕ 3200/3700.

Reyers without rest, bd Aug. Reyers 40, ✉ 1030, ✆ 732 42 42, Fax 732 41 82 – 🛗 TV ☎ 🚗. AE ⓓ E VISA HQ **h**
49 rm ☕ 3150/3350.

XX **Le Cadre Noir,** av. Milcamps 158, ✉ 1030, ✆ 734 14 45 – AE ⓓ E VISA HR **v**
closed Saturday lunch, Sunday dinner, Monday and last 3 weeks July – **Meals** 880/1275.

UCCLE (UKKEL)

County House, square des Héros 2, ✉ 1180, ✆ 375 44 20, Fax 375 31 22 – 🛗 ▤ rest TV ☎ 🚗 – 🏛 25-140. AE ⓓ E VISA. ✻ EX **b**
Meals (open until 11 p.m.) a la carte 1150/1550 – **90 rm** ☕ 4000/5600, 11 suites.

XXX **Les Frères Romano,** av. de Fré 182, ✉ 1180, ✆ 374 70 98, Fax 374 04 18, 🌳 – 🅿. AE ⓓ E VISA FX **d**
closed Sunday and Bank Holidays – **Meals** a la carte 1600/2350.

XX **L'Amandier,** av. de Fré 184, ✉ 1180, ✆ 374 03 95, Fax 374 86 92, 🌳, Open until 11 p.m. – 🅿. AE ⓓ E VISA FX **e**
closed Saturday lunch and Sunday except Bank Holidays – **Meals** a la carte 1500/1800.

XX ✿ **Villa d'Este,** r. Etoile 142, ✉ 1180, ✆ 376 48 48, 🌳, « Terrace » – 🅿. AE ⓓ E VISA
closed Sunday dinner, Monday, July and late December-early January – **Meals** *Lunch 990* – 990/1600, a la carte 1650/2750
Spec. Sole farcie aux poireaux, Fricassée de coquelet à la moutarde de Meaux, Suprême de turbotin au basilic (21 March-21 September).

XX **Blue Elephant,** chaussée de Waterloo 1120, ✉ 1180, ✆ 374 49 62, Fax 375 44 68, Thaï cuisine, « Exotic decor » – ▤. AE ⓓ E VISA GX **j**
closed Saturday lunch – **Meals** *Lunch 850* – a la carte 1050/1650.

XX **La Cité du Dragon,** chaussée de Waterloo 1024, ✉ 1180, ✆ 375 80 80, Fax 375 69 77, 🌳, Chinese cuisine, open until 11.30 p.m., « Exotic garden with fountains » – 🅿. AE ⓓ E VISA GX **c**
Meals 810/2350.

XX **Willy et Marianne,** chaussée d'Alsemberg 705, ✉ 1180, ✆ 343 60 09 – AE ⓓ E VISA EX **r**
closed Tuesday dinner, Wednesday, carnival and 3 weeks July – **Meals** *Lunch 425* – 950.

X **Brasseries Georges,** av. Winston Churchill 259, ✉ 1180, ✆ 347 21 00, Fax 344 02 45, 🌳, Open until midnight – ▤. AE ⓓ E VISA FV **n**
Meals *Lunch 350* – a la carte 1100/1650.

X **De Hoef,** r. Edith Cavell 218, ✉ 1180, ✆ 374 34 17, Fax 375 30 84, 🌳, Grill rest, « 17C inn » – AE ⓓ E VISA FX **q**
closed 10 to 31 July – **Meals** *Lunch 395* – 750.

WATERMAEL-BOITSFORT (WATERMAAL-BOSVOORDE)

XX **Host. Des 3 Tilleuls** 🐦 with rm, Berensheide 8, ✉ 1170, ✆ 672 30 14, Fax 673 65 52, 🌳 – TV ☎ 🅿. AE ⓓ E VISA JCB. ✻ rm
Meals *(closed Sunday and 15 July-15 August) Lunch 1500 b.i.* – 1100 – **7 rm** ☕ 3000/4350.

XX **Les Rives du Gange** with rm, av. de la Fauconnerie 1, ✉ 1170, ✆ 672 16 01, Telex 62661, Fax 672 43 30, 🌳 – 🛗 TV ☎. AE ⓓ E VISA
Meals (Indian cuisine, open until 11.30 p.m.) *Lunch 595* – 990/1600 – **19 rm** ☕ 2480/3480.

XX **Au Vieux Boitsfort,** pl. Bischoffsheim 9, ✉ 1170, ✆ 672 23 32, Fax 660 22 94, 🌳 – AE ⓓ E VISA JCB
closed Saturday lunch and Sunday – **Meals** 1490/1980.

X **L'Entre-Temps,** r. Philippe Dewolfs 7, ✉ 1170, ✆ 672 87 20, Fax 672 87 20, 🌳 – AE ⓓ E VISA
closed Tuesday dinner, Wednesday and 21 July-15 August – **Meals** *Lunch 480* – a la carte 850/1200.

WOLUWÉ-ST-LAMBERT (SINT-LAMBRECHTS-WOLUWE).

Sodehotel M 🐦, av. E. Mounier 5, ✉ 1200, ✆ 775 21 11, Telex 20170, Fax 770 47 80, 🌳 – 🛗 ⇎ ▤ TV ☎ ♿ 🚗 🅿 – 🏛 25-200. AE ⓓ E VISA. ✻ rest
Meals *Lunch 745* – a la carte 1200/1500 – ☕ 595 – **112 rm** 6900, 8 suites.

Lambeau M without rest, av. Lambeau 150, ✉ 1200, ✆ 732 51 70, Fax 732 54 90 – 🛗 TV ☎. AE E VISA HR **u**
24 rm ☕ 2100/3000.

XXX **Mon Manège à Toi,** r. Neerveld 1, ✉ 1200, ☎ 770 02 38, Fax 762 95 80, « Floral garden » - P. AE ① E VISA JCB
closed Saturday, Sunday, Bank Holidays, 7 to 31 July and 24 December-1 January - **Meals** a la carte 2175/3250.

XX **Michel Servais,** r. Th. Decuyper 136, ✉ 1200, ☎ 762 62 95, Fax 771 20 32, 斋 - AE ① E VISA
closed Sunday, Monday and 20 July-20 August - **Meals** *Lunch 1050* - 1250/2050.

XX **Le Relais de la Woluwe,** av. Georges Henri 1, ✉ 1200, ☎ 762 66 36, Fax 762 18 55, 斋, « Terrace and garden » - AE ① E VISA
closed Saturday lunch, Sunday and Christmas week - **Meals** *Lunch 1650* - a la carte 1250/1800

XX **Baalbeck,** bd Brand Whitlock 110, ✉ 1200, ☎ 733 39 06, Lebanese cuisine, open until midnight - AE ① E VISA HS
closed Sunday - **Meals** a la carte approx. 900.

X **The Butterfly,** chaussée de Stockel 294, ✉ 1200, ☎ 763 22 16, Fax 763 22 16 - AE ① E VISA
closed Monday dinner and Tuesday except Bank Holidays - **Meals** *Lunch 495* - 950/1280.

WOLUWÉ-ST-PIERRE (SINT-PIETERS-WOLUWE)

Montgomery ⛜, av. de Tervuren 134, ✉ 1150, ☎ 741 85 11, Fax 741 85 00, Fø, ≘s - |‡| ⇔ ▤ TV ☎ 🚗. AE ① E VISA JCB. ✻ HS
Meals *(closed Saturday, Sunday, Bank Holidays, 15 July-16 August and 23 December-3 January) Lunch 1050* - a la carte 1750/2150 - ☑ 450 - **61 rm** 9000/10000, 2 suites.

XXX ✿ **Des 3 Couleurs** (Tourneur), av. de Tervuren 453, ✉ 1150, ☎ 770 33 21, Fax 770 80 45, 斋, « Terrace » - E VISA
closed Monday, Tuesday, lunch Bank Holidays, mid August-mid September and early January - **Meals** *Lunch 1400* - 2000, a la carte 1900/2300
Spec. Asperges du pauvre aux perles noires, Saumon Liliane, Aile de raie au vin jaune.

XX **Le Vignoble de Margot,** r. Paul Wemaere 2, ✉ 1150, ☎ 779 23 23, Fax 779 05 45 - ▤ AE ① E VISA
closed Saturday lunch, Sunday, Bank Holidays, 21 July-18 August and 22 December-1 January - **Meals** *Lunch 995 b.i.* - 1395/2495.

X **Le Mucha,** av. Jules Dujardin 23, ✉ 1150, ☎ 770 24 14, Fax 770 24 14, 斋, Partly Italian cuisine, open until 11 p.m. - AE ① E VISA
closed Sunday and 1 to 21 September - **Meals** *Lunch 460* - 850/1250.

BRUSSELS ENVIRONS

at Diegem Brussels-Zaventem motorway Diegem exit C Machelen pop. 10 748 - ✉ 1831 Diegem - ⊛ 0 2 :

Holiday Inn, Holidaystraat 7 ☎ 720 58 65, Telex 24285, Fax 720 41 45, Fø, ≘s, 🏊, 🎾 - |‡| ⇔ ▤ TV ☎ P - 🔔 25-500. AE ① E VISA JCB. ✻ rest
Meals (buffets, open until 11 p.m.) *Lunch 1195* - a la carte 1400/1700 - ☑ 575 - **310 rm** 7700/9800.

Sofitel Airport, Bessenveldstraat 15 ☎ 725 11 60, Fax 721 43 45, 斋, ≘s, 🏊 - ⇔ ▤ TV ☎ P - 🔔 25-500. AE ① E VISA. ✻ rest
Meals *(closed Saturday, Sunday and Bank Holidays) Lunch 1250* - a la carte 1350/1800 - ☑ 600 - **120 rm** 7900.

Novotel Airport, Olmenstraat ☎ 725 30 50, Telex 26751, Fax 721 39 58, 斋, 🏊 - |‡| ⇔ ▤ TV ☎ P - 🔔 25-200. AE ① E VISA JCB
Meals (open until midnight) a la carte 800/1400 - ☑ 460 - **206 rm** 4950.

Ibis Airport, Bessenveldstraat 17 ☎ 725 43 21, Fax 725 40 40 - |‡| ⇔ TV ☎ ♿ P - 🔔 25-60. AE ① E VISA JCB
Meals *(closed Friday, Saturday and Sunday) Lunch 555* - 695 - **95 rm** ☑ 2995.

Fimotel Airport, Berkenlaan 5 ☎ 725 33 80, Fax 725 38 10, 斋 - |‡| ⇔ TV ☎ ♿ P - 🔔 25-200. AE ① E VISA. ✻ rest
Meals *Lunch 650* - 800 - **79 rm** ☑ 2200/3700.

at Dilbeek W : 7 km - pop. 36 026 - ✉ 1700 Dilbeek - ⊛ 0 2 :

Relais Delbeccha ⛜, Bodegemstraat 158 ☎ 569 44 30, Fax 569 75 30, 斋, 🌳 - TV ☎ P - 🔔 25-120. AE ① E VISA JCB
closed Sunday dinner - **Meals** *Lunch 950* - a la carte 1300/1750 - ☑ 450 - **14 rm** 3600/4500.

XX **Host. d'Arconati** ⛜ with rm, d'Arconatistraat 77 ☎ 569 35 15, Fax 569 35 04, 斋, « Floral terrace », 🌳 - TV ☎ 🚗 P - 🔔 60. AE E VISA
closed February - **Meals** *(closed Sunday dinner, Monday, Tuesday and 1 week July)* - 1775 - **6 rm** ☑ 2500/3000.

at Dworp (Tourneppe) S : 16 km C Beersel pop. 21 392 - ✉ 1653 Dworp - ⊛ 0 2 :

Kasteel Gravenhof ⛜, Alsembergsesteenweg 676 ☎ 380 44 99, Fax 380 40 60, 斋, « Woodland setting », 🌳 - |‡| TV ☎ P - 🔔 25-120. AE ① E VISA JCB
Meals (Pub rest) *Lunch 595* - a la carte approx. 1200 - ☑ 395 - **24 rm** 3450/7200.

at Grimbergen N : 11 km – pop. 31 110 – ✉ 1850 Grimbergen – ☎ 0 2 :

Abbey, Kerkeblokstraat 5 ✆ 269 63 62, Fax 269 66 88, ♿, ≘s, 🌳 – |‡| ▤ rest ▣ ☎ ⓟ – 🔔 30-200. AE ⓞ E VISA JCB. ✻ rm
closed last 2 weeks July-first week August – **Meals** *(closed Saturday and Sunday) Lunch 1250* – a la carte 1700/2000 – ☕ 400 – **28 rm** 4800/5500.

at Groot-Bijgaarden NW : 7 km Ⓒ Dilbeek pop. 36 026 – ✉ 1702 Groot-Bijgaarden – ☎ 0 2 :

Waerboom without rest, Jozef Mertensstraat 140 ✆ 463 15 00, Fax 463 10 30, ≘s, ▣ – |‡| ▣ ☎ ⓟ – 🔔 25-270. AE ⓞ E VISA. ✻
35 rm ☕ 3300/4600.

Gosset Ⓜ, Alfons Gossetlaan 52 ✆ 466 21 30, Fax 466 18 50, 🍴 – |‡| ▣ ☎ ⓟ – 🔔 25-200. AE ⓞ E VISA. ✻ rm
closed 23 December-2 January – **Meals** *Lunch 350* – a la carte 1000/1350 – ☕ 300 – **48 rm** 2950/3500.

XXXXX ✿✿ **De Bijgaarden,** I. Van Beverenstraat 20 (near castle) ✆ 466 44 85, Fax 463 08 11, ≤, 🍴 – AE ⓞ E VISA
closed Saturday lunch, Sunday, 7 to 15 April and 13 August-4 September – **Meals** 1950/4500, a la carte approx. 3350
Spec. Mêlée de homard et gelée au caviar, Turbot "château" et béarnaise de homard, Faisan à la truffe blanche (15 October-December).

XXXX ✿ **Michel** (Coppens), Schepen Gossetlaan 31 ✆ 466 65 91, Fax 466 90 07, 🍴 – ⓟ. AE ⓞ E VISA
closed Sunday, Monday and August – **Meals** *Lunch 1550* – 2350, a la carte 2200/2500
Spec. Filet de turbot braisé en écailles de pommes de terre aux lentilles et bigorneaux, Selle de chevreuil en aigre-doux d'échalotes, Foie d'oie poêlé et pomme au chèvre frais, déglacé à l'orange.

at Hoeilaart SE : 13 km – pop. 8 327 – ✉ 1560 Hoeilaart – ☎ 0 2 :

XXX ✿ **Aloyse Kloos,** Terhulpsesteenweg 2 (at Groenendaal) ✆ 657 37 37, 🍴 – ⓟ. E VISA
closed Sunday dinner, Monday, 2 weeks Easter and August – **Meals** *Lunch 1400* – 1690, a la carte 1900/2300
Spec. Saumon mariné aux truffes, Ecrevisses à la luxembourgeoise (June-December), Mignardises de cailles aux morilles et girolles.

at Huizingen S : 12 km Ⓒ Beersel pop. 21 392 – ✉ 1654 Huizingen – ☎ 0 2 :

XXX **Terborght,** Oud Dorp 16 (near E 19 - exit 15) ✆ 380 10 10, Fax 380 10 97, 🍴, « Rustic » – ▤ ⓟ. AE ⓞ E VISA. ✻
closed dinner Sunday and Tuesday, Monday, carnival and 15 July-15 August – **Meals** *Lunch 950* – 1750/2400 b.i.

at Kobbegem NW : 11 km Ⓒ Asse pop. 26 432 – ✉ 1730 Kobbegem – ☎ 0 2 :

XXX **Chalet Rose,** Brusselsesteenweg 331 ✆ 452 60 41, Fax 452 26 75, 🍴 – ⓟ. AE ⓞ E VISA
closed Sunday dinner, Monday and last 3 weeks July – **Meals** *Lunch 1275* – a la carte 1300/1750.

XXX **De Plezanten Hof,** Broekstraat 2 ✆ 452 89 39, Fax 452 99 11, 🍴 – ⓟ. AE ⓞ E VISA
closed dinner Tuesday and Sunday, Wednesday, 1 week February and 20 July-12 August – **Meals** *Lunch 1250* – 1600/2250.

at Kraainem E : 12 km – pop. 10 161 – ✉ 1950 Kraainem – ☎ 0 2 :

XX **d'Oude Pastorie,** Pastoorkesweg 1 (Park Jourdain) ✆ 720 63 46, Fax 720 63 46, « Lakeside setting in park » – AE ⓞ E VISA. ✻
closed Monday dinner, Thursday, 15 to 22 April and 12 August-3 September – **Meals** *Lunch 1200* – a la carte approx. 1700.

at Linkebeek S : 12 km – pop. 4 230 – ✉ 1630 Linkebeek – ☎ 0 2 :

XXX **Le Saint-Sébastien,** r. Station 90 ✆ 380 54 90, Fax 380 54 41, 🍴 – ⓟ. ⓞ E VISA
closed Monday and September – **Meals** *Lunch 750* – 1150/1450.

at Machelen NE : 12 km – pop. 10 748 – ✉ 1830 Machelen – ☎ 0 2 :

XXX ✿ **André D'Haese,** Heirbaan 210 ✆ 252 50 72, Fax 253 47 65, 🍴, « Modern interior, terrace with landscaped garden » – ⓟ. AE ⓞ E VISA JCB. ✻
closed Saturday lunch, Sunday, Bank Holidays, 7 to 14 April, 21 July-4 August and 25 December-1 January – **Meals** *Lunch 1300* – 2250/2900, a la carte 2000/2500
Spec. Confit de cailles aux épinards crus, croûtons et lardons, Soupe au pistou et homard norvégien, Ris de veau braisé à brun Zingara.

at Meise N : 14 km – pop. 16 995 – ✉ 1860 Meise – ☎ 0 2 :

XXX **Aub. Napoléon,** Bouchoutlaan 1 ✆ 269 30 78, Fax 269 79 98, Grill rest – ⓟ. AE ⓞ E VISA
closed August – **Meals** *Lunch 1450* – a la carte 1700/2250.

XXX **Koen Van Loven,** Brusselsesteenweg 11 ✆ 270 05 77, Fax 270 05 46 – ⓟ – 🔔 40. AE ⓞ E VISA. ✻
closed Sunday dinner and Monday – **Meals** *Lunch 1175* – 1495/1795.

at Melsbroek NE : 14 km 🄲 Steenokkerzeel pop. 9 806 – ✉ 1820 Melsbroek – ☎ 0 2

XXX **Boetfort,** Sellaerstraat 42 ✆ 751 64 00, Fax 751 62 00, « 17C mansion, park » – Ⓟ – 🏛 25. AE ⓓ E VISA. ✂
closed Wednesday dinner, Saturday lunch, Sunday and carnival week – **Meals** *Lunch 1200* – 1500/1950.

at Nossegem E : 13 km 🄲 Zaventem pop. 23 037 – ✉ 1930 Nossegem – ☎ 0 2 :

XX **Roland Debuyst,** Leuvensesteenweg 614 ✆ 759 23 18, Fax 759 50 08, 🍽 – Ⓟ. AE ⓓ E VISA
closed Saturday lunch, Sunday, Monday dinner, 20 to 27 February and 21 July-16 August – **Meals** *Lunch 1600 b.i.* – 1750/2150.

at Overijse SE : 16 km – pop. 18 661 – ✉ 3090 Overijse – ☎ 0 2 :

XXXX ✿ **Barbizon** (Deluc), Welriekendedreef 95 (at Jezus-Eik) ✆ 657 04 62, Fax 657 40 66, 🍽 « Terrace and garden » – Ⓟ. AE ⓓ E VISA
closed Tuesday, Wednesday, February and 3 weeks August – **Meals** *Lunch 1750* – 2300/3500 a la carte 2300/2800
Spec. Vinaigrette de homard et tomate au corail, Turbotin braisé, sauce au Côtes du jura, Gibier (September-January).

X **Istas,** Brusselsesteenweg 652 (NW : 2 km at Jezus-Eik) ✆ 657 05 11, Fax 657 05 11, 🍽 Pub rest – Ⓟ
closed Wednesday, Thursday and August – **Meals** a la carte 800/1200.

at Schepdaal W : 12 km 🄲 Dilbeek pop. 36 026 – ✉ 1703 Schepdaal – ☎ 0 2 :

🏨 **Lien Zana,** Ninoofsesteenweg 1022 ✆ 569 65 25, Fax 569 64 64, 🏊, 🌳 – 🛗 TV ☎ Ⓟ – 🏛 25. AE ⓓ E
Meals a la carte approx. 900 – **27 rm** ☕ 2400/3200.

at Sint-Genesius-Rode (Rhode-St-Genèse) S : 13 km – pop. 14 853 – ✉ 1640 Sint-Genesius-Rode – ☎ 0 2 :

🏨 **Aub. de Waterloo,** chaussée de Waterloo 212 ✆ 358 35 80, Fax 358 38 06 – 🛗 🚭 TV ☎ Ⓟ – 🏛 25-80. AE ⓓ E VISA JCB
Meals see rest ***L'Arlecchino*** below – **84 rm** ☕ 4450/5300.

XX **L'Arlecchino** - (at Aub. de Waterloo H.), chaussée de Waterloo 212 ✆ 358 34 16, Fax 358 28 96, 🍽, With Trattoria, Italian cuisine – ▤ Ⓟ. AE ⓓ E VISA
Meals – 795/1580 b.i.

X **Bois Savanes,** chaussée de Waterloo 208 ✆ 358 37 78, Fax 354 66 95, 🍽, Thaï cuisine – Ⓟ. AE ⓓ E VISA
closed lunch Monday and Tuesday and 1 to 21 August – **Meals** *Lunch 495* – a la carte approx. 1100.

at Sint-Pieters-Leeuw SO : 13 km – pop. 27 868 – ✉ 1600 Sint-Pieters-Leeuw – ☎ 0 2 :

🏨 **Green Park** Ⓜ 🐕, V. Nonnemanstraat 15 ✆ 331 19 70, Fax 331 03 11, 🍽, « Lakeside setting », 🏋 – 🛗 TV ☎ ♿ Ⓟ – 🏛 40. AE ⓓ E VISA JCB
closed 8 to 26 July – **Meals** *(closed Friday) Lunch 450* – a la carte 1150/1550 – **18 rm** ☕ 3650/4150.

at Strombeek-Bever N : 9 km 🄲 Grimbergen pop. 31 110 – ✉ 1853 Strombeek-Bever – ☎ 0 2 :

XX **Le Val Joli,** Leestbeekstraat 16 ✆ 460 65 43, Fax 460 04 00, 🍽, « Terrace and garden » – Ⓟ. AE E VISA
closed Monday, Tuesday and 4 to 19 June – **Meals** *Lunch 490* – 890/1450.

XX **'t Stoveke,** Jetsestraat 52 ✆ 267 67 25, 🍽, Seafood – AE ⓓ E VISA. ✂
closed Sunday, Monday, Bank Holidays, 3 weeks June, Christmas and New Year – **Meals** *Lunch 1190* – 1720/2300.

at Vilvoorde (Vilvorde) N : 17 km – pop. 29 220 – ✉ 1800 Vilvoorde – ☎ 0 2 :

XX **Barbay,** Romeinsesteenweg 220 (SW : 4 km at Koningslo) ✆ 267 00 45, Fax 267 00 45, 🍽 – AE ⓓ E VISA. ✂
closed Saturday lunch, Sunday and late July – **Meals** *Lunch 895* – a la carte 1050/1800.

at Vlezenbeek W : 11 km 🄲 Sint-Pieters-Leeuw pop. 27 868 – ✉ 1602 Vlezenbeek – ☎ 0 2 :

XX **Philippe Verbaeys,** Dorp 49 ✆ 569 05 25, Fax 569 05 25, 🍽 – AE ⓓ E VISA
closed Monday – **Meals** *Lunch 490* – 990/1490.

X **Aub. Le Saint Esprit,** Postweg 250 (road to the castle of Gaasbeek) ✆ 532 42 18 – AE ⓓ E VISA
closed Monday and dinner Sunday and Tuesday, first 2 weeks March and September – **Meals** a la carte 2000/2500.

at Wemmel N : 12 km – pop. 12 980 – ✉ 1780 Wemmel – ☎ 0 2 :

XX **Parkhof,** Parklaan 7 ✆ 460 42 89, Fax 460 25 10, 🍽, « Terrace » – Ⓟ. AE ⓓ E VISA JCB
closed Wednesday, Thursday and September – **Meals** *Lunch 950* – 1400/1900.

at Wezembeek-Oppem E : 11 km – pop. 11 169 – ✉ 1970 Wezembeek-Oppem – ☎ 0 2 :

XXX **L'Aub. Saint-Pierre,** Sint-Pietersplein 8 ☎ 731 21 79, Fax 731 28 28 – AE ⓓ E VISA
closed Saturday lunch, Sunday, Bank Holidays, 15 July-15 August and 24 December-2 January – **Meals** *Lunch 1490* – a la carte approx. 1800.

at Zaventem Brussels-Zaventem airport motorway – pop. 23 037 – ✉ 1930 Zaventem – ☎ 0 2 :

Sheraton Airport, at airport ☎ 725 10 00, Telex 27085, Fax 725 11 55 – 25-600. AE ⓓ E VISA JCB. rest
Meals ***Concorde*** *Lunch 1375* - a la carte 1350/2450 – 690 – **290 rm** 8900/9900, 7 suites.

XX ✿ **Stockmansmolen** 1st floor, H. Henneaulaan 164 ☎ 725 34 34, Fax 725 75 05, Partly pub rest, « Former watermill » – Ⓟ. AE ⓓ E VISA.
closed Saturday, Sunday and 21 July-15 August – **Meals** *Lunch 1625* – 2175/2650, a la carte 2100/2600
Spec. Salade de homard au melon, curry léger, Sauté de poularde de Bresse aux morilles, Feuilletage aux pommes et sauce au chocolat.

Genval 1322 Brabant Ⓒ Rixensart pop. 19 344 213 ⑲ and 409 G 3 – ☎ 0 2 – 21 km.

Château du Lac Ⓜ, av. du Lac 87 ☎ 655 71 11, Fax 655 74 44, ← lake and woodland, – Ⓟ – 30-1000. AE ⓓ E VISA
Meals see rest ***Le Trèfle à 4*** below – **84 rm** 8250/9900, 1 suite.

Le Manoir without rest, av. Hoover 4 ☎ 655 63 11, Fax 655 64 55, ←, « Park », – Ⓟ – 25. AE ⓓ E VISA
12 rm 8250/9400.

XXXX ✿✿ **Le Trèfle à 4** (Haquin) - at Château du Lac H., av. du Lac 87 ☎ 654 07 98, Fax 653 31 31, ← lake and woodland – Ⓟ. AE ⓓ E VISA
closed Monday, Tuesday and 8 January-9 February – **Meals** *Lunch 1450* – 1950/2950, a la carte 2500/2950
Spec. Rosace de turbot et homard à la nantua, Galette de maïs au foie d'oie poêlé et raisins, Poularde en croûte de sel, crème de cresson aux légumes.

The hotels have entered into certain undertakings towards the readers of this Guide. Make it plain that you have the most recent Guide.

ANTWERP (ANTWERPEN) 2000 212 ⑮ and 409 G 2 – I 2 – pop. 403 072 – ☎ 0 3.

See : Around the Market Square and the Cathedral★★★ : Market Square★ (Grote Markt) FY, Vlaaikensgang★ FY, Cathedral★★★ FY and its tower★★★ FY – Butchers' House★ (Vleeshuis) : Musical instruments★ FY **D** – Rubens' House★★ (Rubenshuis) GZ – Interior★ of St. James' Church (St-Jacobskerk) GY - Hendrik Conscience Place★ GY – St. Charles Borromeo's Church★ (St-Carolus Borromeuskerk) GY – St. Paul's Church (St-Pauluskerk) : interior★ FY – Zoo★★ (Dierentuin) DEU – The port (Haven) FY.

Museums : Maritime "Steen"★ (Nationaal Scheepvaartmuseum Steen) FY – Etnographic Museum★ FY **M1** – Plantin-Moretus★★★ FZ – Mayer Van den Bergh★★ : Mad Meg★★ (Dulle Griet) GZ – Rockox House★ (Rockoxhuis) GY **M4** – Royal Art Gallery★★★ (Koninklijk Museum voor Schone Kunsten) CV **M5** – Museum of Photography★ CV **M6** – Open-air Museum of Sculpture Middelheim★ (Openluchtmuseum voor Beeldhouwkunst).

18 9 at Kapellen N : 15,5 km, G. Capiaulei 2 ☎ (0 3) 666 84 56, - 18 at Aartselaar S : 10 km, Kasteel Cleydael ☎ (0 3) 887 00 79 - 18 at Wommelgem E : 10 km, Uilenbaan 15 ☎ (0 3) 353 02 92 - 18 9 at Broechem E : 13 km, Kasteel Bossenstein ☎ (0 3) 485 64 46.

ℹ (closed Sunday except April-October) Grote Markt 15 ☎ 232 01 03, Fax 231 19 37 – Tourist association of the province, (closed Saturday and Sunday) Karel Oomsstraat 11, ✉ 2018, ☎ 216 28 10, Fax 237 83 65.

Brussels 48 – Amsterdam 159 – Luxembourg 261 – Rotterdam 103.

Plans on following pages

Old Antwerp

Hilton Ⓜ, Groenplaats ☎ 204 12 12, Fax 204 12 13, « Facade of an early 20C department store », – – 30-1000. AE ⓓ E VISA JCB. rest FZ **m**
Meals ***Het Vijfde Seizoen*** *(closed late July-early August)* *Lunch 1275* - 1300/1700 – 675 – **199 rm** 4750/10900, 12 suites.

Alfa Theater Ⓜ, Arenbergstraat 30 ☎ 231 17 20, Fax 233 88 58, – – 25. AE ⓓ E VISA. GZ **t**
Meals *(closed Sunday and Bank Holidays)* *Lunch 590* – a la carte approx. 1200 – **122 rm** 5500, 5 suites.

De Rosier without rest, Rosier 23 ☎ 225 01 40, Fax 231 41 11, « Former 17C residence », – . AE ⓓ E VISA FZ **d**
closed 24, 25, and 26 December and 31 December-2 January – **8 rm** 7500/10000, 4 suites.

De Witte Lelie without rest, Keizerstraat 16 ☎ 226 19 66, Fax 234 00 19, « Typical 17C terraced houses, patio » – . AE ⓓ E VISA GY **z**
closed 20 December-2 January – **7 rm** 6000/15000, 3 suites.

ANTWERPEN

Carnotstr.	EU	3
Dambruggestr.	ETU	39
Gemeentestr.	DU	63
de Keyserlei	DU	103
Leysstr.	DU	123
Offerandestr.	EU	136
Pelikaanstr.	DU	151
Quellinstr.	DU	165
Turnhoutsebaan (BORGERHOUT)	EU	
van Aerdtstr.	DT	3
Amsterdamstr.	DT	4
Ankerrui	DT	6
Ballaerstr.	DV	12
Bolivarplaats	CV	15
Borsbeekbrug	EX	16
van Breestr.	DV	19
Brialmontlei	DV	21
Britselei	DV	22
Broederminstr.	CV	24
Brouwersvliet	DT	25
Brusselstr.	CV	27
Cassiersstr.	DT	31
Charlottalei	DV	33
Cockerillkaai	CV	36
Cuperusstr.	EV	37
Diksmuidelaan	EX	43
Emiel Banningstr.	CV	51
Emiel Vloorsstr.	CX	52
Emile Verhaerenlaan	CT	54
Erwtenstr.	ET	55
van Eycklei	DV	57
Falconplein	DT	58
Franklin Rooseveltpl.	DU	60
Gén. Armstrongweg	CX	64
Gérard Le Grellelaan	DX	66
de Gerlachekaai	CV	67
Gitschotellei	EX	70
Graaf van Egmontstr.	CV	72
Haantjeslei	CDV	79
Halenstr.	ET	81
Hessenplein	DT	84
Jan de Voslei	CX	90
Jan van Gentstr.	CV	91
Jezusstr.	DU	96
Justitiestr.	DV	97
Kasteelpleinstr.	DV	102
Kloosterstr.	CU	105
Kol. Silvertopstr.	CX	106
Koningin Astridplein	DEU	109
Koningin Elisabethlei	DX	110
Korte Winkelstr.	DTU	114
Lange Lobroekstr.	ET	117
Lange Winkelstr.	DT	118
Léopold de Waelplein	CV	120
Léopold de Waelstr.	CV	121
Londenstr.	DT	124
Maria-Henriettalei	DV	129
Mercatorstr.	DEV	130
Namenstr.	CV	133
van den Nestlei	EV	135
Ommeganckstr.	EU	138
Orteliuskaai	DT	141
Osystr.	DU	142
Oude Leeuwenrui	DT	148
Plantinkaai	CU	153
Ploegstr.	EU	154
Pluvierstr.	CU	156
Posthofbrug	EX	157
Prins Albertlei	DX	159
Provinciestr.	EUV	162
Pyckestr.	CX	163
Quinlen Matsijslei	DUV	166
Rolwagenstr.	EV	171
Schijnpoortweg	ET	174
van Schoonhovestr.	DEU	175
Simonsstr.	DEV	178
Sint-Bernardse steenweg	CX	180
Sint-Gummarusstr.	DT	181
Sint-Jansplein	DT	183
Sint-Jozefsstr.	DV	186
Sint-Michielskaai	CU	187
Stuivenbergplein	ET	196
Viaduct Dam	ET	202
Visestr.	ET	204
Volkstr.	CV	207
Vondelstr.	DT	208

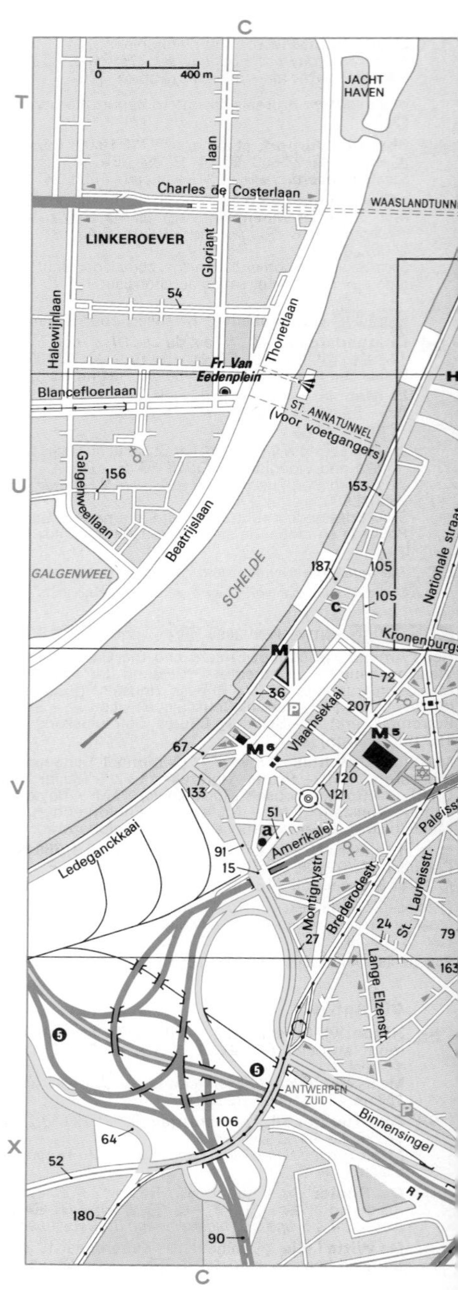

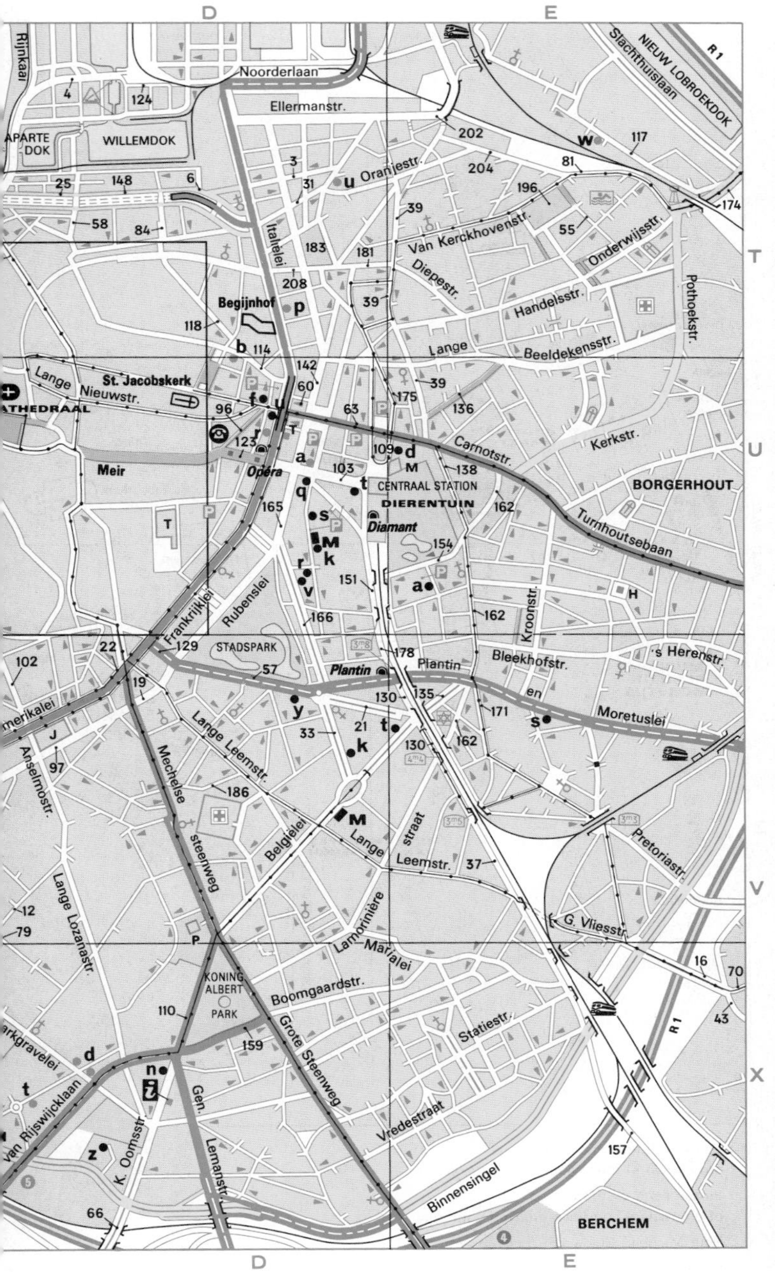

D
E
Noorderlaan
Ellermanstr.
WILLEMDOK
Rijnkaai
NIEUW LOBROEKDOK
Slachthuislaan
R1
Oranjestr.
Italielei
Van Kerckhovenstr.
Onderwijsstr.
Diepestr.
Handelsstr.
Pothoekstr.
Begijnhof
Lange
Beeldekensstr.
Lange Nieuwstr.
St. Jacobskerk
KATHEDRAAL
Meir
Opera
Carnotstr.
Kerkstr.
CENTRAAL STATION
DIERENTUIN
Diamant
BORGERHOUT
Turnhoutsebaan
Frankrijklei
Rubenslei
Kroonstr.
STADSPARK
Plantin
Bleekhofstr.
'sHerenstr.
Plantin en Moretuslei
Amerikalei
Anselmostr.
Lange Leemstr.
Mechelse steenweg
Belgielei
Lange Leemstr.
straat
Pretoriastr.
Lange Lozanastr.
Lamorinière
Marialei
G. Vliesstr.
KONING ALBERT PARK
Boomgaardstr.
Grote Steenweg
Statiestr.
Markgravelei
Van Rijswijcklaan
Gen. Lemanstr.
K. Oomsstr.
Vredestraat
Binnensingel
BERCHEM
T
U
V
X

ANTWERPEN

Street	Grid	No.
Groenplaats	FZ	
Klapdorp	GY	
Meir	GZ	
Nationalestr.	FZ	
Paardenmarkt	GY	
Schoenmarkt	FZ	
Gildekamerstr.	FY	69
Handschoenmarkt	FY	82
Korte Gasthuisstr.	GZ	112
Maria Pijpelinckxstr.	GZ	127
Oude Koornmarkt	FYZ	147
Repenstr.	FY	168
Rosier	FZ	172
Sint-Jansvliet	FZ	184
Sint-Rochusstr.	FZ	189
Steenhouwersvest	FZ	193
Twaalf Maandenstr.	GZ	199
Veemarkt	FY	201
Vleeshouwersstr.	FY	205
Vrijdagmarkt	FZ	213
Wisselstr.	FY	214
Zirkstr.	FY	216
Zwartzusterstr.	FY	217

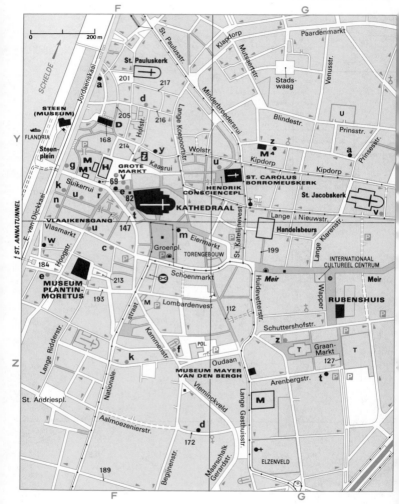

Pleasant hotels and restaurants
are shown in the Guide by a red sign.

Please send us the names
of any where you have enjoyed your stay.

Your **Michelin Guide** will be even better.

't Sandt without rest, Het Zand 17 ☎ 232 93 90, Fax 232 56 13, « 19C residence in rococo style » – 25-150. AE ⓓ E VISA FZ **w**
12 rm 5500/7500, 2 suites.

Rubens without rest, Oude Beurs 29 ☎ 222 48 48, Fax 225 19 40, « Floral inner courtyard » – 25-50. AE ⓓ E VISA. FY **y**
35 rm 5500/6500, 1 suite.

Prinse without rest, Keizerstraat 63 ☎ 226 40 50, Fax 225 11 48 – 25-100. AE E VISA. GY **a**
34 rm 3700/6000, 1 suite.

Villa Mozart, Handschoenmarkt 3 ☎ 231 30 31, Fax 231 56 85, « Elegant interior », – 25. AE ⓓ E VISA JCB FY **e**
Meals (Pub rest) *Lunch 920* – a la carte 1000/1500 – 500 – **25 rm** 3500/5400.

Antigone without rest, Jordaenskaai 11 ☎ 231 66 77, Fax 231 37 74 – 30. AE ⓓ E VISA. FY **a**
17 rm 3000/3500.

XXX **Den Gulden Greffoen,** Hoogstraat 37 ☎ 231 50 46, Fax 233 20 39, « In a 15C residence » – . AE ⓓ E VISA. FZ **u**
closed lunch Saturday and Sunday – **Meals** *Lunch 1450* – a la carte approx. 1800.

XXX **La Rade** 1st floor, E. Van Dijckkaai 8 ☎ 233 37 37, Fax 233 49 63, « Former 19C freemason's lodge » – AE ⓓ E VISA FY **g**
closed Saturday lunch, Sunday, Bank Holidays, carnival week and 8 to 28 July – **Meals** *Lunch 1450* – a la carte 2300/2750.

XXX ✿✿ **'t Fornuis** (Segers), Reyndersstraat 24 ☎ 233 62 70, Fax 233 99 03, « 17C residence, rustic interior » – AE ⓓ E VISA. FZ **c**
closed Saturday, Sunday, Bank Holidays, last 3 weeks August and Christmas-New Year – **Meals** *Lunch 2150* – a la carte 2350/3250
Spec. Barbue au four, mousseline de pommes de terre au caviar, Galettes aux épices et au crabe frais, Ris de veau rôti au chou vert et truffes.

XXX ✿ **De Kerselaar** (Michiels), Grote Pieter Potstraat 22 ☎ 233 59 69, Fax 233 11 49, « Opulent interior » – . AE ⓓ E VISA. FY **n**
closed lunch Saturday and Monday, Sunday, 29 March-8 April and 8 to 21 July – **Meals** *Lunch 1350* – a la carte 1950/2250
Spec. Petits-gris sur salade chaude de champignons des bois aux noisettes, Solettes rôties, macédoine d'artichaut, pommes de terre et champigons aux herbes, Charlotte au chocolat et aux croustilles parfumées à l'orange et au Rhum.

XX **Huis De Colvenier,** St-Antoniusstraat 8 ☎ 226 65 73, Fax 227 13 14, « Late 19C residence » – . AE ⓓ E VISA FZ **k**
closed Saturday lunch, Sunday dinner, Monday, 1 week carnival and late July-early August – **Meals** *Lunch 1200* – 1600/3200 b.i.

XX **Petrus,** Kelderstraat 1 ☎ 225 27 34, Fax 225 27 34, – . AE ⓓ E VISA GZ **z**
closed lunch Saturday and Sunday, Monday and 1 week carnival – **Meals** *Lunch 995 b.i.* – a la carte approx. 1900.

XX **'t Silveren Claverblat,** Grote Pieter Potstraat 16 ☎ 231 33 88, Fax 231 31 46 – AE ⓓ E VISA. FY **k**
closed Tuesday – **Meals** *Lunch 1000* – 1450/2000.

XX **Zirk,** Zirkstraat 29 ☎ 225 25 86, Fax 226 51 77 – AE ⓓ E VISA. FY **d**
closed Saturday lunch, Sunday, Monday, first 2 weeks September and late January – **Meals** *Lunch 1200* – 1800/2400.

XX **P. Preud'homme,** Suikerrui 28 ☎ 233 42 00, Fax 232 82 16, , Open until 11 p.m. – . AE ⓓ E VISA JCB. FY **r**
closed February and Tuesday October-May – **Meals** *Lunch 850* – a la carte 1550/2200.

XX **De Perelaer,** Kammenstraat 75 ☎ 233 42 73, Fax 226 28 51, « 16C residence » – AE ⓓ E VISA FZ **f**
closed lunch Saturday and Monday, Sunday and 15 July-7 August – **Meals** *Lunch 1100* – a la carte 1200/1800.

XX **De Gulden Beer,** Grote Markt 14 ☎ 226 08 41, Fax 232 52 09, , Partly Italian cuisine – . AE ⓓ E VISA. FY **v**
Meals *Lunch 1500* – a la carte approx. 1800.

XX **VIP Diners,** Lange Nieuwstraat 95 ☎ 233 13 17, Fax 233 13 17 – AE ⓓ E VISA GY **v**
closed Saturday lunch, Sunday, Bank Holidays, 2 weeks Easter and last 3 weeks July – **Meals** a la carte 1600/1950.

XX **Het Nieuwe Palinghuis,** St-Jansvliet 14 ☎ 231 74 45, Fax 231 50 53, Seafood – . AE ⓓ E VISA FZ **e**
closed June and holiday Monday and Tuesday – **Meals** *Lunch 1150* – a la carte approx. 1700.

XX ✿ **De Matelote** (Garnich), Haarstraat 9 ☎ 231 32 07, Fax 231 08 13, Seafood – . AE ⓓ E VISA FY **u**
closed lunch Saturday and Monday, Sunday, Bank Holidays, July and 1 to 15 January – **Meals** *Lunch 1600 b.i.* – a la carte 1800/2900
Spec. Légumes froids à l'italienne, Sole à la vinaigrette de pommes de terre (July-December), Barbue à la ciboulette et carottes confites.

XX **In de Schaduw van de Kathedraal,** Handschoenmarkt 17 ☎ 232 40 14, Fax 226 88 14, terrace, Mussels in season – AE ⓓ E VISA. ✻ FY **e**
closed Monday except in season, Tuesday, 10 January-10 February and 13 to 19 November – **Meals** a la carte approx. 1700.

XX **De Manie,** H. Conscienceplein 3 ☎ 232 64 38, Fax 232 64 38, terrace – AE ⓓ E VISA. ✻ GY **u**
closed Wednesday, Sunday and 16 August-1 September – **Meals** *Lunch 1150* – a la carte 1400/1950.

X **Rooden Hoed,** Oude Koornmarkt 25 ☎ 233 28 44, Mussels in season, Antwerp atmosphere – AE E VISA. ✻ FY **t**
closed Wednesday, Thursday, carnival week and mid June-mid July – **Meals** *Lunch 850* – a la carte 1000/1650.

X **Don Carlos,** St-Michielskaai 34 ☎ 216 40 46, Partly Spanish cuisine – ✻ CU **c**
closed Monday – **Meals** (dinner only) a la carte approx. 1200.

Town Centre

Park Lane M, Van Eycklei 32, ✉ 2018, ☎ 285 85 85 and 285 85 80 (rest), Fax 285 85 86, Lö, sauna, pool – lift ⇔ air TV ☎ car – 🏛 25-450. AE ⓓ E VISA JCB. ✻ DV **y**
Meals ***Longchamps*** *(closed Saturday lunch and Sunday dinner) Lunch 850* - 950/1600 – **176 rm** ☕ 5500/6000, 2 suites.

Alfa De Keyser M, De Keyserlei 66, ✉ 2018, ☎ 234 01 35, Fax 232 39 70, Lö, sauna, pool – lift ⇔ air TV ☎ – 🏛 25-160. AE ⓓ E VISA JCB. ✻ DU **t**
Meals *(closed Saturday lunch and Sunday dinner) Lunch 800* – a la carte approx. 1300 – **115 rm** ☕ 6100/8000, 8 suites.

Carlton with 12 apartments in annex, Quinten Matsijslei 25, ✉ 2018, ☎ 231 15 15, Telex 31072, Fax 225 30 90, ← – lift ⇔ air TV ☎ car – 🏛 45-100. AE ⓓ E VISA. ✻ DU **v**
Meals *(closed dinner Friday and Sunday, Saturday lunch, Easter week, first 3 weeks August and Christmas holidays) Lunch 875* – a la carte 1050/1750 – **138 rm** ☕ 5700/6700, 1 suite.

Hylitt M, De Keyserlei 28, ✉ 2018, ☎ 202 68 00 and 227 44 88 (rest), Fax 202 68 90 and 227 45 00 (rest), terrace – lift air TV ☎ car. AE ⓓ E VISA. ✻ DU **q**
Meals ***Gran Duca*** 6th floor, Terrace with ← town (partly Italian cuisine, open until 11 p.m.) a la carte 1250/1600 – ☕ 550 – **50 rm** 3250/4250, 30 suites.

Switel, Copernicuslaan 2, ✉ 2018, ☎ 231 67 80, Telex 33965, Fax 233 02 90, Lö, sauna, pool, ✻ – lift ⇔ air rest TV ☎ car – 🏛 30-1000. AE ⓓ E VISA EU **a**
Meals a la carte 1150/1500 – ☕ 575 – **308 rm** 5025/7470, 2 suites.

Plaza without rest, Charlottalei 43, ✉ 2018, ☎ 218 92 40, Telex 31531, Fax 218 88 23 – lift ⇔ TV ☎ car – 🏛 25. AE ⓓ E VISA. ✻ DV **k**
80 rm ☕ 5400/6900.

Residence without rest, Molenbergstraat 9 ☎ 232 76 75, Fax 233 73 28 – lift TV ☎ car. AE ⓓ E VISA. ✻ DU **f**
☕ 400 – **67 rm** 2500/4000.

Alfa Empire without rest, Appelmansstraat 31, ✉ 2018, ☎ 231 47 55, Fax 233 40 60 – lift ⇔ air TV ☎. AE ⓓ E VISA JCB DU **s**
70 rm ☕ 7100.

Colombus without rest, Frankrijklei 4 ☎ 233 03 90, Fax 226 09 46, Lö, pool – lift TV ☎. AE ⓓ E VISA. ✻ DU **u**
32 rm ☕ 3250/3800.

Alfa Congress, Plantin en Moretuslei 136, ✉ 2018, ☎ 235 30 00, Fax 235 52 31 – lift ⇔ air TV ☎ car P – 🏛 25-120. AE ⓓ E VISA. ✻ rm EV **s**
Meals *Lunch 800* – a la carte approx. 1400 – **66 rm** ☕ 3200/4200.

Eden without rest, Lange Herentalsestraat 25, ✉ 2018, ☎ 233 06 08, Fax 233 12 28 – lift TV ☎ car. AE ⓓ E VISA DU **k**
66 rm ☕ 2500/3000.

XXX ✿ **Corum** (De Koninck), Italiëlei 177 ☎ 232 23 44, Fax 232 24 41 – air. AE ⓓ E VISA. ✻ DT **p**
closed Saturday lunch, Sunday, Monday and 10 to 31 July – **Meals** *Lunch 1250* – a la carte 1700/2200
Spec. Marée du jour, Terrine de foie d'oie au naturel, Pigeon aux pleurottes et thym frais.

XX **Fouquets** 1st floor, De Keyserlei 17, ✉ 2018, ☎ 233 97 42, Fax 226 16 88, terrace, Open until midnight – air. AE ⓓ E VISA DU **a**
Meals *Lunch 995* – a la carte 1200/1800.

XX **De Barbarie,** Van Breestraat 4, ✉ 2018, ☎ 232 81 98, Fax 231 26 78, terrace – AE E VISA. ✻ DV **b**
closed Sunday, Monday and 1 to 15 September – **Meals** *Lunch 1350* – a la carte 1800/2200.

XX **Blue Phoenix,** Frankrijklei 14 ☎ 233 33 77, Fax 233 88 46, Chinese cuisine – air. AE E VISA DU **r**
closed Monday, Saturday lunch and August – **Meals** *Lunch 750* – a la carte 800/1700.

XX **De Zeste,** Lange Dijkstraat 36, ✉ 2060, ☎ 233 45 49, Fax 232 34 18 – air. AE ⓓ E VISA DT **u**
closed Sunday – **Meals** *Lunch 1200* – 1950/2800.

't Lammeke, Lange Lobroekstraat 51 (opposite the slaughterhouse), 2060, 236 79 86, Fax 271 05 16 – . AE VISA ET w
closed Monday, Saturday lunch, 16 July-11 August and 23 to 31 December – **Meals** 975/1475.

Yamayu Santatsu, Ossenmarkt 19 234 09 49, Japanese cuisine – . AE VISA DTU b
closed Sunday lunch, Monday and first 2 weeks August – **Meals** *Lunch 420* – 1500/1700.

South Quarter

Holiday Inn Crowne Plaza, G. Legrellelaan 10, 2020, 237 29 00, Telex 33843, Fax 216 02 96, – 40-800. AE VISA JCB
Meals *Lunch 995* – a la carte 1300/1600 – 575 – **256 rm** 5995, 4 suites.

Sofitel, Desguinlei 94, 2018, 216 48 00, Fax 216 47 12, – 65-500. AE VISA DX z
Meals *Tiffany's Lunch 550* - 1125 – 550 – **215 rm** 6500, 5 suites.

Firean without rest, Karel Oomsstraat 6, 2018, 237 02 60, Fax 238 11 68, « Period residence, Art Deco style » – . AE VISA JCB. DX n
closed 27 July-19 August and 20 December-6 January – **11 rm** 4100/5700, 4 suites.

Industrie without rest, E. Banningstraat 52 238 66 00, Fax 238 86 88 – . AE VISA JCB. CV a
13 rm 2700/3700.

Vateli, Van Putlei 31, 2018, 238 72 52, Fax 238 25 88 – . AE VISA. DX t
closed Saturday lunch, Sunday, Bank Holidays and last 2 weeks July – **Meals** *Lunch 1450 b.i.* – a la carte 1800/2350.

Loncin, Markgravelei 127, 2018, 248 29 89, Fax 248 38 66, , Open until midnight – . VISA. DX d
closed Tuesday, Wednesday and lunch Saturday and Sunday – **Meals** *Lunch 2000 b.i.* – a la carte 2200/2800.

Liang's Garden, Markgravelei 141, 2018, 237 22 22, Fax 248 38 34, Chinese cuisine – . AE VISA. DX d
closed Sunday, 3 weeks July, Christmas and New Year – **Meals** a la carte 1000/1700.

De Poterne, Desguinlei 186, 2018, 238 28 24, Fax 238 59 67 – AE VISA DX u
closed Saturday lunch, Sunday and 21 July-15 August – **Meals** *Lunch 1350* – a la carte approx. 2000.

Suburbs

North – 2030 – 0 3 :

Novotel, Luithagen-Haven 6 542 03 20, Fax 541 70 93, , , – – 25-150. AE VISA
Meals (open until midnight) a la carte approx. 1100 – 425 – **119 rm** 3500/3700.

at Borgerhout E : 3 km C Antwerpen – 2140 Borgerhout – 0 3 :

Scandic Crown, Luitenant Lippenslaan 66 235 91 91, Telex 34479, Fax 235 08 96, , – – 25-230. AE VISA
Meals a la carte approx. 1600 – 550 – **201 rm** 4950, 3 suites.

at Deurne NE : 3 km C Antwerpen – 2100 Deurne – 0 3 :

De Violin, Bosuil 1 324 34 04, Fax 326 33 20, , « Small farmhouse » – . AE VISA
closed Sunday and early August-early September – **Meals** a la carte approx. 2000.

Périgord, Turnhoutsebaan 273 325 52 00 – . AE VISA.
closed Tuesday, Wednesday, Saturday lunch, 1 week carnival and July – **Meals** *Lunch 900* – 1425/1900.

at Ekeren N : 11 km C Antwerpen – 2180 Ekeren – 0 3 :

Hof de Bist, Veltwijcklaan 258 664 61 30, Fax 664 67 24 – . AE VISA
closed Sunday, Monday, Tuesday and August – **Meals** – 2000.

at Wilrijk S : 6 km C Antwerpen – 2610 Wilrijk – 0 3 :

Schans XV, Moerelei 155 828 45 64, Fax 828 93 29, , « Early 20C redoubt » – AE VISA.
closed Thursday dinner, Saturday lunch, Sunday, Bank Holidays, 2 weeks February and 2 weeks July – **Meals** a la carte approx. 2000.

Environs

at Aartselaar S : 10 km – pop. 14 264 – 2630 Aartselaar – 0 3 :

Kasteel Solhof without rest, Baron Van Ertbornstraat 116 877 30 00, Fax 877 31 31, « In an ancient park », – – 40. AE VISA.
closed Christmas-New Year – 600 – **24 rm** 4800/6000.

Host. Kasteelhoeve Groeninghe with rm, Kontichsesteenweg 78 457 95 86, Fax 458 13 68, ≤, , « Restored Flemish farm, country atmosphere », – – 25-150. AE VISA.
closed 4 to 18 August and 22 December-4 January – **Meals** *(closed Saturday lunch, Sunday and Bank Holidays) Lunch 1500* – 2350/2750 – 500 – **7 rm** 3900/5250.

XXX **Kasteel Cleydael** with rm, Cleydaellaan 36 (W : direction Hemiksem) 887 05 04, Fax 887 20 18, « Restored moated feudal castle » - TV ☎ P - 25-50. AE ⓞ E VISA.
closed Saturday lunch, Sunday, Monday, Bank Holidays, 21 July-20 August and 22 December-2 January - **Meals** *Lunch 1750* - a la carte approx. 2300 - **6 rm** 5500/6500, 1 suite.

XX **Villa Verde,** Kleistraat 175 887 56 85, Fax 887 22 56, ←, - P. AE ⓞ E VISA.
closed Monday, Saturday lunch, Sunday dinner, 14 July-4 August and 1 to 16 January - **Meals** *Lunch 1100* - 1800/2450.

at Boechout SE : 9 km - pop. 11 307 - ✉ 2530 Boechout - 0 3 :

XX ✿ **De Schone van Boskoop** (Keersmaekers), Appelkantstraat 10 454 19 31, Fax 454 19 31, , « Terrace with ornamental pool » - P. AE E VISA.
closed Sunday, Monday, 1 week April, last 2 weeks August-first week September and first week January - **Meals** *Lunch 1400* - a la carte approx. 2300
Spec. Carpaccio de St-Jacques à la crème de caviar, Ravioli de foie gras, pied de porc et truffes, Pigeonneau au ris de veau et baies de genèvrier.

at Brasschaat N : 11 km - pop. 33 985 - ✉ 2930 Brasschaat - 0 3 :

XXX **Halewijn,** Donksesteenweg 212 (Ekeren-Donk) 647 20 10, Fax 647 08 95, - AE ⓞ E VISA
closed Monday - **Meals** *Lunch 990* - a la carte approx. 1400.

at Hemiksem SW : 9 km - pop. 9 042 - ✉ 2620 Hemiksem - 0 3 :

Scheldeboord, Scheldestraat 151 877 14 14, Fax 877 12 10, « Scheldt-side setting », - rest TV ☎ P - 25-60. AE ⓞ E VISA.
Meals *(closed Saturday lunch) Lunch 1250* - a la carte approx. 1500 - **20 rm** 3300/3700.

at Kapellen N : 15,5 km - pop. 23 382 - ✉ 2950 Kapellen - 0 3 :

XXX ✿✿ **De Bellefleur** (Buytaert), Antwerpsesteenweg 253 664 67 19, Fax 665 02 01, , « Veranda surrounded by floral gardens » - P. AE ⓞ E VISA
closed Saturday dinner May-September, Saturday lunch, Sunday, 2 weeks February and July - **Meals** *Lunch 1750 b.i.* - 3750 b.i., a la carte 2300/2800
Spec. Ragoût d'écrevisses et champignons, Solette aux chicons et caviar, Chevreuil aux baies de sureau et aux champignons des bois (May-December).

at Kontich S : 12 km - pop. 18 754 - ✉ 2550 Kontich - 0 3 :

XXX **Carême,** Koningin Astridlaan 114 457 63 04, Fax 457 93 02, - P. AE ⓞ E VISA
closed Saturday lunch, Sunday, Monday and July - **Meals** *Lunch 1095* - 1650/2350.

at Ranst E : 12 km - pop. 16 610 - ✉ 2520 Ranst - 0 3 :

XX **Ten Schawijcke,** Schawijkplasweg 14 353 92 32, Fax 353 75 31, « Restored farmhouse manor, rustic » - P. AE ⓞ E VISA.
closed Monday and July - **Meals** (dinner only) 1350/1800.

at Schoten NE : 10 km - pop. 30 168 - ✉ 2900 Schoten - 0 3 :

XXX **Kleine Barreel,** Bredabaan 1147 645 85 84, Fax 645 85 03 - P. AE ⓞ E VISA.
Meals *Lunch 1150* - 1150/1575.

XXX **Uilenspiegel,** Brechtsebaan 277 (3 km on N 115) 651 61 45, Fax 652 08 08, , « Terrace and garden » - P. AE E VISA
closed Monday, Tuesday, last 2 weeks July and last week January - **Meals** *Lunch 975* - 1395/1950.

at Wijnegem E : 10 km - pop. 8 352 - ✉ 2110 Wijnegem - 0 3 :

XXX **Ter Vennen,** Merksemsebaan 278 326 20 60, Fax 326 38 47, , « Terrace » - P. AE ⓞ E VISA
Meals *Lunch 1675* - a la carte 1300/2400.

Kruiningen Zeeland (Netherlands) C Reimerswaal pop. 20 125 212 ⑬ ⑭ and 408 D 7 - 0 113 - 56 km.

Le Manoir , Zandweg 2 (W : 1 km), ✉ 4416 NA, 38 17 53, Fax 38 17 63, ←, - TV ☎ P. AE ⓞ E VISA
closed 2 weeks January - **Meals** see rest ***Inter Scaldes*** below - 28 - **8 rm** 275/450, 2 suites.

XXXX ✿✿ **Inter Scaldes** (Mme Boudeling) - at Le Manoir H., Zandweg 2 (W : 1 km), ✉ 4416 NA, 38 17 53, Fax 38 17 63, , « Terrace-veranda overlooking an English-style garden » - P. AE ⓞ E VISA
closed 1 week October, 2 weeks January and Monday and Tuesday except Bank Holidays - **Meals** 100/175, a la carte 148/195
Spec. Homard fumé, sauce au caviar, Bar légèrement fumé à la tomate, basilic et olives (May-November), Turbot en robe de truffes et son beurre.

BRUGES (BRUGGE) 8000 West-Vlaanderen 213 ③ and 409 C 2 – pop. 114 530 – ☎ 0 50.

See : Procession of the Holy Blood★★★ (Heilig Bloedprocessie) – Historic centre and canals★★★ (Historisch centrum en grachten) – Market square★★ (Markt) AU, Belfry and Halles★★★ (Belfort en Hallen) ≤★★ from the top AU – Market-town★★ (Burg) AU – Basilica of the Holy Blood★ (Basiliek van het Heilig Bloed) : low Chapel★ or St. Basiles Chapel (beneden- of St-Basiliuskapel) AU **B** – Chimney of the "Brugse Vrije"★ in the Palace of the "Brugse Vrije" AU **S** – Rosery quay (Rozenhoedkaai) ≤★★ AU **63** – Dijver ≤★★ AU – St. Boniface bridge (Bonifatiusbrug) : site★★ AU – Beguinage★★ (Begijnhof) AV – Trips on the canals★★★ (Boottocht) AU – Church of Our Lady★ (O.-L.-Vrouwekerk) : tower★★, statue of the Madonna★★, tombstone★★ of Mary of Burgundy★★ AV **N.**

Museums : Groeninge★★★ (Stedelijk Museum voor Schone Kunsten) AU – Memling★★★ (St. John's Hospital) AV – Gruuthuse★ : bust of Charles the Fifth★ (borstbeeld van Karel V) AU **M**[1] – Brangwyn★ AU **M**[4] – Folklore★ (Museum voor Volkskunde) DY **M**[2].

Envir : Zedelgem : baptismal font★ in the St. Lawrence's church SW : 10,5 km – Damme★ NE : 7 km.

18 9 at Sijsele NE : 7 km, Doornstraat 16 ☎ (0 50) 33 35 72, Fax (0 50) 35 89 25.

ℹ Burg 11 ☎ 44 86 86, Fax 44 86 00 and at railway station, Stationsplein – Tourist association of the province, Kasteel Tillegem ✉ 8200, ☎ 38 02 96, Fax 38 02 92.

Brussels 96 – Ghent 45 – Lille 72 – Ostend 28.

Plans on following pages

Town Centre

Holiday Inn Crowne Plaza 🔇, Burg 10 ☎ 34 58 34, Fax 34 56 15, ≤, « Interesting medieval remains and objects in basement », Fō, ≘s, 🏊 – 🛗 ⇔ ▤ TV ☎ ♿ ⇔ P – 🔔 25-400. AE ⓓ E VISA JCB. ✻ AU **a**
Meals *'t Kapittel (closed Saturday lunch and Sunday) Lunch 995* - 1665 – ☐ 600 – **93 rm** 6000/6700, 3 suites.

Sofitel, Boeveriestraat 2 ☎ 34 09 71, Telex 81369, Fax 34 40 53, ≘s, 🏊, 🌳 – 🛗 ⇔ ▤ TV ☎ ⇔ – 🔔 25-200. AE ⓓ E VISA CZ **b**
Meals 950/1600 – **155 rm** ☐ 6000/6500.

De Tuilerieën 🔇 without rest, Dijver 7 ☎ 34 36 91, Fax 34 04 00, ≤, ≘s, 🏊 – 🛗 TV ☎ P – 🔔 25-45. AE ⓓ E VISA JCB AU **c**
25 rm ☐ 7100/12250, 1 suite.

Relais Oud Huis Amsterdam 🔇 without rest, Spiegelrei 3 ☎ 34 18 10, Telex 83121, Fax 33 88 91, ≤, « 17C residence, former Dutch trading post », 🌳 – 🛗 ⇔ TV ☎ ⇔ – 🔔 25. AE ⓓ E VISA JCB. ✻ AT **d**
25 rm ☐ 3900/7500.

De Orangerie 🔇 without rest, Karthuizerinnenstraat 10 ☎ 34 16 49, Telex 82443, Fax 33 30 16, « Period canalside residence » – 🛗 TV ☎ P. AE ⓓ E VISA JCB AU **e**
19 rm ☐ 5950/8950.

Die Swaene 🔇, Steenhouwersdijk 1 ☎ 34 27 98, Fax 33 66 74, ≤, 🏞, « Stylish furnishings », Fō, ≘s, 🏊 – 🛗 TV ☎ P – 🔔 30. AE ⓓ E VISA JCB. ✻ rest AU **p**
Meals *(closed Wednesday, Thursday lunch, 2 weeks February and 2 weeks August) Lunch 1050* – 1850/2250 – **17 rm** ☐ 5250/6600, 2 suites.

Parkhotel without rest, Vrijdagmarkt 5 ☎ 33 33 64, Fax 33 47 63 – 🛗 TV ☎ ⇔ – 🔔 25-250. AE ⓓ E VISA CY **j**
86 rm ☐ 4000/5400.

de'Medici 🔇, Potterierei 15 ☎ 33 98 33, Telex 82227, Fax 33 07 64, « Modern style », Fō, ≘s – 🛗 ⇔ TV ☎ ♿ ⇔ P – 🔔 25-60. AE ⓓ E VISA. ✻ rest CX **g**
Meals (dinner only) 850/1250 – **80 rm** ☐ 3800/4200.

Acacia M without rest, Korte Zilverstraat 3a ☎ 34 44 11, Fax 33 88 17, Fō, ≘s, 🏊 – 🛗 TV ☎ ⇔ P – 🔔 25-40. AE ⓓ E VISA JCB. ✻ AU **n**
34 rm ☐ 3400/5400, 2 suites.

Karos without rest, Hoefijzerlaan 37 ☎ 34 14 48, Telex 82377, Fax 34 00 91, ≘s, 🏊 – 🛗 ▤ TV ☎ P. AE ⓓ E VISA BY **f**
closed 2 January-12 February – **60 rm** ☐ 2500/4800.

Prinsenhof 🔇 without rest, Ontvangersstraat 9 ☎ 34 26 90, Fax 34 23 21 – 🛗 TV ☎ P. AE ⓓ E VISA JCB CY **s**
16 rm ☐ 3300/6500.

Pandhotel without rest., Pandreitje 16 ☎ 34 06 66, Fax 34 05 56, « Opulent interior » – 🛗 TV ☎. AE ⓓ E VISA JCB AU **q**
24 rm ☐ 3890/4690.

Alfa Dante, Coupure 29a ☎ 34 01 94, Fax 34 35 39, ≤ – 🛗 TV ☎ – 🔔 25-60. AE ⓓ E VISA JCB DY **m**
Meals (vegetarian cuisine) *(closed Monday, Tuesday, February and August)* a la carte approx. 900 – **20 rm** ☐ 2650/5250.

Novotel Centrum, Katelijnestraat 65b ☎ 33 75 33, Telex 81799, Fax 33 65 56, 🏞, 🏊, 🌳 – 🛗 ⇔ ▤ TV ☎ ♿ – 🔔 50-400. AE ⓓ E VISA JCB AV **h**
Meals a la carte 800/1250 – ☐ 400 – **126 rm** 3800/4360.

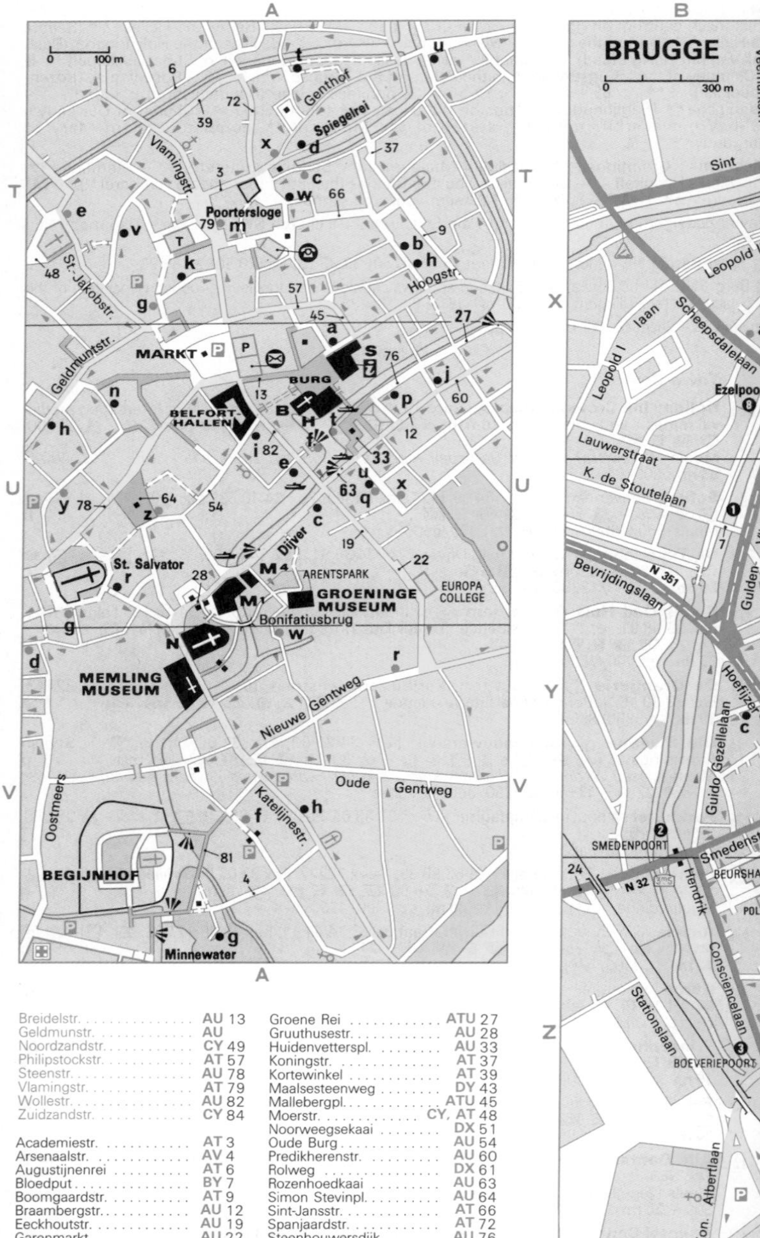

Breidelstr. . . . . AU 13
Geldmunstr. . . . . AU
Noordzandstr. . . . . CY 49
Philipstockstr. . . . . AT 57
Steenstr. . . . . AU 78
Vlamingstr. . . . . AT 79
Wollestr. . . . . AU 82
Zuidzandstr. . . . . CY 84

Academiestr. . . . . AT 3
Arsenaalstr. . . . . AV 4
Augustijnenrei . . . . AT 6
Bloedput . . . . BY 7
Boomgaardstr. . . . . AT 9
Braambergstr. . . . . AU 12
Eeckhoutstr. . . . . AU 19
Garenmarkt . . . . AU 22
Gistelsesteenweg . . . . BZ 24
Gloribusstr. . . . . CZ 25

Groene Rei . . . . ATU 27
Gruuthusestr. . . . . AU 28
Huidenvetterspl. . . . . AU 33
Koningstr. . . . . AT 37
Kortewinkel . . . . AT 39
Maalsesteenweg . . . . DY 43
Mallebergpl. . . . . ATU 45
Moerstr. . . . . CY, AT 48
Noorweegsekaai . . . . DX 51
Oude Burg . . . . AU 54
Predikherenstr. . . . . AU 60
Rolweg . . . . DX 61
Rozenhoedkaai . . . . AU 63
Simon Stevinpl. . . . . AU 64
Sint-Jansstr. . . . . AT 66
Spanjaardstr. . . . . AT 72
Steenhouwersdijk . . . . AU 76
Wijngaardstr. . . . . AV 81
Zwarte Leertouwersstr. . . . . DY 85

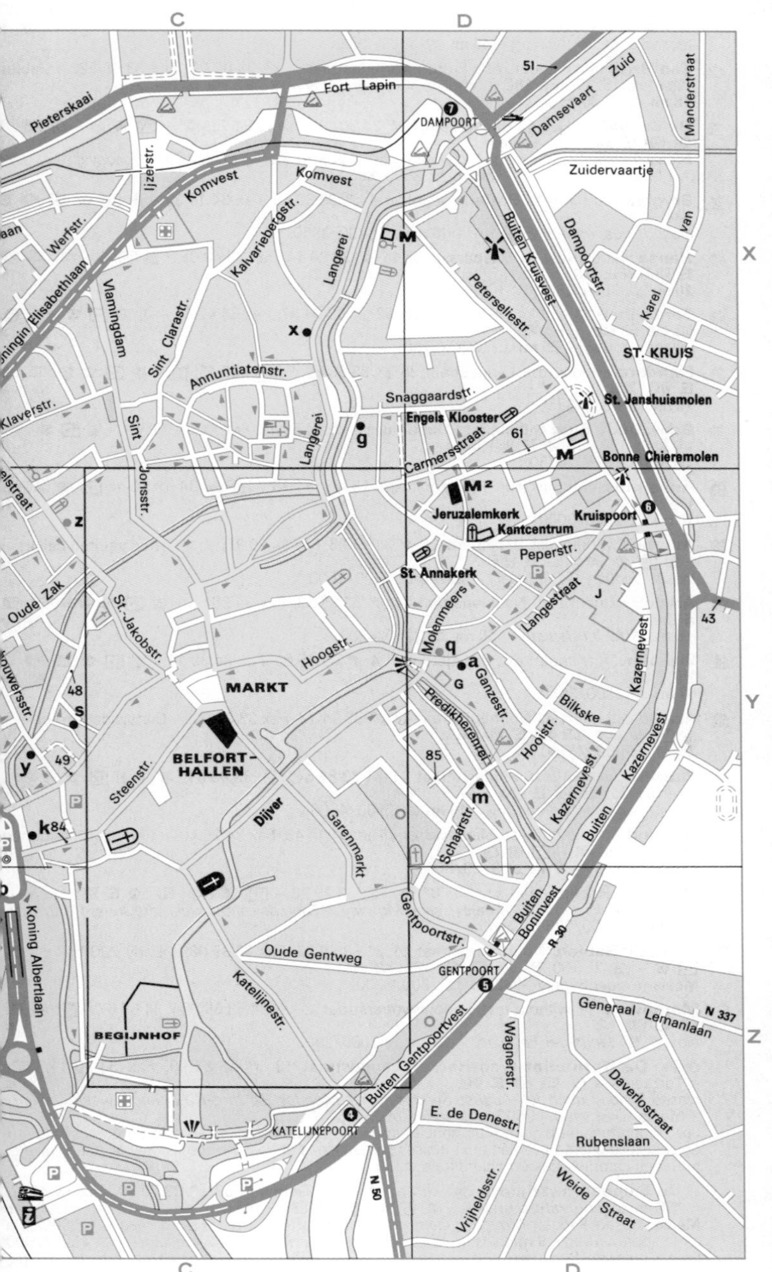

C
D
X
Y
Z
Pieterskaai
Fort Lapin
DAMPOORT
Damsevaart Zuid
Manderstraat
Zuidervaartje
Komvest
Ijzerstr.
Werfstr.
Kalvariebergstr.
Langerei
M
Buiten Kruisvest
Dampoortstr.
Karel
Van
Koningin Elisabethlaan
Vlamingdam
Sint Clarastr.
Peterseliestr.
ST. KRUIS
Annuntiatenstr.
Snaggaardstr.
St. Janshuismolen
Klaverstr.
Sint Jorisstr.
Engels Klooster
Carmersstraat
Bonne Chieremolen
M²
Jeruzalemkerk
Kruispoort
Kantcentrum
Peperstr.
St. Annakerk
Oude Zak
St.-Jakobstr.
Molenmeers
Langestraat
Kazernevest
Hoogstr.
MARKT
Ganzestr.
Predikherenrei
Bilkske
Hooistr.
BELFORT-HALLEN
Steenstr.
Dijver
Garenmarkt
Schaarstr.
Kazernevest
Buiten Kazernevest
Koning Albertlaan
Gentpoortstr.
Buiten Boninvest
R 30
Oude Gentweg
GENTPOORT
Katelijnestr.
Generaal Lemanlaan
N 337
Wagnerstr.
Buiten Gentpoortvest
BEGIJNHOF
Daverlostraat
E. de Denestr.
KATELIJNEPOORT
Rubenslaan
N 50
Vrijheidsstr.
Weide Straat

Portinari without rest, 't Zand 15 34 10 34, Fax 34 41 80 – 25-8 AE E VISA JCB CY
closed 2 to 25 January – **40 rm** 3000/4500.

Jan Brito without rest, Freren Fonteinstraat 1 33 06 01, Fax 33 06 52, « Gable façades, 16, 17 and 18C interior », – . AE E VISA JCB AU
18 rm 2800/5500.

De Castillion, Heilige Geeststraat 1 34 30 01, Fax 33 94 75, – – 25-5 AE E VISA JCB. rest AU
Meals *(closed Sunday dinner and lunch Monday and Tuesday except Bank Holidays)* Lunch 12 – a la carte 2500/2950 – **20 rm** 3500/8500.

Bryghia without rest, Oosterlingenplein 4 33 80 59, Fax 34 14 30 – . AE VISA JCB AT
closed 3 January- 2 February – **18 rm** 3200/3950.

Hansa without rest, N. Desparsstraat 11 33 84 44, Fax 33 42 05 – . AE E VISA JCB. AT
20 rm 3500/3800.

Ter Duinen without rest, Langerei 52 33 04 37, Fax 34 42 16 – AE E VISA JCB. CX
closed January – **20 rm** 2300/3750.

Flanders without rest, Langestraat 38 33 88 89, Fax 33 93 45, – . AE E VISA JCB DY
16 rm 2500/3750.

Gd H. Oude Burg without rest, Oude Burg 5 44 51 11, Fax 44 51 00, – – 25-180. AE E VISA JCB AU
138 rm 3750/4750.

Anselmus without rest, Riddersstraat 15 34 13 74, Fax 34 19 16 – . AE VISA AT
10 rm 2800/3000.

Adornes without rest, St-Annarei 26 34 13 36, Fax 34 20 85, ≤, « Period vaulted cellars – . AE E VISA AT
closed January-14 February – **20 rm** 2500/3500.

Aragon without rest, Naaldenstraat 24 33 35 33, Fax 34 28 05 – . AE E VISA AT
closed 3 to 31 January – **18 rm** 2250/4200.

Biskajer without rest, Biskajersplein 4 34 15 06, Fax 34 39 11 – . AE VISA AT
17 rm 2800/3950.

Azalea without rest, Wulfhagestraat 43 33 14 78, Fax 33 97 00, « Canalside terrace » . AE E VISA JCB CY
25 rm 2800/4700.

Patritius without rest, Riddersstraat 11 33 84 54, Fax 33 96 34, – – 25. AE E VISA JCB AT
closed January-15 February – **16 rm** 2900/4500.

Egmond without rest, Minnewater 15 34 14 45, Fax 34 29 40, « Early 20C residenc in garden », – . AV
closed January – **8 rm** 3200/3600.

Maraboe, Hoefijzerlaan 9 33 81 55, Fax 33 29 28 – . AE E VISA CY
closed 2 weeks carnival – **Meals** *(closed Monday to Thursday and 1 week late June)* 1150/195 – **9 rm** 2000/2950.

Gd H. du Sablon, Noordzandstraat 21 33 39 02, Fax 33 39 08, « Early 20C hall » – – 25-100. AE E VISA JCB. rest AU
Meals (residents only) – **42 rm** 2800/3700.

Montovani without rest, Schouwvegerstraat 11 34 53 66, Fax 34 53 67 – . E VISA. BY
closed 16 January-8 February – **13 rm** 2000/2900.

XXXX ✿✿✿ **De Karmeliet** (Van Hecke), Langestraat 19 33 82 59, Fax 33 10 11, « Terrace » – . AE E VISA DY
closed Sunday lunch July-August, Sunday dinner, Monday, 24 June-8 July and 2 weeks Januar – **Meals** Lunch 2100 – 2600, a la carte 2550/3250
Spec. Suprêmes de pigeon rôtis, saucisson de ses cuisses confites au pied de porc, sauce au épices, Tuile sucrée et salée aux grosses langoustines et chicons confits, Ravioli à la vanille e pommes caramélisées en chaud-froid.

XXX ✿ **De Snippe** (Huysentruyt) with rm, Nieuwe Gentweg 53 33 70 70, Fax 33 76 62 « 18C residence with murals » – . AE E VISA AV
Meals *(closed Sunday, Monday lunch and 15 February-15 March)* Lunch 1950 b.i. – 2500, a la carte approx. 2800 – **9 rm** *(closed 15 February-15 March and Sunday in winter)* 4500/700
Spec. Courgette farcie aux cuisses de grenouilles, St-Pierre au Meursault et cerfeuil sauvage Parfait de poires, croustillant au citron vert.

XXX ⊛ **Den Gouden Harynck** (Serruys), Groeninge 25 ✆ 33 76 37, Fax 34 42 70 - P. AE O E VISA AUV w
closed Sunday, Monday, last 2 weeks July and Christmas - **Meals** *Lunch 1200* - 2000, a la carte approx. 2600
Spec. Filet de turbot aux épices, Pigeonneau à l'embeurré de chou, Gratin de mûres et glace aux pistaches.

XXX **Duc de Bourgogne** with rm, Huidenvettersplein 12 ✆ 33 20 38, Fax 34 40 37, ≤ canals, « Rustic decor and murals of late medieval style » - ▤ rest TV ☎. AE O E VISA JCB
closed 3 weeks July and January - **Meals** *(closed Monday and Tuesday lunch) Lunch 1250* - a la carte approx. 2500 - **10 rm** ⊏ 3500. AU t

XXX **De Witte Poorte,** Jan Van Eyckplein 6 ✆ 33 08 83, Fax 34 55 60, 🍽, « Vaulted dining room, garden » - AE O E VISA JCB AT x
closed Sunday and Monday except Bank Holidays, 2 weeks July and 2 weeks January - **Meals** *Lunch 1100* - 1650/1950.

XXX **Den Braamberg,** Pandreitje 11 ✆ 33 73 70, Fax 33 93 73 - AE E VISA JCB AU u
closed Thursday, Sunday and 15 to 30 July - **Meals** *Lunch 1650 b.i.* - a la carte 1500/1850.

XXX **'t Pandreitje,** Pandreitje 6 ✆ 33 11 90, Fax 34 00 70 - AE O E VISA JCB AU x
closed Wednesday, Sunday, 10 to 16 February, 1 to 14 July and 28 October-3 November - **Meals** *Lunch 1450* - 1950/2450.

XX **'t Bourgoensche Cruyce** ⛵ with rm, Wollestraat 43 ✆ 33 79 26, Fax 34 19 68, ≤ canals and old Flemish houses - |‡| TV ☎. AE O E VISA AU f
closed 17 November-13 December - **Meals** *(closed Tuesday and Wednesday) Lunch 1350* - a la carte 1800/2500 - **8 rm** ⊏ 3400/4400.

XX **'t Stil Ende,** Scheepsdalelaan 12 ✆ 33 92 03, Fax 33 26 22, 🍽 - AE O E VISA BX a
closed Saturday lunch, Sunday dinner, Monday, first week March and late July-early August - **Meals** *Lunch 1200* - 1200/1950.

XX ⊛ **Hermitage** (Dryepondt), Ezelstraat 18 ✆ 34 41 73 - O E VISA JCB CY z
closed Sunday, Monday, 6 to 12 May and 1 to 24 July; last 2 weeks July-August open only Thursday, Friday and Saturday - **Meals** (dinner only) (booking essential) a la carte approx. 2350
Spec. Terrine de foie gras d'oie, Cassolette de queues de langoustines aux fines herbes, Rognon de veau sauté à la liégeoise.

XX **De Lotteburg,** Goezeputstraat 43 ✆ 33 75 35, Fax 33 04 04, 🍽, Seafood - AE O E VISA JCB. ✻ AV d
closed Monday and Tuesday except Bank Holidays, last week July-first week August and last week December - **Meals** *Lunch 995* - 1500/1895.

XX **Kardinaalshof,** St-Salvatorskerkhof 14 ✆ 34 16 91, Fax 34 20 62, Seafood - AE O E VISA AUV g
closed Wednesday, Thursday lunch and first 2 weeks July - **Meals** *Lunch 1050* - 1050/1850.

XX **Patrick Devos,** Zilverstraat 41 ✆ 33 55 66, Fax 33 58 67, « Belle Epoque interior, patio » - AE O E VISA JCB. ✻ AU y
closed 21 July-8 August, 24 to 31 December, Sunday, Monday and Bank Holidays except 1 January - **Meals** *Lunch 800* - 1400/1900.

XX **Spinola,** Spinolarei 1 ✆ 34 17 85, Fax 39 12 01, « Rustic » - AE O E VISA JCB AT c
closed Sunday and Monday lunch except Bank Holidays, last 2 weeks June-first week July and Christmas-New Year - **Meals** a la carte 1200/1500.

XX **Tanuki,** Oude Gentweg 1 ✆ 34 75 12, Fax 34 75 12, Japanese cuisine - ▤. AE O E VISA JCB. ✻ AV f
closed Monday, Tuesday, last 2 weeks February and last 2 weeks July - **Meals** *Lunch 430* - a la carte approx. 1700.

X **Bhavani,** Simon Stevinplein 5 ✆ 33 90 25, Fax 34 89 52, 🍽, Indian cuisine - AE O E VISA JCB AU z
closed Wednesday and Thursday lunch except 15 October-15 February - **Meals** *Lunch 450* - 550/1400.

X **Brasserie Raymond,** Eiermarkt 5 ✆ 33 78 48, Fax 33 78 48, 🍽, Open until 11.30 p.m. - AE O E VISA JCB AT g
closed Tuesday, 10 to 19 March, 1 to 16 July and 18 to 26 November - **Meals** *Lunch 450* - a la carte 1000/1400.

X **René van Puyenbroeck,** St-Jacobstraat 58 ✆ 34 12 24 - AE E VISA. ✻ AT e
closed Sunday dinner, Monday and July - **Meals** *Lunch 950* - a la carte 1150/1800.

X **Brasserie Georges,** Vlamingstraat 58 ✆ 34 35 65, Fax 34 35 65, 🍽, Open until 11.30 p.m. - AE O E VISA JCB AT m
closed Sunday - **Meals** *Lunch 375* - a la carte approx. 1300.

Suburbs

North-West - ✉ 8000 - ☎ 0 50 :

XX **De Gouden Korenhalm,** Oude Oostendsesteenweg 79 (Sint-Pieters) ✆ 31 33 93, Fax 31 18 96, 🍽, « Typical Flemish farmhouse » - P. AE O E VISA
closed Monday, late February and late August-early September - **Meals** *Lunch 995* - 1420/1850.

South – ✉ 8200 – ☎ 0 50 :

🏨 **Novotel Zuid,** Chartreuseweg 20 (Sint-Michiels) ✆ 38 28 51, Telex 81507, Fax 38 79 0
, , – , rest TV ☎ ♿ P – 25-200. AE ⓓ E VISA
Meals *Lunch 500* – a la carte 850/1200 – ☕ 400 – **101 rm** 3300/3900.

XXX **Casserole** (Hotel school), Groene-Poortdreef 17 (Sint-Michiels) ✆ 40 30 30, Fax 40 30 3
, « Garden setting » – P. AE ⓓ E VISA
closed July-24 August – **Meals** (lunch only except Friday and Saturday) *Lunch 950* – a la car
approx. 1700.

South-West – ✉ 8200 – ☎ 0 50 :

🏨 **Host. Pannenhuis** , Zandstraat 2 ✆ 31 19 07, Fax 31 77 66, ≤, , « Terrace ar
garden » – TV ☎ P – 25. AE ⓓ E VISA JCB
Meals *(closed Tuesday dinner, Wednesday, 4 to 20 July and 15 January-2 February) Lunch 12*
– 1650 – **18 rm** ☕ 3250/3950.

XX **Herborist** with rm, De Watermolen 15 (by N 32 : 6 km, then on the right after E 4
St-Andries) ✆ 38 76 00, Fax 39 31 06, , « Inn with country atmosphere », – TV
P. AE E VISA.
closed Sunday dinner, Monday, 26 March-6 April, 26 June-6 July, 26 September-6 Octob
and 26 December-6 January – **Meals** 1750 b.i./3350 b.i. – **4 rm** ☕ 2800/3800.

at Sint-Kruis E : 6 km C Bruges – ✉ 8310 Sint-Kruis – ☎ 0 50 :

🏨 **Wilgenhof** without rest, Polderstraat 151 ✆ 36 27 44, Fax 36 28 21, ≤, « An area
reclaimed land (polder) », – TV ☎ P. AE ⓓ E VISA JCB
closed last week January – **6 rm** ☕ 2500/4100.

XXX **Ronnie Jonkman,** Maalsesteenweg 438 ✆ 36 07 67, Fax 35 76 96, , « Terraces » –
AE ⓓ E VISA JCB
closed Sunday, Monday, 2 weeks Easter, 1 to 15 July and 1 to 15 October – **Meals** *Lunch 1750 b*
– a la carte 2150/2750.

Environs

at Hertsberge S by N 50 : 12,5 km C Oostkamp pop. 20 653 – ✉ 8020 Hertsberge – ☎ 0 50

XXX **Manderley,** Kruisstraat 13 ✆ 27 80 51, , « Terrace and garden » – P. AE ⓓ E VI
closed Thursday dinner September-April, Sunday dinner, Monday, first week October and la
3 weeks January – **Meals** *Lunch 1200* – 1750/2250.

at Ruddervoorde S by N 50 : 12 km C Oostkamp pop. 20 653 – ✉ 8020 Ruddervoorde
☎ 0 50 :

XXX **Host. Leegendael** with rm, Kortrijkstraat 498 (N 50) ✆ 27 76 99, Fax 27 58 80, « Perio
residence, country atmosphere » – TV ☎ P. AE ⓓ E VISA
closed carnival week and 2 weeks August – **Meals** *(closed Wednesday and Sunday dinner) Lunc*
990 – a la carte 1600/2000 – **6 rm** ☕ 1750/2550.

at Varsenare W : 6,5 km C Jabbeke pop. 12 726 – ✉ 8490 Varsenare – ☎ 0 50 :

XXXX **Manoir Stuivenberg** with rm, Gistelsteenweg 27 ✆ 38 15 02, Fax 38 28 92, – TV
☎ P. AE ⓓ E VISA.
Meals *(closed Sunday dinner and Monday) Lunch 1485* – 1895/2350 – **7 rm** ☕ 4450/6500
1 suite.

at Waardamme S by N 50 : 11 km C Oostkamp pop. 20 653 – ✉ 8020 Waardamme
☎ 0 50 :

XXX **Ter Talinge,** Rooiveldstraat 46 ✆ 27 90 61, Fax 28 00 52, , « Terrace » – P. AE E
VISA
closed Wednesday, Thursday, 23 February-8 March and 23 August-6 September
Meals a la carte 1250/1600.

at Zedelgem SW : 10,5 km – pop. 21 005 – ✉ 8210 Zedelgem – ☎ 0 50 :

🏨 **Zuidwege** without rest, Torhoutsesteenweg 128 ✆ 20 13 39, Fax 20 17 39 – TV ☎ P
– 25. AE ⓓ E VISA.
17 rm ☕ 1850/2550.

XX **Ter Leepe,** Torhoutsesteenweg 168 ✆ 20 01 97, Fax 20 88 54 – P. AE ⓓ E VISA
closed Wednesday dinner, Sunday, carnival and 15 to 31 July – **Meals** *Lunch 1300 b.i.* – a la cart
approx. 1600.

Waregem 8790 West-Vlaanderen 213 ⑮ and 409 D 3 – pop. 34 967 – ☎ 0 56 – 47 km

XXXX ✿✿ **'t Oud Konijntje** (Mme Desmedt), Bosstraat 53 (S : 2 km near E 17) ✆ 60 19 37
Fax 60 92 12, , « Floral terrace » – P. AE ⓓ E VISA
closed dinner Thursday and Sunday, Friday, 22 July-13 August and 22 December-4 Januar
– **Meals** *Lunch 1500* – 1950/2750, a la carte 2200/2500
Spec. Langoustines à la crème de Sauternes, Trilogie de la mer en bouillon de fenouil, Canett
de Barbarie au poivre vert et ses cuisses grillées.

LIÈGE 4000 213 ㉒ and 409 J 4 ⑰ N – pop. 155 999 – ✪ 0 41.

See : Citadel ≤★★ DW – Cointe Park ≤★ CX – Old town★★ – Palace of the Prince-Bishops★ : court of honour★★ EY – The Perron★ (market cross) EY **A** – Baptismal font★★★ of St. Bartholomew's church FY – Treasury★★ of St. Paul's Cathedral : reliquary of Charles the Bold★★ EZ – St. James church★★ : vaults of the nave★★ EZ – Altarpiece★ in the St. Denis church EY – Church of St. John : Wooden Calvary statues★ EY – Aquarium★ FZ **D**.

Museums : Provincial Museum of Life in Wallonia★★ EY – Religious and Roman Art Museum★ FY **M5** – Curtius and Glass Museum★ : evangelistary of Notger★★★, collection of glassware★ FY **M1** – Arms★ FY **M3** – Ansembourg★ FY **M2**.

Envir : Blégny-Trembleur★★ NE : 20 km – Baptismal font★ in the church★ of St. Severin SW : 27 km – Visé N : 17 km, Reliquary of St. Hadelin★ in the collegiate church.

r. Bernalmont 2 ☎ 27 44 66, Fax 27 91 92 - at Angleur S : 7,5 km, rte du Condroz 541 ☎ (0 41) 36 20 21, Fax (0 41) 37 20 26 - at Gomzé-Andoumont SE : 18 km, r. Gomzé 30 ☎ (0 41) 60 92 07, Fax (0 41) 60 92 06.

☎ 42 52 14.

En Féronstrée 92 ☎ 21 92 21, Fax 21 92 22 and Gare des Guillemins ☎ 52 44 19 – Tourist association of the province, bd de la Sauvenière 77 ☎ 22 42 10, Fax 22 10 92.

Brussels 97 – Amsterdam 242 – Antwerp 119 – Cologne 122 – Luxembourg 159.

Plans on following pages

Bedford M, quai St-Léonard 36 ☎ 28 81 11, Fax 27 45 75, « Inner garden » – 25-200. AE VISA. — DW **g**
Meals *Lunch 1050* – a la carte 800/1100 – **149 rm** 2550/6950.

Michel Germeau, r. Vennes 151 (Fétinne), ✉ 4020, ☎ 43 72 42, Fax 44 03 86, « Early 20C mansion » – AE VISA — DX **y**
closed Monday, 4 to 13 February, 15 to 30 July and 24 November-3 December – **Meals** *Lunch 990* – 1290/1600.

Old town

Ramada, bd de la Sauveniere 100 ☎ 21 77 11, Fax 21 77 01 – 25-100. AE VISA — EY **t**
Meals *(closed Saturday lunch and Sunday dinner) Lunch 690* – 690 – **105 rm** 6100/6660.

Au Vieux Liège, quai Goffe 41 ☎ 23 77 48, Fax 23 78 60, « 16C residence » – AE VISA — FY **a**
closed Wednesday dinner, Sunday, Bank Holidays, 1 week Easter and mid July-mid August – **Meals** *Lunch 1195* – 1545/2000.

Chez Max, pl. de la République Française 12 ☎ 22 08 59, Fax 22 90 02, , Oyster bar, open until 11 p.m., « Elegant brasserie decorated by Luc Genot » – AE VISA — EY **a**
closed Saturday lunch and Sunday – **Meals** *Lunch 990* – a la carte 1300/1750.

Robert Lesenne, r. Boucherie 9 ☎ 22 07 93, Fax 22 92 33 – AE VISA — FY **m**
closed Saturday lunch, Sunday and first 2 weeks August – **Meals** 1195.

Le Shanghai 1st floor, Galeries Cathédrale 104 ☎ 22 22 63, Fax 23 00 50, Chinese cuisine – AE VISA — EZ **r**
closed Tuesday and 9 to 31 July – **Meals** *Lunch 520* – a la carte approx. 1000.

As Ouhès, pl. du Marché 21 ☎ 23 32 25, Fax 22 30 19, , Oyster bar, open until 11 p.m. – AE VISA — EY **e**
closed Sunday – **Meals** *Lunch 400* – 950.

Enoteca, r. Casquette 5 ☎ 22 24 64, Fax 22 47 72 – VISA — EY **g**
closed Saturday lunch, Sunday and Bank Holidays – **Meals** *Lunch 590* – 1090.

Lalo's Bar, r. Madeleine 18 ☎ 23 22 57, Fax 23 22 57, Italian cuisine, open until 11 p.m. – VISA — EY **d**
closed Saturday lunch, Sunday, Bank Holidays and 15 July-15 August – **Meals** *Lunch 550* – a la carte approx. 900.

Guillemins

L'Héliport, bd Frère-Orban ☎ 52 13 21, ≤, – . AE VISA — CX **b**
closed Sunday and Monday dinner – **Meals** 1395.

La Maison Thaïe, bd d'Avroy 180 ☎ 22 00 91, Fax 21 05 21, Thaï cuisine, open until 11 p.m. – AE VISA — CX **d**
closed Saturday lunch – **Meals** a la carte 850/1400.

Le Duc d'Anjou, r. Guillemins 127 ☎ 52 28 58, Mussels in season, open until 11.30 p.m. – AE VISA — CX **n**
Meals 795.

Outremeuse

Holiday Inn without rest, Esplanade de l'Europe 2, ✉ 4020, ☎ 42 60 20, Fax 43 48 10, ≤, – – 25-50. AE VISA JCB — DX **a**
214 rm 5250/6600, 5 suites.

Simenon, bd de l'Est 16, ✉ 4020, ☎ 42 86 90 – . AE VISA — FZ **x**
Meals (Pub rest, lunch only except July-August) a la carte approx. 800 – 280 – **11 rm** 2000.

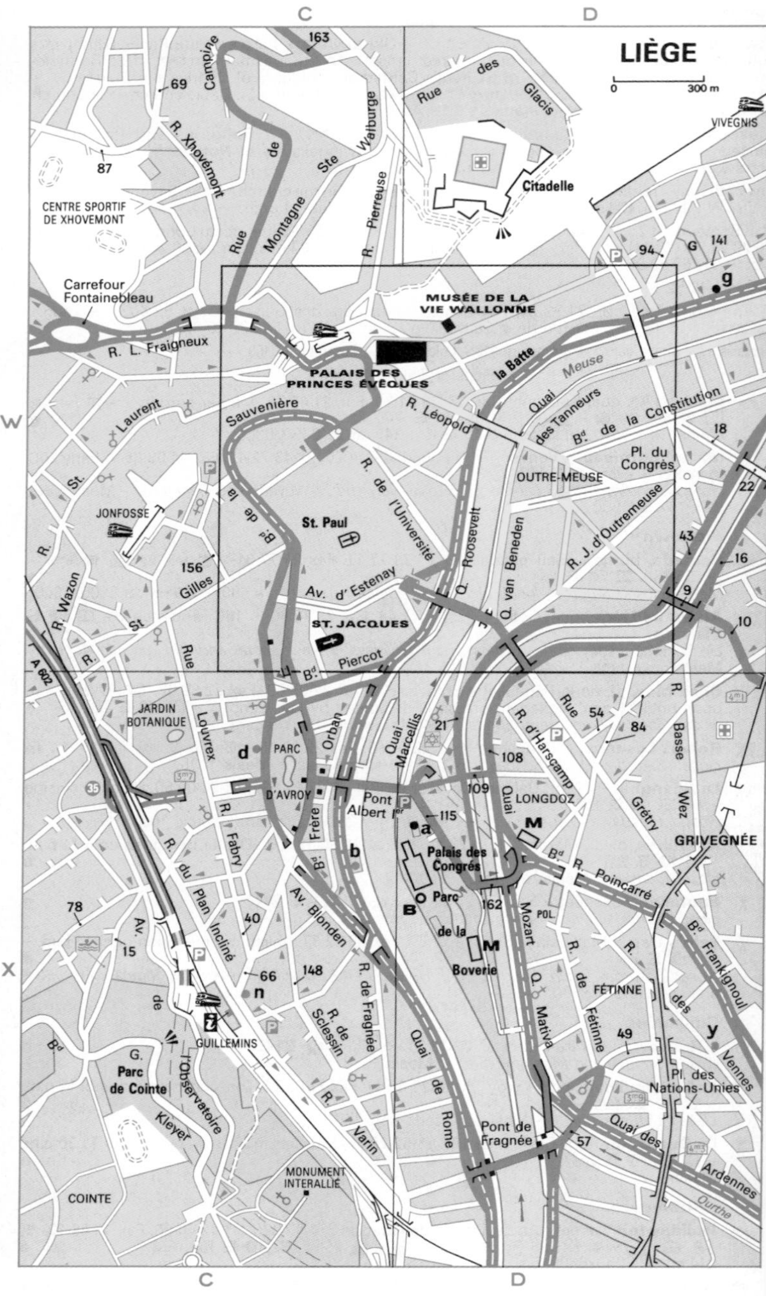
LIÈGE
0
300 m
C
D
W
X
Citadelle
MUSÉE DE LA VIE WALLONNE
PALAIS DES PRINCES ÉVÊQUES
CENTRE SPORTIF DE XHOVEMONT
Carrefour Fontainebleau
R. L. Fraigneux
R. Xhovémont
Rue de Campine
Montagne de Ste Walburge
R. Pierreuse
Rue des Glacis
VIVEGNIS
la Batte
Meuse
Quai des Tanneurs
Bd de la Constitution
R. Léopold
Pl. du Congrès
OUTRE-MEUSE
R. J. d'Outremeuse
Q. Roosevelt
Q. van Beneden
Sauvenière
Bd de la Sauvenière
R. de l'Université
St. Paul
Av. d'Estenay
ST. JACQUES
Bd Piercot
St. Laurent
JONFOSSE
St. Gilles
R. Wazon
A 602
JARDIN BOTANIQUE
Louvrex
PARC D'AVROY
Orban
Frère
Quai Marcellis
Pont Albert Ier
Palais des Congrès
Parc de la Boverie
LONGDOZ
Quai
Rue d'Harscamp
Basse Wez
Grétry
GRIVEGNÉE
Bd R. Poincarré
Bd Frankignoul
R. Fabry
R. du Plan Incliné
Av. Blonden
R. de Fragnée
R. de Sclessin
Quai de Rome
Q. Mativa
Mozart
POL.
R. de Fétinne
FÉTINNE
R. des Vennes
Pl. des Nations-Unies
Quai des Ardennes
Ourthe
Pont de Fragnée
Av. de l'Observatoire
GUILLEMINS
Bd G. Kleyer
Parc de Cointe
COINTE
MONUMENT INTERALLIÉ
R. Varin
163
69
87
94
G
141
g
18
22
43
16
9
10
156
21
54
84
108
109
115
a
b
d
B
M
162
40
66
148
n
78
15
35
49
y
57

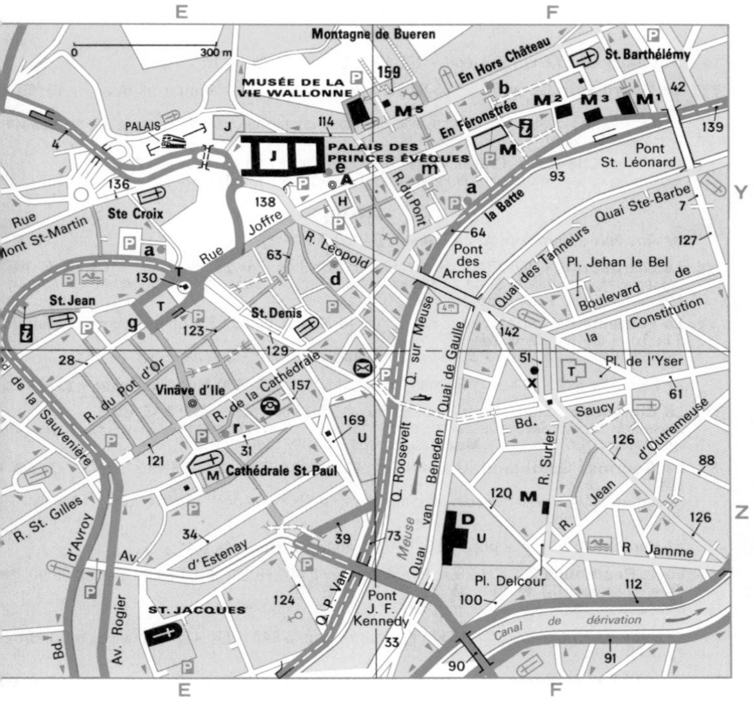

athédrale (R. de la) .... EZ
ı Féronstrée .... FY
ėopold (R.) .... EFY
ont d'Ile .... EY 123
égence (R. de la) ..... EYZ 129
aint-Gilles (R.) .... EZ
inâve d'Ile (R.) .... EZ

cadémie (R. de l') ..... EY 4
dolphe Maréchal (R.) .. FY 7
mercoeur (Pont d') .... DW 9
mercoeur (R. d') ...... DW 10
ois-l'Evêque (R.) ...... CX 15
onaparte (Quai) .... DW 16
onnes-Villes (R. des) ... DW 18
overie (Quai de la) .... DX 21
ressoux (Pont de) ..... DW 22
ruxelles (R. de) .... EY 24
asquette (R. de la) .... EYZ 28
harles Magnette (R.) ... EZ 31
hurchill (Quai) .... FZ 33
larisses (R. des) ...... EZ 34
roisiers (R. des) .... EZ 39

Dartois (R.) .... CX 40
Déportés (Pl. des) ...... FY 42
Dérivation (Quai de la) .. DW 43
Emile de Laveleye (Bd) .. DX 49
Est (Bd de l') .... FYZ 51
Fer (R. du) .... DX 54
Fétinne (Pont de) ...... DX 57
Georges Simenon (R.) .. FZ 61
Gérardrie (R.) .... EY 63
Goffe (Quai de la) ...... FY 64
Guillemins (R. des) .... CX 66
Hauteurs (Bd des) ...... CW 69
van Hoegaerden (Quai) . EFZ 73
Joie (R. de) .... CX 78
Lairesse (R.) .... DX 84
Léon Philippet (Bd) ..... CW 87
Liberté (R. de la) .... FZ 88
Longdoz (Pont de) ..... FZ 90
Longdoz (Quai de) ..... FZ 91
Maastricht (Quai de) .... FY 93
Maghin (R.) .... DW 94
Méan (R.) .... FZ 100
Orban (Quai) .... DX 108

Orban ou de Huy (Pont d') DX 109
Ourthe (Quai de l') ..... FZ 112
Palais (R. du) .... EY 114
Parc (R. du) .... DX 115
Pitteurs (R. des) .... FZ 120
Pont d'Avroy (R.) .... EZ 121
Prémontrés (R. des) .... EZ 124
Puits-en-Soc (R.) .... FZ 126
Ransonnet (R.) .... FY 127
Rép. Française
(Pl. de la) .... EY 130
Saint-Hubert (R.) .... EY 136
Saint-Lambert (Pl.) ..... EY 138
Saint-Léonard (Quai) .... FY 139
Saint-Léonard (R.) ...... DW 141
Saint-Pholien (R. et Pl.) .. FY 142
Serbie (R. de) .... CX 148
Trappé (R.) .... CW 156
Université (R. de l') ..... EYZ 157
Ursulines (Imp. des) .... FY 159
Vennes (Pont des) ..... DX 162
Victor Hugo (Av.) ...... CW 163
20 Août (Pl. du) .... EZ 169

Suburbs

at Chênée E : 7,5 km 🄲 Liège - ✉ 4032 Chênée - ☎ 0 41 :

XXX **Le Gourmet,** r. Large 91 ☎ 65 87 97, Fax 65 38 12, 🏞, « Winter garden » - Ⓟ. AE ⓓ E VISA
closed Monday dinner, Wednesday and Saturday lunch except Bank Holidays, 2 weeks July and first week January - **Meals** *Lunch 1000* - 1000/1700.

XX **Le Vieux Chênée,** r. Gravier 45 ☎ 67 00 92, Fax 67 59 15 - AE ⓓ E VISA
closed Thursday except Bank Holidays and 2 weeks July - **Meals** *Lunch 890* - a la carte 950/1550

Environs

at Ans NW : 4 km - pop. 23 784 - ✉ 4430 Ans - ☎ 0 41 :

XX **Le Marguerite,** r. Walthère Jamar 171 ☎ 26 43 46, Fax 26 38 35, 🏞 - AE ⓓ E VISA
closed Saturday lunch, Sunday, Monday, last 3 weeks July and 23 December-3 January - **Meals** *Lunch 980* - a la carte approx. 1400.

XX **La Fontaine de Jade,** r. Yser 321 ☎ 46 49 72, Fax 63 69 53, Chinese cuisine, open until 11 p.m. - ▤. AE ⓓ E VISA. ✂
closed Tuesday and 16 to 30 August - **Meals** *Lunch 450* - a la carte approx. 900.

at Flémalle SW : 14 km 🄲 Flémalle pop. 23 571 - ✉ 4400 Flémalle-Haute - ☎ 0 41 :

XXX **La Ciboulette,** chaussée de Chokier 96 ☎ 75 19 65, 🏞 - AE ⓓ E VISA
closed Monday, Saturday lunch, dinner Sunday and Wednesday, 2 weeks August and 26 December-6 January - **Meals** *Lunch 1200* - 1200/1690.

XX **Le Gourmet Gourmand,** Grand-Route 411 ☎ 33 07 56, Fax 33 19 21, 🏞 - AE ⓓ E VISA
closed Monday, dinner Tuesday, Wednesday and Thursday and Saturday lunch - **Meals** *Lunch 1250* - 1500/1650.

at Herstal NE : 8 km - pop. 28 596 - ✉ 4040 Herstal - ☎ 0 41 :

Forte Posthouse ⛰, r. Hurbise (by motorway E 40 exit 34) ☎ 64 64 00, Fax 48 06 90, 🏞, 🏊 - |♦| ▤ rest 📺 ☎ Ⓟ - 🏛 25-60. AE ⓓ E VISA
Meals *Lunch 750* - a la carte 850/1800 - **93 rm** ☕ 2600/5700.

at Neuville-en-Condroz S : 18 km 🄲 Neupré pop. 8 643 - ✉ 4121 Neuville-en-Condroz - ☎ 0 41 :

XXXX ✿ **Le Chêne Madame** (Mme Tilkin), av. de la Chevauchée 70 (in Rognacs wood SE : 2 km) ☎ 71 41 27, Fax 71 29 43, « Country Inn » - Ⓟ. AE ⓓ E VISA
closed Monday, dinner Sunday and Thursday, August and 24 and 25 December - **Meals** *Lunch 1800 b.i.* - 2250, a la carte 2000/2400
Spec. Gâteau de sandre farci de petits gris, Salade de lapereau à l'huile de noix, Gibiers en saison

Hasselt 3500 Limburg 213 ⑨ and 409 I 3 - pop. 64 722 - ☎ 0 11 - 42 km.

at Stevoort by N 2 : 5 km to Kermt, then road on the left 🄲 Hasselt - ✉ 3512 Stevoort - ☎ 0 11 :

XXXXX ✿✿ **Scholteshof** (Souvereyns) ⛰ with rm, Kermtstraat 130 ☎ 25 02 02, Fax 25 43 28, ←, 🏞, « 18C farmhouse with vines, kitchen garden, orchard and English style gardens », ✂ - 📺 ☎ Ⓟ - 🏛 25-60. AE ⓓ E VISA
closed 8 to 26 July and 2 to 24 January - **Meals** *(closed Wednesday) Lunch 2650 b.i.* - 3450/4750, a la carte 3500/4400 - ☕ 800 - **11 rm** 4800/14000, 7 suites
Spec. Compression de homard, jarret de veau confit et foie d'oie, Pintadeau farci d'herbes en croûte de sel, Tomate jaune semi-confite, sorbet à l'origan et coulis de baies sauvages (August-30 December).

Namur 5000 Namur 213 ⑳ 214 ⑤ and 409 H 4 - pop. 97 845 - ☎ 0 81 - 61 km.

at Lives-sur-Meuse E : 9 km 🄲 Namur - ✉ 5101 Lives-sur-Meuse - ☎ 0 81 :

XXXX ✿✿ **La Bergerie** (Lefevere), r. Mosanville 100 ☎ 58 06 13, Fax 58 19 39, ←, « Overlooking the valley, terrace and garden with ornamental fountain » - ▤ Ⓟ. AE ⓓ E VISA
closed Sunday dinner in winter, Monday, Tuesday, 3 weeks February and 3 weeks August - **Meals** *Lunch 1750 b.i.* - 2000/2850, a la carte 2100/2500
Spec. Truite de notre vivier au Bleu, Agneau rôti "Bergerie", Le gâteau de crêpes soufflées.

Pepinster 4860 Liège 213 ㉓ and 409 K 4 - pop. 8 885 - ☎ 0 87 - 26 km.

XXX ✿✿ **Host. Lafarque** ⛰ with rm, Chemin des Douys 20 (W : 4 km by N 61, locality Goffontaine) ☎ 46 06 51, Fax 46 97 28, ←, 🏞, « Park », 🌳 - 📺 ☎ Ⓟ. AE ⓓ E VISA. ✂ rm
closed Monday and Tuesday except Bank Holidays, 10 to 31 March and 26 August-5 September - **Meals** *Lunch 1450* - a la carte 2150/3000 - ☕ 400 - **6 rm** 3000/3750
Spec. Croustillant de cervelle de veau, crème au vinaigre à l'échalote, Pied de porc en crépinette de raifort et sauce béarnaise, Ris de veau braisé aux pamplemousses.

St-Vith **4780 Liège 214 ⑨ and 409 L 5 - pop. 8 442 - ✆ 0 80 - 78 km.**

XXX ✿✿ **Zur Post** (Pankert) with rm, Hauptstr. 39 ✆ 22 80 27, Fax 22 93 10 - TV ☎. AE E VISA
closed Sunday dinner, Monday, Tuesday lunch, late June-early July and January - **Meals** *Lunch 1200* - 1800/2500, a la carte 2200/2700 - **8 rm** ☕ 2500/4000
Spec. Fond d'artichaut farci d'une poêlée de foie d'oie aux épinards, Poêlée de homard et St-Jacques à la vanille (October-April), Cochon de lait en cocotte aux éclats de truffes et champignons sauvages (15 December-15 September).

Tongeren **3700 Limburg 213 ㉒ and 409 J 3 - pop. 28 947 - ✆ 0 12 - 19 km.**

at Vliermaal N : 5 km C Kortessem pop. 7 754 - ✉ 3724 Vliermaal - ✆ 0 12 :

XXXX ✿✿ **Clos St. Denis** (Denis), Grimmertingenstraat 24 ✆ 23 60 96, Fax 26 32 07, « 17C farmhouse manor, terrace and garden » - P. AE O E VISA. ✂
closed Monday, Tuesday, 15 to 29 July and 23 December-6 January - **Meals** *Lunch 1500* - 3500/3950, a la carte 2700/3250
Spec. Jarret de veau confit et foie de canard mariné aux truffes façon mille-feuille, Gâteau de tourteau, légumes croquants et fines herbes, St-Pierre rôti au jus de viande et cèpes.

Valkenburg **Limburg (Netherlands) C Valkenburg aan de Geul pop. 18 062 212 ① and 408 I 9 - ✆ 0 43 - 47 km.**

✿✿ **Prinses Juliana** (annexe Residentie - 3 rm and 5 suites), Broekhem 11, ✉ 6301 HD, ✆ 601 22 44, Fax 601 44 05, « Terrace and floral garden » - rest TV ☎ P - 50. AE O E VISA. ✂ rest
closed 1 January - **Meals** *(closed Saturday lunch) Lunch 63* - 90/135, a la carte 103/125 - ☕ 28 - **16 rm** 225/260
Spec. Bouillabaisse à notre façon, Piccatas de foie d'oie aux pommes caramélisées, Carré d'agneau des prés-salés aux fines herbes.

Weert **Limburg (Netherlands) 212 ⑲ and 408 I 8 - pop. 41 370 - ✆ 0 495 - 90 km.**

XX ✿✿ **L'Auberge** (Mertens) Parallelweg 101 (relocation planned Wilhelminasingel 76 - with 16 rm), ✉ 6001 HM, ✆ 53 10 57, Fax 53 10 57 - AE E VISA. ✂
closed Saturday lunch, Sunday, Monday and last 3 weeks July - **Meals** a la carte 101/126
Spec. St-Jacques aux shii-take, à l'anchois et à l'huile de truffes blanches (15 October-15 April), Lièvre à la royale au gratin d'endives et de truffes (15 October-1 January), Gâteau de noisettes caramélisées au parfait de grains de café, crème au Whiskey.

Luxembourg

(LËTZEBUERG) 215 E 4 and 409 L 7 - pop. 75 377.

See : Site★★ - Old Luxembourg★★ G : Place de la Constitution <★★ F, Plateau St. Esprit <★★ G, Chemin de la Corniche★★, <★★ G, The Bock cliff <★★, Bock Casemates★★ G, Boulevard Victor Thorn <★ G 121, Grand-Ducal Palace★ G, Cathedral of Our Lady★ (Notre-Dame) F - Grand-Duchess Charlotte Bridge★ DY - The Trois Glands <★ (Three Acorns) DY.

Museum : National Museum of Art and History★, Gallo Romain section★, Luxembourg life section (decorative arts and folk traditions)★★ G **M**[1].

18 Hoehenhof (Senningerberg) near Airport, rte de Trèves 1, ✉ 2633, ☎ 34 00 90, Fax 34 83 91.

✈ Findel by E 44 : 6 km ☎ 40 08 08 - Air Terminal : pl. de la Gare ☎ 48 11 99.

ℹ Pl. d'Armes, ✉ 2011, ☎ 22 28 09, Fax 47 48 18 - Air Terminus (closed Sunday from November to March), pl. de la Gare, ✉ 1616, ☎ 48 11 99.

Amsterdam 391 - Bonn 190 - Brussels 219.

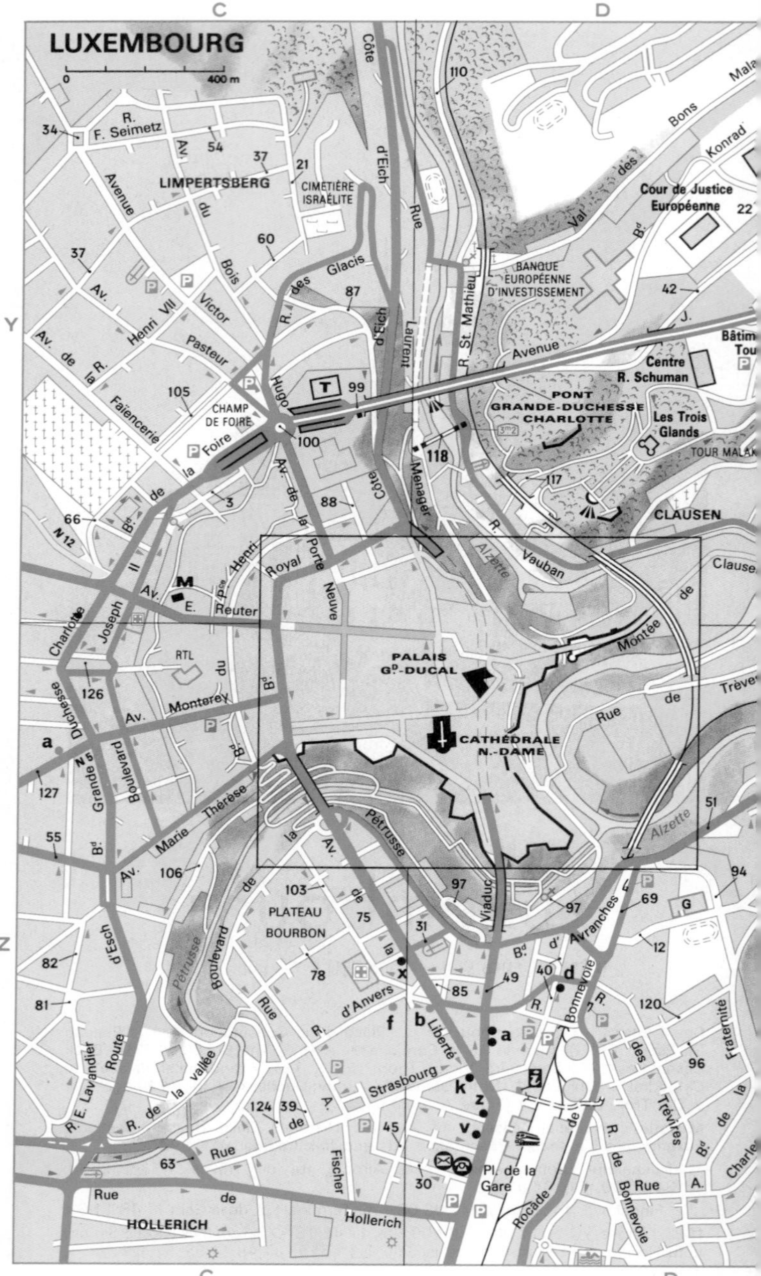

LUXEMBOURG
400 m
LIMPERTSBERG
CIMETIÈRE ISRAÉLITE
BANQUE EUROPÉENNE D'INVESTISSEMENT
Cour de Justice Européenne
Centre R. Schuman
PONT GRANDE-DUCHESSE CHARLOTTE
CHAMP DE FOIRE
Les Trois Glands
TOUR MALAK
CLAUSEN
PALAIS Gᴰ-DUCAL
CATHÉDRALE N.-DAME
RTL
PLATEAU BOURBON
HOLLERICH
Pl. de la Gare

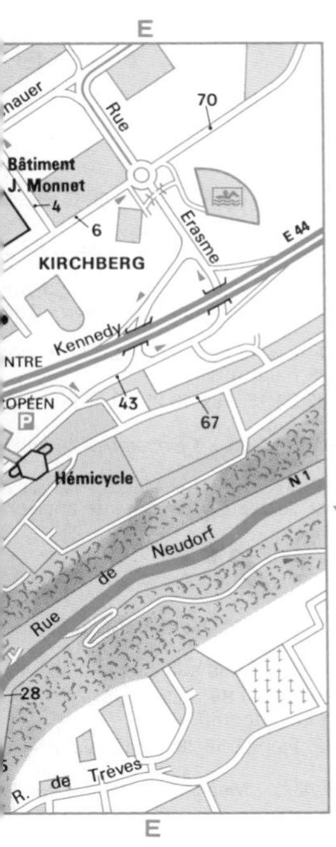

Capucins (R. des) . . . . . F
Chimay (R.) . . . . F 24
Curé (R. du) . . . . F
Fossé (R. du) . . . . F 46
Gare (Av. de la) . . . . . . DZ 49
Grand-Rue . . . . F
Liberté (Av. de la) . . . . . CDZ
Philippe II (R.) . . . . F 91
Porte-Neuve (Av. de la) . CY
Strasbourg (R. de) . . . . . CDZ

Adames (R.) . . . . CY 3
Albert Wehrer (R.) . . . . . EY 4
Alcide de Gasperi (R.) . . EY 6
Aldringen (R.) . . . . F 7
Athénée (R. de l') . . . . . F 9
Auguste Lumière (R.) . . DZ 12
Bains (R. des) . . . . F 13
Boucherie (R. de la) . . . G 15
Bruxelles (Pl. de) . . . . . F 16
Cerisiers (R. des) . . . . . CY 21
Charles-Léon Hammes (R.) . . . . DY 22
Clairefontaine (Pl.) . . . . . FG 27
Clausen (R. de) . . . . EY 28
Commerce (R. du) . . . . . CDZ 30
Diks (R.) . . . . CDZ 31
Eau (R. de l') . . . . G 33
Edouard André (Square) . . . . CY 34
Ermesinde (R.) . . . . CY 37
Etats-Unis (R. des) . . . . . CZ 39
Fort Neipperg (R. du) . . DZ 40
Fort Niedergrünewald (R. du) . . . . DY 42
Fort Thüngen (R. du) . . EY 43
Fort Wedell (R. du) . . . . CDZ 45
Franklin-Roosevelt (Bd) . F 48
Général Patton (Bd du) . DZ 51
Georges Willmar (R.) . . . CY 54
Guillaume (Av.) . . . . CZ 55
Guillaume II (R.) . . . . F 58
Guillaume Schneider (R.) . . . . CY 60
Jean Baptiste Merkels (R.) . . . . CZ 63

Y

Jean Ulveling (Bd) . . . . FG 64
J.P. Probst (R.) . . . . CY 66
Jules Wilhem (R.) . . . . . EY 67
Laboratoire (R. du) . . . . DZ 69
Léon Hengen (R.) . . . . . EY 70
Marché (Pl. du) . . . . . . G 72
Marché aux Herbes (R. du) . . . . FG 73
Martyrs (Pl. des) . . . . . . CZ 75
Michel Rodange (R.) . . CZ 78
Nancy (Pl. de) . . . . CZ 81
Nassau (R. de) . . . . CZ 82
Notre-Dame (R.) . . . . . . F 84
Paris (Pl. de) . . . . DZ 85
Paul Eyschen (R.) . . . . . CY 87
Pescatore (Av.) . . . . CY 88
Pfaffenthal (Montée de) . . . . FG 90
Pierre de Mansfeld (Allée) . . . . DY 93
Pierre et Marie Curie (R.) . . . . DZ 94
Pierre Hentges (R.) . . . . DZ 96
Prague (R. de) . . . . DZ 97
Robert Schuman (Bd) . CY 99
Robert Schuman (Rond-Point) . . . . CY 100
Sainte-Zithe (R.) . . . . . . CZ 103
Scheffer (Allée) . . . . CY 105
Semois (R. de la) . . . . . CZ 106
Sigefroi (R.) . . . . G 108
Sostène Weis (R.) . . . . G 109
Stavelot (R. de) . . . . . . DY 110
Théâtre (Pl. du) . . . . . . F 114
Tour Jacob (Av. de la) . . . . EY 115
Trois Glands (R. des) . . . . DY 117
Vauban (Pont) . . . . DY 118
Verger (R. du) . . . . DZ 120
Victor Thorn (Bd) . . . . . G 121
Willy Georgen (R.) . . . . F 123
Wilson (R.) . . . . CZ 124
Winston Churchill (Pl.) . CZ 126
10 Septembre (Av. du) . . . . CZ 127

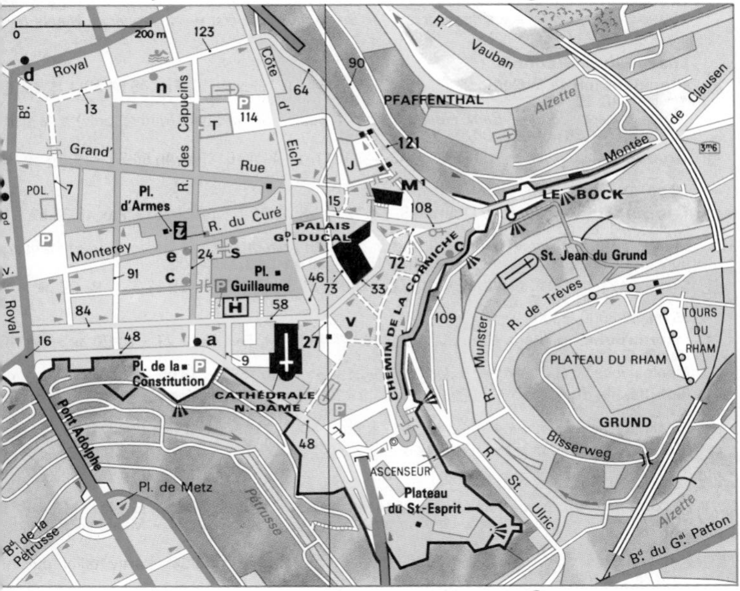

F G
0 200 m
123
Royal
d
n
13
Bd
R. des Capucins
T
114
Côte d'Eich
64
90
R. Vauban
PFAFFENTHAL
Alzette
Montée de Clausen
121
J
M1
Grand' Rue
POL.
7
Pl. d'Armes
R. du Curé
15
PALAIS Gd-DUCAL
108
LE BOCK
CHEMIN DE LA CORNICHE
St. Jean du Grund
Monterey
e
24
S
c
91
Pl. Guillaume
46
73
33
72
R. de Trèves
TOURS DU RHAM
H
58
84
V
109
R. Munster
PLATEAU DU RHAM
16
48
a
27
Royal
9
Pl. de la Constitution
CATHÉDRALE N.-DAME
GRUND
Pont Adolphe
48
Bisserweg
ASCENSEUR
R. St. Ulric
Pl. de Metz
Pétrusse
Plateau du St.-Esprit
Alzette
Bd de la Pétrusse
Bd du Gal Patton
F G

Luxembourg-Centre

Le Royal, bd Royal 12, ✉ 2449, ☎ 4 16 16, Fax 22 59 48, ... - 🅿 - 25-350. AE ⓓ E VISA JCB F
Meals *Le Jardin* *Lunch 950* - a la carte 1200/1800 - **165 rm** 8200/10600, 15 suites.

Cravat, bd Roosevelt 29, ✉ 2450, ☎ 22 19 75, Telex 2846, Fax 22 67 11 - ... 25-70. AE ⓓ E VISA. rest F
Meals *Lunch 480* - 950/1300 - **59 rm** 5400/7200.

Rix without rest, bd Royal 20, ✉ 2449, ☎ 47 16 66, Fax 22 75 35 - ... 🅿. E VISA. F
closed 22 December-2 January - **21 rm** 4280/6280.

XXXX ✿ **Clairefontaine** (Tintinger), pl. de Clairefontaine 9, ✉ 1341, ☎ 46 22 11, Fax 47 08 2... - 🅿. AE ⓓ E VISA G
closed Saturday lunch, Sunday, Bank Holidays, 18 to 25 February, 7 to 14 April, 22 to 24 Jun... 15 August-4 September, 27 Oct.-3 Nov. and 22 to 26 December - **Meals** *Lunch 1840* - 256... a la carte 2050/2700
Spec. Foie gras d'oie au Porto, St-Pierre rôti aux pommes de terre safranées et homard, Tournedo... de lièvre à l'ardennaise (October-November). Wines Riesling, Pinot gris.

XXX ✿ **St-Michel** (Glauben) 1st floor, r. Eau 32, ✉ 1449, ☎ 22 32 15, Fax 46 25 93, « In the ol... city, rustic interior » - AE ⓓ E VISA G
closed Saturday lunch, Sunday, Bank Holidays, 1 to 15 August and 24 December-2 Januar... - **Meals** *Lunch 1750* - a la carte 2250/2700
Spec. St-Jacques gratinées au pistou sur fondue de tomates (September-March), Turbot e... écailles de pommes de terre, sauce persillée, Rognon et ris de veau à la moutarde ancienn... Wines Pinot gris, Riesling Koëppchen.

XXX **Speltz,** r. Chimay 8, ✉ 1333, ☎ 47 49 50, Fax 47 46 77 - AE ⓓ E VISA F
closed Saturday, Sunday, Bank Holidays, 1 to 8 April, 3 to 17 August and 21 Decembe... 5 January - **Meals** *Lunch 1250* - 1250/1450.

XX **La Lorraine,** pl. d'Armes 7, ✉ 1136, ☎ 47 14 36, Fax 47 09 64, ..., Oyster bar and Seafoo... - ... AE ⓓ E VISA F
closed Saturday lunch, Sunday and 15 August-4 September - **Meals** a la carte 2000/240...

XX **Aux Bains** 1st floor, r. Bains 9, ✉ 1212, ☎ 22 44 88, Fax 22 44 89 - AE E VISA F
closed Sunday and Bank Holidays - **Meals** *Lunch 1100* - a la carte 1600/1900.

XX **Thailand,** av. Gaston Diderich 72, ✉ 1420, ☎ 44 27 66, Fax 22 58 28, Thaï cuisine - ... ⓓ E VISA. AV
closed Monday, Saturday lunch and 15 August-early September - **Meals** *Lunch 690* - a la cart... 950/1300.

XX **Am Pays,** r. Curé 20, ✉ 1368, ☎ 22 26 18, Fax 46 24 40, Seafood - AE ⓓ E VISA F
closed Saturday lunch - **Meals** *Lunch 1480* - 1480.

X **Brédewée,** r. Large/Corniche 9, ✉ 1917, ☎ 22 26 96, Fax 46 77 20, ... - AE ⓓ E VIS...
closed Sunday, last week August-first week September and first week January - **Meals** *Lunc... 1200* - 1200/1790. G

Luxembourg-Station

President, pl. de la Gare 32, ✉ 1024, ☎ 48 61 61, Telex 1510, Fax 48 61 80 - ... 40. AE ⓓ E VISA. DZ
Meals *(closed Sunday, Bank Holidays and August-1 September)* (dinner only) a la cart... 1050/1450 - **35 rm** 4600/6400.

Arcotel without rest, av. de la Gare 43, ✉ 1611, ☎ 49 40 01, Fax 40 56 24 - ... ⓓ E VISA. DZ
30 rm 4100/4800.

Central Molitor, av. de la Liberté 28, ✉ 1930, ☎ 48 99 11, Telex 2613, Fax 48 33 82 - ... rest ... AE ⓓ E VISA CDZ
Meals *(closed Saturday, last week July-first 2 weeks August and late December-early January)* (lunch only) *Lunch 340* - a la carte 1100/1550 - **36 rm** 3500/4600.

City Ⓜ without rest, r. Strasbourg 1, ✉ 2561, ☎ 29 11 22, Fax 29 11 33 - ... - 25-70. AE ⓓ E VISA DZ
35 rm 3000/5300.

International, pl. de la Gare 20, ✉ 1616, ☎ 48 59 11, Fax 49 32 27 - ... - 40 AE ⓓ E VISA. rm DZ
Meals *(closed 20 December-5 January)* *Lunch 925* - 925/1395 - **49 rm** 3650/4850.

Nobilis, av. de la Gare 47, ✉ 1611, ☎ 49 49 71, Fax 40 31 01 - ... - 50. AE ⓓ E VISA DZ
Meals (lunch only) *Lunch 295* - a la carte approx. 800 - 300 - **43 rm** 3000/4200.

Marco Polo without rest, r. Fort Neipperg 27, ✉ 2230, ☎ 406 41 41, Fax 40 48 84 - ... AE ⓓ E VISA DZ
18 rm 3100/3650.

XXX **Cordial** 1st floor, pl. de Paris 1, ✉ 2314, ☎ 48 85 38, Fax 40 77 76 - E VISA DZ
closed Friday, Saturday lunch, carnival week and 15 July-15 August - **Meals** *Lunch 1350* - 1350/2500.

XX **Italia** with rm, r. Anvers 15, ✉ 1130, ☎ 48 66 26, Fax 48 08 07, ..., Partly Italian cuisine - ... AE ⓓ E VISA CZ
Meals a la carte 1000/1600 - **20 rm** 2500/3100.

Suburbs

Airport NE : 8 km :

Sheraton Aérogolf ⛰, rte de Trèves, ✉ 1019, ☎ 34 05 71, Telex 2662, Fax 34 02 17, < - |♦| ⇔ ▤ TV ☎ P - 25-120. AE ① E VISA
Meals ***Le Montgolfier*** (open until midnight) *Lunch 950* - a la carte 1200/1950 - ☐ 550 - **145 rm** 6300/9000, 4 suites.

Ibis, rte de Trèves, ✉ 2632, ☎ 43 88 01, Telex 60790, Fax 43 88 02, < - |♦| ▤ TV ☎ & P - 25-80. AE ① E VISA
Meals *Lunch 380* - 750 - **120 rm** ☐ 2900/3900.

Trust Inn without rest, r. Neudorf 679, ✉ 2220, ☎ 42 30 51, Fax 42 30 56 - ▤ TV ☎ P. AE ① E VISA
7 rm ☐ 2200/3500.

Le Grimpereau, r. Cents 140, ✉ 1319, ☎ 43 67 87, Fax 42 60 26, ☂ - P. AE E VISA. ✻
closed Wednesday dinner, Thursday, 1 week carnival, first 3 weeks August and All Saints' week - **Meals** *Lunch 800* - 1250/1850.

at Belair C Luxembourg :

Parc Belair M ⛰, av. du X Septembre 109, ✉ 2551, ☎ 44 23 23, Fax 44 44 84, <, ≘s - |♦| ⇔ ▤ rest TV ☎ ⇔ - 60. AE ① E VISA
Meals *(dinner only except Sunday)* a la carte approx. 1400 - **45 rm** ☐ 5900/6400.

Astoria, av. du X Septembre 14, ✉ 2550, ☎ 44 62 23, Fax 45 82 96 - AE ① E VISA CZ **a**
closed Saturday and 26 December-4 January - **Meals** (lunch only) a la carte 1900/2250.

at Dommeldange (Dummeldéng) N : 5,5 km C Luxembourg :

Inter.Continental ⛰, r. Jean Engling 12, ✉ 1466, ☎ 4 37 81, Telex 3754, Fax 43 60 95, <, ☂, Fō, ≘s, ▣ - |♦| ⇔ ▤ TV ☎ & P - 25-360. AE ① E VISA. ✻ rest
Meals *(closed lunch Saturday and Sunday, August and early January)* *Lunch 1350* - a la carte 1850/2250 - ☐ 620 - **309 rm** 7350/8350, 30 suites.

Parc, rte d'Echternach 120, ✉ 1453, ☎ 43 56 43, Fax 43 69 03, Fō, ≘s, ▣, ☂, ✂ - |♦| TV ☎ & P - 40-2000. AE ① E VISA
Meals (open until 11.30 p.m.) *Lunch 750* - a la carte approx. 1300 - **261 rm** ☐ 3600/4400, 10 suites.

Host. du Grünewald, rte d'Echternach 10, ✉ 1453, ☎ 43 18 82 and 42 03 14 (rest), Fax 42 06 46 and 42 03 14 (rest), ☂ - |♦| TV ☎ P - 25-40. AE ① E VISA. ✻
Meals *(closed Saturday lunch, Sunday, Bank Holidays and 1 to 22 January)* *Lunch 1620* - a la carte 1700/2250 - **25 rm** ☐ 3900/4900, 3 suites.

Upland of Kirchberg (Kürchbierg) :

Sofitel and Europlaza, r. Fort Niedergrünewald 6 (European Centre), ✉ 2015, ☎ 43 77 61, Fax 43 86 58, ≘s, ▣ - |♦| ⇔ ▤ TV ☎ & ⇔ P - 25-300. AE ① E VISA JCB. ✻ rest EY **a**
Meals ***Les Trois Glands*** *(closed Saturday lunch, Sunday dinner, Monday and August)* *Lunch 1100* - a la carte approx. 1400 - ***Brasserie Europa*** a la carte 900/1300 - **357 rm** ☐ 6300/8900, 7 suites.

at the skating-rink of Kockelscheuer (Kockelscheier) S by N 31 :

✿✿ **Patin d'Or** (Berring), rte de Bettembourg 40, ✉ 1899, ☎ 22 64 99, Fax 40 40 11 - ▤ P. AE E VISA. ✻
closed Saturday, Sunday, late August-early September and late December-early January - **Meals** 2000, a la carte 2300/2700
Spec. Queues de langoustines au caviar et œuf brouillé, Rouget de roches en écailles de pommes de terre, brandade aux olives, Joue de bœuf, pied de porc farci et queue de bœuf en feuille de chou (September-May). **Wines** Pinot gris, Riesling Koëppchen.

at Limpertsberg (Lampertsbierg) C Luxembourg :

Bouzonviller, r. A. Unden 138, ✉ 2652, ☎ 47 22 59, Fax 46 43 89, < - E VISA
closed Saturday, Sunday, Bank Holidays, first 3 weeks August and Christmas-New Year - **Meals** *Lunch 1600* - a la carte 1800/2250.

at Rollingergrund (Rolléngergronn) C Luxembourg :

Sieweburen, r. Septfontaines 36, ✉ 2534, ☎ 44 23 56, Fax 44 23 53, <, ☂, « Woodland setting », ☂ - TV ☎ P. E VISA
closed 18 December-8 January - **Meals** (Pub rest) *(closed Wednesday)* *Lunch 340* - a la carte 850/1500 - **13 rm** ☐ 2600/3700.

Environs

at Bridel (Briddel) by N 12 : 7 km C Kopstal pop. 2 974 :

Le Rondeau, r. Luxembourg 82, ✉ 8140, ☎ 33 94 73, Fax 33 37 46 - P. AE E VISA
closed Monday dinner, Tuesday, last 3 weeks August and first 2 weeks January - **Meals** *Lunch 980* - 980/1900.

at Hesperange (Hesper) SE : 5,5 km – pop. 9 918 :

XXX ✿ **L'Agath** (Steichen) with rm, rte de Thionville 274 (Howald), ✉ 5884, ☎ 48 86 87, Fax 48 55 05, ⛱, ⛲ – TV ☎ P – 🏛 60. AE ⓓ E VISA
closed Sunday, Monday, mid July-early August and 22 December-3 January – **Meals** *Lunch 1600* – 1850/3200, a la carte 2100/2600 – **5 rm** ☕ 1800/3300
Spec. Carpaccio de canard fumé aux copeaux de foie gras, Filets de sole et pâtes imprimées aux herbes, Médaillon de ris de veau en feuilleté à l'estragon. Wines Riesling, Pinot gris.

XXX **Klein,** rte de Thionville 432, ✉ 5886, ☎ 36 08 42, Fax 36 08 43 – AE ⓓ E VISA JCB
closed Sunday dinner, Monday and last 2 weeks August – **Meals** *Lunch 1400* – 1650/2500.

at Strassen (Strossen) W : 4 km – pop. 4 919 :

🏨 **L'Olivier** with apartments, rte d'Arlon 140, ✉ 8008, ☎ 313 66 61 and 31 88 13 (rest), Fax 31 36 27, ⛱ – |‡| ⚡ TV ☎ ♿ 🚗 P – 🏛 25-350. AE ⓓ E VISA
Meals *(closed Bank Holidays except Easter and Whitsun) Lunch 890* – 1250/1650 – **42 rm** ☕ 3950/5550, 4 suites.

at Walferdange (Walfer) N : 5 km – pop. 5 818 :

🏨 **Moris** M, pl. des Martyrs, ✉ 7201, ☎ 33 01 05, Fax 33 30 70 – |‡| ▤ rest TV ☎ P – 🏛 50. AE ⓓ E VISA
Meals *(closed Monday)* 1050/1180 – **21 rm** ☕ 2600/3600.

XX **l'Etiquette,** rte de Diekirch 50, ✉ 7220, ☎ 33 51 67, Fax 33 51 69 – P. AE ⓓ E VISA
Meals 750/1000.

Echternach (Iechternach) 215 D 6 and 409 M 6 – pop. 4 211 – 35 km.

at Geyershaff (Geieschhaff) SW : 6,5 km by E 27 C Bech pop. 787 :

XXX ✿✿ **La Bergerie** (Phal), ✉ 6251, ☎ 7 94 64, Fax 7 97 71, ←, ⛱, « Floral country setting » – P. AE ⓓ E VISA
closed Sunday dinner, Monday and 15 January-late February – **Meals** *Lunch 1800* – a la carte 2500/3500
Spec. Foie d'oie au naturel, Homard rôti à la vinaigrette tiède d'herbes, Rosaces de St-Jacques au pilpil. Wines Riesling Koëppchen, Pinot gris.

Paliseul 6850 Luxembourg belge (Belgium) 214 ⑯ and 409 I 6 – pop. 4 770 – ✪ 0 6 – 94 km.

XXX ✿✿ **Au Gastronome** (Libotte) with rm, r. Bouillon 2 (Paliseul-Gare) ☎ 53 30 64, Fax 53 38 91, « Floral garden with ⛱ » – ▤ TV ☎ P. AE ⓓ E VISA
closed Sunday dinner and Monday except Bank Holidays, January-2 February, carnival week and 25 June-5 July – **Meals** *Lunch 1200* – 1950/2750, a la carte 2150/2800 – **9 rm** ☕ 3500/4500
Spec. Pastilla de pied de porc au foie gras, vinaigrette truffée, Gratin de queues d'écrevisses au Champagne et pomme de terre (July-December), Cochon de lait rôti au miel, sauce aux epices

Amsterdam

Noord-Holland 210 J 8 and 408 G 4 – ㉑ S – Pop. 724 096 – ☎ 0 20.

See : Old Amsterdam★★★ – The canals★★★ (Grachten) : Boat trips★ (Rondvaart) – Dam : Royal Palace★ (Koninklijk Paleis) LY, pulpit★ in the New Church★ (Nieuwe Kerk) LY – Beguine Convent★★ (Begijnhof) LY – Flower market★ (Bloemenmarkt) LY – Cromhout Houses★ (Cromhouthuizen) – Reguliersgracht ≤★ – Keizersgracht ≤★ – ≤★ from the sluice bridge Oudezijds Kolk-Oudezijds Voorburgwal MX – Groenburgwal ≤★ LMY – Thin Bridge★ (Magere Brug) MZ – Artis★ (Zoological Garden) – Westerkerk★ KX.

Museums : Amsterdam Historical Museum★★ (Amsterdams Historisch Museum) LY – Madame Tussaud's Scenerama★ : wax museum LY **M¹** – Rijksmuseum★★★ KZ – Vincent van Gogh National Museum★★★ (Rijksmuseum) – Municipal★★ (Stedelijk Museum) : Modern Art – Amstelkringmuseum "Our Dear Lord in the Attic"★ (Museum Amstelkring Ons' Lieve Heer op Solder) : clandestine chapel MX **M⁴** – Rembrandt's House★ (Rembrandthuis) : works by the master MY **M⁵** – Jewish Museum★ (Joods Historisch Museum) MY **M⁶** – Allard Pierson★ : antiquities LY **M⁷** – Tropical Museum★ (Tropenmuseum) – Netherlands Maritime History Museum★ (Nederlands Scheepvaart Museum) – Anne Frank's House KX **M⁸**.

Casino, Max Euweplein 62, ✉ 1017 MB (near Leidseplein) ☎ 620 10 06, Fax 620 36 66.

18 Bauduinlaan 35 ✉ 1165 NE at Halfweg (W : 6 km) ☎ (0 20) 497 78 66 – 9 Zwarte Laantje 4 ✉ 1099 CE at Duivendrecht (S : 5 km) ☎ (0 20) 663 12 86 – 9 Abcouderstraatweg 46 ✉ 1105 AA at Holendrecht (SW : 11 km) ☎ (0 294) 56 53 73 – 9 Buikslotermurdÿk 41 ✉ 1027 AC ☎ (0 20) 632 56 50.

✈ at Schiphol SW : 9,5 km ☎ (0 20) 601 91 11.

ℹ Stationsplein, ✉ 1012 AB ☎ 06-34 03 40 66, Fax 625 28 69.

Brussels 204 – Düsseldorf 227 – The Hague 60 – Luxembourg 419 – Rotterdam 76.

AMSTERDAM
0
200 m
J
K
X
Y
Z
Westerstr.
Anjeliersstr.
Egelantiersstr.
Nieuwe
Leliestr.
Bloem
gracht
Westerkerk
110
Raadhuis straat
Rozengracht
straat
Hartenstr.
Laurier-
gracht
Elandsstr.
Elands
gracht
Runstr.
Wolvenstr.
PRINSEN
GRACHT
KEIZERS
HEREN
Raamstr.
Leidsestraat
Leidse
Kerkstr.
Leidseplein
CASINO
Wetering
schans
Paradiso
Stadhouders
kade
RIJKSMUSE
Hooftstr.
Paulus
Potterstr.
Vondel
Park
Huygensstr.
1e. Constantijn
Overtoom
S 106
S 100
S 105
S 109
Kostverlorenvaart
Hendrikstraat
2e Hugo de Groot
Fr.
Grootstr.
Nassau
kade
Singelgracht
Marnixstr.
Lijnbaans
Hugo de Groot gracht
Da Costa gracht
Clercqstr.
Bilderdijkstr.
Kinkerstr.
J. v. Lennep straat
Lennep kanaal
Jacob van
Bosboom Toussaintstr.
POL.
88
6

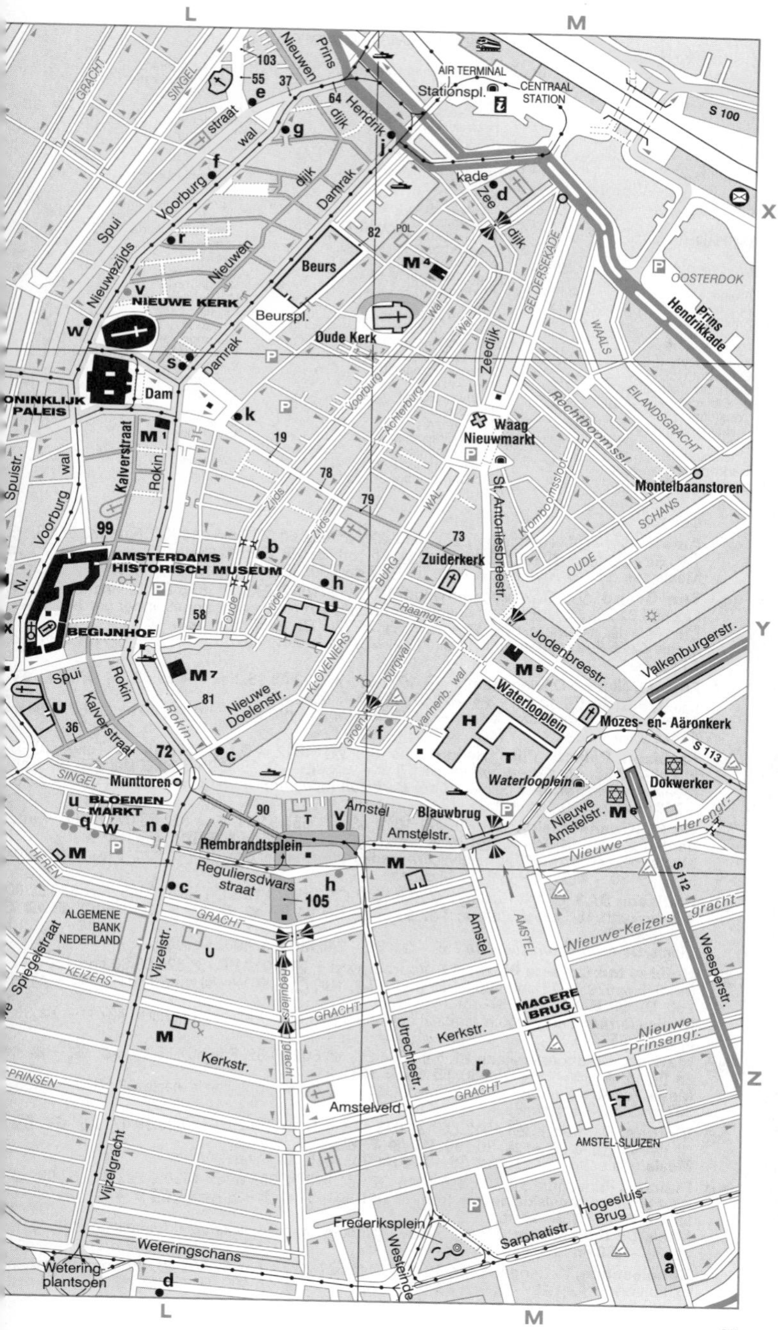

L
M
X
Y
Z
AIR TERMINAL
CENTRAAL STATION
Stationspl.
Prins Hendrikkade
Nieuwendijk
Voorburgwal
Nieuwezijds
Spui
Damrak
Beurs
Beurspl.
Oude Kerk
NIEUWE KERK
KONINKLIJK PALEIS
Dam
Zeedijk
Geldersekade
OOSTERDOK
Waag
Nieuwmarkt
Montelbaanstoren
Rechtboomssl.
Kalverstraat
Rokin
AMSTERDAMS HISTORISCH MUSEUM
BEGIJNHOF
Zuiderkerk
St. Antoniesbreestr.
Jodenbreestr.
Valkenburgerstr.
Waterlooplein
Mozes- en- Aäronkerk
Dokwerker
Munttoren
BLOEMEN MARKT
Rembrandtsplein
Blauwbrug
Amstelstr.
Reguliersdwarsstraat
ALGEMENE BANK NEDERLAND
Vijzelstr.
Amstel
MAGERE BRUG
Kerkstr.
Utrechtestr.
Amstelveld
AMSTEL-SLUIZEN
Vijzelgracht
Weteringschans
Frederiksplein
Sarphatistr.
Hogesluis-Brug
Weesperstr.
Wetering plantsoen
Westeinde

STREET INDEX TO AMSTERDAM TOWN PLAN

van Baerlestr. . . . . JZ 6
Damrak LX
Damstr. . . . . LY 19
Heiligeweg . . . . LY 36
Kalverstr. . . . . LY
Kinkerstr. . . . . JY
Leidsestr. . . . . KYZ
Nieuwendijk LX
P.C. Hooftstr. . . . . KZ
Raadhuisstr. . . . . KXY
Reguliersbreestr. . . . . . . LY 90
Rokin . . . . LY
Rozengracht . . . . JKY
Spui . . . . LY
Utrechtsestr. . . . . MZ

Amstel . . . . MYZ
Amstelstr. . . . . MY
Amstelveld . . . . LMZ
Angeliersstr. . . . . KX
Beursplein LX
Bilderdijkstr. . . . . JY
Blauwbrug . . . . MY
Bosboom Toussaintstr. . . . JYZ
de Clercstr. . . . . JY
Constantijn
Huygensstr. (1e) . . . . . . JZ
Dam . . . . LY
Egelantiersstr. . . . . KX
Elandsgracht . . . . KY
Elandsstr. . . . . JKY
Frederik Hendrikstr. . . . . . JX
Frederikspl. . . . . MZ
Hartenstr. . . . . KY
Hekelveld . . . . LX 37
Hogesluis-Brug . . . . MZ
Hugo de
Grootstr. (2e) . . . . JX
Jodenbreestr. . . . . MY
Kattengat . . . . LX 55
Kerkstr. . . . . KLZ
Langebrugsteeg . . . . LY 58
Laurierstr. . . . . JKY
Leidseplein . . . . KZ
Magerebrug . . . . MZ
Marnixstr. . . . . JXY
Martelaarsgracht . . . . LX 64
Muntplein . . . . LY 72
Nassaukade . . . . JXY
Nieuwe Amstelstr. . . . . . . MY
Nieuwe Doelenstr. . . . . . . LY
Nieuwe Hoogstr. . . . . MY 73
Nieuwe Leliestr. . . . . KX
Nieuwe Spiegelstr. . . . . . . LZ
Nieuwezijds
Voorburgwal . . . . LXY
Nieuwendijk LX
Nieuwmarkt . . . . MY
Oude Doelenstr. . . . . LY 78
Oude Hoogstr. . . . . LMY 79
Oude Turfmarkt . . . . LY 81
Oudebrugsteeg . . . . LMX 82
Paulus Potterstr. . . . . KZ
Prins Hendrikkade . . . . . . LMX
Raamstr. . . . . KY
Reestraat . . . . KY 88
Reguliersdwarsstr. . . . . . . LY
Rembrandtsplein . . . . LMY
Runstr. . . . . KY
Sint-
Antoniesbreestr. . . . . MY
Sint-
Luciensteeg . . . . LY 99
Spuistr. LX
Stadhouderskade . . . . KZ
Stationsplein . . . . MX
Stromarkt . . . . LX 10
Thorbeckepl. . . . . LZ 10
Valkenburgerstr. . . . . MY
Vijzelgracht . . . . LZ
Vijzelstr. . . . . LZ
Vondelstr. . . . . JZ
Waterlooplein . . . . MY
Weesperstr. . . . . MZ
Westeinde . . . . MZ
Westermarkt . . . . KX 11
Westerstr. . . . . KX
Wetering-
plantsoen . . . . LZ
Wetering-
schans . . . . KLZ
Wolvenstr. . . . . KY
Zeedijk . . . . MX

Centre

Amstel, Prof. Tulpplein 1, 1018 GX, 622 60 60, Telex 11004, Fax 622 58 08, – 25-180. MZ
Meals see rest ***La Rive*** below – 30 – **63 rm** 600/850, 16 suites.

The Grand, O.Z. Voorburgwal 197, 1012 EX, 555 31 11, Telex 1307, Fax 555 32 22, « Historic building, authentic Art Nouveau lounges, inner garden », – rest – 25-320. LY
Meals ***Café Roux*** (open until 11 p.m.) *Lunch 38* - a la carte 43/63 – 30 – **155 rm** 545/64 11 suites.

Europe, Nieuwe Doelenstraat 2, 1012 CP, 623 48 36, Fax 624 29 62, – – 25-250. LY
Meals see rest ***Excelsior*** below – ***Le Relais*** (open until midnight) 40/50 – 35 – **96 r** 475/650, 5 suites.

Barbizon Palace, Prins Hendrikkade 59, 1012 AD, 556 45 64, Telex 1018 Fax 624 33 53, – rest – 25-300. rest MX
Meals see rest ***Vermeer*** below – ***Café Barbizon*** (open until 11 p.m.) a la carte 44/77 – – **265 rm** 375/510, 3 suites.

Gd H. Krasnapolsky, Dam 9, 1012 JS, 554 91 11, Fax 622 86 07, « 19C wint garden », – – 25-750. rest LY
Meals see rest ***Edo and Kyo*** below – ***Brasserie Reflet*** (dinner only until 11 p.m.) a la carte appr 55 – 30 – **415 rm** 350/575, 14 suites.

Radisson SAS, Rusland 17, 1012 CK, 623 12 31, Telex 10365, Fax 520 82 « Patio with 18C presbytery », – – 25-150. LY
Meals ***De Palmboom*** *Lunch 48* - 58 – 32 – **246 rm** 375/400, 1 suite.

Holiday Inn Crowne Plaza, N.Z. Voorburgwal 5, 1012 RC, 620 05 00 and 420 22 (rest), Fax 620 11 73 and 420 04 65 (rest), – rm – 2 260. rm LX
Meals ***Dorrius*** (Partly Dutch regional cooking, open until 11 p.m.) a la carte 48/91 – 38 **270 rm** 345/445.

Marriott, Stadhouderskade 21, 1054 ES, 607 55 55, Fax 607 55 11, – – 25-360. KZ
Meals *(closed Sunday and Monday)* (seafood, dinner only) a la carte 53/76 – 33 **387 rm** 325/405, 5 suites.

Victoria, Damrak 1, 1012 LG, 623 42 55, Telex 16625, Fax 625 29 97, – 30-150. rest LMX
Meals a la carte 43/80 – 28 – **286 rm** 395/425, 19 suites.

Pulitzer, Prinsengracht 323, 1016 GZ, 523 52 35, Telex 16508, Fax 627 67 53, « 24 terraced canalside houses from 17 and 18C », – – 25-1 rest KY
Meals ***De Goudsbloem*** *(closed Sunday, Monday and 2 weeks July)* (dinner only) 65/11 – 33 – **230 rm** 395/540, 2 suites.

Renaissance, Kattengat 1, 1012 SZ, 621 22 23, Fax 627 52 45, « Contemporary exhibition », – – 25-400. re LX
Meals a la carte 51/79 – 33 – **419 rm** 465/525, 6 suites.

Barbizon Centre, Stadhouderskade 7, ⊠ 1054 ES, ℰ 685 13 51, Telex 12601, Fax 685 16 11, – – 25-200. AE E VISA JCB. rest
Meals (dinner only) *Lunch 43* – a la carte 65/82 – 38 – **237 rm** 485, 2 suites. KZ **p**

Jolly Carlton M, Vijzelstraat 4, ⊠ 1017 HK, ℰ 622 22 66 and 623 83 20 (rest), Telex 11670, Fax 626 61 83 – – 25-200. AE E VISA JCB. rest LY **n**
Meals ***Caruso*** (Italian cuisine, dinner only until 11 p.m.) *(closed Monday)* 50/90 – **219 rm** 330/560.

American, Leidsekade 97, ⊠ 1017 PN, ℰ 624 53 22, Fax 625 32 36, – – 70-160. AE E VISA JCB. KZ **q**
Meals (Art Deco style pub rest, open until 11.30 p.m.) *Lunch 38* – a la carte approx. 60 – 30 – **185 rm** 295/575, 3 suites.

Ascot, Damrak 95, ⊠ 1012 LP, ℰ 626 00 66, Fax 627 09 82 – – 25-60. AE E VISA JCB. rest LXY **s**
Meals (Swiss cuisine) *Lunch 34* – a la carte 49/68 – 28 – **109 rm** 355/450.

Sofitel, N.Z. Voorburgwal 67, ⊠ 1012 RE, ℰ 627 59 00, Fax 623 89 32, – – 25-60. AE E VISA JCB. LX **r**
Meals (dinner only) 43/60 – 30 – **148 rm** 345/380.

Canal Crown without rest, Herengracht 519, ⊠ 1017 BV, ℰ 420 00 55, Fax 420 09 93 – . AE E VISA JCB
25 – **57 rm** 150/350. LZ **c**

Ambassade without rest, Herengracht 341, ⊠ 1016 AZ, ℰ 626 23 33, Fax 624 53 21, ≤ – . AE E VISA
46 rm 230/285, 6 suites. KY **x**

Canal House without rest, Keizersgracht 148, ⊠ 1015 CX, ℰ 622 51 82, Fax 624 13 17, « Antique furniture », – . AE E VISA.
26 rm 210/260. KX **k**

Estheréa without rest, Singel 305, ⊠ 1012 WJ, ℰ 624 51 46, Fax 623 90 01 – . AE E VISA JCB.
75 rm 300/365. LY **y**

Caransa without rest, Rembrandtsplein 19, ⊠ 1017 CT, ℰ 622 94 55, Fax 622 27 73 – – 25-200. AE E VISA.
66 rm 300/365. LY **v**

Tulip Inn without rest, Spuistraat 288, ⊠ 1012 VX, ℰ 420 45 45, Fax 420 43 00, – . AE E VISA
208 rm 210/240. LY **g**

Cok City M without rest, N.Z. Voorburgwal 50, ⊠ 1012 SC, ℰ 422 00 11, Fax 420 03 57 – . AE E VISA.
106 rm 220/240. LX **f**

Die Port van Cleve, N.Z. Voorburgwal 178, ⊠ 1012 SJ, ℰ 624 48 60, Fax 622 02 40 – – 25-50. AE E VISA.
Meals see rest ***De Blauwe Parade*** below – **116 rm** 287/342. LX **w**

Dikker en Thijs Fenice, Prinsengracht 444, ⊠ 1017 EK, ℰ 626 77 21, Fax 625 89 86 – – 25. AE E VISA
De Prinsenkelder (dinner only until midnight) a la carte approx. 60 – **25 rm** 250/415. KZ **v**

Amsterdam, Damrak 93, ⊠ 1012 LP, ℰ 624 03 96 and 555 06 66 (rest), Telex 10569, Fax 620 47 16 – . AE E VISA JCB
Meals ***De Roode Leeuw*** (Dutch regional cooking) *Lunch 38* - 48 – **80 rm** 209/325. LXY **s**

Wiechmann without rest, Prinsengracht 328, ⊠ 1016 hx, ℰ 626 33 21, Fax 626 89 62 –
36 rm 150/225. KY **c**

Asterisk without rest, Den Texstraat 16, ⊠ 1017 ZA, ℰ 626 23 96, Fax 638 27 90 – . E VISA
29 rm 149/185. LZ **d**

Vondel without rest, Vondelstraat 28, ⊠ 1054 GE, ℰ 612 01 20, Fax 685 43 21, – – 25. AE E VISA JCB
25 – **38 rm** 255/310. JZ **m**

XXXX ✿ **La Rive** - (at Amstel H.), Prof. Tulpplein 1, ⊠ 1018 GX, ℰ 622 60 60, Telex 11004, Fax 622 58 08, ≤, , « Amstel-side setting », – . AE E VISA. MZ **a**
Meals *Lunch 50* – 125/175, a la carte 113/138
Spec. Omelette fourée de risotto truffé et poêlée de homard, Filets de sole aux piments, bouillon acidulé, Noix de ris de veau grillées et gratin de macaronis au Vieux Hollande.

XXX ✿ **Vermeer** - (at Barbizon Palace H.), Prins Hendrikkade 59, ⊠ 1012 AD, ℰ 556 48 85, Telex 10187, Fax 624 33 53 – . AE E VISA JCB. MX **d**
closed Saturday lunch, Sunday, 15 July-19 August and 26 December-3 January – **Meals** *Lunch 50* – 85/125, a la carte 98/122
Spec. Tartare de veau aux truffes et parmesan, Lotte grillée au gros sel, poivron et compote d'aubergine, Soufflé au mascarpone et basilic.

XXX **Excelsior** - (at Europe H.), Nieuwe Doelenstraat 2, ⊠ 1012 CP, ℰ 623 48 36, Fax 624 29 62, ≤, , Open until 11 p.m., – . AE E VISA JCB LY **c**
closed Saturday lunch – **Meals** *Lunch 63* – 75/165 b.i.

XXX **D'Vijff Vlieghen,** Spuistraat 294, ✉ 1012 VX, ℘ 624 83 69, Fax 623 64 04, « Typical 17C houses » - AE ⓓ E VISA JCB LY p
closed 1 January - **Meals** (dinner only) a la carte 68/74.

XXX **Radèn Mas,** Stadhouderskade 6, ✉ 1054 ES, ℘ 685 40 41, Fax 685 39 81, Indonesian cuisine, open until 11 p.m., « Exotic decor » - ▤. AE ⓓ E VISA JCB JKZ k
Meals *Lunch 40* - 55/99.

XXX ✿ **Christophe** (Royer), Leliegracht 46, ✉ 1015 DH, ℘ 625 08 07, Fax 638 91 32 - ▤. AE ⓓ E VISA KX c
closed Sunday and 1 to 5 January - **Meals** (dinner only until 11 p.m.) 75/95, a la carte 104/123
Spec. Ris de veau rôti au romarin et au citron confit, Homard rôti à l'ail doux et aux pommes de terre, Canard sauvage aux figues et au Banyuls (September-January).

XXX **De Blauwe Parade** - (at Die Port van Cleve H.), N.Z. Voorburgwal 178, ✉ 1012 SJ, ℘ 624 00 47, Fax 622 02 40, « Delftware » - AE ⓓ E VISA. 🐕 LX w
Meals *Lunch 28* - 43/100.

XXX **Dynasty,** Reguliersdwarsstraat 30, ✉ 1017 BM, ℘ 626 84 00, Fax 622 30 38, 🏠, Oriental cuisine, « Terrace » - ▤. AE ⓓ E VISA. 🐕 LY
closed January - **Meals** (dinner only until 11 p.m.) a la carte 67/108.

XX **Het Tuynhuys,** Reguliersdwarsstraat 28, ✉ 1017 BM, ℘ 627 66 03, Fax 627 66 03, 🏠, « Terrace » - ▤. AE ⓓ E VISA LY
closed lunch Saturday and Sunday - **Meals** *Lunch 55* - 55/79.

XX **'t Swarte Schaep** 1st floor, Korte Leidsedwarsstraat 24, ✉ 1017 RC, ℘ 622 30 21, Fax 624 82 68, Open until 11 p.m., « 17C Dutch interior » - ▤. AE ⓓ E VISA JCB KZ
closed 30 April, 25, 26 and 31 December and 1 January - **Meals** *Lunch 38* - 43/90.

XX **Les Quatre Canetons,** Prinsengracht 1111, ✉ 1017 JJ, ℘ 624 63 07, Fax 638 45 99 - AE ⓓ E VISA JCB. 🐕 MZ
closed Saturday lunch and Sunday - **Meals** *Lunch 58* - a la carte 84/110.

XX **Tout Court,** Runstraat 13, ✉ 1016 GJ, ℘ 625 86 37, Fax 625 44 11, Open until 11.30 p.m. - AE ⓓ E VISA KY
closed lunch Saturday and Sunday and first week January - **Meals** *Lunch 40* - 50/73.

XX **Indrapura,** Rembrandtsplein 42, ✉ 1017 CV, ℘ 623 73 29, Fax 624 90 78, Indonesian cuisine - ▤. AE ⓓ E VISA JCB. 🐕 LYZ
Meals (dinner only until 11 p.m.) a la carte 49/78.

XX ✿ **Sichuan Food,** Reguliersdwarsstraat 35, ✉ 1017 BK, ℘ 626 93 27, Fax 627 72 81, Chinese cuisine - ▤. AE ⓓ E VISA. 🐕 LY
closed 31 December - **Meals** (dinner only until 11 p.m., booking essential) a la carte 58/7
Spec. Dim Sum, Canard laqué à la pékinoise, Huîtres sautées maison.

XX **Bols Taverne,** Rozengracht 106, ✉ 1016 NH, ℘ 624 57 52, Fax 620 41 94, 🏠 - ▤. AE ⓓ E VISA JCB JKY
closed Sunday, Bank Holidays except Christmas and mid July-mid August - **Meals** *Lunch 55* 59/69.

XX **De Oesterbar,** Leidseplein 10, ✉ 1017 PT, ℘ 623 29 88, Fax 623 21 99, Seafood, open until 1 a.m. - ▤. AE ⓓ E VISA. 🐕 KZ
Meals a la carte approx. 85.

XX **Manchurian,** Leidseplein 10a, ✉ 1017 PT, ℘ 623 13 30, Fax 626 21 05, Oriental cuisine - ▤. AE ⓓ E VISA. 🐕 KZ
closed 31 December - **Meals** 50/90.

XX **Le Pêcheur,** Reguliersdwarsstraat 32, ✉ 1017 BM, ℘ 624 31 21, Fax 624 31 21, 🏠, Seafood, open until midnight - AE ⓓ E VISA JCB. 🐕 LY
closed Sunday - **Meals** *Lunch 48* - 48/59.

XX **Hosokawa,** Max Euweplein 22, ✉ 1017 MB, ℘ 638 80 86, Fax 638 22 19, Japanese cuisine, teppan-yaki, open until 11 p.m. - AE ⓓ E VISA JCB. 🐕 KZ
Meals *Lunch 40* - 85/120.

XX **Treasure,** N.Z. Voorburgwal 115, ✉ 1012 RH, ℘ 626 09 15, Fax 640 12 02, Chinese cuisine - ▤. AE ⓓ E VISA. 🐕 LX
closed Wednesday - **Meals** a la carte 48/80.

XX **Sancerre,** Reestraat 28, ✉ 1016 DN, ℘ 627 87 94, Fax 623 87 49 - AE ⓓ E VISA JCB. KY
Meals (dinner only) 58/86.

XX **Lonny's,** Rozengracht 46, ✉ 1016 ND, ℘ 623 89 50, Fax 615 78 83, Indonesian cuisine « Exotic decor » - ▤. AE ⓓ E VISA JCB. 🐕 KXY
Meals (dinner only until 11 p.m.) 45/85.

XX **Sea Palace,** Oosterdokskade 8, ✉ 1011 AE, ℘ 626 47 77, Fax 620 42 66, Asian cuisine open until 11 p.m., « Floating restaurant with ≤ town » - ▤. AE ⓓ E VISA JCB. 🐕
Meals *Lunch 35* - a la carte 43/58.

X **Tom Yam,** Staalstraat 22, ✉ 1011 JM, ℘ 622 95 33, Fax 624 90 62, Thaï cuisine - ▤. ⓓ E VISA JCB MY
closed 24 to 31 December - **Meals** (dinner only) 53/70.

X **De Gouden Reael,** Zandhoek 14, ✉ 1013 KT, ℘ 623 38 83, « 17C house on old harbour site » - AE ⓓ E VISA. 🐕
closed Sunday and last week December-first week January - **Meals** *Lunch 55* - 55/65.

X **Edo and Kyo** - (at Gd H. Krasnapolsky H.), Dam 9, ✉ 1012 JS, ✆ 554 60 96, Fax 639 31 46, Japanese cuisine – AE ⓓ E VISA JCB. ※ LY k
Meals *Lunch 45* – 65/85.

X **Haesje Claes,** Spuistraat 273, ✉ 1012 VR, ✆ 624 99 98, Fax 627 48 17, « Amsterdam atmosphere » – AE ⓓ E VISA JCB. ※ LY x
Meals *Lunch 25* – 25/45.

X **Bordewijk,** Noordermarkt 7, ✉ 1015 MV, ✆ 624 38 99, 🏖 – AE E VISA
closed Monday, late July-early August and 27 December-2 January – **Meals** (dinner only) a la carte approx. 80.

South and West Quarters

Okura, Ferdinand Bolstraat 333, ✉ 1072 LH, ✆ 678 71 11, Fax 671 23 44, ≘s, ⛶ – |‡| ⇸ ▤ TV ☎ 🚗 P – 🏛 25-650. AE ⓓ E VISA. ※
Meals see rest ***Ciel Bleu*** and ***Yamazato*** below – ***Sazanka*** *(closed lunch Saturday and Sunday)* (Japanese cuisine, teppan-yaki) *Lunch 50* - 44/145 – ***Brasserie Le Camelia*** (open until 11 p.m.) 48 – ☕ 38 – **358 rm** 375/520, 12 suites.

Le Meridien Apollo, Apollolaan 2, ✉ 1077 BA, ✆ 673 59 22, Fax 570 57 44, 🏖, « Terrace with ≤ canal », ⛶ – |‡| ⇸ ▤ rm TV ☎ P – 🏛 25-200. AE ⓓ E VISA JCB. ※ rest
Meals (open until 11 p.m.) *Lunch 55* – a la carte 59/72 – ☕ 30 – **226 rm** 360/450, 2 suites.

Garden, Dijsselhofplantsoen 7, ✉ 1077 BJ, ✆ 664 21 21, Fax 679 93 56 – |‡| ⇸ TV ☎ P – 🏛 25-150. AE ⓓ E VISA JCB. ※
Meals see rest ***Mangerie De Kersentuin*** below – ☕ 35 – **96 rm** 255/465, 2 suites.

Hilton, Apollolaan 138, ✉ 1077 BG, ✆ 678 07 80, Fax 662 66 88, 🏖, ⛶ – |‡| ⇸ ▤ rest TV ☎ P – 🏛 25-350. AE ⓓ E VISA JCB. ※
Meals ***Roberto's*** (Italian cuisine) *Lunch 50* - a la carte 79/150 – ☕ 38 – **268 rm** 385/615, 3 suites.

Mercure a/d Amstel Ⓜ, Joan Muyskenweg 10, ✉ 1096 CJ, ✆ 665 81 81, Telex 13382, Fax 694 87 35, Fø, ≘s, ⛶ – |‡| ⇸ ▤ rm TV ☎ ♿ P – 🏛 25-450. AE ⓓ E VISA. ※
Meals *Lunch 43* – a la carte 60/80 – ☕ 25 – **178 rm** ☕ 270/290.

Memphis without rest, De Lairessestraat 87, ✉ 1071 NX, ✆ 673 31 41, Telex 12450, Fax 673 73 12 – |‡| ⇸ TV ☎ – 🏛 25-60. AE ⓓ E VISA
☕ 28 – **74 rm** 295/370.

Toro ⛰ without rest, Koningslaan 64, ✉ 1075 AG, ✆ 673 72 23, Fax 675 00 31, « Waterside terrace, overlooking the park » – |‡| TV ☎. AE ⓓ E VISA. ※
22 rm ☕ 170/200.

Lairesse without rest, De Lairessestraat 7, ✉ 1071 NR, ✆ 671 95 96, Telex 14275, Fax 671 17 56 – |‡| TV ☎. AE ⓓ E VISA JCB
34 rm ☕ 190/310.

Jan Luyken without rest, Jan Luykenstraat 58, ✉ 1071 CS, ✆ 573 07 30, Telex 16254, Fax 676 38 41 – |‡| TV ☎ 🚗 – 🏛 25-60. AE ⓓ E VISA KZ r
63 rm ☕ 290/435.

Cok Hotels without rest, Koninginneweg 34, ✉ 1075 CZ, ✆ 664 61 11, Fax 664 53 04 – |‡| TV ☎ – 🏛 25-80. AE ⓓ E VISA
155 rm ☕ 155/260.

Villa Borgmann ⛰ without rest, Koningslaan 48, ✉ 1075 AE, ✆ 673 52 52, Fax 676 25 80 – |‡| TV ☎. AE ⓓ E VISA JCB. ※
15 rm ☕ 135/205.

La Casaló ⛰ without rest, Amsteldijk 862, ✉ 1079 LN, ✆ 642 36 80, Fax 644 74 09, ≤, « Floating hotel on the Amstel » – TV ☎. AE ⓓ E VISA
4 rm ☕ 165.

XXX **Ciel Bleu** - (at Okura H.), 23th floor, Ferdinand Bolstraat 333, ✉ 1072 LH, ✆ 678 71 11, Fax 671 23 44, ≤ town, ⛶ – ▤ P. AE ⓓ E VISA. ※
Meals (dinner only until 11 p.m.) 75/118.

XX **Le Garage,** Ruysdaelstraat 54, ✉ 1071 XE, ✆ 679 71 76, Fax 662 22 49, Open until 11 p.m., « Artistic atmosphere in a contemporary and cosmopolitan brasserie » – AE ⓓ E VISA. ※
Meals *Lunch 39* – 70.

XX **Mangerie De Kerstentuin** - (at Garden H.), Dijsselhofplantsoen 7, ✉ 1077 BJ, ✆ 664 21 21, Fax 679 93 56 – ▤. AE ⓓ E VISA JCB. ※
closed Sunday, 31 December and 1 January – **Meals** (dinner only until 11 p.m.) 60/70.

XX **Yamazato** - (at Okura H.), Ferdinand Bolstraat 333, ✉ 1072 LH, ✆ 678 71 11, Telex 16182, Fax 671 23 44, Japanese cuisine, ⛶ – ▤ P. AE ⓓ E VISA. ※
Meals 30/130.

XX **Beddington's,** Roelof Hartstraat 6, ✉ 1071 VH, ✆ 676 52 01, Fax 671 74 29 – AE ⓓ E VISA JCB. ※
closed lunch Saturday and Monday, Sunday, last week July-first week August and last week December-first week January – **Meals** 55/80.

XX **Keyzer,** Van Baerlestraat 96, ✉ 1071 BB, ✆ 671 14 41, Fax 673 73 53, Pub rest, open until 11.30 p.m. – AE ⓓ E VISA. ※
closed Sunday, Easter, Whitsun and Christmas – **Meals** 58/60.

X **Brasserie Van Baerle,** Van Baerlestraat 158, ✉ 1071 BG, ✆ 679 15 32, Fax 671 71 96, 🏖, Pub rest, open until 11 p.m. – AE ⓓ E VISA
closed Saturday and 25 December-1 January – **Meals** 45/68.

Buitenveldert (RAI)

Holiday Inn, De Boelelaan 2, ✉ 1083 HJ, ☎ 646 23 00, Fax 646 47 90 - |‡| ⇔ ▤ TV ☎ ♿ P - 🏛 25-350. AE ⓓ E VISA JCB
Meals (open until 11 p.m.) 55/70 - ☕ 32 - **261 rm** 360/470, 2 suites.

Novotel, Europaboulevard 10, ✉ 1083 AD, ☎ 541 11 23, Telex 13375, Fax 646 28 23 - |‡| ⇔ ▤ TV ☎ ♿ P - 🏛 25-225. AE ⓓ E VISA JCB
Meals (open until midnight) *Lunch 28* - 43 - ☕ 25 - **598 rm** 248/275, 2 suites.

XXX ✿ **Halvemaan,** van Leyenberghlaan 320 (Gijsbrecht van Aemstelpark), ✉ 1082 GM ☎ 644 03 48, Fax 644 17 77, 🏖, « Terrace with ≤ private lake » - P. AE ⓓ E VISA ✕
closed Saturday, Sunday and 24 December-first week January - **Meals** 95/125, a la carte 82/108
Spec. Foie gras brûlé, Ris de veau meunière et ravioli de ragoût de rognon de veau, Bread and butter pudding.

XX **Rosarium,** Amstelpark 1, ✉ 1083 HZ, ☎ 644 40 85, Fax 646 60 04, 🏖, « Floral park » - P - 🏛 300. AE ⓓ E VISA
closed Sunday - **Meals** *Lunch 43* - 60.

North

Galaxy, Distelkade 21, ✉ 1031 XP, ☎ 634 43 66, Telex 18607, Fax 636 03 45 - |‡| ▤ rest TV ☎ P - 🏛 25-250. AE ⓓ E VISA JCB
Meals a la carte approx. 50 - **280 rm** ☕ 215/250.

Suburbs

by motorway The Hague (A 4) - ✆ 0 20 :

Mercure Airport, Oude Haagseweg 20, ✉ 1066 BW, ☎ 617 90 05, Fax 615 90 27 - |‡| ⇔ ▤ TV ☎ ♿ P - 🏛 25-250. AE ⓓ E VISA. ✕ rest
Meals *Lunch 40* - 43/65 - ☕ 25 - **151 rm** 215/290.

Environs

at Amstelveen S : 11 km - pop. 74 059 - ✆ 0 20.

ℹ Plein 1960 nr 2, ✉ 1181 ZM, ☎ 547 51 11, Fax 647 02 88

Grand Hotel M ⛭, Bovenkerkerweg 81 (S : 2,5 km direction Uithoorn), ✉ 1187 XC ☎ 645 55 58, Fax 641 21 21 - |‡| ⇔ TV ☎ ♿ P. AE ⓓ E VISA JCB. ✕
Meals see rest ***Résidence Fontaine Royale*** below, shuttle service - **81 rm** ☕ 270/300 10 suites.

XXX **De Jonge Dikkert,** Amsterdamseweg 104a, ✉ 1182 HG, ☎ 641 13 78, Fax 645 91 62, 🏖 « 17C windmill » - P. AE ⓓ E VISA JCB
Meals *Lunch 55* - 55/75.

XXX **Résidence Fontaine Royale** - (at Grand Hotel), Dr Willem Dreesweg 1 (S : 2 km, direction Uithoorn), ✉ 1185 VA, ☎ 640 15 01, Fax 640 16 51, 🏖 - ▤ P - 🏛 25-225. AE ⓓ E VISA ✕
closed Saturday lunch, Sunday and Monday dinner - **Meals** *Lunch 30* - a la carte 62/89.

XX **Le Pescadou,** Amsterdamseweg 448, ✉ 1181 BW, ☎ 647 04 43, Seafood - ▤. AE ⓓ E VISA JCB
closed lunch Saturday and Sunday and 15 July-15 August - **Meals** *Lunch 50* - a la carte 75/96

at Badhoevedorp SW : 15 km C Haarlemmermeer pop. 103 684 - ✆ 0 20 :

Dorint, Sloterweg 299, ✉ 1171 VB, ☎ 658 81 11, Fax 659 71 01, ≘s, ⛆, ✕ - |‡| ⇔ ▤ TV ☎ ♿ P - 🏛 25-150. AE ⓓ E VISA JCB
Meals *Lunch 40* - a la carte 53/89 - ☕ 28 - **198 rm** 275/360.

XX **De Herbergh** with rm, Sloterweg 259, ✉ 1171 CP, ☎ 659 26 00, Fax 659 83 90, 🏖 - ▤ rest TV ☎ P. AE E VISA. ✕
Meals *(closed last 2 weeks July-first week August)* a la carte approx. 65 - ☕ 15 - **15 rm** 145

at Ouderkerk aan de Amstel S : 10 km C Amstelveen pop. 74 059 - ✆ 0 20

't Jagershuis, Amstelzijde 2, ✉ 1184 VA, ☎ 496 20 20, Fax 496 45 51, ≤, « Inn with Amstel-side terrace », ⚓ - TV ☎ P - 🏛 30. AE ⓓ E VISA JCB. ✕ rest
Meals *Lunch 50* - a la carte approx. 70 - ☕ 25 - **12 rm** 195/245.

XXX **Paardenburg,** Amstelzijde 55, ✉ 1184 TZ, ☎ 496 12 10, Fax 496 40 17, 🏖, « 19C murals riverside terrace » - P. AE ⓓ E VISA JCB. ✕
closed Sunday - **Meals** *Lunch 60* - 60/135.

XX **Klein Paardenburg,** Amstelzijde 59, ✉ 1184 TZ, ☎ 496 13 35, Fax 496 16 90, 🏖 - AE ⓓ E VISA
closed Sunday, Bank Holidays and late December - **Meals** *Lunch 68* - 75/90.

XX **Het Kampje,** Kerkstraat 56, ✉ 1191 JE, ☎ 496 19 43, Fax 496 57 01, 🏖 - AE E VISA JCB
closed Saturday, Sunday, 23 April-14 May and 23 December-6 January - **Meals** *Lunch 40* 50/60.

at Schiphol (international airport) SW : 15 km 🄲 Haarlemmermeer pop. 103 684 - ☎ 0 20 - Casino, Schiphol airport - Central Terminal ☎ (0 23) 571 80 44, Fax (0 23) 571 62 26

Hilton International, Herbergierstraat 1, ✉ 1118 ZK, ☎ 603 45 67, Telex 15186, Fax 648 09 17, - 25-110. AE O E VISA JCB. rest
Meals *(closed Saturday, Sunday and July-August)* a la carte 57/85 - 37 - **265 rm** 415/605, 1 suite.

Blokzijl Overijssel 🄲 Brederwiede pop. 12 128 210 P 6 and 408 I 3 - ☎ 0 527 - 102 km.

Kaatje bij de Sluis, Brouwerstraat 20, ✉ 8356 DV, ☎ 29 18 33, Fax 29 18 36, <, - P. AE O E VISA
closed Monday, Tuesday, February and late December - **Meals** *(closed Monday, Tuesday and Saturday lunch)* *Lunch 65* - 78/135, a la carte 125/145 - 35 - **8 rm** 195/250
Spec. Feuillantines au saumon cru et caviar, Canard sauvage aux betteraves et olives (August-November), Foie d'oie aux asperges vertes, sauce aux truffes.

Haarlem Noord-Holland 210 H 8 and 408 E 4 - pop. 150 213 - ☎ 0 23 - 24 km.

at Overveen W : 4 km 🄲 Bloemendaal pop. 16 737 - ☎ 0 23 :

XXX **De Bokkedoorns,** Zeeweg 53 (W : 2,5 km), ✉ 2051 EB, ☎ 526 36 00, Fax 527 31 43, « Terrace, < lake surrounded by wooded dunes » - P. AE O E VISA.
closed Monday, Saturday lunch, 30 April lunch, 5 and 24 December and 27 December lunch - **Meals** *Lunch 63* - 90/140, 128/153
Spec. Salade de homard caramélisé et foie d'oie au gingembre, Turbot en habit vert, Perdrix à la choucroute et chanterelles (15 September-1 January).

Hoorn Noord-Holland 210 M 2 and 408 G 4 - pop. 60 979 - ☎ 0 229 - 43 km.

XX **De Oude Rosmolen** (Fonk), Duinsteeg 1, ✉ 1621 ER, ☎ 21 47 52, Fax 21 49 38 - AE O E VISA
closed Thursday, 2 weeks February, 11 to 29 August and 30 December-9 January - **Meals** (dinner only, booking essential) 95/135, a la carte 98/123
Spec. Profiteroles à la mousse de foie gras, Canard nantais et ses abats, Pâtisseries maison.

Zaandam Noord-Holland 🄲 Zaanstad pop. 132 508 210 I 8 and 408 F 4 - ㉗ N - ☎ 0 75 - 16 km.

XXX **De Hoop op d'Swarte Walvis,** Kalverringdijk 15 (Zaanse Schans), ✉ 1509 BT, ☎ 616 56 29, Fax 616 24 76, « 18C residence in a museum village », - P. AE O E VISA JCB
closed Saturday lunch January-April and Sunday - **Meals** *Lunch 63* - 90/125, a la carte 89/113
Spec. Langoustines rôties, tartelette aux St-Jacques, Daurade grillée au verjus et cannelle, Filet d'agneau rôti aux courgettes et tomates.

The HAGUE (Den HAAG or 's-GRAVENHAGE) Zuid-Holland 408 D 5 - pop. 445 279 - ☎ 0 70.

ee : Binnenhof★ : The Knight's Room★ (Ridderzaal) JY - Court pool (Hofvijver) <★ HJY - Lange oorhout★ HJX - Madurodam★ - Scheveningen★★.

useums : Mauritshuis★★★ JY - Prince William V art gallery★ (Schilderijengalerij Prins Willem HY M² - Panorama Mesdag★ HX - Mesdag★ - Municipal★★ (Gemeentehuis) - Bredius★ JY.

at Leidschendam E : 6 km, Elzenlaan 31, ✉ 2267 BL, ☎ (0 70) 399 10 96 - 18 at Rijswijk : 5 km, Delftweg 59, ✉ 2289 AL, ☎ (0 70) 319 24 24 - 18 at Wassenaar NE : 11 km, Groot aesebroekseweg 22, ✉ 2243 EC, ☎ (0 70) 517 98 07 and 9 Hoge Klei 1, ✉ 2243 XZ, (0 70) 517 88 99.

Amsterdam-Schiphol NE : 37 km ☎ (0 20) 601 91 11 - Rotterdam-Zestienhoven SE : 17 km (0 10) 446 34 44.

Kon. Julianaplein 30, ✉ 2595 AA, ☎ 0 6-34 03 50 51, Fax 347 21 02.

nsterdam 55 - Brussels 182 - Rotterdam 24 - Delft 13.

Plan on next page

Centre

Des Indes, Lange Voorhout 54, ✉ 2514 EG, ☎ 363 29 32, Fax 356 28 63, « Late 19C residence » - P - 25-60. AE O E VISA JCB. rm JX s
Meals ***Le Restaurant*** *Lunch 55* - 65/100 - 35 - **70 rm** 505, 6 suites.

Promenade, van Stolkweg 1, ✉ 2585 JL, ☎ 352 51 61, Fax 354 10 46, <, « Collection of modern Dutch paintings » - rest P - 25-400. AE O E VISA JCB
Meals ***La Cigogne*** *(closed Saturday and Sunday)* *Lunch 53* - a la carte 72/88 - 30 - **93 rm** 200/386, 4 suites.

Carlton Ambassador, Sophialaan 2, ✉ 2514 JP, ☎ 363 03 63, Fax 360 05 35, « Dutch and English style interior » - P - 25-120. AE O E VISA JCB HX c
Meals *Lunch 40* - 45/98 - 34 - **70 rm** 209/317, 10 suites.

Sofitel, Koningin Julianaplein 35, ✉ 2595 AA, ☎ 381 49 01, Fax 382 59 27 - - 25-100. AE O E VISA
Meals *Lunch 50* - 50 - 30 - **143 rm** 285/340.

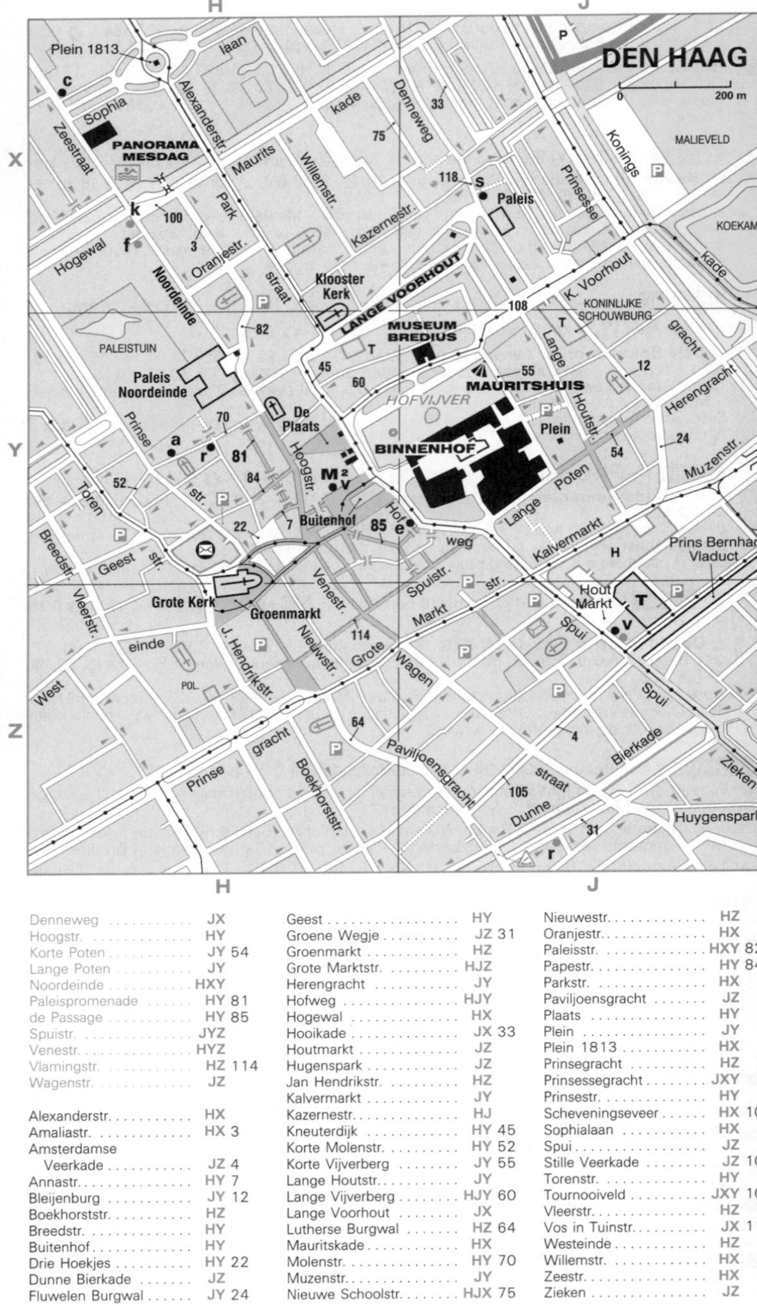

H
J
DEN HAAG
0
200 m
Plein 1813
c
Sophia
laan
Alexanderstr.
Zeestraat
PANORAMA
MESDAG
Maurits
kade
Denneweg
33
75
Willemstr.
Park
Oranjestr.
100
3
k
f
Hogewal
Noordeinde
118
s
Paleis
Kazernestr.
Prinsesse
Konings
MALIEVELD
KOEKAMP
kade
P
Klooster
Kerk
straat
LANGE VOORHOUT
108
K. Voorhout
KONINLIJKE
SCHOUWBURG
gracht
82
PALEISTUIN
MUSEUM
BREDIUS
T
Lange
Houtstr.
12
Paleis
Noordeinde
45
60
55
MAURITSHUIS
HOFVIJVER
Herengracht
70
De
Plaats
Plein
54
24
Muzenstr.
Prinse
a
r
81
BINNENHOF
84
Hoogstr.
M²
v
52
Toren
str.
22
7
Buitenhof
85
e
Hof
weg
Lange
Poten
Kalvermarkt
H
Prins Bernhard
Viaduct
Breedstr.
Geest
str.
Spuistr.
str.
Hout
Markt
T
v
Vleerstr.
Grote Kerk
Groenmarkt
Venestr.
Markt
Spui
eind
114
J. Hendrikstr.
Nieuwstr.
Grote
Wagen
POL.
West
Spui
4
Bierkade
64
gracht
Paviljoensgracht
Zieken
Prinse
Boekhorststr.
straat
105
Dunne
Huygenspark
31
r
X
Y
Z

Bel Air, Johan de Wittlaan 30, ✉ 2517 JR, ✆ 350 20 21, Fax 351 26 82, – – 25-250. – *Meals* *Lunch 40* – a la carte approx. 70 – 28 – **348 rm** 250/265, 2 suites.

Mercure Central without rest, Spui 180, ✉ 2511 BW, ✆ 363 67 00, Telex 32000, Fax 363 93 98, – – 25-110. JZ v
23 – **156 rm** 175/240, 3 suites.

Corona, Buitenhof 42, ✉ 2513 AH, ✆ 363 79 30, Fax 361 57 85, – rest – 30-100. HY v
Meals (Brasserie) 45/50 – 25 – **26 rm** 240/285.

Parkhotel without rest, Molenstraat 53, ✉ 2513 BJ, ✆ 362 43 71, Fax 361 45 25 – – 25-100. HY a
114 rm 153/265.

Novotel, Hofweg 5, ✉ 2511 AA, ✆ 364 88 46, Fax 356 28 89 – – 25-100. HJY e
Meals *Lunch 38* – a la carte 45/60 – 23 – **104 rm** 210, 2 suites.

Paleis without rest, Molenstraat 26, ✉ 2513 BL, ✆ 362 46 21, Fax 361 45 33, – HY r
16 – **20 rm** 155/219.

XXX **De Hoogwerf,** Zijdelaan 20, ✉ 2594 BV, ✆ 347 55 14, Fax 381 95 96, « 17C farm-house, garden » –
closed Sunday and Bank Holidays except Christmas – **Meals** *Lunch 45* – 55/125.

XXX **Da Roberto,** Noordeinde 196, ✉ 2514 GS, ✆ 346 49 77, Fax 362 52 86, Italian cuisine – HX k
closed Saturday lunch and Sunday – **Meals** *Lunch 53* – a la carte approx. 85.

XXX **Royal Dynasty,** Noordeinde 123, ✉ 2514 GG, ✆ 365 25 98, Fax 365 25 22, Asian cuisine – HX k
closed Monday – **Meals** 50/68.

XX ✿ **'t Ganzenest** (Visbeen), Groenewegje 115, ✉ 2515 LP, ✆ 389 67 09, Fax 380 07 41 – JZ r
closed Monday, Tuesday, Easter, Whitsun, 3 weeks August and first week January – **Meals** (dinner only) 53/85, – a la carte approx. 80
Spec. Carpaccio de thon mariné à la vinaigrette de soja, Crème de witlof aux St-Jacques (October-April), Dorade à la purée d'aubergines et tomates confites (May-August).

XX **La Grande Bouffe,** Maziestraat 10, ✉ 2514 GT, ✆ 360 27 23 – HX f
closed lunch Saturday and Sunday, Monday and 30 July-26 August – **Meals** *Lunch 45* – 55/68.

XX **Shirasagi,** Spui 170, ✉ 2511 BW, ✆ 346 47 00, Fax 346 26 01, Japanese cuisine – JZ v
closed lunch Saturday, Sunday and Monday – **Meals** 45/115.

at Scheveningen C 's-Gravenhage – 0 70 – Seaside resort★★ – Casino Kurhaus, Gevers Deijnootplein 30 ✆ 351 26 21, Fax 354 31 83.

Gevers Deijnootweg 1134, ✉ 2586 BX, ✆ 0-6 34 03 50 51, Fax 352 04 26

Kurhaus, Gevers Deijnootplein 30, ✉ 2586 CK, ✆ 416 26 36, Fax 416 26 46, « Former late 19C concert hall » – – 35-480. rest
Meals see rest ***Kandinsky*** below – ***Kurzaal*** (Buffets) 55/63 – 40 – **233 rm** 380/440, 8 suites.

Carlton Beach, Gevers Deijnootweg 201, ✉ 2586 HZ, ✆ 354 14 14, Fax 352 00 20, – – 30-250.
Meals (open until midnight) a la carte approx. 60 – 28 – **183 rm** 235/275.

Europa, Zwolsestraat 2, ✉ 2587 VJ, ✆ 351 26 51, Fax 350 64 73, – – 25-450.
Meals *Lunch 35* – a la carte 55/95 – 23 – **173 rm** 210/325, 1 suite.

XXXX **Kandinsky** - (at Kurhaus H.), Gevers Deijnootplein 30, ✉ 2586 CK, ✆ 416 26 36, Fax 416 26 46, –
closed Saturday lunch, Sunday and 24 and 31 December – **Meals** (dinner only July-August) *Lunch 55* – 80/112.

XXX **Seinpost,** Zeekant 60, ✉ 2586 AD, ✆ 355 52 50, Fax 355 50 93, Seafood –
closed Saturday lunch, Sunday and Bank Holidays – **Meals** *Lunch 53* – 58/65 b.i.

XXX **Radèn Mas,** Gevers Deijnootplein 125, ✉ 2586 CR, ✆ 354 54 32, Fax 354 54 32, Partly Indonesian cuisine –
Meals *Lunch 30* – 48/95.

XX **China Delight,** Dr Lelykade 116, ✉ 2583 CN, ✆ 355 54 50, Fax 354 66 52, Chinese cuisine –
Meals *Lunch 19* – a la carte 49/79.

XX **Bali,** Badhuisweg 1, ✉ 2587 CA, ✆ 350 24 34, Fax 354 03 63, Indonesian cuisine –
Meals (dinner only) 55/70.

Environs

at Leidschendam E : 6 km - pop. 34 038 - ☎ 0 70 :

Green Park, Weigelia 22, ✉ 2262 AB, ☎ 320 92 80, Fax 327 49 07, ←, ⛹ - 🛗 ▤ rest 📺 ☎ 🅿 - 🔊 25-200. AE ⓓ E VISA
Meals *Lunch 38* - 43/58 - **92 rm** ☕ 250/290, 4 suites.

XXX ✿ **Villa Rozenrust,** Veursestraatweg 104, ✉ 2265 CG, ☎ 327 74 60, Fax 327 50 62, 🏠, « Terrace » - 🅿. AE ⓓ E VISA
closed Saturday lunch, Sunday and 29 July-17 August - **Meals** *Lunch 63* - 90/125, a la carte approx. 110
Spec. Dégustation de pâtes, Turbot grillé aux pâtes noires, Agneau de lait au romarin (February-June).

at Voorburg E : 5 km - pop. 39 919 - ☎ 0 70 :

Cadett Ⓜ, Stationsplein 8, ✉ 2275 AZ, ☎ 337 37 37, Fax 337 37 00, 🏠 - 🛗 ⚡ ▤ 📺 ☎ ♿ 🚗 - 🔊 25-160. AE ⓓ E VISA JCB
Meals (buffets) *Lunch 30* - 43 - ☕ 18 - **120 rm** 149/189.

XXX **Savelberg** 🔇 with rm, Oosteinde 14, ✉ 2271 EH, ☎ 387 20 81, Fax 387 77 15, ←, 🏠, « 17C residence with terrace in public park » - 🛗 ⚡ 📺 ☎ 🅿 - 🔊 35. AE ⓓ E VISA JCB
closed 24 December-1 January - **Meals** *(closed Saturday lunch, Sunday and Monday) Lunch 58* - a la carte 98/121 - **14 rm** ☕ 250/495.

XX **Villa la Ruche,** Prinses Mariannelaan 71, ✉ 2275 BB, ☎ 386 01 10, Fax 386 50 64 - ▤. AE ⓓ E VISA
closed Sunday and late December - **Meals** *Lunch 45* - 50.

X **Papermoon,** Herenstraat 175, ✉ 2271 CE, ☎ 387 31 61, Fax 386 80 36, 🏠 - AE E. ✂
closed Monday, last 3 weeks July and last week December-first week January - **Meals** (dinner only) 40/53.

at Wassenaar NE : 11 km - pop. 25 754 - ☎ 0 70 :

Aub. de Kieviet 🔇, Stoeplaan 27, ✉ 2243 CX, ☎ 511 92 32, Fax 511 09 69, 🏠, « Floral terrace » - 🛗 ⚡ ▤ 📺 ☎ ♿ 🅿 - 🔊 25-50. AE ⓓ E VISA JCB
Lunch 40 - 50/60 - ☕ 30 - **23 ch** 225/390, 1 suite.

ROTTERDAM Zuid-Holland 212 ⑤ and 408 E 6 ㉕ N - pop. 598 521 - ☎ 0 10 - Casino JY, Weena 624 ✉ 3012 CN, ☎ 414 77 99, Fax 414 92 33.

See : Lijnbaan★ (Shopping centre) JKY - St. Laurence Church (Grote- of St-Laurenskerk) : interior★ KY - Euromast★ (Tower) ✻★★, ←★ JZ - The harbour★★★ ⛴ KZ.

Museums : History Museum Het Schielandshuis★ KY **M⁴** - Boymans-van Beuningen★★★ JZ - History "De Dubbelde Palmboom"★.

Envir : SE : 7 km, Kinderdijk Windmils★★.

⛳9 Kralingseweg 200, ✉ 3062 CG, ☎ 453 24 97, - ⛳18 at Capelle aan den IJssel, 's Gravenweg 311, ✉ 2905 LB, ☎ (0 10) 442 21 09 - ⛳9 at Rhoon SW : 11 km, Veerweg 2a, ✉ 3161 EX, ☎ (0 10) 501 79 28.

✈ Zestienhoven ☎ 446 34 44.

⛴ Europoort to Kingston-upon-Hull : North Sea Ferries ☎ (0 181) 25 55 00, Fax (0 181) 25 52 15 (information) and 25 55 55 (reservations).

ℹ Coolsingel 67, ✉ 3012 AC, ☎ 0 6-34 03 40 65, Fax 413 01 24 - Central Station, Stationsplein 1, ✉ 3013 AJ, ☎ 0-6-34 03 40 65 - at Schiedam W : 6 km, Buitenhavenweg 9, ✉ 3119 BC, ☎ (0 10) 473 30 00, Fax 473 66 95.

Amsterdam 76 - The Hague 24 - Antwerp 103 - Brussels 148 - Utrecht 57.

Plan opposite

Centre

Parkhotel, Westersingel 70, ✉ 3015 LB, ☎ 436 36 11, Telex 22020, Fax 436 42 12, ⛹, ≘ - 🛗 ⚡ ▤ 📺 ☎ 🅿 - 🔊 25-70. AE ⓓ E VISA JCB. ✂ rm JZ a
Meals *Lunch 43* - a la carte approx. 90 - **187 rm** ☕ 335/385, 2 suites.

Hilton, Weena 10, ✉ 3012 CM, ☎ 414 40 44, Fax 411 88 84 - 🛗 ⚡ ▤ rest 📺 ☎ ♿ 🅿 - 🔊 25-350. AE ⓓ E VISA JCB. ✂ rest KY a
Meals *(closed Saturday lunch) Lunch 35* - a la carte approx. 60 - ☕ 40 - **247 rm** 345/545, 7 suites.

Holiday Inn, Schouwburgplein 1, ✉ 3012 CK, ☎ 433 38 00, Fax 414 54 82 - 🛗 ⚡ 📺 ☎ - 🔊 25-300. AE ⓓ E VISA. ✂ JY e
Meals (dinner only July-August and weekends) *Lunch 45* - 45/65 - ☕ 33 - **97 rm** 275/350 2 suites.

Atlanta, Aert van Nesstraat 4, ✉ 3012 CA, ☎ 411 04 20, Fax 413 53 20 - 🛗 ⚡ 📺 ☎ 🚗 - 🔊 25-400. AE ⓓ E VISA KY e
Meals (dinner only) a la carte approx. 70 - ☕ 23 - **163 rm** 200/265, 1 suite.

ROTTERDAM

Street	Grid	No.
Beursplein	KY	9
Binnenweg	JY	
Botersloot	KY	13
Coolsingel	KY	
Hoogstr.	KY	
Karel Doormanstr.	JY	
Korte Hoogstr.	KY	46
Korte Lijnbaan	JY	48
Lijnbaan	JKY	
Stadhuispl.	KY	93
Aert van Nesstr.	JKY	4
Binnenwegpl.	KY	10
Delftsepl	JY	21
Delftsestr.	JY	22
G.J. de Jonghweg	JZ	24
Grotekerkpl.	KY	30
Haagseveer	KY	33
Jonker Fransstr.	KY	39
Keizerstr.	KY	40
Kruiskade	JKY	51
Kruisplein	JY	52
Nieuwestr.	KY	70
van Oldenbarneveltstr.	JKY	72
Pompenburg	KY	78
Posthoornstr.	KY	79
Scheepstimmermanslaan	KZ	85
Schouwburgplein	JY	88
Veerhaven	KZ	102
Veerkade	KZ	103
van Vollenhovenstr.	KZ	107
Westewagenstr.	KY	110
Witte de Withstr.	KZ	112

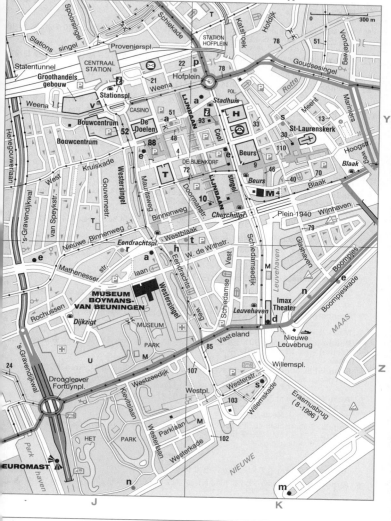

Don't get lost, use **Michelin Maps** which are kept up to date.

New York, Koninginnehoofd 1, ✉ 3072 AD, ☎ 439 05 00, Fax 484 27 01, ≤, 🏞, « Former head office of the Holland-America Line maritime company » – |‡| TV ☎ P – 🏛 25-200 AE ⦿ E VISA. ✗ KZ m
Meals (open until 11 p.m.) *Lunch 35* – 43 – ☕ 15 – **72 rm** 135/250.

Inntel, Leuvehaven 80, ✉ 3011 EA, ☎ 413 41 39, Fax 413 32 22, ≤, 🏋, ≘s, 🏊 – |‡| ⇔ ▤ rest TV ☎ P – 🏛 25-220. AE ⦿ E VISA KZ c
Meals *(open until 11 p.m.)* *Lunch 28* – 40/61 – ☕ 23 – **150 rm** 225/295.

Zuiderparkhotel, Dordtsestraatweg 285, ✉ 3083 AJ, ☎ 485 00 55, Fax 485 63 04, ≘s 🏊 – |‡| TV ☎ P – 🏛 25-300. AE ⦿ E VISA. ✗ rest
Meals 45/83 – ☕ 18 – **117 rm** 148/175, 3 suites.

Pax without rest, Schiekade 658, ✉ 3032 AK, ☎ 466 33 44, Fax 467 52 78 – |‡| TV ☎ P AE ⦿ E VISA JCB
45 rm ☕ 135/250.

Van Walsum, Mathenesserlaan 199, ✉ 3014 HC, ☎ 436 32 75, Telex 20010, Fax 436 44 10 – |‡| TV ☎ P. AE ⦿ E VISA. ✗ rest JZ e
closed 23 December-2 January – **Meals** (dinner residents only) – **25 rm** ☕ 85/160.

Savoy, Hoogstraat 81, ✉ 3011 PJ, ☎ 413 92 80, Fax 404 57 12 – |‡| TV ☎. AE ⦿ E VISA JCB. ✗ rest
Meals *(closed Saturday and Sunday)* (dinner only) a la carte 43/73 – ☕ 25 – **94 rm** 160/175

Scandia, Willemsplein 1, ✉ 3016 DN, ☎ 413 47 90, Fax 412 78 90, ≤ – |‡| ⇔ ▤ rest TV ☎ – 🏛 25-70. AE ⦿ E VISA. ✗ KZ s
closed 24 December-1 January – **Meals** *Lunch 19* – a la carte 51/69 – **104 rm** ☕ 135/190.

XXXX ✿✿ **Parkheuvel** (Helder), Heuvellaan 21, ✉ 3016 GL, ☎ 436 07 66, Fax 436 71 40, 🏞, « Terrace and ≤ maritime trade » – P. AE ⦿ E VISA JZ n
closed Saturday lunch, Sunday and 27 December-2 January – **Meals** *Lunch 88* – 88/138, a la carte 100/123
Spec. Pot-au-feu tiède à la vinaigrette de moutarde, Turbot à la mousseline d'anchois, ragoût de champignons et jus de veau, Délice de veau croquant au foie gras et aux morilles.

XXX **Old Dutch,** Rochussenstraat 20, ✉ 3015 EK, ☎ 436 03 44, Fax 436 78 26, 🏞 – ▤. AE ⦿ E VISA JZ
closed Saturday, Sunday and Bank Holidays – **Meals** *Lunch 53* – 63/78.

XXX **Radèn Mas** 1st floor, Kruiskade 72, ✉ 3012 EH, ☎ 411 72 44, Fax 411 97 11, Indonesian cuisine, « Exotic decor » – ▤. AE ⦿ E VISA. ✗ JY a
Meals *Lunch 33* – a la carte 75/90.

XX **Brasserie La Vilette,** Westblaak 160, ✉ 3012 KM, ☎ 414 86 92, Fax 414 33 91 – ▤. AE ⦿ E VISA JCB JKY t
closed Sunday, 22 July-11 August and 22 December-1 January – **Meals** *Lunch 55* – 55/70.

XX **La Bourgogne,** Delftsestraat 6, ✉ 3013 CJ, ☎ 411 55 75, Fax 411 19 45 – ▤ P. AE ⦿ E VISA JCB JKY p
Meals *Lunch 45* – a la carte 52/73.

XX **De Castellane,** Eendrachtsweg 22, ✉ 3012 LB, ☎ 414 11 59, Fax 214 08 97, 🏞 – AE ⦿ E VISA JZ h
closed Sunday, Bank Holidays, 29 July-19 August and 23 December-5 January – **Meals** *Lunch 48* – 73/95.

XX **Brancatelli,** Boompjes 264, ✉ 3011 XD, ☎ 411 41 51, Fax 404 57 34, Italian cuisine, open until 11 p.m. – ▤. AE ⦿ E VISA. ✗ KZ n
Meals *Lunch 53* – a la carte 63/81.

XX **Boompjes,** Boompjes 701, ✉ 3011 XZ, ☎ 413 60 70, Fax 413 70 87, ≤ Nieuwe Maas (Meuse) – ▤. AE ⦿ E VISA. ✗ KZ e
Meals *Lunch 55* – 70/98.

X **Silhouet** Euromast tower, Parkhaven 20, ✉ 3016 GM, ☎ 436 48 11, Fax 436 22 80, ✳ city and port – ▤. AE ⦿ E VISA. ✗ JZ
closed Sunday, Monday and Bank Holidays – **Meals** (dinner only) a la carte 65/83.

X **Anak Mas,** Meent 72a, ✉ 3011 JN, ☎ 414 84 87, Fax 412 44 74, Indonesian cuisine – ▤ AE ⦿ E VISA JCB KY s
closed Sunday – **Meals** (dinner only) 48.

X **Engels,** Stationsplein 45, ✉ 3013 AK, ☎ 411 95 50, Fax 413 94 21, Multinational cuisines – ▤ P – 🏛 25-800. AE ⦿ E VISA. ✗ JY v
Meals a la carte approx. 45.

Suburbs

Airport N : 2,5 km 🄲 Rotterdam – ✪ 0 10 :

Airport, Vliegveldweg 59, ✉ 3043 NT, ☎ 462 55 66, Fax 462 22 66 – |‡| ⇔ TV ☎ ♿ P – 🏛 25-300. AE ⦿ E VISA
Meals 43/50 – **97 rm** ☕ 205/260, 1 suite.

at Hillegersberg NE : 10 km 🄲 Rotterdam – ✪ 0 10 :

XX **Lommerrijk,** Straatweg 99, ✉ 3054 AB, ☎ 422 00 11, Fax 422 64 96, ≤, 🏞 – ▤ P – 🏛 250. AE ⦿ E VISA
closed Monday – **Meals** a la carte 48/63.

at Kralingen E : 2 km 🄲 Rotterdam - ☎ 0 10 :

Novotel Brainpark, K.P. van der Mandelelaan 150 (near A 16), ✉ 3062 MB, ☎ 453 07 77, Telex 24109, Fax 453 15 03 - 25-625. AE E VISA
Meals (open until 11 p.m.) *Lunch 38* - a la carte approx. 60 - 23 - **196 rm** 169.

In den Rustwat, Honingerdijk 96, ✉ 3062 NX, ☎ 413 41 10, Fax 404 85 40, « 16C residence » - AE E VISA
closed Saturday lunch, Sunday and Bank Holidays - **Meals** *Lunch 60* - 89/105.

at Ommoord NE : 10 km 🄲 Rotterdam - ☎ 0 10 :

Keizershof, Martin Luther Kingweg 7, ✉ 3069 EW, ☎ 455 13 33, Fax 456 80 23, - AE E VISA
closed 24 and 31 December - **Meals** 40/90.

Europoort zone W : 25 km - ☎ 0 181 :

De Beer Europoort, Europaweg 210 (N 15), ✉ 3198 LD, ☎ 26 23 77, Fax 26 29 23, ←, - 25-180. AE E VISA
Meals *Lunch 33* - a la carte approx. 65 - **78 rm** 150/190.

Environs

at Capelle aan den IJssel E : 8 km - pop. 59 364 - ☎ 0 10 :

Barbizon, Barbizonlaan 2 (near A 20), ✉ 2908 MA, ☎ 456 44 55, Telex 26514, Fax 456 78 58, ←, - 30-250. AE E VISA JCB.
Meals *Lunch 48* - 48/68 - 30 - **101 rm** 225/275.

at Rhoon S : 10 km 🄲 Albrandswaard pop. 14 920 - ☎ 0 10 :

Het Kasteel van Rhoon, Dorpsdijk 63, ✉ 3161 KD, ☎ 501 88 96, Fax 501 24 18, ←, « Inside the outbuildings of the mansion » - AE E VISA
closed 5, 25 and 26 December - **Meals** 65/93.

at Schiedam W : 6 km - pop. 72 515 - ☎ 0 10 :

Novotel, Hargalaan 2 (near A 20), ✉ 3118 JA, ☎ 471 33 22, Fax 470 06 56, - rest - 25-150. AE E VISA
Meals (open until 11 p.m.) a la carte approx. 50 - 23 - **133 rm** 159.

La Duchesse, Maasboulevard 9, ✉ 3114 HB, ☎ 426 46 26, Fax 473 25 01, ← Nieuwe Maas (Meuse), - AE E VISA
closed Saturday lunch, Sunday and 31 December - **Meals** *Lunch 55* - 65/85.

Aub. Hosman Frères 1st floor, Korte Dam 10, ✉ 3111 BG, ☎ 426 40 96, Fax 473 00 08, Collection of alcoholic spirits - AE E VISA
closed Sunday and Monday - **Meals** *Lunch 53* - a la carte approx. 75.

Czech Republic

Česká Republika

PRAGUE

PRACTICAL INFORMATION

LOCAL CURRENCY

Crown : 100 CRT = 3.76 US $ (Jan. 96)

PRICES

Prices may change if goods and service costs in the Czech Republic are revised and it is therefore always advisable to confirm rates with the hotelier when making a reservation.

FOREIGN EXCHANGE

It is strongly advised against changing money other than in banks, exchange offices or authorised offices such as large hotels, tourist offices, etc... Banks are usually open on weekdays from 8am to 5pm.

HOTEL RESERVATIONS

In case of difficulties in finding a room through our hotel selection, it is always possible to apply to AVE Wilsonova 2, Prague 1, ✆ 236 25 60. CEDOK Václavské nám 55, Prague 1 ✆ 26 38 83.

POSTAL SERVICES

Post offices are open from 8am to 6pm on weekdays and 2pm on Saturdays.
The **General Post Office** is open 24 hours a day : Jindřišska 14, Prague 1, ✆ 26 41 93.

SHOPPING IN PRAGUE

In the index of street names, those printed in red are where the principal shops are found. Typical goods to be bought include embroidery, puppets, glass, porcelain, ceramics... Shops are generally open from 9am to 7pm.

TIPPING

Hotel, restaurant and café bills include service in the total charge but it is up to you to tip the staff.

CAR HIRE

The international car hire companies have branches in Prague. Your hotel porter should be able to give details and help you with your arrangements.

BREAKDOWN SERVICE

A 24 hour – breakdown service is operated by YELLOW ANGELS, Limuzská 12, Prague 10, ✆ 77 34 55.

SPEED LIMITS - SEAT BELTS - MOTORWAYS TAX

The maximum permitted speed on motorways is 110 km/h - 68 mph, 90 km/h - 56 mph on other roads and 60 km/h - 37 mph in built up areas except where a lower speed limit is indicated.
The wearing of seat belts is compulsory for drivers and passengers.
Driving on motorways is subject to the purchase of a single rate annual road tax obtainable from frontier posts and tourist offices.
In the Czech Republic, drivers must not drink alcoholic beverage at all.

Prague

(PRAHA) Česká Republika 976 F 3 – Pop. 1 215 943 – ✆ 02.

See : Castle District★★★ (Hradčany) ABY : Prague Castle★★★ (Pražský Hrad) BY, St Vitus' Cathedral★★★ (Katedrála sv. Víta) BY, Royal Palace★★ (Královský palác) BY, St George's Basilica and Convent★★ (National Gallery's Collection of Old Czech Art★★★) (Bazilika sv. Jiří/Jiřský Klašter) BY, Hradčany Square★ (Hradčanské náměstí) AY **37**, Schwarzenberg Palace★ (Schwarzenberský Palác) ABY **N**, Loretto★★ (Loreta) AY, Strahov Monastery★★ (Strahovský Klášter) AY – Lesser Town★★★ (Malá Strana) BY : Charles Bridge★★★ (Karlův Most) BCY, Lesser Town Square★★ (Malostranské náměstí) BY, St Nicholas Church★★★ (Sv. Mikuláš) BY, Nerudova Street★★ (Nerudova) BY, Wallenstein Palace★★ (Valdštejnský Palác) BY – Old Town★★★ (Staré Město) CY : Old Town Square★★★ (Staroměstské náměstí) CY, Astronomical Clock★★ (Orloj) CY **B**, Old Town Hall – Extensive view★★★ (Staroměstská radnice) CYB, St Nicolas'★ (Sv. Mikuláš) CY, Týn Church★ (Týnský chrám) CY, Jewish Quarter★★★ (Josefov) CY, Old-New Synagogue★★ (Staronová Synagóga) CY **C**, Old Jewish Cemetery★★ (Starý židovský hřbitov) CY, St Agnes Convent★★ (National Gallery's Collection of 19 C Czech Painting and Sculpture) (Anežský klášter) CY, Celetná Street★★ (Celetná) CDY, Powder Tower★ (Prašná Brána) DY, House of the black Madonna★ (Dům u černe Matky boží) CDY **E**, Municipal House★★ (Obecní Dům) DY **F** – New Town★★★ (Nové Město) CDZ : Wenceslas Square★★★ (Václavské náměstí) CDYZ.

Museums : National Gallery★★★ (Národní Galérie) AY, National Museum★ (Národní muzeum) DZ, National Theatre★★ (Národní divadlo) CZ, Decorative Arts Museum★ (Umělecko průmyslové muzeum) CY **M¹**, City Museum★ (Prague model★★) (Muzeum hlavního města Prahy) DY **M²**, Vila America★ (Dvořák Museum) DZ.

Outskirts : Karlštejn Castle SW : 30 km ET – Konopiště Castle SW : 40 km FT.

18 Golf Club Praha, Motol-Praha 5, ✆ 651 24 64

✈ Ruzyně (Prague Airport) NW 20 km, by road n° 7 ✆ 36 77 60.
Bus to airport : ČSA Bus at airlines Terminal Rásnovka Street
CZECH AIRLINES (ČESKÉ AEROLINIE) Revolučni Street 1, PRAGUE 1 ✆ 24 80 61 11.

ℹ Prague Information Service : Na Příkope 20 (main office), Staroměstské nám 22, and Main Railway Station ✆ 187

CEDOK : Na přikopě 18, Prague 1 ✆ 24 19 71 11, Fax 232 16 56.

Berlin 344 – Dresden 152 – Munich 384 – Nurnberg 287 – Wroclaw 272 – Vienna 291.

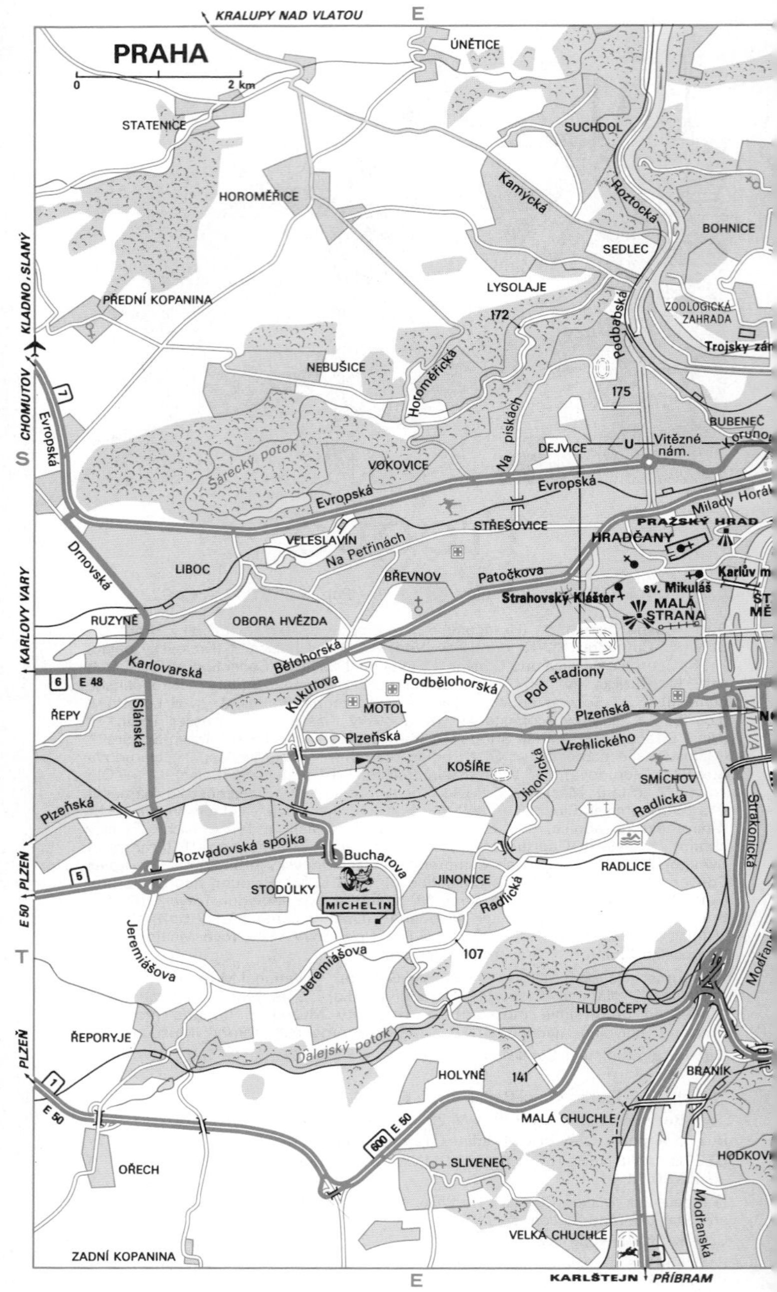

PRAHA
0
2 km
KRALUPY NAD VLATOU
E
ÚNĚTICE
STATENICE
SUCHDOL
HOROMĚŘICE
Kamýcká
Roztocká
BOHNICE
SEDLEC
KLADNO, SLANÝ
PŘEDNÍ KOPANINA
LYSOLAJE
Podbabská
ZOOLOGICKÁ ZAHRADA
172
Trojský zá
NEBUŠICE
Horoměřická
175
CHOMUTOV
Evropská
Na piskách
BUBENEČ
S
Šárecký potok
DEJVICE
Vítězné nám.
VOKOVICE
Evropská
Evropská
Milady Horák
STŘEŠOVICE
PRAŽSKÝ HRAD
VELESLAVÍN
HRADČANY
Drnovská
Na Petřinách
LIBOC
BŘEVNOV
Patočkova
Karlův m
KARLOVY VARY
sv. Mikuláš
Strahovský Klášter
MALÁ STRANA
RUZYNĚ
OBORA HVĚZDA
Bělohorská
Karlovarská
6
E 48
Kukulova
Podbělohorská
Pod stadiony
ŘEPY
Slánská
MOTOL
Plzeňská
Plzeňská
Vrchlického
VLTAVA
KOŠÍŘE
Jinonická
SMÍCHOV
Plzeňská
Radlická
Strakonická
PLZEŇ
Rozvadovská spojka
Bucharova
5
RADLICE
STODŮLKY
JINONICE
MICHELIN
Radlická
E 50
Jeremiášova
Jeremiášova
107
T
Modřanská
HLUBOČEPY
ŘEPORYJE
Dalejský potok
PLZEŇ
7
HOLYNĚ
141
BRANÍK
E 50
600
E 50
MALÁ CHUCHLE
OŘECH
SLIVENEC
HODKOV
Modřanská
VELKÁ CHUCHLE
ZADNÍ KOPANINA
4
KARLŠTEJN
PŘÍBRAM
E

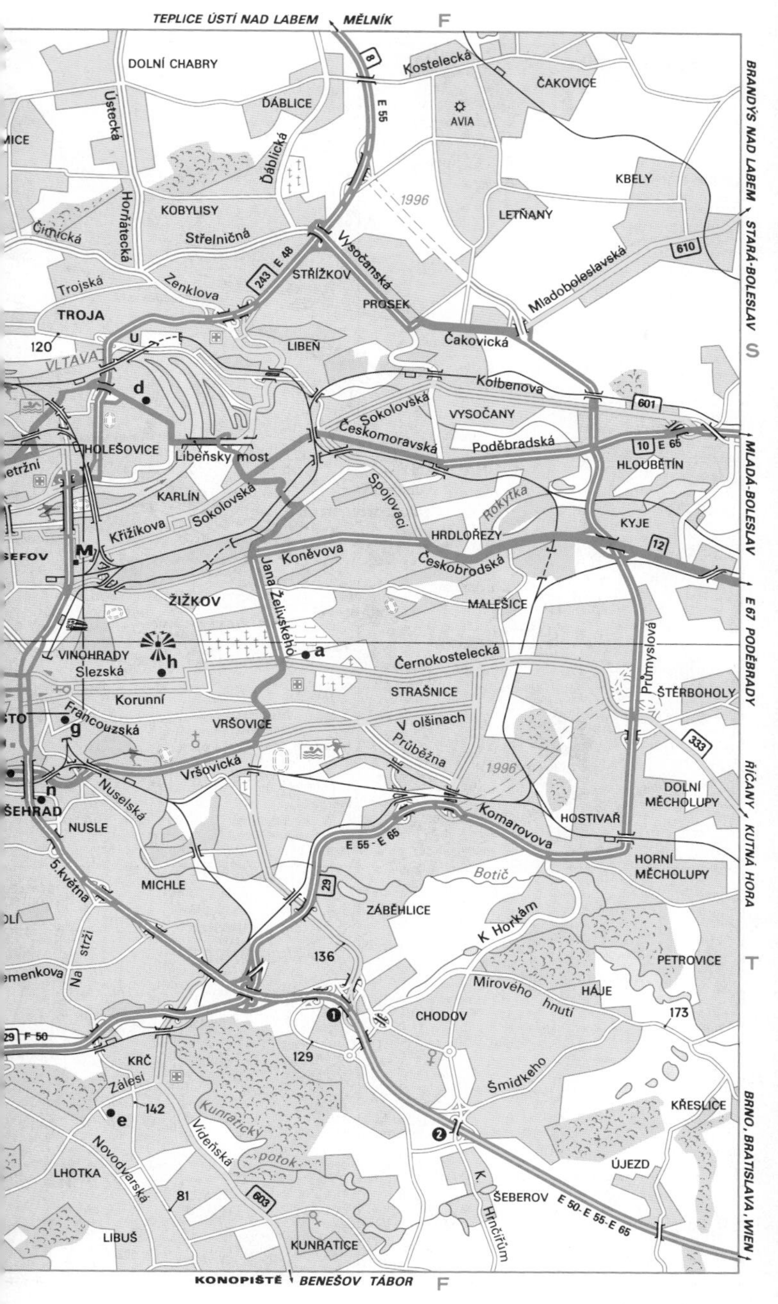
TEPLICE ÚSTÍ NAD LABEM
MĚLNÍK
F
BRANDÝS NAD LABEM
STARÁ-BOLESLAV
S
MLADÁ-BOLESLAV
E 67 PODĚBRADY
ŘÍČANY
KUTNÁ HORA
T
BRNO, BRATISLAVA, WIEN
KONOPIŠTĚ
BENEŠOV TÁBOR
DOLNÍ CHABRY
ĎÁBLICE
ČAKOVICE
AVIA
KBELY
LETŇANY
KOBYLISY
Střelničná
Kostelecká
Ďáblická
Ústecká
Hořňátecká
Čimická
Trojská
Zenklova
TROJA
STŘÍŽKOV
Vysočanská
PROSEK
Mladoboleslavská
Čakovická
LIBEŇ
VLTAVA
Kolbenova
VYSOČANY
Sokolovská
Českomoravská
Poděbradská
HLOUBĚTÍN
HOLEŠOVICE
Libeňský most
KARLÍN
Křižíkova
Spojovací
Rokytka
KYJE
HRDLOŘEZY
Koněvova
Českobrodská
Jana Želivského
MALEŠICE
ŽIŽKOV
VINOHRADY
Slezská
Černokostelecká
STRAŠNICE
ŠTĚRBOHOLY
Korunní
Francouzská
VRŠOVICE
V olšinach
Průmyslová
Průběžná
Vršovická
Nuselská
NUSLE
DOLNÍ MĚCHOLUPY
HOSTIVAŘ
Komarovova
HORNÍ MĚCHOLUPY
E 55 - E 65
Botič
MICHLE
ZÁBĚHLICE
K Horkám
5.května
Na strži
PETROVICE
Mírového hnutí
HÁJE
CHODOV
KRČ
Zálesí
Kunratický potok
Videňská
Novodvorská
Šmidkeho
KŘESLICE
ÚJEZD
LHOTKA
ŠEBEROV
K. Hrnčířům
E 50- E 55- E 65
LIBUŠ
KUNRATICE
1996
E 55
E 48
E 65
F 50
8
243
610
601
10
12
333
29
603
120
136
129
142
173
81
a
d
e
g
h
n
u
M

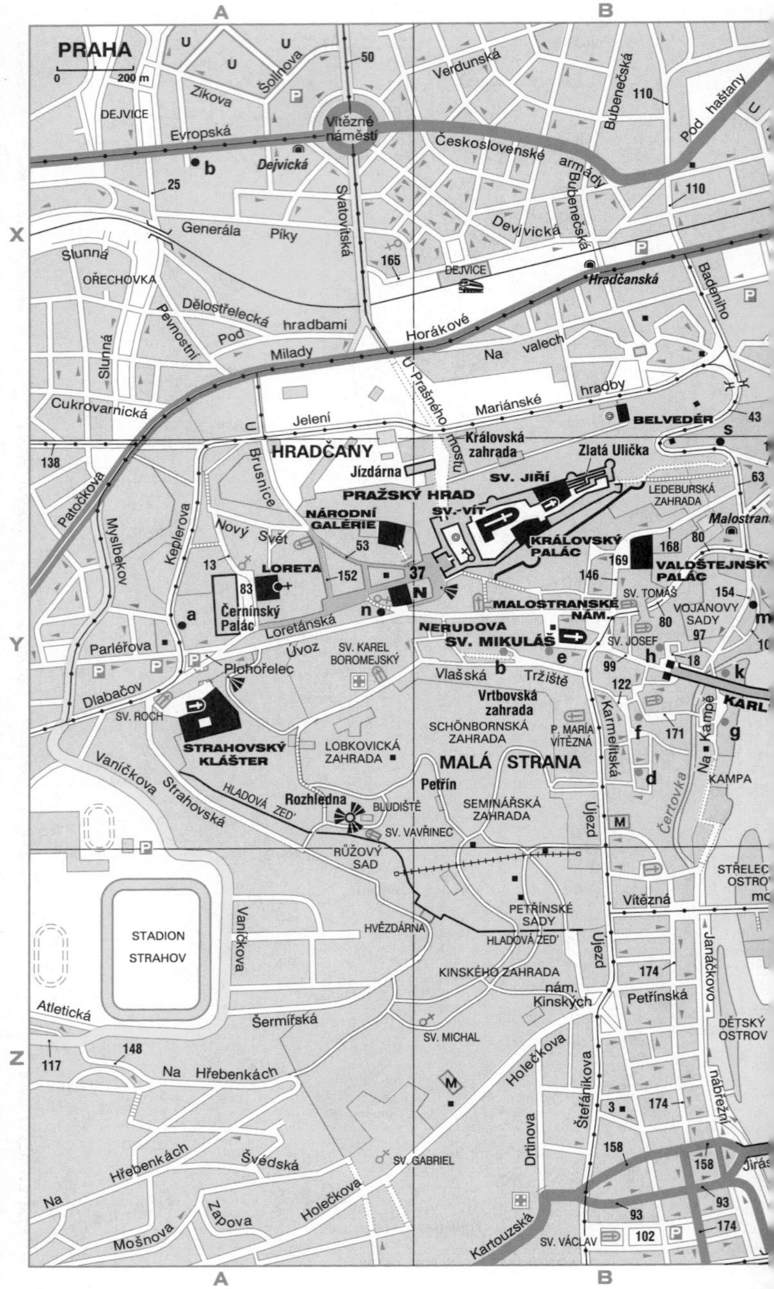
PRAHA
0
200 m
A
B
X
Y
Z
DEJVICE
Evropská
Dejvická
Vítězné náměstí
Svatovítská
Československé armády
Bubenečská
Pod haštany
Verdunská
Zikova
Šolínova
Generála Píky
Dejvická
Hradčanská
Badeniho
Slunná
OŘECHOVKA
Dělostřelecká
Pod hradbami
Pevnostní
Milady Horákové
Na valech
Mariánské hradby
U Prašného mostu
Cukrovarnická
Jelení
HRADČANY
Královská zahrada
BELVEDÉR
Zlatá Ulička
Jízdárna
SV. JIŘÍ
PRAŽSKÝ HRAD
SV. VÍT
NÁRODNÍ GALÉRIE
KRÁLOVSKÝ PALÁC
LEDEBURSKÁ ZAHRADA
Malostranská
VALDŠTEJNSKÝ PALÁC
LORETA
Černínský Palác
Nový Svět
Kepleróva
Mysíbekov
Patočkova
Loretánská
MALOSTRANSKÉ NÁM.
NERUDOVA
SV. MIKULÁŠ
SV. TOMÁŠ
VOJANOVY SADY
SV. JOSEF
Parléřova
Úvoz
SV. KAREL BOROMEJSKÝ
Pohořelec
Vlašská
Tržiště
Dlabačov
SV. ROCH
STRAHOVSKÝ KLÁŠTER
Vrtbovská zahrada
SCHÖNBORNSKÁ ZAHRADA
P. MARIA VÍTĚZNÁ
Karmelitská
LOBKOVICKÁ ZAHRADA
MALÁ STRANA
Na Kampě
KAMPA
KARL
Vaníčkova
Strahovská
HLADOVÁ ZEĎ
Rozhledna
BLUDIŠTĚ
Petřín
SEMINÁŘSKÁ ZAHRADA
Újezd
Čertovka
SV. VAVŘINEC
RŮŽOVÝ SAD
STŘELECKÝ OSTROV
Vítězná
PETŘÍNSKÉ SADY
HVĚZDÁRNA
HLADOVÁ ZEĎ
STADION STRAHOV
Vaníčkova
Janáčkovo nábřeží
KINSKÉHO ZAHRADA
nám. Kinských
Petřínská
Atletická
Šermířská
SV. MICHAL
DĚTSKÝ OSTROV
Na Hřebenkách
Holečkova
Štefánikova
Drtinova
Hřebenkách
Švédská
SV. GABRIEL
Na
Zapova
Holečkova
Mošnova
Kartouzská
SV. VÁCLAV
Jirás
50
110
25
165
43
138
63
13
53
152
37
83
168
80
169
146
154
97
99
18
122
171
174
148
117
3
158
93
102
a
b
e
f
d
g
h
k
m
n
s
N
M
P
U

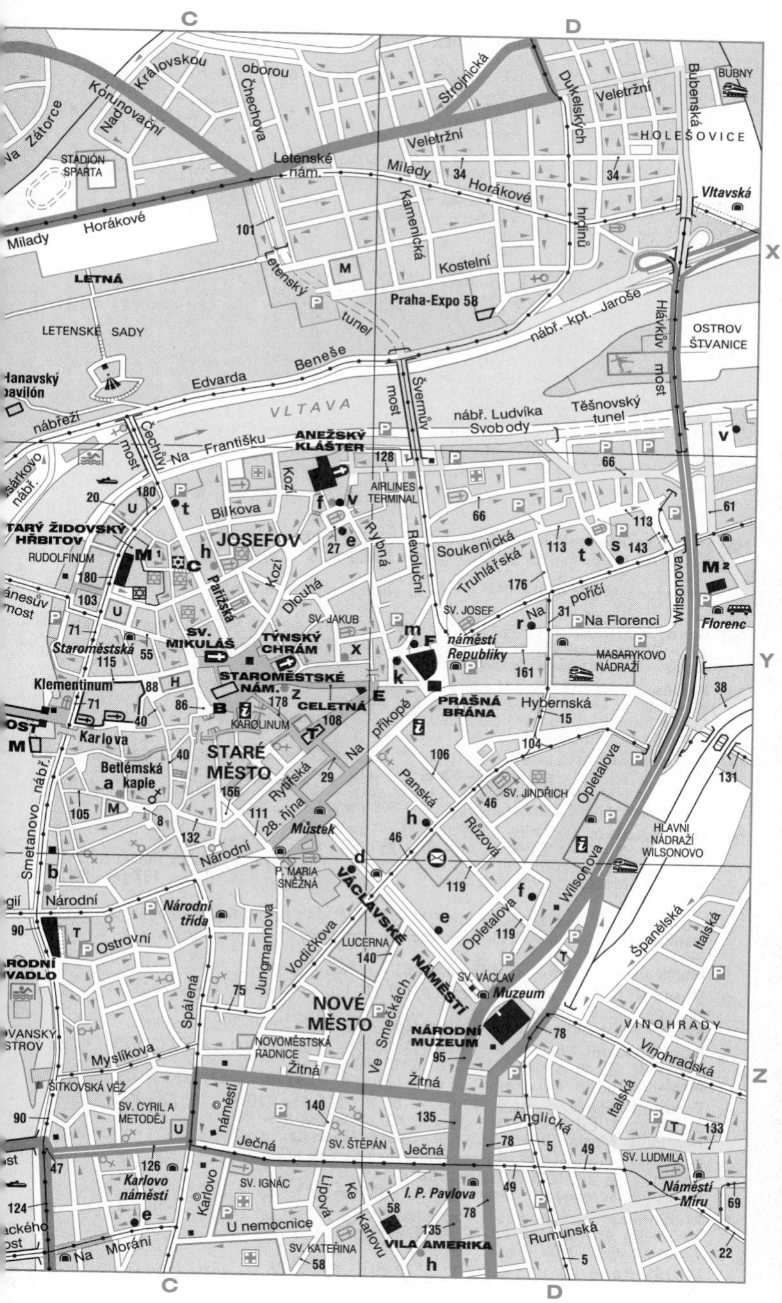
C
D
Královskou
Korunovační
Nad
oborou
Čechova
Strojnická
Dukelských
Veletržní
Bubenská
BUBNY
HOLEŠOVICE
Na Zátorce
STADIÓN SPARTA
Letenské nám.
Veletržní
Milady
Horákové
34
Vltavská
Milady
Horákové
101
Letenský tunel
Kamenická
hrdinů
X
M
Kostelní
LETNÁ
Praha-Expo 58
nábř. kpt. Jaroše
Hlávkův most
OSTROV ŠTVANICE
LETENSKÉ SADY
Beneše
Edvarda
Hanavský pavilón
Švermův most
VLTAVA
nábřeží
Čechův most
nábř. Ludvíka Svobody
Těšnovský tunel
Na Františku
ANEŽSKÝ KLÁŠTER
128
66
AIRLINES TERMINAL
Kozí
Bílkova
JOSEFOV
Rybná
Revoluční
61
113
143
STARÝ ŽIDOVSKÝ HŘBITOV
RUDOLFINUM
180
103
Pařížská
Kozí
Dlouhá
Soukenická
Truhlářská
176
Wilsonova
M²
Mánesův most
SV. JAKUB
SV. JOSEF
Na poříčí
Na Florenci
Florenc
71
Staroměstská
115
55
SV. MIKULÁŠ
TÝNSKÝ CHRÁM
náměstí Republiky
MASARYKOVO NÁDRAŽÍ
161
Y
Klementinum
88
STAROMĚSTSKÉ NÁM.
38
71
86
178
CELETNÁ
108
PRAŠNÁ BRÁNA
Hybernská
15
Karlova
40
KAROLINUM
Na příkopě
104
40
STARÉ MĚSTO
106
Betlémská kaple
Rytířská
29
Panská
Opletalova
131
Smetanovo nábř.
105
8
156
SV. JINDŘICH
46
111
28. října
Můstek
HLAVNÍ NÁDRAŽÍ WILSONOVO
132
Národní
46
Růžová
P. MARIA SNĚŽNÁ
VÁCLAVSKÉ NÁMĚSTÍ
119
Wilsonova
Národní
Národní třída
Opletalova
119
Španělská
Italská
90
Ostrovní
Jungmannova
Vodičkova
LUCERNA
140
NÁRODNÍ DIVADLO
SV. VÁCLAV
Muzeum
75
Spálená
NOVÉ MĚSTO
Ve Smečkách
NÁRODNÍ MUZEUM
78
VINOHRADY
NOVOMĚSTSKÁ RADNICE
95
Vinohradská
Myslíkova
Žitná
Z
ŠITKOVSKÁ VĚŽ
Žitná
SV. CYRIL A METODĚJ
140
135
Italská
90
náměstí
Anglická
133
Ječná
SV. ŠTĚPÁN
Ječná
78
5
49
47
126
SV. LUDMILA
Karlovo náměstí
Karlovo
SV. IGNÁC
Lipová
Ke Karlovu
I. P. Pavlova
49
Náměstí Míru
69
124
58
78
U nemocnice
135
Rumunská
Na Morání
SV. KATEŘINA
VILA AMERIKA
22
58
5
C
D

STREET INDEX TO PRAHA TOWN PLAN

Celetná . . . . . CDY
Na příkopě . . . . . CDY
Národní . . . . . CZ
Václavské náměstí . . . . . CDZ

Arbesovo náměstí . . . . . BZ 3
Bělehradská . . . . . DZ 5
Betlémské náměstí . . . . . CY 8
Cihelná . . . . . BY 10
Černínská . . . . . AY 13
Dlážděná . . . . . DY 15
Dražického náměstí . . . . . BY 18
Dvořákovo nábřeží . . . . . CY 20
Francouzská . . . . . DY 22
Gymnasijní . . . . . AX 25
Haštalské náměstí . . . . . CY 27
Havířská . . . . . CY 29
Havlíčkova . . . . . DY 31
Heřmanova . . . . . DX 34
Hradčanské náměstí . . . . . AY 37
Husitská . . . . . DY 38
Husova . . . . . CY 40
Chotkova . . . . . BX 43
Jindřišská . . . . . DY 46
Jiráskovo náměstí . . . . . CZ 47
Jugoslávská . . . . . DZ 49
Jugoslávských partyzánů . . . . . AX 50
Kanovnická . . . . . AY 53
Kaprova . . . . . CY 55
Kateřinská . . . . . CDZ 58
Ke Štvanici . . . . . DY 61
Klárov . . . . . BY 63

Klimentská . . . . . DY 66
Korunní . . . . . DZ 69
Křižovnická . . . . . CY 71
Lazarská . . . . . CZ 75
Legerova . . . . . DZ 78
Letenská . . . . . BY 80
Libušská . . . . . FT 81
Loretánské náměstí . . . . . AY 83
Malé náměstí . . . . . CY 86
Mariánské náměstí . . . . . CY 88
Masarykovo nábřeží . . . . . CZ 90
Matoušova . . . . . BZ 93
Mezibranská . . . . . DZ 95
Míšeňská . . . . . BY 97
Mostecká . . . . . BY 99
Nad štolou . . . . . CX 101
náměstí 14. října . . . . . BZ 102
náměstí Jana Palacha . . . . . CY 103
náměstí Maxima Gorkého . . . . . DY 104
Náprstkova . . . . . CY 105
Nekázanka . . . . . DY 106
Novoveská . . . . . ET 107
Ovocný trh . . . . . CY 108
Pelléova . . . . . BX 110
Perlová . . . . . CY 111
Petrská . . . . . DY 113
Platnéřská . . . . . CY 115
Pod Stadiony . . . . . AZ 117
Politických vězňů . . . . . DZ 119
Povltavská . . . . . FS 120
Prokopská . . . . . BY 122
Rašínovo nábřeží . . . . . CZ 124

Resslova . . . . . CZ 126
Řásnovka . . . . . DY 128
Ryšaveho . . . . . FT 129
Seifertova . . . . . DY 131
Skořepka . . . . . CY 132
Slezská . . . . . DZ 133
Sokolská . . . . . DZ 135
Sporilovská . . . . . FT 136
Střešovická . . . . . AY 138
Štěpánská . . . . . DZ 140
Štěpařská . . . . . ET 141
Štúrova . . . . . FT 142
Těšnov . . . . . DY 143
Tomášská . . . . . BY 146
Turistiká . . . . . AZ 148
U Bruských Kasáren . . . . . BY 150
U kasáren . . . . . AY 152
U lužického semináře . . . . . BY 154
Uhelný trh . . . . . CY 156
V botanice . . . . . BZ 158
V celnici . . . . . DY 161
Václavkova . . . . . AX 165
Valdštejnská . . . . . BY 168
Valdštejnské náměstí . . . . . BY 169
Velkopřevorské náměstí . . . . . BY 171
V Šáreckém údolí . . . . . ES 172
Výstavní . . . . . FT 173
Zborovská . . . . . BZ 174
Zelená . . . . . ES 175
Zlatnická . . . . . DY 176
Železná . . . . . CY 178
17. listopadu . . . . . CY 180

Intercontinental, Nám. Curieových 43, ✉ 110 00, ☏ 24 88 11 11, Telex 122681, Fax 24 81 12 16, ≤, – 600. AE VISA JCB. — CY **t**
Primator : **Meals** 650/1050 and a la carte – (see also ***Zlatá Praha*** below) – **365 rm** 7400/8200.

Savoy, Keplerova Ul. 6, ✉ 118 00, ☏ 24 30 24 30, Fax 24 30 21 28, « Elegant installation », – rm – 30. AE VISA JCB — AY **a**
Meals – (see ***Hradčany*** below) – **60 rm** 7800/9275, 1 suite.

Palace, Panská 12, ✉ 111 21, ☏ 240 93 111, Telex 123 337, Fax 242 21 240 – rm – 80. AE VISA JCB. — DY **h**
Meals 290 (lunch) and a la carte 380/820 – ***Club Restaurant :*** **Meals** a la carte 910/1605 – **124 rm** 7540/9300, 5 suites.

Renaissance, V Celnici 7, ✉ 110 00, ☏ 2182 1100, Fax 2182 2200, – rm – 250. AE VISA JCB — DY **r**
Potomac : **Meals** *(closed Sunday)* a la carte 640/780 – ***Pavillion :*** **Meals** 450/520 – ***U Korbele :*** **Meals** a la carte 430/770 – **309 rm** 6200/7000, 12 suites.

Hilton Atrium, Pobřežní 1, ✉ 186 00, ☏ 24 84 11 11, Fax 24 81 18 96, ≤, – – 1500. AE VISA JCB. — DX **v**
Chez Louis : **Meals** (dinner only) a la carte 460/920 – ***Praha :*** **Meals** (buffet lunch) 500 – ***Morava :*** **Meals** - Czech specialities - a la carte 305/585 – 325 – **762 rm** 6800/7520, 22 suites.

Hoffmeister, Pod Bruskou 9, ✉ 118 00, ☏ 561 81 55, Fax 530 959, « Elegant installation, collection of Adolf Hoffmeister's artwork » – rm. AE VISA JCB — BXY **s**
Meals a la carte 345/455 – **38 rm** 6100/7800, 4 suites.

Grand H. Bohemia, Králodvorská 4, ✉ 110 00, ☏ 24 804 111, Fax 23 295 45 – – 150. AE VISA JCB — DY **k**
Meals 190 (lunch) and a la carte 505/740 – **78 rm** 2865/3960, 3 suites.

Don Giovanni, Vinohradská 157a, ✉ 130 61, ☏ 67 03 6703, Fax 67 03 6704, ≤, – rm – 300. AE VISA. — FT **a**
Meals (buffet lunch) 490 and a la carte 550/990 – **354 rm** 4271/5347, 46 suites.

Forum, Kongresová 1, ✉ 140 69, ☏ 61 191 111, Fax 420 684, ≤, squash – rm – 290. AE VISA JCB. — FT **n**
Harmonie : **Meals** a la carte 470/930 – ***Ceska :*** **Meals** (buffet only) 680 – **531 rm** 6220/7060.

Diplomat, Europská 15, ✉ 160 00, ☏ 243 94 111, Fax 243 94 215, – rm – 360. AE VISA JCB. — AX **b**
Meals (dinner only) a la carte 440/780 – **382 rm** 6270/7410, 32 suites.

Maximilian without rest., Haštalská 14, ✉ 110 00, ☏ 21 806 111, Fax 21 806 110 – – 90. AE VISA — CY **e**
72 rm 3600/5700, 1 suite.

U Krále Karla, Úvoz 4, ✉ 118 00, ☏ 53 88 05, Fax 53 88 11, « 17C Baroque house, antique furniture » – rm. AE VISA JCB — AY **n**
Meals a la carte 285/690 – **18 rm** 5000/5500.

Villa Voyta, K Novému Dvoru 124, 142 00, 472 55 11, Fax 472 94 26, – rm . AE VISA JCB FT e
Meals 500/900 and a la carte – **13 rm** 4100/6300.

Adria, Václavské Nám. 26, 110 00, 210 81 111, Fax 210 81 300 – – 80. AE VISA. CZ d
Meals 300/400 (lunch) and a la carte 310/630 – **66 rm** 4030/4930, 5 suites.

City H. Moran, Na Moráni 15, 120 00, 249 152 08, Telex 12 21 34, Fax 29 75 33 – . AE VISA JCB. CZ e
Meals 260/810 and a la carte – **57 rm** 4200/5880.

Esplanade, Washingtonova 19, 110 00, 24 21 17 15, Fax 24 22 93 06, « Art Nouveau building » – rm – 58. AE VISA JCB DZ f
Meals *(closed Sunday)* (dinner only) a la carte 299/652 – **64 rm** 5250/7390, 7 suites.

Jalta, Václavské Nám. 45, 110 00, 24 22 91 33, Fax 24 21 38 66 – rest – 150. AE VISA. DZ e
Meals a la carte 285/760 – **79 rm** 5400/6000, 6 suites.

Paříž, U Obecního Domu 1, 110 00, 24 22 21 51, Fax 24 22 54 75, « Neo-Gothic and Art Nouveau architecture » – rest – 55. AE VISA JCB DY m
Meals a la carte 335/870 – **96 rm** 5900/9600, 4 suites.

Alta, Ortenovo Nám. 22, 170 00, 800 252-9, Fax 667 120 11 – rest – 30. AE VISA JCB. FS d
Meals 300/350 and a la carte – **82 rm** 2470/3090, 5 suites.

Ametyst, Jana Masaryka 11, 120 00, 691 1758, Fax 691 1790, – rm rest – 45. AE VISA JCB FT g
Meals 465/837 and a la carte – **84 rm** 3534/4836.

Sieber, Slezská 55, 130 00, 25 83 95, Fax 25 23 90 – . AE VISA.
Meals a la carte 295/375 – **12 rm** 3580/3800. FT h

U Páva, U Lužického Semináře 32, 118 00, 245 10 922, Fax 53 33 79 – rm . AE VISA JCB BY m
Meals 450/700 and a la carte – **6 rm** 4400/4700, 5 suites.

Casa Marcello, Řásnovka 783, 110 00, 231 12 30, Fax 231 33 23, – . AE VISA JCB CY v
Meals - Italian - (buffet lunch) 100/900 and a la carte – **13 rm** 4900/5200, 4 suites.

Bílá Labuť, Biskupská 9, 110 00, 2481 1382, Fax 232 29 05 – . AE VISA. DY t
Meals a la carte 190/550 – **54 rm** 4000/4500.

Harmony, Na Poříčí 31, 110 00, 232 00 16, Fax 231 00 09 – . AE VISA
Meals a la carte 147/340 – **48 rm** 1781/2477, 12 suites. DY s

Union, Ostrcilovo Nám. 4, 128 00, 61 21 48 12, Fax 61 21 48 20 – . AE VISA JCB. FT s
Meals a la carte 148/316 – **56 rm** 2600/3200.

XXXX **Zlatá Praha** (at Intercontinental H.), Nám. Curieových 43, 110 00, 24 88 11 11, Fax 24 81 12 16, < Prague – . AE VISA JCB. CY t
Meals a la carte 640/1650.

XXXX **Hradčany** (at Savoy H.), Keplerova Ul. 6, 118 00, 24 30 24 30, Fax 24 30 21 28 – AE VISA JCB AY a
Meals 380/720 and a la carte.

XXX **Parnas,** Smetanovo Nábřeží 2, 110 00, 24 22 76 14, Fax 24 22 89 32, < – AE VISA
closed 24 December – **Meals** (dinner booking essential) 795/1595 and a la carte. CZ b

XXX **Klub Kampa,** Na Kampě 14, 110 00, 53 99 85 – AE VISA BY g
Meals (dinner only November-February) a la carte 360/800.

XX **V Zatisi,** Liliová 1, Betlémské Nám., 110 00, 24 22 89 77, Fax 24 22 89 32 – AE VISA
closed 24 December – **Meals** 395/795 and a la carte. CY a

XX **David,** Tržiště 21, 110 00, 53 93 25 – AE VISA BY b
Meals (dinner booking essential) a la carte 395/570.

X **Bistrot de Marlène,** Plavecká 4, 120 000, 29 10 77 – AE ET f
closed Saturday lunch, Sunday and Christmas-New Year – **Meals** (booking essential) a la carte 530/810.

X **Kampa Park,** Na Kampě 8b, 110 00, 534 856, Fax 242 129 65, , « Vltava riverside setting, < Charles Bridge » – AE VISA BY k
Meals (dinner booking essential) a la carte 440/725.

X **U Patrona,** Dražického Nám. 4, 110 00, 53 15 12, Fax 24 22 89 32 – AE VISA.
closed 24 December – **Meals** 375/785 and a la carte. BY h

X **Au Saint Esprit,** Elišky Krásnohorské 5, 110 00, 231 00 39, – AE VISA JCB
closed Sunday and Christmas-New Year – **Meals** a la carte 500/1200. CY h

X **La Provence,** Štupartská 9, 110 00, 232 4801, Fax 248 1 6695 – AE VISA CY x
Meals - Mediterranean Bistro - (booking essential) a la carte 349/695.

X **Circle Line Brasserie,** Malostranske Nám. 12, 110 00, 530 308, Fax 2422 8932, Vaulted cellar – AE VISA BY e
closed 24 December – **Meals** - Seafood - 445/1795 and a la carte.

LOCAL ATMOSPHERE AND CZECH CUISINE

XX **U Vladaře,** Maltézské Nám. 10, ✉ 118 00, ✆ 53 81 28, Fax 53 08 42, 余 - AE ⓓ E VISA. ✄ BY f
Meals a la carte 260/660.

XX **U Červeného Kola,** Anežská 2, ✉ 110 00, ✆ 24 81 11 18, Fax 24 81 11 18, « Courtyard terrace » - AE ⓓ E VISA. ✄ CY f
Meals a la carte 295/700.

XX **U Modre Kachnicky,** Nebovidská 6, ✉ 118 00, ✆ 24 51 02 17, Fax 24 51 02 17, « 14C house with modern murals » - AE VISA BY d
Meals (dinner booking essential) a la carte 375/660.

XX **U Sixtů,** Celetná 2, ✉ 110 00, ✆ 24 22 57 24, Fax 24 21 16 71, 13C vaulted cellar - AE ⓓ E VISA JCB CY z
Meals (booking essential) a la carte 400/780.

X **U Kalicha,** Na Bojišti 12, ✉ 120 00, ✆ 29 07 01, Fax 29 19 45, Typical Prague beerhouse - AE ⓓ E VISA JCB DZ h
Meals a la carte 240/420.

Denmark

Danmark

COPENHAGEN

PRACTICAL INFORMATION

LOCAL CURRENCY

Danish Kroner: 100 DKK = 18.01 USD ($) (Jan. 96)

TOURIST INFORMATION

The telephone number and address of the Tourist Information office is given in the text under ℹ.

FOREIGN EXCHANGE

Banks are open between 9.30am and 4.00pm (6.00pm on Thursdays) on weekdays except Saturdays. The main banks in the centre of Copenhagen, the Central Station and the Airport have exchange facilities outside these hours.

MEALS

At lunchtime, follow the custom of the country and try the typical buffets of Scandinavian specialities.
At dinner, the a la carte and set menus will offer you more conventional cooking.

SHOPPING IN COPENHAGEN

Strøget (Department stores, exclusive shops, boutiques).
Kompagnistræde (Antiques). Shops are generally open from 10am to 8pm (Saturday 10am to 5pm).
See also in the index of street names, those printed in red are where the principal shops are found.

THEATRE BOOKINGS

Your hotel porter will be able to make your arrangements or direct you to Theatre Booking Agents.

CAR HIRE

The international car hire companies have branches in Copenhagen – Your hotel porter should be able to give details and help you with your arrangements.

TIPPING

In Denmark, all hotels and restaurants include a service charge. As for the taxis, there is no extra charge to the amount shown on the meter.

SPEED LIMITS

The maximum permitted speed in cities is 50 km/h - 31 mph, outside cities 80 km/h - 50 mph and 110 km/h - 68 mph on motorways. Cars towing caravans 70 km/h – 44 mph and buses 80 km/h – 50 mph also on motorways.
Local signs may indicate lower or permit higher limits. On the whole, speed should always be adjusted to prevailing circumstances. In case of even minor speed limit offences, drivers will be liable to heavy fines to be paid on the spot. If payment cannot be made, the car may be impounded.

SEAT BELTS

The wearing of seat belts is compulsory for drivers and all passengers except children under the age of 3 and taxi passengers.

Copenhagen

(KØBENHAVN) Danmark 985 Q 9 – pop. 622 000, Greater Copenhagen 1 354 000.

See : Tivoli★★★ : April 17 to September 15 BZ – Harbour and Canal Tour★★★ (Kanaltur) : May to September 15 (Gammel Strand and Nyhavn) – Little Mermaid★★★ (Den Lille Havfrue) DX – Strøget★★ BCYZ – Nyhavn★★ DY – Amalienborg★★ : Changing of the Guard at noon DY – Rosenborg Castle★★ (Rosenborg Slot) CX – Christiansborg Palace★★ (Christiansborg Slot) CZ – Old Stock Exchange★★ (Børsen) CZ – Round Tower★★ (Rundetårn) CY **D** – Gråbrødretorv★ CY **28** – Gammel Strand★ CZ **26** – Marble Church★ (Marmorkirke) DY **E** – Royal Chapel and Naval Church★ (Holmen's Kirke) CZ **B** – King's Square★ (Kongens Nytorv) DY – Charlottenborg Palace★ (Charlottenborg Slot) DY **F** – Citadel★ (Kastellet) DX – Christianhavn★ DZ – Botanical Garden★ (Botanisk Have) BX – Frederiksberg Garden★ (Frederiksberg Have) AZ – Town Hall (Rådhus) : World Clock★ (Jens Olsen's Verdensur) BZ **H**.

Museums : Ny Carlsberg Glyptotek★★★ (Glyptoteket) BZ – National Museum★★ (Nationalmuseet) CZ – Royal Museum of Fine Arts★★ (Statens Museum for Kunst) CX – Thorvaldsen Museum★ CZ **M1** Royal Arsenal Museum★ (Tøjhusmuseet) CZ **M2** – Royal Theatre Museum★ (Teaterhistorisk Museum) CZ **M3** – Copenhagen City Museum★ (Bymuseet) AZ **M4**.

Outskirts : Open Air Museum★★ (Frilandsmuseet) NW : 12 km BX – Ordrupgaard Museum★ (Ordrupgaardsamlingen) N : 10 km CX – Dragør★ SW : 13 km DZ – Karen Blixen Museum★ (Karen Blixen Museet) N : 20 km AX – Louisiana Museum of Modern Art★ (Louisiana Museum for moderne kunst) N : 35 km AX.

18 Dansk Golf Union 56 ☎ 43 45 55 55.

✈ Copenhagen/Kastrup SE : 10 km ☎ 31 54 17 01 – Air Terminal : main railway station.

Motorail for Southern Europe : ☎ 33 14 17 01.

Further information from the D S B, main railway station or tourist information centre (see below).

Copenhagen Tourist Information, Bernstorffsgade 1, ✉ 1577 V ☎ 33 11 13 25, Fax 33 93 49 69.

Berlin 385 – Hamburg 305 – Oslo 583 – Stockholm 630.

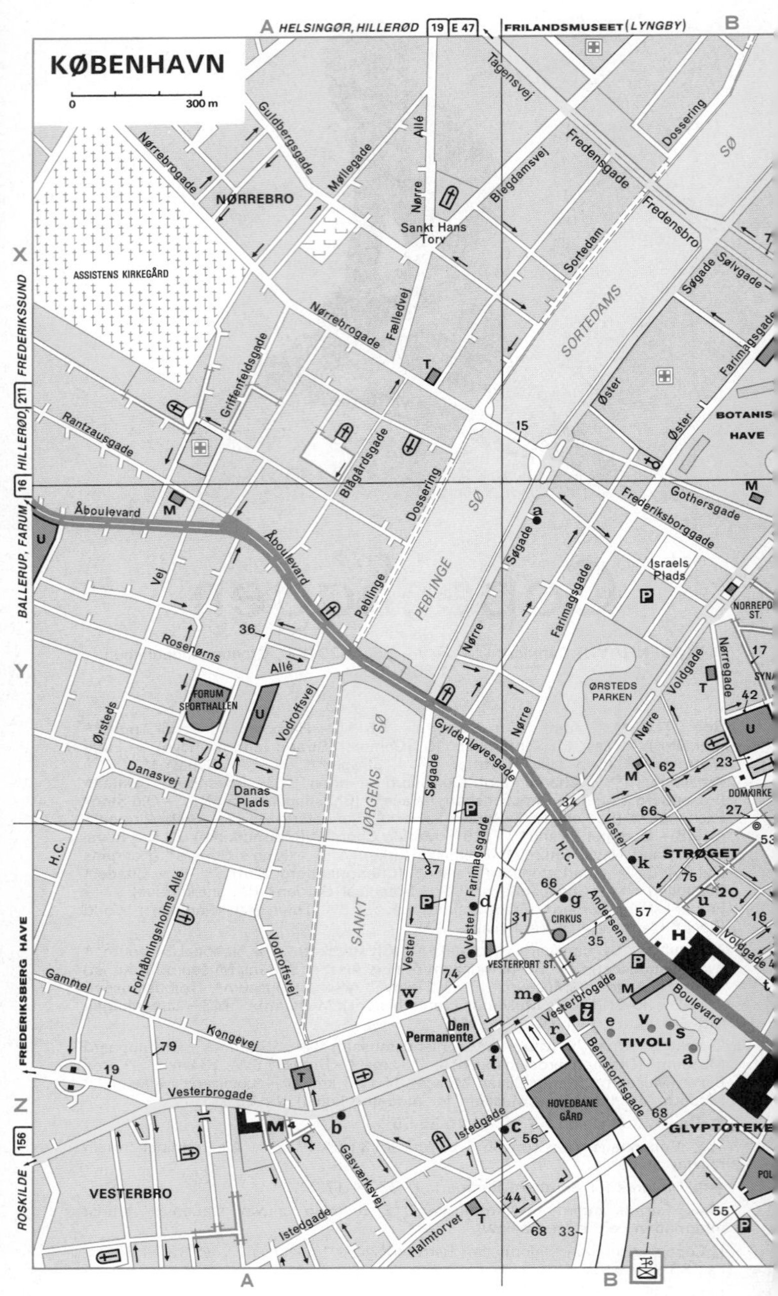
KØBENHAVN
0
300 m
HELSINGØR, HILLERØD
19
E 47
FRILANDSMUSEET (LYNGBY)
FREDERIKSSUND
HILLERØD, 211
16
BALLERUP, FARUM
FREDERIKSBERG HAVE
ROSKILDE
156
NØRREBRO
ASSISTENS KIRKEGÅRD
Nørrebrogade
Guldbergsgade
Møllegade
Nørre Allé
Sankt Hans Torv
Tagensvej
Blegdamsvej
Fredensgade
Fredensbro
Dossering
SØ
Sortedam
SORTEDAMS
Søgade
Sølvgade
Farimagsgade
Østervoldgade
BOTANISK HAVE
Fælledvej
Griffenfeldsgade
Rantzausgade
Blågårdsgade
Dossering
Åboulevard
Peblinge
PEBLINGE
Søgade
Gothersgade
Frederiksborggade
Israels Plads
NØRREPORT ST.
Nørregade
Rosenørns Allé
FORUM SPORTHALLEN
Vodroffsvej
Ørsteds
Danasvej
Danas Plads
ØRSTEDS PARKEN
Nørre Voldgade
Gyldenløvesgade
JØRGENS
SANKT
Søgade
Vester Farimagsgade
H.C. Andersens Boulevard
Vester Voldgade
STRØGET
DOMKIRKE
CIRKUS
VESTERPORT ST.
Vesterbrogade
TIVOLI
Bernstorffsgade
HOVEDBANE GÅRD
GLYPTOTEKET
H.C.
Forhåbningsholms Allé
Vodroffsvej
Gammel Kongevej
Den Permanente
Vesterbrogade
Istedgade
Gasværksvej
Halmtorvet
VESTERBRO
Istedgade
A
B
X
Y
Z

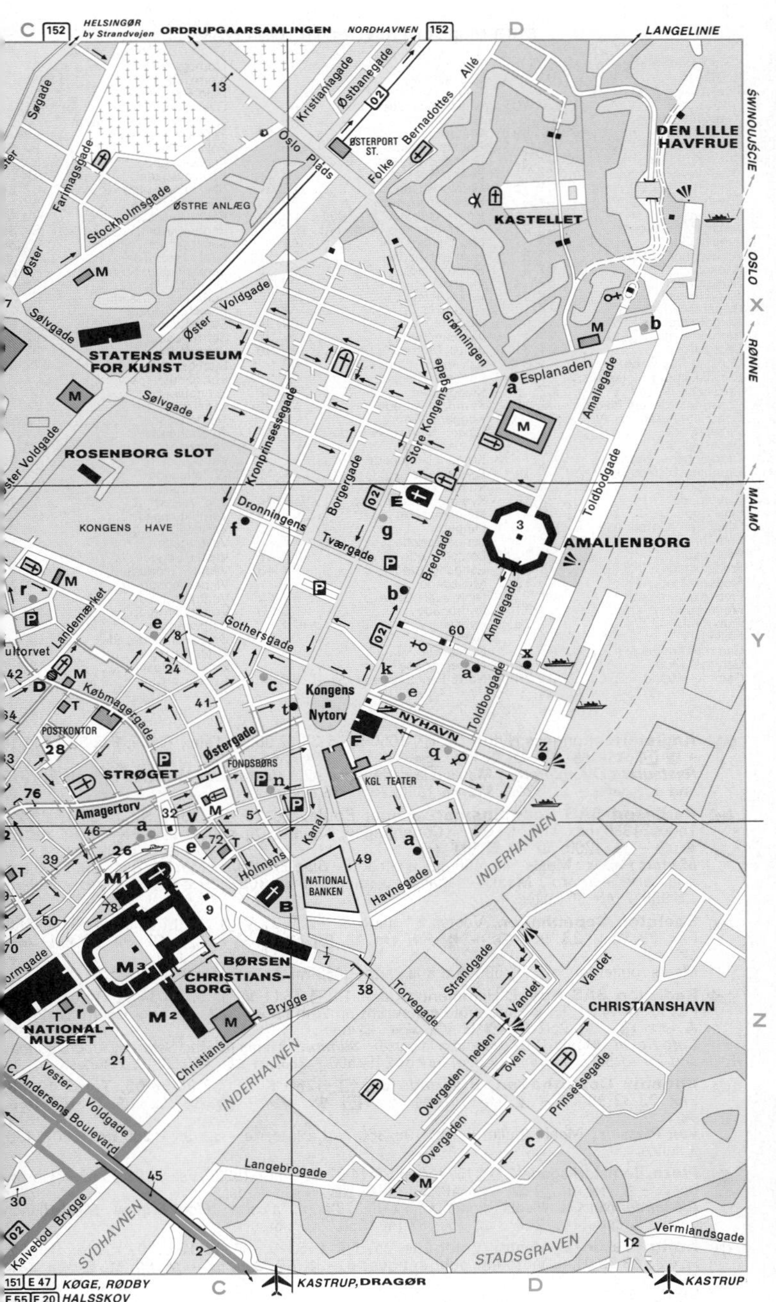
HELSINGØR by Strandvejen
ORDRUPGAARSAMLINGEN
NORDHAVNEN
LANGELINIE
DEN LILLE HAVFRUE
ŚWINOUJŚCIE
OSLO
RØNNE
MALMÖ
KASTELLET
ØSTRE ANLÆG
ØSTERPORT ST.
STATENS MUSEUM FOR KUNST
ROSENBORG SLOT
KONGENS HAVE
AMALIENBORG
Kongens Nytorv
NYHAVN
KGL TEATER
STRØGET
FONDSBØRS
POSTKONTOR
Amagertorv
NATIONAL BANKEN
BØRSEN
CHRISTIANSBORG
NATIONAL-MUSEET
INDERHAVNEN
CHRISTIANSHAVN
SYDHAVNEN
STADSGRAVEN
KØGE, RØDBY
HALSSKOV
KASTRUP, DRAGØR
KASTRUP

STREET INDEX TO KØBENHAVN TOWN PLAN

Amagertorv (Strøget) ..... CY
Bredgade ..... DY
Frederiksberggade (Strøget) ..... BZ 20
Købmagergade ..... CY
Nygade (Strøget) ..... CYZ 52
Nørre Voldgade ..... BY
Store Kongensgade ..... DX
Vesterbrogade ..... ABZ
Vimmelskaftet (Strøget) ..... CY 76
Østergade (Strøget) ..... CY

Amager Boulevard ..... CZ 2
Amaliegade ..... DXY
Amalienborg Plads ..... DY 3
Axeltorv ..... BZ 4
Bernstorffsgade ..... BZ
Blegdamsvej ..... BX
Blågårdsgåde ..... AX
Borgergade ..... DXY
Bremerholm ..... CY 5
Børsgade ..... DZ 7
Christan IX's Gade ..... CY 8
Christiansborg Slotsplads ..... CZ 9
Christians Brygge ..... CZ
Christmas Møllers Plads ..... DZ 12
Dag Hammarskjölds Allé ..... CX 13
Danas Plads ..... AY
Danasvej ..... AY
Dronningens Tværgade ..... CDY
Dronning Louises Bro ..... BX 15
Esplanaden ..... DX
Farvergade ..... BZ 16
Fiolstræde ..... BY 17
Folke Bernadottes Allé ..... DX
Forhåbningsholms Allé ..... AZ
Fredensbro ..... BX
Fredensgade ..... BX
Frederiksberg Allé ..... AZ 19
Frederiksborggade ..... BY
Frederiksholms Kanal ..... CZ 21
Frue Plads ..... BY 23
Fælledvej ..... AX
Gammel Kongevej ..... AZ
Gammel Mønt ..... CY 24
Gammel Strand ..... CZ 26
Gammeltorv ..... BYZ 27
Gasværksvej ..... AZ
Gothersgade ..... BCY
Griffenfeldsgade ..... AX
Grønningen ..... DX
Gråbrødretorv ..... CY 28
Guldbergsgade ..... AX
Gyldenløvesgade ..... AY
Halmtorvet ..... AZ
Hambrosgade ..... CZ 30
Hammerichsgade ..... BZ 31
Havnegade ..... DZ
H.C. Andersens Boulevard ..... BCZ
H.C. Ørsteds Vej ..... AY
Holmens Kanal ..... CDZ
Højbro Plads ..... CY 32
Ingerslevsgade ..... BZ 33
Israels Plads ..... BY
Istedgade ..... AZ
Jarmers Plads ..... BY 34
Jernbanegade ..... BZ 35
Julius Thomsens Gade ..... AY 36
Kalvebod Brygge ..... CZ
Kampmannsgade ..... AZ 37
Knippelsbro ..... DZ 38
Kompagnistræde ..... CZ 39
Kongens Nytorv ..... DY
Kristen Bernikows Gade ..... CY 41
Kristianiagade ..... DX
Kronprinsessegade ..... CXY
Krystalgade ..... BCY 42
Kultorvet ..... CY
Kvægtorvsgade ..... ABZ 44
Landemaerket ..... CY
Langebro ..... CZ 45
Langebrogade ..... CDZ
Læderstræde ..... CYZ 46
Løngangstræde ..... BZ 48
Møllegade ..... AX
Niels Juels Gade ..... DZ 49
Nybrogade ..... CZ 50
Nyhavn ..... DY
Nytorv ..... BZ 53
Nørre Allé ..... AX
Nørrebrogade ..... AX
Nørre Farimagsgade ..... BY
Nørregade ..... BY
Nørre Søgade ..... ABY
Oslo Plads ..... DX
Overgaden neden Vandet ..... DZ
Overgaden oven Vandet ..... DZ
Peblinge Dossering ..... AY
Polititorvet ..... BZ 55
Prinsessegade ..... DZ
Rantzausgade ..... AX
Reventlowsgade ..... BZ 56
Rosenørns Allé ..... AY
Rådhuspladsen ..... BZ 57
Rådhusstræde ..... CZ 59
Sankt Annæ Plads ..... DY 60
Sankt Hans Torv ..... AX
Sankt Peders Stræde ..... BY 62
Skindergade ..... CY 63
Sortedam Dossering ..... BX
Stockholmsgade CX
Store Kannikestræde ..... CY 64
Stormgade ..... CZ
Strandgade ..... DZ
Studiestræde ..... BYZ 66
Sølvgade ..... BCX
Sølvtorvet ..... CX 67
Tagensvej ..... BX
Tietgensgade ..... BZ 68
Toldbodgade ..... DXY
Torvegade ..... DZ
Vandkunsten ..... CZ 70
Webersgade ..... BX 71
Ved Stranden ..... CZ 72
Ved Vesterport ..... AZ 74
Vermlandsgade ..... DZ
Vester Farimagsgade ..... AZ
Vestergade ..... BZ 75
Vester Søgade ..... AYZ
Vester Voldgade ..... BCZ
Vindebrogade ..... CZ 78
Vodroffsvej ..... AYZ
Værnedamsvej ..... AZ 79
Østbanegade ..... DX
Øster Farimagsgade ..... BCX
Øster Søgade ..... BCX
Øster Voldgade CX
Aboulevard ..... AY

Angleterre, Kongens Nytorv 34, ✉ 1050 K, ☎ 33 12 00 95, Telex 15877, Fax 33 12 11 18 – |$| TV ☎ – 400. AE E VISA JCB. CDY t
***Restaurant D'Angleterre :* Meals** a la carte 342/543 – ***Restaurant Wiinblad :* Meals** 75/275 and a la carte – 120 – **112 rm** 1850/2900, 18 suites.

Radisson SAS Scandinavia, Amager Boulevard 70, ✉ 2300 S, ☎ 33 11 23 24, Telex 31330, Fax 31 57 01 93, ≤ Copenhagen, squash – |$| rm rest TV ☎ P – 1200. AE E VISA JCB by Amager Boulevard CZ
***Mamas Papas :* Meals** 145/400 and a la carte – ***Blue Elephant :* Meals** - Thai - 300/900 and a la carte – ***Kyoto :* Meals** - Japanese - (dinner only) 300/800 and a la carte – **506 rm** 999/2145, 36 suites.

Sheraton Copenhagen, Vester S ! gade 6, ✉ 1601 V, ☎ 33 14 35 35, Telex 27450, Fax 33 32 12 23, ≤, – |$| rm TV ☎ – 1200. AE E VISA JCB. rest AZ w
Meals (buffet lunch) 175/500 and a la carte – **463 rm** 995/1950, 2 suites.

Radisson SAS Royal, Hammerichsgade 1, ✉ 1611 V, ☎ 33 14 14 12, Telex 27155, Fax 33 14 14 21, ≤, « Panoramic restaurant on 20th floor », – |$| rm TV ☎ P – 250. AE E VISA JCB. rest BZ m
***Cafe Royal :* Meals** 120/200 and a la carte – ***Summit :* Meals** *(closed Saturday lunch, Sunday and 21 to 30 December)* (buffet lunch) 245/500 – **263 rm** 1490/2240, 2 suites.

Phoenix Copenhagen, Bredgade 37, ✉ 1260 K, ☎ 33 95 95 00, Telex 40068, Fax 33 33 98 33 – |$| rm rest TV ☎ – 80. AE E VISA JCB. DY b
***Von Plessen :* Meals** (buffet lunch) 198/350 and a la carte – 95 – **209 rm** 1090/1490, 3 suites.

Plaza, Bernstorffsgade 4, ✉ 1577 V, ☎ 33 14 92 62, Telex 15330, Fax 33 93 93 62, « Library bar » – |$| rm TV ☎ – 40. AE E VISA JCB. rest BZ r
***Alexander Nevski :* Meals** (dinner only) 218/378 and a la carte – ***Flora Danica :* Meals** (lunch only) a la carte 148/268 – 75 – **87 rm** 1550/2150, 6 suites.

Kong Frederik, Vester Voldgade 25, ✉ 1552 V, ☎ 33 12 59 02, Telex 19702, Fax 33 93 59 01, « Victorian pub, antiques » – |$| TV ☎ – 80. AE E VISA JCB. BZ k
Meals 145/295 and a la carte – 100 – **107 rm** 1350/1650, 3 suites.

Kong Arthur , Nørre Søgade 11, ✉ 1370 K, ☎ 33 11 12 12, Telex 16512, Fax 33 32 61 30, – rm ☎ – 70. AE ⓓ E VISA JCB.
Brochner : **Meals** *(closed Sunday and Bank Holidays)* (buffet lunch)/dinner 175/265 and a la carte – ***Sticks 'n' Sushi*** : **Meals** - Japanese - *(closed Bank Holidays)* (dinner only) 135/160 and a la carte – **107 rm** 945/1245. BY **a**

Palace, Rådhuspladsen 57, ✉ 1550 V, ☎ 33 14 40 50, Telex 19693, Fax 33 14 52 79, – rm ☎ – 40. AE ⓓ E VISA JCB. rest BZ **u**
Meals (buffet lunch) 124/314 and a la carte – **159 rm** 1325/1525.

Radisson SAS Falconer, Falkoner Allé 9, ✉ 2000 Frederiksberg C, ☎ 31 19 80 01, Fax 31 87 11 91, City, – rm ☎ – 2000. AE ⓓ E VISA JCB. by Gammel Kongerej AZ
Meals (buffet lunch) 150/210 and a la carte – **144 rm** 675/1795, 22 suites.

Imperial, Vester Farimagsgade 9, ✉ 1606 V, ☎ 33 12 80 00, Telex 15556, Fax 33 12 80 03 – rm ☎ – 100. AE ⓓ E VISA JCB. AZ **e**
Meals (buffet lunch) 250/450 and a la carte – **163 rm** 1160/2310.

Neptun, Sankt Annae Plads 14-20, ✉ 1250 K, ☎ 33 13 89 00, Fax 33 12 12 50 – ☎ – 60. AE ⓓ E VISA JCB. DY **a**
closed 22 December-2 January – **Meals** *(closed Sunday and July)* 155/285 and a la carte – **118 rm** 1020/1590, 15 suites.

Sophie Amalie, Sankt Annae Plads 21, ✉ 1250 K, ☎ 33 13 34 00, Fax 33 11 77 07, – ☎ – 80. AE E VISA JCB. DY **x**
Meals 180/300 and a la carte – 90 – **130 rm** 805/1620, 4 suites.

71 Nyhavn, Nyhavn 71, ✉ 1051 K, ☎ 33 11 85 85, Fax 33 93 15 85, « Former warehouse » – ☎. AE ⓓ E VISA JCB. DY **z**
Meals *(closed Sunday and Bank Holidays)* (dinner only) 245/282 and a la carte – **76 rm** 995/1560, 6 suites.

Komfort, Løngangstraede 27, ✉ 1468 K, ☎ 33 12 65 70, Telex 16488, Fax 33 15 28 99 – . AE ⓓ E VISA JCB. rest BZ **n**
closed Christmas to 29 December – **Meals** 68/198 and a la carte – 85 – **201 rm** 800/1100.

Grand, Vesterbrogade 9, ✉ 1620 V, ☎ 31 31 36 00, Fax 31 31 33 50 – ☎ – 100. AE ⓓ E VISA JCB. rest AZ **t**
Meals (buffet lunch) 98/180 and a la carte – **144 rm** 775/1155, 2 suites.

Copenhagen Crown without rest., Vesterbrogade 41, ✉ 1620 V, ☎ 31 21 21 66, Fax 31 21 00 66 – ☎ – 25. AE ⓓ E VISA JCB AZ **b**
80 rm 925/1190.

Ascot without rest., Studiestraede 61, ✉ 1554 V, ☎ 33 12 60 00, Telex 15730, Fax 33 14 60 40, – ☎ – 90. AE ⓓ E VISA JCB BZ **g**
113 rm 790/1290, 20 suites.

City without rest., Peder Skrams Gade 24, ✉ 1054 K, ☎ 33 13 06 66, Fax 33 13 06 67 – ☎. AE ⓓ E VISA JCB DZ **a**
81 rm 775/1125.

Copenhagen Star without rest., Colbjørnsensgade 13, ✉ 1652 V, ☎ 31 22 11 00, Fax 31 22 21 99 – rm ☎ – 35. AE ⓓ E VISA JCB ABZ **c**
132 rm 925/1190, 2 suites.

Mercur, 17 Vester Farimagsgade, ✉ 1780 V, ☎ 33 12 57 11, Fax 33 12 57 17, – rm ☎. AE ⓓ E VISA JCB. rest AZ **d**
Meals *(closed Saturday lunch, Sunday and Bank Holidays)* 98/220 and a la carte – **108 rm** 795/955, 1 suite.

Esplanaden without rest., Bredgade 73, ✉ 1260 K, ☎ 33 91 32 00, Fax 33 91 32 39 – ☎. AE ⓓ E VISA JCB. DX **a**
closed 22 December-2 January – **116 rm** 675/970.

Christian IV without rest., Dronningens Tvaergade 45, ✉ 1302 K, ☎ 33 32 10 44, Fax 33 32 07 06 – ☎. AE ⓓ E VISA JCB CY **f**
closed 23 to 27 December – **42 rm** 785/965.

Danmark without rest., Vester Voldgade 89, ✉ 1552 V, ☎ 33 11 48 06, Fax 33 14 36 30 – ☎ . AE ⓓ E VISA JCB BZ **t**
closed 21 December-2 January – **49 rm** 575/925, 2 suites.

XXX ✿ **Kong Hans Kaelder,** Vingårdsstraede 6, ✉ 1070 K, ☎ 33 11 68 68, Fax 33 32 67 68, « Vaulted Gothic cellar » – AE ⓓ E VISA JCB CY **n**
closed Sunday, 27 May, Easter, 1 to 29 July, 22 December-2 January and Bank Holidays – **Meals** (booking essential) (dinner only) 475/675 and a la carte 335/760
Spec. Smoked salmon from our own smokery, Warm foie gras in a raspberry vinegar sauce, Lobster "Tiger Lee".

XX ✿ **Nouvelle,** Gammel Strand 34 (1st floor), ✉ 1202 K, ☎ 33 13 50 18, Fax 33 32 07 97 – AE ⓓ E VISA JCB CZ **a**
closed Saturday lunch, Sunday, July, 22 December-8 January and Bank Holidays – **Meals** 250/465 and a la carte 405/475
Spec. Egg "Nouvelle" filled with lobster, mousseline sauce and sevruga caviar, Bornholm herrings served as appetisers, "Whatnot" with white chocolate and summer berries.

XX ✿ **Kommandanten,** Ny Adelgade 7, ✉ 1104 K, ☎ 33 12 09 90, Fax 33 93 12 23, « 17C town house, contemporary furnishings » – AE ⓓ E VISA JCB CY c
closed Saturday lunch, Sunday, 23 December-4 January and Bank Holidays – **Meals** (booking essential) 285/520 and a la carte 420/560
Spec. Oysters with osetrova caviar, blinis and balsamie granité, Oxtail and lobster served with a parsley potato purée, Chocolate variation.

XX ✿ **Restaurationen,** Møntergade 19, ✉ 1116 K, ☎ 33 14 94 95 – AE ⓓ E VISA CY e
closed Sunday, Monday, July, 23 December-3 January and Bank Holidays – **Meals** (dinner only except in December) 335/405
Spec. Smoked eel and leek terrine, Breast of pheasant in a truffle cream sauce, Caramel ice cream with elderberry jelly and caramelised breadcrumbs.

XX **Leonore Christine,** Nyhavn 9 (1st floor), ✉ 1051 K, ☎ 33 13 50 40, Fax 33 13 50 40 – AE ⓓ E VISA JCB DY e
closed 23 December-1 January – **Meals** 225/395 and a la carte.

XX **St. Gertruds Kloster,** Hauser Plads 32, ✉ 1127 K, ☎ 33 14 66 30, Fax 33 93 93 65, « Part 14C monastic cellars » – ▤. AE ⓓ E VISA JCB CY r
closed Christmas-2 January – **Meals** 165/750 and dinner a la carte.

XX **Era Ora,** Torvegade 62, ✉ 1400 K, ☎ 31 54 06 93, Fax 31 85 07 53 – ⇔ ▤. AE ⓓ E VISA JCB DZ c
closed Sunday, 23 to 26 December and 31 December-1 January – **Meals** - Italian - (dinner only) 385/495.

X **Lumskebugten,** Esplanaden 21, ✉ 1263 K, ☎ 33 15 60 29, Fax 33 32 87 18, 余, « Mid 19C café-pavilion » – AE ⓓ E VISA JCB DX b
closed Saturday lunch, Sunday and 23 December-2 January – **Meals** 265/375 and a la carte.

X **Den Sorte Ravn,** Nyhavn 14, ✉ 1051 K, ☎ 33 13 12 33, Fax 33 13 24 72 – ▤. AE ⓓ E VISA JCB DY q
closed Easter, Whitsun and Christmas – **Meals** 175/245 and a la carte.

X **Den Gyldne Fortun,** Ved Stranden 18, ✉ 1061 K, ☎ 33 12 20 11, Fax 33 93 35 11 – AE ⓓ E VISA JCB CZ e
closed lunch Saturday and Sunday, 3 to 8 April, 3, 16 and 25 to 27 May, 21 December-2 January and Bank Holidays – **Meals** - Seafood - 175/485 and a la carte.

X **Els,** Store Strandstraede 3, ✉ 1255 K, ☎ 33 14 13 41, Fax 33 91 07 00, « 19C murals » – ▤. AE ⓓ E VISA JCB DY k
Meals 96/376 and a la carte.

X **Thorvaldsen,** Gammel Strand 34 (ground floor), ✉ 1202 K, ☎ 33 32 04 00, Fax 33 32 07 97, 余 – AE ⓓ E VISA JCB CZ a
closed dinner 15 September-15 April, Sunday, 22 December-7 January and Bank Holidays – **Meals** 175/225 and a la carte.

in Tivoli : (Entrance fee payable)

XXX **Divan 2,** Vesterbrogade 3, ✉ 1620 V, ☎ 33 12 51 51, Fax 33 91 08 82, ≤, 余, « Floral decoration and terrace » – AE ⓓ E VISA JCB BZ a
1 May-15 September – **Meals** 295/650 and a la carte.

XXX **Belle Terrasse,** Vesterbrogade 3, ✉ 1620 V, ☎ 33 12 11 36, Fax 33 15 00 31, ≤, 余, « Floral decoration and terrace » – AE ⓓ E VISA JCB BZ s
2 May-14 September – **Meals** 195/545 and a la carte.

XXX **Divan 1,** Vesterbrogade 3, ✉ 1620 V, ☎ 33 11 42 42, Fax 33 11 74 07, ≤, 余, « 19C pavilion and terrace » – AE ⓓ E VISA JCB BZ v
2 May-15 September – **Meals** 98/415 and a la carte.

XX **La Crevette,** Vesterbrogade 3, ✉ 1620 V, ☎ 33 14 68 47, Fax 33 14 60 03, ≤, 余, « Part mid 19C pavilion and terrace » – AE ⓓ E VISA JCB BZ e
1 May-15 September – **Meals** - Seafood - 310/425 and a la carte.

SMØRREBRØD

The following list of simpler restaurants and cafés/bars specialize in Danish open sandwiches and are generally open from 10.00am to 4.00pm.

X **Ida Davidsen,** St. Kongensgade 70, ✉ 1264 K, ☎ 33 91 36 55, Fax 33 11 36 55 – AE ⓓ E VISA DY g
closed Saturday, Sunday, July and Christmas-New Year – **Meals** (buffet lunch) a la carte 30/105.

X **Slotskaelderen-Hos Gitte Kik,** Fortunstraede 4, ✉ 1065 K, ☎ 33 11 15 37 – AE ⓓ E VISA JCB CYZ v
closed Sunday, Monday and Bank Holidays – **Meals** (lunch only) 25/68 and a la carte.

X **Sankt Annae,** Sankt Annae Plads 12, ✉ 1250 K, ☎ 33 12 54 97 – ⓓ E VISA JCB DY a
closed Saturday, Sunday and July – **Meals** (lunch only) 35/65.

X **Kanal Caféen,** Frederiksholms Kanal 18, ✉ 1220 K, ☎ 33 11 57 70, Fax 33 13 79 62 – ⓓ E VISA CZ r
closed Saturday and Sunday – **Meals** (lunch only) 30/158 and a la carte.

at Hellerup N : 6 ½ km by Øster Farimagsgade – CX – ✉ 2900 Hellerup :

XX **Saison,** Strandvejen 203, ✉ 2900, ☎ 39 62 48 42, Fax 39 62 56 57 – Ⓟ. AE ⓓ E VISA JCB
closed Sunday, 2 weeks July and Bank Holidays – **Meals** 175/525 and a la carte.

at Klampenborg N : 12 km by Østbanegade - DX - on coast rd - ✉ 2930 :

X **Den Gule Cottage,** Staunings Plaene, Strandvejen 506, ✉ 2930, ☎ 39 64 06 91, Fax 39 64 27 77, ≤, « Thatched cottage beside the sea » - Ⓟ. AE ⓓ E VISA JCB
closed 22 December-2 January - **Meals** 210/445 and a la carte.

at Søllerød N : 16 km by Tagensvej - BX - Lyngbyvej and Road 19 - ✉ 2840 Holte :

XXX **Søllerød Kro,** Søllerødvej 35, ✉ 2840, ☎ 42 80 25 05, Fax 42 80 22 70, « 17C thatched inn, terrace » - Ⓟ. AE ⓓ E VISA JCB. ✻
Meals 150/510 and a la carte 365/530.

at Kastrup Airport SE : 10 km by Amager Boulevard - CZ - ✉ 2300 S :

Dan, Kastruplundgade 15, Kastrup, ✉ 2770, N : 2 ¾ km by coastal rd ☎ 31 51 14 00, Telex 31111, Fax 31 51 37 01, ⛱, ≘s - |♦| ⇔ rm ▤ rest TV ☎ Ⓟ - 🏛 150. AE ⓓ E VISA JCB. ✻ rest
Meals (buffet lunch) 168/265 and a la carte - **228 rm** ☐ 895/1395.

Radisson SAS Globetrotter, Engvej 171, ✉ 2300 S, NW : 2 ½ km by coastal rd ☎ 31 55 14 33, Fax 31 55 81 45, Fδ, ≘s, ▣ - |♦| ⇔ rm TV ☎ Ⓟ - 🏛 360. AE ⓓ E VISA JCB. ✻
Meals (buffet lunch) 170/300 and dinner a la carte - **197 rm** ☐ 1130/1595.

Finland

Suomi

HELSINKI

PRACTICAL INFORMATION

LOCAL CURRENCY

Finnish Mark: 100 FIM = 22.99 USD ($) (Jan. 96)

TOURIST INFORMATION

The Tourist Office is situated near the Market Square, Pohjoisesplanadi 19 ✆ 169 3757 and 174 088. Open from 2 May to 30 September, Monday to Friday 8.30am - 6pm, Saturday and Sunday 10.00am - 3.00pm, and from 1 October to 30 April, Monday to Friday 8.30am - 4.00pm. Hotel bookings are possible from a reservation board situated in airport arrival lounge; information also available free.

FOREIGN EXCHANGE

Banks are open between 9.15am and 4.15pm on weekdays only. Exchange office at Helsinki-Vantaa airport and Helsinki harbour open daily between 6.30am and 11pm.

MEALS

At lunchtime, follow the custom of the country and try the typical buffets of Scandinavian specialities.
At dinner, the a la carte and set menus will offer you more conventionnal cooking. Booking is essential.
Many city centre restaurants are closed for a few days over the Midsummer Day period.

SHOPPING IN HELSINKI

Furs, jewelry, china, glass and ceramics, Finnish handicraft and wood. In the index of street names, those printed in red are where the principal shops are found. Your hotel porter will be able to help you with information.

THEATRE BOOKINGS

A ticket service - Lippupalvelu, Mannerheimintie 5, is selling tickets for cinema, concert and theatre performances - Telephone 6138 6246, open Mon-Fri 9am to 6pm, Sat. 9am to 2pm.

CAR HIRE

The international car hire companies have branches in Helsinki city and at Vantaa airport. Your hotel porter should be able to help you with your arrangements.

TIPPING

Service is normally included in hotel and restaurant bills - Doormen, baggage porters etc. are generally given a gratuity; taxi drivers are usually not tipped.

SPEED LIMITS

The maximum permitted speed on motorways is 120 km/h - 74 mph (in winter 100 km/h - 62 mph), 80 km/h - 50 mph on other roads and 50 km/h - 31 mph in built-up areas.

SEAT BELTS

The wearing of seat belts in Finland is compulsory for drivers and for front and rear seat passagers.

Helsinki

Finland 985 L 21 – Pop. 491 777 – ✆ 90.

See : Senate Square★★★ (Senaatintori) DY 53 : Lutheran Cathedral (Tuomiokirkko) DY, University Library (Yliopiston kirjasto) CY **B**, Government Building (Valtioneuvosto) DY **C**, Sederholm House DY **E** – Market Square★★ (Kauppatori) DY **26** : Uspensky Cathedral (Uspenskin katedraali) DY, Presidential Palace (Presidentinlinna) DY **F**, Havis Amanda Fountain DY **K** – Spa Park★ (Kaivopuisto) DZ ; Esplanade★★ (Eteläesplanadi CY **8**, Pohjoisesplanadi CY **43** ; Aleksanterinkatu★ CDY **2** ; Atheneum Art Museum★★ (Ateneum In Taidemuseo) CY **M1** – Mannerheimintie★★ BCXY : Parliament House (Eduskuntatalo) BX, Rock Church (Temppeliaukion kirkko) BX, National Museum (Kansallismuseo) BX **M2**, Helsinki City Museum (Helsingin kaupunginmuseo) BX **M3**, Finlandia Hall (Finlandia-talo) BX – Sibelius Monument★★ (Sibeliuksen puisto) AX ; Stadium tower (Olympiastadion) BX : view★★.

Sightseeing by sea : Fortress of Suomenlinna★★ ; Seurasaari Open-Air Museum★ (from Kauppatori) ; Helsinki zoo★ (Korkeasaari).

Entertainment : Helsinki Festival★★ (19 August to 1 September).

18 Tali Manor ✆ 550 235.

✈ Helsinki-Vantaa N : 19 km ✆ 821 122 – Finnair Head Office, Tietotie 11 A – 01053 ✆ 818 8114, Fax 818 40 92 – Air Terminal : Hotel Intercontinental, Mannerheimintie 46 – Finnair City Terminal : Abema – Aukio 3, ✆ 818 77 50, Fax 818 77 65.

⛴ To Sweden, Estonia, Poland and boat excursions : contact the City Tourist Office (see below) – Car Ferry : Silja Line – Finnjet Line ✆ 180 41.

ℹ City Tourist Office Pohjoisesplanadi 19 ✆ 169 37 57, Fax 169 38 39 – Automobile and Touring Club of Finland : Autoliitto ✆ 694 00 22, Telex 124 839, Fax 693 25 78.

Lahti 103 – Tampere 176 – Turku 165.

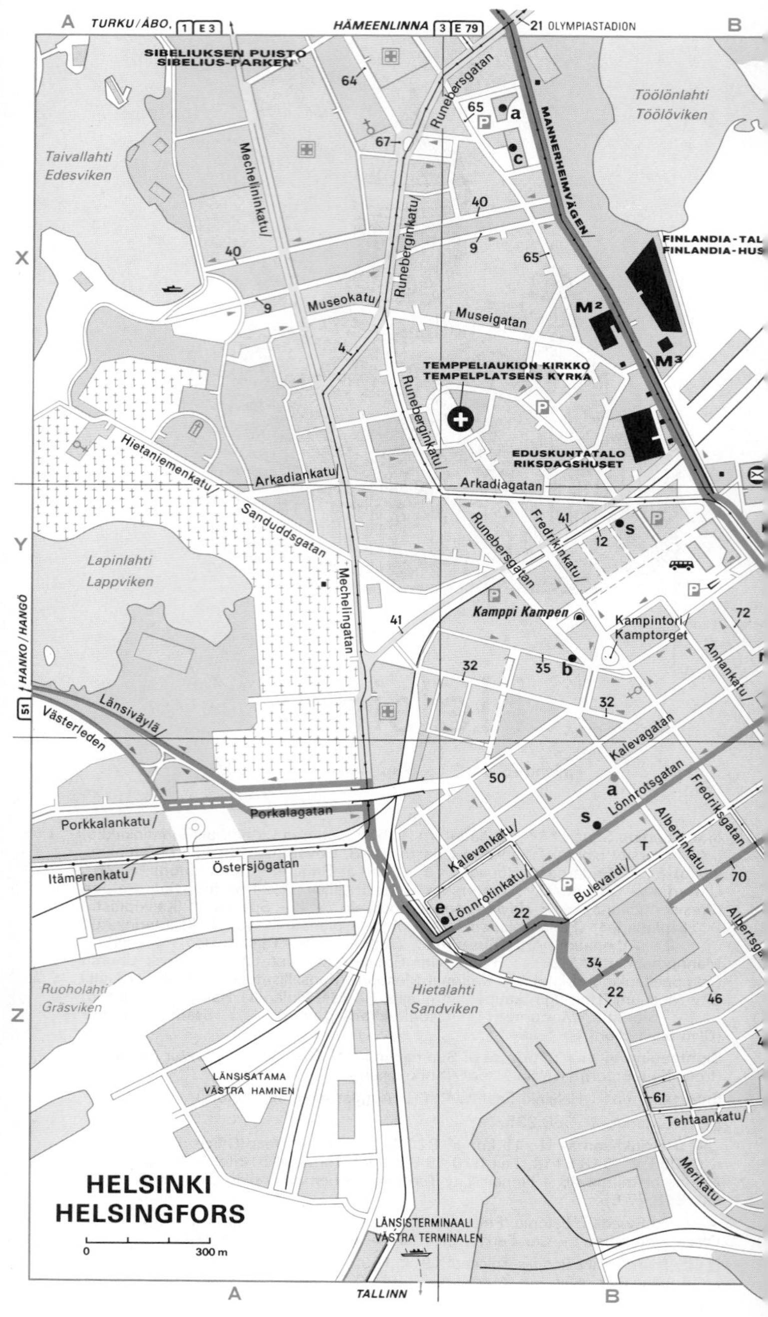

TURKU/ÅBO 1 E 3
HÄMEENLINNA 3 E 79
21 OLYMPIASTADION
SIBELIUKSEN PUISTO
SIBELIUS-PARKEN
Töölönlahti
Töölöviken
Taivallahti
Edesviken
Mechelininkatu
Runebersgatan
Runeberginkatu
MANNERHEIMVÄGEN
FINLANDIA-TAL
FINLANDIA-HUS
Museokatu
Museigatan
TEMPPELIAUKION KIRKKO
TEMPELPLATSENS KYRKA
EDUSKUNTATALO
RIKSDAGSHUSET
Hietaniemenkatu
Arkadiankatu
Arkadiagatan
Sanduddsgatan
Fredrikinkatu
Lapinlahti
Lappviken
Mechelingatan
Kamppi Kampen
Kampintori/
Kamptorget
Annankatu
HANKO/HANGÖ
Länsiväylä
Västerleden
Kalevagatan
Lönnrotsgatan
Fredriksgatan
Albertinkatu
Porkalagatan
Porkkalankatu
Östersjögatan
Itämerenkatu
Kalevankatu
Bulevardi
Lönnrotinkatu
Albertsgatan
Ruoholahti
Gräsviken
Hietalahti
Sandviken
LÄNSISATAMA
VÄSTRA HAMNEN
Tehtaankatu
Merikatu
HELSINKI
HELSINGFORS
0
300 m
LÄNSITERMINAALI
VÄSTRA TERMINALEN
TALLINN

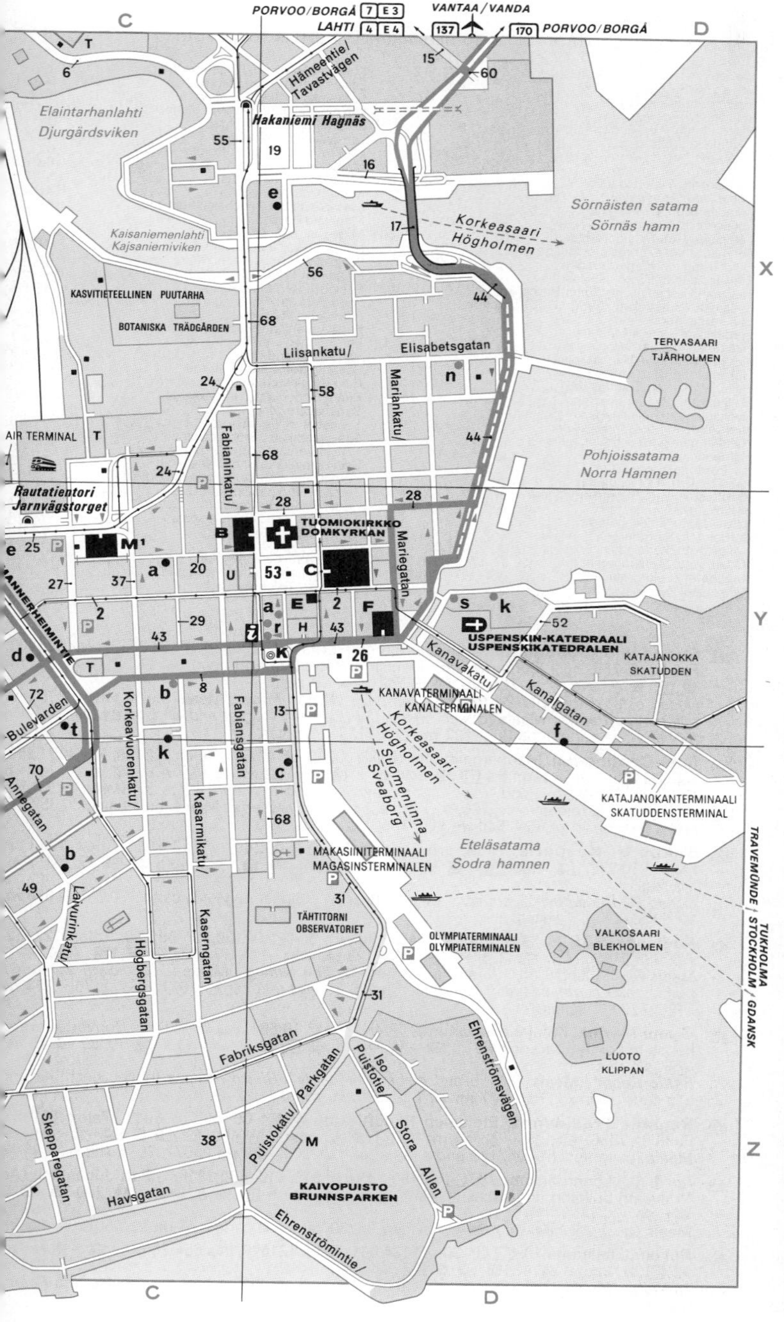

PORVOO/BORGÅ 7 E3
LAHTI 4 E4
VANTAA/VANDA
137
170 PORVOO/BORGÅ
Eläintarhanlahti
Djurgårdsviken
Hämeentie/
Tavastvägen
Hakaniemi Hagnäs
Kaisaniemenlahti
Kajsaniemiviken
Sörnäisten satama
Sörnäs hamn
Korkeasaari
Högholmen
KASVITIETEELLINEN PUUTARHA
BOTANISKA TRÄDGÅRDEN
Liisankatu/
Elisabetsgatan
TERVASAARI
TJÄRHOLMEN
Mariankatu/
Fabianinkatu/
AIR TERMINAL
Pohjoissatama
Norra Hamnen
Rautatientori
Järnvägstorget
TUOMIOKIRKKO
DOMKYRKAN
Mariegatan
MANNERHEIMINTIE
USPENSKIN-KATEDRAALI
USPENSKIKATEDRALEN
KATAJANOKKA
SKATUDDEN
Kanavakatu
Kanalgatan
KANAVATERMINAALI
KANALTERMINALEN
Bulevarden
Korkeavuorenkatu/
Fabiansgatan
Korkeasaari
Högholmen
Suomenlinna
Sveaborg
Annegatan
Kasarmikatu/
KATAJANOKANTERMINAALI
SKATUDDENSTERMINAL
MAKASIINITERMINAALI
MAGASINSTERMINALEN
Eteläsatama
Sodra hamnen
TRAVEMÜNDE / TUKHOLMA / STOCKHOLM / GDANSK
Laivurinkatu/
TÄHTITORNI
OBSERVATORIET
OLYMPIATERMINAALI
OLYMPIATERMINALEN
VALKOSAARI
BLEKHOLMEN
Högbergsgatan
Kaserngatan
Fabriksgatan
Puistotie/
Iso
Parkgatan
Ehrenströmsvägen
LUOTO
KLIPPAN
Skepparegatan
Puistokatu/
Stora
Allen
KAIVOPUISTO
BRUNNSPARKEN
Havsgatan
Ehrenströmintie/

STREET INDEX TO HELSINKI/HELSINGFORS TOWN PLAN

Aleksanterinkatu/Alexandersgatan . . . CDY 2
Fabianinkatu/Fabiansgatan . . . CXYZ
Keskuskatu/Centralgatan . . . CY 27
Kluuvikatu/Glogatan . . . CY 29
Mannerheimintie/Mannerheimvägen . . . BCXY
Mikonkatu/Mikaelsgatan . . . CY 37
Pohjoisesplanadi/Norra esplanaden . . . CDY 43

Albertinkatu/Albertsgatan . . . BZ
Annankatu/Annegatan . . . BCYZ
Arkadiankatu/Arkadiagatan . . . ABX
Bulevardi/Bulevarden . . . BCXY
Caloniuksenkatu/Caloniusgatan . . . AX 4
Ehrenströmintie/Ehrenströmsvägen . . . DZ
Eläintarhantie/Djurgårdsvägen . . . CX 6
Eteläesplanadi/Södra esplanaden . . . CY 8
Eteläinen Hesperiankatu/Södra Hesperiagatan . . ABX 9
Eteläinen Rautatiekatu/Södra Järnvägsgatan . BY 12
Eteläranta/Södra kajen . . . DY 13
Fredrikinkatu/Fredriksgatan . . . BYZ
Haapaniemenkatu/Aspnäsgatan . . . DX 15
Hakaniemenranta/Hagnäskajen . . . DX 16
Hakaniemen silta/Hagnäs bro . . . DX 17
Hakaniemen tori/Hagnäs torg . . . DX 19
Hallituskatu/Regeringsgatan . . . CY 20
Helsinginkatu/Helsingegatan . . . BX 21
Hietalahdenranta/Sandvikskajen . . . BZ 22
Hietaniemenkatu/Sanduddsgatan . . . AXY
Hämeentie/Tavastvägen . . . DX
Iso Puistotie/Stora Allen . . . DZ
Itämerenkatu/Östersjögatan . . . AZ
Kaisaniemenkatu/Kajsaniemigatan . . . CX 24
Kaivokatu/Brunnsgatan . . . CY 25
Kalevankatu/Kalevagatan . . . BYZ
Kampintori/Kamptorget . . . BY
Kanavakatu/Kanalgatan . . . DXY
Kasarmikatu/Kaserngatan . . . CZ
Kauppatori/Salutorget . . . DY 26
Kirkkokatu/Kyrkogatan . . . DY 28
Korkeavuorenkatu/Högbergsgatan . . . CYZ
Laivasillankatu/Skeppsbrogatan . . . DZ
Laivurinkatu/Skepparegatan . . . CZ
Lapinlahdenkatu/Lappviksgatan . . . BY
Liisankatu/Elisabetsgatan . . . DX
Länsiväylä/Västerleden . . . AYZ
Lönnrotinkatu/Lönnrotsgatan . . . BZ
Mallaskatu/Maltgatan . . . BZ
Malminkatu/Malmgatan . . . BY
Mariankatu/Mariegatan . . . DXY
Mechelininkatu/Mechelingatan . . . AXY
Merikatu/Havsgatan . . . BCZ
Museokatu/Museigatan . . . ABX
Neitsytpolku/Jungfrustigen . . . CZ
Pohjoinen Hesperiankatu/Norra Hesperiagatan . ABX
Pohjoinen Rautatiekatu/Norra Järnvägsgatan . ABY
Pohjoisranta/Norra kajen . . . DX
Porkkalankatu/Porkalagatan . . . AZ
Puistokatu/Parkgatan . . . DZ
Punavuorenkatu/Rödbergsgatan . . . BZ
Pursimiehenkatu/Båtsmansgatan . . . BZ
Ratakatu/Bangatan . . . CZ
Rautatientori/Järnvägstorget . . . CY
Runeberginkatu/Runebersgatan . . . ABXY
Ruoholahdenkatu/Gräsviksgatan . . . BZ
Satamakatu/Hamngatan . . . DY
Senaatintori/Senatstorget . . . DY
Siltasaarenkatu/Broholmsgatan . . . CX
Siltavuorenranta/Brobergskajen . . . DX
Snellmaninkatu/Snellmansgatan . . . DX
Sörnäisten rantatie/Sörnäs strandväg . . . DX
Tehtaankatu/Fabriksgatan . . . BCDZ
Telakkakatu/Docksgatan . . . BZ
Topeliuksenkatu/Topeliusgatan . . . AX
Töölönkatu/Tölögatan . . . BX
Töölöntori/Tölötorg . . . AX
Unioninkatu/Unionsgatan . . . DXYZ
Uudenmaankatu/Nylandsgatan . . . BCZ
Yrjönkatu/Georgsgatan . . . BCY

Strand Inter-Continental, John Stenbergin Ranta 4, ⊠ 00530, ✆ 39 351, Telex 12620 Fax 39 35 255, ←, « Contemporary Finnish architecture and decor », ≘s, ◻ - |‡| ⇆ rm ▤ TV ☎ & ⇔ - 🔬 300. AE ① E VISA JCB. ✳ rest DX
closed 5 to 8 April and 24 to 26 December - ***Atrium Plaza :*** **Meals** (buffet lunch) 215 an a la carte - ***Pamir :*** **Meals** *(closed Easter, 21 June-mid August and Christmas)* (dinner onl 535 and a la carte - ☐ 80 - **192 rm** 1208/1367, 8 suites.

Inter-Continental, Mannerheimintie 46, ⊠ 00260, ✆ 40 551, Telex 122159, Fax 405 525 Ƒ₺, ≘s, ◻ - |‡| ⇆ rm ▤ TV ☎ ⇔ Ⓟ - 🔬 700. AE ① E VISA JCB. ✳ rest BX
Galateia : **Meals** - Seafood - *(closed Saturday, Sunday, 5 to 8 April, 28 to 31 March 1997 an Bank Holidays)* (dinner only) 220/410 and a la carte - ***Brasserie :*** **Meals** (buffet lunch) 135/19 and a la carte - ☐ 65 - **540 rm** 960/1350, 12 suites.

Sokos H. Hesperia, Mannerheimintie 50, ⊠ 00260, ✆ 43 101, Telex 12211 Fax 43 10 995, Ƒ₺, ≘s, ◻ - |‡| ⇆ rm ▤ TV ☎ ⇔ Ⓟ - 🔬 400. AE ① E VISA JC ✳ rest BX
closed 22 December-2 January - **Meals** - Russian - (dinner only) a la carte 120/200 - **356 r** ☐ 1150/1430, 4 suites.

Radisson SAS H. Helsinki, Runeberginkatu 2, ⊠ 00100, ✆ 695 80, Telex 12211 Fax 695 87100, Ƒ₺, ≘s - |‡| ⇆ rm ▤ TV ☎ & ⇔ - 🔬 175. AE ① E VISA JCB. ✳
Meals (buffet lunch) 85/196 and a la carte - ***Johan Ludvig :*** **Meals** *(closed Saturday lunc Sunday and summer)* (grill rest.) (buffet lunch) 85 and a la carte 120/175 - ☐ 75 - **253 r** 1120/1220, 7 suites. BY

Grand Marina, Katajanokanlaituri 7, ⊠ 00160, ✆ 16 661, Fax 664 764, « Converted war house in contemporary style », ≘s - |‡| ⇆ rm ▤ TV ☎ & ⇔ Ⓟ - 🔬 70. AE ① E VIS JCB. ✳ rest DYZ
Baltic Room : **Meals** 78/158 and dinner a la carte - ***Bistro :*** **Meals** (buffet lunch) 42 an a la carte approx. 115 - **447 rm** ☐ 690/840, 15 suites.

Ramada Presidentti, Eteläinen Rautatiekatu 4, ⊠ 00100, ✆ 6911, Telex 12195 Fax 694 7886, ≘s, ◻ - |‡| ⇆ rm ▤ TV ☎ & ⇔ - 🔬 400. AE ① E VISA. ✳ rest
Meals (buffet lunch) 105/180 and a la carte - ☐ 30 - **490 rm** 930/1090, 5 suites. BY

Lord ⛬, Lönnrotinkatu 29, ⊠ 00180, ✆ 615 815, Fax 680 1315, « Part Jugendstil (A Nouveau) building, fireplaces », ≘s - |‡| ⇆ rm ▤ rm TV ☎ & ⇔ - 🔬 200. AE ① VISA. ✳ BZ
Meals *(closed Sunday and Bank Holidays)* 85/300 and a la carte - **47 rm** ☐ 650/800, 1 suit

Palace, Eteläranta 10, ⊠ 00130, ✆ 134 561, Telex 121570, Fax 654 786, ←, ≘s - |‡| ⇆ r ▤ TV ☎ ⇔ - 🔬 40. AE ① E VISA. ✳ rest DZ
La Vista : **Meals** - Italian - *(closed Saturday lunch)* 60/200 and a la carte - (see also ***Palac*** below) - **48 rm** ☐ 990/1400, 2 suites.

Sokos H. Vaakuna, Asema-aukio 2, ✉ 00100, ☎ 131 181, Telex 121381, Fax 131 18 234, – rm. – Meals 135/190 and a la carte – **274 rm** 960/1155, 10 suites. BY **n**

Sokos H. Klaus Kurki, Bulevardi 2, ✉ 00120, ☎ 618 911, Telex 121670, Fax 608 538, – rm. – **Meals** (buffet lunch) 50/200 and dinner a la carte – **134 rm** 890/1100, 1 suite. CY **t**

Arctia H. Marski, Mannerheimintie 10, ✉ 00100, ☎ 68 061, Telex 121240, Fax 642 377, – rm – 400. **Meals** 80/160 and a la carte – **226 rm** 845/1145, 6 suites. CY **d**

Seaside, Ruoholahdenranta 3, ✉ 00180, ☎ 69 360, Telex 126122, Fax 69 32 123, – rm – 60. rest **Meals** 75/250 and a la carte – **321 rm** 590/880, 2 suites. ABZ **e**

Seurahuone-Socis, Kaivokatu 12, ✉ 00100, ☎ 69 141, Telex 122234, Fax 691 4010, – rest **Meals** (buffet lunch) 35/182 and dinner a la carte – **118 rm** 630/970. CY **e**

Sokos H. Torni, Yrjönkatu 26, ✉ 00100, ☎ 131 131, Telex 125153, Fax 131 1361, – rm – 40. rest *closed Christmas* – **Meals** *(closed Saturday lunch and Sunday)* 75/350 and a la carte – **152 rm** 960/1150. BY **r**

Rivoli Jardin without rest., Kasarmikatu 40, ✉ 00130, ☎ 177 880, Telex 125 881, Fax 656 988, – *closed Christmas* – **53 rm** 770/890. CYZ **k**

Sokos H. Pasila, Maistraatinportti 3, ✉ 00240, N : 3 km by Mannerheimintie ☎ 148 841, Telex 125809, Fax 143 771, squash – rm – 60. rest *closed 21 to 29 December* – **Meals** (buffet lunch) 70/255 and a la carte – **247 rm** 660/880, 6 suites.

Aurora, Helsinginkatu 50, ✉ 00530, NE : 2 km ☎ 717 400, Telex 125 643, Fax 714 240, squash – rm – 110. rest **Meals** 55/75 and a la carte – **70 rm** 370/440.

Sokos H. Helsinki without rest., Yliopistonkatu 8, ✉ 00100, ☎ 131 401, Telex 121 022, Fax 176 014, – rm *closed Christmas* – **129 rm** 660/800. CY **a**

Anna without rest., Annankatu 1, ✉ 00120, ☎ 648 011, Telex 12 5514, Fax 602 664, – *closed Christmas-New Year* – **59 rm** 330/570, 1 suite. CZ **b**

Palace (at Palace H.), Eteläranta 10 (10th floor), ✉ 00130, ☎ 134 561, Fax 657 474, harbour and city – *closed July lunch, Saturday, Sunday and Bank Holidays* – **Meals** 220/450 and a la carte. DZ **c**

Savoy, Eteläesplanadi 14 (8th floor), ✉ 00130, ☎ 176 571, Fax 628 715, – *closed Saturday, Sunday and Bank Holidays* – **Meals** 118/350 and a la carte. CY **b**

Alexander Nevski, Pohjoisesplanadi 17, ✉ 00170, ☎ 639 610, Fax 631 435 – *closed lunch Sunday and July and 24 to 26 December* – **Meals** - Russian - 120/300 and a la carte. DY **r**

Havis Amanda, Unioninkatu 23, ✉ 00170, ☎ 666 882, Fax 631 435 – *closed Sunday, Easter and 24 to 26 December* – **Meals** - Seafood - (booking essential) 80/270 and a la carte. DY **r**

Sipuli, Kanavaranta 3 (2nd floor), ✉ 00160, ☎ 179 900, Telex 630662, Fax 630 662, « Roof window Uspensky Cathedral (orthodox) » – *closed Saturday, Sunday and 21 June-4 August* – **Meals** (booking essential) (dinner only) 182/245. DY **s**

Svenska Klubben, Maurinkatu 6, ✉ 00170, ☎ 135 4706, Fax 135 4896, « Scottish style house » – *closed Saturday, Sunday and 23 June-15 August* – **Meals** 120/350 and a la carte. DX **n**

Amadeus, Sofiankatu 4, ✉ 00170, ☎ 626 676, Fax 636 064 – *closed Saturday lunch, Sunday, weekends in July and Bank Holidays* – **Meals** 150 (lunch) and dinner a la carte 216/338. DY **a**

Rivoli, Albertinkatu 38, ✉ 00180, ☎ 643 455, Fax 647 780, « Nautical decor » – *closed lunch Saturday and Sunday, 5 to 8 April, 21 to 23 June, 23 to 27 December and Bank Holidays* – **Meals** 84/200 and a la carte. BZ **a**

Kanavaranta, Kanavaranta 3E/F, ✉ 00160, ☎ 6222 633, Fax 6222 616, « Mid 19C harbour warehouse with nautical tavern » – *closed lunch Monday, Saturday and 25 June-12 August, Sunday and Bank Holidays* – **Meals** (booking essential) 55/295 and a la carte 145/255. DY **k**

at Vantaa N : 19 km by A 137 - DX - 90 Helsinki :

Sokos H. Vantaa, Hertaksentie 2, near Tikkurila Railway Station, ✉ 01300, ✆ 857 85
Telex 121775, Fax 8578 5555, - rm - 95. AE E VISA. rest
closed Christmas - **Meals** *(closed Sunday lunch and Bank Holidays)* a la carte 80/154 - **154 rm**
660/800, 8 suites.

Holiday Inn Garden Court, Rälssitie 2, Helsinki Airport, ✉ 01510, ✆ 870 900
Telex 126121, Fax 870 90101, - rm - 30. AE E VISA JCB.
closed Christmas - **Meals** *(closed lunch Saturday and Sunday)* 75/150 and a la carte - **287 rm**
720/820.

Airport H. Rantasipi, Robert Huberin Tie 4, ✉ 01510, ✆ 87051, Telex 121812
Fax 822 846, , - rm - 250. AE E VISA JCB. rest
Meals (buffet lunch) 55/120 and a la carte - **296 rm** 670/770, 4 suites.

France

PARIS AND ENVIRONS - BORDEAUX
CANNES - LILLE - LYONS
MARSEILLES - PRINCIPALITY OF MONACO
NICE - STRASBOURG
VALLEY OF THE LOIRE

PRACTICAL INFORMATION

LOCAL CURRENCY

French Franc: 100 FRF = 20.41 USD ($) (Jan. 96)

TOURIST INFORMATION IN PARIS

Paris "Welcome" Office (Office du Tourisme et des Congrès de Paris - Accueil de France): 127 Champs-Élysées, 8th, ✆ 49 52 53 54, Fax 49 52 53 00
American Express 11 Rue Scribe, 9th, ✆ 47 77 79 79, Fax 47 77 78 75

AIRLINES

AMERICAN AIRLINES: 109, rue Fg-St-Honoré, 8th, ✆ 42 89 05 22, Fax 42 99 99 95
T.W.A.: 6, rue Christophe-Colomb, 8th, ✆ 49 19 20 00, Fax 49 19 20 09
DELTA AIRLINES: 4, rue Scribe, 9th, ✆ 47 68 92 92, Fax 47 68 52 82
BRITISH AIRWAYS: 13 bd de la Madeleine, 1st, ✆ 47 78 14 14, Fax 78 53 34 43
AIR FRANCE: 119 Champs-Élysées, 8th, ✆ 42 99 21 01, Fax 42 99 21 99
AIR INTER: 119 Champs-Élysées, 8th, ✆ 47 23 59 58, Fax 47 23 74 58

FOREIGN EXCHANGE OFFICES

Banks: close at 5pm and at weekends
Orly Airport: daily 6.30am to 11.30pm
Roissy-Charles de Gaulle Airport: daily 7am to 11.30pm

TRANSPORT IN PARIS

Taxis: may be hailed in the street when showing the illuminated sign-available day and night at taxi ranks or called by telephone
Bus-Métro (subway): for full details see the Michelin Plan de Paris nº 11. The metro is quicker but the bus is good for sightseeing and practical for short distances.

POSTAL SERVICES

Local post offices: open Mondays to Fridays 8am to 7pm; Saturdays 8am to noon
General Post Office: 52 rue du Louvre, 1st: open 24 hours

SHOPPING IN PARIS

Department stores: Boulevard Haussmann, Rue de Rivoli and Rue de Sèvres
Exclusive shops and boutiques: Faubourg St-Honoré, Rue de la Paix and Rue Royale, Avenue Montaigne.
Antiques and second-hand goods: Swiss Village (Avenue de la Motte Picquet), Louvre des Antiquaires (Place du Palais Royal), Flea Market (Porte Clignancourt).

TIPPING

Service is generally included in hotel and restaurants bills. But you may choose to leave more than the expected tip to the staff. Taxi-drivers, porters, barbers and theatre or cinema attendants also expect a small gratuity.

BREAKDOWN SERVICE

Certain garages in central and outer Paris operate a 24 hour breakdown service. If you breakdown the police are usually able to help by indicating the nearest one.

SPEED LIMITS

The maximum permitted speed in built up areas is 50 km/h - 31 mph; on motorways the speed limit is 130 km/h - 80 mph and 110 km/h - 68 mph on dual carriageways. On all other roads 90 km/h - 56 mph.

SEAT BELTS

The wearing of seat belts is compulsory for drivers and passengers.

Paris and environs

Maps : 10, 11, 12 G. Paris – ❂ 1.

Population : Paris 2 152 333 ; Ile-de-France region : 10 651 000.
Altitude : Observatory : 60 m ; Place Concorde : 34 m
Air Terminals – To Orly : Esplanade des Invalides, 7th, ✆ 43 17 21 65 – **To Charles de Gaulle** (Roissy) : Palais des Congrès, Porte Maillot, 17th, ✆ 44 09 51 52
Paris'Airports : see Orly and Charles de Gaulle (Roissy)
Railways, motorail : information ✆ 45 82 50 50.

ARRONDISSEMENTS

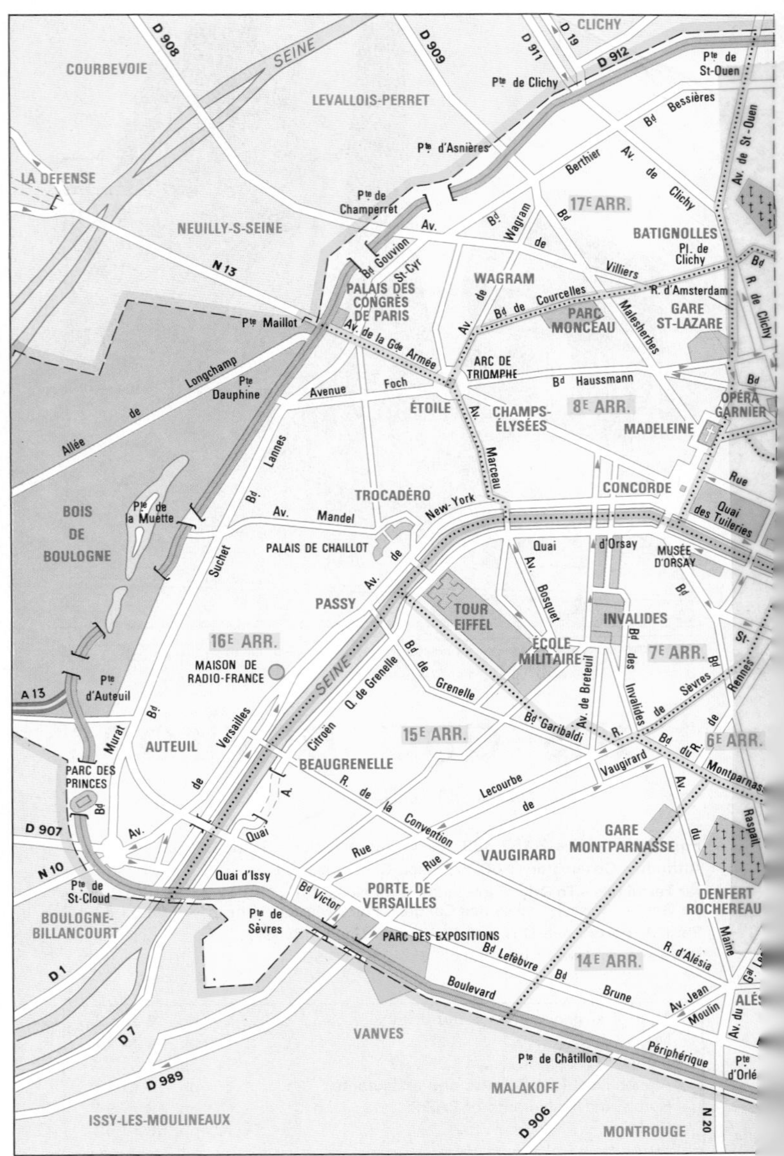

AND DISTRICTS

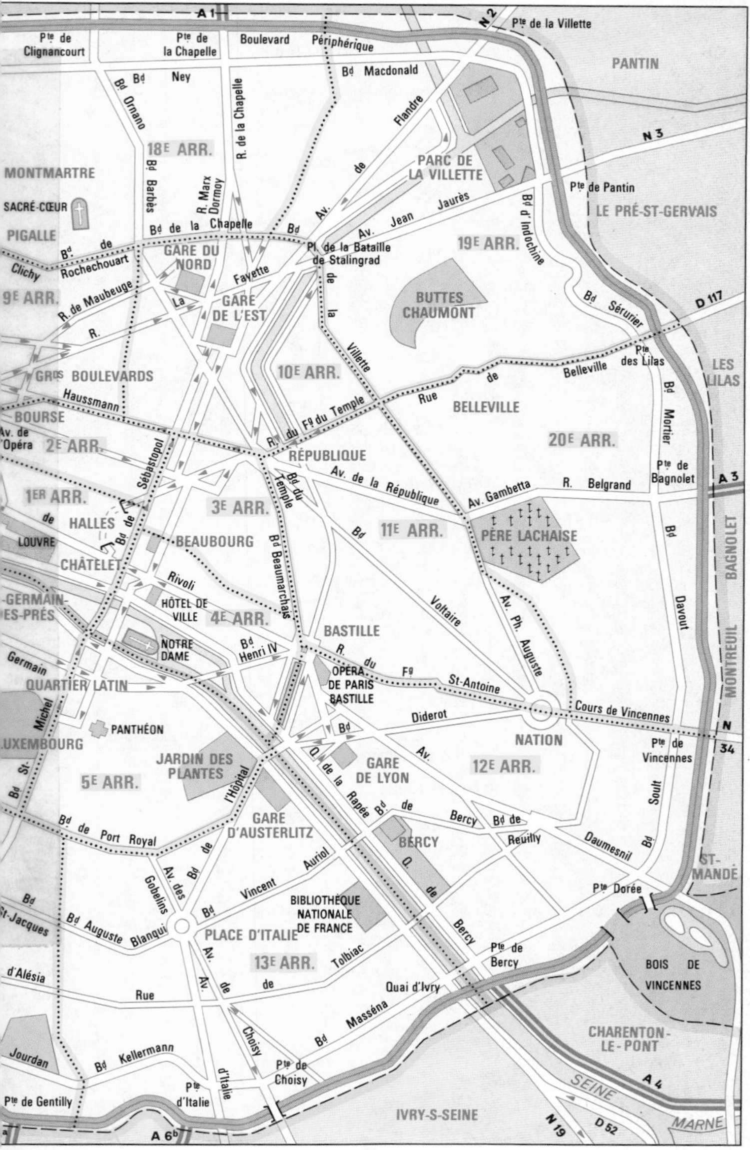

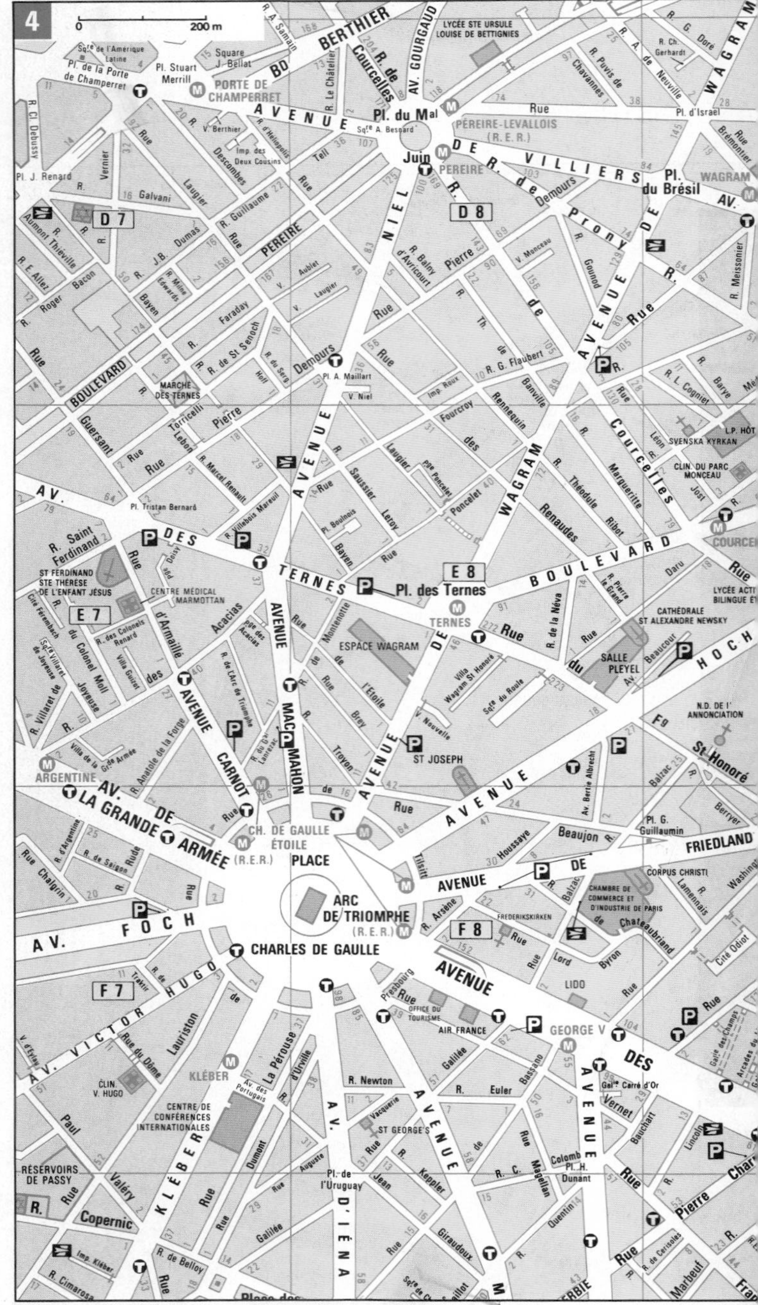
4
0
200 m
Sq.re de l'Amérique Latine
Pl. de la Porte de Champerret
Pl. Stuart Merrill
Square J. Bellat
PORTE DE CHAMPERRET
BD BERTHIER
R. A. Samain
R. Le Châtelier
R. de Courcelles
AV. GOURGAUD
LYCÉE STE URSULE LOUISE DE BETTIGNIES
R. Puvis de Chavannes
R. A. de Neuville
R. Ch. Gerhardt
R. G. Doré
WAGRAM
Pl. d'Israel
R. Bremontier
R. Cl. Debussy
Rue Vernier
R. V. Berthier
R. d'Héliopolis
Imp. des Deux Cousins
Rue Descombes
Rue Laugier
AVENUE
Rue Tell
Sq.re A. Besnard
Pl. du Mal Juin
PEREIRE-LEVALLOIS (R.E.R.)
PEREIRE
AVENUE DE VILLIERS
R. de Prony
R. de Demours
Pl. du Brésil
WAGRAM
AV. DE
Pl. J. Renard
R. Galvani
R. Guillaume
D 7
D 8
R. Aumont Thiéville
R. E. Allez
R. Roger Bacon
R. J.B. Dumas
R. Mme Edwards
R. Bayen
BOULEVARD PEREIRE
V. Aublet
V. Laugier
AVENUE NIEL
R. Balny d'Avricourt
Rue Pierre Demours
V. Monceau
R. Gounod
R. Meissonier
R. Faraday
R. de St Senoch
R. du Serg. Hoff
Rue Th. de Banville
R. G. Flaubert
R. Cardinet
R. Barye
R. L. Cogniet
MARCHÉ DES TERNES
Pl. A. Maillart
V. Niel
Imp. Roux
R. Fourcroy
R. Rennequin
R. Torricelli
R. Pierre Leroux
R. Guersant
Rue Laugier
R. Saussier Leroy
Pge Poncelet
R. Poncelet
WAGRAM
R. Théodule Ribot
R. Margueritte
Rue de Courcelles
R. Léon Jost
SVENSKA KYRKAN
L.P. HÔT
CLIN. DU PARC MONCEAU
R. Marcel Renault
R. Villebois Mareuil
Pl. Boulnois
AV. DES TERNES
Pl. Tristan Bernard
R. Saint Ferdinand
ST FERDINAND STE THÉRÈSE DE L'ENFANT JÉSUS
CENTRE MÉDICAL MARMOTTAN
Pl. des Ternes
E 8
E 7
TERNES
BOULEVARD
R. Renaudes
COURCELLES
R. Daru
LYCÉE ACTI BILINGUE
CATHÉDRALE ST ALEXANDRE NEWSKY
R. Pierre le Grand
R. de la Néva
Rue du Fg St Honoré
SALLE PLEYEL
Av. Beaucour
AV. HOCH
N.D. DE L'ANNONCIATION
Cité Ferembach
R. du Colonel Moll
R. des Colonels Renard
Villa Guizot
R. d'Armaillé
Rue des Acacias
Pge des Acacias
R. de l'Arc de Triomphe
AVENUE MAC MAHON
R. Montenotte
Rue de l'Étoile
ESPACE WAGRAM
Villa Wagram St Honoré
Sq.re du Roule
R. Brey
R. Troyon
V. Nouvelle
ST JOSEPH
Sq.re Villaret de Joyeuse
R. Villaret de Joyeuse
R. Joyeuse
Villa de la Gde Armée
R. Anatole de la Forge
AVENUE CARNOT
R. du Gal Lanrezac
ARGENTINE
AV. DE LA GRANDE ARMÉE
Rue de Tilsitt
AVENUE
Av. Bertie Albrecht
R. Balzac
Rue Berryer
Pl. G. Guillaumin
R. Beaujon
R. Houssaye
FRIEDLAND
AVENUE DE
CH. DE GAULLE ÉTOILE (R.E.R.)
PLACE
R. d'Argentine
R. de Saïgon
Rue Rude
Rue Chalgrin
R. Balzac
CORPUS CHRISTI
CHAMBRE DE COMMERCE ET D'INDUSTRIE DE PARIS
R. Lamennais
R. Washington
ARC DE TRIOMPHE (R.E.R.)
R. Arsène Houssaye
FREDERIKSKIRKEN
Rue de Chateaubriand
AV. FOCH
CHARLES DE GAULLE
F 8
Cité Odiot
Rue Lord Byron
LIDO
AVENUE
R. de Presbourg
R. de Traktir
F 7
AV. VICTOR HUGO
OFFICE DU TOURISME
AIR FRANCE
GEORGE V
V. d'Eylau
Rue du Dôme
Rue Lauriston
CLIN. V. HUGO
KLÉBER
Av. des Portugais
Rue La Pérouse
R. d'Urville
R. Newton
R. Galilée
R. Euler
Rue Bassano
DES CHAMPS
Galie Carré d'Or
Rue Vernet
Galie des Champs
Arcades du
R. Paul Valéry
CENTRE DE CONFÉRENCES INTERNATIONALES
AV. D'IÉNA
R. Vacquerie
ST GEORGE'S
Rue Jean Goujon
AVENUE
Rue de Magellan
Colomb
Pl. H. Dunant
R. C.
R. Bouchart
Lincoln
Rue Pierre Charron
RÉSERVOIRS DE PASSY
R. Copernic
AV. KLÉBER
Rue Dumont d'Urville
R. Auguste Vacquerie
Pl. de l'Uruguay
R. Keppler
Quentin Bauchart
Rue Galilée
Imp. Kléber
R. Cimarosa
R. de Belloy
Place des
Rue Galilée
R. Giraudoux
Sq.re de Ch. Laillot
AVENUE MARCEAU
CHERBIE
R. de Cerisoles
R. Marbeuf
R. Fran

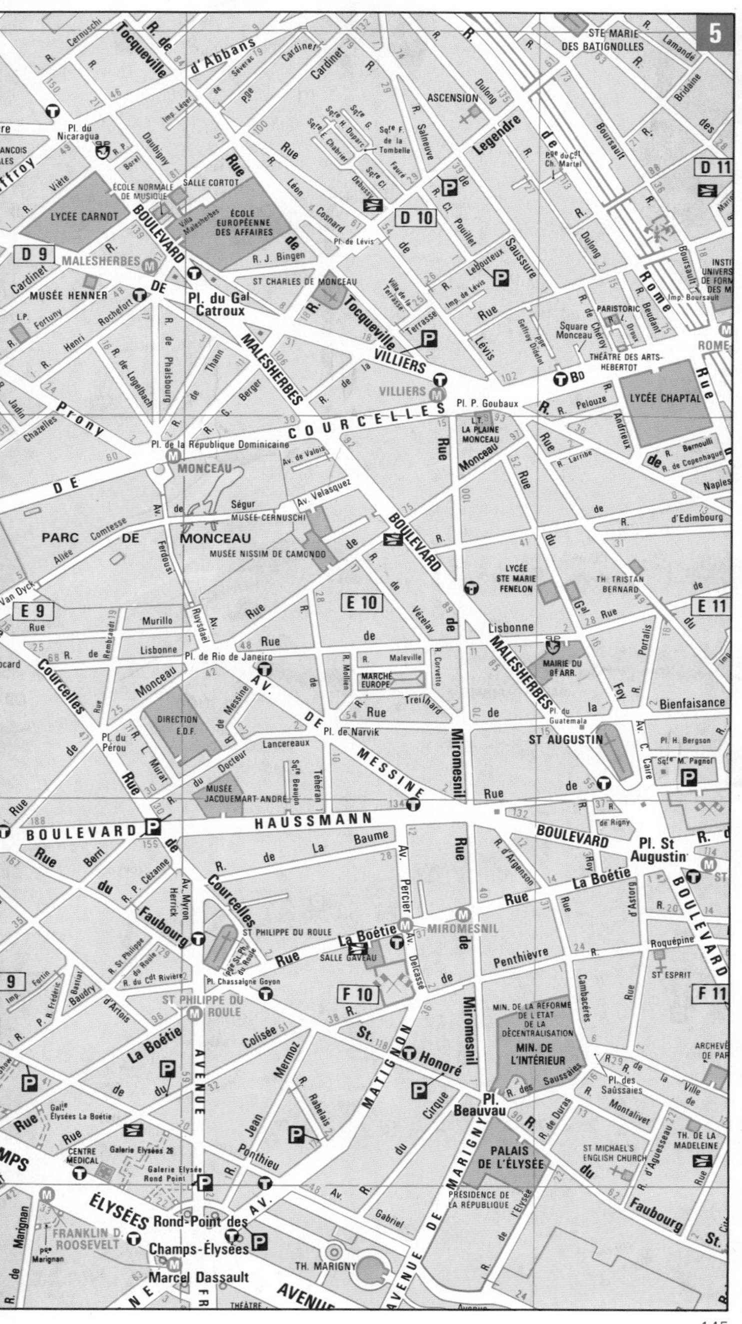
5
D 9
D 10
D 11
E 9
E 10
E 11
F 9
F 10
F 11
R. de Tocqueville
d'Abbans
Cardinet
R. Cardinet
Cernuschi
Pl. du Nicaragua
Daubigny
Borel
Viète
Rue Léon Cosnard
R. Salneuve
ASCENSION
Dulong
Legendre
STE MARIE DES BATIGNOLLES
Lamandé
Bridaine
Boursault
Pge du Cdt Ch. Martel
SALLE CORTOT
ÉCOLE NORMALE DE MUSIQUE
LYCEE CARNOT
Villa Malesherbes
ÉCOLE EUROPÉENNE DES AFFAIRES
BOULEVARD DE MALESHERBES
R. J. Bingen
MALESHERBES
MUSÉE HENNER
Fortuny
Rochefort
Henri
Pl. du Gal Catroux
ST CHARLES DE MONCEAU
Pl. de Lévis
R. Cl. Pouillet
Saussure
Lebouteux
Imp. de Lévis
Rue Lévis
Villa de la Terrasse
Terrasse
VILLIERS
R. de Phalsbourg
R. de Logelbach
de Thann
R. G. Berger
Square Monceau
Geffroy Didelot
PARISTORIC
R. de Chéroy
R. Beudant
Rome
Imp. Boursault
ROME
THÉATRE DES ARTS-HEBERTOT
LYCÉE CHAPTAL
Jadin
Chazelles
Prony
Pl. de la République Dominicaine
COURCELLES
Pl. P. Goubaux
L.T. LA PLAINE MONCEAU
Rue Monceau
R. Pelouze
Andrieux
R. Larribe
R. Bernoulli
R. de Copenhague
Naples
d'Edimbourg
MONCEAU
Av. de Valois
Av. Velasquez
PARC DE MONCEAU
Allée Comtesse de Ségur
Av. Ferdousi
MUSÉE CERNUSCHI
MUSÉE NISSIM DE CAMONDO
Van Dyck
LYCÉE STE MARIE FENELON
TH. TRISTAN BERNARD
Rue du Gal Foy
R. de Vézelay
Portalis
Murillo
Ruysdael
Rembrandt
Lisbonne
Pl. de Rio de Janeiro
R. Maleville
R. Mollien
MARCHÉ EUROPE
R. Corvetto
Treilhard
MAIRIE DU 8e ARR.
Courcelles
DIRECTION E.D.F.
Av. de Messine
Pl. de Narvik
Lancereaux
Sqre Beaujon
Téhéran
Miromesnil
Pl. du Guatemala
ST AUGUSTIN
Av. C. Caire
Bienfaisance
Pl. H. Bergson
Sqre M. Pagnol
Pl. du Pérou
R. L. Murat
R. du Docteur
MUSÉE JACQUEMART ANDRÉ
BOULEVARD HAUSSMANN
R. de Rigny
Pl. St Augustin
R. de La Baume
Av. Percier
R. d'Argenson
Rue La Boétie
Berri
R. P. Cézanne
Av. Myron Herrick
Rue du Faubourg St Honoré
ST PHILIPPE DU ROULE
MIROMESNIL
SALLE GAVEAU
Av. Delcassé
Penthièvre
Cambacérès
R. d'Astorg
Roquépine
ST ESPRIT
R. St Philippe du Roule
R. du Cdt Rivière
Pl. Chassaigne Goyon
Fortin
R. Frédéric Bastiat
Baudry
d'Artois
Colisée
MIN. DE LA RÉFORME DE L'ETAT DE LA DÉCENTRALISATION
MIN. DE L'INTÉRIEUR
Pl. des Saussaies
R. des Saussaies
R. de la Ville l'Evêque
ARCHEVÊ DE PAR
Jean Mermoz
Rabelais
MATIGNON
Honoré
R. du Cirque
Pl. Beauvau
R. de Duras
Montalivet
Galie Élysées La Boétie
CENTRE MEDICAL
Galerie Elysées 26
Galerie Elysée Rond Point
Ponthieu
PALAIS DE L'ÉLYSÉE
PRÉSIDENCE DE LA RÉPUBLIQUE
ST MICHAEL'S ENGLISH CHURCH
R. d'Aguesseau
TH. DE LA MADELEINE
AVENUE DE MARIGNY
Av. Gabriel
R. de l'Elysée
CHAMPS ÉLYSÉES
FRANKLIN D. ROOSEVELT
Pge Marignan
R. de Marignan
Rond-Point des Champs-Élysées Marcel Dassault
TH. MARIGNY
AVENUE
THÉATRE

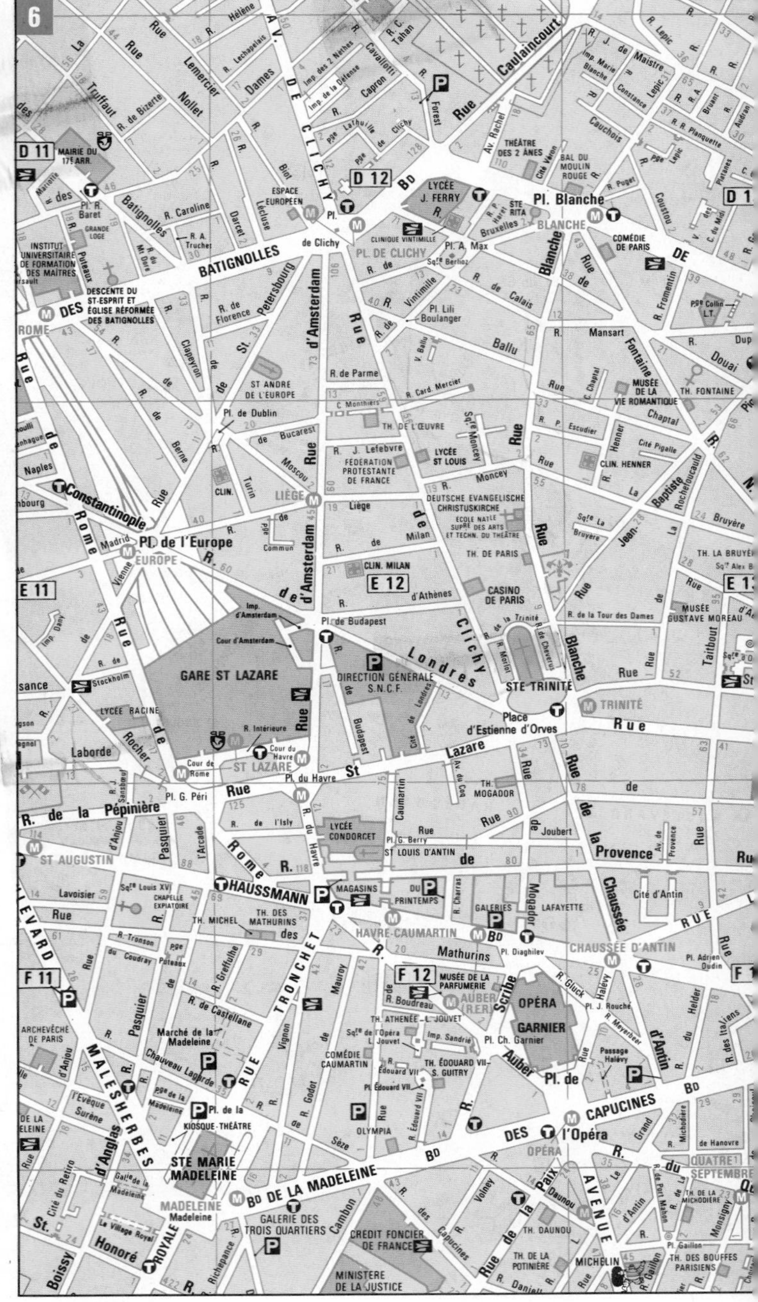
6
D 11
D 12
E 11
E 12
F 11
F 12
MAIRIE DU 17E ARR.
Rue Lemercier
Rue Nollet
R. Hélène
R. Lechapelais
R. Truffaut
R. de Bizerte
AV. DE CLICHY
R. Cavallotti
R. C. Tahan
Rue Caulaincourt
R. Capron
R. Forest
Imp. des 2 Nèthes
Imp. de la Défense
R. Biot
R. Darcet
R. Lécluse
R. Caroline
Batignolles
BATIGNOLLES
ESPACE EUROPÉEN
LYCÉE J. FERRY
CLINIQUE VINTIMILLE
PL. DE CLICHY
Pl. A. Max
Sq. Berlioz
R. de Vintimille
R. de Calais
R. Puteaux
INSTITUT UNIVERSITAIRE DE FORMATION DES MAITRES
GRANDE LOGE
Pl. R. Baret
DESCENTE DU ST-ESPRIT ET ÉGLISE RÉFORMÉE DES BATIGNOLLES
DES
ROME
R. de Florence
R. de St. Petersbourg
Rue d'Amsterdam
Rue de Clichy
R. Clapeyron
R. de Berne
ST ANDRÉ DE L'EUROPE
Pl. de Dublin
R. de Parme
R. Card. Mercier
C. Monthiers
TH. DE L'ŒUVRE
Sq. Moncey
R. Moncey
LYCÉE ST LOUIS
FÉDÉRATION PROTESTANTE DE FRANCE
R. J. Lefebvre
R. de Bucarest
R. de Moscou
R. de Turin
CLIN.
LIÈGE
R. de Liège
R. de Milan
DEUTSCHE EVANGELISCHE CHRISTUSKIRCHE
ECOLE NATLE SUPRE DES ARTS ET TECHN. DU THÉATRE
TH. DE PARIS
CASINO DE PARIS
R. d'Athènes
CLIN. MILAN
Pl. de l'Europe
EUROPE
Constantinople
Rue de Rome
R. de Madrid
R. de Vienne
R. de Naples
Imp. d'Amsterdam
Cour d'Amsterdam
Pl. de Budapest
R. de Londres
DIRECTION GÉNÉRALE S.N.C.F.
GARE ST LAZARE
Cité de Londres
R. de Budapest
R. Intérieure
Cour du Havre
Cour de Rome
ST LAZARE
Pl. du Havre
Rue St Lazare
LYCÉE RACINE
Stockholm
R. du Rocher
Laborde
R. de la Pépinière
Pl. G. Péri
R. d'Anjou
Pasquier
l'Arcade
ST AUGUSTIN
R. de l'Isly
R. du Havre
LYCÉE CONDORCET
Pl. G. Berry
ST LOUIS D'ANTIN
R. Caumartin
Rue de Provence
R. de Rome
HAUSSMANN
MAGASINS DU PRINTEMPS
R. Charras
GALERIES LAFAYETTE
Mogador
TH. MOGADOR
Rue Joubert
Av. du Coq
Place d'Estienne d'Orves
STE TRINITÉ
TRINITÉ
R. de la Trinité
R. Morlot
R. de Châteaudun
Rue Blanche
Pl. Blanche
BLANCHE
MOULIN ROUGE
BAL DU MOULIN ROUGE
THÉATRE DES 2 ÂNES
Cité Véron
Av. Rachel
R. J. de Maistre
R. Lepic
Imp. Marie Blanche
R. Constance
R. Cauchois
R. Puget
R. Coustou
R. Burq
R. Audran
R. Bruant
R. R. Planquette
R. Fromentin
COMÉDIE DE PARIS
STE RITA
R. P. Haret
R. de Bruxelles
R. de Douai
R. Mansart
R. Fontaine
R. Ballu
Pl. Lili Boulanger
V. Ballu
Rue Chaptal
C. Chaptal
MUSÉE DE LA VIE ROMANTIQUE
TH. FONTAINE
R. P. Escudier
R. Henner
Cité Pigalle
CLIN. HENNER
Rue La Rochefoucauld
Jean-Baptiste
Sq. La Bruyère
R. La Bruyère
TH. LA BRUYÈRE
R. de la Tour des Dames
MUSÉE GUSTAVE MOREAU
Taitbout
Chaussée d'Antin
CHAUSSÉE D'ANTIN
Cité d'Antin
Av. de Provence
Lavoisier
Sq. Louis XVI
CHAPELLE EXPIATOIRE
TH. MICHEL
TH. DES MATHURINS
R. des Mathurins
HAVRE-CAUMARTIN
Pl. Diaghilev
R. Tronson du Coudray
Pge Puteaux
R. Greffulhe
R. de Castellane
R. Tronchet
R. Vignon
R. de Mauroy
MUSÉE DE LA PARFUMERIE
AUBER (RER)
R. Boudreau
TH. ATHENÉE - L. JOUVET
Sq. de l'Opéra L. Jouvet
Imp. Sandrié
R. Scribe
OPÉRA GARNIER
R. Gluck
R. Halévy
Pl. J. Rouché
R. Meyerbeer
Pl. Ch. Garnier
Passage Halévy
R. du Helder
R. des Italiens
ARCHEVÊCHÉ DE PARIS
R. d'Anjou
MALESHERBES
Marché de la Madeleine
Chauveau Lagarde
Pge de la Madeleine
Pl. de la Madeleine
KIOSQUE-THÉATRE
COMÉDIE CAUMARTIN
R. Édouard VII
Pl. Édouard VII
TH. ÉDOUARD VII - S. GUITRY
R. Godot de Mauroy
OLYMPIA
R. de Sèze
R. Auber
Pl. de l'Opéra
BD DES CAPUCINES
OPÉRA
R. Grand
R. de Hanovre
R. de la Michodière
QUATRE SEPTEMBRE
STE MARIE MADELEINE
MADELEINE
BD DE LA MADELEINE
Gal. de la Madeleine
Le Village Royal
Cité du Retiro
R. d'Anglas
Boissy
St. Honoré
ROYALE
GALERIE DES TROIS QUARTIERS
R. Cambon
R. Richepance
CREDIT FONCIER DE FRANCE
MINISTERE DE LA JUSTICE
R. des Capucines
R. Volney
Rue de la Paix
R. Daunou
TH. DAUNOU
AVENUE
TH. DE LA POTINIÈRE
R. Danielle
MICHELIN
R. Gaillon
Pl. Gaillon
R. de Port Mahon
TH. DE LA MICHODIÈRE
Monsigny
TH. DES BOUFFES PARISIENS

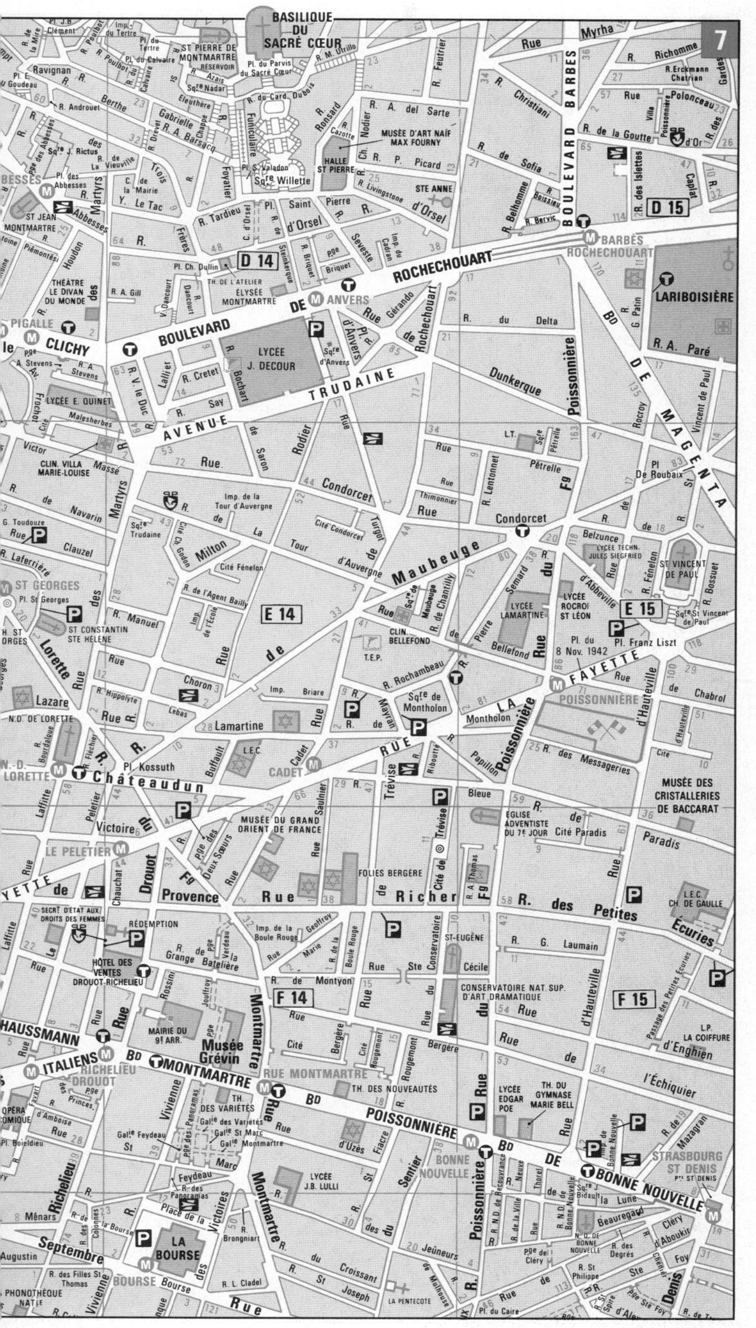
7
BASILIQUE DU SACRÉ CŒUR
ST PIERRE DE MONTMARTRE
Pl. du Parvis du Sacré Cœur
Pl. du Tertre
Pl. du Calvaire
Pl. J.B. Clément
Sq^re Nadar
R. du Card. Dubois
Funiculaire
Sq^re Willette
Pl. S. Valadon
HALLE ST PIERRE
MUSÉE D'ART NAÏF MAX FOURNY
STE ANNE
BOULEVARD BARBÈS
LARIBOISIÈRE
R. A. Paré
BARBÈS ROCHECHOUART
D 14
D 15
ABBESSES
Pl. des Abbesses
ST JEAN MONTMARTRE
BOULEVARD DE ROCHECHOUART
ANVERS
PIGALLE
CLICHY
TH. DE L'ATELIER
ÉLYSÉE MONTMARTRE
Pl. Ch. Dullin
THÉATRE LE DIVAN DU MONDE
LYCÉE J. DECOUR
AVENUE TRUDAINE
LYCÉE E. QUINET
CLIN. VILLA MARIE-LOUISE
Sq^re Trudaine
Cité Fénelon
Rue de Maubeuge
Rue La Tour d'Auvergne
Rue Condorcet
Condorcet
Rue de Dunkerque
R. du Delta
BD DE MAGENTA
Pl. De Roubaix
LYCÉE TECHN. JULES SIEGFRIED
ST VINCENT DE PAUL
Sq^re St Vincent de Paul
E 14
E 15
LYCÉE LAMARTINE
LYCÉE ROCROI ST LÉON
Pl. du 8 Nov. 1942
Pl. Franz Liszt
CLIN. BELLEFOND
T.E.P.
ST GEORGES
Pl. St Georges
ST CONSTANTIN STE HELENE
N.D. DE LORETTE
Rue Lamartine
L.E.C.
CADET
Pl. Kossuth
Rue de Châteaudun
Sq^re de Montholon
RUE LA FAYETTE
POISSONNIÈRE
R. des Messageries
MUSÉE DES CRISTALLERIES DE BACCARAT
MUSÉE DU GRAND ORIENT DE FRANCE
EGLISE ADVENTISTE DU 7^E JOUR
Cité Paradis
LE PELETIER
FOLIES BERGÈRE
Rue Richer
Rue de Provence
R. des Petites Écuries
L.E.C. CH. DE GAULLE
SECR^T D'ETAT AUX DROITS DES FEMMES
RÉDEMPTION
HÔTEL DES VENTES DROUOT-RICHELIEU
ST-EUGÈNE
Rue Ste Cécile
CONSERVATOIRE NAT. SUP. D'ART DRAMATIQUE
F 14
F 15
Passage des Petites Écuries
L.P. LA COIFFURE
Rue d'Enghien
MAIRIE DU 9^E ARR.
Musée Grévin
HAUSSMANN
RICHELIEU DROUOT
ITALIENS
BD MONTMARTRE
RUE MONTMARTRE
TH. DES NOUVEAUTÉS
LYCÉE EDGAR POE
TH. DU GYMNASE MARIE BELL
Rue de l'Échiquier
BD POISSONNIÈRE
BONNE NOUVELLE
BD DE BONNE NOUVELLE
STRASBOURG ST DENIS
OPÉRA COMIQUE
TH. DES VARIÉTÉS
Gal^ie Feydeau
Gal^ie des Variétés
Gal^ie St Marc
Gal^ie Montmartre
LYCÉE J.B. LULLI
N.D. DE BONNE NOUVELLE
LA BOURSE
BOURSE
Place de la Bourse
Rue du Quatre Septembre
R. des Filles St Thomas
PHONOTHÈQUE NAT^LE
Rue du Croissant
R. St Joseph
Rue des Jeûneurs
LA PENTECOTE
Pl. du Caire
Rue Ste Foy
Rue d'Aboukir

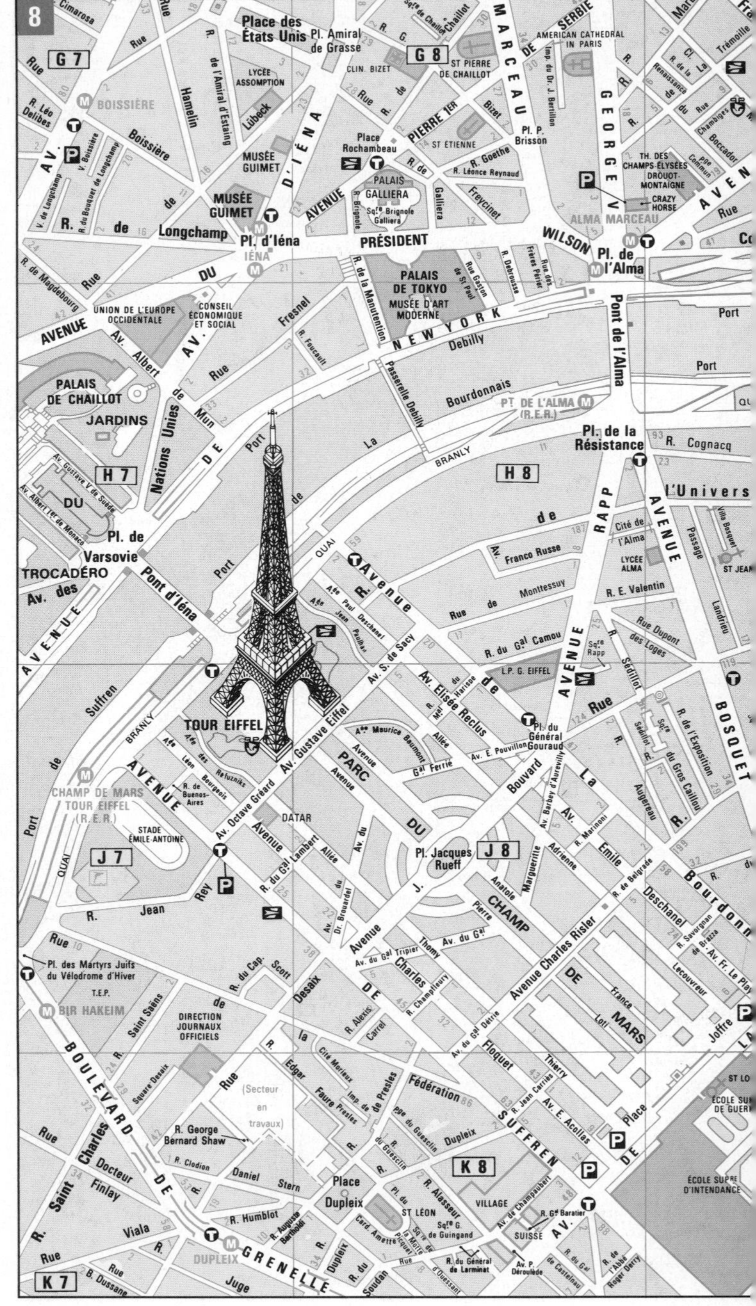
8
G 7
G 8
H 7
H 8
J 7
J 8
K 7
K 8
Place des États Unis
Pl. Amiral de Grasse
LYCÉE ASSOMPTION
CLIN. BIZET
ST PIERRE DE CHAILLOT
AMERICAN CATHEDRAL IN PARIS
MARCEAU
DE SERBIE
GEORGE V
BOISSIÈRE
Boissière
Hamelin
R. de l'Amiral d'Estaing
Lübeck
MUSÉE GUIMET
D'IÉNA
Place Rochambeau
PALAIS GALLIERA
PIERRE 1ER
ST ÉTIENNE
R. Goethe
R. Léonce Reynaud
Freycinet
Galliera
Bizet
Pl. P. Brisson
TH. DES CHAMPS-ÉLYSÉES DROUOT-MONTAIGNE
CRAZY HORSE
ALMA MARCEAU
R. de Longchamp
Pl. d'Iéna
IÉNA
AVENUE PRÉSIDENT WILSON
Pl. de l'Alma
PALAIS DE TOKYO
MUSÉE D'ART MODERNE
R. de la Manutention
R. Debrousse
UNION DE L'EUROPE OCCIDENTALE
CONSEIL ÉCONOMIQUE ET SOCIAL
AVENUE DU
Rue Fresnel
AV. DE NEW YORK
Debilly
Pont de l'Alma
Port
PALAIS DE CHAILLOT
JARDINS
Av. Albert de Mun
Nations Unies
Passerelle Debilly
Bourdonnais
PT DE L'ALMA (R.E.R.)
Pl. de la Résistance
R. Cognacq
QUAI BRANLY
L'Univers
AVENUE RAPP
Cité de l'Alma
LYCÉE ALMA
Av. Franco Russe
R. E. Valentin
Rue de Monttessuy
Pl. de Varsovie
TROCADÉRO
Av. des
Pont d'Iéna
Port
Avenue de La Bourdonnais
Rue Dupont des Loges
R. du Gal Camou
Sqre Rapp
L.P. G. EIFFEL
Av. S. de Sacy
Av. Elisée Reclus
Sédillot
BOSQUET
Suffren
TOUR EIFFEL
Av. Gustave Eiffel
Pl. du Général Gouraud
Av. E. Pouvillon
Bouvard
PARC DU CHAMP DE MARS
CHAMP DE MARS TOUR EIFFEL (R.E.R.)
STADE ÉMILE-ANTOINE
Av. Octave Gréard
DATAR
R. de l'Exposition
du Gros Caillou
Augereau
Av. Émile Deschanel
Pl. Jacques Rueff
Anatole France
Avenue Charles Risler
R. de Belgrade
Jean Rey
Pl. des Martyrs Juifs du Vélodrome d'Hiver
T.E.P.
BIR HAKEIM
DIRECTION JOURNAUX OFFICIELS
BOULEVARD DE GRENELLE
Desaix
R. Alexis Carrel
Rue de la Fédération
Av. du Gal Détrie
Floquet
Thierry
(Secteur en travaux)
R. George Bernard Shaw
R. Clodion
Daniel Stern
Place Dupleix
Square Desaix
Rue Saint Charles
Docteur Finlay
Viala
R. Humblot
DUPLEIX
ST LÉON
VILLAGE SUISSE
ÉCOLE SUPRE D'INTENDANCE
ÉCOLE SUP DE GUERR
Joffre
R. Jean Carriès
Av. E. Acollas
SUFFREN
Juge
B. Dussane
Soudan

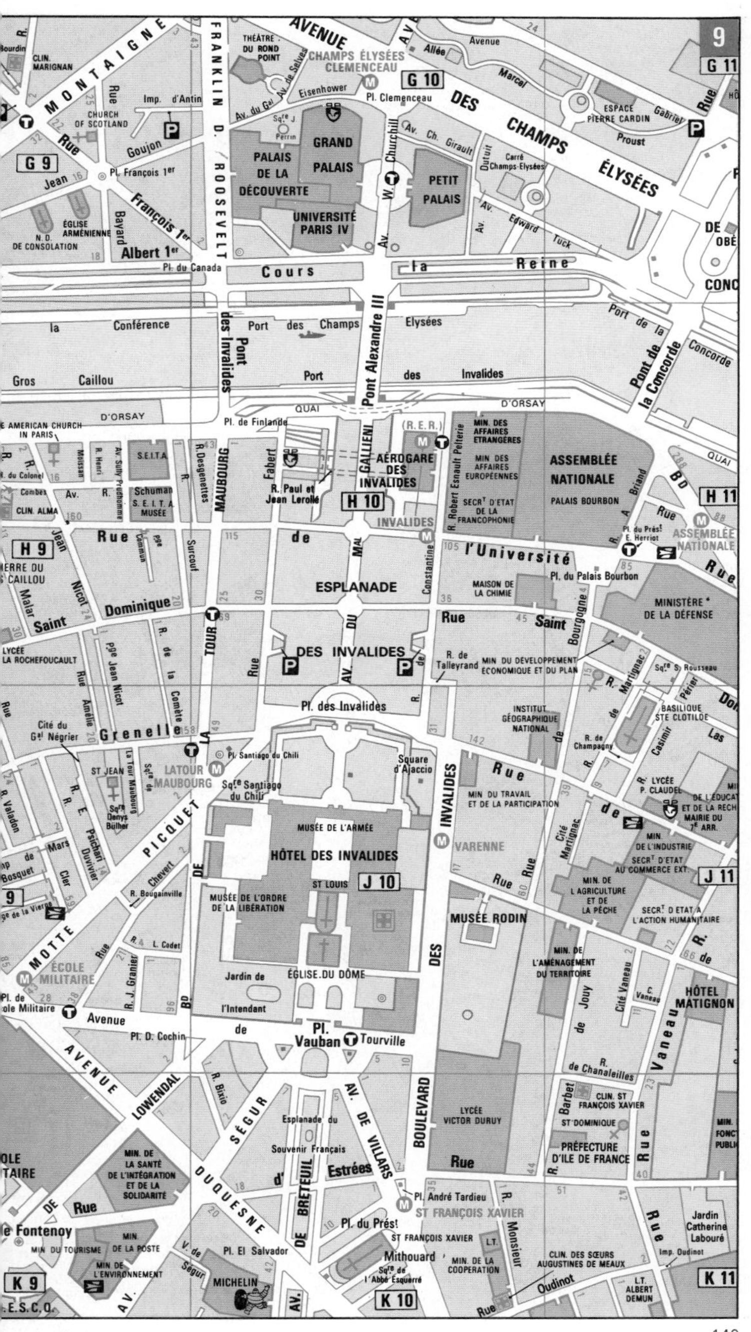
9
G 11
G 10
G 9
H 9
H 10
H 11
J 10
J 11
K 9
K 10
K 11
AVENUE
DES CHAMPS ÉLYSÉES
MONTAIGNE
THÉÂTRE DU ROND POINT
CHAMPS ÉLYSÉES CLEMENCEAU
Pl. Clemenceau
Av. de Selves
Av. du Gal Eisenhower
Allée
Avenue Marcel Proust
ESPACE PIERRE CARDIN
Rue Gabriel
CLIN. MARIGNAN
Rue Bourdin
Imp. d'Antin
CHURCH OF SCOTLAND
Rue Goujon
Rue Jean Goujon
Pl. François 1er
Rue François 1er
FRANKLIN D. ROOSEVELT
Sqre J. Perrin
GRAND PALAIS
PALAIS DE LA DÉCOUVERTE
UNIVERSITÉ PARIS IV
Av. W. Churchill
Av. Ch. Girault
PETIT PALAIS
Rue Dutuit
Carré Champs-Elysées
Av. Edward Tuck
ÉGLISE ARMÉNIENNE
N. D. DE CONSOLATION
Rue Bayard
Albert 1er
Pl. du Canada
Cours la Reine
DE OBÉ
CONC
Port de la Conférence
Port des Champs Elysées
Port de la Concorde
Pont des Invalides
Pont Alexandre III
Pont de la Concorde
Gros Caillou
Port des Invalides
QUAI D'ORSAY
AMERICAN CHURCH IN PARIS
Pl. de Finlande
(R.E.R.)
MIN. DES AFFAIRES ETRANGERES
MIN DES AFFAIRES EUROPÉENNES
SECRT D'ETAT DE LA FRANCOPHONIE
R. Robert Esnault Pelterie
ASSEMBLÉE NATIONALE
PALAIS BOURBON
QUAI
BD
Rue A. Briand
ASSEMBLÉE NATIONALE
Pl. du Prést E. Herriot
R. Moissan
R. Henri
Av. Sully Prudhomme
S.E.I.T.A.
R. du Colonel Combes
Av. Rapp
Schuman
S.E.I.T.A. MUSÉE
CLIN. ALMA
R. Desgenettes
MAUBOURG
R. Fabert
R. Paul et Jean Lerollé
AÉROGARE DES INVALIDES
GALLIENI
INVALIDES
Rue de l'Université
Pge Commun
Rue Jean Nicot
PIERRE DU GROS CAILLOU
Rue Malar
Surcouf
ESPLANADE DES INVALIDES
Constantine
MAISON DE LA CHIMIE
Pl. du Palais Bourbon
MINISTÈRE DE LA DÉFENSE
Rue Saint Dominique
LYCÉE LA ROCHEFOUCAULT
Pge Jean Nicot
R. de la Comète
Rue Amélie
TOUR
Rue
AV. DU MAL
R. de Talleyrand
MIN DU DÉVELOPPEMENT ÉCONOMIQUE ET DU PLAN
Bourgogne
Sqre S. Rousseau
R. de Martignac
Rue Las Cases
Rue Périer
BASILIQUE STE CLOTILDE
Pl. des Invalides
INSTITUT GÉOGRAPHIQUE NATIONAL
R. de Champagny
R. Casimir
Cité du Gal Négrier
Rue de Grenelle
LA TOUR MAUBOURG
Pl. Santiago du Chili
Sqre Santiago du Chili
ST JEAN
La Tour Maubourg
Square d'Ajaccio
BD DES INVALIDES
MIN DU TRAVAIL ET DE LA PARTICIPATION
LYCÉE P. CLAUDEL
MIN. DE L'ÉDUCATION ET DE LA RECHERCHE
MAIRIE DU 7E ARR.
R. Valadon
R. E. Psichari
R. Duvivier
Sqre Denys Bülher
AV. DE LA MOTTE PICQUET
Mars
Rue Cler
MUSÉE DE L'ARMÉE
HÔTEL DES INVALIDES
VARENNE
Cité Martignac
MIN. DE L'INDUSTRIE
SECRT D'ETAT AU COMMERCE EXT.
Rue Chevert
R. Bougainville
ST LOUIS
MUSÉE DE L'ORDRE DE LA LIBÉRATION
Rue de Varenne
MIN. DE L'AGRICULTURE ET DE LA PÊCHE
SECRT D'ETAT A L'ACTION HUMANITAIRE
MUSÉE RODIN
MIN. DE L'AMÉNAGEMENT DU TERRITOIRE
R. L. Codet
R. J. Granier
ÉCOLE MILITAIRE
Jardin de l'Intendant
ÉGLISE DU DÔME
Cité Vaneau
C. Vaneau
HÔTEL MATIGNON
Pl. de l'École Militaire
Avenue de Tourville
Pl. D. Cochin
PL. Vauban
Tourville
Rue de Jouy
R. de Chanaleilles
Rue Vaneau
AVENUE LOWENDAL
R. Bixio
SÉGUR
AV. DE VILLARS
BOULEVARD
Esplanade du Souvenir Français
LYCÉE VICTOR DURUY
Rue Barbet
CLIN. ST FRANÇOIS XAVIER
ST DOMINIQUE
PRÉFECTURE D'ILE DE FRANCE
MIN. FONCT PUBLIQUE
MIN. DE LA SANTÉ DE L'INTÉGRATION ET DE LA SOLIDARITÉ
ÉCOLE MILITAIRE
DUQUESNE
DE BRETEUIL
Rue d'Estrées
Pl. André Tardieu
ST FRANÇOIS XAVIER
Rue Monsieur
Jardin Catherine Labouré
Place de Fontenoy
MIN. DU TOURISME
MIN. DE LA POSTE
MIN. DE L'ENVIRONNEMENT
Pl. du Prést Mithouard
ST FRANÇOIS XAVIER
Sqre de l'Abbé Esquerré
MIN. DE LA COOPERATION
CLIN. DES SŒURS AUGUSTINES DE MEAUX
Rue Oudinot
Imp. Oudinot
L.T. ALBERT DEMUN
V. de Ségur
Pl. El Salvador
MICHELIN
U.N.E.S.C.O.

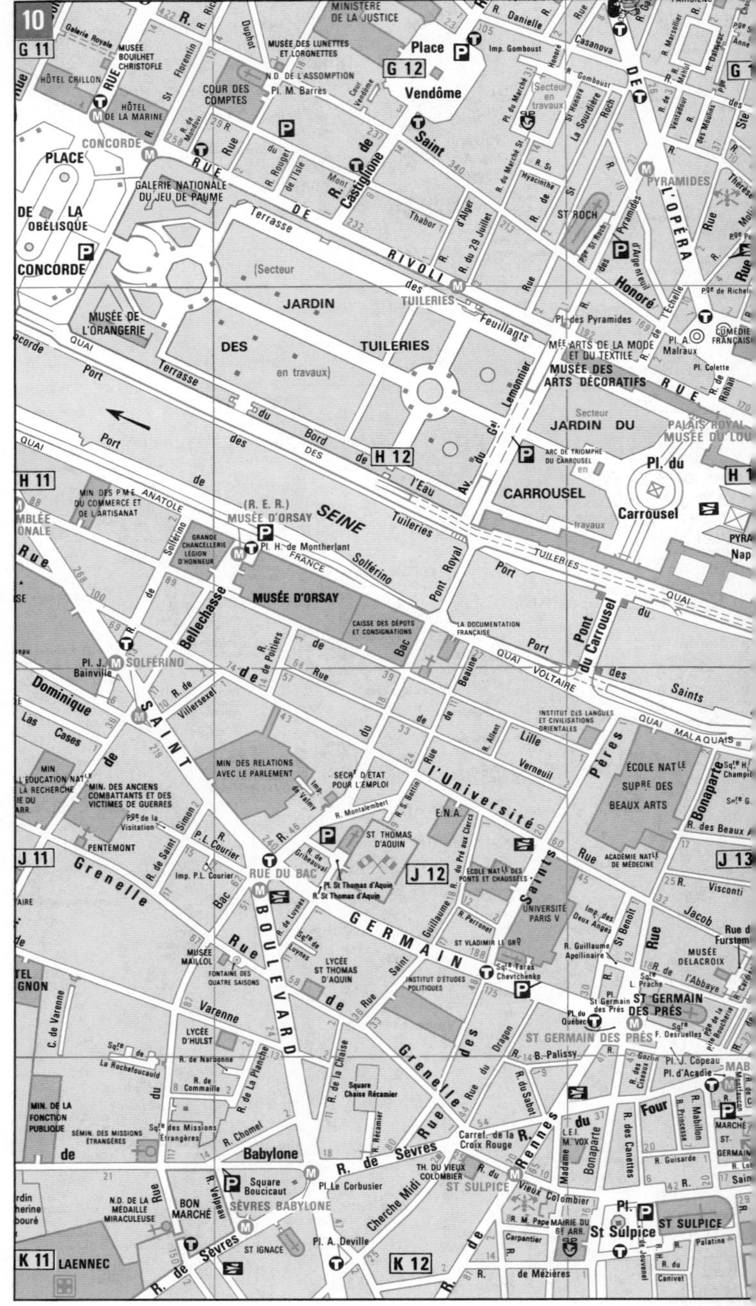
10
G 11
G 12
Galerie Royale
MUSÉE BOUILHET CHRISTOFLE
HÔTEL CRILLON
HÔTEL DE LA MARINE
CONCORDE
PLACE DE LA CONCORDE
OBÉLISQUE
MINISTERE DE LA JUSTICE
MUSÉE DES LUNETTES ET LORGNETTES
N.D. DE L'ASSOMPTION
Pl. M. Barrès
COUR DES COMPTES
Place Vendôme
Imp. Gombout
R. Danielle
Casanova
Secteur en travaux
Pl. du Marché St Honoré
La Sourdière
Roch
PYRAMIDES
AV. DE L'OPÉRA
R. St Hyacinthe
ST ROCH
Pge St Roch
Pyramides
d'Argenteuil
Honoré
Pge de Richelieu
R. de Castiglione
R. de Mont Thabor
R. d'Alger
R. du 29 Juillet
RUE DE RIVOLI
Terrasse
GALERIE NATIONALE DU JEU DE PAUME
(Secteur
JARDIN DES TUILERIES
en travaux)
TUILERIES
des Feuillants
Pl. des Pyramides
MÉE ARTS DE LA MODE ET DU TEXTILE
MUSÉE DES ARTS DÉCORATIFS
Pl. A. Malraux
COMÉDIE FRANÇAISE
Pl. Colette
R. de Rohan
MUSÉE DE L'ORANGERIE
QUAI
Port de la Concorde
Terrasse du Bord de l'Eau
Port des Tuileries
QUAI DES TUILERIES
H 11
H 12
Secteur
JARDIN DU CARROUSEL
en travaux
Av. du Gal Lemonnier
ARC DE TRIOMPHE DU CARROUSEL
Pl. du Carrousel
PALAIS ROYAL MUSÉE DU LOUVRE
QUAI ANATOLE FRANCE
MIN. DES P.M.E. DU COMMERCE ET DE L'ARTISANAT
(R. E. R.) MUSÉE D'ORSAY
SEINE
Pl. H. de Montherlant
GRANDE CHANCELLERIE LÉGION D'HONNEUR
MUSÉE D'ORSAY
CAISSE DES DÉPOTS ET CONSIGNATIONS
Solférino
Pont Royal
Port
LA DOCUMENTATION FRANÇAISE
Pont du Carrousel
QUAI VOLTAIRE
Port des Saints Pères
QUAI MALAQUAIS
INSTITUT DES LANGUES ET CIVILISATIONS ORIENTALES
Rue de Bellechasse
R. de Poitiers
Rue de Lille
Rue de Verneuil
R. de Beaune
R. Allent
Rue du Bac
Pl. J. Bainville
SOLFÉRINO
Rue St Dominique
R. de Villersexel
Las Cases
BOULEVARD SAINT GERMAIN
MIN. DES RELATIONS AVEC LE PARLEMENT
SECRT D'ETAT POUR L'EMPLOI
Imp. de Valmy
R. Montalembert
R. S. Bottin
Rue de l'Université
E.N.A.
ÉCOLE NATLE SUPRE DES BEAUX ARTS
R. Bonaparte
R. des Beaux Arts
MIN. L'ÉDUCATION NATLE LA RECHERCHE
MIN. DES ANCIENS COMBATTANTS ET DES VICTIMES DE GUERRES
Pge de la Visitation
Simon
PENTEMONT
R. P.L. Courier
Imp. P.L. Courier
R. de Saint Simon
ST THOMAS D'AQUIN
R. de Gribeauval
Pl. St Thomas d'Aquin
R. St Thomas d'Aquin
J 11
J 12
J 13
Rue de Grenelle
RUE DU BAC
R. du Pré aux Clercs
ÉCOLE NATLE DES PONTS ET CHAUSSÉES
Rue des Saints Pères
ACADÉMIE NATLE DE MÉDECINE
R. Visconti
Rue Jacob
Rue de Furstemberg
UNIVERSITÉ PARIS V
Imp. des Deux Anges
St Benoit
R. Guillaume Apollinaire
MUSÉE DELACROIX
R. de l'Abbaye
R. Perronet
R. Guillaume
ST VLADIMIR LE GRD
Sqre Taras Chevtchenko
R. de Luynes
Sqre de Luynes
LYCÉE ST THOMAS D'AQUIN
MUSÉE MAILLOL
FONTAINE DES QUATRE SAISONS
INSTITUT D'ÉTUDES POLITIQUES
Rue Saint Guillaume
Sqre L. Prache
Pl. St Germain des Prés
ST GERMAIN DES PRÉS
Pl. du Québec
Sqre F. Desruelles
Rue de Varenne
C. de Varenne
LYCÉE D'HULST
Sqre de La Rochefoucauld
R. de Narbonne
R. de Commaille
R. de La Planche
R. de la Chaise
Square Chaise Récamier
Rue de Grenelle
Rue des Dragon
B. Palissy
R. du Sabot
R. des Ciseaux
Gozlin
Pl. J. Copeau
Pl. d'Acadie
MABILLON
MIN. DE LA FONCTION PUBLIQUE
SÉMIN. DES MISSIONS ÉTRANGÈRES
Sqre des Missions Étrangères
R. Chomel
R. Récamier
Rue de Babylone
Carref. de la Croix Rouge
R. de Rennes
du Four
L.E.I. M. VOX
R. Bonaparte
Madame
R. des Canettes
R. Princesse
R. Mabillon
R. Guisarde
MARCHÉ ST GERMAIN
R. Lobineau
21
R. Velpeau
Square Boucicaut
Pl. Le Corbusier
R. de Sèvres
TH. DU VIEUX COLOMBIER
R. du Vieux Colombier
ST SULPICE
Pl. St Sulpice
ST SULPICE
N.D. DE LA MÉDAILLE MIRACULEUSE
BON MARCHÉ
SÈVRES BABYLONE
Cherche Midi
R. M. Pape Carpentier
MAIRIE DU 6E ARR.
R. Palatine
R. de Jouvenel
R. du Canivet
K 11
LAENNEC
ST IGNACE
Pl. A. Deville
K 12
R. de Mézières

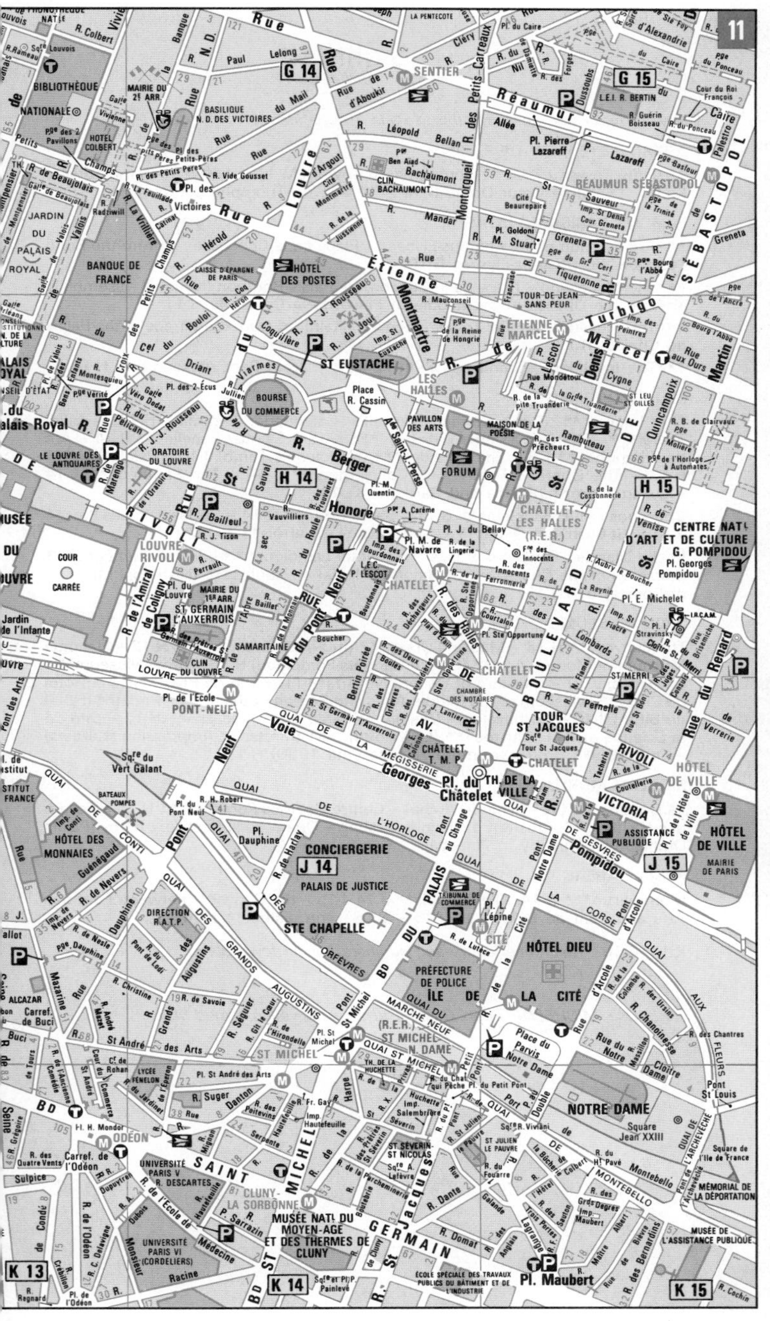

Sights

How to make the most of a trip to Paris – some ideas :

A BIRD'S-EYE VIEW OF PARIS

★★★Eiffel Tower J 7 – ★★★Montparnasse Tower LM 11 – ★★★Notre-Dame Towers K 15 – ★★★Sacré Cœur Dome D 14 – ★★★Arc de Triomphe platform F 8.

FAMOUS PARISIAN VISTAS

★★★Arc de Triomphe – Champs-Élysées – Place de la Concorde : ⩽ from the Rond Point on the Champs-Élysées G 10.

★★★The Madeleine – Place de la Concorde – Palais Bourbon (National Assembly) : ⩽ from the Obelisk in the middle of Place de la Concorde G 11.

★★★The Trocadéro – Eiffel Tower – Ecole Militaire : ⩽ from the terrace of the Palais de Chaillot H 7.

★★★The Invalides – Grand and Petit Palais : ⩽ from Pont Alexandre III H 10.

MAIN MONUMENTS

The Louvre★★★ (Cour Carrée, Perrault's Colonnade, Pyramid) H 13 – Eiffel Tower★★★ J 7 – Notre-Dame Cathedral★★★ K 15 – Sainte-Chapelle★★★ J 14 – Arc de Triomphe★★★ F 8 – The Invalides★★★ (Napoleon's Tomb) J 10 – Palais-Royal★★ H 13 – The Opéra★★ F 12 – The Conciergerie★★ J 14 – The Panthéon★★ L 14 – Luxembourg★★ (Palace and Gardens) KL 13.

Churches : The Madeleine★★ G 11 – Sacré Cœur★★ D 14 – St-Germain-des-Prés★★ J 13 – St-Etienne-du-Mont★★ – St-Germain-l'Auxerrois★★ H 14.

In the Marais : Place des Vosges★★ – Hôtel Lamoignon★★ – Hôtel Guénégaud★★ (Museum of the Chase and of Nature) – Hôtel de Soubise★★ (Historical Museum of France) by HJ 15.

MAIN MUSEUMS

The Louvre★★★ H 13 – Musée d'Orsay★★★ (mid-19C to early 20C) H 12 – National Museum of Modern Art★★★ (Centre Georges-Pompidou) H 15 – Army Museum★★★ (Invalides) J 10 – Museum of Decorative Arts★★ (107 rue de Rivoli) H 13 – Hôtel de Cluny★★ (Museum of the Middle Ages and Roman Baths) K 14 – Rodin★★ (Hôtel de Biron) J 10 – Carnavalet★★ (History of Paris) J 17 – Picasso★★ H 17 – Cité de la Science et de l'Industrie★★★ (La Villette) – Marmottan★★ (Impressionist artists) – Orangerie★★ (from the Impressionists until 1930) H 11.

MODERN MONUMENTS

La Défense★★ (CNIT, Grande Arche) – Centre Georges-Pompidou★★ H 15 – Forum des Halles H 14 – Institut du Monde Arabe★ – Opéra de la Bastille – Bercy (Palais Omnisports, Ministry of Finance).

PRETTY AREAS

Montmartre★★★ D 14 – Ile St-Louis★★ J 14 J 15 – the Quays★★ (between Pont des Arts and Pont de Sully) J 14 J 15 – St Séverin district★★ K 14.

K 14, G 10 : *Reference letters and numbers on the town plans.*

Use ***MICHELIN*** *Green Guide* ***Paris*** *for a well-informed visit.*

ALPHABETICAL LIST (Hotels and restaurants)

A

B

C

D

E

F

G

H - I

O

P

Q

R

S

T

U - V

W

Y - Z

MICHELIN GREEN GUIDES in English

Austria
Belgium Luxemburg
Brussels
California
Canada
Chicago
England :
The West Country
France
Germany
Great Britain
Greece
Ireland
Italy
London
Mexico
Netherlands
New England
New York City
Portugal
Quebec
Rome
Scotland
Spain
Switzerland
Tuscany
Washington DC

HOTELS, RESTAURANTS

Listed by districts and arrondissements

(List of Hotels and Restaurants in alphabetical order, see pp 5 to 8)

G 12: These reference letters and numbers correspond to the squares on the Michelin Map of Paris no 10. Paris Atlas no 11. Map with street index no 12 and Map of Paris no 14.

Consult any of the above publications when looking for a car park nearest to a listed establishment.

Opéra, Palais-Royal, Halles, Bourse.

1st and 2nd arrondissements - 1st: ✉ 75001 - 2nd: ✉ 75002

Ritz, 15 pl. Vendôme (1st) ✆ 43 16 30 30, Telex 220262, Fax 43 16 31 78, « Attractive pool and luxurious fitness centre » - AE GB JCB. rest G 12
Meals see ***Espadon*** below - 180 - **142 rm** 3200/4250, 45 suites.

Meurice, 228 r. Rivoli (1st) ✆ 44 58 10 10, Telex 220256, Fax 44 58 10 15 - rm - 40 - 100. AE GB JCB. rest G 12
Meals see ***Le Meurice*** below - 150 - **134 rm** 2650/3700, 46 suites.

Inter - Continental, 3 r. Castiglione (1st) ✆ 44 77 11 11, Telex 220114, Fax 44 77 14 60, - - 500. AE GB JCB. rest G 12
Café Tuileries ✆ 44 77 10 40 **Meals** a la carte 210/330 - ***La Terrasse Fleurie*** - ✆ **44 77 10 44** *(closed 23 to 31 December, Saturday and Sunday)* **Meals** 310 - 140 - **450 rm** 2500/2700, 40 suites.

Lotti, 7 r. Castiglione (1st) ✆ 42 60 37 34, Telex 240066, Fax 40 15 93 56 - - 25. AE GB JCB G 12
Meals 160/220 and a la carte 330/460 - 120 - **129 rm** 1710/3330.

Westminster, 13 r. Paix (2nd) ✆ 42 61 57 46, Telex 680035, Fax 42 60 30 66 - rm - 40. AE GB JCB G 12
Meals see ***Le Céladon*** below - 110 - **84 rm** 1650/2450, 18 suites.

du Louvre, pl. A. Malraux (1st) ✆ 44 58 38 38, Telex 220412, Fax 44 58 38 01 - - 100. AE GB JCB H 13
Brasserie Le Louvre : **Meals** 98/175 and a la carte 180/240 - 110 - **195 rm** 1350/1950, 4 suites.

Castille M, 37 r. Cambon (1st) ✆ 44 58 44 58, Fax 44 58 44 00, - . AE GB JCB G 12
Il Cortile ✆ 44 58 45 67, Italian rest. *(closed Saturday except September-June and Sunday)* **Meals** 195 and a la carte 220/300 - 120 - **107 rm** 1990/2650, 8 suites, 14 duplex.

Normandy, 7 r. Échelle (1st) ✆ 42 60 30 21, Telex 213035, Fax 42 60 45 81 - - 45. AE GB JCB H 13
L'Échelle *(closed Saturday and Sunday)* **Meals** 170 and a la carte 230/280 - 75 - **110 rm** 1265/1990, 4 suites.

Edouard VII and rest. Le Delmonico, 39 av. Opéra (2nd) ✆ 42 61 56 90, Telex 680217, Fax 42 61 47 73 - - 30. AE GB G 13
Meals *(closed August, Saturday and Sunday)* 168 - 90 - **65 rm** 1200/1400, 4 suites.

Mayfair without rest, 3 r. Rouget-de-Lisle (1st) ✆ 42 60 38 14, Telex 240037, Fax 40 15 04 78 - . AE GB JCB. G 12
85 - **53 rm** 1050/1400.

Royal St-Honoré M without rest, 221 r. St-Honoré (1st) ✆ 42 60 32 79, Telex 215613, Fax 42 60 47 44 - . AE GB JCB G 12
90 - **67 rm** 1250/1950, 5 suites.

Régina, 2 pl. Pyramides (1st) ✆ 42 60 31 10, Telex 670834, Fax 40 15 95 16, - - 30. AE GB JCB. rest H 13
Meals *(closed August, Saturday, Sunday and Bank Holidays)* 160 (lunch), 250/290 and a la carte 240/370 - 90 - **116 rm** 1520/2120, 14 suites.

Cambon without rest, 3 r. Cambon (1st) ✆ 42 60 38 09, Fax 42 60 30 59 – ▯ ▤ TV ☎. AE ⓓ GB JCB G 12
☕ 75 – **42 rm** 1280/1580.

L'Horset Opéra M without rest, 18 r. d'Antin (2nd) ✆ 44 71 87 00, Telex 282676, Fax 42 66 55 54 – ▯ ▤ TV ☎ ♿. AE ⓓ GB JCB G 13
☕ 80 – **54 rm** 990/1350.

Stendhal M without rest, 22 r. D. Casanova (2nd) ✆ 44 58 52 52, Fax 44 58 52 00 – ▯ ▤ TV ☎. AE ⓓ GB JCB G 12
☕ 95 – **20 rm** 1580/1900.

Opéra Richepanse M without rest, 14 r. Richepanse (1st) ✆ 42 60 36 00, Telex 210811, Fax 42 60 13 03 – ▯ ▤ TV ☎. AE ⓓ GB G 12
☕ 65 – **35 rm** 990/1300, 3 suites.

Novotel Les Halles M, 8 pl. M.-de-Navarre (1st) ✆ 42 21 31 31, Fax 40 26 05 79, – ▯ ▤ TV ☎ ♿ – 40 - 100. AE ⓓ GB JCB H 14
Meals a la carte approx. 190 – ☕ 62 – **280 rm** 860/915, 5 suites.

Mansart without rest, 5 r. Capucines (1st) ✆ 42 61 50 28, Telex 214324, Fax 49 27 97 44 – ▯ TV ☎. AE ⓓ GB. G 12
☕ 50 – **57 rm** 610/820.

Favart without rest, 5 r. Marivaux (2nd) ✆ 42 97 59 83, Telex 213126, Fax 40 15 95 58 – ▯ TV ☎ ♿. AE ⓓ GB JCB F 13
☕ 20 – **37 rm** 490/590.

de Noailles M without rest, 9 r. Michodière (2nd) ✆ 47 42 92 90, Telex 290644, Fax 49 24 92 71 – ▯ TV ☎. AE GB JCB G 13
☕ 50 – **58 rm** 700/850.

Louvre Montana without rest, 12 r. St-Roch (1st) ✆ 42 60 35 10, Fax 42 61 12 28 – ▯ TV ☎. AE ⓓ GB JCB G 12
☕ 55 – **25 rm** 580/1090.

Louvre St-Honoré M without rest, 141 r. St-Honoré (1st) ✆ 42 96 23 23, Telex 215044, Fax 42 96 21 61 – ▯ TV ☎ ♿. AE ⓓ GB JCB H 14
☕ 45 – **40 rm** 656/862.

Violet M without rest, 7 r. J. Lantier (1st) ✆ 42 33 45 38, Fax 40 28 03 56 – ▯ TV ☎ ♿. AE ⓓ GB JCB. J 14
☕ 50 – **30 rm** 550/730.

Lautrec Opéra without rest, 8 r. Ambroise (2nd) ✆ 42 96 67 90, Fax 42 96 06 83 – ▯ TV ☎. AE GB JCB. F 13
☕ 30 – **30 rm** 500/850.

Baudelaire Opéra without rest, 61 r. Ste Anne (2nd) ✆ 42 97 50 62, Fax 42 86 85 85 – ▯ TV ☎. AE ⓓ GB JCB G 13
☕ 38 – **24 rm** 480/630, 5 duplex.

Gd H. de Besançon M without rest, 56 r. Montorgueil (2nd) ✆ 42 36 41 08, Fax 45 08 08 79 – ▯ TV ☎. AE ⓓ GB JCB. G 14
☕ 40 – **20 rm** 530/620.

Marsollier Opéra without rest, 13 r. Marsollier (2nd) ✆ 42 96 68 14, Fax 42 60 53 84 – ▯ TV ☎. AE ⓓ GB JCB G 13
☕ 35 – **29 rm** 550/760.

Vivienne without rest, 40 r. Vivienne (2nd) ✆ 42 33 13 26, Fax 40 41 98 19 – ▯ TV ☎. GB F 14
☕ 40 – **44 rm** 360/460.

✿✿ **Espadon** - Hôtel Ritz, 15 pl. Vendôme (1st) ✆ 43 16 30 30, Fax 43 16 31 78, – ▤. AE ⓓ GB JCB. G 12
Meals 380 (lunch)/600 and a la carte 420/760
Spec. Foie gras au vin de Médoc. Blanc de turbot, pommes fondantes au romarin et jus de volaille. Attereaux de pigeon à la ficelle.

✿✿ **Grand Vefour,** 17 r. Beaujolais (1st) ✆ 42 96 56 27, Fax 42 86 80 71, « Pre-Revolutionary (late 18C) Café Style » – ▤. AE ⓓ GB JCB. G 13
closed August, Saturday and Sunday – **Meals** 325 (lunch)/750 and a la carte 570/820
Spec. Ravioles de foie gras, crème truffée. Poissons du lac Léman. Gourmandise au chocolat.

✿ **Le Meurice** - Hôtel Meurice, 228 r. Rivoli (1st) ✆ 44 58 10 50, Telex 220256, Fax 44 58 10 15 – ▤. AE ⓓ GB JCB. G 12
Meals 330 (lunch), 410 b.i./550 and a la carte 340/490
Spec. Terrine de jeunes anguilles au vert. Petit chou de langoustines aux légumes et aux herbes Filet d'agneau au citron confit en pastilla.

XXXX ✿✿ **Drouant,** pl. Gaillon (2nd) ✆ 42 65 15 16, Fax 49 24 02 15, « Home of the Academie Goncourt since 1914 » – ▤. AE ⓓ GB G 13
Meals 300/650 and a la carte 540/730 - ***Café Drouant :*** **Meals** 200, a la carte 260/360
Spec. Ravioles de homard, jus parfumé au basilic. Rouget rôti à la moelle, jus au corail d'oursin. Noix de ris de veau rôtie au vin jaune.

XXXX ✿✿ **Carré des Feuillants** (Dutournier), 14 r. Castiglione (1st) ✆ 42 86 82 82, Fax 42 86 07 71 – ▤. AE ⓓ GB JCB G 12
closed 3 to 25 August, Saturday lunch and Sunday – **Meals** 285 and a la carte 460/590
Spec. Poêlée "minute" de chipirons aux artichauts violets. Emincé de Saint-Jacques en chaud-froid de céleri truffé (Autumn-Winter). Caneton aux pêches blanches et amandes fraîches (Summer).

XXXX ✿✿ **Goumard-Prunier,** 9 r. Duphot (1st) ✆ 42 60 36 07, Fax 42 60 04 54 – ▤. AE ⓓ GB JCB G 12
closed Sunday (except October-March) and Monday – **Meals** - Seafood - 295 (lunch), 390/750 and a la carte 410/670
Spec. Ravioli de crustacés. Turbot de ligne rôti à l'arête. Poêlée de petits rougets de roche entiers.

XXXX ✿✿ **Gérard Besson,** 5 r. Coq Héron (1st) ✆ 42 33 14 74, Fax 42 33 85 71 – ▤. AE ⓓ GB JCB H 14
closed Saturday (except dinner from 15 September-15 June) and Sunday – **Meals** 280 (lunch)/520 and a la carte 440/640
Spec. Tartelette Lucullus au coulis de truffes. Poularde de Bresse à la serviette. Fenouil confit aux épices (dessert).

XXX ✿ **Le Céladon** - Hôtel Westminster, 15 r. Daunou (2nd) ✆ 47 03 40 42, Fax 42 60 30 66 – ▤. AE ⓓ GB JCB G 12
closed August, Saturday and Sunday – **Meals** 220/350 and a la carte 320/490
Spec. "Cépière" de homard. Turbot et céleri rave au parfum de truffes. Crumble de pommes vertes à la crème de nougat.

XXX **Pierre " A la Fontaine Gaillon ",** pl. Gaillon (2nd) ✆ 47 42 63 22, Fax 47 42 82 84, 🏠 – ▤. AE ⓓ GB G 13
closed Saturday lunch and Sunday – **Meals** 165 and a la carte 220/380.

XXX ✿ **Mercure Galant,** 15 r. Petits-Champs (1st) ✆ 42 97 53 85, Fax 42 96 08 89 – AE GB G 13
closed Saturday lunch, Sunday and Bank Holidays – **Meals** 230/290 and a la carte 300/440
Spec. Salade de homard breton aux agrumes. Poissons. Mille et une feuilles "Mercure".

XXX **Chez Vong,** 10 r. Grande-Truanderie (1st) ✆ 40 39 99 89, Fax 42 33 38 15 – ▤. AE ⓓ GB
closed Sunday – **Meals** - Chinese and Vietnamese rest. - 150 and a la carte 180/300. H 15

XXX **Au Pied de Cochon** (24 hr service), 6 r. Coquillière (1st) ✆ 42 36 11 75, Fax 45 08 48 90, brasserie – ▤. AE ⓓ GB H 14
Meals 185 and a la carte 170/330.

XXX **La Corbeille,** 154 r. Montmartre (2nd) ✆ 40 26 30 87, Fax 40 26 08 20 – ▤. AE GB. ✂
closed August, Saturday lunch and Sunday – **Meals** 195/275. G 14

XX **Chez Pauline,** 5 r. Villédo (1st) ✆ 42 96 20 70, Fax 49 27 99 89, bistro – AE ⓓ GB JCB
closed Saturday except dinner from 16 September-31 March and Sunday – **Meals** 220 and a la carte 280/550. G 13

XX **Rôtisserie Monsigny,** 1 r. Monsigny (2nd) ✆ 42 96 16 61, Fax 42 97 40 97 – ▤. AE GB JCB G 13
closed 10 to 25 August and Saturday lunch – **Meals** 159 and a la carte approx. 250.

XX **Saudade,** 34 r. Bourdonnais (1st) ✆ 42 36 30 71 – ▤. AE GB. ✂ H 14
closed Sunday – **Meals** - Portuguese rest. - 129 and a la carte 180/320.

XX **Kinugawa,** 9 r. Mont-Thabor (1st) ✆ 42 60 65 07, Fax 42 60 45 21 – ▤. AE ⓓ GB JCB. ✂ G 12
closed 23 December-7 January and Sunday – **Meals** - Japanese rest. - 155 (lunch), 245/700 and a la carte 280/390.

XX **Gaya Rive Droite,** 17 r. Duphot (1st) ✆ 42 60 43 03, Fax 42 60 04 54, « Attractive glazed tile panels » – ▤. AE GB G 12
closed Sunday – **Meals** - Seafood - a la carte 230/360.

XX ✿ **Pierre Au Palais Royal,** 10 r. Richelieu (1st) ✆ 42 96 09 17, Fax 42 96 09 62 – AE ⓓ GB
closed 27 July-31 August, Saturday, Sunday and Bank Holidays – **Meals** 225 and a la carte 250/410 H 13
Spec. Foie gras chaud au vinaigre de Xérès. Quenelles de brochet. Boeuf ficelle "à la ménagère".

XX **Le Poquelin,** 17 r. Molière (1st) ✆ 42 96 22 19, Fax 42 96 05 72 – ▤. AE ⓓ GB JCB G 13
closed 1 to 20 August, Saturday lunch and Sunday – **Meals** 189 and a la carte 270/410.

XX **La Passion,** 41 r. Petits Champs (1st) ✆ 42 97 53 41 – ▤. AE GB. ✂ G 13
closed Saturday lunch and Sunday – **Meals** 150/200 and a la carte 300/450.

XX **Armand Au Palais Royal,** 4 r. Beaujolais (1st) ✆ 42 60 05 11, Fax 42 96 16 24 – AE GB
closed Saturday lunch and Sunday – **Meals** 180 (lunch)/250. G 13

XX **Chez Fabrice,** 38 r. Croix des Petits-Champs (1st) ✆ 40 20 06 46 – AE GB H 14
closed Saturday lunch and Sunday – **Meals** 125/225.

XX ✿ **Pile ou Face,** 52bis r. N.-D.-des-Victoires (2nd) ✆ 42 33 64 33, Fax 42 36 61 09 – ▤. GB G
closed August, 23 December-1 January, Saturday, Sunday and Bank Holidays – **Meals** 24 (lunch), 280/320 and a la carte 280/400
Spec. Crêpe de semoule de blé aux escargots de Bourgogne. Pigeonneau rôti à l'huile de truff Glace au yaourt, biscuit concassé et confiture de cassis.

XX **Vaudeville,** 29 r. Vivienne (2nd) ✆ 40 20 04 62, Fax 49 27 08 78, brasserie – AE ⓓ GB
Meals a la carte 180/270 ♁. G

XX **Le Grand Colbert,** 2 r. Vivienne (2nd) ✆ 42 86 87 88, Fax 42 86 82 65, brasserie – AE ⓓ GB G
closed 10 to 20 August – **Meals** 160 and a la carte 180/260 ♁.

XX **Bonne Fourchette,** 320 r. St-Honoré, in the backyard (1st) ✆ 42 60 45 27 – ▤. ⓓ GB.
closed August, February Holidays, Sunday lunch and Saturday – **Meals** 118/158 and a la car 200/310. G

XX **Le Soufflé,** 36 r. Mont-Thabor (1st) ✆ 42 60 27 19, Fax 42 60 54 98 – ▤. AE ⓓ GB JCB
closed Sunday – **Meals** 175/250 and a la carte 200/310. G

XX **Le Petit Bourbon,** 15 r. Roule (1st) ✆ 40 26 08 93 – AE GB H
closed August, Saturday lunch, Sunday and Monday – **Meals** 110/245.

XX **Le Saint Amour,** 8 r. Port Mahon (2nd) ✆ 47 42 63 82 – ▤. AE ⓓ GB JCB G
closed 28 July-23 August, Saturday except dinner from September-June, Sunday and Bank Holidays – **Meals** 165 and a la carte 220/350.

XX **Chez Gabriel,** 123 r. St-Honoré (1st) ✆ 42 33 02 99 – ▤. AE ⓓ GB JCB. H
closed 7 to 28 August, 21 December-2 January and Sunday – **Meals** 150/220.

XX **Les Cartes Postales,** 7 r. Gomboust (1st) ✆ 42 61 02 93, Fax 42 61 02 93 – GB JCB
closed Saturday lunch and Sunday – **Meals** (booking essential) 135 (lunch), 200/350 and a la carte 230/330. G

X **A la Grille St-Honoré,** 15 pl. Marché St-Honoré (1st) ✆ 42 61 00 93, Fax 47 03 31 64 – ▤ AE ⓓ GB. G
closed 1 to 20 August, 23 December-2 January, Monday except dinner in October and November and Sunday – **Meals** 180 and a la carte 260/370.

X **Yvan sur Seine,** 26 quai Louvre (1st) ✆ 42 36 49 52 – ▤. AE GB H
closed lunch Saturday and Sunday – **Meals** 98 (lunch)/138 b.i. and a la carte 170/260 ♁.

X **Caveau du Palais,** 19 pl. Dauphine (1st) ✆ 43 26 04 28, Fax 43 26 81 84 – AE GB J
closed Sunday – **Meals** 184 and a la carte 200/380.

X **Paul,** 15 pl. Dauphine (1st) ✆ 43 54 21 48 – AE GB J
closed Monday – **Meals** a la carte 200/360.

X **Le Petit Restaurant,** 50 r. Richelieu (1st) ✆ 40 15 97 39 – AE GB G
closed August, Saturday and Sunday – **Meals** 160.

X **Le Ruban Bleu,** 29 r. Argenteuil (1st) ✆ 42 61 47 53 – ⓓ GB G
closed 3 August-1 September, 24 December-1 January, Saturday and Sunday – **Meals** a la cart 180/260.

X **Chez Georges,** 1 r. Mail (2nd) ✆ 42 60 07 11, bistro – ▤. AE GB JCB G
closed 1 to 20 August, Sunday and Bank Holidays – **Meals** a la carte 190/350.

X **La Poule au Pot,** 9 r. Vauvilliers (1st) ✆ 42 36 32 96, bistro – GB H
closed Monday – **Meals** (dinner only) 160 and a la carte 200/270.

X **Lescure,** 7 r. Mondovi (1st) ✆ 42 60 18 91, bistro – GB G
closed August, Saturday dinner and Sunday – **Meals** 100 and a la carte 80/170.

X **Le Souletin,** 6 r. Vrillière (1st), ✆ 42 61 43 78, bistro – GB G
closed Sunday and Bank Holidays – **Meals** a la carte approx. 180.

Bastille, République, Hôtel de Ville.

3rd, 4th and 11th arrondissements.
3rd: ✉ 75003
4th: ✉ 75004
11th: ✉ 75011

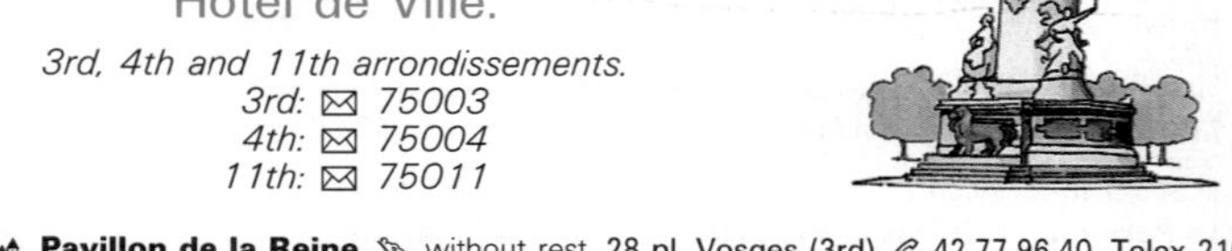

Pavillon de la Reine without rest, 28 pl. Vosges (3rd) ✆ 42 77 96 40, Telex 21616C Fax 42 77 63 06 – ▤ TV ☎ . AE ⓓ GB JCB J
☕ 95 – **31 rm** 1500/2100, 14 suites, 10 duplex.

Jeu de Paume without rest, 54 r. St-Louis-en-l'Ile (4th) ✆ 43 26 14 18, Fax 40 46 02 76 « 17C tennis court » – ☎ – 30. AE ⓓ GB JCB K
☕ 80 – **32 rm** 895/1295.

Bretonnerie without rest, 22 r. Ste-Croix-de-la-Bretonnerie (4th) ✆ 48 87 77 63, Fax 42 77 26 78 – 🛗 📺 ☎. GB. ✻ J 16
closed 28 July-25 August – ☕ 45 – **27 rm** 630/750, 3 suites.

Bel Air Ⓜ without rest, 5/7 r. Rampon (11th) ✆ 47 00 41 57, Fax 47 00 21 56 – 🛗 📺 ☎. AE ⓓ GB. ✻ G 17
☕ 45 – **48 rm** 500/610.

Caron de Beaumarchais Ⓜ without rest, 12 r. Vieille-du-Temple (4th) ✆ 42 72 34 12, Fax 42 72 34 63 – 🛗 ▤ 📺 ☎. AE ⓓ GB JCB J 16
☕ 48 – **19 rm** 620/690.

Méridional without rest, 36 bd Richard-Lenoir (11th) ✆ 48 05 75 00, Fax 43 57 42 85 – 🛗 📺 ☎. AE ⓓ GB JCB J 18
☕ 45 – **36 rm** 600.

Beaubourg without rest, 11 r. S. Le Franc (4th) ✆ 42 74 34 24, Fax 42 78 68 11 – 🛗 📺 ☎. AE ⓓ GB. ✻ H 15
☕ 38 – **28 rm** 490/580.

Rivoli Notre Dame without rest, 19 r. Bourg Tibourg (4th) ✆ 42 78 47 39, Fax 40 29 07 00 – 🛗 📺 ☎. AE ⓓ GB JCB. ✻ J 16
☕ 40 – **31 rm** 500/630.

Verlain without rest, 97 r. St-Maur (11th) ✆ 43 57 44 88, Fax 43 57 32 06 – 🛗 ▤ 📺 ☎. AE ⓓ GB JCB G 19
☕ 40 – **38 rm** 490/520.

Lutèce without rest, 65 r. St-Louis-en-l'Ile (4th) ✆ 43 26 23 52, Fax 43 29 60 25 – 🛗 ▤ 📺 ☎. GB. ✻ K 16
☕ 45 – **23 rm** 830/850.

Stella Ⓜ without rest, 14 r. Neuve St-Pierre (4th) ✆ 44 59 28 50, Fax 44 59 28 79 – 🛗 ▤ 📺 ☎. AE ⓓ GB JCB J 17
☕ 50 – **20 rm** 556/662.

Gd H. Prieuré without rest, 20 r. Grand Prieuré (11th) ✆ 47 00 74 14, Fax 49 23 06 64 – 📺 ☎. AE GB. ✻ G 17
☕ 30 – **32 rm** 300/370.

Allegro République Ⓜ without rest, 39 r. J.-P. Timbaud (11th) ✆ 48 06 64 97, Fax 48 05 03 38 – 🛗 📺 ♿. AE GB G 18
☕ 35 – **42 rm** 365/420.

Croix de Malte Ⓜ without rest, 5 r. Malte (11th) ✆ 48 05 09 36, Fax 43 57 02 54 – 🛗 ⚹ 📺 ☎. AE ⓓ GB JCB. ✻ H 17
☕ 45 – **29 rm** 470/535.

Beauséjour Ⓜ without rest, 71 av. Parmentier (11th) ✆ 47 00 38 16, Fax 43 55 47 89 – 🛗 ⚹ 📺 ☎. AE ⓓ GB H 18
☕ 30 – **31 rm** 290/350.

Place des Vosges without rest, 12 r. Birague (4th) ✆ 42 72 60 46, Fax 42 72 02 64 – 📺 ☎. AE ⓓ GB JCB J 17
☕ 30 – **16 rm** 315/460.

XXXX ✿✿✿ **L'Ambroisie** (Pacaud), 9 pl. des Vosges (4th) ✆ 42 78 51 45 – AE GB. ✻ J 17
closed 4 to 25 August, February Holidays, Sunday and Monday – **Meals** a la carte 680/990
Spec. Feuillantine de queues de langoustines aux graines de sésame, sauce curry. Croustillant d'agneau de Sisteron au confit de légumes, semoule composée. Tarte fine sablée au cacao amer.

XXX **Miravile,** 72 quai Hôtel de Ville (4th) ✆ 42 74 72 22, Fax 42 74 67 55 – ▤. AE GB J 15
closed 1 to 21 August, Saturday lunch and Sunday – **Meals** 290/400 b.i..

XXX **Ambassade d'Auvergne,** 22 r. Grenier St-Lazare (3rd) ✆ 42 72 31 22, Fax 42 78 85 47 – ▤. AE GB H 15
closed 1 to 15 August – **Meals** 160/300 b.i. and a la carte 190/290.

XX ✿ **Benoît,** 20 r. St-Martin (4th) ✆ 42 72 25 76, Fax 42 72 45 68, bistro J 15
closed August – **Meals** 200 and a la carte 330/460
Spec. Ballotine de canard au foie gras. Saint-Jacques au naturel (September-April). Selle d'agneau en rognonnade.

XX **Bofinger,** 5 r. Bastille (4th) ✆ 42 72 87 82, Fax 42 72 97 68, brasserie, « Belle Epoque decor » – AE ⓓ GB JCB J 17
Meals 169 b.i. and a la carte 180/310.

XX **Pyrénées Cévennes "Chez Philippe",** 106 r. Folie-Méricourt (11th) ✆ 43 57 33 78 – ▤. AE ⓓ GB G 17
closed August, Saturday and Sunday – **Meals** a la carte 230/380.

XXX ✿ **A Sousceyrac** (Asfaux), 35 r. Faidherbe (11th) ✆ 43 71 65 30, Fax 40 09 79 75 – ▤. GB J
closed Saturday lunch and Sunday – **Meals** 175
Spec. Foie gras d'oie ou de canard. Cassoulet. Lièvre à la royale "Gaston Richard" (season).

XX **L'Excuse,** 14 r. Charles V (4th) ✆ 42 77 98 97, Fax 42 77 88 55 – AE GB J
closed 5 to 20 August and Sunday – **Meals** 165 and a la carte 230/360.

XX **Thaï Elephant,** 43 r. Roquette (11th) ✆ 47 00 42 00, Fax 47 00 45 44, « Typical decor » ▤. AE ⓓ GB J
closed Saturday lunch – **Meals** - Thai rest. - 150 (lunch), 275/300 and a la carte 190/250.

XX **L'Alisier,** 26 r. Montmorency (3rd) ✆ 42 72 31 04, Fax 42 72 74 83 – AE GB. H
closed August, Saturday and Sunday – **Meals** 150 b.i. (lunch)/175.

XX **L'Aiguière,** 37bis r. Montreuil (11th) ✆ 43 72 42 32, Fax 43 72 96 36 – ▤. AE ⓓ GB
closed Saturday lunch and Sunday – **Meals** 135 b.i./248 b.i. and a la carte 270/330. K

XX **Les Amognes,** 243 r. Fg St-Antoine (11th) ✆ 43 72 73 05 – GB K
closed 11 to 26 August, 24 December to 1 January, Monday lunch and Sunday – **Meals** 18

XX **La Table Richelieu,** 276 bd Voltaire (11th) ✆ 43 72 31 23 – ▤. AE GB K
closed Saturday lunch – **Meals** 149 b.i./260.

XX **Chardenoux,** 1 r. J. Vallès (11th) ✆ 43 71 49 52, bistro, « Early 20C decor » – AE GB.
closed August, Saturday lunch and Sunday – **Meals** a la carte 170/290. K

X **Bistrot du Dôme,** 2 r. Bastille (4th) ✆ 48 04 88 44, Fax 48 04 00 59 – ▤. AE GB J
Meals - Seafood - a la carte approx. 230.

X **Au Bascou,** 38 r. Réaumur (3rd) ✆ 42 72 69 25, bistro – AE GB G
closed 1 to 21 August, Saturday lunch and Sunday – **Meals** a la carte 170/250.

X **Le Bistrot de Bofinger,** 6 r. Bastille (4th) ✆ 42 72 05 23, Fax 42 72 97 68 – ▤. AE ⓓ G JCB J
Meals 165 b.i. and a la carte 140/210.

X **Le Grizzli,** 7 r. St-Martin (4th) ✆ 48 87 77 56, , bistro – AE GB J
closed 24 December-2 January and Sunday – **Meals** 120 (lunch)/155 and a la carte 160 250 .

X **Le Navarin,** 3 av. Philippe Auguste (11th) ✆ 43 67 17 49 – GB JCB K
closed Saturday lunch and Sunday dinner – **Meals** 119/158 .

X **Astier,** 44 r. J.-P. Timbaud (11th) ✆ 43 57 16 35, bistro – GB G
closed 19 April-2 May, August, 20 December-2 January, Saturday and Sunday – **Meals** 13

X **Le Maraîcher,** 5 r. Beautreillis (4th) ✆ 42 71 42 49 – GB K
closed 15 August-1 September, Monday lunch and Sunday – **Meals** 175/295 and a la car 210/290.

X **Le Monde des Chimères,** 69 r. St-Louis-en-l'Ile (4th) ✆ 43 54 45 27, Fax 43 29 84 88 – G
closed February Holidays, Sunday and Monday – **Meals** 160 and a la carte 250/390. K

X **Anjou-Normandie,** 13 r. Folie-Méricourt (11th) ✆ 47 00 30 59 – GB H
closed 15 July-21 August, Monday dinner, Friday dinner, Saturday and Sunday – **Meals** 137/16 and a la carte 170/280 .

X **Les Fernandises,** 19 r. Fontaine au Roi (11th) ✆ 48 06 16 96, bistro – GB G
closed 1 to 21 August, Sunday and Monday – **Meals** 130 and a la carte 170/260.

Quartier Latin, Luxembourg, Jardin des Plantes.

5th and 6th arrondissements.
5th: ✉ 75005
6th: ✉ 75006

Lutétia, 45 bd Raspail (6th) ✆ 49 54 46 46, Telex 270424, Fax 49 54 46 00 – ▤ TV – 300. AE ⓓ GB JCB K 1
Meals see *Le Paris* below - ***Brasserie Lutétia*** ✆ 49 54 46 76 **Meals** 128/245 – 125 – **234 rm** 1500/2100, 30 suites.

Relais Christine M without rest, 3 r. Christine (6th) ✆ 43 26 71 80, Telex 20260 Fax 43 26 89 38 – ▤ TV ☎ . AE ⓓ GB JCB J 1
95 – **36 rm** 1670/1770, 15 duplex.

Relais St-Germain M without rest, 9 carrefour de l'Odéon (6th) ✆ 43 29 12 05 Fax 46 33 45 30, « Attractive interior » – kitchenette ▤ TV ☎. AE ⓓ GB JCB K 1
22 rm 1280/1930.

Relais Médicis M without rest, 23 r. Racine (6th) ✆ 43 26 00 60, Fax 40 46 83 39, « Tastefu decor » – ▤ TV ☎. AE ⓓ GB JCB K 1
16 rm 930/1480.

Quality Inn Rive Gauche M without rest, 34 r. Abbé Grégoire (6th) 42 22 00 56, Fax 42 22 05 39 – AE GB JCB L 12
72 – **134 rm** 920/990.

Abbaye St-Germain without rest, 10 r. Cassette (6th) 45 44 38 11, Fax 45 48 07 86 – AE GB. K 12
42 rm 900/1500, 4 duplex.

Left Bank St-Germain without rest, 9 r. Ancienne Comédie (6th) 43 54 01 70, Fax 43 26 17 14 – AE GB JCB K 13
30 – **31 rm** 895/990.

Madison M without rest, 143 bd St-Germain (6th) 40 51 60 00, Fax 40 51 60 01 – AE GB JCB J 13
55 rm 760/1500.

Victoria Palace without rest, 6 r. Blaise-Desgoffe (6th) 45 44 38 16, Fax 45 49 23 75 – AE GB L 11
50 – **85 rm** 840/1300.

Sainte Beuve M without rest, 9 r. Ste-Beuve (6th) 45 48 20 07, Fax 45 48 67 52 – AE GB JCB L 12
80 – **22 rm** 700/1300.

Angleterre without rest, 44 r. Jacob (6th) 42 60 34 72, Fax 42 60 16 93 – AE GB. J 13
52 – **24 rm** 630/1100, 3 suites.

Littré without rest, 9 r. Littré (6th) 45 44 38 68, Fax 45 44 88 13 – 25. AE GB JCB. L 11
50 – **93 rm** 950/990, 4 suites.

St-Grégoire M without rest, 43 r. Abbé Grégoire (6th) 45 48 23 23, Fax 45 48 33 95 – AE GB JCB L 12
60 – **20 rm** 790/1390.

Latitudes St-Germain M without rest, 7-11 r. St-Benoit (6th) 42 61 53 53, Telex 213531, Fax 49 27 09 33 – AE GB J 13
70 – **117 rm** 1040.

La Villa M without rest, 29 r. Jacob (6th) 43 26 60 00, Fax 46 34 63 63, « Contemporary decor » – AE GB JCB J 13
80 – **29 rm** 900/1800, 3 suites.

St-Germain-des-Prés without rest, 36 r. Bonaparte (6th) 43 26 00 19, Fax 40 46 83 63 – rm GB J 13
50 – **30 rm** 750/1300.

Les Rives de Notre-Dame M without rest, 15 quai St-Michel (5th) 43 54 81 16, Fax 43 26 27 09, – AE GB JCB. J 14
85 – **11 rm** 995/1650.

Ferrandi without rest, 92 r. Cherche-Midi (6th) 42 22 97 40, Fax 45 44 89 97 – AE GB JCB L 11
60 – **41 rm** 600/980.

Villa des Artistes M without rest, 9 r. Grande Chaumière (6th) 43 26 60 86, Telex 204080, Fax 43 54 73 70 – AE GB JCB L 12
59 rm 600/860.

Panthéon without rest, 19 pl. Panthéon (5th) 43 54 32 95, Fax 43 26 64 65, – AE GB JCB. L 14
closed 1 to 21 August – 45 – **34 rm** 670/790.

Grands Hommes without rest, 17 pl. Panthéon (5th) 46 34 19 60, Fax 43 26 67 32, – AE GB JCB. L 14
45 – **32 rm** 670/790.

Le Régent M without rest, 61 r. Dauphine (6th) 46 34 59 80, Fax 40 51 05 07 – AE GB JCB J 13
55 – **25 rm** 750/950.

Résidence Henri IV M without rest, 50 r. Bernardins (5th) 44 41 31 81, Fax 46 33 93 22 – kitchenette AE GB JCB. K 15
40 – **8 rm** 700/900, 5 suites.

Odéon H. M without rest, 3 r. Odéon (6th) 43 25 90 67, Fax 43 25 55 98 – AE GB JCB. K 13
55 – **33 rm** 700/1300.

de Fleurie without rest, 32 r. Grégoire de Tours (6th) 43 29 59 81, Fax 43 29 68 44 – AE GB. K 13
50 – **29 rm** 650/1200.

Prince de Conti M without rest, 8 r. Guénégaud (6th) 44 07 30 40, Fax 44 07 36 34 – AE GB. J 13
60 – **26 rm** 750/990.

Jardins du Luxembourg M without rest, 5 imp. Royer-Collard (5th) 40 46 08 88, Fax 40 46 02 28 – AE GB JCB. L 14
50 – **25 rm** 800.

Belloy St-Germain M without rest, 2 r. Racine (6th) ✆ 46 34 26 50, Fax 46 34 66 18 – lift TV ☎. AE GB JCB K 14
☕ 40 – **50 rm** 690/1200.

des Saints-Pères without rest, 65 r. Sts-Pères (6th) ✆ 45 44 50 00, Fax 45 44 90 83 – lift TV ☎. AE GB J 12
☕ 55 – **36 rm** 720/1620, 3 suites.

Sully St-Germain M without rest, 31 r. Écoles (5th) ✆ 43 26 56 02, Fax 43 29 74 42, fitness – lift air-conditioning TV ☎. AE ① GB JCB. no dogs K 15
☕ 50 – **56 rm** 600/800.

Royal St-Michel M without rest, 3 bd St-Michel (5th) ✆ 44 07 06 06, Fax 44 07 36 25 – lift air-conditioning TV ☎. AE ① GB JCB K 14
☕ 40 – **39 rm** 740/1160.

de l'Odéon without rest, 13 r. St-Sulpice (6th) ✆ 43 25 70 11, Fax 43 29 97 34, « 16C house » – lift air-conditioning TV ☎. AE ① GB JCB K 13
☕ 50 – **29 rm** 630/920.

Select M without rest, 1 pl. Sorbonne (5th) ✆ 46 34 14 80, Telex 201207, Fax 46 34 51 79 – lift air-conditioning TV ☎. AE ① GB JCB K 14
☕ 30 – **67 rm** 650/890.

Jardin de l'Odéon M without rest, 7 r. C. Delavigne (6th) ✆ 46 34 23 90, Fax 43 25 28 12 – lift TV ☎ wheelchair access. AE GB JCB K 13
☕ 50 – **41 rm** 606/1012.

Clos Médicis M without rest, 56 r. Monsieur Le Prince (6th) ✆ 43 29 10 80, Fax 43 54 26 90 – lift non-smoking air-conditioning TV ☎ wheelchair access. AE ① GB JCB K 14
☕ 60 – **38 rm** 706/1212.

St-Christophe without rest, 17 r. Lacépède (5th) ✆ 43 31 81 54, Fax 43 31 12 54 – lift TV ☎. AE ① GB L 15
☕ 50 – **31 rm** 750.

Au Manoir St-Germain des Prés without rest, 153 bd St-Germain (6th) ✆ 42 22 21 65, Fax 45 48 22 25 – lift non-smoking air-conditioning TV ☎. AE ① GB JCB J 12
☕ 40 – **32 rm** 750/990.

Aramis St-Germain without rest, 124 r. Rennes (6th) ✆ 45 48 03 75, Fax 45 44 99 29 – lift TV ☎ – seminars 30. AE ① GB JCB. no dogs L 12
☕ 45 – **42 rm** 550/850.

Parc St-Séverin without rest, 22 r. Parcheminerie (5th) ✆ 43 54 32 17, Fax 43 54 70 71 – lift TV ☎. AE ① GB. no dogs K 14
☕ 50 – **27 rm** 500/1500.

Notre Dame without rest, 1 quai St-Michel (5th) ✆ 43 54 20 43, Fax 43 26 61 75, view – lift TV ☎. AE ① GB JCB K 14
☕ 40 – **23 rm** 590/790, 3 duplex.

Jardin de Cluny without rest, 9 r. Sommerard (5th) ✆ 43 54 22 66, Fax 40 51 03 36 – lift air-conditioning TV ☎. AE ① GB JCB. no dogs K 14
☕ 45 – **40 rm** 620/800.

Marronniers quiet without rest, 21 r. Jacob (6th) ✆ 43 25 30 60, Fax 40 46 83 56 – lift air-conditioning TV ☎. no dogs J 13
☕ 46 – **37 rm** 715/870.

Albe without rest, 1 r. Harpe (5th) ✆ 46 34 09 70, Fax 40 46 85 70 – lift non-smoking TV ☎. AE ① GB JCB. no dogs K 14
☕ 40 – **45 rm** 530/625.

Maxim M without rest, 28 r. Censier (5th) ✆ 43 31 16 15, Fax 43 31 93 87 – lift non-smoking TV ☎. AE ① GB JCB M 15
☕ 45 – **36 rm** 470/535.

California H. without rest, 32 r. Écoles (5th) ✆ 46 34 12 90, Fax 46 34 75 52 – lift TV ☎. AE ① GB K 14-15
☕ 40 – **44 rm** 500/700.

La Sorbonne without rest, 6 r. Victor Cousin (5th) ✆ 43 54 58 08, Telex 206373, Fax 40 51 05 18 – lift TV ☎. AE GB K 14
☕ 35 – **37 rm** 415/490.

Pleasant hotels and restaurants
are shown in the Guide by a red sign.
Please send us the names
of any where you have enjoyed your stay.
Your Michelin Guide will be even better.

XXXXX ... X

XXXXX ✿✿ **Tour d'Argent** (Terrail), 15 quai Tournelle (5th) ✆ 43 54 23 31, Fax 44 07 12 04, < Notre-Dame, « Small museum showing the development of eating utensils. In the cellar : an illustrated history of wine » - ▤. AE ⓓ GB JCB K 16
closed Monday - **Meals** 395 and a la carte 800/1 150
Spec. Quenelles de brochet "André Terrail". Canard "Tour d'Argent". Flambée de pêche à l'eau-de-vie de framboise.

XXXX ✿✿ **Jacques Cagna,** 14 r. Gds Augustins (6th) ✆ 43 26 49 39, Fax 43 54 54 48, « Old Parisian house » - ▤. AE ⓓ GB JCB J 14
closed 1 to 21 August, Christmas-New Year, Saturday lunch and Sunday - **Meals** 260/490 and a la carte 500/680
Spec. Lotte de Cancale en cocotte à l'estragon. Poularde de Houdan en deux services. Gibier (season).

XXXX ✿ **Paris** - Hôtel Lutétia, 45 bd Raspail (6th) ✆ 49 54 46 90, Telex 270424, Fax 49 54 46 00, « "Art Deco" decor » - ▤. AE ⓓ GB JCB K 12
closed 27 July-25 August, Saturday and Sunday - **Meals** 260 (lunch), 360/565 and a la carte 380/510
Spec. Turbot au sel de Guérande. Jarret de veau cuit en cocotte. Le "tout chocolat".

XXX **Relais Louis XIII,** 1 r. Pont de Lodi (6th) ✆ 43 26 75 96, Fax 44 07 07 80, « 16C cellar, fine furniture » - ▤. AE ⓓ GB JCB J 14
closed 21 July-19 August, Monday lunch and Sunday - **Meals** 195 (lunch), 250/350 and a la carte 450/570.

XXX **Le Procope,** 13 r. Ancienne Comédie (6th) ✆ 43 26 99 20, Fax 43 54 16 86, « Former 18C literary café » - ▤. AE ⓓ GB K 13
Meals 106 (lunch)/185 and a la carte 180/320 ♁.

XX **Aub. des Deux Signes,** 46 r. Galande (5th) ✆ 43 25 46 56, Fax 46 33 20 49, « Medieval decor » - AE ⓓ GB JCB K 14
closed August, Saturday lunch and Sunday - **Meals** 150 (lunch)/230 and a la carte 360/520.

XX **Campagne et Provence,** 25 quai Tournelle (5th) ✆ 43 54 05 17, Fax 43 29 74 93 - ▤. GB
closed Monday lunch, Saturday lunch and Sunday - **Meals** 110 and a la carte 180/240. K 15

XX **Le Chat Grippé,** 87 r. Assas (6th) ✆ 43 54 70 00 - ▤. AE GB LM 13
closed August, Saturday lunch and Monday - **Meals** 160 (lunch), 240/325 and a la carte 260/370.

XX **Yugaraj,** 14 r. Dauphine (6th) ✆ 43 26 44 91, Fax 46 33 50 77 - ▤. AE ⓓ GB JCB. ✽
Meals - Indian rest. - 130 (lunch), 180/220 and a la carte 200/290. J 14

XX **La Truffière,** 4 r. Blainville (5th) ✆ 46 33 29 82, Fax 46 33 64 74 - ▤. AE ⓓ GB L 15
closed 1 to 20 August and Monday - **Meals** 98 (lunch), 125/298 and a la carte 200/280 ♁.

XX **Dodin-Bouffant,** 25 r. F.-Sauton (5th) ✆ 43 25 25 14, Fax 43 29 52 61 - ▤. AE ⓓ GB JCB
closed Saturday lunch and Sunday - **Meals** 180 b.i. (lunch), 235/600 and a la carte 240/370. K 15

XX **Marty,** 20 av. Gobelins (5th) ✆ 43 31 39 51, Fax 43 37 63 70, brasserie - AE ⓓ GB JCB
Meals 189/269 b.i. and a la carte 190/330 ♁. M 15

XX ✿ **La Timonerie** (de Givenchy), 35 quai Tournelle (5th) ✆ 43 25 44 42 - GB K 15
closed 1 to 15 March, Monday lunch and Sunday - **Meals** 230 and a la carte 270/370
Spec. Foie gras rôti sur pomme de terre séchée au four. Sandre rôti, choux et pommes de terre en vinaigrette. Tarte fine au chocolat.

XX **Mavrommatis,** 42 r. Daubenton (5th) ✆ 43 31 17 17, Fax 43 36 13 08 - ▤. GB. ✽ M 15
closed Monday and lunch except Saturday and Sunday - **Meals** - Greek rest. - a la carte 160/250.

XX **Bistrot d'Alex,** 2 r. Clément (6th) ✆ 43 54 09 53 - ▤. AE GB JCB K 13
closed 24 December-2 January, Saturday lunch and Sunday - **Meals** 140/170 and a la carte 170/300.

XX **Joséphine "Chez Dumonet",** 117 r. Cherche Midi (6th) ✆ 45 48 52 40, Fax 42 84 06 83, bistro - GB L 11
closed August, Saturday and Sunday - **Meals** a la carte 180/310 - **La Rôtisserie :** ✆ 42 22 81 19 *(closed July, Monday and Tuesday)* **Meals** 150 bc.

XX **Le Rond de Serviette,** 97 r. Cherche-Midi (6th) ✆ 45 44 01 02, Fax 42 22 50 10 - ▤. AE ⓓ GB JCB L 11
closed 28 July-18 August, Saturday lunch and Sunday - **Meals** 138 b.i./168 and a la carte 180/250 ♁.

XX **Chez Toutoune,** 5 r. Pontoise (5th) ✆ 43 26 56 81, Fax 43 25 35 93 - AE GB K 15
closed Monday lunch and Sunday - **Meals** 108 (lunch)/158.

XX **L'Arrosée,** 12 r. Guisarde (6th) ✆ 43 54 66 59, Fax 43 54 66 59 - ▤. AE ⓓ GB JCB. ✽
closed 7 to 22 August, Saturday lunch and Sunday lunch - **Meals** 149/210 and a la carte 265/465. K 13

XX **La Marlotte,** 55 r. Cherche Midi (6th) ✆ 45 48 86 79, Fax 45 44 34 80 - AE ⓓ GB JCB. ✽
closed August, Saturday and Sunday - **Meals** a la carte 180/260. K 12

XX **Chez Maître Paul,** 12 r. Monsieur-le-Prince (6th) ✆ 43 54 74 59, Fax 46 34 58 33 - AE ⓓ GB
closed Saturday lunch and Sunday - **Meals** 190 b.i. and a la carte 190/330. K 13

XX **Les Bouchons de François Clerc,** 12 r. Hôtel Colbert (5th) ✆ 43 54 15 34, Fax 46 34 68 07 - AE GB K 15
closed Saturday lunch and Sunday - **Meals** 219.

XX **La Bastide Odéon,** 7 r. Corneille (6th) ✆ 43 26 03 65, Fax 44 07 28 93 – GB K 13
closed 5 to 26 August, Sunday and Monday – **Meals** 180.

XX **Inagiku,** 14 r. Pontoise (5th) ✆ 43 54 70 07, Fax 40 51 74 44 – ▤. GB JCB K 15
closed 15 to 31 August, lunch from 1 to 14 August and Sunday – **Meals** - Japanese rest. - 88 (lunch), 148/248 and a la carte 230/290.

X **L'Épi Dupin,** 11 r. Dupin (6th) ✆ 42 22 64 56 – GB K 12
closed Saturday lunch and Sunday – **Meals** 153.

X **Au Grilladin,** 6 r. Mézières (6th) ✆ 45 48 30 38 – AE GB K 12
closed 27 July-26 August, 21 December-3 January, Monday lunch and Sunday – **Meals** 159 and a la carte 190/270.

X **Les Bookinistes,** 53 quai Grands Augustins (6th) ✆ 43 25 45 94, Fax 43 25 23 07 – ▤. AE GB JCB J 14
closed Saturday lunch and Sunday – **Meals** 160 and a la carte 200/250.

X **La Timbale St-Bernard,** 16 r. Fossés St-Bernard (5th) ✆ 46 34 28 28, Fax 46 34 66 26 – AE ⓓ GB. ✻ K 15
closed 1 to 21 August, Saturday lunch and Sunday – **Meals** 135/165 and a la carte approx. 220.

X **Le Palanquin,** 12 r. Princesse (6th) ✆ 43 29 77 66 – GB K 13
closed 7 to 21 August and Sunday – **Meals** - Vietnamese rest. - 68 (lunch), 99/145 and a la carte 150/230.

X **Moulin à Vent "Chez Henri",** 20 r. Fossés-St-Bernard (5th) ✆ 43 54 99 37, bistro – GB. ✻ K 15
closed August, Sunday and Monday – **Meals** 170 and a la carte 240/320.

X **Dominique,** 19 r. Bréa (6th) ✆ 43 27 08 80, Fax 43 26 88 35 – AE ⓓ GB L 12
closed 21 July-19 August, Monday lunch and Sunday – **Meals** - Russian rest. - 170 and a la carte 230/310.

X **Rôtisserie d'en Face,** 2 r. Christine (6th) ✆ 43 26 40 98, Fax 43 54 54 48 – ▤. AE GB JCB
closed Saturday lunch and Sunday – **Meals** 159 (lunch)/198. J 14

X **Rôtisserie du Beaujolais,** 19 quai Tournelle (5th) ✆ 43 54 17 47, Fax 44 07 12 04 – GB
closed Monday – **Meals** a la carte 170/280. K 15

X **Allard,** 41 r. St-André-des-Arts (6th) ✆ 43 26 48 23, Fax 46 33 04 02, bistro – ▤. AE ⓓ GB JCB K 14
closed Sunday – **Meals** 150 (lunch)/200 and a la carte 260/380.

X **Moissonnier,** 28 r. Fossés-St-Bernard (5th) ✆ 43 29 87 65, bistro – GB K 15
closed 26 July-3 September, Sunday dinner and Monday – **Meals** a la carte 180/250.

X **Atelier Maître Albert,** 1 r. Maître Albert (5th) ✆ 46 33 13 78, Fax 44 07 01 86 – ▤. AE GB
closed Sunday – **Meals** (dinner only) 160/230 b.i.. K 15

X **Bistrot du Port,** 13 quai Montebello (5th) ✆ 40 51 73 19 – ▤. GB K 15
closed 22 to 30 December, 2 to 15 January and Monday – **Meals** (dinner only) 138.

X **Balzar,** 49 r. Écoles (5th) ✆ 43 54 13 67, Fax 44 07 14 91, brasserie – ▤. AE GB K 14
closed August, Christmas-New Year – **Meals** a la carte 150/280.

X **Valérie Tortu,** 11 r. Grande Chaumière (6th) ✆ 46 34 07 58, Fax 46 34 06 84 – AE GB
closed August, Saturday lunch and Sunday – **Meals** 80/158 and a la carte 170/220. L 12

X **Bistro de la Grille,** 14 r. Mabillon (6th) ✆ 43 54 16 87, bistro – GB K 13
Meals 90 (lunch)/150 ♁.

Faubourg-St-Germain, Invalides, École Militaire.

7th arrondissement.
7th: ✉ 75007

Montalembert Ⓜ, 3 r. Montalembert ✆ 45 49 68 68, Fax 45 49 69 49, ⛱, « Original decor » – |♦| ▤ TV ☎ – 🏛 25. AE ⓓ GB. ✻ rm J 12
Meals 170 (lunch)(brunch Sunday 185)and a la carte 250/350 – ☕ 100 – **51 rm** 1625/2080, 5 suites.

Cayré Ⓜ without rest, 4 bd Raspail ✆ 45 44 38 88, Telex 270577, Fax 45 44 98 13 – |♦| ⊁ TV ☎. AE ⓓ GB JCB J 12
☕ 50 – **119 rm** 900.

Duc de Saint-Simon without rest, 14 r. St-Simon ✆ 44 39 20 20, Telex 203277, Fax 45 48 68 25, « Tastefully furnished interior » – 🛗 📺 ☎. 🚫 J 11
☕ 70 – **29 rm** 1050/1500, 5 suites.

La Bourdonnais, 111 av. La Bourdonnais ✆ 47 05 45 42, Telex 201416, Fax 45 55 75 54 – 🛗 📺 ☎. ⓓ GB JCB J 9
Meals see rest. ***La Cantine des Gourmets*** below – ☕ 37 – **57 rm** 490/670, 3 suites.

Bellechasse Ⓜ without rest, 8 r. Bellechasse ✆ 45 50 22 31, Fax 45 51 52 36 – 🛗 ⇔ 📺 ☎ ♿. AE ⓓ GB JCB H 11
☕ 75 – **41 rm** 910.

Le Tourville Ⓜ without rest, 16 av. Tourville ✆ 47 05 62 62, Fax 47 05 43 90 – 🛗 ▤ 📺 ☎. AE ⓓ GB J 9
☕ 60 – **30 rm** 790/990.

Lenox Saint-Germain without rest, 9 r. Université ✆ 42 96 10 95, Fax 42 61 52 83 – 🛗 📺 ☎. AE ⓓ GB JCB J 12
☕ 45 – **32 rm** 590/780.

Splendid Ⓜ without rest, 29 av. Tourville ✆ 45 51 24 77, Telex 206879, Fax 44 18 94 60 – 🛗 📺 ☎ ♿. AE ⓓ GB. 🚫 J 9
☕ 46 – **48 rm** 630/990.

Bourgogne et Montana without rest, 3 r. Bourgogne ✆ 45 51 20 22, Fax 45 56 11 98 – 🛗 📺 ☎. AE ⓓ GB JCB H 11
☕ 65 – **30 rm** 685/920, 4 suites.

Sèvres Vaneau Ⓜ without rest, 86 r. Vaneau ✆ 45 48 73 11, Fax 45 49 27 74 – 🛗 ⇔ 📺 ☎. AE ⓓ GB JCB K 11
☕ 75 – **39 rm** 840.

Eiffel Park H. Ⓜ without rest, 17 bis r. Amélie ✆ 45 55 10 01, Telex 202950, Fax 47 05 28 68 – 🛗 📺 ☎ ♿ – 🎤 40. AE ⓓ GB JCB. 🚫 J 9
☕ 53 – **36 rm** 795/835.

Les Jardins d'Eiffel Ⓜ without rest, 8 r. Amélie ✆ 47 05 46 21, Telex 206582, Fax 45 55 28 08 – 🛗 ⇔ ▤ 📺 ☎ ♿ 🚗. AE ⓓ GB JCB H 9
☕ 60 – **80 rm** 700/960.

Verneuil St-Germain without rest, 8 r. Verneuil ✆ 42 60 82 14, Fax 42 61 40 38 – 🛗 📺 ☎. AE ⓓ GB. 🚫 J 12
☕ 50 – **26 rm** 650/950.

Muguet Ⓜ without rest, 11 r. Chevert ✆ 47 05 05 93, Fax 45 50 25 37 – 🛗 📺 ☎. AE GB J 9
☕ 42 – **45 rm** 420/490.

Relais Bosquet without rest, 19 r. Champ-de-Mars ✆ 47 05 25 45, Fax 45 55 08 24 – 🛗 📺 ☎ ♿. AE ⓓ GB J 9
☕ 53 – **40 rm** 660/810.

du Cadran Ⓜ without rest, 10 r. Champ-de-Mars ✆ 40 62 67 00, Fax 40 62 67 13 – 🛗 ⇔ ▤ 📺 ☎. AE ⓓ GB. 🚫 J 9
☕ 50 – **42 rm** 850/980.

Élysées Maubourg without rest, 35 bd La Tour Maubourg ✆ 45 56 10 78, Fax 47 05 65 08 – 🛗 📺 ☎. AE ⓓ GB JCB H 10
☕ 45 – **30 rm** 570/710.

de Varenne 🌿 without rest, 44 r. Bourgogne ✆ 45 51 45 55, Fax 45 51 86 63 – 🛗 📺 ☎. AE GB J 10
☕ 45 – **24 rm** 510/690.

Beaugency without rest, 21 r. Duvivier ✆ 47 05 01 63, Fax 45 51 04 96 – 🛗 📺 ☎. AE ⓓ GB JCB J 9
30 rm ☕ 530/660.

Londres without rest, 1 r. Augereau ✆ 45 51 63 02, Fax 47 05 28 96 – 🛗 📺 ☎. AE ⓓ GB JCB J 8
☕ 50 – **30 rm** 595.

Bersoly's without rest, 28 r. Lille ✆ 42 60 73 79, Fax 49 27 05 55 – 🛗 📺 ☎. GB J 13
closed August – ☕ 50 – **16 rm** 580/680.

France without rest, 102 bd La Tour Maubourg ✆ 47 05 40 49, Fax 45 56 96 78 – 🛗 📺 ☎ ♿. AE GB J 9
☕ 35 – **60 rm** 380/490.

Champ-de-Mars without rest, 7 r. Champ-de-Mars ✆ 45 51 52 30, Fax 45 51 64 36 – 🛗 📺 ☎. AE GB J 9
☕ 35 – **25 rm** 360/420.

L'Empereur without rest, 2 r. Chevert ✆ 45 55 88 02, Fax 45 51 88 54 – 🛗 📺 ☎. AE GB J 9
☕ 37 – **38 rm** 421/466.

Turenne without rest, 20 av. Tourville ✆ 47 05 99 92, Fax 45 56 06 04 – 🛗 📺 ☎. AE ⓓ GB J 9
☕ 38 – **34 rm** 320/515.

Résidence Orsay without rest, 93 r. Lille ✆ 47 05 05 27, Fax 47 05 29 48 – 🛗 📺 ☎. GB. 🚫 H 11
closed August – ☕ 35 – **32 rm** 250/490.

XXXX ✿ **Jules Verne,** Eiffel Tower : 2nd platform, lift in south leg ✆ 45 55 61 44, Fax 47 05 29 41, ≤ Paris – ▤. AE ⓓ GB. ✈ J 7
Meals 300 (lunch), 680/770 (except Sunday lunch)and a la carte 490/660
Spec. Fricassée de petites seiches au foie gras de canard poêlé. Langoustines et crabes aux pommes croustillantes et asperges. Entrecôte de veau de Corrèze, jus à l'oseille.

XXXX ✿✿✿ **Arpège** (Passard), 84 r. Varenne ✆ 45 51 47 33, Fax 44 18 98 39 – ▤. AE ⓓ GB JCB J 10
closed Sunday lunch and Saturday – **Meals** 390 (lunch)/790 and a la carte 520/800
Spec. Aiguillettes de homard et navet à l'aigre-doux au romarin. Poulet de Janzé fumé et ravioles de foie gras à la fondue d'oignons. Tomate farcie confite aux douze saveurs.

XXXX ✿✿ **Le Divellec,** 107 r. Université ✆ 45 51 91 96, Fax 45 51 31 75 – ▤. AE ⓓ GB JCB. ✈ H 10
closed 23 December-3 January, Sunday and Monday – **Meals** - Seafood - 290 (lunch)and a la carte 440/750
Spec. Homard à la presse avec son corail. Saint-Pierre braisé au citron confit. Raviole de saumon avec crevettes grises et bigorneaux.

XXXX ✿✿ **Duquesnoy,** 6 av. Bosquet ✆ 47 05 96 78, Fax 44 18 90 57 – ▤. AE GB H 9
closed 1 to 15 August, Saturday lunch and Sunday – **Meals** 250 (lunch), 450/550 and a la carte 440/600
Spec. Saint-Jacques fumées "minute", pommes de terre au caviar (October-March). Chartreuse de pigeonneau au foie gras, sauce aux truffes. Millefeuille léger, poire caramélisée, sauce et crème glacée aux noix.

XXX ✿ **Paul Minchelli,** 54 bd La Tour Maubourg ✆ 47 05 89 86, Fax 45 56 03 84 – ▤. GB J 9
closed August, Sunday, Monday and Bank Holidays – **Meals** - Seafood - a la carte 310/520
Spec. Galette d'anchois et beignets d'arêtes. Pibales à l'ail. Saumon au bouillon de poivre.

XXX ✿ **La Cantine des Gourmets,** 113 av. La Bourdonnais ✆ 47 05 47 96, Fax 45 51 09 29 – ▤. AE GB J 9
Meals 240 b.i. (lunch), 320/420 and a la carte 350/470
Spec. Croustilles de langoustines à la fondue de poireau. Noisettes d'agneau de Lozère en fine croûte d'olives. Dôme moelleux choco-caramel, soufflé aux marrons (Winter).

XXX **Le Petit Laurent,** 38 r. Varenne ✆ 45 48 79 64, Fax 45 44 15 95 – AE ⓓ GB J 11
closed August, Saturday lunch and Sunday – **Meals** 185/250 and a la carte 250/370.

XXX ✿ **La Boule d'Or,** 13 bd La Tour Maubourg ✆ 47 05 50 18, Fax 47 05 91 21 – ▤. AE ⓓ GB JCB H 10
Meals 170/210
Spec. Foie gras frais de canard. Chausson de langoustines. Soufflé chaud au citron.

XX ✿ **Le Bellecour** (Goutagny), 22 r. Surcouf ✆ 45 51 46 93, Fax 45 50 30 11 – ▤. AE ⓓ GB H 9
closed August, Saturday except dinner from 15 September-15 June and Sunday – **Meals** 160 (lunch), 250/420 and a la carte 320/450
Spec. Truffière de Saint-Jacques (15 December-30 March). Quenelles de brochet "maison". Lièvre à la cuillère (10 October-31 January).

XX **La Maison de l'Amérique Latine,** 217 bd St-Germain ✆ 45 49 33 23, Fax 40 49 03 94, 🍴, « 18C mansion, terrace opening onto the garden » – AE GB. ✈ J 11
closed 5 to 26 August, Saturday, Sunday and Bank Holidays – **Meals** (lunch only except May-October) 195 (lunch)and a la carte 300/340.

XX **Beato,** 8 r. Malar ✆ 47 05 94 27 – ▤. AE GB. ✈ H 9
closed August, Christmas-New-Year, Sunday and Monday – **Meals** - Italian rest. - 145 (lunch)and a la carte 230/330 ♁.

XX **Ferme St-Simon,** 6 r. St-Simon ✆ 45 48 35 74, Fax 40 49 07 31 – ▤. AE ⓓ GB J 11
closed 3 to 19 August, Saturday lunch and Sunday – **Meals** 170 (lunch)/190 and a la carte 260/340.

XX **Au Quai d'Orsay,** 49 quai d'Orsay ✆ 45 51 58 58, Fax 45 56 98 42 – AE ⓓ GB H 9
closed Saturday lunch and Sunday – **Meals** 190 and a la carte 240/290.

XX ✿ **Récamier,** 4 r. Récamier ✆ 45 48 86 58, Fax 42 22 84 76, 🍴 – ▤. AE ⓓ GB JCB K 12
closed Sunday – **Meals** 300 b.i. (lunch)and a la carte 270/420
Spec. Oeufs en meurette. Mousse de brochet sauce Nantua. Sauté de boeuf bourguignon.

XX **Les Glénan,** 54 r. Bourgogne ✆ 47 05 96 65 – ▤. AE GB J 10
closed 3 August-2 September, February Holidays, Saturday and Sunday – **Meals** 195 b.i. and a la carte 270/340.

XX **Le Bamboche,** 15 r. Babylone ✆ 45 49 14 40, Fax 45 49 14 44 – AE GB K 11
closed 3 to 25 August, Saturday lunch and Sunday – **Meals** 180 and a la carte 240/370.

XX **D'Chez Eux,** 2 av. Lowendal ✆ 47 05 52 55, Fax 45 55 60 74 – AE ⓓ GB J 9
closed 5 to 20 August and Sunday – **Meals** 250 (lunch)and a la carte 220/420.

XX **Foc Ly,** 71 av. Suffren ✆ 47 83 27 12 – ▤. AE GB K 8
closed Monday in July-August – **Meals** - Chinese and Thai rest. - 110/160 b.i. and a la carte 180/200.

XX **Gildo,** 153 r. Grenelle ✆ 45 51 54 12, Fax 45 51 57 42 – ▤. AE GB J 9
closed 25 July-24 August, Monday lunch and Sunday – **Meals** - Italian rest. - 150 b.i. (lunch)and a la carte 240/420.

XX **Le Champ de Mars,** 17 av. La Motte-Picquet ✆ 47 05 57 99, Fax 44 18 94 69 – AE ⓓ GB
closed 15 July-15 August and Monday – **Meals** 118/159 and a la carte 200/300. J 9

XX **Tan Dinh,** 60 r. Verneuil ✆ 45 44 04 84, Fax 45 44 36 93 J 12
closed 1 August-1 September and Sunday – **Meals** - Vietnamese rest. - a la carte 270/310.

X **Gaya Rive Gauche,** 44 r. Bac ✆ 45 44 73 73, Fax 42 60 04 54 – AE GB J 12
closed August and Sunday – **Meals** - Seafood - a la carte 250/330.

X **Vin sur Vin,** 20 r. Monttessuy ✆ 47 05 14 20 – GB H 8
closed 1 to 20 August, 23 December-3 January, Saturday except dinner from October-April, Monday lunch and Sunday – **Meals** a la carte 240/330.

X **Eiffel Park,** 39 av. La Motte-Picquet ✆ 45 55 90 20, Fax 44 18 36 73 – AE ⓓ GB JCB
Meals 175 b.i.. H 9

X **Le P'tit Troquet,** 28 r. Exposition ✆ 47 05 80 39, bistro – GB J 9
closed 1 to 21 August, Saturday lunch and Sunday – **Meals** 135 (lunch), 145/163.

X **Thoumieux** with rm, 79 r. St-Dominique ✆ 47 05 49 75, Fax 47 05 36 96, brasserie – ▤ rest TV ☎. GB H 9
closed August except rest. – **Meals** 72/150 🍷 – ☕ 35 – **10 rm** 600/650.

X **Clémentine,** 62 av. Bosquet ✆ 45 51 41 16 – AE GB J 9
closed 15 to 31 August, Saturday lunch, Sunday and Bank Holidays – **Meals** 149 and a la carte 180/250 🍷.

X **Chez Collinot,** 1 r. P. Leroux ✆ 45 67 66 42 – GB K 11
closed August, Saturday (except dinner September-May) and Sunday – **Meals** 135.

X **Le Sédillot,** 2 r. Sédillot ✆ 45 51 95 82, « Art Nouveau decor » – AE GB H 8
closed 7 to 21 August, Saturday lunch and Sunday – **Meals** 120 (dinner), 135/200.

X **La Fontaine de Mars,** 129 r. St-Dominique ✆ 47 05 46 44, Fax 47 05 11 13, ☂, bistro – AE GB J 9
closed Sunday – **Meals** a la carte 180/300.

X **L'Oeillade,** 10 r. St-Simon ✆ 42 22 01 60 – ▤. GB J 11
closed 4 to 25 August, Saturday lunch and Sunday – **Meals** 138 and a la carte approx. 210.

X **Le Maupertu,** 94 bd La Tour Maubourg ✆ 45 51 37 96 – GB J 10
closed 12 to 20 August, Saturday lunch and Sunday – **Meals** 135 and a la carte 200/290.

X **Du Côté 7ème,** 29 r. Surcouf ✆ 47 05 81 65, bistro – AE GB H 9-10
closed 14 to 28 August, 24 December-1 January and Monday – **Meals** 175 b.i..

X **Au Bon Accueil,** 14 r. Monttessuy ✆ 47 05 46 11 – GB H 8
closed August, 25 December-1 January, Saturday lunch and Sunday – **Meals** 120 and a la carte approx. 220.

X **La Calèche,** 8 r. Lille ✆ 42 60 24 76, Fax 47 03 31 10 – ▤. AE ⓓ GB JCB J 12
closed 3 to 26 August, 23 December-1 January, Saturday and Sunday – **Meals** 100/175 and a la carte 180/270.

X **Aub. Bressane,** 16 av. La Motte-Picquet ✆ 47 05 98 37, Fax 47 05 92 21 – AE GB H 9
closed Saturday lunch – **Meals** 140 b.i. (lunch)and a la carte 160/260.

X **Le Florimond,** 19 av. La Motte-Picquet ✆ 45 55 40 38 – GB H 9
closed 4 to 20 August, Saturday lunch and Sunday – **Meals** 100/155 and a la carte 170/270 🍷.

X **Apollon,** 24 r. J. Nicot ✆ 45 55 68 47, Fax 47 05 13 60 – GB H 9
closed Sunday – **Meals** - Greek rest. - 128 and a la carte 150/210.

Champs-Élysées, St-Lazare, Madeleine.

8th arrondissement.
8th: ✉ 75008

🏨 **Plaza Athénée,** 25 av. Montaigne ✆ 47 23 78 33, Fax 47 20 20 70 – |‡| ▤ TV ☎ – 🏛 30 - 100. AE ⓓ GB JCB. ✂ rest G 9
Meals see rest. ***Régence*** and ***Relais Plaza*** below – ☕ 160 – **210 rm** 2950/4650, 42 suites.

🏨 **Crillon,** 10 pl. Concorde ✆ 44 71 15 00, Telex 290204, Fax 44 71 15 02 – |‡| ✈ ▤ TV ☎ – 🏛 30 - 60. AE ⓓ GB JCB G 11
Meals see ***Les Ambassadeurs*** and ***L'Obélisque*** below – ☕ 155 – **163 rm** 3200/4100, 45 suites.

🏨 **Bristol,** 112 r. Fg St-Honoré ✆ 42 66 91 45, Telex 280961, Fax 42 66 68 68, ♿, ▣, ☂ – |‡| ▤ rm TV ☎ 🚗 – 🏛 30 - 60. AE ⓓ GB JCB. ✂ F 10
Meals see ***Bristol*** below – ☕ 165 – **153 rm** 2500/4500, 40 suites.

George V, 31 av. George-V ✆ 47 23 54 00, Fax 47 20 40 00, – |‡| ▤ TV ☎ – 🏛 30 - 600. AE ⓓ GB JCB G 8
Les Princes : **Meals** 240/450 and a la carte 300/530 – ***Le Grill*** – ✆ **47 23 60 80** *(closed August, Saturday and Sunday)* **Meals** 198/280 and a la carte 240/420, – ☕ 140 – **221 rm** 1800/2800, 39 suites.

Royal Monceau, 37 av. Hoche ✆ 42 99 88 00, Telex 650361, Fax 42 99 89 90, , « Pool and fitness centre » – |‡| ▤ TV ☎ – 🏛 25 - 100. AE ⓓ GB JCB. ✻ E 8
Meals see ***Le Jardin*** below ***Carpaccio*** ✆ 42 99 98 90, Italian rest. *(closed August)* **Meals** a la carte 310/460 – ☕ 190 – **180 rm** 2450/3350, 39 suites.

Prince de Galles, 33 av. George-V ✆ 47 23 55 11, Telex 651627, Fax 47 20 96 92, – |‡| ⇷ ▤ TV ☎ – 🏛 40 - 110. AE ⓓ GB JCB. ✻ G 8
Jardin des Cygnes : **Meals** 260/350 (Sunday brunch only 280) and a la carte 360/510 – ☕ 145 – **138 rm** 2250/3100, 30 suites.

Vernet, 25 r. Vernet ✆ 44 31 98 00, Telex 651347, Fax 44 31 85 69 – |‡| ▤ TV ☎. AE ⓓ GB. ✻ rest F 8
Meals see ***Les Élysées*** below – ☕ 120 – **54 rm** 1550/2250, 3 suites.

de Vigny M without rest, 9 r. Balzac ✆ 40 75 04 39, Telex 651822, Fax 40 75 05 81, « Tasteful decor » – |‡| ⇷ ▤ TV ☎ 🚗. AE ⓓ GB JCB F 8
☕ 90 – **25 rm** 1900/2200, 12 suites.

San Régis, 12 r. J. Goujon ✆ 44 95 16 16, Fax 45 61 05 48, « Tasteful decor » – |‡| ▤ rm TV ☎. AE ⓓ GB. ✻ G 9
Meals 200/250 and a la carte 300/460 – ☕ 110 – **34 rm** 1650/2850, 10 suites.

La Trémoille, 14 r. La Trémoille ✆ 47 23 34 20, Telex 640344, Fax 40 70 01 08 – |‡| ▤ TV ☎ – 🏛 25. AE ⓓ GB JCB G 9
Meals 190 and a la carte 230/360 – ☕ 100 – **93 rm** 1950/2930, 14 suites.

Lancaster, 7 r. Berri ✆ 40 76 40 76, Telex 640991, Fax 40 76 40 00, – |‡| TV ☎. AE ⓓ GB JCB F 9
Meals *(closed Saturday and Sunday)* 230 – ☕ 120 – **52 rm** 1950/2650, 7 suites.

Élysées Star M without rest, 19 r. Vernet ✆ 47 20 41 73, Fax 47 23 32 15 – |‡| ▤ TV ☎ – 🏛 30. AE ⓓ GB JCB F 8
☕ 90 – **38 rm** 1700/1900.

Balzac M, 6 r. Balzac ✆ 44 35 18 00, Telex 651298, Fax 42 25 24 82 – |‡| ▤ TV ☎. AE ⓓ GB JCB F 8
Bice ✆ 44 35 18 18, Italian rest. *(closed 3 to 28 August, 21 December-3 January, Saturday lunch and Sunday)* **Meals** a la carte 250/360 – ☕ 90 – **56 rm** 1830/2200, 14 suites.

Golden Tulip St-Honoré M, 220 r. Fg St-Honoré ✆ 49 53 03 03, Telex 650657, Fax 40 75 02 00 – |‡| kitchenette ⇷ ▤ TV ☎ ♿ 🚗 – 🏛 190. AE ⓓ GB JCB. ✻ rm
Relais Vermeer *(closed 4 to 25 August, Saturday lunch and Sunday)* **Meals** 180 and a la carte 290/420 – ☕ 110 – **54 rm** 1500/1800, 18 suites. E 8

Château Frontenac without rest, 54 r. P. Charron ✆ 47 23 55 85, Fax 47 23 03 32 – |‡| TV ☎ – 🏛 25. AE ⓓ GB. ✻ G 9
☕ 85 – **102 rm** 930/1450, 4 suites.

Sofitel Arc de Triomphe, 14 r. Beaujon ✆ 45 63 04 04, Telex 650902, Fax 42 25 36 81 – |‡| ⇷ ▤ rest TV ☎ – 🏛 40. AE ⓓ GB JCB F 8
Le Clovis *(closed August, Christmas-New Year, Saturday, Sunday and Bank Holidays)* **Meals** 220 and a la carte 310/440 – ☕ 100 – **129 rm** 1650/1900, 6 suites.

Bedford, 17 r. de l'Arcade ✆ 44 94 77 77, Telex 290506, Fax 44 94 77 97 – |‡| ▤ TV ☎ – 🏛 80. AE GB. ✻ rest F 11
Meals *(closed 29 July-25 August, Saturday and Sunday)* (lunch only) 200 and a la carte 230/340 – ☕ 70 – **137 rm** 790/960, 11 suites.

Warwick M, 5 r. Berri ✆ 45 63 14 11, Telex 642295, Fax 45 63 75 81 – |‡| ⇷ ▤ TV ☎ – 🏛 30 - 110. AE ⓓ GB. ✻ rest F 9
Meals see ***La Couronne*** below – ☕ 110 – **142 rm** 1800/2700, 5 suites.

California, 16 r. Berri ✆ 43 59 93 00, Telex 644634, Fax 45 61 03 62, – |‡| ⇷ ▤ TV ☎ – 🏛 25 - 90. AE ⓓ GB JCB. ✻ rest F 9
Meals *(closed Sunday)* (lunch only) 170 – ☕ 120 – **160 rm** 1800/2200, 13 duplex.

Résidence du Roy M without rest, 8 r. François 1er ✆ 42 89 59 59, Telex 648452, Fax 40 74 07 92 – |‡| kitchenette ▤ TV ☎ ♿ 🚗 – 🏛 25. AE ⓓ GB JCB G 9
☕ 80, 28 suites1220/1720, 4 studios, 3 duplex.

Queen Elizabeth, 41 av. Pierre-1er-de-Serbie ✆ 47 20 80 56, Telex 641179, Fax 47 20 89 19 – |‡| ⇷ ▤ TV ☎ – 🏛 25 - 30. AE ⓓ GB JCB G 8
Meals *(closed August and Sunday)* (lunch only) 170/230 b.i. – ☕ 90 – **53 rm** 1200/1800, 12 suites.

Concorde St-Lazare, 108 r. St-Lazare ✆ 40 08 44 44, Fax 42 93 01 20, « 19th century lobby, remarkable billiards room » – |‡| ⇷ ▤ TV ☎ – 🏛 150. AE ⓓ GB JCB. ✻
Café Terminus : **Meals** 140(dinner), 155/250, a la carte approx. 350, – ☕ 97 – **295 rm** 1300/1900, 5 suites. E 12

Napoléon without rest, 40 av. Friedland ✆ 47 66 02 02, Fax 47 66 82 33 – |‡| TV ☎ – 🏛 100. AE ⓓ GB JCB F 8
☕ 85 – **70 rm** 1250/1750, 32 suites.

Claridge-Bellman without rest, 37 r. François 1er ☎ 47 23 54 42, Telex 641150, Fax 47 23 08 84 – AE GB. – 70 – **42 rm** 1150/1350. G 9

Beau Manoir without rest, 6 r. de l'Arcade ☎ 42 66 03 07, Fax 42 68 03 00, « Attractive interior » – AE GB JCB **29 rm** 995/1155, 3 suites. F 11

Sofitel Champs-Élysées M, 8 r. J. Goujon ☎ 43 59 52 41, Fax 42 25 06 59, – – 150. AE GB JCB G 9
Les Saveurs ☎ 45 63 17 44 *(closed dinner Saturday and Sunday)* **Meals** a la carte 190/300 – 85 – **40 rm** 1500/1800.

Chateaubriand M without rest, 6 r. Chateaubriand ☎ 40 76 00 50, Telex 641012, Fax 40 76 09 22 – AE GB JCB. 65 – **28 rm** 1100/1400. F 9

Montaigne M without rest, 6 av. Montaigne ☎ 47 20 30 50, Telex 648051, Fax 47 20 94 12 – AE GB JCB 95 – **29 rm** 1300/1850. G 9

Royal Alma M without rest, 35 r. J. Goujon ☎ 42 25 83 30, Telex 641428, Fax 45 63 68 64 – AE GB JCB. 95 – **61 rm** 1380/1620, 3 suites. G 9

Paris St-Honoré without rest, 15 r. Boissy d'Anglas ☎ 44 94 14 14, Telex 281908, Fax 44 94 14 28 – AE GB 90 – **112 rm** 860/1330. G 11

de l'Élysée without rest, 12 r. Saussaies ☎ 42 65 29 25, Fax 42 65 64 28 – AE GB JCB. 60 – **32 rm** 700/980. F 11

Élysées-Ponthieu and Résidence without rest, 24 r. Ponthieu ☎ 42 25 68 70, Telex 640053, Fax 42 25 80 82 – kitchenette AE GB JCB 75 – **92 rm** 920/1600, 6 suites. F 9

Royal H. M without rest, 33 av. Friedland ☎ 43 59 08 14, Telex 651465, Fax 45 63 69 92 – AE GB JCB 90 – **58 rm** 1250/1950. F 8

Concortel without rest, 19 r. Pasquier ☎ 42 65 45 44, Telex 660228, Fax 42 65 18 33 – AE GB 50 – **46 rm** 570/750. F 11

Powers without rest, 52 r. François 1er ☎ 47 23 91 05, Telex 642051, Fax 49 52 04 63 – AE GB JCB 65 – **53 rm** 806/1262. G 9

Résidence Monceau without rest, 85 r. Rocher ☎ 45 22 75 11, Fax 45 22 30 88 – AE GB JCB. 50 – **51 rm** 685. E 11

Mathurins M without rest, 43 r. Mathurins ☎ 44 94 20 94, Fax 44 94 00 44 – AE GB JCB. 65 – **33 rm** 800/1200, 3 suites. F 11

Castiglione, 40 r. Fg St-Honoré ☎ 44 94 25 25, Telex 281906, Fax 42 65 12 27 – – 80. AE GB **Meals** 125/160 – 60 – **114 rm** 1250/1500. G 11

New Roblin and rest. Le Mazagran, 6 r. Chauveau-Lagarde ☎ 44 71 20 80, Telex 285154, Fax 42 65 19 49 – AE GB JCB. rest F 11
Meals *(closed Saturday, Sunday and Bank Holidays)* 115 and a la carte 170/270 – 60 – **75 rm** 700/900, 3 suites.

L'Arcade M without rest, 9 r. de l'Arcade ☎ 53 30 60 00, Fax 40 07 03 07 – – 25. AE GB JCB 55 – **41 rm** 770/940, 4 duplex. F 11

West-End without rest, 7 r. Clément-Marot ☎ 47 20 30 78, Fax 47 20 34 42 – AE GB JCB 55 – **54 rm** 700/1300. G 9

Lido M without rest, 4 passage Madeleine ☎ 42 66 27 37, Fax 42 66 61 23 – AE GB JCB **32 rm** 830/980. F 11

Galiléo M without rest, 54 r. Galilée ☎ 47 20 66 06, Fax 47 20 67 17 – AE GB JCB. 50 – **27 rm** 800/950. F 8

Étoile Friedland M without rest, 177 r. Fg St-Honoré ☎ 45 63 64 65, Fax 45 63 88 96 – AE GB JCB 75 – **40 rm** 1300. F 9

Queen Mary M without rest, 9 r. Greffulhe ☎ 42 66 40 50, Telex 285419, Fax 42 66 94 92 – AE GB JCB. 69 – **36 rm** 710/890. F 12

Franklin Roosevelt without rest, 18 r. Clément-Marot ✆ 47 23 61 66, Fax 47 20 44 30 – G 9
☕ 55 – **45 rm** 795/895.

Atlantic H. without rest, 44 r. Londres ✆ 43 87 45 40, Telex 285477, Fax 42 93 06 26 – E 12
☕ 52 – **88 rm** 510/890.

Waldorf Madeleine M without rest, 12 bd Malesherbes ✆ 42 65 72 06, Fax 40 07 10 45 – F 11
☕ 50 – **45 rm** 1100/1400.

Flèche d'Or M without rest, 29 r. Amsterdam ✆ 48 74 06 86, Telex 660641, Fax 48 74 06 04 – E 12
☕ 35 – **61 rm** 550/820.

Rochambeau without rest, 4 r. La Boétie ✆ 42 65 27 54, Fax 42 66 03 81 – F 11
☕ 50 – **50 rm** 800.

Cordélia without rest, 11 r. Greffulhe ✆ 42 65 42 40, Fax 42 65 11 81 – F 11
☕ 50 – **30 rm** 740/850.

Newton Opéra without rest, 11 bis r. de l'Arcade ✆ 42 65 32 13, Fax 42 65 30 90 – F 11
☕ 50 – **31 rm** 690.

Mayflower without rest, 3 r. Chateaubriand ✆ 45 62 57 46, Telex 640727, Fax 42 56 32 38 – F 9
☕ 50 – **24 rm** 690/970.

Élysées Mermoz M without rest, 30 r. J. Mermoz ✆ 42 25 75 30, Fax 45 62 87 10 – F 10
☕ 45 – **21 rm** 690/850, 5 suites.

Fortuny without rest, 35 r. de l'Arcade ✆ 42 66 42 08, Fax 42 66 00 32 – F 11
☕ 50 – **30 rm** 680/730.

Plaza Haussmann without rest, 177 bd Haussmann ✆ 45 63 93 83, Fax 45 61 14 30 – F 9
☕ 30 – **41 rm** 645/830.

L'Orangerie without rest, 9 r. Constantinople ✆ 45 22 07 51, Fax 45 22 16 49 – E 11
☕ 35 – **29 rm** 570/670.

Arc Élysée M without rest, 45 r. Washington ✆ 45 63 69 33, Fax 45 63 76 25 – F 9
☕ 55 – **23 rm** 756/922.

Colisée without rest, 6 r. Colisée ✆ 43 59 95 25, Fax 45 63 26 54 – F 9
☕ 45 – **45 rm** 640/850.

Lavoisier-Malesherbes without rest, 21 r. Lavoisier ✆ 42 65 10 97, Fax 42 65 02 43 – F 11
☕ 32 – **32 rm** 420/470.

XXXXX ✿✿ **Les Ambassadeurs** - Hôtel Crillon, 10 pl. Concorde ✆ 44 71 16 16, Telex 290204, Fax 44 71 15 02, « 18C decor » – G 11
Meals 340 (lunch)/610 and a la carte 500/630
Spec. Moelleux de pommes ratte, médaillons de homard à la civette. Suprême de pintade fermière poêlée à l'étouffée. Truffe glacée à la fleur de thym frais.

XXXXX ✿✿✿ **Taillevent** (Vrinat), 15 r. Lamennais ✆ 44 95 15 01, Fax 42 25 95 18 – F 9
closed 20 July-20 August, Saturday, Sunday and Bank Holidays – **Meals** (booking essential) a la carte 560/780
Spec. Boudin de homard à la nage. Pigeon rôti en bécasse. Soufflé chaud aux fruits.

XXXXX ✿✿ **Lasserre,** 17 av. F.-D.-Roosevelt ✆ 43 59 53 43, Fax 45 63 72 23, « Retractable roof » – G 10
closed 4 August-2 September, Monday lunch and Sunday – **Meals** a la carte 550/760
Spec. Saint-Jacques poêlées au beurre de truffes (September-April). Lapereau rôti à la crème de ciboulette. Macarons passion-orange.

XXXXX ✿✿✿ **Lucas Carton** (Senderens), 9 pl. Madeleine ✆ 42 65 22 90, Fax 42 65 06 23, « Authentic 1900 decor » – G 11
closed 3 to 27 August, 22 December-7 January, Saturday lunch and Sunday – **Meals** 395 (lunch), 600/1850 and a la carte 640/1 230
Spec. Foie gras de canard au chou. Homard à la vanille. Canard Apicius rôti au miel et aux épices.

XXXXX ✿✿ **Ledoyen,** carré Champs-Élysées (1st floor) ☎ 47 42 35 98, Fax 47 42 55 01, - see also rest. *Le Cercle* – ▤ P. AE ① GB JCB G 10
closed August, Saturday and Sunday – **Meals** 290 (lunch), 520/590 and a la carte 500/800
Spec. Truffes en feuilleté de pommes de terre (late December-late February). Homard en waterzooï. Tronçon de turbot rôti à la bière de garde et oignons frits.

XXXXX ✿✿ **Laurent,** 41 av. Gabriel ☎ 42 25 00 39, Fax 45 62 45 21, ☂, « Pleasant summer terrace » – AE ① GB. ✈ G 10
closed Saturday lunch, Sunday and Bank Holidays – **Meals** 380 and a la carte 540/980
Spec. Foie gras de canard aux haricots noirs pimentés. Tête de veau gribiche ou ravigote. Les deux soufflés "Laurent".

XXXXX ✿ **Bristol** - Hôtel Bristol, 112 r. Fg St-Honoré ☎ 42 66 91 45, Telex 280961, Fax 42 66 68 68 – ▤. AE ① GB JCB. ✈ F 10
Meals 345/630 and a la carte 530/770
Spec. Salade de langoustines et croustillant de pommes de terre. Médaillon de lotte au beurre de thym et "chiffons" d'aubergines. Tête de veau au chou caramélisé et tanin de brouilly.

XXXXX ✿ **Régence** - Hôtel Plaza Athénée, 25 av. Montaigne ☎ 47 23 78 33, Telex 650092, Fax 47 20 20 70, ☂ – ▤. AE ① GB JCB G 9
Meals 320 (lunch)and a la carte 500/620
Spec. Ravigote de homard, vinaigrette coraillée. Filet d'agneau rôti, concassé de champignons au thym. Dôme au caramel mousseux parfumé de café fort.

XXXX ✿✿ **Les Élysées** - Hôtel Vernet, 25 r. Vernet ☎ 44 31 98 98, Fax 44 31 85 69, « Fine glass roof » – ▤. AE ① GB JCB. ✈ F 8
closed 29 July-23 August, 23 to 27 December, Saturday and Sunday – **Meals** 320 (lunch), 370/490 and a la carte 380/580
Spec. Morue rôtie aux tomates confites. Rougets de roche en filets poêlés à la tapenade. Chausson feuilleté au chocolat amer, crème glacée aux fèves de cacao.

XXXX ✿ **Chiberta,** 3 r. Arsène-Houssaye ☎ 45 63 77 90, Fax 45 62 85 08 – ▤. AE ① GB JCB
closed 1 to 27 August, Saturday and Sunday – **Meals** 290 and a la carte 420/610 F 8
Spec. Turbot rôti au raifort sur mousseline de champignons. Ris de veau braisé à la vanille et badiane. Macaron à la crème et sorbet fromage blanc.

XXXX ✿ **La Marée,** 1 r. Daru ☎ 43 80 20 00, Fax 48 88 04 04 – ▤. AE ① GB E 8
closed 26 July-27 August, Saturday and Sunday – **Meals** - Seafood - a la carte 360/610
Spec. Langoustines rôties au beurre de carottes. Turbotin rôti aux cèpes et foie gras (September-October). Râble de lièvre à la "Caladoise" (October-December).

XXX ✿ **Le Jardin** - Hôtel Royal Monceau, 37 av. Hoche ☎ 42 99 98 70, Fax 42 99 89 94, ☂ – ▤. AE ① GB JCB
closed Saturday, Sunday and Bank Holidays except August – **Meals** 280 (lunch), 340/430 and a la carte 430/610
Spec. Langoustines rôties au poivre. Carré d'agneau au fenouil sauvage et ses légumes farcis à la niçoise. Damier de chocolat guanaja.

XXX ✿ **La Couronne** - Hôtel Warwick, 5 r. Berri ☎ 45 63 78 49, Telex 642295, Fax 45 63 38 50 – ▤. AE ① GB. ✈ F 9
closed August, Saturday lunch and Sunday – **Meals** 230/320 and a la carte 280/470
Spec. Pot-au-feu d'agneau à l'anis étoilé. Sandre rôti au four. "Arpège" d'arômes chocolat vanillé.

XXX ✿ **Copenhague,** 142 av. Champs-Élysées (1st floor) ☎ 44 13 86 26, Fax 42 25 83 10, ☂ – ▤. AE ① GB JCB. ✈ F 8
closed 4 to 31 August, 1 to 7 January, Saturday lunch, Sunday and Bank Holidays – **Meals** - Danish rest. - 240/270 and a la carte 280/440 - **Flora Danica** ☎ 44 13 86 29 **Meals** 148b.i./255 and a la carte 230/360
Spec. Saumon mariné à l'aneth. Suprême de poule des neiges aux airelles (October-March). Gratin de rhubarbe aux fraises (March-October).

XXX **Le 30 - Fauchon,** 30 pl. Madeleine ☎ 47 42 56 58, Fax 47 42 96 02, ☂ – ▤. AE ① GB JCB
closed Sunday – **Meals** 245 (dinner)and a la carte 280/420. F 12

XXX **Yvan,** 1bis r. J. Mermoz ☎ 43 59 18 40, Fax 45 63 78 69 – ▤. AE ① GB JCB F-G 10
closed Saturday lunch and Sunday – **Meals** 178/298 and a la carte approx. 320.

XXX **Le Marcande,** 52 av. Miromesnil ☎ 42 65 19 14, Fax 40 76 03 27, ☂ – AE GB F 10
closed 9 to 26 August, Saturday and Sunday – **Meals** 240 and a la carte 250/390.

XXX ✿ **Vancouver** (Decout), 4 r. Arsène-Houssaye ☎ 42 56 77 77, Fax 42 56 50 52 – ▤. AE GB
closed 27 July-18 August, 25 December-2 January, Saturday, Sunday and Bank Holidays – **Meals** - Seafood - a la carte 280/370 F 8
Spec. Carpaccio de Saint-Jacques au colombo (October-May). "Dim Sum" de langoustines aux épices. Bouillabaisse parisienne.

XXX **L'Obélisque** - Hôtel Crillon, 6 r. Boissy-d'Anglas ☎ 44 71 15 15, Fax 44 71 15 02 – ▤. AE ① GB JCB G 11
closed August and Bank Holidays – **Meals** (booking essential) 270.

XXX **Relais-Plaza** - Hôtel Plaza Athénée, 21 av. Montaigne ☎ 47 23 46 36, Telex 650092, Fax 47 20 20 70 – ▤. AE ① GB JCB G 9
closed August – **Meals** 290 b.i. (lunch)and a la carte 360/480.

XXX **Indra,** 10 r. Cdt-Rivière ☎ 43 59 46 40, Fax 44 07 31 19 – ▤. AE ① GB F 9
closed Sunday – **Meals** - Indian rest. - 195 (lunch), 220/300 and a la carte 200/275.

XX **La Luna,** 69 r. Rocher ✆ 42 93 77 61, Fax 40 08 02 44 – ▤. AE GB JCB E 11
closed Sunday – **Meals** - Seafood - a la carte 290/390.

XX **Les Géorgiques,** 36 av. George-V ✆ 40 70 10 49 – ▤. AE ⓓ GB JCB. ✻ G 8
closed Saturday lunch and Sunday – **Meals** 180 (lunch)/360 and a la carte 340/490.

XX **Chez Tante Louise,** 41 r. Boissy-d'Anglas ✆ 42 65 06 85, Fax 42 65 28 19 – ▤. AE ⓓ GB JCB F 11
closed August, Saturday lunch and Sunday – **Meals** 190 and a la carte 230/350.

XX **Le Sarladais,** 2 r. Vienne ✆ 45 22 23 62, Fax 45 22 23 62 – ▤. AE GB E 11
closed August, Saturday lunch and Sunday – **Meals** 145 (dinner)/200 and a la carte 220/380.

XX **Le Grenadin,** 46 r. Naples ✆ 45 63 28 92, Fax 45 61 24 76 – ▤. AE GB E 11
closed Saturday except dinner September-May and Sunday – **Meals** 265/330.

XX **Le Cercle Ledoyen,** carré Champs-Élysées (ground floor) ✆ 47 42 76 02, Fax 47 42 55 01, G 10
☂ – ▤. AE ⓓ GB JCB. ✻
closed Sunday – **Meals** a la carte 220/270.

XX **Hédiard,** 21 pl. Madeleine ✆ 43 12 88 99, Fax 43 12 88 98 – ▤. AE ⓓ GB JCB F 11
closed Sunday – **Meals** a la carte 230/300.

XX **Boeuf sur le Toit,** 34 r. Colisée ✆ 43 59 83 80, Fax 45 63 45 40, brasserie – ▤. AE ⓓ GB F 10
Meals a la carte 180/270 ♁.

XX **La Fermette Marbeuf 1900,** 5 r. Marbeuf ✆ 53 23 08 00, Fax 53 23 08 09, « 1900 decor with original ceramics and stained glass windows » – ▤. AE ⓓ GB G 9
Meals 169 and a la carte 210/370 ♁.

XX ✿ **Marius et Janette,** 4 av. George-V ✆ 47 23 41 88, Fax 47 23 07 19, ☂ – ▤. AE ⓓ GB JCB G 8
Meals - Seafood - 300 b.i. and a la carte 330/480
Spec. Moules de pleine mer grillées au thym frais (late August-early November). Bar en croûte de sel de Guérande. Merlan frit sauce tartare (late April-early October).

XX **Androuët,** 41 r. Amsterdam ✆ 48 74 26 93, Fax 49 95 02 54 – ▤. AE ⓓ GB E 12
closed 4 to 27 August, Saturday lunch, Monday lunch and Sunday – **Meals** - Cheese specialities - 175 (lunch), 195/250 and a la carte 220/340.

XX **Suntory,** 13 r. Lincoln ✆ 42 25 40 27, Fax 45 63 25 86 – ▤. AE ⓓ GB JCB. ✻ F 9
closed Saturday lunch and Sunday – **Meals** - Japanese rest. - 135 (lunch), 420/590 and a la carte 360/460.

XX **Le Lloyd's,** 23 r. Treilhard ✆ 45 63 21 23, Fax 45 63 21 23 – AE GB E 10
closed 25 December-1 January, Saturday and Sunday – **Meals** a la carte 210/310.

XX **Stresa,** 7 r. Chambiges ✆ 47 23 51 62 – ▤. AE ⓓ GB G 9
closed August, 20 December-3 January, Saturday dinner and Sunday – **Meals** - Italian rest. - (booking essential) a la carte 240/350.

XX **Village d'Ung et Li Lam,** 10 r. J. Mermoz ✆ 42 25 99 79 – ▤. AE ⓓ GB F 10
Meals - Chinese and Thai rest. - 105/149 and a la carte 160/220.

XX **Kinugawa,** 4 r. St-Philippe du Roule ✆ 45 63 08 07, Fax 42 60 45 21 – ▤. AE ⓓ GB JCB. ✻ F 9
closed 23 December-7 January and Sunday – **Meals** - Japanese rest. - 155 (lunch), 247/700 and a la carte 280/390.

XX **Bistrot du Sommelier,** 97 bd Haussmann ✆ 42 65 24 85, Fax 53 75 23 23 – ▤. AE GB F 11
closed August, Christmas-New Year, Saturday and Sunday – **Meals** 390 b.i. (dinner)and a la carte 270/390.

XX **Le Pichet,** 68 r. P. Charron ✆ 43 59 50 34, Fax 45 63 07 82 – ▤. AE ⓓ GB GF 9
closed Sunday – **Meals** a la carte 270/450.

XX **L'Alsace** (24 hr service), 39 av. Champs-Élysées ✆ 43 59 44 24, Fax 42 89 06 62, ☂, brasserie – ▤. AE ⓓ GB F 9
Meals 185 and a la carte 180/350 ♁.

XX **Tong Yen,** 1bis r. J. Mermoz ✆ 42 25 04 23, Fax 45 63 51 57 – ▤. AE ⓓ GB F 10
closed 1 to 25 August – **Meals** - Chinese rest. - a la carte 200/290.

X **Ferme des Mathurins,** 17 r. Vignon ✆ 42 66 46 39 – ⓓ GB F 12
closed August, Sunday and Bank Holidays – **Meals** 160/210 and a la carte 190/330.

X **Bistrot de Marius,** 6 av. George-V ✆ 40 70 11 76, ☂ – AE ⓓ GB JCB G 8
Meals - Seafood - a la carte 200/260.

X **L'Appart',** 9 r. Colisée ✆ 53 75 16 34, Fax 53 76 15 39 – ▤. AE GB JCB F 9
Meals 160 b.i. (lunch) and a la carte 200/260.

X **Le Boucoléon,** 10 r. Constantinople ✆ 42 93 73 33 – GB JCB. ✻ E 11
closed 1 to 21 August, Saturday lunch, Sunday and Bank Holidays – **Meals** 90/150 and a la carte 140/210.

Opéra, Gare du Nord, Gare de l'Est, Grands Boulevards.

9th and 10th arrondissements.
9th: ✉ 75009
10th: ✉ 75010

Grand Hôtel Inter-Continental, 2 r. Scribe (9th) ✆ 40 07 32 32, Telex 220875, Fax 42 66 12 51, - - 300. AE ⓓ GB JCB. rest F 12
Meals see ***Rest. Opéra*** and ***Brasserie Café de la Paix*** below - ***La Verrière*** ✆ 40 07 31 00 *(closed dinner Saturday and Sunday)* **Meals** 175(dinner)/305 - ☕ 160 - **492 rm** 1700/2800, 22 suites.

Scribe, 1 r. Scribe (9th) ✆ 44 71 24 24, Telex 214653, Fax 42 65 39 97 - - 50. AE ⓓ GB JCB. rest F 12
Meals see ***Les Muses*** below - ***Le Jardin des Muses :*** **Meals** 140 and a la carte 160/230, - ☕ 105 - **206 rm** 1950/2450, 11 suites.

Ambassador, 16 bd Haussmann (9th) ✆ 44 83 40 40, Telex 285912, Fax 40 22 08 74 - - 110. AE ⓓ GB JCB F 13
Venantius ✆ 48 00 06 38 *(closed August, Saturday and Sunday)* **Meals** 220/340 and a la carte 280/470 - ☕ 122 - **298 rm** 1450/1750.

Commodore, 12 bd Haussmann (9th) ✆ 42 46 72 82, Telex 280601, Fax 47 70 23 81 - - 25. AE ⓓ GB JCB F 13
Cancans (brasserie) **Meals** 89 - ***Le Carvery*** - **(lunch only)**- *(closed July-August, Saturday and Sunday)* **Meals** 220 - ☕ 95 - **151 rm** 1250/1650, 11 suites.

Terminus Nord M without rest, 12 bd Denain (10th) ✆ 42 80 20 00, Fax 42 80 63 89 - - 80. AE ⓓ GB JCB E 16
☕ 75 - **247 rm** 940/990.

Lafayette M without rest, 49 r. Lafayette (9th) ✆ 42 85 05 44, Telex 283025, Fax 49 95 06 60 - . AE ⓓ GB JCB F 14
☕ 75 - **97 rm** 910, 6 suites.

St-Pétersbourg, 33 r. Caumartin (9th) ✆ 42 66 60 38, Telex 680001, Fax 42 66 53 54 - rest - 25. AE ⓓ GB JCB. rest F 12
Le Relais *(closed August, Saturday and Sunday)* **Meals** 140 and a la carte 180/270 - ☕ 70 - **100 rm** 840/925.

Brébant, 32 bd Poissonnière (9th) ✆ 47 70 25 55, Telex 280127, Fax 42 46 65 70 - rest - 25 - 100. AE ⓓ GB JCB F 14
Vieux Pressoir : **Meals** 98/159 and a la carte 160/320 - ☕ 48 - **122 rm** 760/890.

L'Horset Pavillon, 38 r. Échiquier (10th) ✆ 42 46 92 75, Telex 283905, Fax 42 47 03 97 - . AE ⓓ GB JCB F 15
Meals *(closed Saturday, Sunday and Bank Holidays)* 165 b.i. and a la carte 170/260 - ☕ 80 - **92 rm** 850/950.

Franklin M without rest, 19 r. Buffault (9th) ✆ 42 80 27 27, Fax 48 78 13 04 - . AE ⓓ GB E 14
☕ 75 - **68 rm** 780/990.

Blanche Fontaine without rest, 34 r. Fontaine (9th) ✆ 45 26 72 32, Fax 42 81 05 52 - . AE GB. D 13
☕ 40 - **45 rm** 507/540, 4 suites.

Carlton's H. without rest, 55 bd Rochechouart (9th) ✆ 42 81 91 00, Fax 42 81 97 04, « Roof top panoramic terrace, ≤ Paris » - . AE ⓓ GB JCB D 14
☕ 45 - **103 rm** 615/665.

Bergère without rest, 34 r. Bergère (9th) ✆ 47 70 34 34, Telex 290668, Fax 47 70 36 36 - . AE ⓓ GB JCB. F 14
☕ 50 - **134 rm** 690/990.

Anjou-Lafayette without rest, 4 r. Riboutté (9th) ✆ 42 46 83 44, Fax 48 00 08 97 - . AE ⓓ GB JCB E 14
☕ 40 - **39 rm** 460/590.

Paix République without rest, 2 bis bd St-Martin (10th) ✆ 42 08 96 95, Telex 680632, Fax 42 06 36 30 - . AE ⓓ GB. G 16
☕ 40 - **45 rm** 550/980.

Frantour Paris-Est M without rest, 4 r. 8 Mai 1945 (cour d'Honneur gare de l'Est)(10th) ✆ 44 89 27 00, Fax 44 89 27 49 - - 250. AE GB E 16
☕ 55 - **45 rm** 550/1050.

Touraine Opéra M without rest, 73 r. Taitbout (9th) ✆ 48 74 50 49, Fax 42 81 26 09 - . AE ⓓ GB E 13
☕ 75 - **39 rm** 780/990.

Albert 1er [M] without rest, 162 r. Lafayette (10th) ✆ 40 36 82 40, Fax 40 35 72 52 - |‡| ▤ TV ☎. AE ⓓ GB JCB E 16
☐ 40 - **57 rm** 440/555.

Opéra Cadet [M] without rest, 24 r. Cadet (9th) ✆ 48 24 05 26, Telex 282287, Fax 42 46 68 09 - |‡| ▤ TV ☎ ♿ 🚗. AE ⓓ GB JCB F 14
☐ 65 - **82 rm** 735/820, 3 suites.

Mercure Monty [M] without rest, 5 r. Montyon (9th) ✆ 47 70 26 10, Fax 42 46 55 10 - |‡| ⇹ TV ☎ - 🏛 50. AE ⓓ GB JCB F 14
☐ 60 - **71 rm** 660/690.

Corona ⛰ without rest, 8 cité Bergère (9th) ✆ 47 70 52 96, Telex 281081, Fax 42 46 83 49 - |‡| TV ☎ ♿. AE ⓓ GB JCB F 14
☐ 45 - **56 rm** 570/690, 4 suites.

Trinité Plaza without rest, 41 r. Pigalle (9th) ✆ 42 85 57 00, Telex 280110, Fax 45 26 41 20 - |‡| TV ☎. AE ⓓ GB JCB E 13
☐ 30 - **42 rm** 570/660.

Résidence du Pré without rest, 15 r. P. Sémard (9th) ✆ 48 78 26 72, Fax 42 80 64 83 - |‡| TV ☎. AE ⓓ GB E 15
☐ 50 - **40 rm** 425/485.

du Pré without rest, 10 r. P. Sémard (9th) ✆ 42 81 37 11, Telex 660549, Fax 40 23 98 28 - |‡| TV ☎. AE ⓓ GB. 🐕 E 15
☐ 50 - **41 rm** 445/575.

Axel without rest, 15 r. Montyon (9th) ✆ 47 70 92 70, Telex 282200, Fax 47 70 43 37 - |‡| ⇹ ▤ TV ☎. AE ⓓ GB JCB F 14
☐ 45 - **38 rm** 640/750.

Monterosa [M] without rest, 30 r. La Bruyère (9th) ✆ 48 74 87 90, Fax 42 81 01 12 - |‡| ⇹ TV ☎. AE ⓓ GB. 🐕 E 13
☐ 32 - **36 rm** 400/600.

Printania without rest, 19 r. Château d'Eau (10th) ✆ 42 01 84 20, Fax 42 39 55 12 - |‡| TV ☎. AE ⓓ GB. 🐕 F 16
☐ 42 - **51 rm** 536/742.

Moulin [M] without rest, 39 r. Fontaine (9th) ✆ 42 81 93 25, Fax 40 16 09 90 - |‡| ⇹ TV ☎. AE ⓓ GB JCB D 13
☐ 75 - **50 rm** 785.

Capucines without rest, 6 r. Godot de Mauroy (9th) ✆ 47 42 25 05, Fax 42 68 05 05 - |‡| TV ☎. AE ⓓ GB JCB F 12
☐ 38 - **45 rm** 520/600.

Modern' Est without rest, 91 bd Strasbourg (10th) ✆ 40 37 77 20, Fax 40 37 17 55 - |‡| TV ☎. GB. 🐕 - ☐ 30 - **30 rm** 385/470. E 16

Alba ⛰ without rest, 34 ter r. La Tour d'Auvergne (9th) ✆ 48 78 80 22, Fax 42 85 23 13 - |‡| kitchenette TV ☎. AE GB JCB. 🐕 E 14
☐ 40 - **25 rm** 500/700.

Ibis Lafayette without rest, 122 r. Lafayette (10th) ✆ 45 23 27 27, Fax 42 46 73 79 - |‡| ⇹ TV ☎ ♿. AE ⓓ GB E 16
☐ 40 - **70 rm** 410/455.

St-Laurent [M] without rest, 5 r. St-Laurent (10th) ✆ 42 09 59 79, Fax 42 09 83 50 - |‡| TV ☎ ♿. AE ⓓ GB JCB - ☐ 45 - **44 rm** 550/650. EF 16

Suède without rest, 106 bd Magenta (10th) ✆ 40 36 10 12, Fax 40 36 11 98 - |‡| ⇹ TV ☎. AE ⓓ GB JCB - ☐ 45 - **52 rm** 535. E 15-16

Champagne-Mulhouse without rest, 87 bd Strasbourg (10th) ✆ 42 09 12 28, Fax 42 09 48 12 - |‡| ⇹ TV ☎. AE ⓓ GB JCB E 15
☐ 45 - **31 rm** 535.

Montréal without rest, 23 r. Godot-de-Mauroy (9th) ✆ 42 65 99 54, Fax 49 24 07 33 - |‡| ⇹ TV ☎. AE ⓓ GB F 12
closed August - ☐ 35 - **14 rm** 285/600, 5 suites.

XXXX ✿ **Rest. Opéra** - Grand Hôtel Inter-Continental, pl. Opéra (9th) ✆ 40 07 30 10, Telex 220875, Fax 40 07 33 86, « Second Empire decor » - ▤. AE ⓓ GB JCB. 🐕 F 12
closed August, Saturday and Sunday - **Meals** 230 (lunch)/335 b.i. and a la carte 320/550
Spec. Tête de veau sautée, ravioles de pieds mitonnés. Fricassée de poularde de Bresse étuvée au vin jaune. Conversation aux amandes.

XXXX ✿ **Les Muses** - Hôtel Scribe, 1 r. Scribe (9th) ✆ 44 71 24 26, Fax 42 65 39 97 - ▤. AE ⓓ GB JCB. 🐕 F 12
closed August, Saturday, Sunday and Bank Holidays - **Meals** 210/270 and a la carte approx. 350
Spec. Saumon d'Ecosse rôti aux épices à la rose. Salmis de palombe aux pignons de pin, gratin de girolles (October-February). Tarte soufflée à la mascarpone et aux fruits rouges poivrés.

XXX ✿ **La Table d'Anvers** (Conticini), 2 pl. Anvers (9th) ✆ 48 78 35 21, Fax 45 26 66 67 – ▤. AE GB D 14
closed Saturday lunch and Sunday – **Meals** 180 (lunch)/250 and a la carte 410/575
Spec. Croustillant de langoustines en fondue épicée. Selle d'agneau rôtie, curry sec aux aromates. Croquettes au chocolat coulant.

XXX **Charlot "Roi des Coquillages",** 12 pl. Clichy (9th) ✆ 48 74 49 64, Fax 40 16 11 00 – ▤. AE ⓓ GB D 12
Meals - Seafood - 185 and a la carte 240/340.

XXX **Le Louis XIV,** 8 bd St-Denis (10th) ✆ 42 08 56 56, Fax 42 08 23 50 – AE ⓓ GB G 15
Meals 195 b.i. and a la carte 210/430.

XX **Au Chateaubriant,** 23 r. Chabrol (10th) ✆ 48 24 58 94, Collection of paintings – ▤. AE GB. ✂ E 15
closed August, Sunday and Monday – **Meals** - Italian rest. - 159 and a la carte 230/320.

XX **Brasserie Café de la Paix** - Grand Hôtel Inter-Continental, 12 bd Capucines (9th) ✆ 40 07 30 20, Telex 220875, Fax 40 07 33 86, ⛱ – ▤. AE ⓓ GB JCB F 12
Meals a la carte 240/360 ♁.

XX **Julien,** 16 r. Fg St-Denis (10th) ✆ 47 70 12 06, Fax 42 47 00 65, « Belle Epoque brasserie » – ▤. AE ⓓ GB F 15
Meals a la carte 180/270 ♁.

XX **Grand Café Capucines** (24 hr service), 4 bd Capucines (9th) ✆ 47 42 19 00, Fax 47 42 74 22, brasserie, « Belle Epoque decor » – ▤. AE ⓓ GB F 13
Meals 185 and a la carte 190/340 ♁.

XX **Grange Batelière,** 16 r. Grange Batelière (9th) ✆ 47 70 85 15 – AE GB G 10
closed August, Saturday lunch, Sunday and Bank Holidays – **Meals** 198/295 and a la carte 260/360.

XX **Le Quercy,** 36 r. Condorcet (9th) ✆ 48 78 30 61 – AE ⓓ GB E 14
closed 2 August-3 September, Sunday and Bank Holidays – **Meals** 152 and a la carte 190/340.

XX **Bistrot Papillon,** 6 r. Papillon (9th) ✆ 47 70 90 03 – ▤. AE ⓓ GB E 15
closed 6 to 14 April, 3 to 26 August, Saturday and Sunday – **Meals** 140 and a la carte 210/280 ♁.

XX **Comme Chez Soi,** 20 r. Lamartine (9th) ✆ 48 78 00 02, Fax 42 85 09 78 – ▤. AE GB JCB E 14
closed August, Saturday, Sunday and Bank Holidays – **Meals** 140/230 and a la carte 220/340.

XX **Au Petit Riche,** 25 r. Le Peletier (9th) ✆ 47 70 68 68, Fax 48 24 10 79, bistro, « Late 19C decor » – ▤. AE ⓓ GB JCB F 13
closed Sunday – **Meals** 160 and a la carte 190/320 ♁.

XX **Brasserie Flo,** 7 cour Petites-Écuries (10th) ✆ 47 70 13 59, Fax 42 47 00 80, « 1900 decor » – ▤. AE ⓓ GB F 15
Meals a la carte 180/270 ♁.

XX **Terminus Nord,** 23 r. Dunkerque (10th) ✆ 42 85 05 15, Fax 40 16 13 98, brasserie – ▤. AE ⓓ GB E 16
Meals a la carte 180/270 ♁.

XX **Le Saintongeais,** 62 r. Fg Montmartre (9th) ✆ 42 80 39 92 – AE ⓓ GB E 14
closed 12 to 18 August, Saturday and Sunday – **Meals** 135 and a la carte 180/260.

XX **La P'tite Tonkinoise,** 56 r. Fg Poissonnière (10th) ✆ 42 46 85 98 – ⓓ GB F 15
closed 1 August-5 September, 22 December-5 January, Sunday and Monday – **Meals** - Vietnamese rest. - 133 (lunch)and a la carte 160/230 ♁.

X **Wally Le Saharien,** 36 r. Rodier (9th) ✆ 42 85 51 90, Fax 42 81 22 77 – ✂ E 14
closed Sunday – **Meals** - North African rest. - 150 (lunch)/240.

X **I Golosi,** 6 r. Grange Batelière (9th) ✆ 48 24 18 63, « Venetian decor » – ▤. GB F 14
closed August, Saturday dinner and Sunday – **Meals** - Italian rest - a la carte 170/230.

X **L'Oenothèque,** 20 r. St-Lazare (9th) ✆ 48 78 08 76, Fax 40 16 10 27 – ▤. GB E 13
closed 12 to 31 August, Saturday and Sunday – **Meals** a la carte 220/360.

X **Aux Deux Canards,** 8 r. Fg Poissonnière (10th) ✆ 47 70 03 23 – AE ⓓ GB JCB F 15
closed 1 to 20 August, Saturday lunch and Sunday – **Meals** 110 and a la carte 140/210.

X **L'Alsaco Winstub,** 10 r. Condorcet (9th) ✆ 45 26 44 31 – AE GB E 15
closed August, Saturday lunch and Sunday – **Meals** 78 (lunch), 85/168 b.i. and a la carte 130/240.

X **Chez Jean,** 52 r. Lamartine (9th) ✆ 48 78 62 73, Fax 48 78 62 73, bistro – GB E 14
closed 24 December-1 January, Saturday lunch and Sunday – **Meals** 165.

X **Bistro de Gala,** 45 r. Fg Montmarte (9th) ✆ 40 22 90 50 – ▤. AE ⓓ GB F 14
closed 20 July-20 August, Saturday lunch and Sunday – **Meals** 150 and a la carte 150/210.

X **Relais Beaujolais,** 3 r. Milton (9th) ✆ 48 78 77 91, bistro – GB E 14
closed August, Saturday and Sunday – **Meals** 130 (lunch)and a la carte 130/210.

Bistro des Deux Théâtres, 18 r. Blanche (9th) ✆ 45 26 41 43, Fax 48 74 08 92 – ▤. AE GB E 12
Meals 169 b.i..

L'Excuse Mogador, 21 r. Joubert (9th) ✆ 42 81 98 19 – GB F 12
closed August, 24 to 31 December, Monday dinner, Saturday and Sunday – **Meals** 75 (lunch)/93 and a la carte approx. 130.

Bastille, Gare de Lyon, Place d'Italie, Bois de Vincennes.

12th and 13th arrondissements.
12th: ✉ 75012
13th: ✉ 75013

Novotel Gare de Lyon M, 2 r. Hector Malo (12th) ✆ 44 67 60 00, Telex 214014, Fax 44 67 60 60, – ▤ TV ☎ – 150. AE GB JCB L 18
Meals a la carte approx. 160 – 62 – **253 rm** 810/930.

Pavillon Bastille M without rest, 65 r. Lyon (12th) ✆ 43 43 65 65, Fax 43 43 96 52 – ▤ TV ☎. AE GB JCB K 18
80 – **25 rm** 955/1375.

Novotel Bercy, 86 r. Bercy (12th) ✆ 43 42 30 00, Fax 43 45 30 60, – ▤ TV ☎ – 30 - 60. AE GB M 19
Meals 138 and a la carte approx. 180 – 62 – **128 rm** 730/760.

Mercure Tolbiac M without rest, 21 r. Tolbiac (13th) ✆ 45 84 61 61, Fax 45 84 43 38 – ▤ TV ☎ – 25. AE GB JCB P 18
60 – **71 rm** 690/770.

Mercure Pont de Bercy without rest, 6 bd Vincent Auriol (13th) ✆ 45 82 48 00, Fax 45 82 19 16 – ▤ TV ☎ – 40. AE GB M 18
60 – **89 rm** 810.

Mercure Place d'Italie M without rest, 178 bd Vincent Auriol (13th) ✆ 44 24 01 01, Telex 203424, Fax 44 24 07 07 – TV ☎ – 50. AE GB N 16
62 – **70 rm** 680/785.

Mercure Blanqui without rest, 25 bd Blanqui (13th) ✆ 45 80 82 23, Fax 45 81 45 84 – ▤ TV ☎. AE GB JCB P 15
60 – **50 rm** 690/750.

Quatre Saisons Bastille M without rest, 67 r. Lyon (12th) ✆ 40 01 07 17, Telex 214223, Fax 40 01 07 27 – ▤ TV ☎ – 25. AE GB JCB K 18
70 – **36 rm** 760/950.

Allegro Nation M without rest, 33 av. Dr A. Netter (12th) ✆ 40 04 90 90, Fax 40 04 99 20 – ▤ TV ☎. AE GB JCB M 12
40 – **49 rm** 470/570.

Slavia without rest, 51 bd St-Marcel (13th) ✆ 43 37 81 25, Fax 45 87 05 03 – TV ☎. AE GB. M 16
35 – **37 rm** 345/385, 6 suites.

Résidence Vert Galant, 43 r. Croulebarbe (13th) ✆ 44 08 83 50, Fax 44 08 83 69 – TV ☎. AE GB JCB. rm N 15
Meals see rest. ***Etchegory*** below – 40 – **15 rm** 400/500.

Terminus-Lyon without rest, 19 bd Diderot (12th) ✆ 43 43 24 03, Fax 43 44 09 00 – TV ☎. AE GB JCB. L 18
40 – **60 rm** 520/540.

Modern H. Lyon without rest, 3 r. Parrot (12th) ✆ 43 43 41 52, Telex 220083, Fax 43 43 81 16 – TV ☎. AE GB JCB. L 18
39 – **48 rm** 495/570.

Média without rest, 22 r. Reine Blanche (13th) ✆ 45 35 72 72, Fax 43 31 43 31 – TV ☎. AE GB M 15
closed August – 35 – **18 rm** 340/525, 3 duplex.

Ibis Bercy, 77 r. Bercy (12th) ✆ 43 42 91 91, Telex 216391, Fax 43 42 34 79, – ▤ rest TV ☎ – 25 - 160. AE GB M 19
Meals 99 b.i. – 40 – **368 rm** 455/465.

Relais de Lyon without rest, 64 r. Crozatier (12th) ✆ 43 44 22 50, Telex 216690, Fax 43 41 55 12 – TV ☎. AE GB. K 19
40 – **34 rm** 426/542.

Touring Hôtel Magendie without rest, 2 r. Magendie (13th) 43 36 13 61, Fax 43 36 47 48 – GB
113 rm 320/390. N 14

Ibis without rest, 177 r. Tolbiac (13th) 45 80 16 60, Fax 45 80 95 80 – AE GB
39 – **60 rm** 395/420. P 15

Viator without rest, 1 r. Parrot (12th) 43 43 11 00, Fax 43 43 10 89 – AE GB.
35 – **45 rm** 320/370. L 18

Nouvel H. without rest, 24 av. Bel Air (12th) 43 43 01 81, Fax 43 44 64 13 – AE GB
40 – **28 rm** 360/535. L 21

XXX **Au Pressoir** (Seguin), 257 av. Daumesnil (12th) 43 44 38 21, Fax 43 43 81 77 – AE GB
closed August, Saturday and Sunday – **Meals** 400 and a la carte 380/500 M 22
Spec. Salade de pommes de terre roseval au foie gras. Huîtres en gelée, vinaigrette aux échalotes (October-May). Ris et rognon de veau au coulis de truffes.

XXX **Train Bleu,** Gare de Lyon (12th) 43 43 09 06, Fax 43 43 97 96, brasserie, « Murals depicting the journey from Paris to the Mediterranean » – AE GB
Meals (1st floor) 250 b.i. and a la carte 230/440. L 18

XXX **L'Oulette,** 15 pl. Lachambeaudie (12th) 40 02 02 12, – AE GB N 20
closed Saturday lunch and Sunday – **Meals** 160/240 b.i. and a la carte 170/360.

XX **Au Trou Gascon,** 40 r. Taine (12th) 43 44 34 26, Fax 43 07 80 55 – AE GB JCB
closed 3 August-1 September, 28 December-5 January, Saturday lunch and Sunday – **Meals** (booking essential) 190 (lunch)/280 b.i. and a la carte 290/410 M 21
Spec. Petits chipirons en piperade froide (June-October). Petit pâté chaud de cèpes. Volaille de Chalosse truffée.

XX **La Gourmandise,** 271 av. Daumesnil (12th) 43 43 94 41 – AE GB M 22
closed 4 to 18 August, Monday dinner and Sunday – **Meals** 145/175 and a la carte 260/370.

XX **Au Petit Marguery,** 9 bd Port-Royal (13th) 43 31 58 59, bistro – AE GB M 15
closed August, 24 December-3 January, Sunday and Monday – **Meals** 165 (lunch), 205/325 and a la carte 210/330.

XX **La Frégate,** 30 av. Ledru-Rollin (12th) 43 43 90 32 – AE GB L 18
closed August, Saturday and Sunday – **Meals** - Seafood - 160/300 and a la carte 280/400.

XX **Le Luneau,** 5 r. Lyon (12th) 43 43 90 85, brasserie – AE GB JCB L 18
Meals 137 and a la carte 200/310.

XX **La Flambée,** 4 r. Taine (12th) 43 43 21 80 – AE GB M 20
closed 1 to 21 August and Sunday – **Meals** 125/199 b.i. and a la carte 190/300.

XX **Le Traversière,** 40 r. Traversière (12th) 43 44 02 10 – AE GB K 18
closed August and Sunday dinner – **Meals** 120 (lunch)/150 and a la carte 210/340.

X **L'Escapade en Touraine,** 24 r. Traversière (12th) 43 43 14 96 – GB JCB L 18
closed 2 to 31 August, Saturday, Sunday and Bank Holidays – **Meals** 110/140 and a la carte 150/270.

X **Le Quincy,** 28 av. Ledru-Rollin (12th) 46 28 46 76, bistro – L 17
closed 15 August-15 September, Saturday, Sunday and Monday – **Meals** a la carte 220/370.

X **Etchégorry,** 41 r. Croulebarbe (13th) 44 08 83 51, Fax 44 08 83 69 – AE GB JCB
closed Sunday – **Meals** 135/170 and a la carte 210/290. N 15

X **Anacréon,** 53 bd St-Marcel (13th) 43 31 71 18 – AE GB. M 16
closed August, Sunday and Monday – **Meals** 110 (lunch)/180.

X **Le Temps des Cerises,** 216 r. Fg St-Antoine (12th) 43 67 52 08, Fax 43 67 60 91 – AE GB
closed Monday – **Meals** 97/224 and a la carte 220/300. K 20

X **St-Amarante,** 4 r. Biscornet (12th) 43 43 00 08, bistro – GB K 18
closed 14 July-15 August, Saturday and Sunday – **Meals** (booking essential) a la carte approx. 170.

X **Chez Françoise,** 12 r. Butte aux Cailles (13th) 45 80 12 02, Fax 45 65 13 67, bistro – AE GB.
closed 11 to 17 March, 1 to 28 August, Saturday lunch and Sunday – **Meals** 72 b.i. (lunch), 99/146 and a la carte 150/230. P 15

X **A la Biche au Bois,** 45 av. Ledru-Rollin (12th) ✆ 43 43 34 38 - AE ⓓ GB K 18
closed 14 July-15 August, 25 December-1 January, Saturday and Sunday - **Meals** 100/118 and a la carte 130/210 ♁.

X **Le Rhône,** 40 bd Arago (13th) ✆ 47 07 33 57, ☂ - GB N 14
closed August, Saturday, Sunday and Bank Holidays - **Meals** 75/160 and a la carte 130/200 ♁.

X **Le Terroir,** 11 bd Arago (13th) ✆ 47 07 36 99, bistro - GB N 15
closed 1 to 7 April, 1 to 21 August, Christmas-New Year, Saturday lunch and Sunday - **Meals** 98 (lunch), 200/300 and a la carte 160/300.

X **Les Zygomates,** 7 r. Capri (12th) ✆ 40 19 93 04, Fax 40 19 93 04, bistro - GB. ✻
closed August, Saturday except dinner in winter and Sunday - **Meals** 75 (lunch)/130 and a la carte 160/210 ♁. N 21

Vaugirard, Gare Montparnasse, Grenelle, Denfert-Rochereau.

14th and 15th arrondissements.
14th: ✉ 75014
15th: ✉ 75015

Hilton Ⓜ, 18 av. Suffren (15th) ✆ 44 38 56 00, Telex 200955, Fax 44 38 56 10, ☂ - |♦| ⇌ ▤ TV ☎ ♿ ⇔ - 🏛 25 - 400. AE ⓓ GB JCB J 7
Western ✆ 44 38 56 37 **Meals** 139 and a la carte 170/250 ♁ - ***La Terrasse*** - ✆ **44 38 56 37 Meals** 140(lunch)/158(dinner) and a la carte 170/230 ♁ - ☕ 150 - **444 rm** 1765/2365, 18 suites.

Nikko Ⓜ, 61 quai Grenelle (15th) ✆ 40 58 20 00, Telex 205811, Fax 45 75 42 35, ←, Ⅎ, ⊡ - |♦| ⇌ ▤ TV ☎ ♿ ⇔ - 🏛 25 - 600. AE ⓓ GB JCB K 6
Meals see ***Les Célébrités*** below - ***Brasserie Pont Mirabeau :*** **Meals** 160 and a la carte 220/300 - ***Benkay - Japanese rest.*** **Meals** 135(lunch), 300/690 and a la carte 240/440 - ☕ 85 - **758 rm** 1480/2180, 6 suites.

Méridien Montparnasse, 19 r. Cdt Mouchotte (14th) ✆ 44 36 44 36, Telex 200135, Fax 44 36 49 00, ← - |♦| ⇌ ▤ rm TV ☎ ♿ ⇔ - 🏛 25 - 1 000. AE ⓓ GB JCB M 11
Meals see ***Montparnasse 25*** below - ***Justine*** ✆ 44 36 44 00 **Meals** 195/230 and a la carte 190/300, ♁ - ☕ 95 - **917 rm** 1400/1550, 36 suites.

Sofitel Porte de Sèvres Ⓜ, 8 r. L. Armand (15th) ✆ 40 60 30 30, Telex 200432, Fax 45 57 04 22, ←, panoramic indoor pool, Ⅎ - |♦| ⇌ ▤ TV ☎ ⇔ - 🏛 25 - 800. AE ⓓ GB JCB. ✻ rest N 5
Meals see ***Le Relais de Sèvres*** below - ***La Tonnelle*** (brasserie) **Meals** 128b.i. - ☕ 95 - **524 rm** 1350, 14 suites.

Sofitel St-Jacques Ⓜ, 17 bd St-Jacques (15th) ✆ 40 78 79 80, Telex 270740, Fax 45 88 43 93 - |♦| ⇌ ▤ TV ☎ ♿ ⇔ - 🏛 25 - 1 200. AE ⓓ GB JCB N 13-14
Le Français *(closed August)* **Meals** 195 - ☕ 95 - **783 rm** 1000/1500, 14 suites.

Mercure Porte de Versailles Ⓜ, 69 bd Victor (15th) ✆ 44 19 03 03, Telex 205628, Fax 48 28 22 11 - |♦| ⇌ ▤ TV ☎ ♿ ⇔ - 🏛 25 - 250. AE ⓓ GB N 7
Meals 99/150 - ☕ 70 - **91 rm** 1097/1164.

Mercure Montparnasse Ⓜ, 20 r. Gaîté (14th) ✆ 43 35 28 28, Telex 201532, Fax 43 27 98 64 - |♦| ⇌ ▤ TV ☎ ♿ ⇔ - 🏛 80. AE ⓓ GB JCB. ✻ rest M 11
Bistrot de la Gaîté ✆ 43 22 86 46 **Meals** 125 b.i./175 b.i. - ☕ 70 - **178 rm** 980, 7 suites.

L'Aiglon without rest, 232 bd Raspail (14th) ✆ 43 20 82 42, Fax 43 20 98 72 - |♦| TV ☎ ⇔. AE ⓓ GB JCB M 12
☕ 35 - **38 rm** 480/710, 9 suites.

Adagio Vaugirard Ⓜ, 257 r. Vaugirard (15th) ✆ 40 45 10 00, Telex 250709, Fax 40 45 10 10, ☂, Ⅎ - |♦| ⇌ ▤ rest TV ☎ ♿ ⇔ - 🏛 25 - 200. AE ⓓ GB JCB
Meals 165 and a la carte approx. 220 - ☕ 70 - **184 rm** 690/895, 3 suites. M 9

Mercure Tour Eiffel Ⓜ without rest, 64 bd Grenelle (15th) ✆ 45 78 90 90, Fax 45 78 95 55 - |♦| ⇌ ▤ TV ☎ ♿ ⇔ - 🏛 30. AE ⓓ GB K 7
☕ 68 - **64 rm** 940.

Lenox Montparnasse without rest, 15 r. Delambre (14th) ✆ 43 35 34 50, Fax 43 20 46 64 - |♦| TV ☎. AE ⓓ GB JCB. ✻ M 12
☕ 45 - **52 rm** 520/640.

Raspail Montparnasse without rest, 203 bd Raspail (14th) ✆ 43 20 62 86, Fax 43 20 50 79 - |♦| ▤ TV ☎. AE ⓓ GB JCB. ✻ M 12
☕ 50 - **38 rm** 560/1210.

Alésia Montparnasse without rest, 84 r. R. Losserand (14th) ✆ 45 42 16 03, Fax 45 42 11 60 - |♦| ⇌ TV ☎. AE ⓓ GB JCB N 10
☕ 42 - **45 rm** 490/550.

Mercure Paris XV [M] without rest, 6 r. St-Lambert (15th) 45 58 61 00, Telex 206936, Fax 45 54 10 43 - 25. AE GB M 7
55 - **56 rm** 720.

Versailles without rest, 213 r. Croix-Nivert (15th) 48 28 48 66, Fax 45 30 16 22 - AE GB N 7
45 - **41 rm** 495/575.

Alizé Grenelle without rest, 87 av. É. Zola (15th) 45 78 08 22, Fax 40 59 03 06 - AE GB JCB L 7
37 - **50 rm** 420/500.

Beaugrenelle St-Charles without rest, 82 r. St-Charles (15th) 45 78 61 63, Fax 45 79 04 38 - AE GB JCB K 7
37 - **51 rm** 380/490.

L'Alligator without rest, 39 r. Delambre (14th) 43 35 18 40, Fax 43 35 30 71 - AE GB M 12
45 - **35 rm** 540/590.

Tour Eiffel Dupleix [M] without rest, 11 r. Juge (15th) 45 78 29 29, Fax 45 78 60 00 - AE GB K 7
45 - **40 rm** 450/660.

Arès without rest, 7 r. Gén. de Larminat (15th) 47 34 74 04, Telex 206083, Fax 47 34 48 56 - AE GB K 8
45 - **43 rm** 530/650.

Orléans Palace H. without rest, 185 bd Brune (14th) 45 39 68 50, Telex 205490, Fax 45 43 65 64 - 35. AE GB JCB R 11
52 - **92 rm** 510/580.

Abaca Messidor without rest, 330 r. Vaugirard (15th) 48 28 03 74, Fax 48 28 75 17, - AE GB JCB M 8
53 - **72 rm** 500/950.

Acropole without rest, 199 bd Brune (14th) 45 39 64 17, Fax 45 42 18 21 - AE GB. R 12
30 - **43 rm** 356/402.

Wallace without rest, 89 r. Fondary (15th) 45 78 83 30, Telex 283155, Fax 40 58 19 43 - AE GB JCB L 8
60 - **35 rm** 600/700.

Terminus Vaugirard without rest, 403 r. Vaugirard (15th) 48 28 18 72, Fax 48 28 56 34 - GB. N 7
closed 16 to 26 December - 45 - **90 rm** 470/580.

Apollon Montparnasse without rest, 91 r. Ouest (14th) 43 95 62 00, Fax 43 95 62 10 - AE GB JCB. N 10-11
35 - **33 rm** 395/470.

Lilas Blanc [M] without rest, 5 r. Avre (15th) 45 75 30 07, Fax 45 78 66 65 - AE GB JCB K 8
closed 1 to 21 August - 32 - **32 rm** 380/455.

Ariane Montparnasse without rest, 35 r. Sablière (14th) 45 45 67 13, Fax 45 45 39 49 - AE GB N 11
35 - **30 rm** 395/460.

Carladez Cambronne without rest, 3 pl. Gén. Beuret (15th) 47 34 07 12, Fax 40 65 95 68 - AE GB M 9
34 - **27 rm** 380/430.

Modern H. Val Girard without rest, 14 r. Pételle (15th) 48 28 53 96, Fax 48 28 69 94 - AE GB JCB M 8
36 - **39 rm** 375/450.

Châtillon H. without rest, 11 square Châtillon (14th) 45 42 31 17, Fax 45 42 72 09 - GB. P 11
32 - **31 rm** 330/360.

Daguerre without rest, 94 r. Daguerre (14th) 43 22 43 54, Fax 43 20 66 84 - AE GB JCB. N 11
38 - **30 rm** 380/440.

Résidence St-Lambert without rest, 5 r. E. Gibez (15th) 48 28 63 14, Fax 45 33 45 50 - AE GB JCB N 8
42 - **48 rm** 490/550.

Istria without rest, 29 r. Campagne Première (14th) 43 20 91 82, Fax 43 22 48 45 - AE GB JCB M 12
40 - **26 rm** 470/580.

Aberotel without rest, 24 r. Blomet (15th) 40 61 70 50, Fax 40 61 08 31 - AE GB L 8
40 - **28 rm** 430/520.

Idéal [M] without rest, 96 av. É. Zola (15th) 45 79 09 79, Fax 45 79 73 59 - AE GB L 7
40 - **35 rm** 400/440.

des Bains without rest, 33 r. Delambre (14th) ☎ 43 20 85 27, Fax 42 79 82 78 – 🛗 TV ☎
☕ 45 – **41 rm** 378/430. M 12

du Lion without rest, 1 av. Gén. Leclerc (14th) ☎ 40 47 04 00, Fax 43 20 38 18 – 🛗 TV
☎. AE ⓓ GB N 12
☕ 50 – **33 rm** 370/570.

Fondary without rest, 30 r. Fondary (15th) ☎ 45 75 14 75, Fax 45 75 84 42 – 🛗 TV ☎. AE
GB L 8
☕ 38 – **20 rm** 395.

Parc without rest, 60 r. Beaunier (14th) ☎ 45 40 77 02, Fax 45 40 81 99 – 🛗 TV ☎. AE GB
☕ 30 – **24 rm** 350/390. R 12

Pasteur without rest, 33 r. Dr Roux (15th) ☎ 47 83 53 17, Fax 45 66 62 39 – 🛗 TV ☎. GB
closed late July-late August – ☕ 40 – **19 rm** 315/440. M 10

XXXX ✿ **Les Célébrités** - Hôtel Nikko, 61 quai Grenelle (15th) ☎ 40 58 20 00, Telex 205811, Fax 45 75 42 35, ≤ – ▤. AE ⓓ GB JCB K 6
closed August – **Meals** 290/390 and a la carte 350/580
Spec. Langoustines poêlées aux échalotes grises. Blanc de turbot à la tomate fraîche et au basilic. Lièvre à la royale (late September-mid-December).

XXXX ✿ **Montparnasse 25** - Hôtel Méridien Montparnasse, 19 r. Cdt Mouchotte (14th) ☎ 44 36 44 25, Telex 200135, Fax 44 36 49 03 – ▤ P. AE ⓓ GB JCB. ✂ M 11
closed 3 August-2 September, Saturday and Sunday – **Meals** 240 (lunch), 300/390 and a la carte 330/450
Spec. Tian de homard breton, rattes et tomates confites à l'huile d'olive (June-September). Sole aux épices, nouilles frites aux jeunes pousses. Royal de lièvre de Sologne, gros macaroni au foie gras (October-December).

XXXX ✿ **Relais de Sèvres** - Hôtel Sofitel Porte de Sèvres, 8 r. L. Armand (15th) ☎ 40 60 30 30, Telex 200432, Fax 45 57 04 22 – ▤. AE ⓓ GB JCB. ✂ N 5
closed August, 24 to 31 December, Saturday, Sunday and Bank Holidays – **Meals** 320 and a la carte 300/400
Spec. Marbré de joue de porc aux ris de veau et foie gras. Grosses langoustines rôties au bouillon d'herbes. Lasagnes de ris de veau croustillants aux tomates confites et langue écarlate.

XXX ✿ **Morot Gaudry,** 6 r. Cavalerie (15th) (8th floor) ☎ 45 67 06 85, Fax 45 67 55 72, 🍽 – 🛗
▤. AE ⓓ GB K 8
closed Saturday and Sunday – **Meals** 230 b.i. (lunch), 390/550 b.i. and a la carte 300/450
Spec. Blanc de turbot à l'huile vierge au basilic. Croustillant de pigeon au miel, noix et raisins (April-September). Lièvre à la royale (late September-late December).

XXX **Mille Colonnes,** 20 bis r. Gaîté (14th) ☎ 40 47 08 34, Fax 40 64 37 49, 🍽 – ▤. AE
GB M 11
closed 3 to 20 August, Saturday and Sunday – **Meals** 180/245 and a la carte 250/350.

XXX **Armes de Bretagne,** 108 av. Maine (14th) ☎ 43 20 29 50, Fax 43 27 84 11 – ▤. AE ⓓ
GB N 11
closed August, Saturday lunch and Sunday – **Meals** - Seafood - 200 and a la carte 260/420.

XXX ✿ **Le Duc,** 243 bd Raspail (14th) ☎ 43 20 96 30, Fax 43 20 46 73 – ▤. AE GB M 12
closed Sunday, Monday and Bank Holidays – **Meals** - Seafood - a la carte 320/490
Spec. Poissons crus et grillés. Crustacés.

XXX **Moniage Guillaume,** 88 r. Tombe-Issoire (14th) ☎ 43 22 96 15, Fax 43 27 11 79 – AE ⓓ
GB JCB P 12
closed Sunday – **Meals** 195 b.i. (lunch)/245 and a la carte 340/490.

XXX **Pavillon Montsouris,** 20 r. Gazan (14th) ☎ 45 88 38 52, Fax 45 88 63 40, ≤, 🍽, « 1900 pavilion beside the park » – P. AE ⓓ GB. ✂ R 14
Meals 199/265.

XXX **Le Dôme,** 108 bd Montparnasse (14th) ☎ 43 35 25 81, Fax 42 79 01 19, brasserie – ▤. AE
ⓓ GB LM 12
closed Monday – **Meals** - Seafood - a la carte 280/420.

XXX **Lous Landès,** 157 av. Maine (14th) ☎ 45 43 08 04, Fax 45 45 91 35 – ▤. AE ⓓ GB
closed August, Saturday lunch and Sunday – **Meals** 190/300 and a la carte 300/440. N 11

XXX **Chen,** 15 r. Théâtre (15th) ☎ 45 79 34 34, Fax 45 79 07 53 – ▤. AE ⓓ GB JCB K 6
closed Sunday – **Meals** - Chinese rest. - 170 (dinner), 200/450 and a la carte 210/350.

XX **Lal Qila,** 88 av. É. Zola (15th) ☎ 45 75 68 40, Fax 45 79 68 61, « Original decor » – ▤. AE
GB L 7
Meals - Indian rest. - 55 (lunch), 125/250 and a la carte 120/230.

XX **Philippe Detourbe,** 8 r. Nicolas Charlet (15th) ☎ 42 19 08 59, Fax 45 67 09 13 – ▤. AE ⓓ
GB L 10
closed August, Saturday lunch and Sunday – **Meals** 160 (lunch)/180.

XX **Yves Quintard,** 99 r. Blomet (15th) ✆ 42 50 22 27, Fax 42 50 22 27 - GB M 8
closed 7 to 20 August, Saturday lunch and Sunday - **Meals** 125 (lunch), 175/280 and a la carte 180/260.

XX **La Dînée,** 85 r. Leblanc (15th) ✆ 45 54 20 49, Fax 40 60 74 88 - AE GB JCB M 5
closed 1 to 21 August, Sunday lunch and Saturday - **Meals** 160 (lunch)/280 and a la carte 230/370.

XX **La Chaumière des Gourmets,** 22 pl. Denfert-Rochereau (14th) ✆ 43 21 22 59 - AE GB
closed 29 July to 20 August, Saturday lunch and Sunday - **Meals** 165/245 and a la carte 270/380. N 12

XX **Vishnou,** 13 r. Cdt Mouchotte (14th) ✆ 45 38 92 93, Fax 44 07 31 19, 🏠 - AE ⓓ GB M 11
closed Sunday - **Meals** - Indian rest. - 150 b.i. (lunch), 220/230 b.i. and a la carte 210/270.

XX **Bistro 121,** 121 r. Convention (15th) ✆ 45 57 52 90, Fax 45 57 14 69 - ▤. AE ⓓ GB JCB
Meals 168/285 and a la carte 210/360. M 7

XX **La Coupole,** 102 bd Montparnasse (14th) ✆ 43 20 14 20, Fax 43 35 46 14, « 1920 Parisian brasserie » - AE ⓓ GB L 12
Meals a la carte 180/270 ♁.

XX **Aux Senteurs de Provence,** 295 r. Lecourbe (15th) ✆ 45 57 11 98, Fax 45 58 66 84 - AE ⓓ GB JCB M 6
closed 12 to 18 August, Saturday lunch and Sunday - **Meals** - Seafood - 136 and a la carte 190/290.

XX **Petite Bretonnière,** 2 r. Cadix (15th) ✆ 48 28 34 39, Fax 48 28 20 90 - AE GB JCB N 7
closed August, Saturday lunch and Sunday - **Meals** 185 b.i./290 b.i. and a la carte 230/330.

XX **Napoléon et Chaix,** 46 r. Balard (15th) ✆ 45 54 09 00 - ▤. AE GB M 5
closed August, 1 to 7 January, Saturday lunch and Sunday - **Meals** a la carte 200/320.

XX **Monsieur Lapin,** 11 r. R. Losserand (14th) ✆ 43 20 21 39, Fax 43 21 84 86 - GB N 11
closed August, Saturday lunch and Monday - **Meals** 160/300 and a la carte 260/400.

XX **Le Caroubier,** 122 av. Maine (14th) ✆ 43 20 41 49 - ▤. GB N 11
closed 15 July-15 August and Monday - **Meals** - North African rest. - 130 and a la carte 160/180 ♁.

XX **L'Etape,** 89 r. Convention (15th) ✆ 45 54 73 49 - ▤. AE GB M 6
closed Christmas Holidays, Saturday (except lunch from September-June) and Sunday - **Meals** 170/200 b.i. and a la carte 160/270.

XX **Le Copreaux,** 15 r. Copreaux (15th) ✆ 43 06 83 35 - GB M 9
closed August, Saturday lunch and Sunday - **Meals** 130/200 b.i. and a la carte 190/260.

XX **Le Clos Morillons,** 50 r. Morillons (15th) ✆ 48 28 04 37, Fax 48 28 70 77 - AE GB N 8
closed 8 to 20 August, Saturday lunch and Sunday - **Meals** 165/285 and a la carte 250/380.

XX **Les Vendanges,** 40 r. Friant (14th) ✆ 45 39 59 98, Fax 45 39 74 13 - AE GB R 11
closed 5 to 31 August and Sunday - **Meals** 200.

XX **Filoche,** 34 r. Laos (15th) ✆ 45 66 44 60 - GB. ❀ K 8
closed 20 July-26 August, 21 December-3 January, Saturday and Sunday - **Meals** 160 and a la carte 190/260.

XX **La Giberne,** 42bis av. Suffren (15th) ✆ 47 34 82 18 - AE ⓓ GB JCB J 8
closed August, Saturday lunch and Sunday - **Meals** 120 b.i. (lunch), 168/185 and a la carte 180/340 ♁.

XX **Pierre Vedel,** 19 r. Duranton (15th) ✆ 45 58 43 17, Fax 45 58 42 65, bistro - GB M 6
closed Christmas-New Year, Saturday except dinner from October-April and Sunday - **Meals** a la carte 220/330.

XX **La Gauloise,** 59 av. La Motte-Picquet (15 th) ✆ 47 34 11 64, Fax 42 24 18 73, 🏠 - AE ⓓ GB
closed Saturday lunch - **Meals** a la carte 200/380 ♁. K 8

XX **La Chaumière,** 54 av. F. Faure (15th) ✆ 45 54 13 91 - AE ⓓ GB M 7
closed 26 July-26 August, February Holidays, Monday dinner and Tuesday - **Meals** 175 b.i. and a la carte 200/300.

XX **Mina Mahal,** 25 r. Cambronne (15th) ✆ 47 34 19 88 - ▤. AE ⓓ GB L 8
Meals - Indian rest. - 52 (lunch), 99/138 and a la carte 120/210.

X **de la Tour,** 6 r. Desaix (15th) ✆ 43 06 04 24 - GB J 8
closed August, Saturday lunch and Sunday - **Meals** 110 (lunch)/175 and a la carte 190/280.

X **L'Épopée,** 89 av. É. Zola (15th) ✆ 45 77 71 37 - AE GB L 7
closed Saturday lunch and Sunday - **Meals** 175 and a la carte 200/300.

X **A La Bonne Table,** 42 r. Friant (14th) ✆ 45 39 74 91 - GB R 11
closed July, 24 December-4 January, Saturday and Sunday - **Meals** 153 (dinner)and a la carte 190/330.

X **Chez Yvette,** 46bis bd Montparnasse (15th) ✆ 42 22 45 54, bistro - GB L 11
closed Saturday and Sunday - **Meals** a la carte 160/250.

X **Bistrot du Dôme,** 1 r. Delambre (14th) ✆ 43 35 32 00 - ▤. AE GB M 12
Meals - Seafood - a la carte 180/250.

X **La Cagouille,** 10 pl. Constantin Brancusi (14th) ✆ 43 22 09 01, Fax 45 38 57 29, 🏠 - AE GB JCB M 11
closed 24 December-3 January - **Meals** - Seafood - 250 b.i. and a la carte 200/330.

X **Le Gastroquet,** 10 r. Desnouettes (15th) ✆ 48 28 60 91 - AE GB N 7
closed August, Saturday and Sunday - **Meals** 149 and a la carte 190/280.

X **Les Cévennes,** 55 r. Cévennes (15th) ✆ 45 54 33 76, Fax 44 26 46 95 - AE GB. ✻ L 6
closed 10 to 28 August, Saturday lunch and Sunday - **Meals** 155 and a la carte 180/250.

X **La Datcha Lydie,** 7 r. Dupleix (15th) ✆ 45 66 67 77 - AE GB K 8
closed 12 July-31 August and Wednesday - **Meals** - Russian rest. - 80/128 b.i. and a la carte 150/260.

X **Chez Pierre,** 117 r. Vaugirard (15th) ✆ 47 34 96 12, bistro - ▤. AE GB JCB L 11
closed 2 to 28 August, Saturday dinner Easter-September, Saturday lunch, Sunday and Bank Holidays - **Meals** 98 (lunch)/130 and a la carte 180/240.

X **L'Armoise,** 67 r. Entrepreneurs (15th) ✆ 45 79 03 31 - ▤. GB L 7
closed 1 to 20 August, Saturday lunch and Sunday - **Meals** 128 ♈.

X **Le Père Claude,** 51 av. La Motte-Picquet (15th) ✆ 47 34 03 05, Fax 40 56 97 84 - AE GB
Meals 99/155 and a la carte 220/380. K 8

X **L'Amuse Bouche,** 186 r. Château (14th) ✆ 43 35 31 61 - AE GB N 11
closed 5 to 19 August, Saturday lunch and Sunday - **Meals** (booking essential) 160.

X **La Régalade,** 49 av. J. Moulin (14th) ✆ 45 45 68 58, Fax 45 40 96 74, bistro - ▤. GB
closed mid July-mid August, Saturday lunch, Sunday and Monday - **Meals** (booking essential) 165. R 11

X **L'Os à Moelle,** 3 r. Vasco de Gama (15th) ✆ 45 57 27 27, bistro - GB M 6
closed 22 July-22 August, Sunday and Monday - **Meals** 145 (lunch)/190 ♈.

X **L'Agape,** 281 r. Lecourbe (15th) ✆ 45 58 19 29 - GB M 7
closed August, Saturday lunch and Sunday - **Meals** 120.

X **Le St-Vincent,** 26 r. Croix-Nivert (15th) ✆ 47 34 14 94, bistro - ▤. AE GB L 8
closed 11 to 18 August, Saturday lunch and Sunday - **Meals** a la carte 170/240 ♈.

X **Le Petit Mâchon,** 123 r. Convention (15th) ✆ 45 54 08 62, bistro - AE ⓓ GB N 7
closed 1 to 21 August and Sunday - **Meals** 88 b.i./148 b.i..

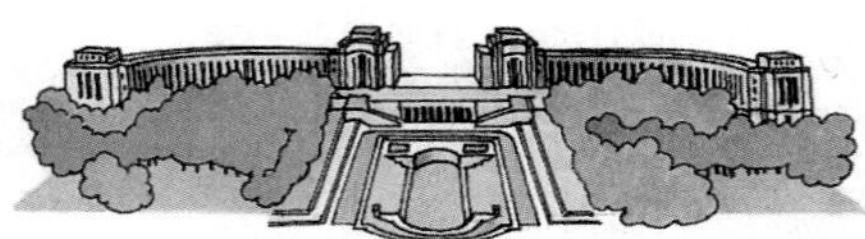

Passy, Auteuil, Bois de Boulogne, Chaillot, Porte Maillot.

16th arrondissement.
16th: ✉ 75016

Le Parc Victor Hugo M ♨, 55 av. R. Poincaré ✉ 75116 ✆ 44 05 66 66, Telex 643862, Fax 44 05 66 00, ☂, « Fine English furniture » - ▮ ⇹ ▤ TV ☎ ♿ - 🏛 30 - 250. AE ⓓ GB JCB. ✻ rest G 6
Meals see ***Jöel Robuchon*** below - ***Le Relais du Parc*** ✆ 44 05 66 10 **Meals** a la carte 210/390 - ☕ 120 - **107 rm** 1990/2650, 10 suites, 3 duplex.

Raphaël, 17 av. Kléber ✉ 75116 ✆ 44 28 00 28, Telex 645356, Fax 45 01 21 50, « Elegant period decor, fine furniture » - ▮ ⇹ ▤ TV ☎ - 🏛 50. AE ⓓ GB JCB F 7
Meals *(closed Saturday and Sunday)* 280 and a la carte 300/450 - ☕ 120 - **64 rm** 1670/2520, 23 suites.

St-James Paris ♨, 43 av. Bugeaud ✉ 75116 ✆ 44 05 81 81, Fax 44 05 81 82, ☂, « Elegant neo classic style », ⛹, ⛱ - ▮ ▤ TV ☎ P - 🏛 25. AE ⓓ GB JCB. ✻ rest
Meals *(closed Saturday, Sunday and Bank Holidays)* (residents only) 290/300 b.i. and a la carte 290/440 - ☕ 95 - **20 rm** 1550/1980, 20 suites3600, 8 duplex 2400. F 5

Baltimore M, 88bis av. Kléber ✉ 75116 ✆ 44 34 54 54, Telex 645284, Fax 44 34 54 44 - ▮ ⇹ ▤ TV ☎ - 🏛 30 - 100. AE ⓓ GB JCB G 7
Bertie's ✆ 44 34 54 34 - English rest. *(closed 1 to 15 August)* **Meals** 160(lunch), 195/250 and a la carte 210/330 - ☕ 120 - **104 rm** 1690/2950.

K. Palace M without rest, 81 av. Kléber ✉ 75116 ✆ 44 05 75 75, Fax 44 05 74 74, « Contemporary decor », ⛹ - ▮ kitchenette ⇹ TV ☎ 🚗. AE ⓓ GB JCB G 7
☕ 105 - **82 rm** 1510/2610.

Villa Maillot M without rest, 143 av. Malakoff ✉ 75116 ✆ 45 01 25 22, Telex 649808, Fax 45 00 60 61 - ▮ ⇹ ▤ TV ☎ ♿ - 🏛 25. AE ⓓ GB JCB F 6
☕ 100 - **39 rm** 1500/1700, 3 suites.

Pergolèse M without rest, 3 r. Pergolèse ✉ 75116 ☏ 40 67 96 77, Telex 651618, Fax 45 00 12 11, « Contemporary decor » – 🛗 ▤ TV ☎. AE ⓓ GB JCB E 6
☕ 75 – **40 rm** 860/1520.

Élysées Régencia M without rest, 41 av. Marceau ✉ 75016 ☏ 47 20 42 65, Telex 644965, Fax 49 52 03 42, « Attractive decor » – 🛗 ⇆ ▤ TV ☎. AE ⓓ GB JCB. ✻ G 8
☕ 80 – **41 rm** 1260/1700.

Majestic without rest, 29 r. Dumont d'Urville ✉ 75116 ☏ 45 00 83 70, Telex 640034, Fax 45 00 29 48 – 🛗 ⇆ ▤ TV ☎. AE ⓓ GB JCB F 7
☕ 60 – **27 rm** 1170/1470, 3 suites.

Garden Elysée M ⛱ without rest, 12 r. St-Didier ✉ 75116 ☏ 47 55 01 11, Telex 648157, Fax 47 27 79 24 – 🛗 ▤ TV ☎ ♿. AE ⓓ GB JCB. ✻ G 7
☕ 80 – **48 rm** 1475/1625.

Alexander without rest, 102 av. V. Hugo ✉ 75116 ☏ 45 53 64 65, Telex 645373, Fax 45 53 12 51 – 🛗 TV ☎. AE ⓓ GB JCB. ✻ G 6
☕ 75 – **62 rm** 840/1320.

Floride Etoile, 14 r. St-Didier ✉ 75116 ☏ 47 27 23 36, Telex 643715, Fax 47 27 82 87 – 🛗 ⇆ ▤ rest TV ☎ – 🎤 40. AE ⓓ GB JCB. ✻ G 7
Meals coffee shop - *(closed August, Saturday dinner and Sunday)* a la carte approx. 150 – ☕ 45 – **60 rm** 820/850.

Rond-Point de Longchamp without rest, 86 r. Longchamp ✉ 75116 ☏ 45 05 13 63, Telex 640883, Fax 47 55 12 80 – 🛗 ⇆ ▤ TV ☎ – 🎤 40. AE ⓓ GB G 6
☕ 65 – **57 rm** 1000/1500.

Frémiet without rest, 6 av. Frémiet ✉ 75016 ☏ 45 24 52 06, Fax 42 88 77 46 – 🛗 ▤ TV ☎. AE ⓓ GB JCB J 6
☕ 40 – **34 rm** 650/850.

Union H. Étoile without rest, 44 r. Hamelin ✉ 75116 ☏ 45 53 14 95, Telex 645217, Fax 47 55 94 79 – 🛗 kitchenette TV ☎. AE ⓓ GB JCB G 7
☕ 42 – **29 rm** 720/830, 13 suites.

Élysées Sablons M without rest, 32 r. Greuze ✉ 75116 ☏ 47 27 10 00, Fax 47 27 47 10 – 🛗 ⇆ TV ☎ ♿. AE ⓓ GB JCB G 6
☕ 75 – **41 rm** 825/1040.

Elysées Bassano without rest, 24 r. Bassano ✉ 75116 ☏ 47 20 49 03, Telex 645280, Fax 47 23 06 72 – 🛗 ⇆ TV ☎. AE ⓓ GB JCB G 8
☕ 75 – **40 rm** 850/910.

Massenet without rest, 5bis r. Massenet ✉ 75116 ☏ 45 24 43 03, Telex 640196, Fax 45 24 41 39 – 🛗 TV ☎. AE ⓓ GB JCB. ✻ J 6
☕ 40 – **41 rm** 500/760.

Victor Hugo without rest, 19 r. Copernic ✉ 75116 ☏ 45 53 76 01, Telex 645939, Fax 45 53 69 93 – 🛗 TV ☎. AE ⓓ GB JCB G 7
☕ 45 – **75 rm** 654/798.

Résidence Bassano M without rest, 15 r. Bassano ✉ 75116 ☏ 47 23 78 23, Telex 649872, Fax 47 20 41 22 – 🛗 kitchenette ▤ TV ☎. AE ⓓ GB JCB G 8
☕ 65 – **28 rm** 750/1200, 3 suites.

Sévigné without rest, 6 r. Belloy ✉ 75116 ☏ 47 20 88 90, Fax 40 70 98 73 – 🛗 TV ☎. AE ⓓ GB JCB G 7
☕ 48 – **30 rm** 640/760.

Résidence Impériale M without rest, 155 av. Malakoff ✉ 75116 ☏ 45 00 23 45, Telex 651158, Fax 45 01 88 82 – 🛗 ⇆ ▤ TV ☎. AE ⓓ GB JCB E 6
☕ 55 – **37 rm** 740/800.

Les Jardins du Trocadéro M, 35 r. Franklin ✉ 75116 ☏ 53 70 17 70, Fax 53 70 17 80 – 🛗 ⇆ ▤ TV ☎. AE ⓓ GB JCB H 6
Meals (coffee shop) a la carte approx. 100 – ☕ 65 – **16 rm** 950/2250, 5 suites.

Royal Élysées without rest, 6 av. V. Hugo ✉ 75116 ☏ 45 00 05 57, Telex 648323, Fax 45 00 13 88 – 🛗 ▤ TV ☎. AE ⓓ GB JCB. ✻ F 7
☕ 50 – **35 rm** 1100/1200.

Kléber without rest, 7 r. Belloy ✉ 75116 ☏ 47 23 80 22, Fax 49 52 07 20 – 🛗 TV ☎ P. AE ⓓ GB JCB G 7
☕ 50 – **23 rm** 690/840.

Murat without rest, 119 bis bd Murat ✉ 75016 ☏ 46 51 12 32, Fax 46 51 70 01 – 🛗 TV ☎. AE ⓓ GB. ✻ M 3
☕ 45 – **28 rm** 650/700.

Résidence Chambellan Morgane M without rest, 6 r. Keppler ✉ 75116 ☏ 47 20 35 72, Fax 47 20 95 69 – 🛗 TV ☎. AE ⓓ GB. ✻ GF 8
☕ 50 – **20 rm** 650/800.

Étoile Maillot without rest, 10 r. Bois de Boulogne (angle r. Duret) ✉ 75116 ☏ 45 00 42 60, Fax 45 00 55 89 – 🛗 TV ☎. AE ⓓ GB F 6
☕ 40 – **27 rm** 530/690.

Ambassade without rest, 79 r. Lauriston ✉ 75116 ☏ 45 53 41 15, Fax 45 53 30 80 – 🛗 TV ☎. AE ⓓ GB JCB G 7
☕ 40 – **38 rm** 430/535.

Résidence Foch without rest, 10 r. Marbeau ✉ 75116 ✆ 45 00 46 50, Fax 45 01 98 68 – F 6
TV ☎. AE ⓓ GB
☕ 45 – **21 rm** 700/775, 4 suites.

Passy Eiffel without rest, 10 r. Passy ✉ 75016 ✆ 45 25 55 66, Fax 42 88 89 88 – ▤ rm J 6
TV ☎. AE ⓓ GB JCB
☕ 40 – **50 rm** 586/662.

Résidence Marceau without rest, 37 av. Marceau ✉ 75116 ✆ 47 20 43 37, Fax 47 20 14 76 G 8
– TV ☎. AE ⓓ GB JCB.
closed 5 to 25 August – ☕ 35 – **30 rm** 530/650.

Longchamp without rest, 68 r. Longchamp ✉ 75116 ✆ 47 27 13 48, Fax 47 55 68 26 – G 6
TV ☎. AE ⓓ GB JCB
☕ 50 – **23 rm** 600/750.

Beauséjour Ranelagh without rest, 99 r. Ranelagh ✉ 75016 ✆ 42 88 14 39, J 4
Fax 40 50 81 21 – TV ☎. AE GB
☕ 35 – **30 rm** 450/750.

Eiffel Kennedy M without rest, 12 r. Boulainvilliers ✉ 75016 ✆ 45 24 45 75, K 5
Fax 42 30 83 32 – TV ☎. AE ⓓ GB JCB
☕ 45 – **30 rm** 480/630.

Hameau de Passy M without rest, 48 r. Passy ✉ 75016 ✆ 42 88 47 55, Fax 42 30 83 72 J 5-6
– TV ☎ ♿. AE ⓓ GB JCB
☕ 30 – **32 rm** 490/530.

Keppler without rest, 12 r. Keppler ✉ 75116 ✆ 47 20 65 05, Fax 47 23 02 29 – TV ☎. F 8
AE GB.
☕ 30 – **49 rm** 450/460.

Nicolo without rest, 3 r. Nicolo ✉ 75116 ✆ 42 88 83 40, Fax 42 24 45 41 – TV ☎. GB J 6
JCB
☕ 35 – **28 rm** 360/450.

XXXX ✿✿✿ **Joël Robuchon,** (change of name expected during the second half of 1996) 59 av. R. Poincaré ✉ 75116 ✆ 47 27 12 27, Fax 47 27 31 22, « Elegant mansion with Art Nouveau decor » – ▤. GB G 6
closed 8 July-5 August, Saturday and Sunday – **Meals** 890/1200 and a la carte 700/1 100
Spec. Gelée de caviar à la crème de chou-fleur. Tarte friande de truffes aux oignons et lard fumé (December-March). Lièvre à la royale (October-December).

XXXX ✿✿ **Vivarois** (Peyrot), 192 av. V. Hugo ✉ 75116 ✆ 45 04 04 31, Fax 45 03 09 84 – ▤. AE ⓓ GB JCB G 5
closed August, Saturday and Sunday – **Meals** 345 (lunch)and a la carte 420/720
Spec. Grecque de légumes. Viennoise de turbot. Rognon de veau "noble cru".

XXXX ✿✿ **Faugeron,** 52 r. Longchamp ✉ 75116 ✆ 47 04 24 53, Fax 47 55 62 90 – AE GB JCB. G 7
closed August, 23 December-3 January, Saturday except dinner from October-April and Sunday – **Meals** 290 (lunch), 550 b.i./650 and a la carte 440/610
Spec. Oeufs coque à la purée de truffes. Truffes (January-March). Gibier (15 October-10 January).

XXX ✿ **Prunier-Traktir,** 16 av. V. Hugo ✉ 75116 ✆ 44 17 35 85, Fax 44 17 90 10, « Art Deco decor » – ▤. AE ⓓ GB JCB FG 8
closed 16 July-16 August, Monday lunch and Sunday – **Meals** - Seafood - a la carte 330/580
Spec. Tartare de poissons aux huîtres. Gratin de crustacés "Thermidor" en coque d'araignée. Parfait glacé à l'eau de vie de mirabelle.

XXX ✿ **Toit de Passy** (Jacquot), 94 av. P. Doumer (6th floor) ✉ 75016 ✆ 45 24 55 37, Fax 45 20 94 57, – ▤ P. AE GB HJ 5
closed Saturday lunch and Sunday – **Meals** 200 (lunch), 300/510 and a la carte 390/510
Spec. Foie gras poêlé à la polenta et aux raisins. Pigeonneau en croûte de sel de Guérande embeurrée de choux au lard fumé. Tarte aux pommes caramélisée à l'envers.

XXX **Tsé-Yang,** 25 av. Pierre 1er de Serbie ✉ 75016 ✆ 47 20 70 22, Fax 49 52 03 68, « Tasteful decor » – ▤. AE ⓓ GB JCB. G 8
Meals - Chinese rest. - 245/285 and a la carte 220/340.

XXX **Pavillon Noura,** 21 av. Marceau ✉ 75116 ✆ 47 20 33 33, Fax 47 20 60 31, – ▤. AE ⓓ GB. G 8
Meals - Lebanese rest. - 156 (lunch), 200/320 and a la carte 170/200.

XXX ✿ **Port Alma** (Canal), 10 av. New-York ✉ 75116 ✆ 47 23 75 11 – ▤. AE ⓓ GB H 8
closed August and Sunday – **Meals** - Seafood - 200 (lunch)and a la carte 300/440
Spec. Langoustines rôties aux courgettes, aubergines et tomates épicées. Sole à l'huile d'olive. Soufflé au chocolat.

XXX ✿ **Relais d'Auteuil** (Pignol), 31 bd Murat ✉ 75016 ✆ 46 51 09 54, Fax 40 71 05 03 – ▤. AE GB L 3
closed 4 to 25 August, Saturday lunch and Sunday – **Meals** 250 (lunch), 410/520 and a la carte 400/520
Spec. Amandine de foie gras de canard. Dos de bar au poivre concassé. Madeleines au miel de bruyère, glace miel et noix.

XXX ✿ **Le Pergolèse** (Corre), 40 r. Pergolèse ✉ 75116 ✆ 45 00 21 40, Fax 45 00 81 31 – AE GB
closed August, Saturday and Sunday – **Meals** 230/320 and a la carte 290/390 F 6
Spec. Ravioli de langoustines à la duxelles de champignons. Carré d'agneau rôti, pommes purée. Moelleux au chocolat, glace vanille.

XXX **Chez Ngo,** 70 r. Longchamp ✉ 75116 ✆ 47 04 53 20, Fax 47 04 53 20 – ▤. AE ⓓ GB JCB. ✻ G 6
Meals - Chinese and Thai rest. - 98 b.i. (lunch)/168 and a la carte 130/190.

XX **Al Mounia,** 16 r. Magdebourg ✉ 75116 ✆ 47 27 57 28 – ▤. AE GB. ✻ G 7
closed 10 July-31 August and Sunday – **Meals** - Moroccan rest. - (dinner : booking essential) a la carte 230/280.

XX ✿ **Conti,** 72 r. Lauriston ✉ 75116 ✆ 47 27 74 67, Fax 47 27 37 66 – ▤. AE ⓓ GB G 7
closed 2 to 25 August, 30 December-6 January, Saturday and Sunday – **Meals** - Italian rest. - 198 (lunch)and a la carte 310/410
Spec. Calamars "à la Genovese" (1 July-15 October). Cariucco "à la Livournaise" (November-February). Figues rôties aux amaretti au "vino santo" (September-October).

XX **Carré Kléber,** 11bis r. Magdebourg ✉ 75016 ✆ 47 55 82 08, Fax 47 55 80 09 – ▤. AE ⓓ GB G 7
closed 1 to 22 August and 24 to 30 December – **Meals** 180/285.

XX **Giulio Rebellato,** 136 r. Pompe ✉ 75116 ✆ 47 27 50 26 – ▤. AE GB JCB. ✻ G 6
closed August and Sunday – **Meals** - Italian rest. - 200/300 and a la carte 270/350.

XX ✿ **Fontaine d'Auteuil** (Grégoire), 35bis r. La Fontaine ✉ 75016 ✆ 42 88 04 47 – ▤. AE ⓓ GB
closed 4 to 25 August, 9 to 16 February, Saturday lunch and Sunday – **Meals** 175 (lunch), 230/350 and a la carte 270/390 K 5
Spec. Poulet du Gatinais au vinaigre d'Orléans. Rable de lièvre à la beauceronne (15 October-31 December). Millefeuille.

XX **Tang,** 125 r. de la Tour ✉ 75116 ✆ 45 04 35 35, Fax 45 04 58 19 – AE GB. ✻ H 5
closed August and Monday – **Meals** - Chinese and Thai rest. - 200 and a la carte 200/300.

XX **Villa Vinci,** 23 r. P. Valéry ✉ 75116 ✆ 45 01 68 18 – ▤. AE GB F 7
closed August, Saturday and Sunday – **Meals** - Italian rest. - 175 (lunch)and a la carte 210/360.

XX **Paul Chêne,** 123 r. Lauriston ✉ 75116 ✆ 47 27 63 17, Fax 47 27 53 18 – ▤. AE ⓓ GB
closed 20 to 27 August, 21 December-1 January, Saturday lunch and Sunday – **Meals** 200/250 and a la carte 230/360. G 6

XX **Sous l'Olivier,** 15 r. Goethe ✉ 75116 ✆ 47 20 84 81, Fax 47 20 73 75 – GB G 8
closed 2 to 26 August, Saturday, Sunday and Bank Holidays – **Meals** 155 and a la carte 230/320.

XX **Palais du Trocadéro,** 7 av. Eylau ✉ 75116 ✆ 47 27 05 02, Fax 47 27 25 51 – ▤. AE GB
Meals - Chinese rest. - 100 (lunch), 150/200 and a la carte 140/250 ♁. H 6

XX ✿ **La Petite Tour** (Israël), 11 r. de la Tour ✉ 75116 ✆ 45 20 09 31 – AE ⓓ GB JCB
closed August and Sunday – **Meals** a la carte 270/430 H 6
Spec. Pétales de Saint-Jacques grillées sur salade d'endives et de mâche (October-March). Fleurs de courgettes soufflées à la mousse de Saint-Jacques (May-September). Râble de lièvre sauce smitane (October-December).

XX **Marius,** 82 bd Murat ✉ 75016 ✆ 46 51 67 80, ☂ – AE GB M 2
closed August, Saturday lunch and Sunday – **Meals** a la carte 200/300.

XX **Chez Géraud,** 31 r. Vital ✉ 75016 ✆ 45 20 33 00, Fax 45 20 46 60, « Attractive Longwy porcelain mural » – AE GB H 5
closed August, Saturday except dinner from October-February and Sunday – **Meals** 200 and a la carte 230/360.

XX **San Francisco,** 1 r. Mirabeau ✉ 75016 ✆ 46 47 84 89, Fax 46 47 75 44 – ▤. AE ⓓ GB
closed 12 to 18 August and Sunday – **Meals** - Italian rest. - a la carte 210/320. L 5

XX **Bellini,** 28 r. Lesueur ✉ 75116 ✆ 45 00 54 20, Fax 45 00 11 74 – ▤. AE GB F 7
closed August, 23 December-3 January, Saturday lunch and Sunday – **Meals** - Italian rest. - 180 and a la carte 240/320.

X **Beaujolais d'Auteuil,** 99 bd Montmorency ✉ 75016 ✆ 47 43 03 56, Fax 46 51 27 81, bistro – GB K 3
closed Saturday lunch and Sunday – **Meals** 119 b.i./139 b.i. and a la carte 170/260.

X **La Butte Chaillot,** 110 bis av. Kléber ✉ 75116 ✆ 47 27 88 88, Fax 47 04 85 70 – ▤. AE GB JCB G 7
Meals 210 and a la carte 220/320.

X **Le Cuisinier François,** 19 r. Le Marois ✉ 75016 ✆ 45 27 83 74, Fax 45 27 83 74 – AE GB
closed August, Wednesday dinner, Sunday dinner and Monday – **Meals** 160 and a la carte 200/300 ♁. M 3

X **Bistrot de l'Étoile,** 19 r. Lauriston ✉ 75016 ✆ 40 67 11 16, Fax 45 00 99 87 – ▤. AE GB JCB F 7
closed Saturday lunch and Sunday – **Meals** a la carte 190/240.

X **Le Driver's,** 6 r. G. Bizet ✉ 75016 ✆ 47 23 61 15, Fax 47 23 80 17 – ▤. AE ⓓ GB
closed 10 to 20 August, Saturday lunch and Sunday – **Meals** a la carte 130/210. G 8

X **Vin et Marée,** 2 r. Daumier ✉ 75016 ✆ 46 47 91 39, Fax 46 47 69 07 – AE ⓓ GB
Meals - Seafood - a la carte 140/200. M 3

X **Noura,** 27 av. Marceau ✉ 75116 ✆ 47 23 02 20, Fax 49 52 01 26 – AE ⓓ GB G 8
Meals - Lebanese rest. - a la carte 140/200.

X **Lac Hong,** 67 r. Lauriston ✉ 75116 ✆ 47 55 87 17 – GB. ⚘ G 7
closed 11 to 31 August and Sunday – **Meals** - Vietnamese rest. - 98 (lunch)and a la carte 160/280.

in the Bois de Boulogne :

XXXX ✿✿ **Pré Catelan,** rte Suresnes ✉ 75016 ✆ 44 14 41 14, Fax 45 24 43 25, ☂, ⛱ – P. AE ⓓ GB JCB H 2
closed February Holidays, Sunday dinner and Monday – **Meals** 290 (lunch), 550/750 and a la carte 490/750
Spec. Petit pot de crème prise à l'araignée de mer. Risotto noir de langoustines au basilic. Fondant de couenne au jus de truffe persillé.

XXXX **Grande Cascade,** allée de Longchamp (opposite the hippodrome) ✉ 75016 ✆ 45 27 33 51, Fax 42 88 99 06, ☂ – P. AE ⓓ GB
closed 23 December-14 January – **Meals** 285 (lunch)and a la carte 460/650.

Clichy, Ternes, Wagram.

17th arrondissement.
17th: ✉ 75017

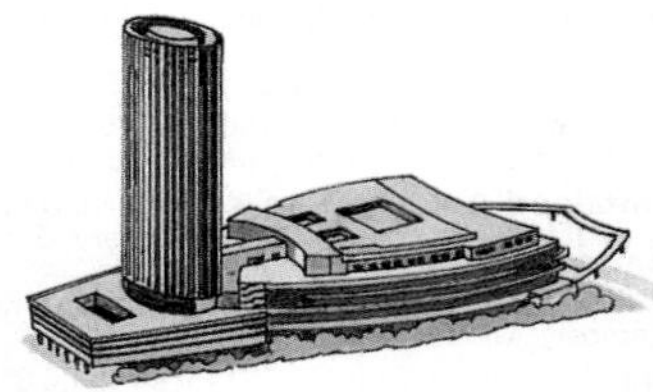

Concorde La Fayette M, 3 pl. Gén. Koenig ✆ 40 68 50 68, Fax 40 68 50 43, « Panoramic bar on 34th floor with ≤ Paris » – |‡| ⇎ ▤ TV ☎ – 🏛 40 - 2 000. AE ⓓ GB JCB
Meals see ***Étoile d'Or*** below - ***L'Arc-en-Ciel*** ✆ 40 68 51 25 **Meals** 225 ♖ – ***Les Saisons*** - (coffee shop) ✆ **40 68 51 19 Meals** 149 ♖ – ☕ 98 – **950 rm** 1450/1850, 20 suites. E 6

Le Meridien M, 81 bd Gouvion St-Cyr ✆ 40 68 34 34, Telex 651179, Fax 40 68 31 31 – |‡| ⇎ ▤ TV ☎ ♿ – 🏛 50 - 800. AE ⓓ GB JCB E 6
Meals see ***Clos de Longchamp*** below - ***Café l'Arlequin*** ✆ 40 68 30 85 **Meals** 158/250 and a la carte 200/320 – ***Le Yamato*** ✆ 40 68 30 41, ***Japanese rest.*** *(closed Aug., 1 to 7/01, Saturday lunch, Sunday, Monday and Bank Holidays)* **Meals** 170 (lunch) 200/250 and a la carte 190/280 – ☕ 95 – **1 007 rm** 1450/2300, 17 suites.

Splendid Etoile without rest, 1bis av. Carnot ✆ 45 72 72 00, Fax 45 72 72 01 – |‡| ▤ TV ☎. AE ⓓ GB. ⚘ F 7
☕ 85 – **57 rm** 930/1700.

Quality Inn Pierre M without rest, 25 r. Th.-de-Banville ✆ 47 63 76 69, Telex 643003, Fax 43 80 63 96 – |‡| ⇎ TV ☎ ♿ – 🏛 30. AE ⓓ GB JCB D 8
☕ 68 – **50 rm** 810/970.

Balmoral without rest, 6 r. Gén. Lanrezac ✆ 43 80 30 50, Fax 43 80 51 56 – |‡| ⇎ TV ☎. AE ⓓ GB E 7
☕ 40 – **57 rm** 500/800.

Regent's Garden without rest, 6 r. P. Demours ✆ 45 74 07 30, Telex 640127, Fax 40 55 01 42, « Garden » – |‡| TV ☎. AE ⓓ GB JCB E 7
☕ 40 – **39 rm** 650/940.

Magellan ⛵ without rest, 17 r. J.B.-Dumas ✆ 45 72 44 51, Fax 40 68 90 36, ⛱ – |‡| TV ☎. AE ⓓ GB. ⚘ D 7
☕ 40 – **75 rm** 580/615.

Étoile St-Ferdinand without rest, 36 r. St-Ferdinand ✆ 45 72 66 66, Fax 45 74 12 92 – |‡| ▤ TV ☎. AE ⓓ GB JCB E 6-7
☕ 50 – **42 rm** 820/880.

Banville without rest, 166 bd Berthier ✆ 42 67 70 16, Telex 643025, Fax 44 40 42 77 – |‡| TV ☎. AE GB D 8
☕ 45 – **39 rm** 635/760.

Mercure Etoile M without rest, 27 av. Ternes ✆ 47 66 49 18, Fax 47 63 77 91 – |‡| ⇎ ▤ TV ☎. AE ⓓ GB E 8
☕ 65 – **56 rm** 880.

Champerret-Villiers M without rest, 129 av. Villiers ✆ 47 64 44 00, Fax 47 63 10 58 – |‡| TV ☎. AE ⓓ GB JCB. ⚘ D 7
☕ 60 – **45 rm** 585/675.

de Neuville without rest, 3 r. Verniquet ✆ 43 80 26 30, Fax 43 80 38 55 – TV ☎. AE ① GB C 8
55 – **28 rm** 706/712.

Cheverny M without rest, 7 villa Berthier ✆ 43 80 46 42, Fax 47 63 26 62 – TV ☎. AE ① GB D 7
40 – **48 rm** 520/660.

Neva M without rest, 14 r. Brey ✆ 43 80 28 26, Fax 47 63 00 22 – TV ☎ ♿. AE ① GB. E 8
41 – **31 rm** 495/745.

Étoile Pereire without rest, 146 bd Péreire ✆ 42 67 60 00, Fax 42 67 02 90 – TV ☎. AE ① GB. D 7
54 – **21 rm** 560/1000, 5 duplex.

Mercédès without rest, 128 av. Wagram ✆ 42 27 77 82, Fax 40 53 09 89 – TV ☎. AE ① GB D 9
50 – **37 rm** 590/680.

Étoile Park H. without rest, 10 av. Mac Mahon ✆ 42 67 69 63, Fax 43 80 18 99 – TV ☎. AE ① GB JCB E 8
closed 24 December-1 January – 52 – **28 rm** 490/722.

Monceau without rest, 7 r. Rennequin ✆ 47 63 07 52, Fax 47 66 84 44 – TV ☎. AE ① GB JCB E 8
75 – **25 rm** 760/815.

Tilsitt Étoile without rest, 23 r. Brey ✆ 43 80 39 71, Telex 640629, Fax 47 66 37 63 – TV ☎. AE ① GB JCB E 8
50 – **39 rm** 570/780.

Monceau Étoile without rest, 64 r. Levis ✆ 42 27 33 10, Fax 42 27 59 58 – TV ☎. AE GB. D 10
30 – **26 rm** 600/650.

Harvey without rest, 7bis r. Débarcadère ✆ 45 74 27 19, Fax 40 68 03 56 – TV ☎. AE ① GB JCB E 6
40 – **32 rm** 500/720.

Royal Magda without rest, 7 r. Troyon ✆ 47 64 10 19, Fax 47 64 02 12 – TV ☎. AE ① GB. E 8
45 – **26 rm** 650/730, 11 suites.

Abrial M without rest, 176 r. Cardinet ✆ 42 63 50 00, Fax 42 63 50 03 – TV ☎ ♿. AE GB JCB C 11
45 – **80 rm** 590/640.

Astrid without rest, 27 av. Carnot ✆ 44 09 26 00, Telex 642065, Fax 44 09 26 01 – TV ☎. AE ① GB JCB E 7
50 – **40 rm** 450/715.

Champerret-Héliopolis M without rest, 13 r. Héliopolis ✆ 47 64 92 56, Fax 47 64 50 44 – TV ☎ ♿. AE ① GB JCB D 7
38 – **22 rm** 350/640.

Campanile, 4 bd Berthier ✆ 46 27 10 00, Fax 46 27 00 57, – TV ☎ ♿ – 40. AE ① GB B 10
Meals 92 b.i./119 b.i. – 34 – **247 rm** 416.

XXXX ✿✿ **Guy Savoy,** 18 r. Troyon ✆ 43 80 40 61, Fax 46 22 43 09 – . AE GB JCB E 8
closed Saturday lunch and Sunday – **Meals** 820 and a la carte 590/760
Spec. Foie gras de canard au sel gris et gelée de canard. Bar en écailles grillées aux épices douces. "Craquant moelleux" vanille et pomme, jus minute.

XXXX ✿✿ **Michel Rostang,** 10 r. Rennequin ✆ 47 63 40 77, Fax 47 63 82 75, « Elegant decor » – . AE ① GB JCB D 8
closed 1 to 15 August, Saturday lunch and Sunday – **Meals** 298 (lunch), 540/720 and a la carte 540/760
Spec. Millefeuille de langoustines de Bretagne "poireaux-pommes de terre". Truffes (15 December-15 March). Canette de Bresse au sang.

XXX ✿ **Étoile d'Or** - Hôtel Concorde La Fayette, 3 pl. Gén. Koenig ✆ 40 68 51 28, Fax 40 68 50 43 – . AE ① GB JCB E 6
closed 2 to 10 March, August, Saturday and Sunday – **Meals** 270 and a la carte 310/510
Spec. Cocktail d'araignée de mer à la vinaigrette d'étrilles. Joue de boeuf en ravigote. Soufflé chaud au chocolat.

XXX ✿ **Le Clos Longchamp** - Hôtel Méridien, 81 bd Gouvion St-Cyr (Pte Maillot) ✆ 40 68 00 70, Telex 651179, Fax 40 68 30 81 – . AE ① GB JCB E 6
closed 5 to 25 August, 23 to 29 December, Saturday, Sunday and Bank Holidays – **Meals** 250 (lunch)and a la carte 380/570
Spec. Crevettes vapeur au vinaigre de champagne. Noix de Saint-Jacques au parfum de Siam (October-April). Grenadin de porc fermier.

XXX ✿ **Manoir de Paris,** 6 r. P. Demours ✆ 45 72 25 25, Fax 45 74 80 98 – ▤. AE ⓓ GB
closed Saturday (except dinner from September-June) and Sunday – **Meals** 280/400 and a la carte 290/400 E 7
Spec. Pastilla de lapereau au romarin, carottes et navets glacés au miel. Pigeonneau des Hautes-Alpes au macis et polenta. Tarte fine au chocolat "Manjari" et poires tièdies.

XXX ✿✿ **Apicius** (Vigato), 122 av. Villiers ✆ 43 80 19 66, Fax 44 40 09 57 – ▤. AE ⓓ GB JCB D 8
closed August, Saturday and Sunday – **Meals** 300 (lunch), 480/550 and a la carte 400/620
Spec. Langoustines façon "tempura". Chaud-froid de homard. Pigeon désossé et farci.

XXX ✿✿ **Amphyclès** (Groult), 78 av. Ternes ✆ 40 68 01 01, Fax 40 68 91 88 – ▤. AE ⓓ GB JCB
closed Saturday lunch and Sunday – **Meals** 680/820 and a la carte 530/760 E 7
Spec. Araignée de mer en carapace. Bar de ligne de l'île de Sein au court-bouillon truffé. Noix de ris de veau des mendiants, fondue de pois gourmands.

XXX ✿ **Le Sormani** (Fayet), 4 r. Gén. Lanrezac ✆ 43 80 13 91, Fax 40 55 07 37 – ▤. AE GB
closed 1 to 21 August, Saturday, Sunday and Bank Holidays – **Meals** - Italian rest. - 350 b.i. (lunch), 400 b.i./450 b.i. and a la carte 310/420 E 7
Spec. Soupe de coquillettes au lard et aux cèpes (October-February). Ravioli de chèvre à la truffe noire. Lasagne de pommes de terre à la morue.

XXX ✿ **Faucher,** 123 av. Wagram ✆ 42 27 61 50, Fax 46 22 25 72 – AE GB D 8
closed Saturday lunch and Sunday – **Meals** 380 and a la carte 220/340
Spec. Millefeuille de boeuf cru et pousses d'épinards, sauce digoinaise. Filets de rouget à l'huile d'olive, macaroni farcis. Moelleux tiède au chocolat.

XXX **Pétrus,** 12 pl. Mar. Juin ✆ 43 80 15 95, Fax 43 80 06 96 – ▤. AE ⓓ GB D 8
closed 1 August-1 September – **Meals** - Seafood - 250/480 b.i. and a la carte 350/510.

XXX ✿ **Timgad** (Laasri), 21 r. Brunel ✆ 45 74 23 70, Fax 40 68 76 46, « Moorish decor » – ▤. AE ⓓ GB. ✂ E 7
Meals - North African rest. - a la carte 200/290
Spec. Couscous princier. Pastilla. Tagine.

XXX **Augusta,** 98 r. Tocqueville ✆ 47 63 39 97, Fax 42 27 21 71 – ▤. GB C 9
closed 5 to 26 August, Saturday except dinner from October-April and Sunday – **Meals** - Seafood - a la carte 320/540.

XXX **Il Ristorante,** 22 r. Fourcroy ✆ 47 63 34 00 – ▤. AE GB D 8
closed 5 to 20 August and Sunday – **Meals** - Italian rest. - 165 (lunch)and a la carte 240/380.

XX ✿ **Le Petit Colombier** (Fournier), 42 r. Acacias ✆ 43 80 28 54, Fax 44 40 04 29 – AE GB
closed 1 to 18 August, Sunday lunch and Saturday – **Meals** 200 (lunch), 350/450 b.i. and a la carte 330/450 E 7
Spec. Oeufs rôtis à la broche aux truffes fraîches (15 December-end February). Civet de lièvre à la française et pâtes fraîches (September-December). Tournedos rossini.

XX **La Table de Pierre,** 116 bd Péreire ✆ 43 80 88 68, Fax 47 66 53 02, 🏠 – ▤. AE GB
closed Saturday lunch and Sunday – **Meals** 210/350 and a la carte 220/380. D 8

XX **Graindorge,** 15 r. Arc de Triomphe ✆ 47 54 00 28, Fax 44 09 84 51 – AE GB E 7
closed Saturday lunch and Sunday – **Meals** 165 (lunch), 188/230 and a la carte 200/290.

XX **Les Bouchons de François Clerc,** 22 r. Terrasse ✆ 42 27 31 51, Fax 42 27 45 76, 🏠 – ▤. AE GB. ✂ D 10
closed Saturday lunch and Sunday – **Meals** 117 (lunch)/219.

XX **Billy Gourmand,** 20 r. Tocqueville ✆ 42 27 03 71 – AE GB D 10
closed 5 to 25 August, Saturday except dinner from September-June, Sunday and Bank Holidays – **Meals** 160 and a la carte 240/390.

XX **Le Beudant,** 97 r. des Dames ✆ 43 87 11 20 – ▤. AE ⓓ GB JCB D 11
closed 11 to 30 August, Saturday lunch and Sunday – **Meals** 155/300 and a la carte 230/330.

XX **Les Béatilles,** 11 bis r. Villebois-Mareuil ✆ 45 74 43 80, Fax 45 74 43 81 – ▤. GB E 7
closed 2 to 26 August, 22 December-4 January, Saturday and Sunday – **Meals** 150/290 and a la carte 170/240.

XX **La Truite Vagabonde,** 17 r. Batignolles ✆ 43 87 77 80, Fax 43 87 31 50, 🏠 – AE GB
closed Sunday dinner – **Meals** 180 and a la carte 260/370. D 11

XX **Taïra,** 10 r. Acacias ✆ 47 66 74 14, Fax 47 66 74 14 – ▤. AE ⓓ GB E 7
closed 12 to 18 August, Saturday lunch and Sunday – **Meals** - Seafood - 160/330 and a la carte 280/360.

XX **Aub. des Dolomites,** 38 r. Poncelet ✆ 42 27 94 56 – AE GB JCB E 8
closed August, Saturday lunch and Sunday – **Meals** 135/188 and a la carte 230/370.

XX **Les Marines de Pétrus,** 27 av. Niel ✆ 47 63 04 24, Fax 44 15 92 20 – ▤. AE ⓓ GB
closed August – **Meals** - Seafood - a la carte 200/330. D 8

XX **La Niçoise,** 4 r. P. Demours ✆ 45 74 42 41, Fax 45 74 80 98 – ▤. AE ⓓ GB E 7
closed Saturday (except dinner from September-June) and Sunday – **Meals** 125 b.i./165.

XX **La Petite Auberge,** 38 r. Laugier ✆ 47 63 85 51 – GB D 7-8
closed 4 to 27 August, Sunday dinner and Monday lunch – **Meals** (booking essential) 160 and a la carte 200/320.

XX **La Braisière,** 54 r. Cardinet ☏ 47 63 40 37, Fax 47 63 04 76 - AE GB D 9
closed August, Saturday and Sunday - **Meals** 175 and a la carte 220/330.

XX **Baumann Ternes,** 64 av. Ternes ☏ 45 74 16 66, Fax 45 72 44 32, brasserie - ▤. AE ⓓ GB E 7
Meals 163 and a la carte 180/320 ♢.

XX **La Soupière,** 154 av. Wagram ☏ 42 27 00 73, Fax 46 22 27 09 - ▤. AE GB D 9
closed 10 to 20 August, Saturday lunch and Sunday - **Meals** 138/240 and a la carte 200/320.

XX **Epicure 108,** 108 r. Cardinet ☏ 47 63 50 91 - GB D 10
closed 12 to 24 August, Saturday lunch and Sunday - **Meals** 175/250.

XX **Chez Laudrin,** 154 bd Péreire ☏ 43 80 87 40 - ▤. AE GB D 7
closed Saturday dinner from October-April and Sunday - **Meals** 165/230 and a la carte 250/370.

XX **Chez Guyvonne,** 14 r. Thann ☏ 42 27 25 43, Fax 42 27 25 43 - AE GB. ✻ D 10
closed 22 July-19 August, 24 December-2 January, Saturday and Sunday - **Meals** 150/260 and a la carte 270/410 ♢.

XX **Chez Georges,** 273 bd Péreire ☏ 45 74 31 00, Fax 45 74 02 56, bistro - GB E 6
closed August - **Meals** a la carte 210/350.

XX **Ballon des Ternes,** 103 av. Ternes ☏ 45 74 17 98, Fax 45 72 18 84, brasserie - AE GB
closed 1 to 20 August - **Meals** a la carte 180/300. E 6

XX **Chez Léon,** 32 r. Legendre ☏ 42 27 06 82, bistro - ⓓ GB D 10
closed August, Saturday and Sunday - **Meals** 135/185.

X **La Rôtisserie d'Armaillé,** 6 r. Armaillé ☏ 42 27 19 20, Fax 40 55 00 93 - ▤. AE GB JCB
closed Saturday lunch and Sunday - **Meals** 198 and a la carte approx. 270. E 7

X **L'Impatient,** 14 passage Geffroy Didelot ☏ 43 87 28 10 - GB D 10-11
closed 5 to 25 August, Monday dinner, Saturday and Sunday - **Meals** 100/285 and a la carte 200/300.

X **Mère Michel,** 5 r. Rennequin ☏ 47 63 59 80, bistro - AE GB E 8
closed 5 to 25 August, Saturday lunch and Sunday - **Meals** (booking essential) 85 (lunch)/145 and a la carte 160/260.

X **Caves Petrissans,** 30 bis av. Niel ☏ 42 27 83 84, Fax 40 54 87 56, ☂, bistro - AE GB D 8
closed 3 to 25 August, Saturday, Sunday and Bank Holidays - **Meals** 165 and a la carte 190/290.

X **Bistro du 17e,** 108 av. Villiers ☏ 47 63 32 77, Fax 42 27 67 66 - ▤. AE GB D 8
Meals 169 b.i..

X **Bistrot d'à Côté Flaubert,** 10 r. G. Flaubert ☏ 42 67 05 81, Fax 47 63 82 75 - AE GB
Meals a la carte 210/300. D 8

X **Bistrot de l'Étoile,** 13 r. Troyon ☏ 42 67 25 95 - ▤. AE GB E 8
closed Saturday lunch and Sunday - **Meals** a la carte 210/270.

Montmartre, La Villette, Belleville.

18th, 19th and 20th arrondissements.
18th: ✉ 75018
19th: ✉ 75019
20th: ✉ 75020

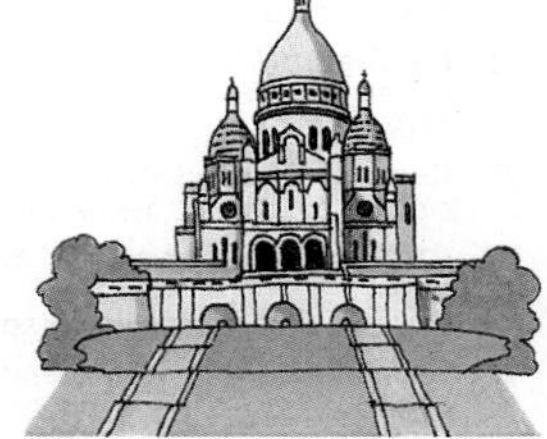

Terrass'H. Ⓜ, 12 r. J. de Maistre (18th) ☏ 46 06 72 85, Fax 42 52 29 11, ☂, « Rooftop terrace, ≤ Paris » - |♦| ⇆ ▤ rest TV ☎ - 🏛 90. AE ⓓ GB JCB C 13
La Terrasse ☏ 44 92 34 00 **Meals** 125b.i./165 ♢ - ☕ 75 - **88 rm** 950/1260, 13 suites.

Mercure Montmartre without rest, 1 r. Caulaincourt (18th) ☏ 44 69 70 70, Telex 285605, Fax 44 69 70 71 - |♦| ⇆ ▤ TV ☎ ♿ - 🏛 120. AE ⓓ GB D 12
☕ 68 - **308 rm** 831/897.

Roma Sacré Coeur without rest, 101 r. Caulaincourt (18th) ☏ 42 62 02 02, Fax 42 54 34 92 - |♦| TV ☎. AE ⓓ GB JCB C 14
☕ 37 - **57 rm** 410/480.

des Arts without rest, 5 r. Tholozé (18th) ☏ 46 06 30 52, Fax 46 06 10 83 - |♦| TV ☎. AE GB
☕ 30 - **50 rm** 420/470. D 13

Eden H. without rest, 90 r. Ordener (18th) ☏ 42 64 61 63, Fax 42 64 11 43 - |♦| TV ☎. AE ⓓ GB JCB B 14
☕ 35 - **35 rm** 365/400.

Regyn's Montmartre without rest, 18 pl. Abbesses (18th) ✆ 42 54 45 21, Fax 42 23 76 6 - TV ☎. AE GB D 1
40 - **22 rm** 375/455.

Palma without rest, 77 av. Gambetta (20th) ✆ 46 36 13 65, Fax 46 36 03 27 - TV ☎. A GB G 2
33 - **32 rm** 340/395.

Super H. without rest, 208 r. Pyrénées (20th) ✆ 46 36 97 48, Fax 46 36 26 10 - TV ☎ AE GB G 2
closed August - 32 - **32 rm** 280/500.

H. Le Laumière without rest, 4 r. Petit (19th) ✆ 42 06 10 77, Fax 42 06 72 50 - TV ☎ GB D 1
32 - **54 rm** 255/380.

Al'Hôtel M, 2 av. Prof. A. Lemierre (20th) ✆ 43 63 16 16, Fax 43 63 31 32 - TV ☎ - 100. AE GB J 2
Meals 90/130 - 35 - **325 rm** 400/440.

Crimée without rest, 188 r. Crimée (19th) ✆ 40 36 75 29, Fax 40 36 29 57 - TV ☎. A GB C 1
30 - **31 rm** 280/340.

Damrémont without rest, 110 r. Damrémont (18th) ✆ 42 64 25 75, Fax 46 06 74 64 - ☎. AE GB JCB. B 1
40 - **35 rm** 350/490.

XXX ✿ **Beauvilliers** (Carlier), 52 r. Lamarck (18th) ✆ 42 54 54 42, Fax 42 62 70 30, « 190 decor, terrace » - AE GB JCB. C 1
closed Monday lunch and Sunday - **Meals** 185 (lunch)/400 b.i. and a la carte 420/550
Spec. Fond d'artichaut farci de tourteau, sauce pistache. Rognonnade de veau et grenadin au essences de truffes. Timbale de macaroni aux ris de veau et morilles (April-August).

XXX **Pavillon Puebla,** Parc Buttes-Chaumont, entrance : av. Bolivar, r. Botzaris (19th ✆ 42 08 92 62, Fax 42 39 83 16, « Pleasant setting in the park » - P. AE GB E 1
closed Sunday and Monday - **Meals** 186/240 and a la carte 360/490.

XXX **La Crème du Homard,** 128 bis bd Clichy (18th) ✆ 45 22 47 08, Fax 45 22 44 72 - A GB D 1
Meals - Seafood - 190/350 and a la carte 240/430.

XXX **Au Cochon d'Or,** 192 av. J.-Jaurès (19th) ✆ 42 45 46 46, Fax 42 40 43 90 - AE G JCB C 2
Meals 240 and a la carte 280/460 - **Bistrot du Cochon d'Or : Meals** 100/150 bc.

XX **La Chaumière,** 46 av. Secrétan (19th) ✆ 42 06 54 69 - AE GB JCB E 1
closed 1 to 15 August and Sunday except Bank Holidays - **Meals** 143/198 b.i. and a la cart 190/350.

XX **Cottage Marcadet,** 151 bis r. Marcadet (18th) ✆ 42 57 71 22 - GB. C 1
closed 3 August-1 September and Sunday - **Meals** 210 b.i. and a la carte 260/350.

XX **Au Boeuf Couronné,** 188 av. J. Jaurès (19th) ✆ 42 39 44 44, Fax 42 39 17 30 - AE G JCB C 2
closed Sunday - **Meals** 150 and a la carte 190/340.

XX **Les Allobroges,** 71 r. Grands-Champs (20th) ✆ 43 73 40 00 - GB K 2
closed August, Sunday, Monday and Bank Holidays - **Meals** 89/159 and a la carte 200/30

XX **Au Clair de la Lune,** 9 r. Poulbot (18th) ✆ 42 58 97 03 - AE GB JCB D 1
closed 1 to 15 March, Sunday dinner and Monday - **Meals** 165 and a la carte 230/310.

X **La Verrière,** 10 r. Gén. Brunet (19th) ✆ 40 40 03 30, Fax 40 40 03 30 - GB E 2
closed 1 to 21 August, Sunday and Monday - **Meals** 190.

X **Aucune Idée ?,** 2 pl. St-Blaise (20th) ✆ 40 09 70 67 - AE GB H 2
closed 5 to 18 August, Sunday dinner and Monday - **Meals** 155/165 and a la carte 180/32

X **Marie-Louise,** 52 r. Championnet (18th) ✆ 46 06 86 55, bistro - GB B 1
closed late July-early September, Sunday, Monday and Bank Holidays - **Meals** 130/220 an a la carte 150/220.

X **L'Étrier,** 154 r. Lamarck (18th) ✆ 42 29 14 01, bistro - GB C 1
closed August, Monday dinner and Sunday - **Meals** (booking essential) 80 (lunch), 160/300 b and a la carte approx. 280.

X **L'Oriental,** 76 r. Martyrs (18th) ✆ 42 64 39 80, Fax 42 64 39 80 - AE GB. D 1
closed 1 to 25 August and Sunday - **Meals** - North African rest. - 78 (lunch)/190 b.i. and a carte 140/180.

ENVIRONS

The outskirts of Paris up to 25Km

When calling the following places from the provinces dial 1 + eight-digit number.

K 11: These reference letters and numbers correspond to the squares on the **Michelin plans of Parisian suburbs** nos 18, 20, 22, 24.

La Défense **92** Hauts-de-Seine 101 ⑭, 18 – ✉ 92400 Courbevoie.

See : Quarter★★ : perspective★ from the parvis.

Paris 8,5.

Sofitel CNIT M, 2 pl. Défense ✆ 46 92 10 10, Telex 613782, Fax 46 92 10 50 – rm – 25. AE GB JCB. rest U-V 19
Meals see ***Les Communautés*** below – 95 – **141 rm** 1460/1700, 6 suites.

Sofitel La Défense M, 34 cours Michelet by ring road, exit La Défense 4 ✉ 92060 Puteaux ✆ 47 76 44 43, Telex 612189, Fax 47 73 72 74 – – 80. AE GB V 20
Les 2 Arcs *(closed Sunday lunch and Saturday)* **Meals** 295 (lunch) and a la carte 260/340 – ***Le Botanic*** *(lunch only)* **Meals** 265 and a la carte 210/280 – 80 – **150 rm** 1350.

Novotel La Défense M, 2 bd Neuilly ✆ 47 78 16 68, Telex 630288, Fax 47 78 84 71, ← – – 25 - 150. AE GB JCB V 21
Meals a la carte approx. 180 – 62 – **280 rm** 770/790.

Ibis La Défense M, 4 bd Neuilly ✆ 47 78 15 60, Fax 47 78 94 16, – – 120. AE GB V 21
Meals 99 b.i. – 39 – **284 rm** 475.

XXX **Les Communautés** - Hôtel Sofitel CNIT, 2 pl. Défense, 5th floor ✆ 46 92 10 30 – . AE GB JCB. U-V 19
closed Saturday and Sunday – **Meals** 175 (dinner)/300 and a la carte approx. 280.

Marne-la-Vallée **77206** S.-et-M. 101 ⑲.

18 of Bussy-St-Georges (private) ✆ 64 66 00 00 ; 9 18 of Disneyland Paris ✆ 60 45 69 14.

Paris 28.

at Collégien - pop. 2 331 alt. 105 – ✉ 77080 :

Novotel M, at Motorway junction Lagny A 4 ✆ 64 80 53 53, Fax 64 80 48 37, , , – P – 300. AE GB
Meals 120 – 53 – **197 rm** 480/500.

at Disneyland Paris access by Highway A 4 and Disneyland exit.

See : Disneyland Paris Park★★★

Disneyland Hôtel M, ✆ (1) 60 45 65 00, Fax (1) 60 45 65 33, ←, « Victorian style architecture, at the entrance to the Disneyland Resort », , , – P – 50. AE GB JCB.
California Grill (dinner only) **Meals** 295 – ***Inventions :*** **Meals** 180 (lunch)/250 – 150 – **478 rm** 1995/3245, 18 suites.

New-York M, ✆ (1) 60 45 73 00, Fax (1) 60 45 73 33, ←, , « Evokes the architecture of Manhattan », , , , – P – 1 500. AE GB JCB.
Manhattan Restaurant : **Meals** 195, enf. 65 – ***Parkside Diner :*** **Meals** a la carte approx. 150 – 80 – **536 rm** 1025/1225, 31 suites.

Newport Bay Club M, ✆ (1) 60 45 55 00, Fax (1) 60 45 55 33, ←, « In the style of a New England seaside resort », , , – P – 50. AE GB JCB.
Cape Cod : **Meals** 125 (lunch)/150 – ***Yacht Club*** – **(dinner only out of season) Meals** 150/230, a la carte dinner – 55 – **1 083 rm** 895/1095, 14 suites.

Séquoia Lodge M, ✆ 60 45 51 00, Fax 60 45 51 33, ←, « The atmosphere of an American mountain lodge », , , – P – 120. AE GB JCB.
Hunter's Grill : **Meals** 90/145 – ***Beaver Creek Tavern*** – **(dinner only out of season) Meals** a la carte approx. 150 – 55 – **997 rm** 795/995, 14 suites.

Cheyenne, ✆ 60 45 62 00, Fax 60 45 62 33, , « Resembles a frontier town of the American Wild West » – rest P. AE GB JCB.
Chuck Wagon Café : **Meals** a la carte approx. 110 – 45 – **1 000 rm** 695.

Santa Fé M, ✆ 60 45 78 00, Fax 60 45 78 33, , « Evokes a New Mexican pueblo » – rest P. AE GB JCB.
La Cantina (self service) **Meals** a la carte approx. 120 – 45 – **1 000 rm** 595.

Orly (Paris Airports) **94396** Val-de-Marne 101 ㉖, 24 - pop. 21 646.
✈ ✆ 49 75 15 15.
Paris 15.

Hilton Orly M, near airport station ✉ 94544 ✆ 45 12 45 12, Telex 265971, Fax 45 12 45 0 - |‡| ⇔ ▤ TV ☎ ♿ P - 🏨 300. AE ⓓ GB JCB AR 3
Meals 195/220 and a la carte 170/290 🍷 - ☕ 95 - **357 rm** 990/1150.

Mercure M, N 7, Z.I. Nord, Orly tech ✉ 94547 ✆ 46 87 23 37, Telex 265665 Fax 46 87 71 92 - |‡| ⇔ ▤ TV ☎ ♿ P - 🏨 80. AE ⓓ GB
Meals a la carte 150/240 🍷 - ☕ 61 - **194 rm** 600/640.

Orly Airport South :

XX **Le Clos St-Germain,** 3rd floor ✉ 94542 ✆ 49 75 78 23, Fax 49 75 36 69, ← - ▤. AE ⓓ GB
Meals a la carte 180/320 🍷.

Orly Airport West :

XXXX ✿ **Maxim's,** 2nd floor ✉ 94546 ✆ 46 86 87 84, Fax 46 87 05 39 - ▤. AE ⓓ GB
closed August, 24 December-2 January, Saturday, Sunday and Bank Holidays - **Meals** 250 an a la carte 280/450
Spec. Langoustines et noix de Saint-Jacques rôties au sel d'ail (October-April). Etuvée de homar et Saint-Jacques au jus de moules et Sauternes (October-April). Selle d'agneau des Pyrénée poêlée, endives et carottes au coriandre.

See also ***Rungis***

Europe — If the name of the hotel is not in bold type, on arrival ask the hotelier his prices.

Roissy-en-France (Paris Airports) **95700** Val-d'Oise 101 ⑧ - pop. 2 054 alt. 85.
✈ ✆ 48 62 22 80.
Paris 26.

at Roissy-Town :

Copthorne M, allée Verger ✆ 34 29 33 33, Fax 34 29 03 05, 🍽, Fб, 🏊 - |‡| ⇔ ▤ TV ☎ ♿ 🚗 - 🏨 150. AE ⓓ GB JCB. ✻ rest
Brasserie l'Europe *(closed Saturday and Sunday)* **Meals** 250 - ☕ 75 - **237 rm** 1050/1250

Holiday Inn, allée Verger ✆ 34 29 30 00, Telex 605143, Fax 34 29 90 52, Fб - |‡| ⇔ ▤ TV ☎ ♿ P - 🏨 120. AE ⓓ GB JCB
Meals a la carte approx. 160 🍷 - ☕ 87 - **243 rm** 805/1150.

Mercure, allée Verger ✆ 34 29 40 00, Telex 605205, Fax 34 29 00 18, 🍽, 🌳 - |‡| ⇔ ▤ TV ☎ ♿ P - 🏨 200. AE ⓓ GB
Meals 141 🍷 - ☕ 67 - **198 rm** 760/960, 4 suites.

Ibis M, av. Raperie ✆ 34 29 34 34, Telex 688413, Fax 34 29 34 19 - |‡| ⇔ ▤ TV ☎ ♿ 🚗 - 🏨 150. AE ⓓ GB
Meals 99 b.i. - ☕ 42 - **315 rm** 490.

in the airport area :

Hilton M, Roissypole ✆ 49 19 77 77, Fax 49 19 77 78, Fб, 🏊 - |‡| ⇔ ▤ TV ☎ ♿ 🚗 - 🏨 1 000. AE ⓓ GB. ✻ rest
Le Gourmet *(closed 22 July-21 August, Saturday and Sunday)* **Meals** 230 - ***La Verrière :*** **Meals** 179 b.i. - ☕ 85 - **383 rm** 1200/1700, 4 suites.

Sofitel M, ✆ 49 19 29 29, Telex 230166, Fax 49 19 29 00, 🍽, 🏊, 🎾 - |‡| ⇔ ▤ TV ☎ ♿ P - 🏨 150. AE ⓓ GB JCB
Meals 109 b.i./150 b.i. and a la carte 160/240 - ☕ 80 - **344 rm** 850/1400, 8 suites.

Novotel M, ✆ 48 62 00 53, Telex 232397, Fax 48 62 00 11 - |‡| ⇔ ▤ TV ☎ ♿ P - 🏨 25 - 100. AE ⓓ GB JCB
Meals a la carte approx. 180 - ☕ 60 - **201 rm** 660.

in the airport nr. 1 :

XXX **Maxim's,** ✆ 48 62 24 34, Fax 48 62 45 96 - ▤. AE ⓓ GB. ✻
closed August, Saturday and Sunday - **Meals** 220/290 and a la carte 300/510.

Z.I. Paris Nord II - ✉ 95912 :

Hyatt Regency M 🐦, 351 av. Bois de la Pie ✆ 48 17 12 34, Telex 230930, Fax 48 17 17 17 🍽, « Original contemporary decor », Fб, 🏊, 🎾 - |‡| ⇔ ▤ TV ☎ ♿ P - 🏨 250. AE ⓓ GB JCB
Brasserie Espace : **Meals** 190 - ***Le Mirage :*** **Meals** a la carte 170/230 - ☕ 85 - **383 rm** 1200/1500, 5 suites.

Rungis **94150** Val-de-Marne 101 ㉖, 24 - pop. 2 939 alt. 80.
Paris 14.

at Pondorly : Access : from Paris, Highway A 6 and take Orly Airport exit ; from outside of Paris, A 6 and Rungis exit :

Pullman Orly M, 20 av. Ch. Lindbergh ✉ 94656 ✆ 46 87 36 36, Fax 46 87 08 48, – 180. AE GB AM 29
La Rungisserie : **Meals** 170 – ▭ 62 – **190 rm** 650.

Holiday Inn M, 4 av. Ch. Lindbergh ✉ 94656 ✆ 46 87 26 66, Telex 265803, Fax 45 60 91 25 – 150. AE GB AM 29
Meals 140/260 – ▭ 70 – **168 rm** 825/1025.

Novotel M, Zone du Delta, 1 r. Pont des Halles ✆ 45 12 44 12, Fax 45 12 44 13, – 150. AE GB
Meals a la carte approx. 160 – ▭ 58 – **181 rm** 620.

Ibis, 1 r. Mondétour ✉ 94656 ✆ 46 87 22 45, Fax 46 87 84 72, – 100. AE GB AM 29
Meals 99 b.i. – ▭ 39 – **119 rm** 320.

Versailles P **78000** Yvelines 101 ㉒, 22 - pop. 87 789 alt. 130.

See : Castel★★★ Y – Gardens★★★ (fountain display★★★ (grandes eaux) and illuminated night performances★★★ (fêtes de nuit) in summer) – Ecuries Royales★ Y – The Trianons★★ – Lambinet Museum★ Y **M**.

of la Boulie (private) ✆ 39 50 59 41 by ③ : 2,5 km.

Tourist Office 7 r. Réservoirs ✆ 39 50 36 22, Fax 39 50 68 07.

Paris 20 ①.

Plan on next page

Trianon Palace M, 1 bd Reine ✆ 30 84 38 00, Telex 698863, Fax 39 49 00 77, ≤, park, « Tasteful early 20C decor », – rm – 30. AE GB JCB
Meals see *Les Trois Marches* below - *Grill :* **Meals** a la carte 200/310 – ▭ 110 – **69 rm** 1500/1800, 25 suites. Y **r**

Sofitel Château de Versailles M, 2 av. Paris ✆ 39 53 30 31, Telex 697042, Fax 39 53 87 20, – 150. AE GB JCB Y **a**
Meals *(closed Saturday lunch)* 159 – ▭ 75 – **146 rm** 900, 6 suites.

Le Pavillon Trianon M, 1 bd Reine ✆ 30 84 38 00, Telex 699210, Fax 39 51 57 79, – 300. AE GB JCB X **r**
Brasserie La Fontaine ✆ 30 84 38 47 **Meals** 165 and a la carte 160/300 – ▭ 75 – **98 rm** 900.

Printania M without rest, 19 r. Ph. de Dangeau ✆ 39 50 44 10, Fax 39 50 65 11 – 35. AE GB JCB Y **n**
▭ 38 – **60 rm** 360/380.

Résidence du Berry without rest, 14 r. Anjou ✆ 39 49 07 07, Telex 689058, Fax 39 50 59 40 – . AE GB Z **s**
closed 20 December-5 January – ▭ 40 – **38 rm** 410/480.

Ibis M without rest, 4 av. Gén. de Gaulle ✆ 39 53 03 30, Fax 39 50 06 31 – . AE GB Y **u**
▭ 35 – **85 rm** 370/470.

XXXX ✿✿ **Les Trois Marches** (Vié), 1 bd Reine ✆ 39 50 13 21, Fax 30 21 01 25, ≤, – . AE GB JCB X **r**
closed August, Sunday and Monday – **Meals** 510/750 and a la carte 480/720
Spec. Galette de pommes de terre, lard et caviar. Carré d'agneau de Pauillac rôti, ragoût d'abats. Bavarois au thé fumé, glace à la rose et crème à la fleur d'oranger.

XXX ✿ **La Grande Sirène,** 25 r. Mar. Foch ✆ 39 53 08 08, Fax 39 53 37 15 – . AE GB.
closed 28 July-28 August, February Holidays, Sunday and Monday – **Meals** 178 (lunch)/225 and a la carte 290/430 Y **v**
Spec. Huîtres frémies "Viroflay" au beurre d'agrumes (September-March). Saint-Pierre rôti au jus de veau. "Coup de foudre" au chocolat amer.

XXX **Rescatore,** 27 av. St-Cloud ✆ 39 25 06 34, Fax 39 02 12 04 – AE GB Y **s**
closed August, Sunday dinner and Monday – **Meals** - Seafood - 180 and a la carte 210/320.

XX **Le Potager du Roy,** 1 r. Mar.-Joffre ✆ 39 50 35 34, Fax 30 21 69 30 – . AE GB Z **r**
closed Sunday dinner and Monday – **Meals** 165 and a la carte 210/430.

XX **La Marée de Versailles,** 22 r. au Pain ✆ 30 21 73 73, Fax 39 50 55 87 – . GB Y **t**
closed 29 July-19 August, 23 December-2 January, Monday dinner and Sunday – **Meals** - Seafood - 260 and a la carte 200/270.

XX **La Rôtisserie,** 30 bis r. Réservoirs ✆ 39 50 70 02, Fax 39 02 24 84 – AE GB Y **f**
Meals 138 and a la carte approx. 200.

XX **Pascal Le Fahler,** 22 r. Satory ✆ 39 50 57 43, Fax 39 49 04 66 – GB. Y **m**
closed Saturday lunch and Sunday – **Meals** 125/180 and a la carte 230/320.

X **La Cuisine Bourgeoise,** 10 bd Roi ✆ 39 53 11 38, Fax 39 53 25 26 – GB XY **k**
closed 8 to 29 August, Wednesday dinner and Thursday – **Meals** 105 (lunch)/158 and a la carte approx. 220.

VERSAILLES

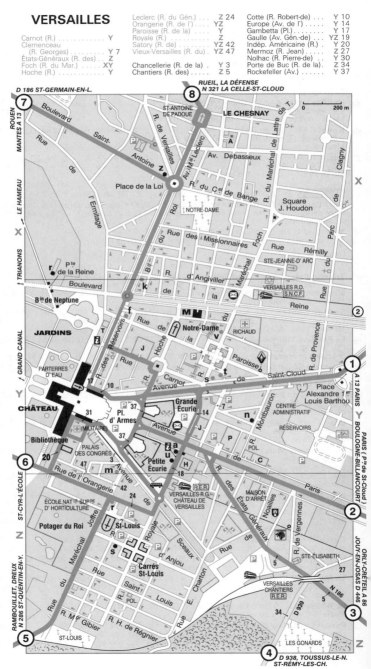

Rue	Carroyage
Carnot (R.)	Y
Clemenceau (R. Georges)	Y 7
États-Généraux (R. des)	Z
Foch (R. du Mar.)	XY
Hoche (R.)	Y
Leclerc (R. du Gén.)	Z 24
Orangerie (R. de l')	YZ
Paroisse (R. de la)	Y
Royale (R.)	Z
Satory (R. de)	YZ 42
Vieux-Versailles (R. du)	YZ 47
Chancellerie (R. de la)	Y 3
Chantiers (R. des)	Z 5
Cotte (R. Robert-de)	Y 10
Europe (Av. de l')	Y 14
Gambetta (Pl.)	Y 17
Gaulle (Av. Gén.-de)	YZ 19
Indép. Américaine (R.)	Y 20
Mermoz (R. Jean)	Z 27
Nolhac (R. Pierre-de)	Y 30
Porte de Buc (R. de la)	Z 34
Rockefeller (Av.)	Y 37

at Le Chesnay - pop. 29 542 alt. 120 - ✉ 78150 :

Novotel Ⓜ, 4 bd St-Antoine ☎ 39 54 96 96, Fax 39 54 94 40 - ⫶ ⫶ ▤ TV ☎ ♿ 🚗 - 🏛 25 - 150. AE ⓓ GB X z
Meals a la carte approx. 180 - ☕ 58 - **105 rm** 540/565.

Mercure Ⓜ without rest, r. Marly-le-Roi, in front of Commercial Centre Parly II ☎ 39 55 11 41, Telex 695205, Fax 39 55 06 22 - ⫶ ⫶ ▤ rm TV ☎ ♿ P - 🏛 70. AE ⓓ GB JCB
☕ 52 - **80 rm** 570.

Ibis Ⓜ without rest, av. Dutartre, Commercial Centre Parly II ☎ 39 63 37 93, Fax 39 55 18 66 - ⫶ ⫶ TV ☎ ♿. AE ⓓ GB
☕ 39 - **72 rm** 375.

Le Chesnoy, 24 r. Pottier ☎ 39 54 01 01 - ▤. AE ⓓ GB
closed 5 to 26 August, Sunday dinner and Monday - **Meals** 178.

Le Connemara, 41 rte Rueil ☎ 39 55 63 07 - AE GB
closed 1 to 21 August, February Holidays, Sunday and Monday - **Meals** 140 (lunch)/165 and a la carte 240/340.

AND BEYOND...

Joigny 89300 Yonne 65 ④ - pop. 9 697 alt. 79.
See : Vierge au Sourire★ in St-Thibault's Church - Côte St-Jacques ≤★ 1,5 km by D 20
of Roncemay ✆ 86 73 68 87.
Tourist Office 4 quai H.-Ragobert ✆ 86 62 11 05, Fax 86 91 76 38.
Paris 147 - Auxerre 27 - Gien 75 - Montargis 59 - Sens 30 - Troyes 76.

✿✿✿ **La Côte St-Jacques** (Lorain) M, 14 fg Paris ✆ 86 62 09 70, Fax 86 91 49 70, ≤ « Tasteful decor », - - 30. AE GB
Meals (Sunday booking essential) 380 (lunch)/720 and a la carte 540/730 - 110 - **25 rm** 720/1750, 4 suites
Spec. Huîtres bretonnes en petite terrine océane. Noix de Saint-Jacques, endives et chanterelles. Poularde de Bresse à la vapeur de champagne. Wines Chardonnay, Irancy.

Pontoise 95300 Val d'Oise 106 ⑤ - pop. 27 150 alt. 48.
Tourist Office 6 pl. Petit-Martroy ✆ (1) 30 38 24 45, Fax (1) 30 73 54 84.
Paris 36 - Beauvais 50 - Dieppe 135 - Mantes-la-Jolie 39 - Rouen 91.

at Cormeilles-en-Vexin NW : 9,5 km by D 915 - alt. 111 - ✉ 95830 :

✿✿ **Gérard Cagna,** on D 915 ✆ (1) 34 66 61 56, Fax (1) 34 66 40 31, « Garden » - AE GB
closed 2 to 25 August, 23 to 28 December, Sunday dinner, Tuesday dinner and Monday -
Meals 200/500 b.i.
Spec. Douceur de pigeon au foie gras et griottes. Soufflé de foie gras et pôelée d'artichaut. Profiteroles à la vanille Bourbon.

Rheims 51100 Marne 56 ⑥ ⑯ - pop. 180 620 alt. 85.
See : Cathedral★★★ - St-Remi Basilica★★ : interior★★★ - Palais du Tau★★ - Champagne cellars★ - Place Royale★ - Porte Mars★ - Hôtel de la Salle★ - Foujita Chapel★ - Library★ of Ancient College des Jésuites - St-Remi Museum★★ - Hôtel le Vergeur Museum★ - Fine Arts Museum★ - Historical centre of the French motor industry★.
Envir. : Fort de la Pompelle : German helmets★ 9 km to the SE by N 44.
Rheims-Champagne ✆ 26 03 60 14 at Gueux, to the NW by N 31-E 46 : 9,5 km.
Rheims-Champagne ✆ 26 07 15 15, to the N : 6 km.
✆ 36 35 35 35.
Tourist Office 2 r. Guillaume-de-Machault ✆ 26 77 45 25, Fax 26 77 45 27 - A.C. de Champagne 7 bd Lundy ✆ 26 47 34 76, Fax 26 88 52 24.
Paris 144 - Brussels 214 - Châlons-en-Champagne 48 - Lille 199 - Luxembourg 232.

✿✿✿ **Boyer "Les Crayères"** M, 64 bd Vasnier ✆ 26 82 80 80, Fax 26 82 65 52, ≤ « Elegant mansion in park », - AE GB
closed 23 December-13 January - **Meals** *(closed Tuesday lunch and Monday)* (booking essential) a la carte 520/740 - 102 - **16 rm** 990/1940, 3 suites
Spec. Ravioli de homard et ris de veau. Filet de bar de ligne grillé, poêlée de légumes à la coriandre. Filet d'agneau pané à la truffe. Wines Champagne.

Saulieu 21210 Côte-d'Or 65 ⑰ - pop. 2 917 alt. 535.
Tourist Office r. d'Argentine ✆ 80 64 00 21, Fax 80 64 21 96.
Paris 249 - Autun 41 - Avallon 38 - Beaune 64 - Clamecy 76 - Dijon 73.

✿✿✿ **La Côte d'Or** (Loiseau) M, 2 r. Argentine **(e)** ✆ 80 90 53 53, Fax 80 64 08 92 « Tasteful inn with flowered garden » - - 30. AE GB JCB
Meals 390 (lunch), 680/890 and a la carte 530/920 - 120 - **24 rm** 310/980, 3 duplex
Spec. Jambonnettes de grenouilles à la purée d'ail et au jus de persil. Sandre à la fondue d'échalote sauce vin rouge. Blanc de volaille au foie gras chaud et purée truffée. Wines Givry, Marsannay.

Vézelay 89450 Yonne 65 ⑮ - pop. 571 alt. 285.
See : Ste-Madeleine Basilica★★★ : tower ★.
Envir. : Site★ of Pierre-Perthuis SE : 6 km.
Tourist Office r. St-Pierre ✆ 86 33 23 69, Fax 86 33 34 00.
Paris 223 - Auxerre 51 - Avallon 15 - Château-Chinon 60 - Clamecy 22.

at St-Père : SE : 3 km by D 957 - alt. 148 - ✉ 89450.
See : Church of N.-Dame★

✿✿✿ **L'Espérance** (Meneau), ✆ 86 33 39 10, Fax 86 33 26 15, ≤, « Conservatory restaurant opening onto the garden », - rest - 50. AE GB JCB
Meals *(closed February, Wednesday lunch and Tuesday except Bank Holidays)* (booking essential) 380 (lunch), 700/900 and a la carte 600/1 000 - 140 - **34 rm** 680/1500, 6 suites
Spec. Galets de pommes de terre au caviar. Homard au lait d'amande, vinaigrette au curry. Veau au "caramel amer". Wines Vézelay, Chablis.

BORDEAUX P 33000 Gironde 71 ⑨ – pop. 210 336 alt. 4 Greater Bordeaux 696 364 h.

See : 18C Bordeaux : façades along the quayside★★ EX, Esplanade des Quinconces DX, Grand Théâtre★★ DX, Notre-Dame Church★ DX, Allées de Tourny DX, – Cours Clemenceau DX, Place Gambetta DX, Cours de l'Intendance DX – Old Bordeaux★★ : Place de la Bourse★★ EX, Place du Parlement★ EX **109**, St-Michel Basilica★ EY, Great Bell★ (Grosse Cloche) EY **D** – Pey-Berland district : St-André Cathedral★ DY (Pey-Berland Tower★ **E**) – Mériadeck district CY – Battle-Cruiser Colbert★ – World Wine Centre (Centre mondial du vin) – Museums : Fine Arts★★ (Beaux-Arts CDY **M³**, Decorative Arts★ DY **M²**, Aquitaine★★ DY **M⁴** – Entrepôt Laîné★★ : museum of contemporary art★.

18 Golf Bordelais ☎ 56 28 56 04, to the NW D109 : 4 km ; 18 18 de Bordeaux Lac ☎ 56 50 92 72, to the N by D 209 : 10 km ; 18 18 of Medoc at Louens ☎ 56 70 21 10 to the NW by N 215 and D 1 : 16 km ; 9 9 9 9 Internat. of Bordeaux-Pessac ☎ 56 36 24 47 to the SW by N 250 : 16 km ; 9 of Artigues ☎ 56 86 49 26, E by D 241 : 8 km.

✈ of Bordeaux-Mérignac : ☎ 56 34 50 00, to the W : 11 km.

☎ 36 35 35 35.

Tourist Office 12 cours 30-Juillet ☎ 56 44 28 41, Fax 56 81 89 21 at the Gare St-Jean ☎ 56 91 64 70 and the airport, arrivals Hall ☎ 52 34 39 39 - Bordeaux wine Exhibition (Maison du vin de Bordeaux) 3 cours 30-Juil. (Information, wine-tasting - closed weekends from mid Oct.-mid May) ☎ 56 00 22 66 DX – A.C. du Sud-Ouest 8 pl. Quiconces ☎ 56 44 22 92.

Paris 579 – Lyons 531 – Nantes 324 – Strasbourg 919 – Toulouse 245.

Plans on following pages

Burdigala M, 115 r. G. Bonnac ☎ 56 90 16 16, Telex 572981, Fax 56 93 15 06 – AE GB JCB — CX **r**
Meals 180/280 – 80 – **68 rm** 830/1460, 8 suites, 7 duplex.

Mercure Château Chartrons M, 81 cours St-Louis ✉ 33300 ☎ 56 43 15 00, Telex 573938, Fax 56 69 15 21, – rest – 150. AE GB
Meals 100/200 – 56 – **144 rm** 455/570.

Holiday Inn Garden Court, 30 r. de Tauzia ✉ 33800 ☎ 56 92 21 21, Telex 573848, Fax 56 91 08 06, – – 70. AE GB — FZ **v**
Meals 95/130 b.i. – 60 – **89 rm** 420.

Novotel Bordeaux-Centre M, 45 cours Mar. Juin ☎ 56 51 46 46, Telex 573749, Fax 56 98 25 56, – – 80. AE GB JCB — CY **m**
Meals a la carte approx. 160 – 51 – **138 rm** 465/495.

Claret M, Cité Mondiale du Vin, 18 parvis des Chartrons ☎ 56 01 79 79, Fax 56 01 79 00, – – 800. AE GB
Meals 100/140 – 60 – **97 rm** 505/570.

Ste-Catherine without rest, 27 r. Parlement Ste-Catherine ☎ 56 81 95 12, Fax 56 44 50 51 – – 40. AE GB JCB — DX **m**
70 – **84 rm** 530/1200.

Normandie without rest, 7 cours 30-Juillet ☎ 56 52 16 80, Fax 56 51 68 91 – – 30. AE GB JCB — DX **z**
50 – **100 rm** 300/660.

Gd H. Français without rest, 12 r. Temple ☎ 56 48 10 35, Fax 56 81 76 18 – AE GB — DX **v**
60 – **35 rm** 360/630.

Majestic without rest, 2 r. Condé ☎ 56 52 60 44, Fax 56 79 26 70 – AE GB JCB — DX **a**
50 – **50 rm** 390/590.

Le Bayonne M without rest, 4 r. Martignac ☎ 56 48 00 88, Fax 56 52 03 79 – AE GB — DX **f**
closed 23 December-5 January – 55 – **36 rm** 370/630.

Presse M without rest, 6 r. Porte Dijeaux ☎ 56 48 53 88, Fax 56 01 05 82 – AE GB — DX **k**
35 – **29 rm** 240/380.

Continental without rest, 10 r. Montesquieu ☎ 56 52 66 00, Fax 56 52 77 97 – AE GB — DX **b**
35 – **50 rm** 290/350.

Royal St-Jean without rest, 15 r. Ch. Domercq ✉ 33800 ☎ 56 91 72 16, Fax 56 94 08 32 – AE GB JCB — FZ **u**
45 – **37 rm** 330/440.

Opéra without rest, 35 r. Esprit des Lois ☎ 56 81 41 27, Fax 56 51 78 80 – GB — DX **n**
35 – **27 rm** 200/290.

XXXX ✿ **Le Chapon Fin** (Garcia), 5 r. Montesquieu ☎ 56 79 10 10, Fax 56 79 09 10, « Authentic 1900 rocaille decor » – AE GB JCB — DX **p**
closed Monday except September-June and Sunday – **Meals** 150 (lunch), 260/400 and a la carte 360/560
Spec. Ravioles de langoustines au citron vert. Noisettes d'agneau à l'estragon. Lamproie à la bordelaise. Wines Entre-Deux-Mers, Graves.

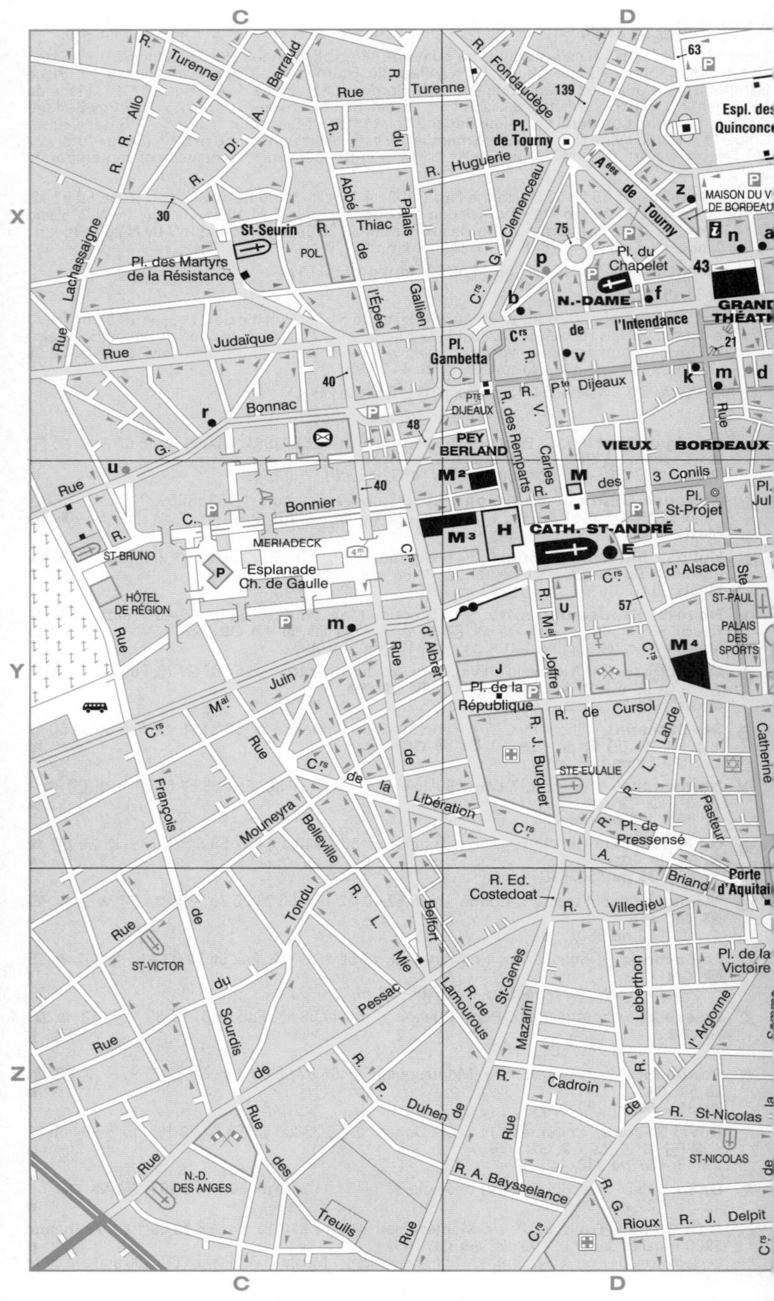

*To go a long way quickly, use **Michelin Maps** at scale of 1: 1 000 000.*

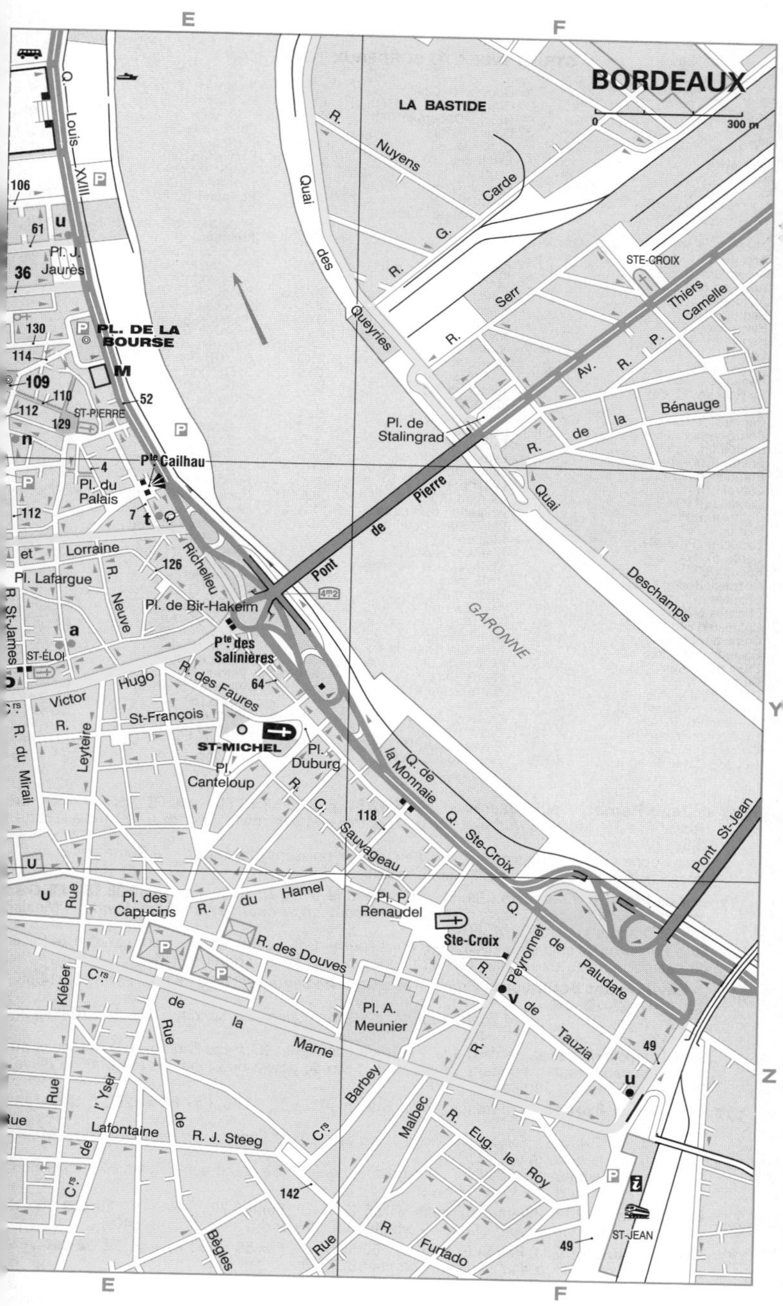

Ensure that you have up to date **Michelin maps** in your car.

STREET INDEX TO BORDEAUX TOWN PLAN

XXX ✿ **Jean Ramet,** 7 pl. J. Jaurès ✆ 56 44 12 51, Fax 56 52 19 80 – ▤. AE GB EX **u**
closed 4 to 25 August, Saturday lunch and Sunday – **Meals** 155 (lunch), 250/300 and a la carte 280/430
Spec. Soupe de grenouilles au cresson. Panaché de poissons aux épices. "La Route des Epices" (dessert). **Wines** Pessac-Léognan, Saint-Emilion.

XXX ✿ **Les Plaisirs d'Ausone** (Gauffre), 10 r. Ausone ✆ 56 79 30 30, Fax 56 51 38 16 – AE GB EY **t**
closed 15 to 30 August, February Holidays, Monday lunch, Saturday lunch and Sunday – **Meals** 165/300 and a la carte 270/350
Spec. Fricassée de sole et Saint-Jacques aux cèpes (1 October-30 March). Gourmandise de foies de canard. Agneau de Pauillac rôti à l'ail doux crémé. **Wines** Entre-Deux-Mers.

XXX ✿ **Pavillon des Boulevards** (Franc), 120 r. Croix de Seguey ✆ 56 81 51 02, Fax 56 51 14 58, terrace – ▤. AE ① GB
closed 10 to 27 August, 1 to 10 January, Saturday lunch and Sunday – **Meals** 220 (lunch), 270/420 and a la carte 320/450
Spec. Liégeois de caviar, homard à la crème de châtaignes (October-February). Sole "servie au plat", artichauts sautés. Fondant au chocolat, glace au poivre de Chine. **Wines** Côtes de Blaye, Premières Côtes de Bordeaux.

XXX ✿ **Le Vieux Bordeaux** (Bordage), 27 r. Buhan ✆ 56 52 94 36, Fax 56 44 25 11, terrace – ▤. AE ① GB EY **a**
closed 4 to 25 August, February Holidays, Saturday lunch, Sunday and Bank Holidays – **Meals** 155/260 and a la carte 200/330
Spec. Confit d'aubergines "Bayaldi". Bar grillé sur galette de crabe aux poivrons. Fondant noix de coco, glace au rhum. **Wines** Graves.

XXX **La Chamade,** 20 r. Piliers de Tutelle ✆ 56 48 13 74, Fax 56 79 29 67 – ▤. AE GB DX **d**
closed 5 to 11 August and Sunday – **Meals** 100/290 and a la carte 210/340.

XX **Didier Gélineau,** 26 r. Pas St Georges ✆ 56 52 84 25, Fax 56 51 93 25 – ▤. AE ① GB JCB EX **n**
closed Saturday lunch and Sunday – **Meals** 100/250.

XX **Le Buhan,** 28 r. Buhan ✆ 56 52 80 86 – AE GB EY **a**
closed 18-26 August, February Holidays, Sunday except lunch from September-June and Monday – **Meals** 135 b.i./285.

L'Oiseau Bleu, 65 cours Verdun ✆ 56 81 09 39, Fax 56 81 09 39 – ▤. AE GB
closed 1 to 21 August, Saturday lunch and Sunday – **Meals** 102 (lunch)/150.

Bistro du Sommelier, 163 r. G. Bonnac ✆ 56 96 71 78, Fax 56 24 52 36, ☂ – AE GB
closed Saturday lunch and Sunday – **Meals** 116. CY **u**

at Parc des Expositions : North of the town – ✉ 33300 Bordeaux :

Sofitel Aquitania M, ✆ 56 50 83 80, Telex 570557, Fax 56 39 73 75, ≤, ⛱ – |♦| ⇆ ▤ TV ☎ P – 🏛 25 - 400. AE ⦿ GB
Le Flore (closed 2 December-2 January) **Meals** 110/185 – ☕ 75 – **206 rm** 680.

Novotel-Bordeaux Lac M, ✆ 56 50 99 70, Telex 570274, Fax 56 43 00 66, ≤, ☂, ⛱, ⛱ – |♦| ⇆ ▤ TV ☎ ♿ P – 🏛 200. AE ⦿ GB
Meals 95/150 – ☕ 50 – **176 rm** 430/470.

Mercure Pont d'Aquitaine, ✆ 56 43 36 72, Fax 56 50 23 95, ☂, ⛱, ⛱ – |♦| ⇆ ▤ TV ☎ ♿ P – 🏛 80. AE ⦿ GB
closed 15 December-15 January – **Meals** 100/180 b.i. – ☕ 50 – **100 rm** 550.

at Bouliac SE : 8 km – alt. 74 – ✉ 33270 :

❀ **Le St-James** M ⚘, pl. C. Hostein, near church ✆ 57 97 06 00, Fax 56 20 92 58, ≤ Bordeaux, ☂, « Original contemporary decor », ⛱, ⛱ – |♦| ▤ rm TV ☎ P. AE ⦿ GB. ⛌
Meals 185 b.i./360 and a la carte 280/420 - ***Le Bistroy*** ✆ 57 97 06 06 *(closed Sunday)* **Meals** a la carte approx. 150 – ☕ 75 – **17 rm** 600/1300
Spec. Filet de rouget froid au safran, purée d'artichaut à l'huile d'olive. Homard rôti aux pommes de terre et gousses d'ail. Pigeon grillé aux épices. Wines Premières Côtes de Bordeaux, Pessac-Léognan.

to the W :

at the airport 11 km by A 630 : from the North, exit nr 11b, from the South, exit nr 11 – ✉ 33700 Mérignac :

Mercure Aéroport M, 1 av. Ch. Lindbergh ✆ 56 34 74 74, Telex 573953, Fax 56 34 30 84, ☂, ⛱ – |♦| ⇆ ▤ TV ☎ ♿ P – 🏛 110. AE ⦿ GB
Meals 120 ⅓ – ☕ 55 – **105 rm** 600/620.

Novotel, av. J. F. Kennedy ✆ 56 34 10 25, Telex 540320, Fax 56 55 99 64, ☂, ⛱, ⛱ – |♦| ⇆ ▤ TV ☎ ♿ P – 🏛 50. AE ⦿ GB JCB
Meals a la carte approx. 160 – ☕ 50 – **137 rm** 460/485.

Soretel, 97 av. J.-F. Kennedy ✆ 56 34 33 08, Fax 56 34 01 90, ☂, ⛱ – |♦| TV ☎ ♿ P – 🏛 25. AE ⦿ GB
Meals 80/150 ⅓ – ☕ 38 – **60 rm** 295/315.

Eugénie-les-Bains 40320 Landes 82 ① – pop. 467 alt. 65 – Spa (12 Feb.-Nov.).

ℹ Tourist Office (Feb.-Dec.) ✆ 58 51 13 16.
Bordeaux 151.

❀❀❀ **Les Prés d'Eugénie** (Guérard) M ⚘, ✆ 58 05 06 07, Telex 540470, Fax 58 51 10 10, ≤, ☂, « Elegantly decorated 19C mansion, park », ⛱, ✂ – |♦| TV ☎ P – 🏛 50. AE ⦿ GB. ⛌
closed 2 December-27 February – **Meals** (low-calorie menu for residents only) 320 - ***rest. Michel Guérard*** (booking essential) *(closed Thursday lunch and Wednesday except 12/7-10/9 and Bank Holidays)* **Meals** 390/690 and a la carte 460/610 – ☕ 110 – **28 rm** 1300/1500, 7 suites
Spec. Oreiller moelleux de mousserons et morilles aux asperges. Dorade royale au plat. Trois sorbets servis "comme un jardin". Wines Tursan blanc, Côtes de Gascogne.
Le Couvent des Herbes M ⚘,, ≤, park, « 18C convent » – TV ☎ P. AE ⦿ GB. ⛌ rest
closed 2 December-27 February – see ***Les Prés d'Eugénie*** and ***Michel Guérard*** – ☕ 110 – **5 rm** 1500/1700, 3 suites.

Maison Rose M ⚘ (see also rest. Michel Guérard), ✆ 58 05 06 07, Fax 58 51 10 10, « Guesthouse ambience », ⛱, ⛱ – kitchenette TV ☎ ♿ P. AE ⦿ GB. ⛌
closed 2 to 21 December and 5 January-9 February – **Meals** (residents only) – ☕ 70 – **27 rm** 470/580, 5 suites.

La Ferme aux Grives, ✆ 58 51 19 08, Fax 58 51 10 10, « Reconstructed country inn », ⛱ – P. GB
closed 3 January-8 February, Monday dinner and Tuesday from 11 September-11 July except Bank Holidays – **Meals** 175.

Pons 17800 Char.-Mar. 71 ⑤ – pop. 4 412 alt. 39.

ℹ Syndicat d'Initiative Donjon de Pons (15 June-15 Sept.) ✆ 46 96 13 21.
Bordeaux 95.

at Mosnac S : 11 km by Bordeaux road and D 134 – alt. 23 – ✉ 17240 :

❀❀ **Moulin de Marcouze** (Bouchet) M ⚘ with rm, ✆ 46 70 46 16, Fax 46 70 48 14, park, « Elegant inn on the banks of the River Seugne », ⛱ – ▤ TV ☎ ♿ P. AE GB JCB
closed January, February, Wednesday lunch and Tuesday from October-March – **Meals** 160/420 and a la carte 300/480 – ☕ 75 – **10 rm** 525/700
Spec. Tarte de pommes de terre et saumon fumé, chantilly au caviar. Gigot d'agneau de sept heures à la cuillère. Pêche glacée sur granité de champagne.

CANNES **06400** Alpes-Mar. 84 ⑨, 115 ㉟ ㊳ – pop. 68 676 alt. 2 – Casinos Carlton Casino BY, Palm Beach (temp. closed) X, Municipal BZ.

See : Site★★ – Seafront★★ : Boulevard★★ BCDZ and Pointe de la Croisette★ X – ≤★ from th Mount Chevalier Tower AZ **V** – The Castre Museum★ (Musée de la Castre) AZ – Tour into th Hills★ (Chemin des Collines) NE : 4 km V – The Croix des Gardes X **E** ≤★ W : 5 km then 15 mn

18 Country-Club of Cannes-Mougins ✆ 93 75 79 13 by ⑤ : 9 km ; 9 18 Golf-Club of Cannes Mandelieu ✆ 93 49 55 39 by ② : 6,5 km ; 18 Royal Mougins Golf Club at Mougins ✆ 92 92 49 6 by ④ : 10 km ; 18 Riviera Golf Club at Mandelieu ✆ 93 38 32 55 by ② : 8 km.

Tourist Office "SEMEC", Palais des Festivals ✆ 93 39 24 53, Fax 93 39 37 06 and railway statio ✆ 93 99 19 77, Fax 93 39 40 19 – A.C. 12bis r. L. Blanc ✆ 93 39 38 94.

Paris 903 ⑤ – Aix-en-Provence 146 ⑤ – Grenoble 312 ⑤ – Marseilles 159 ⑤ – Nice 32 ⑤ – Toulon 121 ⑤.

Plans on following pages

Carlton Inter-Continental, 58 bd Croisette ✆ 93 06 40 06, Telex 470720, Fax 93 06 40 2 ≤, Lб, – |‡| ▤ TV ☎ ♿ – 25 - 250. AE ① GB JCB. CZ
Meals see ***La Belle Otéro*** and ***La Côte*** below - ***Brasserie Carlton :*** **Meals** 225 – ☕ 135 – **338 r** 1400/3690, 28 suites.

Martinez, 73 bd Croisette ✆ 92 98 73 00, Telex 470708, Fax 93 39 67 82, ≤, – |‡| ▤ TV ☎ – 600. AE ① GB JCB DZ
Meals see ***La Palme d'Or*** below - ***L'Orangeraie*** ✆ 92 98 74 12 *(closed 15 February-15 Marc and lunch from Easter-September)* **Meals** 180 – ☕ 115 – **430 rm** 1450/4000, 12 suites.

Majestic, 14 bd Croisette ✆ 92 98 77 00, Telex 470787, Fax 93 38 97 90, ≤, – |‡| ▤ TV ☎ ♿ – 400. AE ① GB JCB BZ
closed 25 November-20 December – ***Villa des Lys :*** **Meals** 240/460 – ☕ 120 – **263 r** 1400/3900, 24 suites.

Noga Hilton M, 50 bd Croisette ✆ 92 99 70 00, Telex 470013, Fax 92 99 70 11, « Rooftop swimming pool and terraces ≤ Cannes », Lб, – |‡| ▤ TV ☎ ♿ – 800. AE ① GB JCB. rest CZ
La Scala : Italian rest. **Meals** 230bi(lunch)/295 – ***Le Grand Bleu*** – **(brasserie)** *(closed Februar* **Meals** 180/185 – ☕ 115 – **196 rm** 1450/4990, 33 suites.

Gray d'Albion M, 38 r. Serbes ✆ 92 99 79 79, Telex 470744, Fax 93 99 26 10, – |‡| ▤ TV ☎ ♿ – 30 - 200. AE ① GB JCB BZ
Royal Gray : **Meals** 188/265 – ☕ 97 – **172 rm** 1000/1650, 14 suites.

L'Horset-Savoy M, 5 r. F. Einessy ✆ 92 99 72 00, Telex 461873, Fax 93 68 25 59, – |‡| ▤ TV ☎ ♿ – 90. AE ① GB CZ
Meals 160 – ☕ 98 – **101 rm** 950/1250, 5 suites.

Sofitel Méditerranée, 2 bd J. Hibert ✆ 92 99 73 00, Telex 470728, Fax 92 99 73 29, « Rooftop swimming pool and restaurant ≤ bay of Cannes » – |‡| ▤ TV ☎ – 10 AE ① GB JCB AZ
closed 25 November-26 December – ***Le Méditerranée*** ✆ 92 99 73 02 *(closed Sunday dinne and Monday from 1 January-6 April)* **Meals** 180(lunch)/230 – ***Le Palmyre*** – ✆ **92 99 73 10 Mea** 120 – ☕ 95 – **145 rm** 800/1595, 5 suites.

Belle Plage M without rest, 6 r. J. Dollfus ✆ 93 06 25 50, Fax 93 99 61 06 – |‡| ▤ TV ♿ – 50. AE ① GB JCB AZ
☕ 70 – **48 rm** 960/1460.

Pullman Beach M without rest, 13 r. Canada ✆ 93 94 50 50, Telex 470034, Fax 93 68 35 3 – |‡| ▤ TV ☎. AE ① GB JCB DZ
closed 5 to 25 December – ☕ 90 – **93 rm** 1070/1500.

Splendid without rest, 4 r. F. Faure ✆ 93 99 53 11, Telex 470990, Fax 93 99 55 02, ≤ – |‡| kitchenette ▤ TV ☎. AE ① GB BZ
☕ 50 – **64 rm** 590/890.

Amarante M, 78 bd Carnot ✆ 93 39 22 23, Fax 93 39 40 22, – |‡| ▤ TV ☎ – 25. AE ① GB JCB V
Meals 120/160 b.i. – ☕ 55 – **71 rm** 850.

Sun Riviera M without rest, 138 r. d'Antibes ✆ 93 38 22 11, Fax 93 06 77 77, – |‡| ▤ TV ☎ ♿. AE ① GB JCB CZ
☕ 85 – **42 rm** 810/1800.

Cristal M, 15 rd-pt Duboys d'Angers ✆ 93 39 45 45, Fax 93 38 64 66, – |‡| ▤ ☎. AE ① GB JCB CZ
Meals *(closed late November-late December and Monday from October-May)* 135/300 – ☕ 8 – **51 rm** 860/1900.

Victoria without rest, rd-pt Duboys d'Angers ✆ 93 99 36 36, Fax 93 38 03 91, – |‡| ▤ ☎. AE ① GB JCB CZ
closed November and December – ☕ 60 – **25 rm** 750/1150.

Fouquet's without rest, 2 rd-pt Duboys d'Angers ✆ 93 38 75 81, Fax 92 98 03 39 – ▤ ☎. AE ① GB JCB CZ
closed 1 November-26 December – ☕ 60 – **10 rm** 1100/1300.

Paris without rest, 34 bd Alsace ✆ 93 38 30 89, Telex 470995, Fax 93 39 04 61, |‡| ▤ TV ☎ – 25. AE ① GB JCB. CY
closed 20 November to 29 December – ☕ 60 – **50 rm** 550/720, 4 suites.

Embassy, 6 r. Bône ☎ 93 38 79 02, Fax 93 99 07 98, – 50. AE GB JCB DY j
Meals 120 – 40 – **60 rm** 500/850.

Mondial without rest, 1 r. Tesseire ☎ 93 68 70 00, Fax 93 99 39 11 – AE GB CY e
55 – **56 rm** 600/770.

America without rest, 13 r. St-Honoré ☎ 93 68 36 36, Fax 93 68 04 58 – AE GB JCB. BZ r
closed 25 November to 27 December – 60 – **28 rm** 495/745.

Villa de l'Olivier without rest, 5 r. Tambourinaires ☎ 93 39 53 28, Fax 93 39 55 85, – AE GB. AZ e
52 – **24 rm** 575/715.

Château de la Tour, 10 av. Font-de-Veyre by ③ ✉ 06150 Cannes-La-Bocca ☎ 93 47 34 64, Fax 93 47 86 61, – AE GB JCB. rest
Meals *(closed 15 November-25 December)* 90/120 – 35 – **42 rm** 550/615.

Beau Séjour, 5 r. Fauvettes ☎ 93 39 63 00, Fax 92 98 64 66, – rm AE GB JCB. rest AZ d
closed November-mid December – **Meals** 120/150 – 60 – **45 rm** 650/750.

Ligure without rest, 5 pl. Gare ☎ 93 39 03 11, Fax 93 39 19 48 – AE GB BY n
35 – **36 rm** 450/750.

Abrial without rest, 24 bd Lorraine ☎ 93 38 78 82, Telex 470761, Fax 92 98 67 41 – AE GB JCB CY s
56 – **50 rm** 710.

Alsace H. without rest, 40 bd Alsace ☎ 93 38 50 70, Fax 93 38 20 44 – AE GB JCB CY d
45 – **30 rm** 575/620.

Albert 1er without rest, 68 av. Grasse ☎ 93 39 24 04, Fax 93 38 83 75 – GB AY d
30 – **11 rm** 300/340.

Molière without rest, 5 r. Molière ☎ 93 38 16 16, Fax 93 68 29 57 – AE GB JCB. CYZ t
closed 15 November-20 December – 40 – **45 rm** 390/580.

Des Congrès et Festivals without rest, 12 r. Teisseire ☎ 93 39 13 81, Fax 93 39 56 28 – rm AE GB CY p
closed December – 40 – **20 rm** 300/600.

XXXXX ✿✿ **La Belle Otéro** - Hôtel Carlton Inter-Continental, 58 bd Croisette, 7th floor ☎ 93 68 00 33, Fax 93 39 09 06, – AE GB JCB CZ e
closed 9 June-8 July, 27 October-19 November, Sunday and Monday except July-August – **Meals** (dinner only July-August) 290 b.i. (lunch), 390/590 and a la carte 540/740
Spec. Grillade de dorade aux olives de Nice. Filet mignon de veau fermier poêlé en jus de truffe. Gratiné de figues fraîches aux saveurs orientales (July-late September). **Wines** Côtes de Provence.

XXXXX ✿✿ **La Palme d'Or** - Hôtel Martinez, 73 bd Croisette ☎ 92 98 74 14, Telex 470708, Fax 93 39 67 82, <, – AE GB JCB DZ n
closed mid November-Christmas, Tuesday (except dinner from 15 June-15 September) and Monday – **Meals** 295 b.i. (lunch), 350/580 and a la carte 510/810
Spec. Mélange d'herbes et salades tendres, pannequets de légumes de Provence farcis. Pavé de loup cuit croustillant, jus de fenouil à la badiane. Aiguillette de cannette au citron et olives. **Wines** Côtes de Provence.

XXXXX ✿ **La Côte** - Hôtel Carlton Intercontinental, 58 bd Croisette ☎ 93 06 40 23, Telex 470720, Fax 93 06 40 25, – AE GB JCB. CZ e
April-October and closed Tuesday and Wednesday – **Meals** 275 b.i. (lunch), 350/460 and a la carte 300/530
Spec. Escalope de foie gras de canard poêlé au vinaigre balsamique. Saint-Pierre au citron confit. Maraîchère de pigeonneau aux navets confits. **Wines** Côtes de Provence.

XXX **Poêle d'Or,** 23 r. États-Unis ☎ 93 39 77 65, Fax 93 40 45 59 – AE GB CZ v
closed 1 to 7 July, February Holidays, Sunday dinner in winter, Tuesday lunch in summer and Monday – **Meals** (weekends : booking essential) 125 (lunch), 169/350 and a la carte 310/430.

XXX **Gaston et Gastounette,** 7 quai St-Pierre ☎ 93 39 47 92, Fax 93 99 45 34, – AE GB AZ v
closed 1 to 20 December – **Meals** 125 (lunch)/200 and a la carte 260/450.

XX **Festival,** 52 bd Croisette ☎ 93 38 04 81, Fax 93 38 13 82, – AE GB CZ p
closed mid November-23 December – **Meals** 180/220.

XX **Le Mesclun,** 16 r. St-Antoine ☎ 93 99 45 19, Fax 93 47 68 29 – AE GB AZ t
closed 20 November-20 December and Wednesday out of season – **Meals** (dinner only) 175.

XX **Maître-Pierre,** 6 r. Mar. Joffre ☎ 93 99 36 30 – AE GB BY r
closed Wednesday dinner from 15 September-15 June – **Meals** 110/165.

XX **La Mirabelle,** 24 r. St-Antoine ☎ 93 38 72 75, Fax 93 90 66 95, « Provençal style » – AE GB JCB AZ a
closed 1 to 20 December, 1 to 15 February and Tuesday – **Meals** (dinner only) 185/255.

XX **La Cigale,** 1 r. Florian ☎ 93 39 65 79, – AE GB JCB CZ d
closed 1 to 15 November, Sunday dinner and Monday – **Meals** 125/165.

CANNES

André (R. du Cdt) . . . . CZ
Antibes (R. d') . . . . BCY
Belges (R. des) . . . . . . BZ 12
Chabaud (R.) . . . . CY 22
Croisette (Bd de la) . . . BDZ
Félix-Faure (R.) . . . . ABZ
Foch (R. du Mar.) . . . . BY 44
Joffre (R. du Mar.) . . . . BY 60
Riouffe (R. Jean de) . . BY 98

Albert-Édouard (Jetée). BZ
Alexandre-III (Bd) . . . . . X 2
Alsace (Bd) . . . . BDY
Anc. Combattants d'Afrique du Nord (Av.) . . . . . AYZ 4
Bachaga Saïd Boualam (Av.) . . . . . AY 5
Beauséjour (Av.) . . . . . DYZ
Beau-Soleil (Bd) . . . . . . X 10
Blanc (R. Louis) . . . . . . AYZ
Broussailles (Av. des) . V 16
Buttura (R.) . . . . BZ 17
Canada (R. du) . . . . DZ
Carnot (Bd) X
Carnot (Square) . . . . V 20
Castre (Pl. de la) . . . . . AZ 21
Clemenceau (R. G.) . . . AZ
Coteaux (Av. des) V
Croix-des-Gardes (Bd) . VX 29
Delaup (Bd) . . . . AY 30
Dr-Pierre Gazagnaire (R.) . AZ 32
Dr-R. Picaud (Av.) X
Dollfus (R. Jean) . . . . . AZ 33
Faure (R. Félix) . . . . ABZ
Favorite (Av. de la) . . . X 38
Ferrage (Bd de la) . . . . ABY 40
Fiesole (Av.) . . . . X 43
Gallieni (R. du Mar.) . . BY 48
Gaulle (Pl. Gén.-de) . . . BZ 51
Gazagnaire (Bd Eugène) . X
Grasse (Av. de) . . . . VX 53
Guynemer (Bd) . . . . AY
Haddad-Simon (R. Jean) . CY 54
Hespérides (Av. des) . . X 55
Hibert (Bd Jean) . . . . AZ
Hibert (R.) . . . . AZ
Isola-Bella (Av. d') . . . X
Jaurès (R. Jean) . . . . BCY
Juin (Av. Mar.) . . . . . DZ
Koenig (Av. Gén.) . . . DY
Lacour (Bd Alexandre) . X 62
Latour-Maubourg (R.) . DZ
Lattre-de-T. (Av. de) . AY 63
Laubeuf (Quai Max) . AZ
Leader (Bd) . . . . VX 64
Lérins (Av. de) . . . . . . X 65
Lorraine (Bd. de) . . . . CDY
Macé (R.) . . . . CZ 66
Madrid (Av. de) . . . . . . DZ
Meynadier (R.) . . . . . ABY
Midi (Bd du) X
Mimont (R. de) . . . . . . BY
Mont-Chevalier (R. du) . AZ 72
Montfleury (Bd) . . . . . CDY 74
Monti (R. Marius) . . . AY 75
Moulin (Bd du) . . . . . . AY 76
Noailles (Av. J.-de) . . X
Observatoire (Bd de l') . X 84
Oxford (Bd d') . . . . . . V 87
Pantiero (la) . . . . ABZ
Paradis-Terrestre (Corniches du) . . . . V 88
Pasteur (R.) . . . . DZ
Pastour (R. Louis) . . . AY 90
Perier (Bd du) . . . . . . V 92
Perrissol (R. Louis) . . . AZ 93
Petit-Juas (Av. du) . . . VX
Pins (Bd des) . . . . X 95
Pompidou (Espl. G.) . . BZ
Prince-de-Galles (Av. du) X 97
République (Bd de la) . X
Riou (Bd du) VX
Roi-Albert 1er (Av.) . . X
Rouguière (R.) . . . . . . BY 100
St-Nicolas (Av.) . . . . . BY 105
St-Pierre (Quai) . . . . . AZ
Sardou (R. Léandre) . X 108
Serbes (R. des) . . . . . BZ 110
Source (Bd de la) . . . . X 112
Stanislas (Pl.) . . . . AY
Strasbourg (Bd de) . . CDY
Teisseire (R.) . . . . CY 114
Tuby (Bd Victor) . . . . AYZ 11
Vallauris (Av. de) . . . . VX 11
Vallombrosa (Bd) . . . AY 11
Vautrin (Bd Gén.) . . . DZ
Vidal (R. du Cdt) . . . . CY 12
Wemyss (Av. Amiral Wester) . X 12

LE CANNET

Aubarède (Ch. de l') . V 8
Bellevue (Pl.) . . . . V 13
Bréguières (Ch. de) . . V 14
Cannes (R. des) . . . . V 19
Carnot (Bd de) V
Cheval (Av. Maurice) . V 23
Collines (Ch. des) . . . V
Doumer (Bd Paul) . . . V
Écoles (R. des) . . . . . V 34
Four-à-Chaux (Bd du) . V 45
Gambetta (Bd) . . . . . V 50
Gaulle (Av. Gén.-de) . V
Jeanpierre (Av. Maurice) . V 58
Mermoz (Av. Jean) . . V 67
Monod (Bd Jacques) . V 68
Mont-Joli (Av. du) . . . V 73
N.-D.-des-Anges (Av.) . V 79
Olivet (Ch. de l') . . . . V 85
Olivetum (Av. d') . . . . V 86
Paris (R. de) . . . . V 89
Pinède (Av. de la) . . . V 94
Pompidou (Av. Georges) V 96
République (Bd de la) . V
Roosevelt (Av. Franklin) . V
St-Sauveur (R.) . . . . . V 10
Victor-Hugo (R.) . . . . V 11
Victoria (Av.) V

VALLAURIS

Cannes (Av. de) . . . . V 18
Clemenceau (Av. G.) . V 25
Fournas (Av. du) . . . . V 46
Golfe (Av. du) . . . . . . V 52
Isnard (Pl. Paul) . . . . . V 56
Rouvier (Bd Maurice) . V 10
Tapis-Vert (Av. du) . . V 11

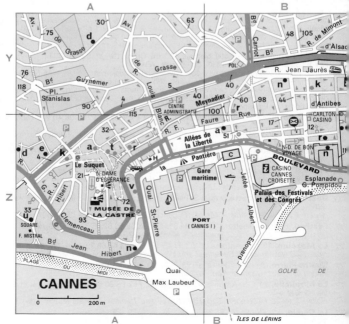

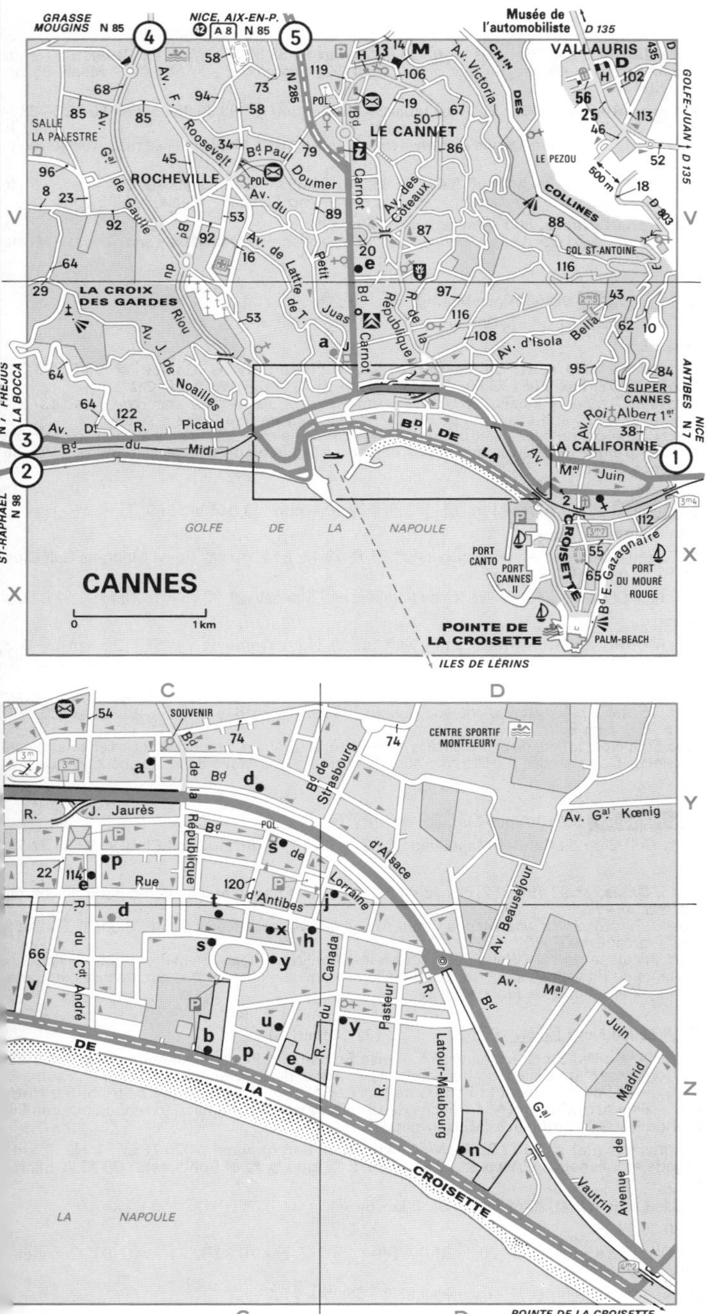

CANNES
LE CANNET
ROCHEVILLE
VALLAURIS
LA CROIX DES GARDES
LA CALIFORNIE
SUPER CANNES
GOLFE DE LA NAPOULE
POINTE DE LA CROISETTE
PORT CANTO
PORT CANNES II
PORT DU MOURÉ ROUGE
PALM-BEACH
ILES DE LÉRINS
COL ST-ANTOINE
LE PEZOU
SALLE LA PALESTRE
Musée de l'automobiliste
GRASSE MOUGINS N 85
NICE, AIX-EN-P. A 8 N 85
GOLFE-JUAN D 135
ANTIBES N 7
NICE
ST-RAPHAEL N 98
LA BOCCA
CENTRE SPORTIF MONTFLEURY
SOUVENIR
Bd de la République
Bd de Strasbourg
Bd d'Alsace
Av. Beauséjour
Av. Gal Kœnig
R. J. Jaurès
Rue d'Antibes
Bd de Lorraine
R. du Cdt André
R. du Canada
R. Pasteur
R. Latour-Maubourg
Bd Gal Vautrin
Av. Mal Juin
Avenue de Madrid
DE LA CROISETTE
LA NAPOULE
POINTE DE LA CROISETTE

XX **Côté Jardin,** 12 av. St-Louis ✆ 93 38 60 28, Fax 93 38 60 28, 🍽 - ▤. AE GB X
closed February, Monday except dinner from May-September and Sunday - **Meals** 95 b. (lunch)/170.

XX **Taverna Romana,** 10 r. St-Dizier (quartier du Suquet) ✆ 93 39 96 05, Fax 93 68 54 38 ▤. AE GB AZ
closed 1 to 15 November and Sunday except July-August - **Meals** - Italian rest. - (dinner only) 135/185.

X **Au Bec Fin,** 12 r. 24 Août ✆ 93 38 35 86, Fax 93 38 43 47 - ▤. AE ⓓ GB BY
closed 20 December-20 January, Saturday dinner and Sunday - **Meals** 90/115 ♁.

X **Aux Bons Enfants,** 80 r. Meynadier - ✆ AZ
closed August, 24 December-2 January, Saturday dinner except in season and Sunday - **Meals** 90.

Juan-les-Pins **06160** Alpes-Mar. 84 ⑨, 115 ㉟ ㊴.

ℹ Tourist Office 51 bd Ch.-Guillaumont ✆ 92 90 53 05.

Cannes 8,5.

🏨 ✿✿ **Juana and rest. La Terrasse** ≫, la Pinède, av. G. Gallice ✆ 93 61 08 70, Telex 470778, Fax 93 61 76 60, 🍽, 🏊, 🌴 - |⇕| ▤ rm TV ☎ P. AE GB
April-late October - **Meals** *(closed Wednesday except July-August and Bank Holidays)* 260 (lunch), 395/620 and a la carte 500/670 - ☕ 95 - **45 rm** 950/2050, 5 suites
Spec. Cannelloni de supions et palourdes à l'encre de seiche. Selle d'agneau de Pauillac cuite en terre d'argile. Millefeuille aux fraises des bois à la crème de mascarpone. Wines Côtes de Provence, Palette.

Mougins **06250** Alpes-Mar. 84 ⑨, 115 ㉔ ㊳ - pop. 13 014 alt. 260.

See : Site★.

18 Country Club de Cannes-Mougins ✆ 93 75 79 13, E : 2 km ; 18 Royal Mougins Golf Club ✆ 92 92 04 03, O : 2,5 km.

ℹ Tourist Office av. J.-Ch. Mallet (closed Sunday and Monday) ✆ 93 75 87 67, Fax 92 92 04 03

Cannes 7.

XXXX ✿✿ **Moulin de Mougins** (Vergé) with rm, at Notre-Dame-de-Vie SE : 2,5 km by D ✆ 93 75 78 24, Fax 93 90 18 55, 🍽, « Converted 16C oil mill », 🌳 - ▤ TV ☎ P. AE ⓓ GB
closed 8 to 18 January and 12 February to 14 March - **Meals** *(closed Monday except dinner from 15 July-31 August and Thursday lunch)* 305 b.i. (lunch), 615/740 and a la carte 560/790 - ☕ 75 - **5 rm** 800/900
Spec. Poupeton de fleur de courgette à la truffe noire. Loup aux poivrons doux et artichauts confits. Cotelettes d'agneau des Alpilles en croûte de champignons. Wines Bandol blanc, Côtes de Provence.

La Napoule **06210** Alpes-Mar. 84 ⑧, 115 ㉞.

9 18 Golf Club de Cannes-Mandelieu ✆ 93 49 55 39 ; 18 Riviera Golf Club ✆ 93 38 32 55

Cannes 9,5.

XXXX ✿✿ **L'Oasis,** ✆ 93 49 95 52, Fax 93 49 64 13, 🍽, « Shaded and flowered patio » - ▤. AE ⓓ GB JCB
closed Sunday dinner and Monday from November-March - **Meals** 275 b.i. (lunch), 350/650 and a la carte 440/620
Spec. Fricassée de sot l'y-laisse et d'écrevisses (April-November). Saint-Pierre rôti en tian aux senteurs de Provence (spring-summer). Selle de chevreuil en noisettes aux myrtilles (autumn-winter). Wines Côtes de Provence.

LILLE P **59000** Nord 51 ⑯, 111 ㉒ - pop. 172 142 alt. 10.

See : **Old Lille★★ : Old Stock Exchange★★ (Vieille Bourse)** EY, **Place du Général-de-Gaule** EY **66** **Hospice Comtesse★ (panelled timber vault★★)** EY, **Rue de la Monnaie★** EY **120** - **Vauban's Citadel★** BV - **St-Sauveur district : Paris Gate★** EFZ, **≤★ from the top of the belfry of the Hôtel de Ville** FZ - **Fine Arts Museum★★★ (Musée des Beaux-Arts)** EZ **(scheduled to reopen autumn 96)** - **Général de Gaulle's Birthplace (Maison natale)** EY.

9 of Flandres (private) ✆ 20 72 20 74, N : 4,5 km ; 18 of Sart (private) ✆ 20 72 02 51, NE : 7 km ; 18 of Brigode at Villeneuve d'Ascq ✆ 20 91 17 86, E : 9 km ; 18 18 of Bondues ✆ 20 23 20 62, N : 9,5 km.

✈ of Lille-Lesquin : ✆ 20 49 68 68, S : 8 km by A1.

🚗 ✆ 36 35 35 35.

ℹ Tourist Office Palais Rihour ✆ 20 30 81 00, Telex 110213, Fax 20 30 82 24 - A.C. 8 r. Quennette ✆ 20 55 21 41.

Paris 221 - Brussels 116 - Ghent 71 - Luxembourg 312 - Strasbourg 525 .

Plans on following pages

Alliance M, 17 quai du Wault ✉ 59800 ☎ 20 30 62 62, Fax 20 42 94 25, « Former 17C convent » – 🛗 ⚡ 📺 ☎ ♿ 🅿 – 🏫 120. AE ⓓ GB JCB. ✱ rest BV **d**
Meals 98/195 – ☕ 70 – **75 rm** 670, 8 suites.

Carlton, 3 r. Paris ✉ 59800 ☎ 20 13 33 13, Telex 110400, Fax 20 51 48 17 – 🛗 ⚡ ▤ 📺 ☎ ♿ 🅿 – 🏫 25 - 100. AE ⓓ GB JCB EY **u**
Brasserie Jean (closed Sunday lunch) **Meals** a la carte 150/230, 🍷 – ☕ 70 – **57 rm** 800/1020, 3 suites.

Novotel Lille Centre M, 116 r. Hôpital Militaire ✉ 59800 ☎ 20 30 65 26, Fax 20 30 04 04 – 🛗 ⚡ ▤ 📺 ☎ ♿ – 🏫 30. AE ⓓ GB EY **s**
Meals a la carte approx. 160 – ☕ 51 – **102 rm** 550/600.

Gd H. Bellevue without rest, 5 r. J. Roisin ✉ 59800 ☎ 20 57 45 64, Fax 20 40 07 93 – 🛗 ⚡ 📺 ☎ – 🏫 50. AE ⓓ GB JCB EY **z**
☕ 62 – **61 rm** 450/615.

Mercure Royal M without rest, 2 bd Carnot ✉ 59800 ☎ 20 51 05 11, Fax 20 74 01 65 – 🛗 ⚡ 📺 ☎ – 🏫 25. AE ⓓ GB JCB EY **h**
☕ 53 – **102 rm** 480.

Fimotel M, 75 bis r. Gambetta ☎ 20 42 90 90, Fax 20 57 14 24 – 🛗 ⚡ 📺 ☎ ♿ 🚗 – 🏫 80. AE ⓓ GB JCB EZ **e**
Meals *(closed Friday dinner, Sunday lunch and Saturday)* 89/115 🍷 – ☕ 40 – **98 rm** 370.

Paix without rest, 46 bis r. Paris ✉ 59800 ☎ 20 54 63 93, Fax 20 63 98 97 – 🛗 📺 ☎. AE ⓓ GB EY **r**
☕ 38 – **35 rm** 340/430.

Treille M without rest, 7 pl. L. de Bettignies ✉ 59800 ☎ 20 55 45 46, Fax 20 51 51 69 – 🛗 📺 ☎ – 🏫 40. AE ⓓ GB EY **d**
☕ 45 – **40 rm** 350/380.

Ibis Centre M, av. Ch. St-Venant ✉ 59800 ☎ 20 55 44 44, Fax 20 31 06 25, 🍽 – 🛗 ⚡ 📺 ☎ ♿ 🚗 – 🏫 25 - 70. AE ⓓ GB FYZ **a**
Meals 99 b.i. – ☕ 35 – **151 rm** 350.

Lille Europe M without rest, allée de Liège, av. Le Corbusier ☎ 20 21 41 51, Fax 20 21 41 59 – 🛗 📺 ☎ ♿ 🅿. AE ⓓ GB FY **m**
☕ 38 – **97 rm** 340.

Ibis Opéra M without rest, 21 r. Lepelletier ✉ 59800 ☎ 20 06 21 95, Fax 20 74 91 30 – 🛗 ⚡ 📺 ☎. AE ⓓ GB EY **b**
☕ 36 – **60 rm** 340.

Nord H., 46 r. Fg d'Arras ☎ 20 53 53 40, Fax 20 53 20 95 – 🛗 📺 ☎ 🅿 – 🏫 40. AE ⓓ GB
Meals 80 (dinner), 98/138 🍷 – ☕ 35 – **80 rm** 270/290.

✻ **A L'Huîtrière,** 3 r. Chats Bossus ✉ 59800 ☎ 20 55 43 41, Fax 20 55 23 10, « Original decoration with ceramics in the fish shop » – ▤. AE ⓓ GB EY **g**
closed 22 July-23 August, dinner Sunday and Bank Holidays – **Meals** 260 and a la carte 300/420
Spec. Huîtres et produits de la mer. Homard aux légumes façon "waterzoï". Saint-Pierre au thym aux écailles de pommes de terre.

Le Sébastopol, 1 pl. Sébastopol ☎ 20 57 05 05, Fax 20 40 11 31 – AE GB EZ **a**
closed sunday July-August and Saturday lunch – **Meals** 150/260 and a la carte 290/370.

La Laiterie, 138 av. Hippodrome at Lambersart NW : 2 km ✉ 59130 Lambersart ☎ 20 92 79 73, Fax 20 22 16 19, 🍽, 🌳 – 🅿. AE ⓓ GB AV **s**
closed Sunday dinner – **Meals** 150/260 and a la carte 330/490.

Le Paris, 52 bis r. Esquermoise ✉ 59800 ☎ 20 55 29 41 – AE ⓓ GB EY **f**
closed beginning August-beginning September and Sunday except Bank Holidays – **Meals** 205/342 b.i..

Baan Thaï, 22 bd J.-B. Lebas ☎ 20 86 06 01, Fax 20 86 03 23 – AE GB. ✱ EZ **s**
closed 22 July-18 August, Saturday lunch and Sunday – **Meals** - Thai rest. - 100 (lunch), 150/220.

Le Club, 16 r. Pas ✉ 59800 ☎ 20 57 01 10, Fax 20 57 39 69 – AE ⓓ GB EY **n**
closed 1 to 20 August, Christmas-New Year, Monday dinner and Sunday – **Meals** 138/208 🍷.

Le Champlain, 13 r. N. Leblanc ☎ 20 54 01 38, Fax 20 40 07 28, 🍽 – AE ⓓ GB. ✱
closed 4 to 25 August, Saturday lunch and dinner Sunday and Monday – **Meals** 145 b.i. (lunch), 165/350 b.i.. EZ **u**

Le Cardinal, 84 façade Esplanade ✉ 59800 ☎ 20 06 58 58, Fax 20 51 42 59 – AE GB
closed 12 to 18 August, Saturday lunch and Sunday – **Meals** 260 b.i.. BV **x**

Le Varbet, 2 r. Pas ✉ 59800 ☎ 20 54 81 40, Fax 20 57 55 18 – AE ⓓ GB EY **t**
closed 18 July-21 August, Christmas-1 January, Sunday, Monday and Bank Holidays – **Meals** 165.

Le Bistrot Tourangeau, 61 bd Louis XIV ✉ 59800 ☎ 20 52 74 64, Fax 20 85 06 39 – AE GB CV **t**
closed Sunday – **Meals** (booking essential) 100/149.

Le Queen, l'Écume des Mers, 10 r. Pas ✉ 59800 ☎ 20 54 95 40, Fax 20 54 96 66 – ▤. AE GB EY **n**
closed 27 July-21 August, Sunday lunch in July, dinner Sunday and Bank Holidays – **Meals** 98 🍷.

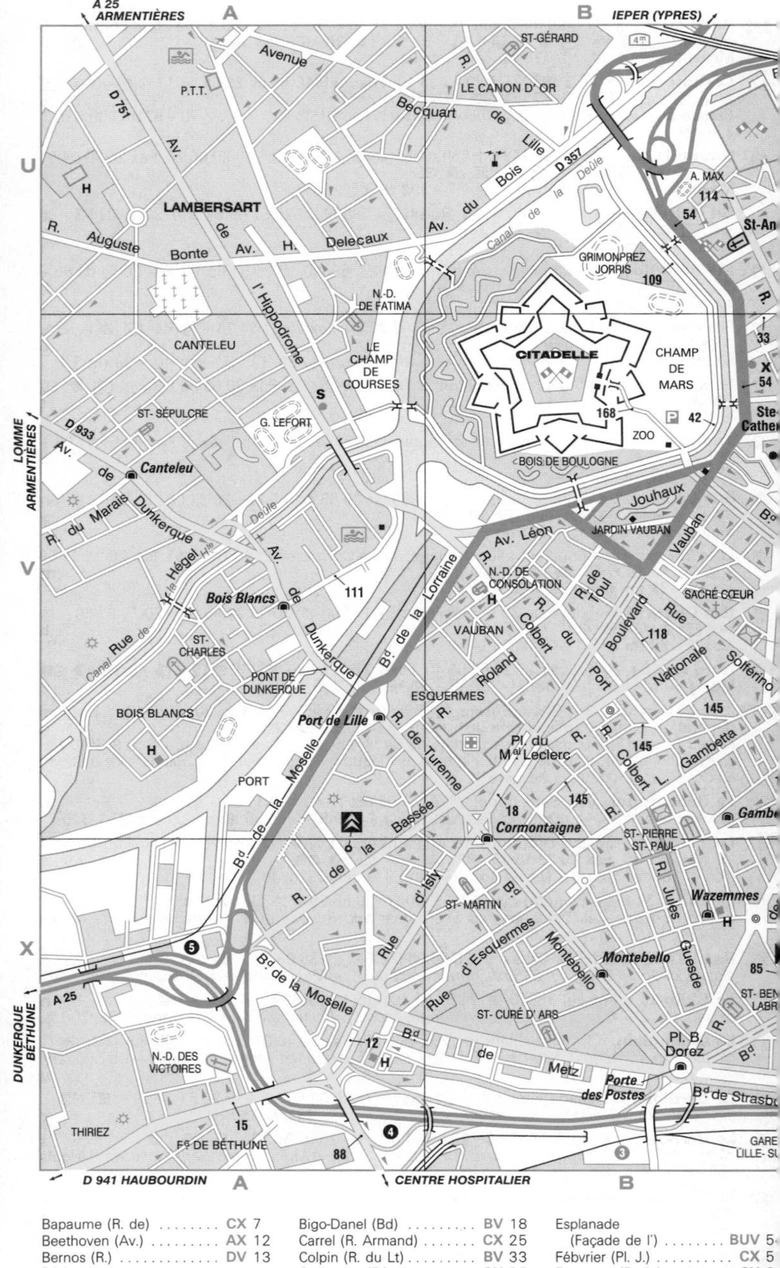

Bapaume (R. de) . . . . CX 7
Beethoven (Av.) . . . . AX 12
Bernos (R.) . . . . DV 13
Béthune
(R. du Fg-de) . . . . AX 15

Bigo-Danel (Bd) . . . . BV 18
Carrel (R. Armand) . . . . CX 25
Colpin (R. du Lt) . . . . BV 33
Courmont (R.) . . . . CX 37
Cuvier (Av.) . . . . BV 42

Esplanade
(Façade de l') . . . . BUV 5
Fébvrier (Pl. J.) . . . . CX 5
Fontenoy (R. de) . . . . CX 6
Gaulle (R. du Gén.-de) . . . . CU 6

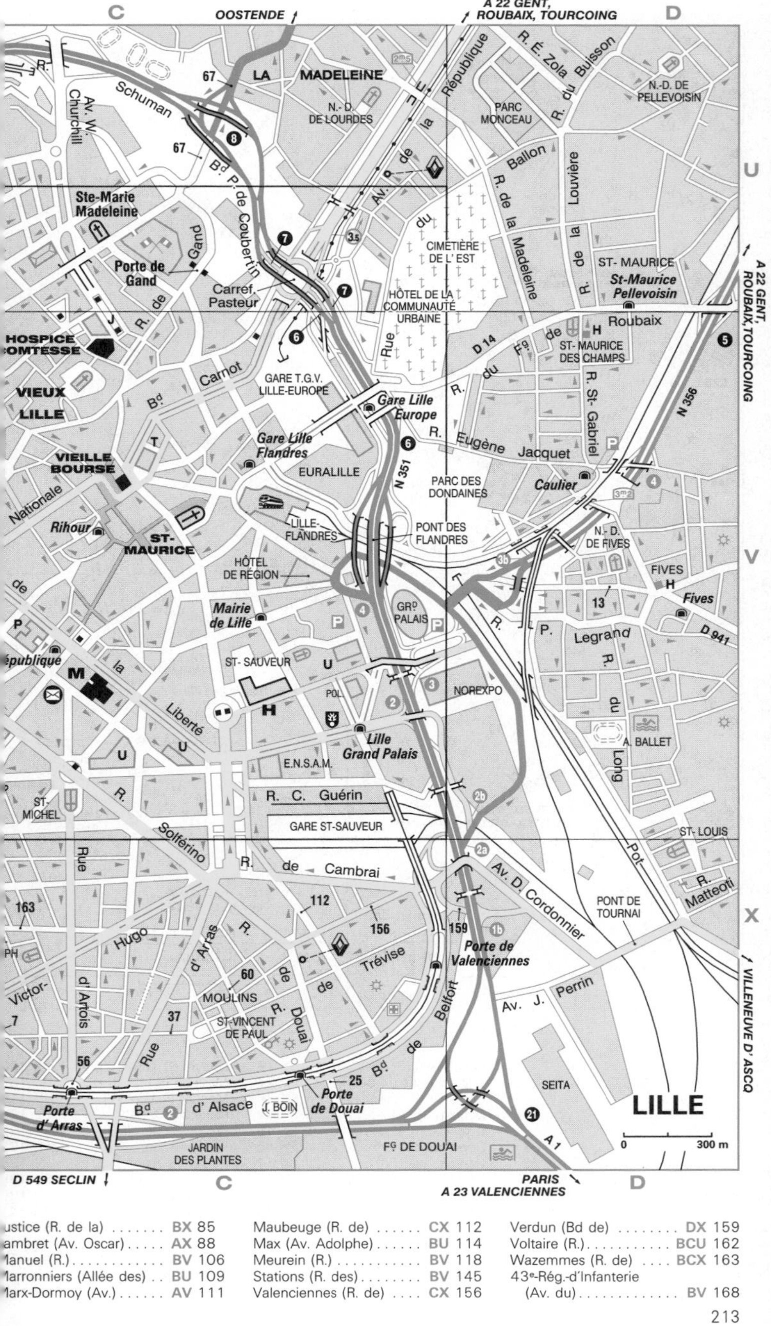
C
OOSTENDE
A 22 GENT, ROUBAIX, TOURCOING
D
LA MADELEINE
N.-D. DE LOURDES
N.-D. DE PELLEVOISIN
PARC MONCEAU
Ste-Marie Madeleine
Porte de Gand
Carref. Pasteur
CIMETIÈRE DE L' EST
HÔTEL DE LA COMMUNAUTÉ URBAINE
ST- MAURICE
St-Maurice Pellevoisin
A 22 GENT, ROUBAIX, TOURCOING
HOSPICE COMTESSE
VIEUX LILLE
GARE T.G.V. LILLE-EUROPE
Gare Lille Europe
ST- MAURICE DES CHAMPS
Gare Lille Flandres
VIEILLE BOURSE
EURALILLE
PARC DES DONDAINES
Caulier
Rihour
ST- MAURICE
LILLE-FLANDRES
PONT DES FLANDRES
N.-D. DE FIVES
HÔTEL DE RÉGION
FIVES
Fives
Mairie de Lille
GRD PALAIS
République
ST- SAUVEUR
NOREXPO
Lille Grand Palais
A. BALLET
E.N.S.A.M.
ST-MICHEL
R. C. Guérin
GARE ST-SAUVEUR
ST- LOUIS
R. de Cambrai
PONT DE TOURNAI
Porte de Valenciennes
VILLENEUVE D' ASCQ
MOULINS
ST-VINCENT DE PAUL
SEITA
Porte d' Arras
Porte de Douai
J. BOIN
LILLE
JARDIN DES PLANTES
FG DE DOUAI
0
300 m
D 549 SECLIN
C
PARIS
A 23 VALENCIENNES
D

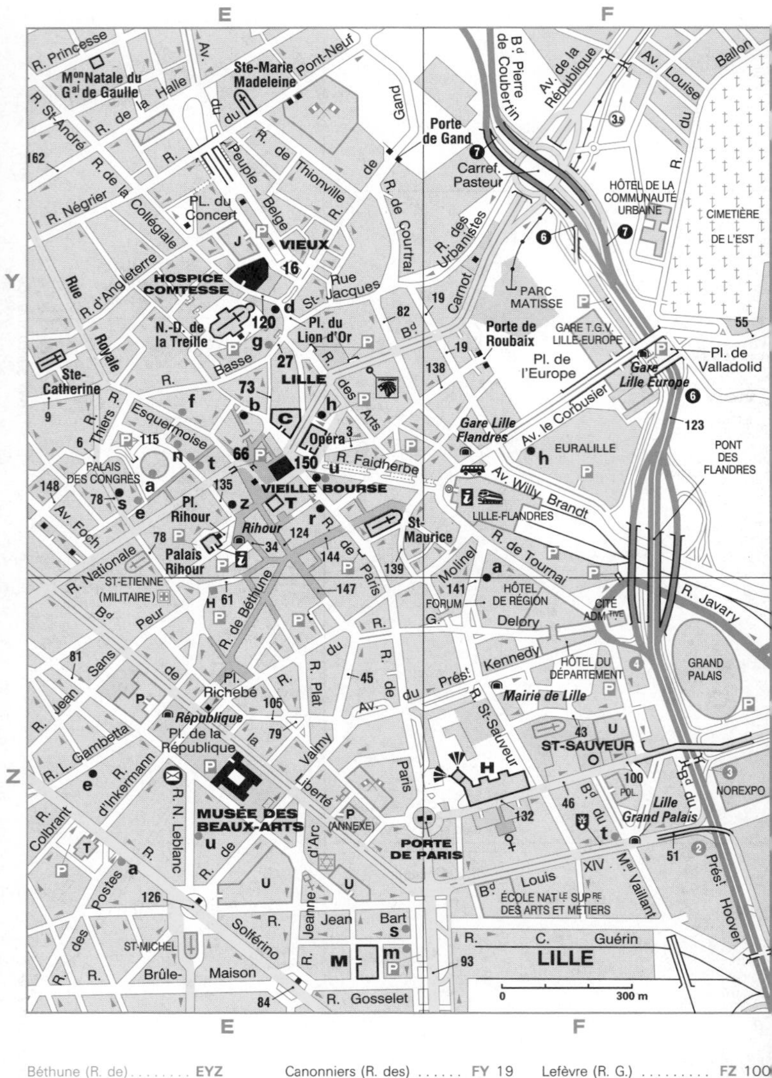

Béthune (R. de) . . . . EYZ
Esquermoise (R.) . . . . EY
Faidherbe (R.) . . . . EY
Gambetta (R. Léon) . . . . . EZ
Gaulle (Pl. Gén.-de)
(Grand Place) . . . . EY 66
Grande Chaussée (R. de la) EY 73
Monnaie (R. de la) . . . . . . EY 120
Nationale (R.) . . . . EYZ
Neuve (R.) . . . . EY 123

Anatole-France (R.) . . . . . . EY 3
Arsenal (Pl. de l') . . . . EY 6
Barre (R. de la) . . . . EY 9
Bettignies (Pl. L. de) . . . . . EY 16
Canonniers (R. des) . . . . . . FY 19
Chats-Bossus (R. des) . . . . . EY 27
Comédie (R. de la) . . . . EY 34
Debierre (R. Ch.) . . . . FZ 43
Delesalle (R. E.) . . . . EZ 45
Déportés (R. des) . . . . FY 46
Dr.-Calmette (Bd) . . . . FY 51
Faubourg de Roubaix . . . . . FY 55
Fosses (R. des) . . . . EYZ 61
Hôpital-Militaire (R.) . . . . . . EY 78
Jacquart (Pl.) . . . . EZ 79
Jacquemars-Giélée (R.) . . . . EZ 81
Jardins (R. des) . . . . EY 82
Jeanne-d'Arc (Pl.) . . . . EZ 84
Lebas (Bd J.-B.) . . . . FZ 93
Lefèvre (R. G.) . . . . FZ 100
Maillotte (R.) . . . . EZ 105
Mendès-France (Pl.) . . . . . . EY 115
Pasteur (Bd. L.) . . . . FY 125
Philippe-le-Bon (Pl.) . . . . . . EZ 126
Réduit (R. du) . . . . FZ 132
Roisin (R. Jean) . . . . EY 135
Roubaix (R. de) . . . . EFY 138
St-Génois (R.) . . . . EY 139
St-Venant (Av. Ch.) . . . . . . FYZ 141
Sec-Arembault (R. du) . . . . EY 144
Tanneurs (R. des) . . . . EYZ 147
Tenremonde (R.) . . . . EY 148
Théâtre (Pl. du) . . . . EY 150
Voltaire (R.) . . . . EY 162

XX **Lutterbach,** 10 r. Faidherbe ✉ 59800 ☎ 20 55 13 74 - AE ⓓ GB EY **u**
closed 29 July-11 August - **Meals** 100/130 ♂.

XX **La Coquille,** 60 r. St-Étienne ✉ 59800 ☎ 20 54 29 82, Fax 20 54 29 82, 17C house - GB
closed 1 to 25 August, February Holidays, Saturday lunch and Sunday - **Meals** 128 b.i. (lunch), 155/210. EY **e**

XX **Charlot II,** 26 bd J.-B. Lebas ☎ 20 52 53 38 - AE GB EZ **m**
closed 22 July to 18 August, Saturday lunch, Sunday and dinner on Bank Holidays - **Meals** - Seafood - a la carte 210/330.

X **Le Hochepot,** 6 r. Nouveau Siècle ☎ 20 54 17 59, Fax 20 54 32 67, 🏛 - GB EY **a**
closed 1 to 20 August, Saturday lunch, Sunday and Bank Holidays - **Meals** 140/180.

at Marcq-en-Baroeul - pop. 36 601 alt. 15 - ✉ 59700 :

Sofitel M, av. Marne, by N 350 : 5 km ☎ 20 72 17 30, Telex 132785, Fax 20 89 92 34 - |♦| ⇔ ▤ TV ☎ ♿ P - 🏃 200. AE ⓓ GB JCB
L'Europe ☎ 20 65 80 60 **Meals** 98/150, ♂ - ☕ 75 - **125 rm** 750/1300.

XXX **Septentrion,** parc du Château Vert Bois, by N 17 : 9 km ☎ 20 46 26 98, Fax 20 46 38 33, 🏛, « In a park with a lake » - P. AE ⓓ GB
closed 1 to 3 August, winter holidays, Sunday dinner, Thursday dinner and Monday - **Meals** 150/290.

XXX **L'Épicurien,** 18 av. Flandre by N 350 : 4 km ☎ 20 45 82 15, Fax 20 45 82 15, 🏛 - P. GB
closed Sunday dinner - **Meals** 135/290 and a la carte 170/290.

at Lille-Lesquin Airport by A 1 : 8 km - ✉ 59810 Lesquin :

Mercure Lille Aéroport M 🐕, ☎ 20 87 46 46, Fax 20 87 46 47 - |♦| ⇔ ▤ TV ☎ ♿ P - 🏃 25 - 800. AE ⓓ GB JCB
Grill La Flamme* : Meals** a la carte 160/220 - ***Le Poêlon *(closed Saturday and Sunday)* **Meals** a la carte 90/140 - ☕ 58 - **212 rm** 490/580.

Novotel Lille Aéroport, ☎ 20 62 53 53, Fax 20 97 36 12, 🏛, 🏊, 🌳 - ⇔ ▤ rest TV ☎ P - 🏃 25 - 200. AE ⓓ GB
Meals a la carte approx. 160 ♂ - ☕ 50 - **92 rm** 460/480.

Agena without rest, ✉ 59155 Faches-Thumesnil ☎ 20 60 13 14, Fax 20 97 31 79 - TV ☎ ♿ P. AE GB JCB
☕ 48 - **40 rm** 340/370.

at Englos by A 25 : 10 km (exit Lomme) - alt. 46 - ✉ 59320 :

Novotel Lille Englos M, ☎ 20 10 58 58, Fax 20 10 58 59, 🏛, 🏊, 🌳 - ⇔ TV ☎ ♿ P - 🏃 60. AE ⓓ GB
Meals a la carte approx. 160 ♂ - ☕ 49 - **124 rm** 420/445.

at Verlinghem by D 257 : 8 km - pop. 2 182 alt. 27 - ✉ 59237 :

XXX ✿ **Château Blanc,** 20 rte Lambersart ☎ 20 40 71 02, Fax 20 40 99 40, 🏛, park - P. AE GB
closed 5 to 18 August, Sunday dinner and Monday - **Meals** 250/300 and a la carte 260/380
Spec. Saint-Jacques rôties au jus de pomme verte (October-April). Blanc de turbot poêlé, moelle pochée et bière de garde. Pigeon rôti au pain d'épices.

When travelling through Europe
use the MICHELIN red-cover map series, nos 980 to 991.

LYONS P **69000** Rhône 74 ⑪ ⑫ - pop. 415 487 alt. 175.

See : Site★★★ (panorama★★ from Fourvière) - Fourvière hill : Notre-Dame Basilica EX, Museum of Gallo-Roman Civilization★★ (Claudian tables★★★) EY **M³**, Roman ruins EY - Old Lyons★★ : Rue St-Jean★ FX, St-Jean Cathedral★ FY, Hôtel de Gadagne★ (Lyons Historical Museum★ and International Marionette Museum★) EX **M¹**Guignol de Lyon FX **N** - Central Lyons (Peninsula) : to the North, Place Bellecour FY, Hospital Museum (pharmacy★) FY **M⁸**, Museum of Printing and Banking★★ FX **M⁶**, Place des Terreaux FX, Hôtel de Ville FX, Palais St-Pierre, Fine Arts Museum (Beaux-Arts)★★ FX **M⁴** - to the South, St-Martin-d'Ainay Basilica (capitals★) FY, Weaving and Textile Museum★★★ FY **M²**, Decorative Arts Museum★★ FY **M⁵** - La Croix-Rousse : Silkweavers'House FV **M¹¹**, Trois Gaules Amphitheatre FV **E** - Tête d'Or Park★ GHV - Guimet Museum of Natural History★★ GV **M⁷** - Historical Information Centre on the Resistance and the Deportation★ FZ **M⁹**.

Envir. : Rochetaillée : Henri Malartre Car Museum★★, 12 km to the North.

⛳18 Verger-Lyon at St-Symphorien-d'Ozon ☎ 78 02 84 20, to the S : 14 km ; ⛳9 ⛳18 Lyon-Chassieu at Chassieu ☎ 78 90 84 77, E : 12 km by D 29 ; ⛳18 Salvagny (private) at the Tour of Salvagny ☎ 78 48 83 60, junction Lyon-Ouest : 8 km.

✈ of Lyon-Satolas ☎ 72 22 72 21, E : 27 km by A 43.

🚗 ☎ 36 35 35 35.

ℹ Tourist Office pl. Bellecour ☎ 78 42 25 75, Fax 78 42 04 32 - A.C. du Rhône 7 r. Grolée ☎ 78 42 51 01.

Paris 462 - Geneva 151 - Grenoble 105 - Marseilles 313 - St-Étienne 60 - Turin 300.

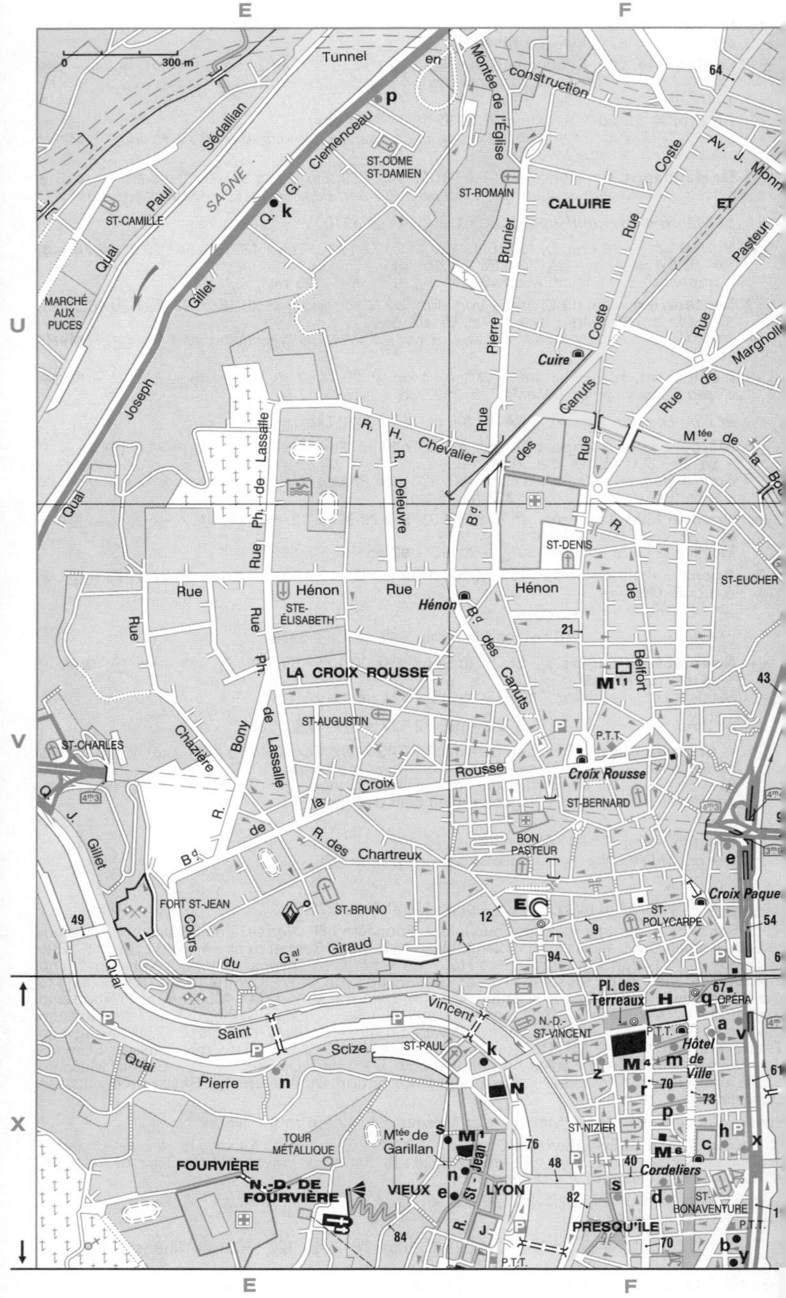
E
F
U
V
X
0
300 m
Tunnel en construction
SAÔNE
Quai Paul Sédallian
Quai Joseph Gillet
Q. G. Clemenceau
ST-COME ST-DAMIEN
ST-CAMILLE
MARCHÉ AUX PUCES
Montée de l'Église
ST-ROMAIN
CALUIRE ET
Rue Pierre Brunier
Rue Coste
Av. J. Monn
Rue Pasteur
Cuire
Rue des Canuts
Rue de Margnolle
Mtée de la Bou
R. H. Chevalier
R. Deleuvre
Rue Ph. de Lassalle
Bd des Canuts
ST-DENIS
ST-EUCHER
Rue Hénon
STE-ÉLISABETH
Hénon
LA CROIX ROUSSE
M11
Rue de Belfort
ST-AUGUSTIN
ST-CHARLES
Rue Chazière
R. Bony
P.T.T.
Croix Rousse
Bd de la Croix Rousse
ST-BERNARD
R. des Chartreux
BON PASTEUR
Q. J. Gillet
FORT ST-JEAN
ST-BRUNO
Cours du Gal Giraud
Croix Paquet
ST-POLYCARPE
Quai Saint Vincent
Pl. des Terreaux
OPÉRA
N.-D.-ST-VINCENT
Hôtel de Ville
Quai Pierre Scize
ST-PAUL
ST-NIZIER
TOUR MÉTALLIQUE
Mtée de Garillan
FOURVIÈRE
N.-D. DE FOURVIÈRE
VIEUX LYON
R. St-Jean
Cordeliers
ST-BONAVENTURE
PRESQU'ÎLE
P.T.T.
64
21
43
49
12
9
4
94
54
67
61
70
73
76
48
40
82
84
70

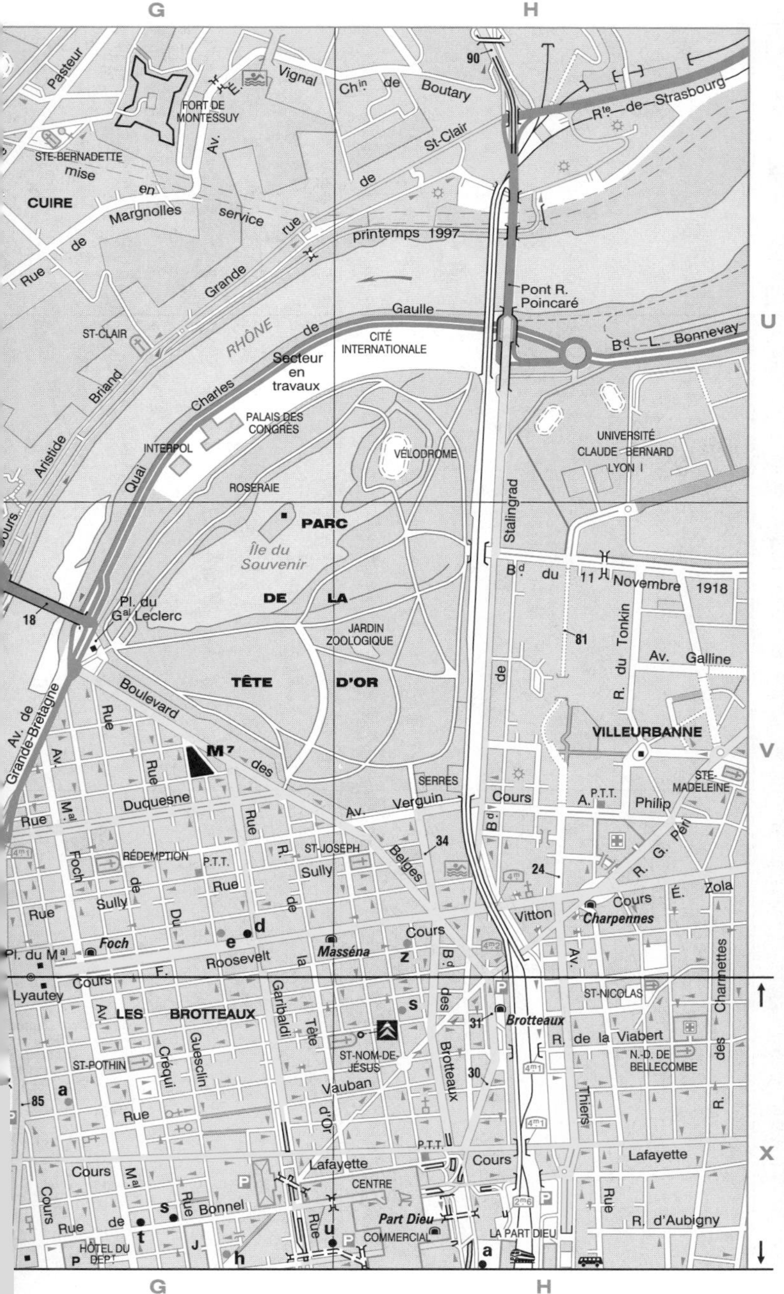
G
H
U
V
X
FORT DE MONTESSUY
STE-BERNADETTE
CUIRE
Pasteur
Vignal
Chin de Boutary
Rte de Strasbourg
Av. de St-Clair
mise en service printemps 1997
Rue de Margnolles
Grande rue
Pont R. Poincaré
Gaulle
Bd L. Bonnevay
ST-CLAIR
RHÔNE
CITÉ INTERNATIONALE
Secteur en travaux
Quai Charles de
Aristide Briand
PALAIS DES CONGRÈS
INTERPOL
VÉLODROME
UNIVERSITÉ CLAUDE BERNARD LYON I
ROSERAIE
PARC DE LA TÊTE D'OR
Île du Souvenir
Stalingrad
Bd du 11 Novembre 1918
Pl. du Gal Leclerc
JARDIN ZOOLOGIQUE
R. du Tonkin
Av. Galline
Av. de Grande-Bretagne
Boulevard des Belges
VILLEURBANNE
SERRES
Av. Verguin
Cours A. Philip
P.T.T.
STE-MADELEINE
Duquesne
Rue Mal Foch
RÉDEMPTION
ST-JOSEPH
Rue Sully
R. G. Péri
Cours É. Zola
Charpennes
Cours Vitton
Foch
Masséna
Pl. du Mal Lyautey
Cours F. Roosevelt
LES BROTTEAUX
ST-NICOLAS
Brotteaux
R. de la Viabert
Garibaldi
Tête d'Or
ST-NOM-DE-JÉSUS
N.-D. DE BELLECOMBE
ST-POTHIN
Créqui
Guesclin
Vauban
Bd des Brotteaux
Thiers
R. des Charmettes
Cours Lafayette
CENTRE COMMERCIAL
Part Dieu
LA PART DIEU
Rue Bonnel
R. d'Aubigny
HÔTEL DU DÉPT
Cours
90
18
81
34
24
31
30
85
M7
a
d
e
z
s
t
u
h
J

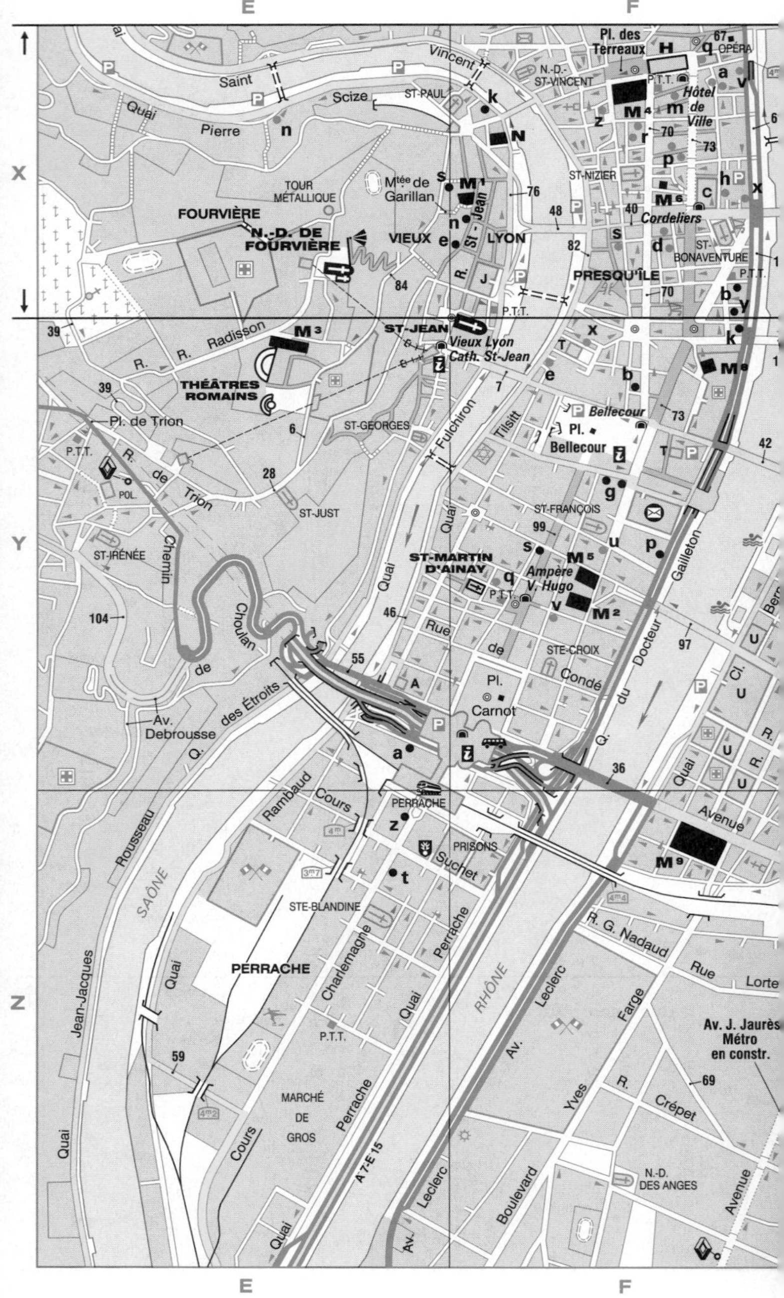
E
F
X
Y
Z
Quai
Saint
Vincent
Quai
Pierre
Scize
ST-PAUL
Pl. des Terreaux
H
q
67
OPÉRA
N.-D.-ST-VINCENT
P.T.T.
a
v
Hôtel de Ville
k
n
N
M 4
m
z
r
70
73
p
TOUR MÉTALLIQUE
Mtée de Garillan
s
M 1
76
ST-NIZIER
h
x
c
M 6
FOURVIÈRE
N.-D. DE FOURVIÈRE
48
40
Cordeliers
VIEUX
e
R. St-Jean
LYON
82
s
d
ST-BONAVENTURE
84
J
PRESQU'ÎLE
70
b
y
39
R. Radisson
M 3
ST-JEAN
Vieux Lyon
Cath. St-Jean
x
T
k
R.
THÉÂTRES ROMAINS
39
7
e
b
M 8
Pl. de Trion
6
ST-GEORGES
Fulchiron
Tilsitt
Bellecour
73
Pl. Bellecour
42
P.T.T.
R. de Trion
T
POL.
28
g
ST-JUST
Quai
ST-FRANÇOIS
99
s
u
p
Gailleton
ST-IRÉNÉE
Chemin
ST-MARTIN D'AINAY
M 5
Ampère V. Hugo
q
P.T.T.
v
M 2
104
Choulan
Quai
46
Rue
de
STE-CROIX
Condé
du
Docteur
97
55
A
Pl.
Carnot
Cl.
de
Av. Debrousse
des Étroits
Q.
a
36
Q.
R.
R.
Quai
Rousseau
Rambaud
Cours
PERRACHE
z
Avenue
PRISONS
Suchet
t
M 9
SAÔNE
STE-BLANDINE
Perrache
R. G. Nadaud
Rue
Lorte
Quai
PERRACHE
Charlemagne
Quai
RHÔNE
Leclerc
Farge
Jean-Jacques
P.T.T.
Av.
Av. J. Jaurès Métro en constr.
59
MARCHÉ DE GROS
Perrache
Yves
R.
Crépet
69
Quai
Cours
A 7-E 15
Leclerc
Boulevard
N.-D. DES ANGES
Avenue
Quai
Av.
E
F

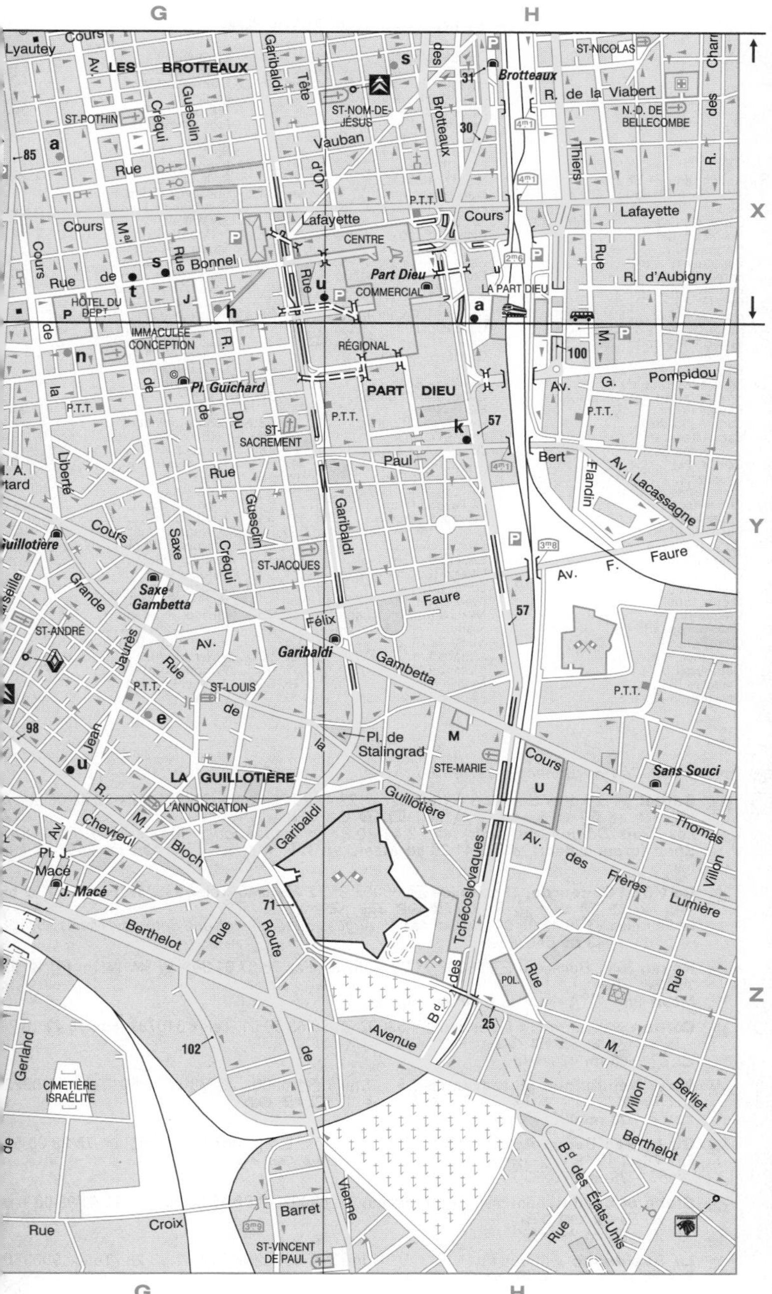
G
H
X
Y
Z
LES BROTTEAUX
Brotteaux
ST-NICOLAS
R. de la Viabert
N.-D. DE BELLECOMBE
ST-POTHIN
ST-NOM-DE-JÉSUS
Vauban
Cours Lafayette
Lafayette
CENTRE
Part Dieu
COMMERCIAL
LA PART DIEU
R. d'Aubigny
HÔTEL DU DÉPT
IMMACULÉE CONCEPTION
RÉGIONAL
PART DIEU
Pl. Guichard
Av. G. Pompidou
ST-SACREMENT
P.T.T.
Paul Bert
Av. Lacassagne
Flandin
ST-JACQUES
Av. F. Faure
Félix Faure
Garibaldi
Saxe Gambetta
Guillotière
ST-ANDRÉ
Gambetta
ST-LOUIS
Pl. de Stalingrad
STE-MARIE
Sans Souci
LA GUILLOTIÈRE
L'ANNONCIATION
Cours de la Guillotière
Av. Thomas
Villon
Av. des Frères Lumière
Chevreul
Bloch
Pl. J. Macé
J. Macé
Tchécoslovaques
Berthelot
Route de Vienne
POL.
Avenue Berthelot
M. Berliet
Rue Villon
CIMETIÈRE ISRAÉLITE
Gerland
B^d des États-Unis
Barret
ST-VINCENT DE PAUL
Croix
Rue
Jean Jaurès
Créqui
Guesclin
Saxe
Liberté
Garibaldi
Tête d'Or
Brotteaux
Thiers
Bonnel
85
31
30
100
57
98
71
102
25

STREET INDEX TO LYON TOWN PLAN

Guillotière (Grande R. de la) . . . . . GYZ
Jaurès (Av. J.) . . . . . GY
La Part Dieu . . . . . HXY
République (R. de la) . . . . FXY 73
Terme (Rue) . . . . . FV 94
Victor-Hugo (Rue) . . . . . FY 99
Vitton (Cours) . . . . . HV

Annonciade (R. de l') . . . . . FV 4
Antiquaille (R. de l') . . . . . EY 6
Aubigny (R. d') . . . . . HX
Barret (R. Croix) . . . . . GZ
Belfort (R. de) . . . . . FV
Belges (Bd des) . . . . . GHV
Bellecour (Place) . . . . . FY
Berliet (R. M.) . . . . . HZ
Bernard (Quai Cl.) . . . . . FY
Bert (R. P.) . . . . . GHY
Berthelot (Av.) . . . . . GHZ
Bloch (R. M.) . . . . . GZ
Bonaparte (Pont) . . . . . FY 7
Bonnel (R. de) . . . . . GX
Bony (R.) . . . . . EV
Boucle (Montée de la) . . . . FU
Brotteaux (Bd des) . . . . . HVX
Burdeau (Rue) . . . . . FV 9
Canuts (Bd des) . . . . . FUV
Carmélites (Montée des) . . . . . FV 12
Carnot (Pl.) . . . . . FY
Charlemagne (Cours) . . . . . EZ
Charmettes (R. des) . . . . . HVX
Chartreux (R. des) . . . . . EV
Chazière (Rue) . . . . . EV
Chevreul (Rue) . . . . . GYZ
Choulans (Chin de) . . . . . EY
Churchill (Pt W.) . . . . . GV 18
Condé (R. de) . . . . . FY
Courmont (Quai J.) . . . . . FX 19
Crepet (Rue) . . . . . FZ
Créqui (R. de) . . . . . GVY
Croix-Rousse (Bd de) . . . . . EFV
Croix-Rousse (Grande R. de la) . . . . . FV 21
Debrousse (Av.) . . . . . EY
Deleuvre (R.) . . . . . EUV
Dr-Gailleton (Quai) . . . . . FY
Du Guesclin (Rue) . . . . . GVY
Duquesne (Rue) . . . . . GV
Epargne (R. de l') . . . . . HZ 25
Etroits (Quai des) . . . . . EY
Farge (Bd Y.) . . . . . FZ
Farges (R. des) . . . . . EY 28
Faure (Av. F.) . . . . . GHY
Favre (Bd J.) . . . . . HX 30
Ferry (Pl. J.) . . . . . HX 31
Flandin (R. M.) . . . . . HXY
France (Bd A.) . . . . . HV 34
Frères Lumière (Av. des) . . HZ
Fulchiron (Quai) . . . . . EY
Gallieni (Pont) . . . . . FY 36
Gambetta (Cours) . . . . . GHY
Garibaldi (Rue) . . . . . GVZ
Garillan (Montée de) . . . . . EFX
Gaulle (Q. Ch. de) . . . . . GHU
Gerland (R. de) . . . . . GZ
Gerlier (R. Cardinal) . . . . . EY 39
Gillet (Quai J.) . . . . . EUV
Giraud (Cours Gén.) . . . . . EV
Grande-Bretagne (Av. de) . . . . . GV
Grenette (Rue) . . . . . FX 40
Guillotière (Pt de la) . . . . . FY 42
Hénon (Rue) . . . . . EFV
Herbouville (Cours d') . . . . . FV 43
Joffre (Quai Mar.) . . . . . EY 46
Juin (Pt Alphonse) . . . . . FX 48
Jutard (Pl. A.) . . . . . GY
Koening (Pt Gén.) . . . . . EV 49
La Fayette (Cours) . . . . . GHX
La Fayette (Pont) . . . . . GX 51
Lassagne (Quai A.) . . . . . FV 54
Lassalle (R. Ph. de) . . . . . EUV
Leclerc (Av.) . . . . . EFZ
Leclerc (Pl. Gén.) . . . . . GV
Liberté (Cours de la) . . . . GXY
Lortet (Rue) . . . . . FZ
Lyautey (Pl. Mar.) . . . . . GVX
Marchand (Pt Kitchener) . . EY 55
Marius Vivier Merle (Bd) . . HY 57
Marseille (R. de) . . . . . GY
Montrochet (R. P.) . . . . . EZ 59
Morand (Pont) . . . . . FVX 60
Moulin (Quai J.) . . . . . FX 61
Nadaud (R. G.) . . . . . FZ
Peissel (R. F.) . . . . . FU 64
Perrache (Quai) . . . . . EZ
Pompidou (Av. G.) . . . . . HY
Pradel (Pl. L.) . . . . . FX 67
Pré Gaudry (Rue) . . . . . FZ 69
Prés. Herriot (R. du) . . . . . FX 70
Radisson (R. R.) . . . . . EY
Rambaud (Quai) . . . . . EYZ
Repos (R. du) . . . . . GZ 71
Rolland (Quai R.) . . . . . FX 76
Roosevelt (Cours F.) . . . . GVX
St-Antoine (Quai) . . . . . FX 82
St-Barthélemy (Montée) . . . . . EX 84
St-Jean (Rue) . . . . . FX
St-Vincent (Quai) . . . . . EFX
Sarrail (Quai Gén.) . . . . . GX 85
Saxe (Av. Mar. de) . . . . . GXY
Scize (Quai P.) . . . . . EX
Sedallian (Quai P.) . . . . . EU
Serbie (Quai de) . . . . . GV
Stalingrad (Bd de) . . . . . GHU
Stalingrad (Pl. de) . . . . . GHY
Suchet (Cours) . . . . . EFZ
Sully (Rue) . . . . . GV
Tassigny (Pt de Lattre de) . . . . . FV 93
Tchécoslovaques (Bd des) . . . . . HZ
Terreaux (Pl. des) . . . . . FX
Tête d'Or (Rue) . . . . . GVX
Thiers (Av.) . . . . . HVX
Tilsitt (Quai) . . . . . FY
Trion (Pl. de) . . . . . EY
Trion (R. de) . . . . . EY
Université (Pont de l') . . . FY 97
Université (R. de l') . . . . . GY 98
Vauban (Rue) . . . . . GHX
Verguin (Av.) . . . . . HV
Viabert (R. de la) . . . . . HX
Vienne (Rte de) . . . . . GZ
Villette (R. de la) . . . . . HY 10
Villon (Rue) . . . . . HZ
Vitton (Cours) . . . . . HV
Vivier (R. du) . . . . . GZ 10
Wilson (Pont) . . . . . FY 10
1re Div. Fr. Libre (Av.) . . . . . EY 10

Hotels

Town Centre (Bellecour-Terreaux) :

Sofitel M, 20 quai Gailleton ✉ 69002 ☎ 72 41 20 20, Telex 330225, Fax 72 40 05 50, – 200. AE GB JCB FY
Les Trois Dômes (8th floor) ☎ 72 41 20 97 *(closed August)* **Meals** 170/250 – ***So Shop*** **(ground floor)** ☎ **72 41 20 80 Meals** 94/125, – 77 – **138 rm** 940, 29 su tes.

Gd Hôtel Concorde, 11 r. Grolée ✉ 69002 ☎ 72 40 45 45, Telex 330244, Fax 78 37 52 5 – 80. AE GB JCB. rest FX
Le Fiorelle : ☎ 78 42 99 84 *(closed 3 to 19 August, Sunday lunch and Saturday)* **Meals** 98/16 – 69 – **143 rm** 650/930.

Royal, 20 pl. Bellecour ✉ 69002 ☎ 78 37 57 31, Fax 78 37 01 36 – rm GB JCB FY
Meals 98/142 – 68 – **80 rm** 680/920.

Carlton without rest, 4 r. Jussieu ✉ 69002 ☎ 78 42 56 51, Telex 310787, Fax 78 42 10 – AE GB FX
57 – **83 rm** 420/695.

Plaza République M without rest, 5 r. Stella ✉ 69002 ☎ 78 37 50 50, Telex 31022 Fax 78 42 33 34 – – 35. AE GB FY
58 – **78 rm** 485/750.

Gd H. des Beaux-Arts without rest, 75 r. Prés. E. Herriot ✉ 69002 ☎ 78 38 09 5 Fax 78 42 19 19 – – 25. AE GB JCB FX
57 – **79 rm** 360/620.

Globe et Cécil without rest, 21 r. Gasparin ✉ 69002 ☎ 78 42 58 95, Fax 72 41 99 06 – AE GB JCB FY
50 – **65 rm** 399/550.

La Résidence without rest, 18 r. V. Hugo ✉ 69002 ☎ 78 42 63 28, Telex 90095 Fax 78 42 85 76 – AE GB FY
35 – **64 rm** 298/330.

Perrache :

Château Perrache, 12 cours Verdun ✉ 69002 ✆ 72 77 15 00, Telex 330500, Fax 78 37 06 56, « Art Nouveau decor » – 250. AE GB JCB EY a
Les Belles Saisons : **Meals** 137/177 – ☐ 67 – **123 rm** 490/840.

Charlemagne M, 23 cours Charlemagne ✉ 69002 ✆ 72 77 70 00, Fax 78 42 94 84, – 120. AE GB EZ t
Meals *(closed August, Saturday and Sunday)* 85/140 – ☐ 52 – **116 rm** 395/545.

Berlioz M without rest, 12 cours Charlemagne ✉ 69002 ✆ 78 42 30 31, Telex 330862, Fax 72 40 97 58 – AE GB JCB EZ z
☐ 40 – **38 rm** 237/353.

at Vaise :

Saphir M, 18 r. L. Loucheur ✉ 69009 ✆ 78 83 48 75, Fax 78 83 30 81 – – 50. AE GB
Meals 95/150 – ☐ 50 – **111 rm** 450/470.

Vieux-Lyon :

✿ **Villa Florentine** M, 25 montée St-Barthélémy ✉ 69005 ✆ 72 56 56 56, Fax 72 40 90 56, ← Lyon, – AE GB EFX s
Les Terrasses de Lyon : **Meals** 160(lunch), 270/380 and a la carte 310/440 – ☐ 80 – **16 rm** 1200/1900, 3 suites
Spec. Homard tiède à la lyonnaise. Saint-Jacques grillées à l'émulsion de corail. Couronne d'agneau de lait aux anchois de Collioure. Wines Condrieu, Côte-Rôtie.

Cour des Loges M, 6 r. Boeuf ✉ 69005 ✆ 78 42 75 75, Fax 72 40 93 61, « Contemporary decor in houses of Old Lyons » – – 40. AE GB JCB FX n
Les Loges : **Meals** à la carte approx. 270 – ☐ 110 – **53 rm** 1150/1800, 10 suites.

✿ **Tour Rose** (Chavent) M, 22 r. Boeuf ✉ 69005 ✆ 78 37 25 90, Fax 78 42 26 02, « 17C house, tasteful silk themed decor », – AE GB JCB EFX e
Meals *(closed Sunday)* 295/595 and a la carte 420/600 – ☐ 95 – **6 rm** 950/1650, 6 suites, 4 duplex
Spec. Saumon mi-cuit au fumoir. Salade de pommes de terre à la crème de caviar. Foie chaud de canard et filet de rouget barbet poêlés aux lentilles confites à l'ail. Wines Brouilly, Viognier.

Phénix H. M without rest, 7 quai Bondy ✉ 69005 ✆ 78 28 24 24, Fax 78 28 62 86 – – 35. AE GB FX k
☐ 65 – **36 rm** 620/1080.

La Croix-Rousse (bank of the River Saône) :

Lyon Métropole M, 85 quai J. Gillet ✉ 69004 ✆ 78 29 20 20, Fax 78 39 99 20, – – 350. AE GB EU k
Les Eaux Vives : **Meals** 150/290, enf. 100 – **Grill : Meals** 80/122 – ☐ 70 – **119 rm** 570/670.

Les Brotteaux :

Olympique without rest, 62 r. Garibaldi ✉ 69006 ✆ 78 89 48 04, Fax 78 89 49 97 – AE GB GV d
☐ 30 – **23 rm** 255/285.

La Part-Dieu :

Holiday Inn Crowne Plaza M, 29 r. Bonnel ✉ 69003 ✆ 72 61 90 90, Fax 72 61 17 54, – – 300. AE GB JCB GX t
Meals 105/190 – ☐ 80 – **156 rm** 895/1500.

Pullman Part-Dieu M, 129 r. Servient (32nd floor) ✉ 69003 ✆ 78 63 55 00, Telex 380088, Fax 78 63 55 20, ← Lyons and Rhône Valley – – 170. AE GB JCB. rest GX u
L'Arc-en-Ciel *(closed 15 July-21 August and Saturday lunch)* **Meals** 195/295 – ***La Ripaille*** **– grill (ground floor)** *(closed Sunday, dinner Friday and Saturday except 15 July-21 August)* **Meals** 97 – ☐ 70 – **245 rm** 560/790.

Mercure La Part-Dieu M, 47 bd Vivier-Merle ✉ 69003 ✆ 72 13 51 51, Telex 306469, Fax 72 13 51 99 – – 80. AE GB JCB HX a
Meals *(closed lunch Saturday and Sunday from 13 July-18 August)* 110/170 b.i. – ☐ 57 – **124 rm** 585/615.

Créqui M without rest, 158 r. Créqui ✉ 69003 ✆ 78 60 20 47, Fax 78 62 21 12 – AE GB GX s
☐ 47 – **28 rm** 360/390.

Ibis La Part-Dieu Gare, pl. Renaudel ✉ 69003 ✆ 78 95 42 11, Fax 78 60 42 85, – – 40. AE GB HY k
Meals 99 b.i. – ☐ 35 – **144 rm** 345.

La Guillotière :

Ibis Université M without rest, 51 r. Université ✉ 69007 ✆ 78 72 78 42, Fax 78 69 24 36 – AE GB GY u
☐ 36 – **53 rm** 345.

Gerland :

Mercure Gerland M, 70 av. Leclerc ✉ 69007 ℘ 72 71 11 11, Telex 305484, Fax 72 71 11 00, , – | ▤ TV ☎ ♿ – 200. AE ① GB JCB
Meals 127 b.i. – ☐ 56 – **194 rm** 510/680.

Montchat-Monplaisir :

Relais Mercure Park H., 4 r. Prof. Calmette ✉ 69008 ℘ 78 74 11 20, Telex 380230, Fax 78 01 43 38, – | TV ☎ . AE ① GB
Meals *(closed 10 to 26 August, 27 December-2 January, Sunday lunch and Saturday)* 100/130 – ☐ 48 – **72 rm** 380/425.

at Bron - pop. 39 683 alt. 204 - ✉ 69500 :

Novotel Bron M, av. J. Monnet ℘ 78 26 97 48, Fax 78 26 45 12, , , – | ▤ TV ☎ ♿ P – 25 - 800. AE ① GB
Meals a la carte approx. 180 – ☐ 50 – **189 rm** 495/520.

Restaurants

XXXXX ✿✿✿ **Paul Bocuse,** bridge of Collonges N : 12 km by the banks of River Saône (D 433, D 51) ✉ 69660 Collonges-au-Mont-d'Or ℘ 72 42 90 90, Fax 72 27 85 87 – ▤ P. AE ① GB
Meals 450/740 and a la carte 480/700
Spec. Soupe aux truffes. Rouget barbet en écailles de pommes de terre. Volaille de Bresse. Wines Saint-Véran, Brouilly.

XXXX ✿ **Orsi,** 3 pl. Kléber ✉ 69006 ℘ 78 89 57 68, Fax 72 44 93 34, , « Elegant decor » – ▤. AE GB JCB GV **e**
closed Sunday except Bank Holidays – **Meals** 240 (lunch), 400/500 and a la carte 300/490
Spec. Ravioles de foie gras au jus de porto. Homard et rouget en barigoule d'artichaut. Pigeonneau rôti en cocotte aux gousses d'ail confites. Wines Mâcon-Clessé, Côte-Rôtie.

XXXX ✿✿ **Léon de Lyon** (Lacombe), 1 r. Pleney ✉ 69001 ℘ 78 28 11 33, Fax 78 39 89 05 – ▤. AE GB JCB FX **r**
closed 11 to 19 August and Sunday – **Meals** 280 (lunch), 490/600 and a la carte 420/500
Spec. Cochon de lait, foie gras et oignons confits en terrine rustique. Brochet de la Dombes en quenelle et meunière, étuvée de grenouilles. Six desserts sur le thème de la praline. Wines Chiroubles, Saint-Véran.

XXX **Christian Têtedoie,** 54 quai Pierre Scize ✉ 69005 ℘ 78 29 40 10, Fax 72 07 05 65 – ▤ P. AE GB EX **n**
closed August, Saturday lunch and Sunday except Bank Holidays – **Meals** 160/280 and a la carte 240/360.

XXX **Aub. de Fond-Rose,** 23 quai Clemenceau ✉ 69300 Caluire-et-Cuire ℘ 78 29 34 61, Fax 72 00 28 67, , « Shaded and flowered garden, aviary » – P. AE ① GB JCB EU **p**
closed 2 to 10 November, February Holidays, Monday from 15 September-15 May and dinner Sunday and Bank Holidays – **Meals** 140/460 and a la carte 250/360.

XXX ✿ **Nandron,** 26 quai J. Moulin ✉ 69002 ℘ 78 42 10 26, Fax 78 37 69 88 – ▤. AE ① GB JCB FX **x**
closed 26 July-25 August and Saturday – **Meals** 200 (lunch), 300/450 and a la carte 310/500
Spec. Terrine de queue de boeuf et lapereau en gelée. Quenelle de brochet à la Nantua. Rognon de veau rôti en cocotte au thym. Wines Côtes-du-Rhône, Beaujolais.

XXX **Fédora,** 249 r. M. Mérieux ✉ 69007 ℘ 78 69 46 26, Fax 72 73 38 80, – AE ① GB
closed 11 to 18 August, 22 December-4 January, Saturday lunch and Sunday – **Meals** - Seafood - 139/420 and a la carte 250/420 .

XXX ✿ **Mère Brazier,** 12 r. Royale ✉ 69001 ℘ 78 28 15 49, Fax 78 28 63 63, « Lyonnaise atmosphere » – AE ① GB FV **e**
closed 26 July-27 August, Saturday (except dinner August-May) and Sunday – **Meals** 170/370 and a la carte 200/300
Spec. Fond d'artichaut au foie gras. Quenelle au gratin. Volaille "demi-deuil". Wines Brouilly, Saint-Joseph.

XXX **Le Saint Alban,** 2 quai J. Moulin ✉ 69001 ℘ 78 30 14 89, Fax 72 00 88 82 – ▤. AE GB FX **v**
closed 1 to 21 August, February Holidays, Saturday lunch, Sunday and Bank Holidays – **Meals** 150/295 and a la carte 260/360.

XX **Le Passage,** 8 r. Plâtre ✉ 69001 ℘ 78 28 11 16, Fax 72 00 84 34 – ▤. AE GB FX **r**
closed Saturday lunch, Sunday and Bank Holidays – **Meals** 150 (lunch), 220/290.

XX ✿ **L'Alexandrin** (Alexanian), 83 r. Moncey ✉ 69003 ℘ 72 61 15 69, Fax 78 62 75 57 – ▤. AE GB GX **h**
closed 28 April-1 May, 16 to 20 May, 4 to 26 August, 22 December-5 January, Sunday, Monday and Bank Holidays – **Meals** 160/208 and a la carte 260/370
Spec. Buchettes de saumon fumé et palourdes roses en gelée de livèche. Filet de boeuf au jus de truffes. Feuillantine et sorbet "pur cacao". Wines Saint-Joseph, Saint-Péray.

XX ✿ **Aub. de l'Ile** (Ansanay), quartier St-Rambert, Ile Barbe ✉ 69009 ☎ 78 83 99 49, Fax 78 47 80 46 – P. AE ⊙ GB. ✂
closed 5 to 19 August, February Holidays, Sunday dinner and Monday – **Meals** 150 (lunch), 185/380 and a la carte 320/410
Spec. Nage d'huîtres au saumon et caviar (September to March). Noix de Saint-Jacques rôties au céleri (September to March). Canon d'agneau en croûte d'olives noires (Easter to October). Wines Morgon, Condrieu.

XX **Gourmet de Sèze,** 129 r. Sèze ✉ 69006 ☎ 78 24 23 42, Fax 78 24 23 42 – ▤. AE GB
closed 1 to 21 August, February Holidays, Saturday lunch and Sunday – **Meals** (booking essential) 125/250. HV **z**

XX **Fleur de Sel,** 7 r. A. Perrin ✉ 69002 ☎ 78 37 40 37, Fax 78 37 26 37 – GB FY **q**
closed August, Saturday lunch and Sunday – **Meals** 120 (lunch), 198/260.

XX **Thierry Gache,** 37 r. Thibaudière ✉ 69007 ☎ 78 72 81 77, Fax 78 72 01 75 – ▤. AE GB
closed Sunday dinner – **Meals** 99 b.i. (lunch), 125/265. GY **e**

XX **La Tassée,** 20 r. Charité ✉ 69002 ☎ 78 37 02 35, Fax 72 40 05 91 – ▤. AE ⊙ GB JCB
closed Saturday July-August and Sunday – **Meals** 130/260 ♨. FY **u**

XX **Gervais,** 42 r. P. Corneille ✉ 69006 ☎ 78 52 19 13, Fax 72 74 99 14 – AE ⊙ GB GX **a**
closed 14 July-15 August, Sunday and Bank Holidays – **Meals** 98 (lunch), 150/185 ♨.

XX **Tante Alice,** 22 r. Remparts d'Ainay ✉ 69002 ☎ 78 37 49 83 – ▤. AE GB FY **v**
closed 27 July-26 August, Friday dinner and Saturday – **Meals** 94/194 ♨.

XX **La Voûte,** 11 pl. A. Gourju ✉ 69002 ☎ 78 42 01 33, Fax 78 37 36 41 – ▤. AE ⊙ GB
closed Sunday – **Meals** 115 (lunch), 122/137. FY **e**

XX **Le Nord,** 18 r. Neuve ✉ 69002 ☎ 78 28 24 54, Fax 78 28 76 58, ☂ – ▤. AE GB FX **p**
Meals brasserie 120/158.

XX **La Pinte à Gones,** 59 r. Ney ✉ 69006 ☎ 78 24 81 75 – ▤. AE GB HX **s**
closed August, 24 December-2 January, Saturday lunch, Sunday and Bank Holidays – **Meals** 85/148 ♨.

XX **Assiette et Marée,** 49 r. Bourse ✉ 69002 ☎ 78 37 36 58 – ▤. GB FX **h**
Meals - Seafood - 100 b.i. and a la carte 140/190.

XX **Chez Jean-François,** 2 pl. Célestins ✉ 69002 ☎ 78 42 08 26, Fax 72 40 04 51 – ▤. AE GB JCB FY **x**
closed 4 to 9 April, 20 July to 21 August, Sunday and Bank Holidays – **Meals** 90/160 ♨.

X **Les Muses de l'Opéra,** pl. Comédie, 7th floor of the Opera ✉ 69001 ☎ 72 00 45 58, Fax 78 29 34 01, ≤, ☂ – ▤. AE GB FX **q**
Meals 89/149.

X **Assiette et Marée,** 26 r. Servient ☎ 78 62 89 94, Fax 78 60 39 27 – ▤. GB GY **n**
closed 15 to 19 August, 24 to 31 December and Sunday – **Meals** - Seafood - a la carte 140/190.

BOUCHONS : **Regional specialities and wine tasting in a lyonnaise atmosphere**

X **Le Garet,** 7 r. Garet ✉ 69001 ☎ 78 28 16 94, Fax 72 00 06 84 – ▤. AE GB FX **a**
closed 15 July-15 August, 23 December-1 January, Saturday and Sunday – **Meals** (booking essential) 86/115 ♨.

X **Chez Sylvain,** 4 r. Tupin ✉ 69002 ☎ 78 42 11 98 – GB FX **s**
closed 7 to 27 August, February Holidays, Saturday and Sunday – **Meals** (booking essential) 65/109 dinner a la carte.

X **Café des Fédérations,** 8 r. Major Martin ✉ 69001 ☎ 78 28 26 00 – AE GB FX **z**
closed 15 July-16 August, Saturday and Sunday – **Meals** 110 (lunch)/145.

X **La Meunière,** 11 r. Neuve ✉ 69001 ☎ 78 28 62 91 – AE ⊙ GB FX **p**
closed 14 July-15 August, Sunday and Monday – **Meals** (booking essential) 95/145.

X **Le Jura,** 25 r. Tupin ✉ 69002 ☎ 78 42 20 57 – AE GB FX **d**
closed 27 July-18 August, Monday lunch from October-April, Saturday from May-September and Sunday – **Meals** (booking essential) a la carte approx. 160.

X **Au Petit Bouchon "chez Georges",** 8 r. Garet ✉ 69001 ☎ 78 28 30 46 – GB FX **a**
closed 5 to 25 August, February Holidays, Saturday and Sunday – **Meals** 82/110 and dinner a la carte.

X **Chez Hugon,** 12 rue Pizay ✉ 69001 ☎ 78 28 10 94 – ⊙ GB FX **m**
closed August, Saturday and Sunday – **Meals** (booking essential) 110/135.

Environs

to the NE :

at Rillieux-la-Pape : 7 km by N 83 and N 84 - pop. 30 791 alt. 269 – ✉ 69140 :

XXX ✿ **Larivoire** (Constantin), chemin des Iles ☎ 78 88 50 92, Fax 78 88 35 22, ☂ – P. GB
closed 16 to 22 August, Monday lunch and Tuesday – **Meals** 160 (lunch), 200/400 and a la carte 320/400
Spec. Ravioles de tourteau, jus à l'estragon. Papillote de sandre au poivre de Sechuan. Canard des Dombes laqué "poivre et miel". Wines Crozes-Hermitage, Saint-Véran.

to the E :

at the Satolas airport : 27 km by A 43 - ✉ 69125 Lyon Satolas Airport :

Sofitel Satolas M without rest, 3rd floor ☎ 72 23 38 00, Telex 380480, Fax 72 23 98 00, ← - AE GB JCB
70 - **120 rm** 780.

XXX **La Grande Corbeille,** 1st floor ☎ 72 22 71 76, Fax 72 22 71 72, ← - AE GB JCB
closed August, Saturday and Sunday - **Meals** 185/350 and a la carte 220/340.

X **Le Bouchon,** 1st floor ☎ 72 22 71 86, Fax 72 22 71 72 - AE GB
Meals brasserie 105/180.

to the NW :

Porte de Lyon - motorway junction A 6 N 6 Exit road signposted Limonest N : 10 km - ✉ 69570 Dardilly :

Novotel Lyon Nord M, ☎ 72 17 29 29, Telex 330962, Fax 78 35 08 45, - 150. AE GB
Meals a la carte approx. 160 - 49 - **107 rm** 440/480.

Mercure Lyon Nord, ☎ 78 35 28 05, Telex 330045, Fax 78 47 47 15, - rest - 30 - 80. AE GB JCB
Meals 125 - 48 - **165 rm** 320/400.

Ibis Lyon Nord M, ☎ 78 66 02 20, Fax 78 47 47 93, - - 30. AE GB
Meals 81/120 - 36 - **64 rm** 325/355.

at Dardilly by D 77 - pop. 6 688 alt. 338 - ✉ 69570 :

XXX **Le Panorama,** at Dardilly-le-Haut, in front of church ☎ 78 47 40 19, Fax 78 43 20 31, - AE GB
closed Sunday dinner and Monday - **Meals** 155/330 and a la carte 290/440.

Annecy P **74000** H.-Savoie 74 ⑥ - pop. 49 644 alt. 448.

See : Old Annecy★★ : Descent from the Cross★ in church of St-Maurice, Palais de l'Isle★, rueSte-Claire★, bridge over the thiou ≤★ - Château★ - Jardins de l'Europe★ - Crêt du Maure forest★ : ≤★★ 3 km on the D 41.

Envir. : Tour of the lake★★★ 39 km (or 1 hour 30 min by boat).

18 of the lac d'Annecy ☎ 50 60 12 89 : 10 km by D 909 ; 9 18 of Giez ☎ 50 44 48 41.

of Annecy-Haute Savoie : T.A.T. ☎ 50 27 30 30, by N 508 and D 14 : 4 km.

Tourist Office Clos Bonlieu 1 r. J. Jaurès ☎ 50 45 00 33, Fax 50 51 87 20 - A.C. 15 r. Préfecture ☎ 50 45 09 12, Fax 50 23 61 31.

at Veyrier-du-Lac E : 5,5 km - pop. 1 967 alt. 504 - ✉ 74290

XXXXX ✿✿✿ **Aub. de l'Éridan** (Veyrat) M with rm, 13 Vieille rte des Pensières ☎ 50 60 24 00, Fax 50 60 23 63, ≤ lake, - AE GB JCB
closed 19 February-7 March - **Meals** *(closed Wednesday except June-September)* 365 (lunch), 595/995 and a la carte 700/900 - 195 - **11 rm** 1650/4850
Spec. Ravioli de légumes aux senteurs de sous-bois. Carré d'agneau au pimpiolet. Les trois crèmes brûlées à la découverte des Aravis. Wines Chignin-Bergeron, Mondeuse.

Chagny **71150** S.-et-L. 69 ⑨ - pop. 5 346 alt. 215.

Tourist Office 2 r. des Halles ☎ 85 87 25 95.

Lyons 145.

✿✿✿ **Lameloise** M, pl. d'Armes ☎ 85 87 08 85, Telex 801086, Fax 85 87 03 57, « Old Burgundian house, tasteful decor » - AE GB JCB
closed 18 December-23 January, Wednesday except dinner 1 July-30 September and Thursday lunch - **Meals** (booking essential) 370/600 and a la carte 390/560 - 90 - **17 rm** 650/1500
Spec. Ravioli d'escargots de Bourgogne dans leur bouillon d'ail doux. Pigeonneau rôti à l'émietté de truffes. Griottines au chocolat noir sur marmelade d'oranges. Wines Rully, Chassagne-Montrachet.

Fleurie **69820** Rhône 74 ① - pop. 1 105 alt. 320.

Lyons 59.

XXX ✿✿ **Aub. du Cep,** pl. Église ☎ 74 04 10 77, Fax 74 04 10 28 - AE GB
closed 30 July-7 August, mid December-mid January, Sunday dinner and Monday - **Meals** (booking essential) 190/400 and a la carte 270/450
Spec. Cuisses de grenouilles rôties. Queues d'écrevisses en petit ragoût. Volaille mijotée au vin de Fleurie. Wines Beaujolais, Fleurie.

Mionnay 01390 Ain 74 ② – pop. 1 103 alt. 276.
Lyons 23.

✿✿ **Alain Chapel,** ✆ 78 91 82 02, Fax 78 91 82 37, « Flowered garden » – TV ☎ P. AE ⓓ GB
closed January, Tuesday lunch and Monday except Bank Holidays – **Meals** 310 (lunch), 570/790 – ☕ 87 – **13 rm** 600/800
Spec. Lapin de quatre heures (April-September). Moelleux de pommes de terre et langoustines. Poulette en vessie (July-September). Wines Mâcon-Clessé, Morgon.

Montrond-les-Bains 42210 Loire 73 ⑱ – pop. 3 627 alt. 356 – Spa (March-November) – Casino.

18 Forez ✆ 77 30 86 85 at Craintilleux, S : 12 km by N 82 and D 16.

Syndicat d'Initiative 1 r. des Ecoles ✆ 77 94 64 74, Fax 77 54 51 96.

Lyons 62.

✿✿ **Host. La Poularde** (Etéocle), ✆ 77 54 40 06, Fax 77 54 53 14 – TV ☎ – 30. AE ⓓ GB JCB
closed 2 to 15 January, Tuesday lunch and Monday except Bank Holidays – **Meals** (Sunday : booking essential) 210/550 and a la carte 450/750 – ☕ 78 – **11 rm** 320/520, 3 duplex
Spec. "Crescendo" de saumon. Choisi d'agneau de lait (February-June). Pigeonneau du Forez cuit à l'os. Wines Condrieu, Saint-Joseph.

Roanne SP 42300 Loire 73 ⑦ – pop. 41 756 alt. 265.

9 of Champlong at Villerest ✆ 77 69 70 60.

✈ Roanne-Renaison ✆ 77 66 83 55, W : 5 km by D 9.

Tourist Office cours République ✆ 77 71 51 77, Fax 77 70 96 62 – A.C. 24 r. Rabelais ✆ 77 71 31 67.

Lyons 87.

✿✿✿ **Troisgros** M, pl. Gare ✆ 77 71 66 97, Fax 77 70 39 77, « Tasteful contemporary decor », – TV ☎. AE ⓓ GB JCB
closed 1 to 15 August, February Holidays, Tuesday dinner and Wednesday – **Meals** (booking essential) 300 (lunch), 560/700 and a la carte 440/650 – ☕ 110 – **15 rm** 700/1400, 4 suites
Spec. Beignets de cuisses de grenouilles au raifort. Tronçon de turbot cuit à l'étouffée. Pièce de boeuf du charolais au poivre éclaté. Wines Côte Roannaise, Bourgogne blanc.

Valence P 26000 Drôme 77 ⑫ – pop. 63 437 alt. 126.
See : House of the Heads (Maison des Têtes)★ – Interior★ of the cathedral – Champ de Mars ≤★ – Red chalk sketches by Hubert Robert★★ in the museum.

9 of Chanalets ✆ 75 55 16 23 ; 18 of St-Didier ✆ 75 59 67 01, E : 14 km by D 119 ; 18 of Bourget ✆ 75 59 41 71 at Montmeyran.

✈ of Valence-Chabeuil ✆ 75 85 26 26, SE : 5 km by D 68.

Tourist Office Parvis de la Gare ✆ 75 44 90 44, Fax 75 44 90 41 – A.C. 33 bis av. F. Faure ✆ 75 43 61 07, Fax 75 55 62 04.

Lyons 101.

XXXX ✿✿ **Pic** with rm, 285 av. V. Hugo, Motorway exit sign posted Valence-Sud ✆ 75 44 15 32, Fax 75 40 96 03, « Shaded garden » – TV ☎ P. AE ⓓ GB JCB
closed 5 to 21 August, Sunday dinner except Bank Holidays – **Meals** (Sunday : booking essential) 290 (lunch), 560/660 and a la carte 550/770 – ☕ 100 – **5 rm** 750/1000
Spec. Langoustines poêlées à l'huile d'olive et truffes. Tresse de loup et saumon au poivron doux. Strate de boeuf et foie de canard au vin de Cornas. Wines Condrieu, Hermitage.

at Pont-de-l'Isère to the N by N 7 : 9 km – alt. 120 – ✉ 26600 :

XXXX ✿✿ **Michel Chabran** M with rm, N 7 ✆ 75 84 60 09, Fax 75 84 59 65, – TV ☎. AE ⓓ GB
Meals 215 b.i. (lunch), 290/795 and a la carte 480/610 – ☕ 80 – **12 rm** 400/690
Spec. Marbré de caille au foie gras de canard. Saint-Pierre rôti entier, pommes rissolées grand-mère. Dos d'agneau cuit à l'os aux gousses d'ail. Wines Crozes-Hermitage, Saint-Joseph.

Don't confuse :

Comfort of hotels : 🏨🏨🏨🏨🏨 ... 🏨
Comfort of restaurants : XXXXX ... X
Quality of the cuisine : ✿✿✿, ✿✿, ✿, **Meals**

Vienne 38200 Isère 74 ⑪ ⑫ - pop. 29 449 alt. 160.

See : Site★ - St-Maurice cathedral★★ - Temple of Augustus and Livia★★ - Roman Theatre★ - Church★ and cloisters★ of St-André-le-Bas - Mont Pipet Esplanade ←★ - Old church of St-Pierre★ : lapidary museum★ - Sculpture group★ in the church of Ste-Colombe.

Tourist Office 3 cours Brillier ✆ 74 85 12 62, Fax 74 31 75 98.

Lyons 31.

✿✿ **La Pyramide** M, 14 bd F. Point ✆ 74 53 01 96, Telex 308058, Fax 74 85 69 73, - 25. AE GB
Meals *(closed Thursday lunch and Wednesday from 15 September-15 June)* 275 b.i. (lunch), 430/630 and a la carte 480/690 - 90 - **20 rm** 770/950, 4 suites
Spec. Gratin de queues d'écrevisses (15 June-15 October). "Piano" au praliné, amandes et noisettes. Wines Condrieu, Côtes-du-Rhône.

Vonnas 01540 Ain 74 ② - pop. 2 381 alt. 200.

Lyons 63.

✿✿✿ **Georges Blanc** M , ✆ 74 50 90 90, Fax 74 50 08 80, « Elegant inn on the banks of the Veyle, flowered garden », - . AE GB
closed 2 January-8 February - **Meals** *(closed Thursday except dinner from 15 June-15 September and Monday)* (booking essential) 460/830 and a la carte 480/770 - 95 - **32 rm** 900/1800, 6 suites
Spec. Crêpe parmentière au saumon et caviar. Pot-au-feu bressan aux trois volailles, bouillon corsé à l'huile de truffe. "Panouille" bressane glacée à la confiture de lait. Wines Mâcon, Chiroubles.

When driving through towns
use the plans in the ***MICHELIN*** *Red Guide.*

Features indicated include :
throughroutes and by-passes,
traffic junctions and major squares,
new streets, car parks, pedestrian streets...
All this information is revised annually.

MARSEILLES P 13000 B.-du-R. 84 ⑬ - pop. 800 550.

See : N.-D.-de-la-Garde Basilica ※★★★ - Old Port★★ - Palais Longchamp★ GS : Fine Arts Museum★, Natural History Museum★ - St-Victor Basilica★ : crypt★★ DU - Old Major Cathedral★ DS **N** - Pharo Parc ←★ DU - Hôtel du département et Dôme-Nouvel Alcazar★ - Vieille charité★★ (Mediterranean archeology) DS **R** - Museums : Grobet-labadié★★ GS **M**[7], Cantini★ FU **M**[5], Vieux Marseille★ DT **M**[2], History of Marseille★ ET **M**[1] - Fish market (quai des Belges ET **5**).

Envir. : Corniche road★★ of Callelongue S : 13 km along the sea front.

Exc. : Château d'If★★ (※★★★) 1 h 30.

18 of Marseilles-Aix ✆ 42 24 20 41 to the N : 22 km ; 18 of Allauch-Marseilles (private) ✆ 91 05 20 60, junction Marseilles-East : 15 km, by D 2 and D 4A ; 9 18 Country Club of la Salette ✆ 91 27 12 16, E : 10 km by A 50.

Marseilles-Provence : ✆ 42 78 21 00, to the N : 28 km.

✆ 36 35 35 35.

Tourist Office 4 Canebière, 13001 ✆ 91 54 91 11, Fax 91 33 05 03 and St-Charles railway station ✆ 91 50 59 18 - A.C. of Provence 149 bd Rabatau, 13010 ✆ 91 78 83 00.

Paris 772 - Lyons 312 - Nice 188 - Turin 407 - Toulon 64 - Toulouse 401.

Plans on following pages

Sofitel Vieux Port M, 36 bd Ch. Livon ✉ 13007 ✆ 91 52 90 19, Telex 401270, Fax 91 31 46 52, ←, « Panoramic restaurant ← old port », - 80. AE GB DU **n**
Meals 210 - 70 - **127 rm** 660/990, 3 suites.

Concorde-Palm Beach M , 2 prom. G. Pompidou ✉ 13008 ✆ 91 16 19 00, Fax 91 16 19 39, ←, , - 400. AE GB JCB. rest
La Réserve : **Meals** 178/209 - ***Les Voiliers :*** **Meals** 117, - 65 - **145 rm** 675.

✿✿ **Le Petit Nice** (Passédat) M , anse de Maldormé (turn off when level with no 160 Corniche Kennedy) ✉ 13007 ✆ 91 59 25 92, Fax 91 59 28 08, , « Villas overlooking the sea, elegant decor, ← », - P. AE GB
Meals *(closed Saturday lunch and Sunday from November-early April)* 310 b.i. (lunch), 590/750 and a la carte 500/780 - 115 - **13 rm** 1000/1900, 3 suites
Spec. Compressé de "bouille-abaisse" port d'Orient. Tronçon de loup "Lucie Passédat". Blue lobster "Nono's way". Wines Palette, Bandol.

Gd H. Mercure-Vieux Port M, r. Neuve St-Martin ✉ 13001 ✆ 91 39 20 00, Telex 401886, Fax 91 56 24 57, ≤, 余 – 闈 ⇌ ▤ TV ☎ ♿ 🚗 – 🏃 200. AE ⓓ GB JCB EST **g**
Oursinade : ✆ 91 39 20 14 *(closed August, Saturday lunch and Sunday)* **Meals** 168/198 🍷 – *Oliveraie :* **Meals** (lunch only) 125 🍷 – ☕ 60 – **199 rm** 399/600.

Mercure Beauvau without rest, 4 r. Beauvau ✉ 13001 ✆ 91 54 91 00, Telex 401778, Fax 91 54 15 76, ≤, « Antiques » – 闈 ⇌ ▤ TV ☎ – 🏃 25. AE ⓓ GB ET **r**
☕ 65 – **71 rm** 500/750.

Holiday Inn M, 103 av. Prado ✉ 13008 ✆ 91 83 10 10, Fax 91 79 84 12 – 闈 ⇌ ▤ TV ☎ ♿ 🚗 – 🏃 170. AE ⓓ GB JCB
Meals *(closed Saturday and Sunday)* 95/450 – ☕ 55 – **119 rm** 510/610, 4 suites.

Novotel Vieux Port M, 36 bd Ch. Livon ✉ 13007 ✆ 91 59 22 22, Fax 91 31 15 48, ≤, 余, 🏊 – 闈 ⇌ ▤ TV ☎ ♿ 🚗 – 🏃 200. AE ⓓ GB DU **n**
Meals 118 🍷 – ☕ 50 – **90 rm** 510/590.

New H. Bompard 🌿 without rest, 2 r. Flots Bleus ✉ 13007 ✆ 91 52 10 93, Fax 91 31 02 14, 🏊, 🌳 – 闈 kitchenette ▤ TV ☎ ♿ 🅿. AE ⓓ GB JCB
☕ 45 – **46 rm** 400.

St-Ferréol's M without rest, 19 r. Pisançon ✉ 13001 ✆ 91 33 12 21, Fax 91 54 29 97 – 闈 ▤ TV ☎. AE GB FU **h**
closed 1 to 21 August – ☕ 39 – **19 rm** 306/462.

Mascotte M without rest, 5 La Canebière ✉ 13001 ✆ 91 90 61 61, Fax 91 90 95 61 – 闈 ⇌ ▤ TV ☎ ♿. AE ⓓ GB ET **s**
☕ 42 – **45 rm** 300/440.

New H. Astoria without rest, 10 bd Garibaldi ✉ 13001 ✆ 91 33 33 50, Fax 91 54 80 75 – 闈 ▤ TV ☎. AE ⓓ GB JCB FT **f**
☕ 38 – **58 rm** 310.

Alizé M without rest, 35 quai Belges ✉ 13001 ✆ 91 33 66 97, Fax 91 54 80 06, ≤ – 闈 ▤ TV ☎. AE ⓓ GB ETU **b**
☕ 35 – **37 rm** 275/355.

New H. Sélect without rest, 4 allées Gambetta ✉ 13001 ✆ 91 50 65 50, Telex 402175, Fax 91 50 45 56 – 闈 ▤ TV ☎ – 🏃 25. AE ⓓ GB JCB FS **k**
☕ 38 – **60 rm** 295.

Castellane M without rest, 31 r. Rouet ✉ 13006 ✆ 91 79 27 54, Fax 91 25 44 07 – 闈 ▤ TV ☎ 🚗. AE ⓓ GB GV **f**
☕ 45 – **53 rm** 290/330.

Hermès without rest, 2 r. Bonneterie ✉ 13002 ✆ 91 90 34 51, Fax 91 91 14 44 – 闈 ▤ TV ☎. AE GB ET **a**
☕ 30 – **28 rm** 255/390.

XXX **Patalain,** 49 r. Sainte ✉ 13001 ✆ 91 55 02 78, Fax 91 54 15 29 – ▤. AE ⓓ GB EU **f**
closed 14 July-4 September, Saturday lunch, Sunday and Bank Holidays – **Meals** 150 (lunch), 180/370 and a la carte 250/380.

XXX **La Ferme,** 23 r. Sainte ✉ 13001 ✆ 91 33 21 12, Fax 91 33 81 21 – ▤. AE ⓓ GB EU **m**
closed August, Saturday lunch and Sunday – **Meals** 148 (lunch)/215 and a la carte 280/330.

XXX ✿ **Miramar** (Minguella), 12 quai Port ✉ 13002 ✆ 91 91 10 40, Fax 91 56 64 31, 余 – ▤. AE ⓓ GB JCB ET **v**
closed 3 to 25 August, 23 December-6 January and Sunday – **Meals** a la carte 310/400 🍷
Spec. Bouillabaisse. Filet de loup au beurre de "Pisala". Croustillant de Saint-Pierre au beurre de miel. Wines Cassis, Côtes de Provence.

XXX **Jambon de Parme,** 67 r. La Palud ✉ 13006 ✆ 91 54 37 98 – ▤. AE ⓓ GB JCB FU **s**
closed 13 July-28 August, Sunday dinner and Monday – **Meals** 185 and a la carte 230/320.

XX **L'Ambassade des Vignobles,** 42 pl. aux Huiles ✉ 13001 ✆ 91 33 00 25, Fax 91 54 25 60 – ▤. AE GB EU **h**
closed 5 August-2 September, Saturday lunch and Sunday – **Meals** 150/300 b.i..

XX **René Alloin,** 9 pl. Amiral Muselier (by prom. G. Pompidou) ✉ 13008 ✆ 91 77 88 25, Fax 91 77 76 84, 余 – GB
closed Saturday lunch, Sunday dinner and Monday lunch – **Meals** 135 (lunch), 185/250.

XX **Michel-Brasserie des Catalans,** 6 r. Catalans ✉ 13007 ✆ 91 52 30 63, Fax 91 59 23 05 – ▤. AE GB JCB
Meals - Seafood - a la carte 360/500.

XX **Les Arcenaulx,** 25 cours d'Estienne d'Orves ✉ 13001 ✆ 91 54 77 06, Fax 91 54 76 33, 余, « Bookshop and restaurant in original decor » – ▤. AE ⓓ GB JCB EU **s**
closed Sunday – **Meals** 135/280.

XX **Brasserie New-York,** 33 quai Belges ✉ 13001 ✆ 91 33 60 98, Fax 91 33 29 46, 余 – ▤. AE ⓓ GB ETU **b**
Meals 145 and a la carte 190/280 🍷.

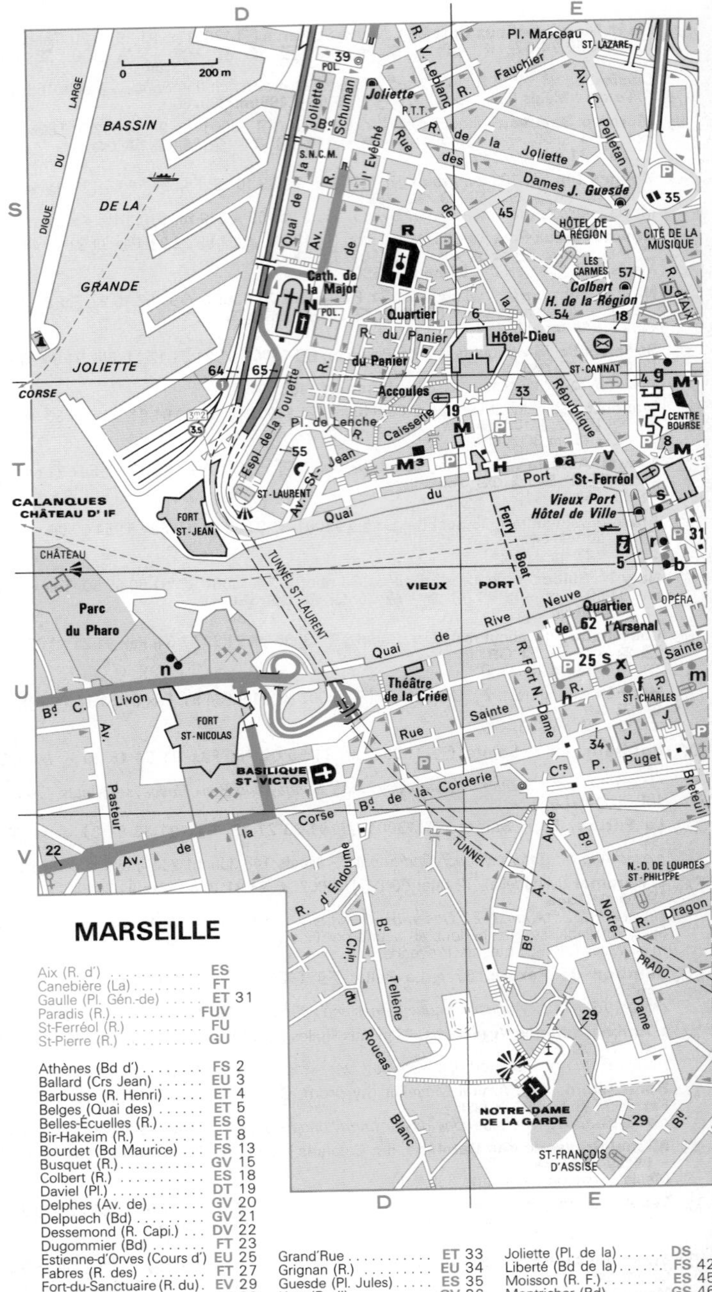

MARSEILLE

Aix (R. d')	ES	
Canebière (La)	FT	
Gaulle (Pl. Gén.-de)	ET	31
Paradis (R.)	FUV	
St-Ferréol (R.)	FU	
St-Pierre (R.)	GU	

Athènes (Bd d')	FS	2
Ballard (Crs Jean)	EU	3
Barbusse (R. Henri)	ET	4
Belges (Quai des)	ET	5
Belles-Écuelles (R.)	ES	6
Bir-Hakeim (R.)	ET	8
Bourdet (Bd Maurice)	FS	13
Busquet (R.)	GV	15
Colbert (R.)	ES	18
Daviel (Pl.)	DT	19
Delphes (Av. de)	GV	20
Delpuech (Bd)	GV	21
Dessemond (R. Capi.)	DV	22
Dugommier (Bd)	FT	23
Estienne-d'Orves (Cours d')	EU	25
Fabres (R. des)	FT	27
Fort-du-Sanctuaire (R. du)	EV	29
Garibaldi (Bd)	FT	30
Grand'Rue	ET	33
Grignan (R.)	EU	34
Guesde (Pl. Jules)	ES	35
Iéna (R. d')	GV	36
Joliette (Pl. de la)	DS	
Liberté (Bd de la)	FS	42
Moisson (R. F.)	ES	45
Montricher (Bd)	GS	46

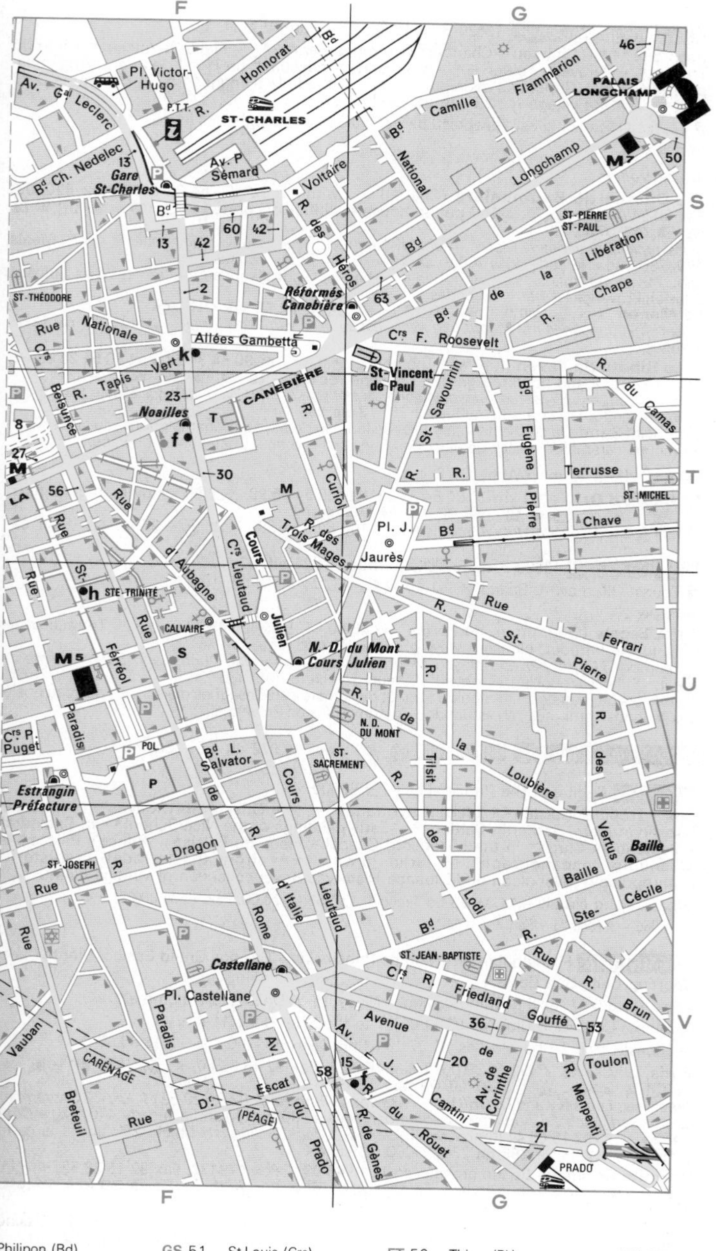

Philipon (Bd) . . . . **GS** 51
Raynouard (Traverse) . . . **GV** 53
Sadi-Carnot (Pl.) . . . . **ES** 54
St-Laurent (R.) . . . . **DT** 55

St-Louis (Crs) . . . . **FT** 56
Ste-Barbe (R.) . . . . **ES** 57
Ste-Philomène (R.) . . . . **FV** 58
Sembat (R. Marcel) . . . **FS** 60

Thiars (Pl.) . . . . **EU** 62
Thierry (Crs J.) . . . . **GS** 63
Tourette (Quai) . . . . **DS** 64
Vaudoyer (Av.) . . . . **DS** 65

Les Baux-de-Provence 13520 B.-du-R. 84 ① – pop. 457 alt. 185.

See : Site★★★ – Château – Charloun Rieu monument ≤★★ – Place St-Vincent★ – Rue du Trencat★ – Paravelle Tower ≤★ – Yves-Brayer museum★ (in Hôtel des Porcelet) – Shepherds' Festival (Christmas midnight mass) – Cathédrale d'Images★ N : 1 km on the D 27 – ✱★★★ of the village N : 2,5 km on the D 27.

Tourist Office Ilôt "Post Tenebras Lux" ✆ 90 54 34 39, Fax 90 54 51 15.

Marseilles 83.

in the Vallon :

XXXXX ✿✿ **Oustaù de Baumanière** (Charial) with rm, ✆ 90 54 33 07, Telex 420203, Fax 90 54 40 46, ≤, « 16C period house tastefully decorated », – ▤ TV ☎ P. AE ⓓ GB JCB
closed mid January-early March, Thursday lunch and Wednesday 1 November-1 April – **Meals** 470/730 and a la carte 410/700 – ☕ 115 – **7 rm** 1250, 4 suites
Spec. Ravioli de truffes. Filets de rougets au basilic. Gigot d'agneau en croûte. Wines Coteaux d'Aix-en-Provence-les-Baux, Gigondas.

Le Manoir without rest, ≤, – ▤ TV ☎ P. AE ⓓ GB JCB
closed mid January-early March and Wednesday 1 November-1 April – ☕ 115 – **5 rm** 1250, 4 suites.

XXX ✿ **La Riboto de Taven** (Novi and Theme) with rm, ✆ 90 54 34 23, Fax 90 54 38 88, ≤, « Terrace and flowered garden near the rocks » – P. AE ⓓ GB JCB
closed 9 January-15 March, Tuesday dinner out of season and Wednesday – **Meals** 198 (lunch), 298/420 and a la carte 360/490 – ☕ 80 – **3 rm** 990
Spec. Saint-Pierre à la crème de rattes. Filet de taureau de pays aux champignons sauvages. Tarte au fenouil caramélisé. Wines Côteaux des Baux-de-Provence, Châteauneuf-du-Pape.

road of Arles to the SW by D 78^F :

La Cabro d'Or, à 1 km ✆ 90 54 33 21, Fax 90 54 45 98, ≤, « Flowered gardens », – ▤ rm TV ☎ P – 60. AE ⓓ GB JCB
Meals *(closed Tuesday lunch and Monday)* 165 (lunch)/290 – ☕ 70 – **23 rm** 715, 8 suites.

Carry-le-Rouet 13620 B.-du-R. 84 ⑫ – pop. 5 224 alt. 5.

Tourist Office av. A. Briand ✆ 42 44 93 56, Fax 42 44 52 03.

Marseilles 27.

XXXX ✿✿ **L'Escale** (Clor), prom. du Port ✆ 42 45 00 47, Fax 42 44 72 69, « Terrace overlooking the harbour, pleasant view », – AE GB
1 February-31 October and closed Monday except dinner July-August and Sunday dinner – **Meals** (Sunday : booking essential) 320 and a la carte 400/530
Spec. Filets de rougets en ratatouille. Ragoût de la marée aux lasagnes maison. Ris de veau poêlé aux oignons compotés. Wines Bandol, Coteaux d'Aix-en-Provence.

MONACO (Principality of) 84 ⑩, 115 ㉗ ㉘ – pop. 29 972 alt. 65 – Casino.

Monaco Capital of the Principality – ✉ 98000.

See : Tropical Garden★★ (Jardin exotique) : ≤★ – Observatory Caves★ (Grotte de l'Observatoire) – St-Martin Gardens★ – Early paintings of the Nice School★★ in Cathedral – Recumbent Christ★ in the Misericord Chapel – Place du Palais★ – Prince's Palace★ – Museums : oceanographic★★ (aquarium★★, ≤★★ from the terrace), Prehistoric Anthropology★, Napoleon and Monaco History★, Royal collection of vintage cars★.

Urban racing circuit – A.C.M. 23 bd Albert-1er ✆ 93 15 26 00, Fax 93 25 80 08.

Paris 956 – ◆ Nice 21 – San Remo 44.

Monte-Carlo Fashionable resort of the Principality – Casinos Grand Casino, Monte-Carlo Sporting Club, Sun Casino.

See : Terrace★★ of the Grand casino – Museum of Dolls and Automata★.

18 Monte-Carlo Golf Club ✆ 93 41 09 11 to the S by N 7 : 11 km.

Tourist Office 2A bd Moulins ✆ 92 16 61 66, Telex 469760, Fax 92 16 60 00.

Paris, pl. Casino ✆ 92 16 30 00, Telex 469925, Fax 92 16 38 50, ≤, – ▤ TV ☎ – 25 - 70. AE ⓓ GB JCB. rest
Meals see ***Louis XV*** and ***Le Grill*** below - ***Terrasse-Empire*** ✆ 92 16 29 52 *(1 July-22 September and closed lunch 26 August-22 September)* **Meals** 280 (lunch) and a la carte 470/770 - ***Côté Jardin*** – ✆ **92 16 68 44 (lunch only)** *(closed 1 July-25 August)* **Meals** 290 and a la carte 300/410 – ☕ 140 – **159 rm** 2200/3000, 41 suites.

Hermitage, square Beaumarchais ✆ 92 16 40 00, Telex 479432, Fax 92 16 38 52, ≤, « Dining room in Baroque style », – ▤ TV ☎ P – 25-80. AE ⓓ GB JCB. rest
Meals 200 (lunch), 320/440 – ☕ 140 – **220 rm** 1750/2600, 16 suites.

Loews M, 12 av. Spélugues ✆ 93 50 65 00, Telex 479435, Fax 93 30 01 57, ≤, Casino and cabaret, – ▤ TV ☎ – 30 - 1 200. AE ⓓ GB JCB. rest
L'Argentin (dinner only) **Meals** 310 – ***Le Pistou :*** *(15 June-30 September)* **Meals** 190(lunch)/350bi – ***Café de la Mer :*** *(June-September)* **Meals** a la carte 180/320 – ☕ 110 – **500 rm** 1350/1750, 33 suites.

Métropole Palace [M], 4 av. Madone ☎ 93 15 15 15, Telex 489836, Fax 93 25 24 44, – AE GB JCB
Le Jardin : **Meals** 200/250, enf. 130 – ☐ 140 – **123 rm** 1250/1450, 18 suites.

Beach Plaza [M], av. Princesse Grace, à la Plage du Larvotto ☎ 93 30 98 80, Telex 479617, Fax 93 50 23 14, <, « Attractive resort with » – – 50 - 300. AE GB JCB. rest
La Pergola (closed Sunday and Monday) **Meals** (dinner only) a la carte 300/420 – ***La Terrasse :*** **Meals** 195/220 – ☐ 125 – **304 rm** 1600/2500, 9 suites.

Mirabeau [M], 1 av. Princesse Grace ☎ 92 16 65 65, Telex 479413, Fax 93 50 84 85, <, – – 25 - 100. AE GB JCB. rest
Meals see ***La Coupole*** below – ☐ 140 – **99 rm** 1300/2000, 4 suites.

Alexandra without rest, 35 bd Princesse Charlotte ☎ 93 50 63 13, Fax 92 16 06 48 – . AE GB JCB.
☐ 59 – **56 rm** 700/850.

Balmoral, 12 av. Costa ☎ 93 50 62 37, Telex 479436, Fax 93 15 08 69, < – . AE GB JCB.
Meals coffee shop *(closed November, Sunday dinner and Monday)* 150 – ☐ 75 – **80 rm** 600/850.

XXXXX ✿✿✿ **Le Louis XV** - Hôtel de Paris, pl. Casino ☎ 92 16 30 01, Telex 469925, Fax 92 16 69 21, – P. AE GB JCB.
closed 1 to 30 December, 11 to 26 February, Wednesday except dinner 19 June-21 August and Tuesday – **Meals** 780/890 and a la carte 670/940
Spec. Légumes mijotés à la truffe noire écrasée. Pigeonneau et foie gras de canard sur la braise. "Louis XV" au croustillant de pralin. Wines Bellet, Côtes de Provence.

XXXX ✿ **Grill de l'Hôtel de Paris,** pl. Casino ☎ 92 16 29 66, Telex 469925, Fax 92 16 38 50, « Rooftop restaurant with sliding roof and < the Principality » – P. AE GB JCB.
closed 7 January-5 February – **Meals** a la carte 520/870
Spec. Grosses langoustines rôties et légumes en barigoule (autumn-winter). Poissons de Méditerranée. Soufflés. Wines Côtes de Provence.

XXXX ✿ **La Coupole** - Hôtel Mirabeau, 1 av. Princesse Grace ☎ 92 16 66 99, Telex 479413, Fax 93 50 84 85, – P. AE GB JCB.
closed August – **Meals** 300/430 and a la carte 390/540
Spec. Queues de langoustines rôties, coulis de haricots cocos à l'infusion de verveine (summer). Carré d'agneau à l'huile aromatisée aux herbes de la garrigue. Tarte chaude au chocolat et son sorbet.

XXX **L'Hirondelle (Thermes Marins),** 2 av. Monte-Carlo ☎ 92 16 49 47, Fax 92 16 49 49, < port and the Rock, – . AE GB JCB.
closed Sunday dinner – **Meals** 260 and a la carte 290/420.

XXX **Le Saint Benoit,** 10 ter av. Costa ☎ 93 25 02 34, Fax 93 30 52 64, < port and Monaco, – . AE GB JCB
closed 23 December-7 January and Monday – **Meals** 165/230 and a la carte 250/330.

XX **Café de Paris,** pl. Casino ☎ 92 16 20 20, Fax 92 16 38 58, , « 1900 brasserie decor » – . AE GB JCB
Meals a la carte 200/300.

X **Polpetta,** 6 av. Roqueville ☎ 93 50 67 84 – GB
closed 15 to 31 October, 3 to 24 February, Saturday lunch and Tuesday – **Meals** - Italian rest. - 150.

at Monte-Carlo-Beach (06 Alpes-Mar.) at 2,5 km – ✉ 06190 Roquebrune-Cap-Martin :

Monte-Carlo Beach H. [M], ☎ 93 28 66 66, Telex 462010, Fax 93 78 14 18, < sea and Monaco, , « Extensive swimming complex », – rm P. AE GB JCB. rest
5 April-7 October – **Meals** (dinner only) a la carte 300/420 – ***La Potinière*** *(late May-16 September/(lunch only)* **Meals** a la carte 310/450 – ***Le Rivage :*** **Meals** a la carte 210/300 – ☐ 140 – **41 rm** 2350/2550, 3 suites.

NICE

P **06000** Alpes-Mar. 84 ⑨ ⑩, 115 ㉖ ㉗ – pop. 342 439 alt. 6 – Casino Ruhl FZ.

See : Site★★ – Promenade des Anglais★★ EFZ – Old Nice★ : Château <★★ JZ, Interior★ of church of St-Martin-St-Augustin HY **D**, Balustraded staircase★ of the Palais Lascaris HZ **K**, Interior★ of Ste-Reparate Cathedral HZ **L**, St-Jacques Church★ HZ **N**, Decoration★ of St-Giaume's Chapel HZ **R** – Mosaic★ by Chagall in Law Faculty DZ **U** – Palais des Arts★ HJY – Miséricorde Chapel★ HZ **S** – Cimiez : Monastery★ (Masterpieces★★ of the early Nice School in the church) HV **Q**, Roman Ruins★ HV – Museums : Marc Chagall★★ GX, Matisse★ HV **M2**, Fine Arts Museum★★ DZ **M**, Masséna★ FZ **M1** – Modern and Contemporary Art★★ HY – Parc Phoenix★ – Carnival★★★ (before Shrove Tuesday).

Envir. : St-Michel Plateau <★★, E : 9,5 km by D 2564.

✈ of Nice-Côte d'Azur ☎ 93 21 30 12, to the SW : 7 km.

☎ 36 35 35 35.

i Tourist Office av. Thiers ☎ 93 87 07 07, Fax 93 16 85 16 - 2 r. Massenet ☎ 93 87 60 60 and Nice-Ferber near the Airport ☎ 93 83 32 64 and at the Airport, Terminal 1 ☎ 93 21 41 11 – A.C. 9 r. Massenet ☎ 93 87 18 17, Fax 93 88 90 00.

Paris 932 – Cannes 32 – Genova 194 – Lyons 472 – Marseilles 188 – Turin 220.

NICE

Félix-Faure (Av.) . . . . . GZ 21
France (R. de) . . . . . . DFZ
Gambetta (Bd) . . . . . . EXZ
Gioffredo (R.) . . . . HY
Hôtel-des-Postes (R.) . . HY 30
Liberté (R. de la) . . . . . GZ 35
Masséna
(Espace, Pl.) . . . . . . GZ
Masséna (R.) . . . . FGZ 43
Médecin (Av. J.) . . . . . FGY 44
Paradis (R.) . . . . GZ 55
Pastorelli (R.) . . . . GY 58
République (Av. de la) . JXY 64

Alberti (R.) . . . . GHY 2
Alsace-Lorraine (Jardin) EZ 3
Armée-du-Rhin (Pl.) . . . JX 5
Auriol (Pont V.) . . . . . . JV 7
Bellanda (Av.) . . . . HV 10
Berlioz (R.) . . . . FY 12
Bonaparte (R.) . . . . JY 13
Carnot (Bd) . . . . JZ 15
Desambrois (Av.) . . . . GHX 18
Diables-Bleus
(Av. des) . . . . JX 19
Gallieni (Av.) . . . . HJX 23
Gautier (Pl. P.) . . . . HZ 25
Ile-de-Beauté
(Pl. de l') . . . . JZ 32
J.-Jaurès (Bd) . . . . . . HYZ 33

Lunel (Quai) . . . . JZ 37
Meyerbeer (R.) . . . . FZ 45
Monastère
(Av. et Pl. du) . . . . HV 46

Moulin (Pl. J.) . . . . HY 4
Parvis
(de l'Europe) . . . . JX 5
Passy (R. F.) . . . . EY 5

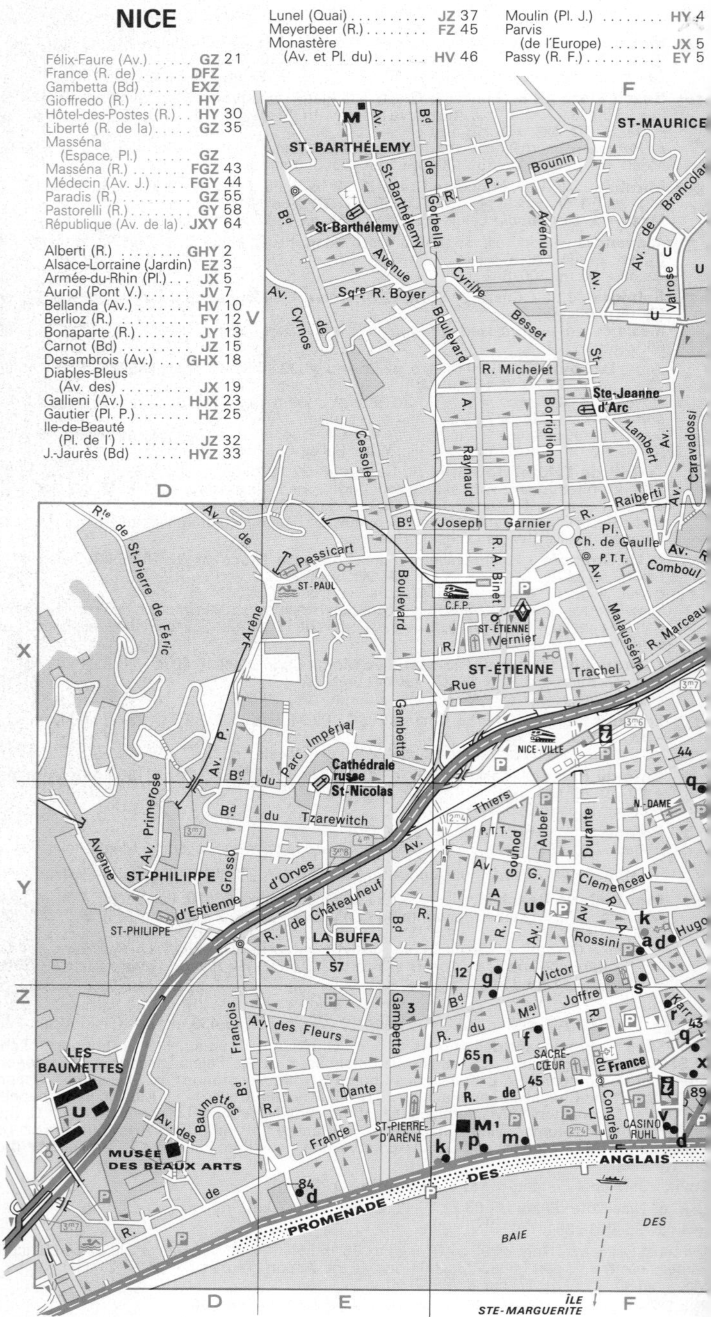

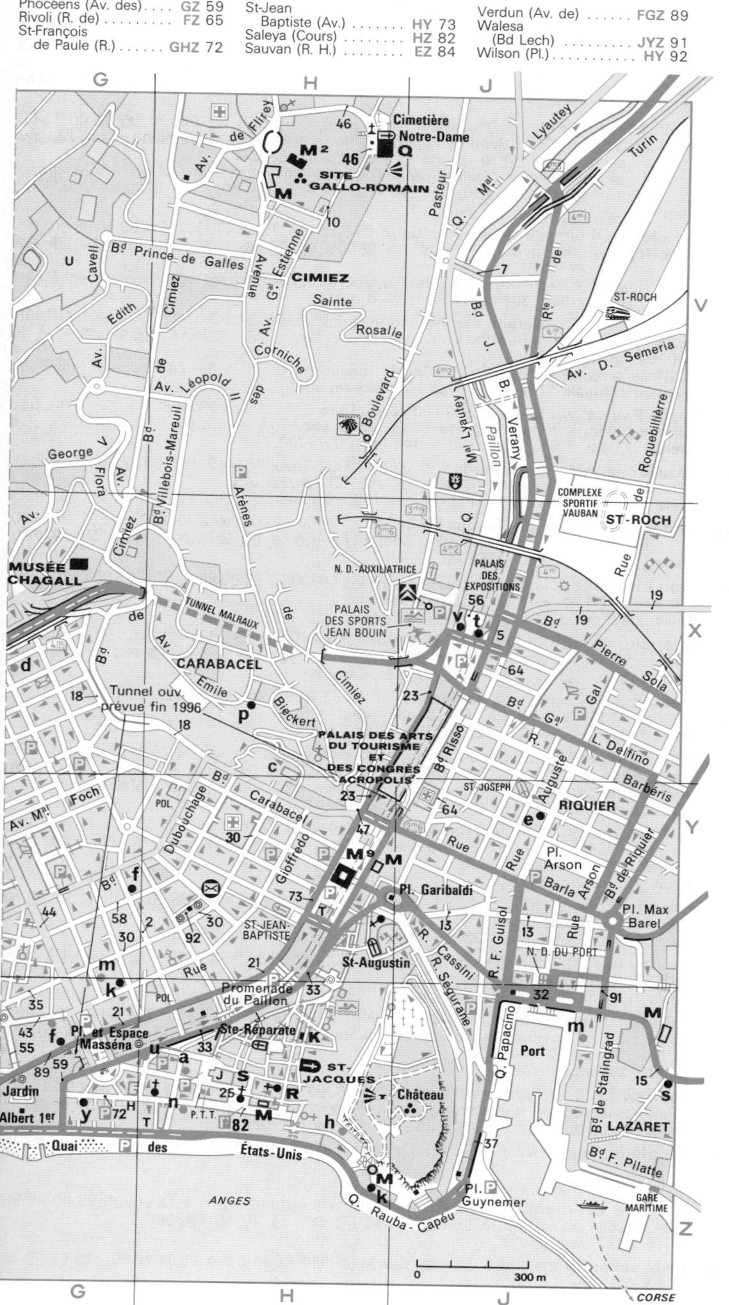

Cimetière Notre-Dame
SITE GALLO-ROMAIN
CIMIEZ
Bd Prince de Galles
Av. Gal Estienne
Sainte Rosalie
Corniche
Av. Léopold II
Bd Villebois-Mareuil
Boulevard Pasteur
Q. Mal Lyautey
Bd J. B. Verany
Paillon
Turin
Av. D. Semeria
ST-ROCH
COMPLEXE SPORTIF VAUBAN
Rue de Roquebillière
MUSÉE CHAGALL
TUNNEL MALRAUX
CARABACEL
Av. Emile Bieckert
Tunnel ouv. prévue fin 1996
N. D.-AUXILIATRICE
PALAIS DES EXPOSITIONS
PALAIS DES SPORTS JEAN BOUIN
PALAIS DES ARTS DU TOURISME ET DES CONGRÈS ACROPOLIS
Bd Pierre Sola
Bd Gal L. Delfino
Bd Risso
ST-JOSEPH
RIQUIER
Rue Barberis
Bd Carabacel
Dubouchage
Gioffredo
Av. Mal Foch
Pl. Garibaldi
Rue Arson
Pl. Arson
Barla
Bd de Riquier
Pl. Max Barel
ST-JEAN-BAPTISTE
St-Augustin
R. Cassini
R. Ségurane
R. F. Guisol
N. D. DU PORT
Promenade du Paillon
Pl. et Espace Masséna
Ste-Réparate
ST-JACQUES
Château
Q. Papacino
Port
Bd de Stalingrad
LAZARET
Bd F. Pilatte
Jardin Albert 1er
Quai des États-Unis
ANGES
Q. Rauba-Capeu
Pl. Guynemer
GARE MARITIME
CORSE
0
300 m

Négresco, 37 promenade des Anglais 93 16 64 00, Telex 460040, Fax 93 88 35 68, <, « 17C, 18C, Empire and Napoléon III furnishings » – 50 - 200. AE GB JCB FZ k
Meals see *Chantecler* below - ***La Rotonde :*** **Meals** 115/155, a la carte Sunday – 120 – **132 rm** 1630/2350, 18 suites.

Palais Maeterlinck M, 6 km by Inferior Corniche 06300 92 00 72 00, Fax 92 04 18 10, <, « Swimming pool, garden and terraces overlooking sea », – kitchenette P – 25. AE GB
closed January-mid March – ***Le Mélisande*** *(closed Sunday dinner and Monday in November and December)* **Meals** 140(lunch), 180/240 – 110 – **9 rm** 1750/2700, 10 suites2200/8000, 9 duplex.

Méridien M, 1 promenade des Anglais 93 82 25 25, Telex 470361, Fax 93 16 08 90, « Rooftop swimming pool, < bay » – – 25 - 200. AE GB JCB FZ d
L'Habit Blanc *: (October-April)* **Meals** 160/240, – ***La Terrasse*** *(May-September)* **Meals** 130/200, – 95 – **306 rm** 1250/1650, 8 suites.

Abela H. M, 223 promenade des Anglais 06200 93 37 17 17, Telex 461635, Fax 93 71 21 71, « Rooftop swimming pool < bay », – – 30 - 180. AE GB JCB DZ a
Les Mosaïques *(closed July-August)* **Meals** 155(lunch), 195/225 – ***La Piscine*** – **grill** *(open July-August)* **Meals** 145/255 – 90 – **321 rm** 900/1500, 12 suites.

Élysée Palace M, r. Sauvan 93 86 06 06, Telex 970336, Fax 93 44 50 40, « Rooftop swimming pool < Nice » – – 45. AE GB JCB EZ d
Meals a la carte 220/290 – 95 – **143 rm** 1000/1300.

Plaza Concorde, 12 av. Verdun 93 87 80 41, Telex 461443, Fax 93 82 50 70, <, « Rooftop terrace » – – 260. AE GB JCB GZ f
Meals 145/210 – 80 – **178 rm** 750/1500, 5 suites.

Sofitel M, 2-4 parvis de l'Europe 06300 92 00 80 00, Telex 461800, Fax 93 26 27 00, « Panoramic rooftop swimming pool », – – 50. AE GB JX t
Meals 115/175 – 80 – **152 rm** 1000.

Beau Rivage M, 24 r. St-François-de-Paule 06300 93 80 80 70, Fax 93 80 55 77, – – 35. AE GB GZ y
Meals grill 250 – 95 – **118 rm** 700/1800.

Splendid, 50 bd V. Hugo 93 16 41 00, Telex 460938, Fax 93 87 02 46, « Rooftop swimming pool < Nice » – – 30 - 100. AE GB JCB. rest FYZ g
Meals 145 – 75 – **113 rm** 820/1090, 14 suites.

West End, 31 promenade des Anglais 93 88 79 91, Telex 460879, Fax 93 88 85 07, <, – – 120. AE GB JCB FZ p
Meals 115/175 – 60 – **123 rm** 700/1300, 3 suites.

Westminster Concorde, 27 promenade des Anglais 93 88 29 44, Telex 460872, Fax 93 82 45 35, – rm – 150. AE GB JCB. rest FZ m
Le Farniente *(closed November and Sunday from 15 October-15 April)* **Meals** (dinner only July-August) 170/200 b.i. – 85 – **102 rm** 700/1200.

La Pérouse , 11 quai Rauba-Capéu 06300 93 62 34 63, Telex 461411, Fax 93 62 59 41, « < Nice and Baie des Anges », – rm . AE GB JCB. rest HZ k
Meals grill *(open : 15 May-15 September)* a la carte approx. 200 – 80 – **64 rm** 870/1300.

Atlantic, 12 bd V. Hugo 93 88 40 15, Telex 460840, Fax 93 88 68 60, – – 50. AE GB JCB FY d
Meals 130/200 – 80 – **123 rm** 600/850.

Holiday Inn M, 20 bd V. Hugo 93 16 55 00, Fax 93 16 55 55, – – 90. AE GB JCB. FY a
Meals 120/155 – 85 – **131 rm** 700/1060.

Pullman Nice without rest, 28 av. Notre-Dame 93 13 36 36, Telex 470662, Fax 93 62 61 69, « Hanging garden on 2nd floor, on 8th floor, < » – – 25 - 120. AE GB JCB FXY q
70 – **201 rm** 595/685.

Novotel M, 8-10 Parvis de l'Europe 06300 93 13 30 93, Fax 93 13 09 04, « Panoramic rooftop swimming pool » – – 80. AE GB JX v
Meals a la carte approx. 160 – 52 – **173 rm** 540/590.

Napoléon without rest, 6 r. Grimaldi 93 87 70 07, Fax 93 16 17 80 – . AE GB FZ r
60 – **83 rm** 510/720.

Mercure Promenade des Anglais M without rest, 2 r. Halévy 93 82 30 88, Telex 970656, Fax 93 82 18 20 – – 25. AE GB FZ v
75 – **122 rm** 840/890.

Ambassador without rest, 8 av. de Suède 93 87 90 19, Fax 93 82 14 90 – . AE GB JCB FZ x
15 February-15 November – 50 – **45 rm** 520/850.

Petit Palais without rest, 10 av. E. Bieckert ☎ 93 62 19 11, Fax 93 62 53 60, ≤ Nice and sea – AE GB JCB HX p
50 – **25 rm** 530/780.

Mercure Masséna without rest, 58 r. Gioffredo ☎ 93 85 49 25, Telex 470192, Fax 93 62 43 27 – AE GB JCB GZ k
65 – **116 rm** 520/795.

Apogia without rest, 26 r. Smolett ✉ 06300 ☎ 93 89 18 88, Fax 93 89 16 06 – AE GB JCB JY e
51 – **101 rm** 480/560.

Grimaldi without rest, 15 r. Grimaldi ☎ 93 87 73 61, Fax 93 88 30 05 – AE GB JCB FY s
50 – **24 rm** 600/800.

Windsor, 11 r. Dalpozzo ☎ 93 88 59 35, Fax 93 88 94 57, – rm AE GB. rest FZ f
Meals (coffee shop) *(closed Sunday)* a la carte approx. 150 – 40 – **60 rm** 415/670.

Gounod without rest, 3 r. Gounod ☎ 93 88 26 20, Fax 93 88 23 84 – AE GB JCB FYZ g
60 – **41 rm** 515/590, 6 suites.

Vendôme without rest, 26 r. Pastorelli ☎ 93 62 00 77, Telex 461762, Fax 93 13 40 78 – AE GB JCB GY f
40 – **51 rm** 410/550, 5 duplex.

Agata without rest, 46 bd Carnot ✉ 06300 ☎ 93 55 97 13, Fax 93 55 67 38 – AE GB JCB JZ s
40 – **45 rm** 400/550.

Régence without rest, 21 r. Masséna ☎ 93 87 75 08, Fax 93 82 41 31 – AE GB JCB FZ q
35 – **37 rm** 335/380.

Trianon without rest, 15 av. Auber ☎ 93 88 30 69, Fax 93 88 11 35 – AE GB FY u
35 – **32 rm** 230/320.

Marbella without rest, 120 bd Carnot ✉ 06300 ☎ 93 89 39 35, Fax 92 04 22 56, ≤ Coastline – AE GB.
30 – **17 rm** 230/430.

XXXXX ✿✿ **Chantecler** - Hôtel Négresco, 37 promenade des Anglais ☎ 93 16 64 00, Telex 460040, Fax 93 88 35 68 – AE GB JCB FZ k
closed mid November-mid December – **Meals** 255 b.i. (lunch), 395/560 and a la carte 450/650
Spec. Ravioli ouvert aux artichauts, pointes d'asperges et langoustines à l'huile d'olive (mid January-mid May). Filets de daurade royale, jus de légumes à la grecque. Composition de rougets aux courgettes, tomates et basilic en aïoli. Wines Côtes de Provence.

XXX **L'Ane Rouge,** 7 quai Deux-Emmanuel ✉ 06300 ☎ 93 89 49 63, Fax 93 89 49 63 – AE GB JZ m
closed Wednesday – **Meals** 148/198 and a la carte 240/330.

XX **Le Florian,** 22 r. A. Karr ☎ 93 88 86 60, Fax 93 87 31 98 – GB FY k
closed Saturday lunch and Sunday – **Meals** a la carte 180/310.

XX **Boccaccio,** 7 r. Masséna ☎ 93 87 71 76, Fax 93 82 09 06, « Carvel decor » – AE GB JCB GZ f
Meals - Seafood - 120 (lunch) and a la carte 200/360.

XX **Les Dents de la Mer,** 2 r. St-François-de-Paule ✉ 06300 ☎ 93 80 99 16, Fax 93 85 05 78, « Unusual decor depicting a submerged galleon » – AE GB JCB HZ n
Meals - Seafood - 148/199.

XX **Flo,** 4 r. S. Guitry ☎ 93 13 38 38, Fax 93 13 38 39, brasserie, « Former theatre » – AE GB GYZ m
Meals 101 b.i./145 b.i..

XX **Don Camillo,** 5 r. Ponchettes ✉ 06300 ☎ 93 85 67 95, Fax 93 13 97 43 – AE GB HZ h
closed 1 to 15 December, Monday lunch and Sunday – **Meals** - Niçoise and Italian specialities - 200/320.

XX **L'Univers,** 54 bd J. Jaurès ✉ 06300 ☎ 93 62 32 22, Fax 93 62 55 69 – AE GB HZ u
closed Sunday July-August – **Meals** 125/190.

XX **La Toque Blanche,** 40 r. Buffa ☎ 93 88 38 18, Fax 93 88 38 18 – GB FZ n
closed Sunday (except lunch September-June) and Monday – **Meals** 145/290.

X **Mireille,** 19 bd Raimbaldi ☎ 93 85 27 23 – GB GX d
closed 10 June-3 July, 2 to 10 October, Monday and Tuesday – **Meals** - One dish only : paella - 110/145.

X **La Merenda,** 4 r. Terrasse ✉ 06300 HZ a
closed August, February, Saturday, Sunday, Monday and Bank Holidays – **Meals** - Niçoise specialities - a la carte approx. 180.

at the airport : 7 km – ✉ 06200 Nice :

Campanile, 459 promenade des Anglais ☎ 93 21 20 20, Fax 93 83 83 96 – – 25 - 80. AE GB
Meals 92 b.i./119 b.i. – 34 – **170 rm** 370.

XXX **Ciel d'Azur,** aérogare 1, 2e étage ☎ 93 21 36 36, Fax 93 21 35 31 – AE GB JCB
Meals (lunch only) 235/290.

St-Martin-du-Var **06670** Alpes-Mar. 84 ⑨, 115 ⑯ – pop. 1 869 alt. 110.

Nice 26.

XXXX ✿✿ **Jean-François Issautier,** to the S : 3 km on N 202 ✆ 93 08 10 65, Fax 93 29 19 73 – ▤ P. AE ⓓ GB
closed 14 to 23 October, late February-late March, Sunday (except lunch 8 September-30 June) and Monday – **Meals** (booking essential) 210 (lunch), 320/515 and a la carte 430/580
Spec. Grosses crevettes poêlées en robe de pomme de terre. Poisson de Méditerranée rôti au jus de tomate, sauce pistou. "Cul" d'agneau de Sisteron à la menthe fraîche. Wines Côtes de Provence, Coteaux d'Aix.

STRASBOURG P **67000** B.-Rhin 62 ⑩ – pop. 252 338 alt. 143.

See : Cathedral★★★ : Astronomical clock★ – La Petite France★★ : rue du Bains-aux-Plantes★★ HJZ – Barrage Vauban ☀★★ – Ponts couverts★ – Place de la Cathédrale★ KZ **26** : maison Kammerzell★ KZ **e** – Mausoleum★★ in St-Thomas Church JZ – Place Kléber★ – Hôtel de Ville★ KY **H** – Orangery★ – Palais de l'Europe★ – Museum of Oeuvre N.-Dame★★ KZ **M¹** – Boat trips on the Ill river and the canals★ KZ – Museums★★ (decorative Arts, Fine Arts, Archeology) in the Palais Rohan★ KZ – Alsatian Museum★★ KZ **M²** – Historical Museum★ KZ **M³** – Guided tours of the Port★ by boat.

⛳9 ⛳9 ⛳9 at Illkirch-Graffenstaden (private) ✆ 88 66 17 22, to the S : 5 km ; ⛳18 of the Wantzenau at Wantzenau (private) ✆ 88 96 37 73, NE : 12 km by D 468 ; ⛳18 of Kempferhof at Plobsheim ✆ 88 98 72 72, S by D 468 : 15 km.

✈ of Strasbourg International : ✆ 88 64 67 67, SW : 12 km by D 392.

🚗 ✆ 36 35 35 35.

ℹ Tourist Office 17 pl. de la Cathédrale ✆ 88 52 28 28, Fax 88 52 28 29, pl. Gare and Pont Europe – A.C. 5 av. Paix ✆ 88 36 04 34, Fax 88 36 00 63.

Paris 490 – Basle 145 – Bonn 360 – Bordeaux 915 – Frankfurt 218 – Karlsruhe 81 – Lille 545 – Luxembourg 223 – Lyons 485 – Stuttgart 157.

Plans on following pages

Régent Petite France M without rest, 5 r. Moulins ✆ 88 76 43 43, Telex 880418, Fax 88 76 43 76, ←, « Former ice factory on the banks of River Ill - contemporary decor », – |‡| ⊁ ▤ TV ☎ ♿ – 🚗 – 25 - 60. AE ⓓ GB JCB JZ **z**
closed 21 December-1 January – ☕ 87 – **63 rm** 1050/1800, 5 suites, 4 duplex.

Hilton, av. Herrenschmidt ✆ 88 37 10 10, Telex 890363, Fax 88 36 83 27, – |‡| ⊁ ▤ TV ☎ ♿ P – 25 - 300. AE ⓓ GB JCB
La Maison du Boeuf ✆ 88 35 72 31 *(closed Saturday lunch and Sunday)* **Meals** 180(lunch)/280 – ***Le Jardin*** ✆ **88 35 72 61 Meals** 156/177 ♁ – ☕ 93 – **241 rm** 1050/1280, 5 suites.

Sofitel M, pl. St-Pierre-le-Jeune ✆ 88 32 99 30, Telex 870894, Fax 88 32 60 67, , patio – |‡| ⊁ ▤ TV ☎ 🚗 – 25 - 150. AE ⓓ GB JY **s**
L'Alsace Gourmande ✆ 88 75 11 10 **Meals** a la carte 170/300, ♁ – ☕ 85 – **158 rm** 995.

Beaucour M without rest, 5 r. Bouchers ✆ 88 76 72 00, Fax 88 76 72 60, « Old Alsatian houses elegantly decorated » – |‡| ▤ TV ☎ ♿ – 30. AE ⓓ GB KZ **k**
☕ 65 – **49 rm** 550/950.

Régent Contades M without rest, 8 av. Liberté ✆ 88 15 05 05, Fax 88 15 05 15, « 19C mansion », – |‡| ⊁ ▤ TV ☎. AE ⓓ GB LY **f**
☕ 87 – **45 rm** 770/1500.

Maison Rouge without rest, 4 r. Francs-Bourgeois ✆ 88 32 08 60, Telex 880130, Fax 88 22 43 73, « Tasteful decor » – |‡| TV ☎ ♿ – 40. AE ⓓ GB JZ **g**
☕ 65 – **142 rm** 540/590.

Monopole-Métropole without rest, 16 r. Kuhn ✆ 88 14 39 14, Telex 890366, Fax 88 32 82 55, « Alsatian and contemporary decor » – |‡| ⊁ TV ☎ 🚗. AE ⓓ GB JCB HY **p**
closed 23 December-5 January – ☕ 65 – **94 rm** 400/600.

Holiday Inn, 20 pl. Bordeaux ✆ 88 37 80 00, Telex 890515, Fax 88 37 07 04, – |‡| ⊁ ▤ TV ☎ ♿ P – 50 - 500. AE ⓓ GB JCB. ✂ rest
Meals 150 ♁ – ☕ 85 – **170 rm** 920/1090.

Europe without rest, 38 r. Fossé des Tanneurs ✆ 88 32 17 88, Fax 88 75 65 45, « Half timbered Alsatian house, beautiful 1/50th copy of the Cathedral » – |‡| ⊁ TV ☎ 🚗 – 40. AE GB JCB JZ **g**
closed 22 to 29 December – ☕ 44 – **60 rm** 370/550.

France without rest, 20 r. Jeu des Enfants ✆ 88 32 37 12, Fax 88 22 48 08 – |‡| TV ☎ 🚗 – 30. AE GB JY **v**
☕ 60 – **66 rm** 450/650.

Mercure Centre M without rest, 25 r. Thomann ✆ 88 75 77 88, Telex 880955, Fax 88 32 08 66 – |‡| ⊁ ▤ TV ☎ ♿ 🚗. AE ⓓ GB JY **q**
☕ 57 – **98 rm** 650.

Novotel Centre Halles M, 4 quai Kléber ✆ 88 21 50 50, Fax 88 21 50 51 – |‡| ⊁ ▤ TV ☎ ♿ – 25 - 100. AE ⓓ GB JY **k**
Meals a la carte approx. 160 ♁ – ☕ 57 – **97 rm** 540/570.

Grand Hôtel without rest, 12 pl. Gare ☎ 88 32 46 90, Telex 870011, Fax 88 32 16 50 – AE GB
65 – **83 rm** 380/610. HY **m**

Plaza, 10 pl. Gare ☎ 88 15 17 17, Fax 88 15 17 15, – AE GB JCB
La Brasserie : **Meals** 97, enf. 40 – 58 – **72 rm** 460/530, 6 suites. HY **m**

Carlton M without rest, 14 pl. Gare ☎ 88 32 62 39, Fax 88 75 94 82 – – 30. AE GB
50 – **60 rm** 420/470. HY **v**

Cathédrale M without rest, 12 pl. Cathédrale ☎ 88 22 12 12, Fax 88 23 28 00 – AE GB JCB
48 – **32 rm** 420/800, 3 duplex. KZ **n**

des Rohan without rest, 17 r. Maroquin ☎ 88 32 85 11, Fax 88 75 65 37 – AE GB JCB
50 – **36 rm** 410/695. KZ **u**

La Dauphine without rest, 30 r. 1e Armée ☎ 88 36 26 61, Fax 88 35 50 07 – AE GB
closed 23 December-2 January – 60 – **45 rm** 390/550.

Dragon M without rest, 2 r. Ecarlate ☎ 88 35 79 80, Telex 871102, Fax 88 25 78 95 – AE GB.
closed 23 to 27 December – 56 – **32 rm** 430/640. JZ **d**

Relais Mercure without rest, 3 r. Maire Kuss ☎ 88 32 80 80, Fax 88 23 05 39, – – 30. AE GB
49 – **52 rm** 370/450. HY **e**

Pax, 24 r. Fg National ☎ 88 32 14 54, Fax 88 32 01 16, – – 25 - 70. AE GB JCB
closed 24 December-2 January – **Meals** *(closed Sunday from November-February)* 85/110 – 36 – **106 rm** 330/370. HYZ **u**

Couvent du Franciscain without rest, 18 r. Fg de Pierre ☎ 88 32 93 93, Fax 88 75 68 46 – AE GB
closed 22 December-5 January – 40 – **43 rm** 270/310. JY **e**

Continental without rest, 14 r. Maire Kuss ☎ 88 22 28 07, Fax 88 32 22 25 – AE GB.
closed 24 to 30 December – 38 – **48 rm** 297/340. HY **s**

XXXX ✿✿✿ **Au Crocodile** (Jung), 10 r. Outre ☎ 88 32 13 02, Fax 88 75 72 01, « Elegant decor » – AE GB
closed 8 to 29 July, 22 December-1 January, Sunday and Monday – **Meals** 300 (lunch), 400/650 and a la carte 430/650 KY **x**
Spec. Timbale de sandre à la laitance de carpe. Lobe de foie d'oie truffé cuit tel un baeckeoffe. Groseilles et physalis en gelée de gentiane à l'orange. Wines Riesling.

XXXX ✿✿✿ **Buerehiesel** (Westermann), set in the Orangery Park ☎ 88 61 62 24, Fax 88 61 32 00, ←, park, « Reconstructed authentic Alsatian farmhouse with conservatory » – AE GB
closed 6 to 22 August, 22 December-5 January, February Holidays, Tuesday and Wednesday – **Meals** 290 (lunch), 340/650 and a la carte 430/700
Spec. Persillé de pintade au foie gras de canard. Schniederspäetle et cuisses de grenouilles poêlées au cerfeuil. Poulette "pattes noires" cuite comme un baeckeoffe. Wines Pinot noir, Riesling.

XXX **Maison Kammerzell and H. Baumann** M with rm, 16 pl. Cathédrale ☎ 88 32 42 14, Fax 88 23 03 92, « Attractive 16C Alsatian house » – rm – 120. AE GB
Meals 190/260 and a la carte 200/300 – 55 – **9 rm** 420/630. KZ **e**

XXX **Zimmer,** 8 r. Temple Neuf ☎ 88 32 35 01, Fax 88 32 42 28 – AE GB KY **y**
closed 29 July to 19 August and Sunday – **Meals** 170/350.

XXX **Maison des Tanneurs dite "Gerwerstub",** 42 r. Bain aux Plantes ☎ 88 32 79 70, Fax 88 22 17 26, « Old Alsatian house on the banks of the River Ill » – AE GB JZ **t**
closed 21 July-12 August, 30 December-21 January, Sunday and Monday – **Meals** a la carte 230/320.

XXX **Estaminet Schloegel,** 19 r. Krütenau ☎ 88 36 21 98, Fax 88 36 21 98 – AE GB LZ **q**
closed Sunday – **Meals** 110 (lunch), 210/290 and a la carte 250/320.

XX ✿ **Julien,** 22 quai Bateliers ☎ 88 36 01 54, Fax 88 35 40 14 – AE GB KZ **x**
closed 5 to 25 August, Christmas-New Year, Sunday and Monday – **Meals** 195 (lunch)/280 and a la carte 300/390
Spec. Foie gras d'oie poêlé au verjus de rhubarbe. Médaillons de lotte en croûte de poireaux et vinaigrette d'herbes. Noisettes de selle d'agneau en croûte persillée. Wines Klevner, Riesling.

XX **Au Gourmet Sans Chiqué,** 15 r. Ste-Barbe ☎ 88 32 04 07, Fax 88 22 42 40 – AE GB
closed 1 to 21 August, Monday lunch and Sunday – **Meals** 148 (lunch), 285/380. JZ **b**

XX **Pont des Vosges,** 15 quai Koch ☎ 88 36 47 75, Fax 88 25 16 85, – AE GB LY **h**
closed Saturday lunch, Sunday and Bank Holidays – **Meals** a la carte 170/230.

XX **Zuem Sternstebele,** 17 r. Tonneliers ☎ 88 21 01 01, – AE GB KZ **h**
closed Monday lunch and Sunday – **Meals** (booking essential) a la carte 150/270.

STRASBOURG

Division Leclerc (R. de la) . JKZ
Grandes Arcades (R. des) . JKY
Kléber (Place) . . . . JY
Maire Kuss (R. du) . . . . . HY 120
Mésange (R. de la) . . . . . JKY 136
Nuée-Bleue (R. de la) KY
Vieux-Marché-aux-Poissons (R. du) . . . . . KZ 228
22 Novembre (R. du) HJY

Abreuvoir (R. de l') . . . . . LZ 3
Alsace (Av. d') . . . . LY 4
Arc-en-ciel (R. de l') . . . . . KLY 7
Austerlitz (Pl. d') . . . . KZ
Austerlitz (R. d') . . . . KZ 10
Auvergne (Pont d') . . . . . LY 12
Bain-aux-Plantes (R. du) . HJZ
Bateliers (Quai des) . . . . . KZ
Bouchers (R. des) . . . . . . KZ
Broglie (Place) . . . . KY
Brulée (Rue) . . . . KY
Castelnau (R. Gén. de) . . . KY 25
Cathédrale (Pl. de la) . . . . KZ 26
Château (Place du) . . . . . . KZ
Chaudron (R. du) . . . . KY 28
Cheveux (R. des) . . . . JZ 29
Clément (Place) . . . . JY 30
Corbeau (Cour du) . . . . . . KZ
Corbeau (Pl. du) . . . . KZ 31
Corbeau (Pont du) . . . . KZ
Cordiers (R. des) . . . . KZ 32
Course (Pte R. de la) . . . . . HY 34
Dentelles (R. des) . . . . JZ 36
Desaix (Quai) . . . . HY 37
Dôme (Rue du) . . . . KY
Douane (R. de la) . . . . KZ 40
Dunant (R. Henri) . . . . HZ 42
Etudiants (R. des) . . . . KY 45
Ecarlate (R. de l') . . . . JZ 46
Faisan (Pont du) . . . . JZ 47
Finkmatt (Quai) . . . . JKY 49
Finkwiller (Quai) . . . . JZ 51
Foch (Rue du Mar.) . . . . . . KY 52
Fonderie (R. de la) . . . . . KY
Fossé-des-Tanneurs (R. du) JZ 57
Fossé-des-Treize (R. du) . KY 58
Francs-Bourgeois (R. des) JZ 60
Frères (R. des) . . . . KYZ
Frères-Matthis (R. des) . . HZ 61
Frey (Quai Ch.) . . . . JZ 63
Grand'Rue . . . . HJZ
Grande-Boucherie (Pl. de la) KZ 76
Gutemberg (Place) . . . . . KZ
Hallebardes (R. des) . . . . KZ
Halles (Place des) . . . . . . HJY
Haute-Montée (R.) . . . . . . JY 82
Homme-de-Fer (Pl. de l') . JY 90
Hôpital-Militaire (R. de l') . LZ 91
Humann (Rue) . . . . HZ 94
Jeu-des-Enfants (R. du) . . JY 97
Joffre (R. du Mar.) . . . . . . LY
Juifs (Rue des) . . . . KY
Kageneck (Rue) . . . . HY
Kellermann (Quai) . . . . . . JY 10
Kléber (Quai) . . . . JY
Koch (Quai) . . . . LY 10

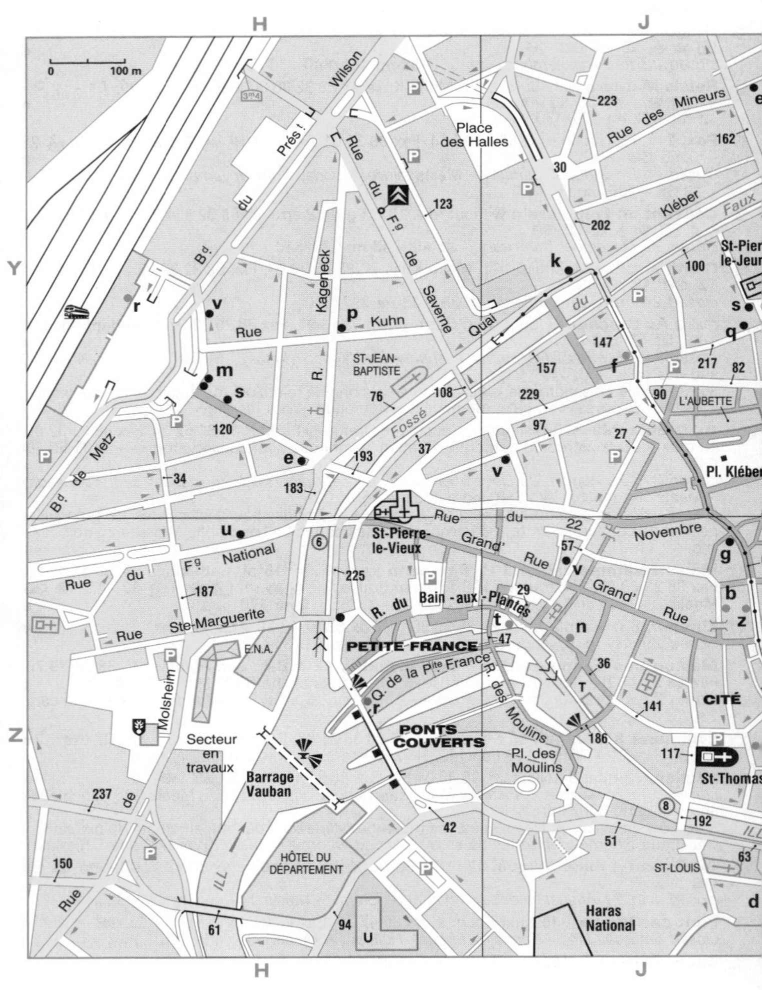

Rue	Carré	N°
Krutenau (Rue de la)	LZ	106
Kuhn (Rue)	HY	
Kuss (Pont)	HY	108
Lamey (R. Auguste)	LY	109
Lezay-Marnésia (Quai)	LY	114
Liberté (Av. de la)	LY	
Luther (Rue Martin)	JZ	117
Maire (Quai du)	LY	118
Marais-Vert (R. du)	HY	123
Marché-aux-Cochons-de-Lait (Pl. du)	KZ	124
Marché-Gayot (Pl. du)	KYZ	126
Marché-Neuf (Pl. du)	KYZ	127
Maroquin (R. du)	KZ	129
Marseillaise (Av. de la)	LY	
Mercière (Rue)	KZ	135
Metz (Bd de)	HY	
Mineurs (R. des)	JY	
Molsheim (R. de)	HZ	
Monnaie (R. de la)	JZ	141
Moulins (R. des)	JZ	
Munch (Rue)	LZ	142
National (R. du Fg)	HZ	
Noyer (Rue du)	JY	147
Obernai (Rue d')	HZ	150
Orphelins (R. des)	LZ	
Outre (R. de l')	KY	153
Paix (Av. de la)	KLY	154
Parchemin (R. du)	KY	156
Paris (Quai de)	JY	157
Pêcheurs (Q. des)	LY	
Pierre (R. du Fg de)	JY	162
Pont Royal	LY	
Président Wilson (Bd)	HY	
Récollets (R. des)	KLY	172
République (Pl. de la)	KY	
St-Étienne (Place)	KLY	
St-Gothard (R. du)	LZ	181
St-Jean (Quai)	HY	183
St-Martin (Pont)	JZ	186
St-Michel (Rue)	HZ	187
St-Nicolas (Pont)	KZ	189
St-Nicolas (Quai)	KZ	
St-Pierre-le-Jeune (Pl.)	JKY	190
St-Thomas (Pont)	JZ	192
St-Thomas (Quai)	JKZ	193
Ste-Marguerite (R.)	HZ	
Sanglier (R. du)	KY	194
Saverne (Pont de)	HY	195
Saverne (R. du Fg de)	HY	
Schœpflin (Quai)	KY	
Sébastopol (R. de)	JY	202
Serruriers (R. des)	JKZ	205
Sturm (Quai J.)	KY	
Temple Neuf (Pl. du)	KY	213
Temple Neuf (R. du)	KY	214
Théâtre (Pont du)	KY	216
Thomann (Rue)	KZ	217
Tonneliers (Rue des)	KZ	220
Travail (Rue du)	JY	223
Turckheim (Quai)	HZ	225
Veaux (R. des)	KLZ	
Vieux-Marché-aux-Vins (R. du)	JY	229
Vosges (Av. des)	LY	
Wasselonne (R. de)	HZ	237
Zurich (R. de)	LZ	
Zurich (Place de)	LZ	243
1re Armée (R. de la)	KZ	244

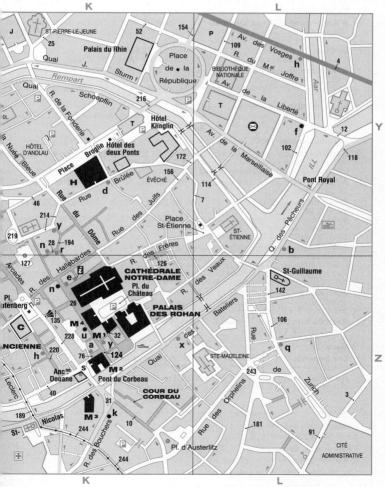

XX **Bec Doré,** 8 quai Pêcheurs ✆ 88 35 39 57 – ▤. AE ⓓ GB LY b
closed 15 to 30 August, 3 to 10 January, Tuesday lunch and Monday – **Meals** a la carte 140/230 ♁.

XX **Au Boeuf Mode,** 2 pl. St-Thomas ✆ 88 32 39 03, Fax 88 21 90 80 – AE ⓓ GB JZ k
closed Sunday – **Meals** 95 (lunch), 150/195 ♁.

XX **Le Benjamin,** 3 r. Dentelles ✆ 88 75 16 67, Fax 88 75 16 67 – AE GB JZ
closed 1 to 15 January, Monday lunch and Sunday – **Meals** 49 (lunch), 110/158 b.i..

XX **Buffet Gare,** pl. Gare ✆ 88 32 68 28, Fax 88 32 88 34 – AE ⓓ GB HY
Meals 68/100 ♁.

X **Ami Schutz,** 1 r. Ponts Couverts ✆ 88 32 76 98, Fax 88 32 38 40, 🏠 – AE ⓓ GB HZ
Meals 165/169 ♁.

X **Au Rocher du Sapin,** 6 r. Noyer ✆ 88 32 39 65, Fax 88 75 60 99, 🏠 – GB JY
closed Sunday and Monday – **Meals** - Alsatian rest. - 88/105 ♁.

WINSTUBS : Regional specialities and wine tasting in a typical Alsatian atmosphere :

X **Zum Strissel,** 5 pl. Gde Boucherie ✆ 88 32 14 73, Fax 88 32 70 24, rustic decor – ▤. GB
closed 4 to 31 July, February Holidays, Sunday except Bank Holidays and Monday – **Meals** 60/130 ♁. KZ

X **S'Burjerstuewel (Chez Yvonne),** 10 r. Sanglier ✆ 88 32 84 15, Fax 88 23 00 18 – GB
closed 14 July-15 August, 22 December-2 January, Monday lunch and Sunday – **Meals** (booking essential) a la carte 140/220 ♁. KYZ

X **Le Clou,** 3 r. Chaudron ✆ 88 32 11 67, Fax 88 75 72 83 – AE GB KY
closed Wednesday lunch, Sunday and Bank Holidays – **Meals** 125/200 b.i..

X **S'Munsterstuewel,** 8 pl. Marché aux Cochons de Lait ✆ 88 32 17 63, Fax 88 21 96 02, 🏠 – AE ⓓ GB KZ
closed 28 July-20 August, February Holidays, Sunday and Monday – **Meals** 128 b.i. and a la carte 150/250.

X **La Petite Mairie,** 8 r. Brûlée ✆ 88 32 83 06 – GB KY
closed August, Saturday dinner and Sunday except December – **Meals** 110 (lunch), 150/200 ♁.

Environs

at La Wantzenau NE by D 468 : 12 km - pop. 4 394 alt. 130 - ✉ 67610 :

Hôtel Au Moulin 🔇, S : 1,5 km by D 468 ✆ 88 59 22 22, Fax 88 59 22 00, ≤, « Old water mill on a branch of the River Ill », 🌳 – |‡| TV ☎ P. AE GB
closed 24 December-2 January – **Meals** see rest. ***Au Moulin*** below – ☕ 55 – **19 rm** 330/440

A la Gare without rest, 32 r. Gare ✆ 88 96 63 44, Fax 88 96 64 95 – TV ☎ P. GB. 🐕
☕ 28 – **15 rm** 180/250.

XXX **Relais de la Poste** M with rm, 21 r. Gén. de Gaulle ✆ 88 96 20 64, Fax 88 96 36 84, 🏠 🌳 – |‡| ▤ rest TV ☎ ♿ P. AE ⓓ GB
hotel : closed 27 December-20 January – **Meals** *(closed 22 July-4 August, 27 December-20 January, Saturday lunch, Sunday dinner and Monday lunch)* 175 (lunch), 225/395 and a la carte 290/400 ♁ – ☕ 50 – **19 rm** 300/550.

XXX ✿ **A la Barrière** (Sutter), 3 rte Strasbourg ✆ 88 96 20 23, Fax 88 96 25 59, 🏠 – P. AE ⓓ GB
closed 12 to 31 August, February Holidays, Tuesday dinner and Wednesday – **Meals** (Sunday booking essential) 150 (lunch)/250 and a la carte 270/480 ♁
Spec. Lièvre à la royale (November). Bouillon de Saint-Jacques et lentilles (winter). Foie gras d'oie cuit au torchon et berewecke. Wines Sylvaner, Riesling.

XXX **Zimmer,** 23 r. Héros ✆ 88 96 62 08, Fax 88 96 37 40, 🏠 – AE ⓓ GB
closed 14 July-7 August, 19 January-5 February, Sunday dinner and Monday – **Meals** 135/33 and a la carte 210/360 ♁.

XX **Rest. Au Moulin** - Hôtel Au Moulin, S : 1,5 km by D 468 ✆ 88 96 20 01, 🏠, « Floral garden » – ▤ P. AE ⓓ GB
closed 4 to 24 July, 31 December to 16 January, Sunday dinner and dinner Bank Holidays – **Meals** 140/365 ♁.

XX **Les Semailles,** 10 r. Petit-Magmod ✆ 88 96 38 38, 🏠 – GB. 🐕
closed 15 August-6 September, Saturday lunch, Sunday dinner and Monday – **Meals** 160/220

XX **Au Soleil,** 1 quai Bateliers ✆ 88 96 20 29, Fax 88 96 20 29, 🏠 – P. AE GB
closed 17 February-2 March and Thursday dinner – **Meals** 52 (lunch), 125/275 ♁.

Pleasant hotels and restaurants are shown in the Guide by a red sign.
Please send us the names of any where you have enjoyed your stay.
Your Michelin Guide will be even better.

XXXXX ... X

Illhaeusern **68970** H.-Rhin 62 ⑲ - pop. 578 alt. 173.
Strasbourg 60.

La Clairière M without rest, rte Guémar ☎ 89 71 80 80, Fax 89 71 86 22, – TV ☎ P. GB
closed 1 January-1 March – 70 – **26 rm** 430/980.

XXXXX ✿✿✿ **Auberge de l'Ill** (Haeberlin), ☎ 89 71 89 00, Fax 89 71 82 83, « Elegant installation, on the banks of the River Ill, ≤ floral gardens » – P. AE GB
closed 5 February-8 March, Monday except lunch April-October and Tuesday – **Meals** (booking essential) 500/710 and a la carte 500/660
Spec. Gelée de maquereau, radis "ostergrüss" et livèche (June-September). Filets de carpe et perche aux haricots cocos blancs. Canard Colvert laqué aux épices (August-January). Wines Pinot blanc, Riesling.

H. des Berges M, ☎ 89 71 87 87, Fax 89 71 87 88, ≤, « Resembling a tobacco shed in the Ried country », – rm TV ☎ AE GB JCB
Meals see ***Aub. de l'Ill*** – 130 – **7 rm** 1450/1700.

Lembach **67510** B.-Rhin 57 ⑲ - pop. 1 710 alt. 190.
Tourist Office rte Bitche ☎ 88 94 43 16, Fax 88 94 20 04.
Strasbourg 55.

XXXX ✿✿ **Aub. Cheval Blanc** (Mischler), 4 rte Wissembourg ☎ 88 94 41 86, Fax 88 94 20 74, « Old coaching inn », – P. AE GB
closed 8 to 26 July, 3 to 21 February, Monday and Tuesday – **Meals** 175/410 and a la carte 300/380
Spec. Farandole de quatre foies d'oie chauds. Suprême de sandre et "schniderspattle". Médaillons de chevreuil "Fleckenstein" (25 May-10 February). Wines Pinot blanc, Muscat.

Marlenheim **67520** B.-Rhin 62 ⑨ - pop. 2 956 alt. 195.
Strasbourg 20.

XXXX ✿✿ **Le Cerf** (Husser) with rm, ☎ 88 87 73 73, Fax 88 87 68 08, – TV ☎ P. AE GB
closed Tuesday and Wednesday – **Meals** 250 b.i. (lunch), 295/500 and a la carte 260/370 – 60 – **15 rm** 300/600
Spec. Ravioles de foie de canard fumé en pot-au-feu. Choucroute au cochon de lait rôti et foie gras fumé. Aumônière aux griottines, coulis de framboises, glace au fromage blanc. Wines Pinot noir, Riesling.

For the quickest route use the MICHELIN Main Road Maps :

970 Europe, 976 Czech Republic-Slovak Republic, 980 Greece, 984 Germany,
985 Scandinavia-Finland, 986 Great Britain and Ireland, 987 Germany-Austria-Benelux,
988 Italy, 989 France, 990 Spain-Portugal *and* 991 Yugoslavia.

VALLEY OF THE LOIRE

Tours P **37000** I.-et-L. 64 ⑮ - pop. 129 509 alt. 60.
See : Cathedral quarter★★ : Cathedral★★ CDY, Fine Arts Museum★★ CDY, Historial de Touraine★ (château) CY M³, The Psalette★ CY, – Place Grégoire de Tours★ DY 46 – Old Tours★★ : Place Plumereau★ ABY, hôtel Gouin★ BY, rue Briçonnet★ AY 12 – St-Julien quarter★ : Craft Guilds Museum★★ (Musée du Compagnonnage) BY, Beaune-Semblançay Garden★ BY B – St-Cosme Priory★ W : 3 km – Museum of military transport and trains★ – Meslay Tithe Barn★ (Grange de Meslay) NE : 10 km by N 10.
18 of Touraine ☎ 47 53 20 28, domaine de la Touche at Ballan-Miré, SW : 14 km by D 751 ;
18 of Ardrée ☎ 47 56 77 38, NW : 14 km by N 138.
of Tours-St-Symphorien : T.A.T ☎ 47 54 19 46, NE : 7 km.
Tourist Office 78 r. Bernard Palissy ☎ 47 70 37 37, Fax 47 61 14 22 – A.C. 4 pl. J. Jaurès ☎ 47 05 50 19.
Paris 234 – Angers 109 – Bordeaux 346 – Chartres 140 – Clermont-Ferrand 335 – Limoges 220 – Le Mans 80 – Orléans 115 – Rennes 219 – St-Étienne 474.

Plans on following pages

✿✿ **Jean Bardet** M, 57 r. Groison ✉ 37100 ☎ 47 41 41 11, Telex 752463, Fax 47 51 68 72, ≤, « Flowered park, attractive kitchen garden », – TV ☎ P. AE GB JCB
Meals *(closed Monday lunch April-October, Sunday dinner and Monday November-March)* 270/750 and a la carte 510/630 – 120 – **16 rm** 650/1000, 5 suites
Spec. Aumônière de légumes, fleurette d'herbes. Fricassée de petites anguilles au vinaigre de vin de Bourgueil. Pintadeau fermier truffé, parmentier de charlotte. Wines Vouvray, Saint-Nicolas de Bourgueil.

Univers and rest. La Touraine M, 5 bd Heurteloup ☎ 47 05 37 12, Telex 751460, Fax 47 61 51 80, « Murals depicting famous past visitors » – TV ☎ – 120. AE GB CZ u
Meals 130/170 – 65 – **75 rm** 650/1200, 10 suites.

TOURS

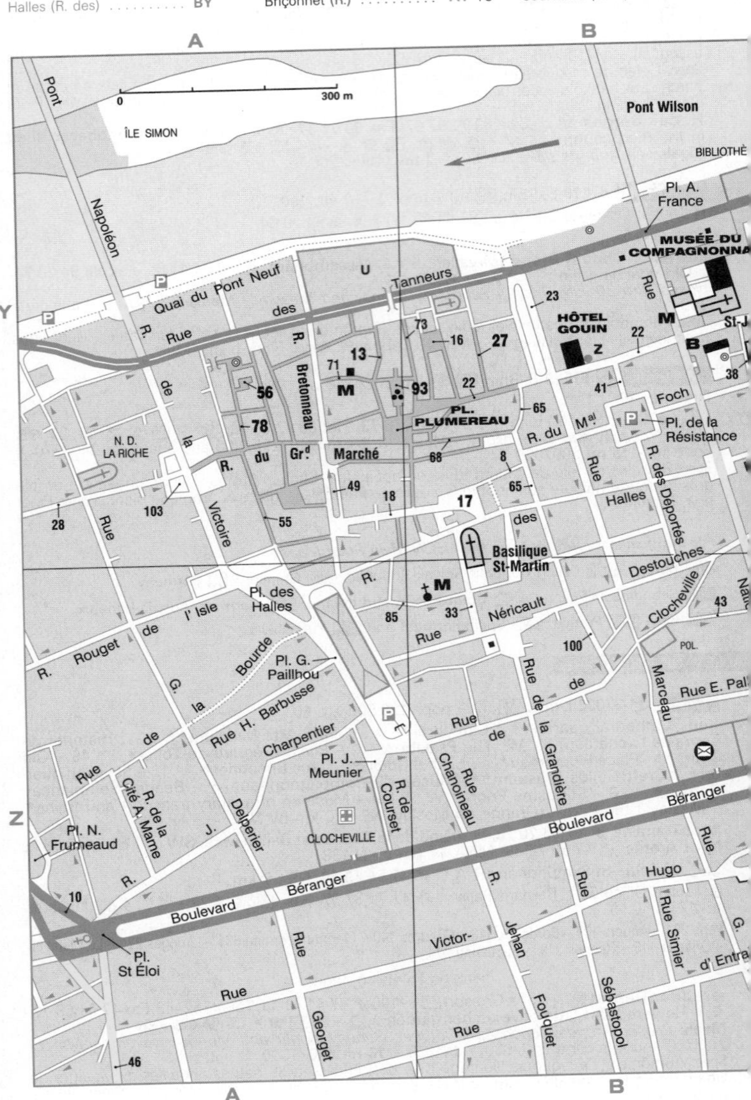

A
B
Y
Z
0
300 m
ÎLE SIMON
Pont Wilson
Pont Napoléon
BIBLIOTHÈ
Pl. A. France
MUSÉE DU COMPAGNONNA
Quai du Pont Neuf
Rue des Tanneurs
U
HÔTEL GOUIN
R. de la Victoire
R. Bretonneau
PL. PLUMEREAU
Foch
R. du Mal
Pl. de la Résistance
N. D. LA RICHE
R. du Grd Marché
Rue des Halles
R. des Déportés
Basilique St-Martin
Destouches
Clocheville
Rue Néricault
Pl. des Halles
R. Rouget de l'Isle
Bourde
Pl. G. Paillhou
Rue H. Barbusse
Charpentier
Pl. J. Meunier
R. de Courset
Rue Chanoineau
Rue de la Grandière
Rue Marceau
Rue E. Pal
Boulevard Béranger
CLOCHEVILLE
Pl. N. Frumeaud
R. de la Cité A. Mame
Delperier
Rue G. de la J.
POL.
Rue Victor-Hugo
Rue Simier
R. Jehan Fouquet
Rue Sébastopol
Rue Georget
Pl. St Éloi
d'Entra

Cygne (R. du) . . . . CY 29
Descartes (R.) . . . . BZ 33
Dolve (R. de la) . . . . BZ 35
Favre (R. Jules) . . . . BY 38
Fusillés (R. des) . . . . BY 41
Gambetta (R.) . . . . BZ 43
Giraudeau (R.) . . . . AZ 46
Grand-Marché (Pl. du) . . . . AY 49
Grégoire-de-Tours (Pl.) . . . . DY 52

Grosse-Tour (R. de la) . . . . . AY 55
Herbes (Carroi aux) . . . . . . AY 56
Lavoisier (R.) . . . . CY 60
Marceau (R.) . . . . DY 61
Merville (R. du Prés.) . . . . . BY 65
Meusnier (R. Gén.) . . . . DY 66
Monnaie (R. de la) . . . . BY 68
Mûrier (R. du) . . . . AY 71
Paix (R. de la) . . . . BY 73

Petit-Cupidon (R. du) . . . . DY 77
Petit-St-Martin (R. du) . . . . AY 78
Petites-Boucheries (Pl. des) . . . . DY 80
Racine (R.) . . . . DY 84
Rapin (R.) . . . . AZ 85
St-Pierre-le-Puellier (Pl.) . . ABY 93
Sully (R. de) . . . . BZ 100
Victoire (Pl. de la) . . . . . . AY 103

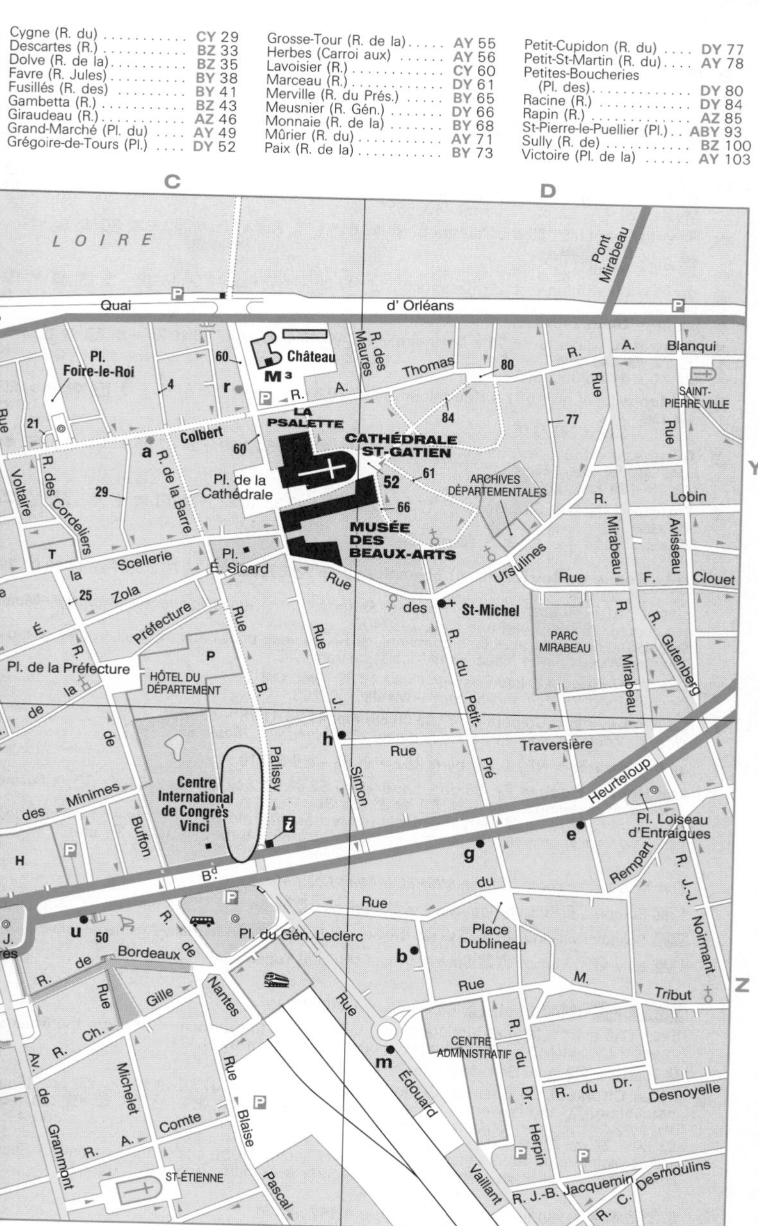

Harmonie M without rest, 15 r. F. Joliot-Curie ☎ 47 66 01 48, Telex 752587, Fax 47 61 66 38 – kitchenette TV ☎ & – 40. AE GB JCB DZ b
closed 25 December-5 January – 55 – **48 rm** 450/750, 6 suites.

Mercure M, 4 pl. Thiers ☎ 47 05 50 05, Telex 752740, Fax 47 20 22 07 – rest TV ☎ & – 70. AE GB
Meals 145/240 b.i. – 56 – **120 rm** 395/490.

Holiday Inn M, 15 r. Ed. Vaillant ☎ 47 31 12 12, Fax 47 38 53 35, – rm TV ☎ & – 50. AE GB JCB DZ m
Meals 120 – 60 – **105 rm** 440/665.

Royal without rest, 65 av. Grammont ☎ 47 64 71 78, Fax 47 05 84 62 – TV ☎ & – 35. AE GB
39 – **50 rm** 335/398.

du Manoir without rest, 2 r. Traversière ☎ 47 05 37 37, Fax 47 05 16 00 – TV ☎ P. AE GB CZ h
30 – **20 rm** 240/320.

Central H. without rest, 21 r. Berthelot ☎ 47 05 46 44, Fax 47 66 10 26 – TV ☎ & P. AE GB JCB CY k
40 – **41 rm** 330/600.

Criden without rest, 65 bd Heurteloup ☎ 47 20 81 14, Fax 47 05 61 65 – TV ☎ . AE GB JCB DZ g
33 – **33 rm** 265/315.

Mirabeau without rest, 89 bis bd Heurteloup ☎ 47 05 24 60, Fax 47 05 31 09 – TV ☎ . AE GB JCB DZ e
38 – **25 rm** 200/290.

Fimotel M, 247 r. Giraudeau ☎ 47 37 00 36, Fax 47 38 50 91 – TV ☎ & P – 40. AE GB
Meals 75/115 – 36 – **48 rm** 280.

XXX ✿ **La Roche Le Roy** (Couturier), 55 rte St-Avertin ✉ 37200 ☎ 47 27 22 00, Fax 47 28 08 39 – P. AE GB
closed 3 to 26 August, February Holidays, Saturday lunch, Sunday dinner and Monday – **Meals** 160 (lunch), 200/350 and a la carte 240/400
Spec. Blanc de turbot et huîtres en marinière. Ris de veau braisé aux morilles. Soufflé chaud à l'orange. Wines Chinon blanc, Saint-Nicolas-de-Bourgueil.

XX **Les Tuffeaux,** 21 r. Lavoisier ☎ 47 47 19 89 – . GB CY r
closed Monday lunch and Sunday – **Meals** 100/200.

XX **La Ruche,** 105 r. Colbert ☎ 47 66 69 83, Fax 47 20 41 76 – . GB CY a
closed Christmas Holidays, Sunday dinner and Monday – **Meals** 85/145 .

at Rochecorbon NE : 6 km by N 152 - alt. 58 - ✉ 37210 :

Les Hautes Roches M, 86 quai Loire ☎ 47 52 88 88, Fax 47 52 81 30, <, , « Former troglodyte dwelling », – TV ☎ P. AE GB
closed mid January-mid March – **Meals** *(closed Sunday dinner out of season and Monday except dinner in season)* 150 (lunch), 270/355 – 85 – **8 rm** 995/1200, 3 suites.

For the quickest route use the ***MICHELIN Main Road Maps*** *:*

970 Europe, 976 Czech Republic-Slovak Republic, 980 Greece, 984 Germany,

985 Scandinavia-Finland, 986 Great Britain and Ireland, 987 Germany-Austria-Benelux,

988 Italy, 989 France, 990 Spain-Portugal *and* 991 Yugoslavia.

Amboise 37400 I.-et-L. 64 ⑯ – pop. 10 982 alt. 60.

See : Château★★ (son et lumière show) : <★★ from the terrace, <★★ from the Minimes tower – Clos-Lucé★ – Chanteloup Pagoda★ SW : 3 km by D 431.

Tourist Office quai Gén.-de-Gaulle ☎ 47 57 01 37, Fax 47 57 14 35.

✿✿ **Le Choiseul,** 36 quai Ch. Guinot ☎ 47 30 45 45, Fax 47 30 46 10, <, , « Elegant installation, and flowered garden » – rest TV ☎ P – 80. AE GB JCB
closed 24 November-18 January – **Meals** 200 b.i. (lunch), 220/400 and a la carte 300/420 – 80 – **28 rm** 700/1200
Spec. Millefeuille de saumon fumé et radis noir. Caneton croisé à la soubise de navets. Sablés aux quetsches, glace au chèvre frais. Wines Touraine Amboise, Touraine Mesland.

Bracieux 41250 L.-et-Ch. 64 ⑱ – pop. 1 157 alt. 70.

Tours 82.

XXXX ✿✿ **Bernard Robin,** ☎ 54 46 41 22, Fax 54 46 03 69, , « Garden » – AE GB.
closed 20 December-20 January, Tuesday dinner and Wednesday except July-August – **Meals** (booking essential) 200/615 and a la carte 330/640
Spec. Salade de pigeon et homard. Queue de boeuf en hachis parmentier, jus aux truffes fraîches. Gibier (October-December). Wines Montlouis, Chinon.

Onzain **41150** L.-et-Ch. 64 ⑯ – pop. 3 080 alt. 69.
Tours 47.

✿✿ **Domaine des Hauts de Loire** M, NW : 3 km by D 1 and private lane ✆ 54 20 72 57, Fax 54 20 77 32, « Elegant hunting lodge in a park », – TV ☎ P – 70. AE GB.
closed 1 December-5 February – **Meals** *(closed Tuesday lunch and Monday in February and March)* 290/350 and a la carte 360/520 – 85 – **25 rm** 900/1400, 10 suites
Spec. Huîtres en gelée au caviar et choux brocoli (October-June). Salade d'anguilles à la vinaigrette d'échalotes. Pigeonneau du Vendômois au jus de presse. Wines Sauvignon, Touraine-Mesland.

Romorantin-Lanthenay **41200** L.-et-Ch. 64 ⑱ – pop. 17 865 alt. 93.
Tourist Office pl. Paix ✆ 54 76 43 89, Fax 54 76 96 24.
Tours 91.

✿✿ **Gd H. Lion d'Or** M, 69 r. Clemenceau ✆ 54 94 15 15, Fax 54 88 24 87, « Tasteful decor, floral patio » – rest TV ☎ P – 50. AE GB
closed mid February-late March – **Meals** (booking essential) 410/600 and a la carte 480/600 – 110 – **13 rm** 600/2000, 3 suites
Spec. Persillade de petites anguilles à l'oseille. Langoustines bretonnes rôties à la poudre d'épices douces. Fraises confites au vin rouge et lait glacé (May-September). Wines Bourgueil, Vouvray.

Germany

Deutschland

BERLIN – COLOGNE – DRESDEN
DÜSSELDORF – FRANKFURT ON MAIN
HAMBURG – HANOVER – LEIPZIG
MUNICH – STUTTGART

PRACTICAL INFORMATION

LOCAL CURRENCY

Deutsche Mark: 100 DEM = 69.76 USD ($) (Jan. 96)

TOURIST INFORMATION

Deutsche Zentrale für Tourismus (DZT) :
Beethovenstr. 69, 60325 Frankfurt, ☎ 069/7 57 20, Fax 069/75 19 03
Hotel booking service :
Allgemeine Deutsche Zimmerreservierung (ADZ)
Corneliusstr. 34, 60325 Frankfurt, ☎ 069/74 07 67
Fax 069/75 10 56

AIRLINES

DEUTSCHE LUFTHANSA AG: Wilhelmshöher Allee 256, 34119 Kassel, ☎ 01803/803803, Fax 0561/9933115
AIR CANADA: 60311 Frankfurt, Friedensstr. 7, ☎ 069/27 11 51 11, Fax 27 11 51 12
AIR FRANCE: 60311 Frankfurt, Friedensstr. 11, ☎ 069/2 56 61 00, Fax 23 05 81
AMERICAN AIRLINES: 60329 Frankfurt, Wiesenhüttenplatz 26, ☎ 01803/242324, Fax 069/23 19 82
BRITISH AIRWAYS: 60329 Frankfurt, Düsseldorfer Str. 1, ☎ 0130/3636, Fax 069/23 45 58
JAPAN AIRLINES: 60311 Frankfurt, Roßmarkt 15, ☎ 0130/6878, Fax 069/29 57 84
SABENA: 60313 Frankfurt, Große Eschenheimer Str. 39 a, ☎069/29 90 06 94, Fax 29 90 06 50
SAS: 60528 Frankfurt, Saonestr. 3, ☎ 069/66 44 61 50, Fax 666 83 79
TWA: 60486 Frankfurt, Hamburger Allee 2, ☎ 069/77 06 01, Fax 77 41 23

FOREIGN EXCHANGE

Is possible in banks, savings banks and at exchange offices.
Hours of opening from Monday to Friday 8.30am to 12.30pm and 2.30pm to 4pm except Thursday 2.30pm to 6pm.

SHOPPING

In the index of street names, those printed in red are where the principal shops are found.

BREAKDOWN SERVICE

ADAC: for the addresses see text of the towns mentioned
AvD: Lyoner Str. 16, 60528 Frankfurt-Niederrad, ☎ 069/6 60 60, Fax 069/660 62 10
In Germany the ADAC (emergency number 01802/22 22 22), and the AvD (emergency number 0130/99 09), make a special point of assisting foreign motorists. They have motor patrols covering main roads.

TIPPING

In Germany, prices include service and taxes. You may choose to leave a tip if you wish but there is no obligation to do so.

SPEED LIMITS

The speed limit, generally, in built up areas is 50 km/h - 31 mph and on all other roads it is 100 km/h - 62mph. On motorways and dual carriageways, the recommended speed limit is 130 km/h - 80 mph.

SEAT BELTS

The wearing of seat belts is compulsory for drivers and passengers.

Berlin

L Berlin 987 ⑱ ⑲, 984 ⑮ ⑯, 414 L 8 - Pop. 3 500 000 - alt. 40 m. - ☎ 030.

MUSEUMS, GALLERIES

Pergamon Museum★★★ PY - Old National Gallery★ (Alte Nationalgalerie) PY **M 1** - Bode-Museum★★ PY **M 2** - Altes Museum★ PY **M3** - Museum of Decorative Arts★ (Kunstgewerbemuseum) NZ **M 4** - New National Gallery★ (Neue Nationalgalerie) NZ **M 5** - Schloß Charlottenburg★★ (Equestrian Statue of the Great Elector★★, Historical Rooms★, Porcelain Room★★) - National Gallery★★ White Hall★ (Nationalgalerie, Weißer Saal) - Golden Gallery★★ (Goldene Galerie) EY - Antique Museum★ (Antikenmuseum) (Ancient Treasure★★★) EY **M 6** - Egyptian Museum★ (Ägyptisches Museum) (Bust of Queen Nefrititi★★) EY **M 6** - Dahlem Museums★★★ (Museum Dahlem) (Painting Gallery★★, Sculpture Department★★, Drawing and Prints Department★, Ethnographic Museum★★) by Rheinbabenallee EZ - Museum of Transport and Technology★ (Museum für Verkehr und Technik) GZ **M 8** - Käthe-Kollwitz-Museum★ LXY **M 9** - Berlin Museum★ GY - Museum of Decorative Arts★ (at Schloß Köpenick) (Kunstgewerbemuseum) by Stralauer Allee HY.

HISTORIC BUILDINGS AND MONUMENTS, STREETS, SQUARES

Brandenburg Gate★★ (Brandenburger Tor) NZ - Unter den Linden★ NPZ - Gendarmenmarkt★ PZ - State Opera House★ (Deutsche Staatsoper) PZ - Neue Wache★ PY - Arsenal★★ (Zeughaus) PY - Nikolaiviertel★ RZ - Philharmonie★★★ NZ - Kurfürstendamm★ JLY - Martin-Gropius-Building★ NZ - Olympic Stadium★ (Olympia Stadion) by Kaiserdamm EY - Nikolai Church★ (Nikolaikirche) RZ.

PARKS, GARDENS, LAKES

Zoological Park★★ (Zoologischer Garten) MX - Castle Park of Charlottenburg★ (Schloßpark Charlottenburg) (at Belvedere Historical Porcelain Exhibition★) EY - Botanical Gardens★★ (Botanischer Garten) by Rheinbabenallee EZ - Grunewald Forest★ (at Grunewald Lake : Hunting Lodge★) by Rheinbabenallee EZ - Havel★ and Peacook Island★ by Clay-Allee EZ - Wannsee★★ by Clay-Allee EZ.

18 Berlin-Wannsee, Am Stölpchenweg, ☎ 8 05 50 75 - 9 Kladower Damm 182, ☎ 365 76 60.

✈ Tegel, ☎ 4 10 11 - ✈ Schönefeld (S : 25 km), 6 09 10.

🚗 Berlin - Wannsee, ☎ 8 03 20 81.

Exhibition Grounds (Messegelände), ☎ 3 03 80, Fax 30 38 23 25.

ℹ Berlin Tourist-Information, Europa-Center (Budapester Straße), ✉ 10787 ☎ 2 62 60 31, Telex 183356, Fax 21 23 25 20.

ADAC, Berlin-Wilmersdorf, Bundesallee 29 ✉ 10717, ☎ 8 68 60, Fax 86 16 025.

Frankfurt/Oder 105 - Hamburg 289 - Hannover 288 - Leipzig 183 - Rostock 222.

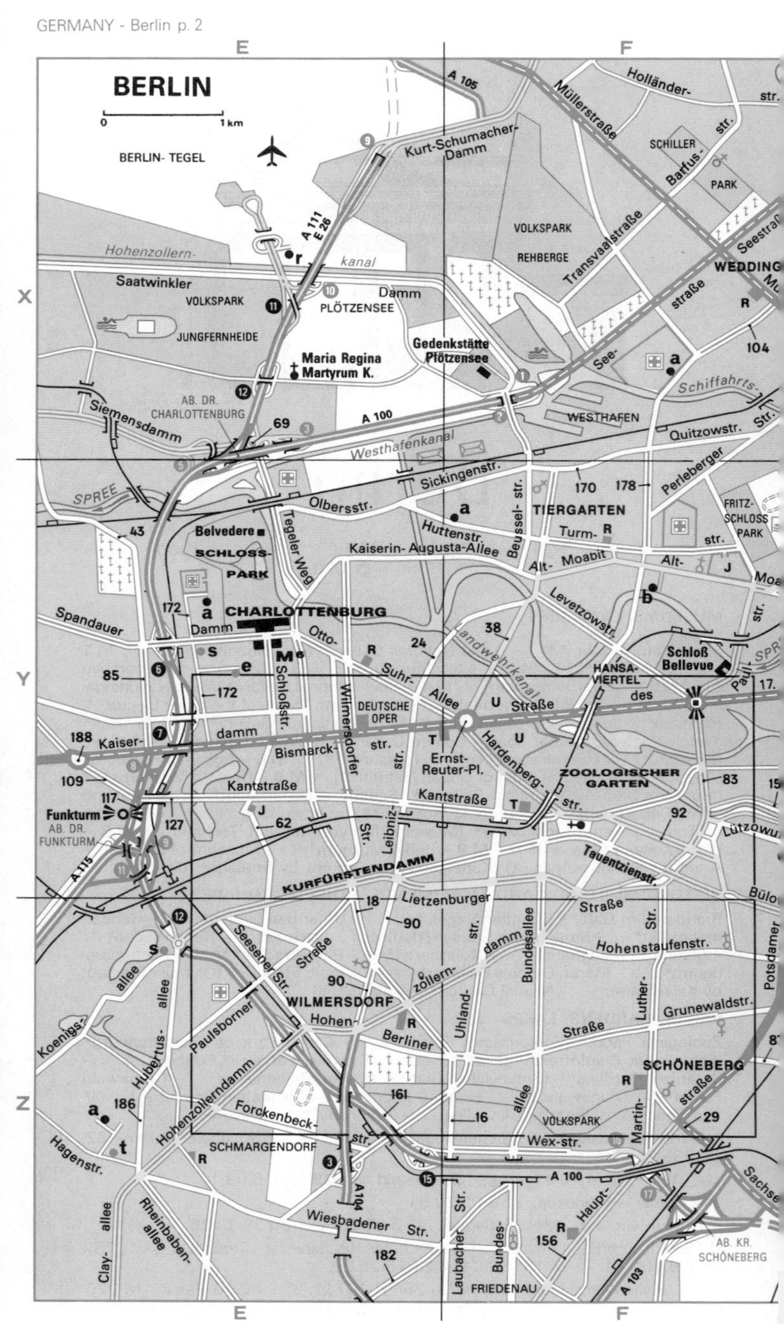
BERLIN
0
1 km
BERLIN- TEGEL
Hohenzollern-
kanal
Saatwinkler
Damm
VOLKSPARK
JUNGFERNHEIDE
PLÖTZENSEE
Maria Regina
Martyrum K.
Gedenkstätte
Plötzensee
Kurt-Schumacher-
Damm
A 105
A 111
E 26
Holländer-
str.
Müllerstraße
SCHILLER
PARK
Barfus-
str.
VOLKSPARK
REHBERGE
Transvaalstraße
Seestraße
WEDDING
See-
straße
Schiffahrts-
WESTHAFEN
Quitzowstr.
Westhafenkanal
A 100
AB. DR.
CHARLOTTENBURG
Siemensdamm
SPREE
Sickingenstr.
Olbersstr.
Perleberger
TIERGARTEN
Beussel- str.
Turm- str.
FRITZ-
SCHLOSS
PARK
Belvedere
SCHLOSS-
PARK
Tegeler Weg
Huttenstr.
Kaiserin- Augusta-Allee
Alt- Moabit
Levetzowstr.
CHARLOTTENBURG
Spandauer
Damm
Otto-
Suhr-
Allee
Landwehrkanal
HANSA-
VIERTEL
Schloß
Bellevue
Schloßstr.
Wilmersdorfer
str.
DEUTSCHE
OPER
Straße
des
17.
Kaiser-
damm
Bismarck-
str.
Ernst-
Reuter-Pl.
Hardenberg-
str.
ZOOLOGISCHER
GARTEN
Kantstraße
Funkturm
AB. DR.
FUNKTURM
A 115
Leibniz-
str.
KURFÜRSTENDAMM
Tauentzienstr.
Lützowu
Lietzenburger
Straße
Hohenstaufenstr.
Seesener Str.
Straße
zollern-
damm
Uhland-
str.
Bundesallee
WILMERSDORF
Hohen-
Berliner
Straße
Grunewaldstr.
Luther-
str.
Potsdamer
Paulsborner
Koenigs-
allee
Hubertus-
allee
SCHÖNEBERG
Hohenzollerndamm
Forckenbeck-
str.
SCHMARGENDORF
VOLKSPARK
Wex-str.
Martin-
Luther-
A 100
A 104
Haupt-
Hagenstr.
Rheinbaben-
allee
Clay-
allee
Wiesbadener
Str.
Laubacher
Str.
Bundes-
FRIEDENAU
AB. KR.
SCHÖNEBERG
A 103
Sachse

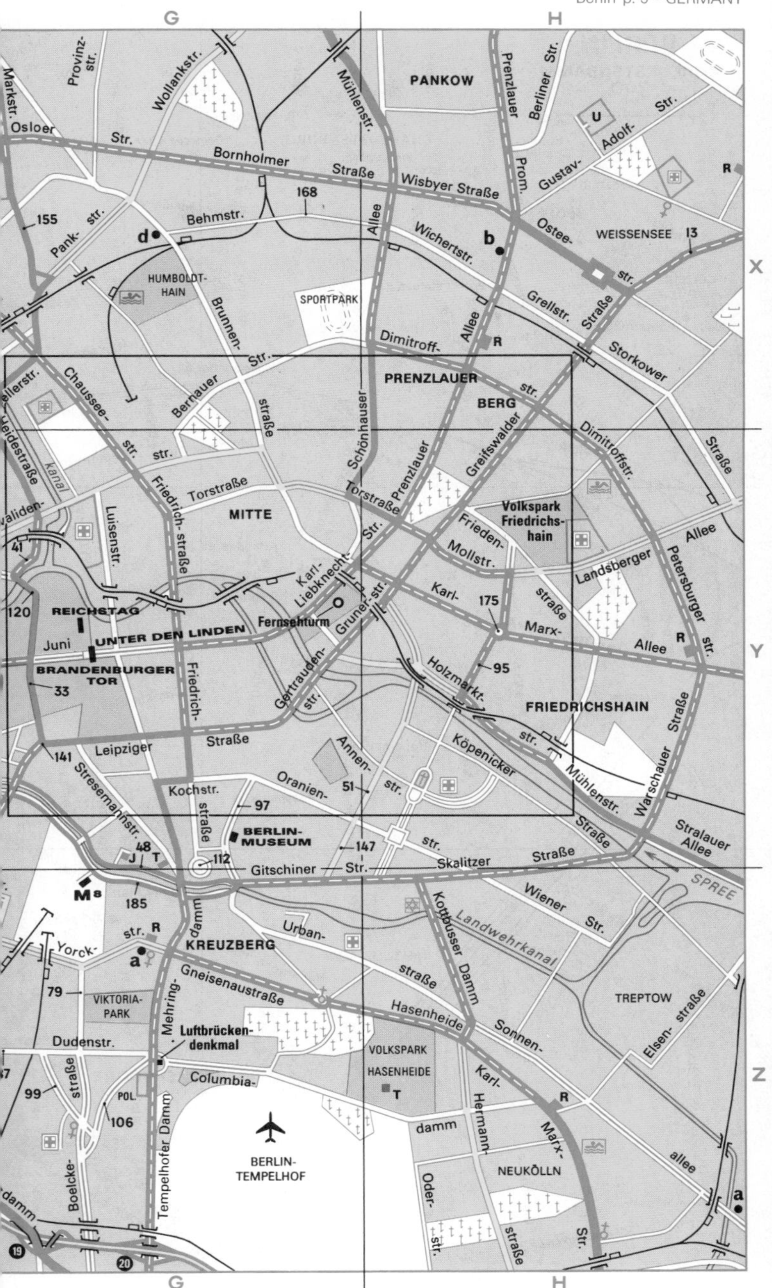

G
H
X
Y
Z
PANKOW
WEISSENSEE
PRENZLAUER BERG
MITTE
FRIEDRICHSHAIN
KREUZBERG
TREPTOW
NEUKÖLLN
HUMBOLDT-HAIN
SPORTPARK
Volkspark Friedrichshain
REICHSTAG
UNTER DEN LINDEN
BRANDENBURGER TOR
Fernsehturm
BERLIN-MUSEUM
VIKTORIA-PARK
Luftbrücken-denkmal
VOLKSPARK HASENHEIDE
BERLIN-TEMPELHOF
SPREE
Landwehrkanal
Osloer Str.
Bornholmer Straße
Wisbyer Straße
Schönhauser Allee
Prenzlauer Allee
Greifswalder Straße
Karl-Marx-Allee
Leipziger Straße
Gitschiner Str.
Skalitzer Straße
Kottbusser Damm
Hasenheide
Columbia-damm
Tempelhofer Damm
Karl-Marx-Str.
Torstraße
Friedrichstraße
Chausseestr.
Brunnenstr.
Stresemannstr.
Yorckstr.
Gneisenaustraße
Urbanstraße
Oranienstr.
Köpenicker Str.
Holzmarktstr.
Mühlenstr.
Warschauer Straße
Stralauer Allee
Petersburger Str.
Landsberger Allee
Dimitroffstr.
Storkower Straße
Ostseestr.

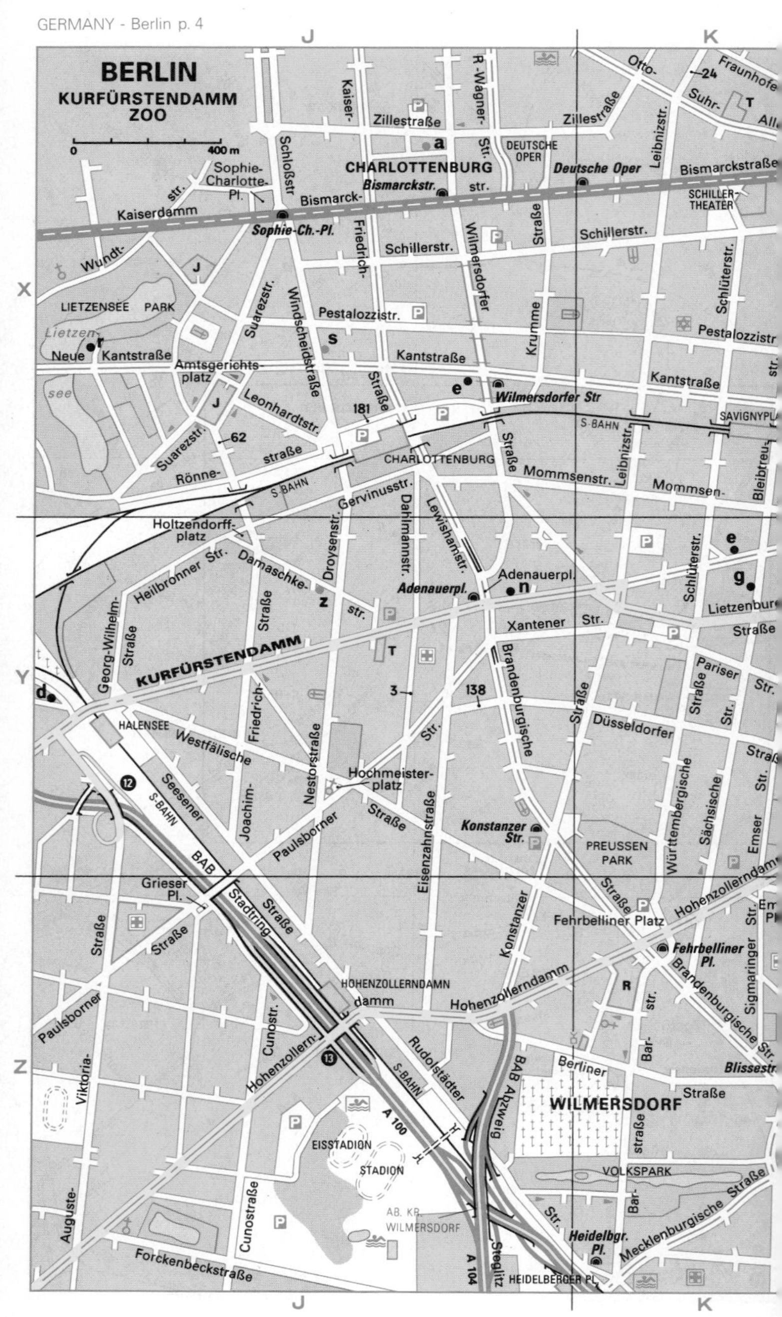
BERLIN
KURFÜRSTENDAMM
ZOO
0
400 m
J
K
X
Y
Z
CHARLOTTENBURG
WILMERSDORF
Kaiser-
Zillestraße
R.-Wagner-Str.
Otto-
Fraunhofer
Suhr-
Allee
Leibnizstr.
DEUTSCHE OPER
Deutsche Oper
Bismarckstraße
Bismarckstr.
Bismarck-
str.
SCHILLER-THEATER
Sophie-Charlotte-Pl.
Sophie-Ch.-Pl.
Schloßstr.
Kaiserdamm
Wundt-
str.
Friedrich-
Schillerstr.
Wilmersdorfer
Straße
Schlüterstr.
LIETZENSEE PARK
Lietzensee
Neue Kantstraße
Suarezstr.
Windscheidstraße
Pestalozzistr.
Pestalozzistr
Krumme
Kantstraße
Amtsgerichtsplatz
Leonhardtstr.
Wilmersdorfer Str
S-BAHN
SAVIGNYPL.
Suarezstr.
Rönne-
straße
CHARLOTTENBURG
Mommsenstr.
Mommsen-
Bleibtreu-
Holtzendorffplatz
Gervinusstr.
Droysenstr.
Dahlmannstr.
Lewishamstr.
Heilbronner Str.
Damaschke-
str.
Adenauerpl.
Lietzenburger
Straße
Xantener Str.
Georg-Wilhelm-Straße
KURFÜRSTENDAMM
Brandenburgische
Pariser Str.
HALENSEE
Westfälische
Joachim-Friedrich-
Nestorstraße
Hochmeisterplatz
Düsseldorfer
Württembergische
Sächsische
Emser
Seesener
Paulsborner
Straße
Eisenzahnstraße
Konstanzer Str.
PREUSSEN PARK
BAB
Grieser Pl.
Stadtring
Fehrbelliner Platz
Fehrbelliner Pl.
Hohenzollerndamm
Konstanzer
HOHENZOLLERNDAMM
damm
Rudolstädter
Bar-
str.
Brandenburgische Str.
Sigmaringer
Paulsborner
Viktoria-
Cunostr.
Hohenzollern-
BAB Abzweig
Berliner
Straße
Blissestr.
EISSTADION
STADION
A 100
VOLKSPARK
Cunostraße
AB. KR. WILMERSDORF
Auguste-
Forckenbeckstraße
A 104
Steglitz
Heidelbgr. Pl.
HEIDELBERGER PL.
Mecklenburgische Straße

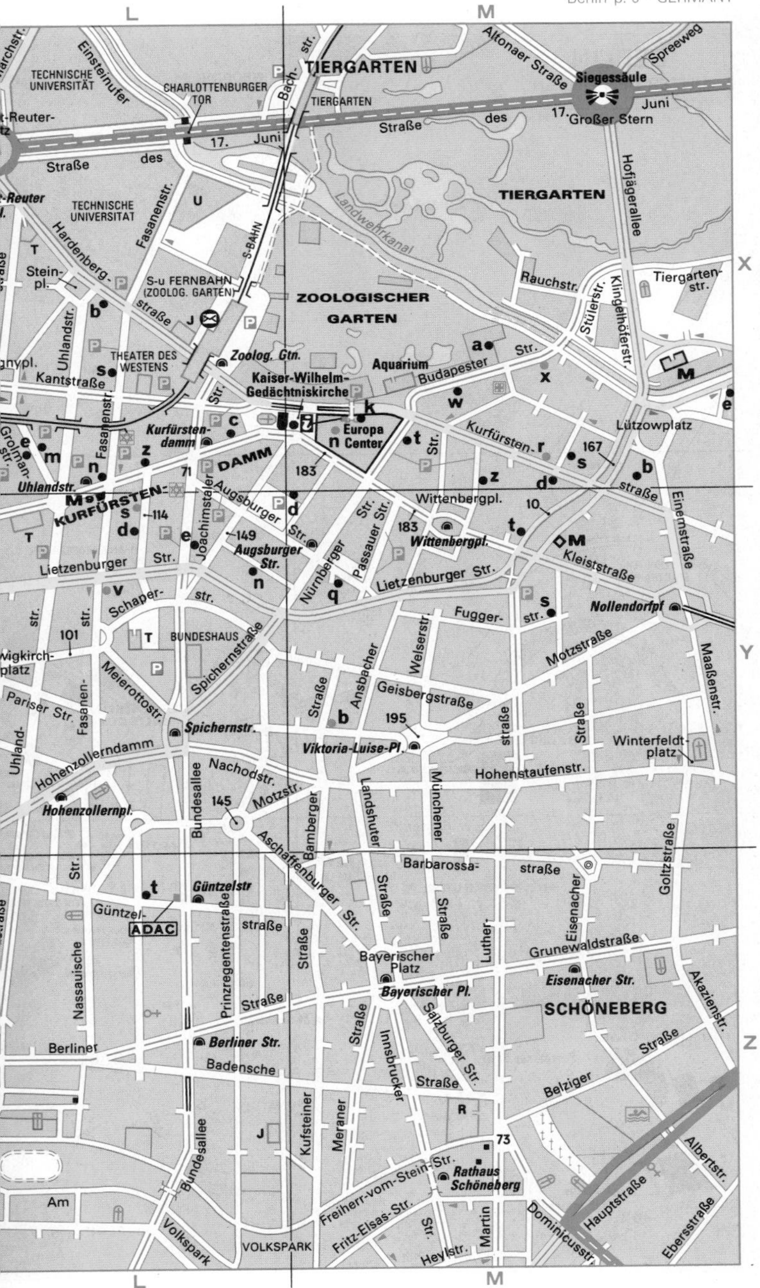
L
M
X
Y
Z
TIERGARTEN
TECHNISCHE UNIVERSITÄT
Einsteinufer
CHARLOTTENBURGER TOR
Bach-str.
Altonaer Straße
Spreeweg
Siegessäule
17. Juni
Großer Stern
Straße des 17. Juni
Hofjägerallee
TECHNISCHE UNIVERSITAT
Fasanenstr.
S-BAHN
Landwehrkanal
Hardenberg-straße
Stein-pl.
S-u FERNBAHN (ZOOLOG. GARTEN)
ZOOLOGISCHER GARTEN
Rauchstr.
Tiergarten-str.
Stülerstr.
Klingelhöferstr.
Uhlandstr.
THEATER DES WESTENS
Zoolog. Gtn.
Aquarium
Budapester Str.
Kantstraße
Kaiser-Wilhelm-Gedächtniskirche
Europa Center
Lützowplatz
Grolman-str.
Kurfürsten-damm
Kurfürsten-straße
KURFÜRSTEN-DAMM
Uhlandstr.
Augsburger Str.
Nürnberger Str.
Passauer Str.
Wittenbergpl.
Einemstraße
Kleiststraße
Joachimstaler Str.
Augsburger Str.
Lietzenburger Str.
Schaper-str.
BUNDESHAUS
Fugger-str.
Nollendorfpl.
Spichernstraße
Motzstraße
Welserstr.
Ansbacher Straße
Geisbergstraße
Maaßenstr.
Meierottostr.
Pariser Str.
Fasanen-str.
Spichernstr.
Viktoria-Luise-Pl.
Winterfeldt-platz
Hohenzollerndamm
Nachodstr.
Motzstr.
Hohenstaufenstr.
Hohenzollernpl.
Bundesallee
Landshuter
Münchener
Bamberger
Aschaffenburger Str.
Barbarossa-straße
Goltzstraße
Eisenacher Straße
Güntzelstr
Güntzel-straße
ADAC
Nassauische Str.
Prinzregentenstraße
Bayerischer Platz
Bayerischer Pl.
Luther-straße
Grunewaldstraße
Eisenacher Str.
SCHÖNEBERG
Akazienstr.
Berliner Str.
Salzburger Str.
Innsbrucker Straße
Badensche Straße
Belziger Straße
Kufsteiner
Meraner
Rathaus Schöneberg
Freiherr-vom-Stein-Str.
Fritz-Elsas-Str.
Martin Luther Str.
Heylstr.
Dominicusstr.
Hauptstraße
Albertstr.
Ebersstraße
Am Volkspark
VOLKSPARK

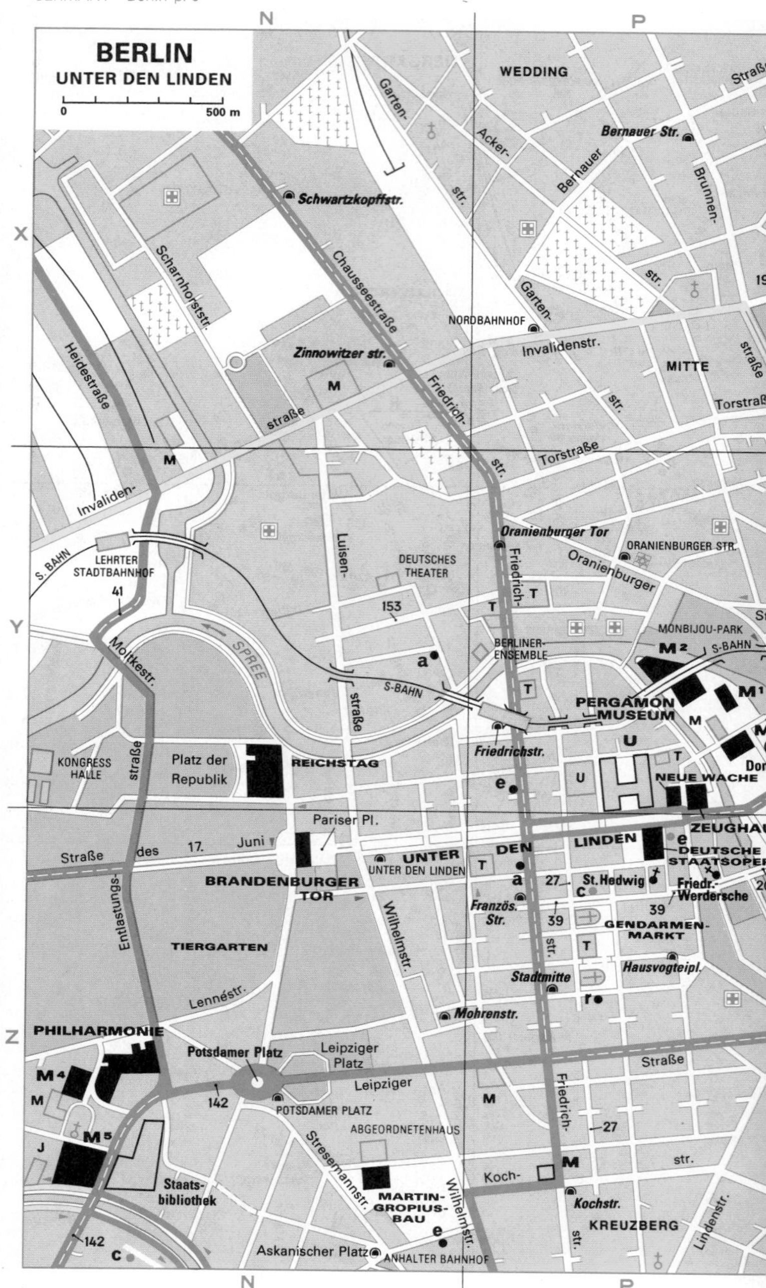
BERLIN
UNTER DEN LINDEN
0
500 m
N
P
X
Y
Z
WEDDING
Bernauer Str.
Bernauer
Brunnen-
Acker-
str.
Garten-
Schwartzkopffstr.
Scharnhorststr.
Chausseestraße
Zinnowitzer str.
NORDBAHNHOF
Invalidenstr.
MITTE
Heidestraße
straße
Friedrich-
str.
Torstraße
Invaliden-
Oranienburger Tor
ORANIENBURGER STR.
Oranienburger
LEHRTER STADTBAHNHOF
S. BAHN
41
Luisen-
DEUTSCHES THEATER
153
Friedrich-
MONBIJOU-PARK
S-BAHN
BERLINER-ENSEMBLE
SPREE
Moltkestr.
S-BAHN
straße
PERGAMON MUSEUM
Friedrichstr.
KONGRESS HALLE
straße
Platz der Republik
REICHSTAG
NEUE WACHE
Pariser Pl.
Straße
des
17.
Juni
UNTER
DEN
LINDEN
UNTER DEN LINDEN
ZEUGHA
DEUTSCHE STAATSOPER
BRANDENBURGER TOR
St. Hedwig
Friedr.-Werdersche
27
39
Französ. Str.
GENDARMEN-MARKT
Entlastungs-
TIERGARTEN
Wilhelmstr.
Hausvogteipl.
Stadtmitte
Lennéstr.
Mohrenstr.
PHILHARMONIE
Potsdamer Platz
Leipziger Platz
Straße
Leipziger
142
POTSDAMER PLATZ
Friedrich-
27
ABGEORDNETENHAUS
Stresemannstr.
Staats-bibliothek
MARTIN-GROPIUS-BAU
Koch-
str.
Kochstr.
Wilhelmstr.
KREUZBERG
Lindenstr.
142
Askanischer Platz
ANHALTER BAHNHOF
str.

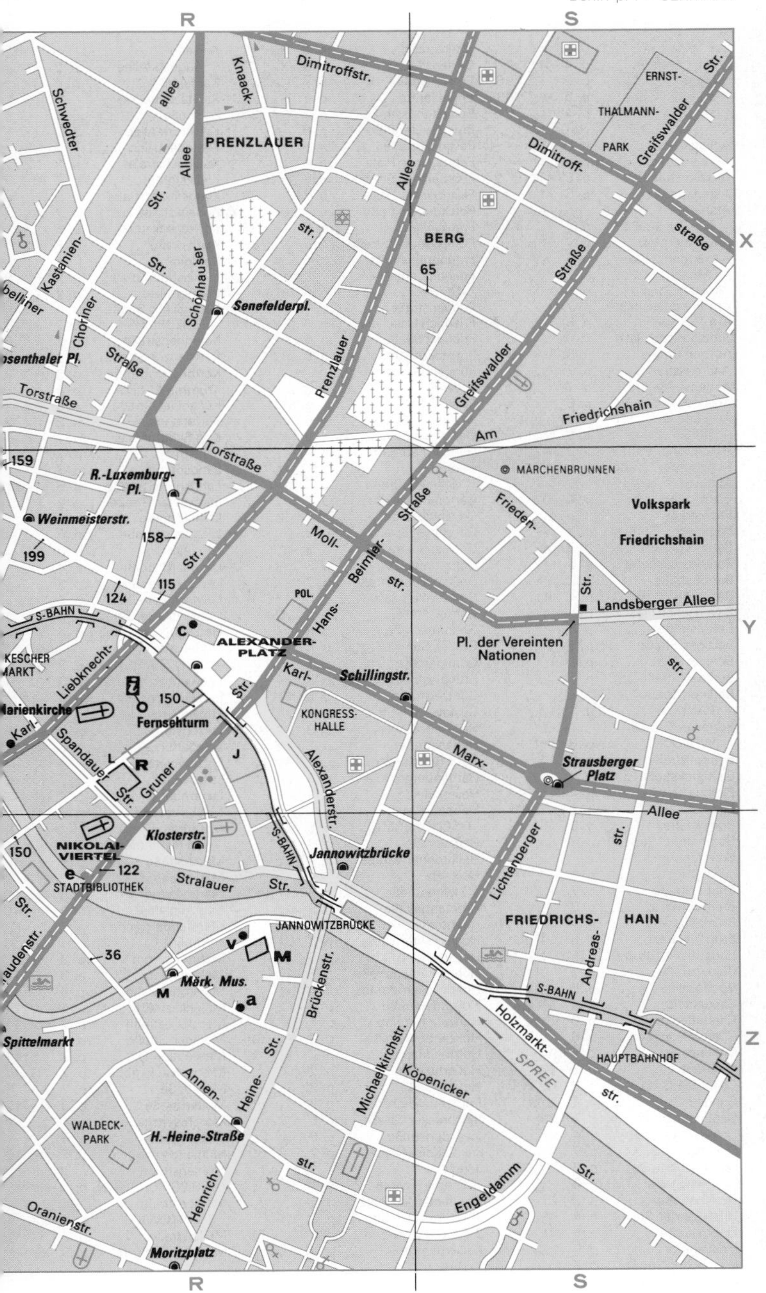
R
S
Dimitroffstr.
Knaack-
allee
Schwedter
PRENZLAUER
ERNST-
THÄLMANN-
PARK
Dimitroff-
Greifswalder
Str.
Allee
Str.
BERG
straße
X
Kastanien-
Str.
Schönhauser
65
Senefelderpl.
Choriner
Straße
Prenzlauer
Greifswalder
Friedrichshain
Am
Torstraße
Torstraße
159
R.-Luxemburg-
Pl.
T
MÄRCHENBRUNNEN
Frieden-
Volkspark
Friedrichshain
Weinmeisterstr.
158
199
Moll-
Straße
Beimler-
str.
Str.
124
115
POL.
Hans-
Str.
Landsberger Allee
S-BAHN
C
ALEXANDER-
PLATZ
Pl. der Vereinten
Nationen
Y
Liebknecht-
Karl-
Schillingstr.
str.
150
Fernsehturm
KONGRESS-
HALLE
Karl-
Spandauer
Alexanderstr.
Marx-
Strausberger
Platz
L
R
J
Gruner
Str.
Allee
NIKOLAI-
VIERTEL
Klosterstr.
S-BAHN
Lichtenberger
str.
150
e
122
STADTBIBLIOTHEK
Jannowitzbrücke
Stralauer
Str.
JANNOWITZBRÜCKE
FRIEDRICHS-
HAIN
Andreas-
Str.
36
V
M
Märk. Mus.
M
a
Brückenstr.
S-BAHN
Holzmarkt-
Z
Spittelmarkt
HAUPTBAHNHOF
SPREE
Str.
Annen-
Heine-
Michaelkirchstr.
Köpenicker
str.
WALDECK-
PARK
H.-Heine-Straße
str.
Heinrich-
Str.
Engeldamm
Oranienstr.
Moritzplatz
R
S

Continued p. 9

STREET INDEX TO BERLIN TOWN PLANS (Concluded)

Town Centre (Berlin - City, -Charlottenburg, -Schöneberg and -Wilmersdorf

Kempinski Hotel Bristol Berlin, Kurfürstendamm 27, ✉ 10719, ☎ 88 43 40, Telex 185651, Fax 8836075, Massage, – rm – 250. AE VISA JCB — LX **n**
Kempinski-Restaurant : *(closed Monday)* **Meals** à la carte 57/93 – ***Kempinski-Eck :*** **Meals** à la carte 47/80 – **315 rm** 372/594 – 29 suites.

Grand Hotel Esplanade, Lützowufer 15, ✉ 10785, ☎ 25 47 80, Telex 185986, Fax 2651171, (conference boat with own landing stage), « Modern hotel featuring contemporary art », Massage, – rm – 300. AE VISA JCB. rest — MX **e**
Meals see also ***Harlekin*** below – ***Eckkneipe*** **Meals** à la carte 34/51 – **402 rm** 409/708 – 17 suites.

Maritim Grand Hotel, Friedrichstr. 158, ✉ 10117, ☎ 2 02 70, Fax 20273362, Massage, – rm – 100. AE VISA JCB. rest — PZ **a**
Le Grand Silhouette see below – ***Coelln*** (outstanding wine list) **Meals** 39 (buffet lunch) and à la carte 51/96 – **Goldene Gans :** *(dinner only)* **Meals** à la carte 30/60 – **358 rm** 404/718 – 20 suites.

Inter-Continental, Budapester Str. 2, ✉ 10787, ☎ 2 60 20, Telex 184380, Fax 260280760, Massage, – rm – 800. AE VISA. rest — MX **a**
Meals see also ***Zum Hugenotten*** below ***L.A. Café :*** **Meals** à la carte 38/68 – **511 rm** 377/609 – 40 suites.

Palace, Budapester Str. 42 (Europa-Centre), ✉ 10789, ☎ 2 50 20, Telex 184825, Fax 2626577, free entrance to the thermal recreation centre – rm – 260. AE VISA JCB. rest — MX **k**
First Floor *(closed Saturday lunch, Sunday and 8 July - 11 August)* **Meals** à la carte 66/99 ***Alt Nürnberg :*** **Meals** à la carte 35/48 – **321 rm** 307/588 – 18 suites.

Berlin, Lützowplatz 17, ✉ 10785, ☎ 2 60 50, Fax 26052715, – rm rest – 500. AE VISA JCB. rest — MX **b**
Meals 32 (buffet lunch) and à la carte 49/80 – **690 rm** 260/420 – 7 suites.

Radisson SAS-Hotel Berlin, Karl-Liebknecht-Str. 5, ✉ 10178, ☎ 2 38 28, Telex 304754, Fax 23827590, Massage, – rm – 360. AE E VISA JCB RY s
Meals à la carte 43/87 – **567 rm** 290/550 – 17 suites.

Berlin Hilton (with Kroneflügel), Mohrenstr. 30, ✉ 10117, ☎ 2 38 20, Telex 305776, Fax 23824269, – rm – 300. AE E VISA JCB
La Cupole (dinner only, closed Sunday - Monday) **Meals** à la carte 60/115 – ***Fellini*** (Italian rest.) *(dinner only, closed Sunday - Monday)* **Meals** à la carte 45/87 – **Mark Brandenburg : Meals** à la carte 43/85 – **502 rm** 236/652 – 12 suites. PZ r

Steigenberger Berlin, Los-Angeles-Platz 1, ✉ 10789, ☎ 2 12 70, Telex 181444, Fax 212117, Massage, – rm – 3600. AE E VISA JCB. rest MY d
Park-Restaurant *(weekdays dinner only, Sunday lunch only, closed Monday)* **Meals** à la carte 50/76 – ***Berliner Stube*** **: Meals** à la carte 33/59 – **397 rm** 319/586 – 11 suites.

Holiday Inn Crown Plaza, Nürnberger Str. 65, ✉ 10787, ☎ 21 00 70, Telex 182877, Fax 2132009, Massage, – rm – 120. AE E VISA JCB. rest MX t
Meals à la carte 50/76 – **425 rm** 318/506 – 10 suites.

Schweizerhof, Budapester Str. 21, ✉ 10787, ☎ 2 69 60, Telex 185501, Fax 2696900, Massage, – rm – 340. AE E VISA JCB MX w
Meals *(closed Sunday - Monday)* (dinner only) à la carte 60/82 – **430 rm** 325/555 – 10 suites.

Savoy, Fasanenstr. 9, ✉ 10623, ☎ 31 10 30, Fax 31103333, – rm – 50. AE E VISA JCB. rest LX s
Meals à la carte 48/80 – **125 rm** 262/450 – 6 suites.

Brandenburger Hof, Eislebener Str. 14, ✉ 10789, ☎ 21 40 50, Fax 21405100, « Modernized Wilhelminian mansion with Bauhaus furniture » – – 25. AE E VISA JCB. rest LY n
Die Quadriga (dinner only) *(closed Saturday - Sunday, 1 - 14 January and 20 July - 18 August)* **Meals** à la carte 76/100 – ***Der Wintergarten*** **: Meals** à la carte 46/73 – **87 rm** 290/445.

Mondial, Kurfürstendamm 47, ✉ 10707, ☎ 88 41 10, Telex 182839, Fax 88411150, – – 50. AE E VISA. rest KY e
Meals à la carte 47/77 – **75 rm** 220/480.

Maritim Pro Arte, Friedrichstr. 150, ✉ 10117, ☎ 2 03 35, Fax 20334209, – rm – 1050. AE E VISA JCB PY e
Meals *(closed Sunday - Monday)* (dinner only) à la carte 51/80 – **403 rm** 324/558 – 29 suites.

President, An der Urania 16, ✉ 10787, ☎ 21 90 30, Telex 184018, Fax 2141200, – rm – 40. AE E VISA MY t
Meals *(closed Sunday)* à la carte 44/67 – **188 rm** 257/375 – 6 suites.

Seehof, Lietzensee-Ufer 11, ✉ 14057, ☎ 32 00 20, Fax 32002251, ≤, « Garden terrace », – rest – 40. AE E VISA. rest JX r
Meals à la carte 56/76 – **77 rm** 245/444.

Luisenhof without rest, Kopenicker Str. 92, ✉ 10179, ☎ 2 70 05 43, Fax 2797983, « Elegant installation » – – 25. AE E VISA JCB RZ a
28 rm 195/270.

Forum-Hotel Berlin, Alexanderplatz, ✉ 10178, ☎ 2 38 90, Telex 307680, Fax 23894305, – rm – 300. AE E VISA JCB RY c
Meals à la carte 35/70 – **1006 rm** 250/367.

Ambassador, Bayreuther Str. 42, ✉ 10787, ☎ 21 90 20, Telex 184259, Fax 21902380, Massage, – rm rest – 70. AE E VISA JCB MX z
Meals à la carte 32/64 – **199 rm** 250/440.

Alsterhof, Augsburger Str. 5, ✉ 10789, ☎ 21 24 20, Fax 2183949, Massage, – rm – 20. AE E VISA JCB MY q
Meals à la carte 42/58 – **200 rm** 225/390.

Berlin Excelsior Hotel, Hardenbergstr. 14, ✉ 10623, ☎ 3 15 50, Fax 31551002, – rm rest – 60. AE E VISA JCB. rest LX b
Meals à la carte 37/65 – **320 rm** 245/385.

Residenz, Meinekestr. 9, ✉ 10719, ☎ 88 44 30, Telex 183082, Fax 8824726 – . AE E VISA. rest LY d
Meals à la carte 53/88 – **88 rm** 220/310.

Am Zoo without rest, Kurfürstendamm 25, ✉ 10719, ☎ 88 43 70, Telex 183835, Fax 88437714 – – 30. AE E VISA JCB LX z
136 rm 245/395.

Hamburg, Landgrafenstr. 4, ✉ 10787, ☎ 26 47 70, Telex 184974, Fax 2629394 – rm – 80. AE E VISA JCB. rest MX s
Meals à la carte 40/65 – **240 rm** 225/320.

Sorat Art'otel without rest, Joachimstalerstr. 28, ✉ 10719, ☎ 88 44 70, Fax 88447700, « Modern hotel with exhibition of contemporary art » – . AE E VISA JCB LY e
75 rm 255/375.

Hecker's Hotel without rest, Grolmanstr. 35, ✉ 10623, ✆ 8 89 00, Telex 184954, Fax 8890260 – rest. LX e
72 rm 240/340.

Queens Hotel without rest, Güntzelstr. 14, ✉ 10717, ✆ 87 02 41, Telex 182948, Fax 8619326 – . LZ t
109 rm 217/342.

Sylter Hof, Kurfürstenstr. 116, ✉ 10787, ✆ 2 12 00, Fax 2142826 – – 80. rest MX d
Meals *(Sunday lunch only)* à la carte 25/41 – **160 rm** 197/352 – 18 suites.

Concept Hotel, Grolmanstr. 41, ✉ 10623, ✆ 88 42 60, Telex 183389, Fax 88426500, – – 45. LX m
Meals à la carte 34/59 – **100 rm** 240/350 – 3 suites.

Abacus Spreehotel without rest, Wallstr. 59, ✉ 10179, ✆ 2 73 60, Fax 2736950 – – 55. RZ v
158 rm 170/280.

Kanthotel without rest, Kantstr. 111, ✉ 10627, ✆ 32 30 26, Telex 183330, Fax 3240952 – . JX e
55 rm 229/269.

Schloßparkhotel, Heubnerweg 2a, ✉ 14059, ✆ 3 22 40 61, Fax 3258861, – – 50. EY a
Meals à la carte 40/63 – **39 rm** 189/285.

Albrechtshof, Albrechtstr. 8, ✉ 10117, ✆ 30 88 60, Fax 30886100, – – 70. rest NY a
Meals à la carte 35/56 – **99 rm** 195/365 – 11 suites.

Holiday Inn Garden Court without rest, Bleibtreustr. 25, ✉ 10707, ✆ 88 09 30, Fax 88093939 – – 15. KY g
73 rm 245/285.

Boulevard without rest, Kurfürstendamm 12, ✉ 10719, ✆ 88 42 50, Fax 88425450 – – 30. LX c
57 rm 198/320.

Kronprinz without rest (restored 1894 house), Kronprinzendamm 1, ✉ 10711, ✆ 89 60 30, Fax 8931215 – – 25. JY d
66 rm 185/295.

Kurfürstendamm am Adenauerplatz without rest, Kurfürstendamm 68, ✉ 10707, ✆ 88 46 30, Telex 184630, Fax 8825528 – – 35. JY n
34 rm 170/270 – 4 suites.

Scandotel Castor without rest, Fuggerstr. 8, ✉ 10777, ✆ 21 30 30, Fax 21303160 – . MY s
78 rm 210/265.

Delta without rest, Pohlstr. 58, ✉ 10785, ✆ 26 00 20, Fax 26002111 – . FY c
47 rm 150/300.

XXXX **Le Grand Silhouette** - Maritim Grand Hotel, Friedrichstr. 158, ✉ 10117, ✆ 20 27 45 00, Fax 20273362 – . PZ a
closed Sunday - Monday and 4 weeks July - August – **Meals** (dinner only) 125/198 and à la carte 89/129.

XXXX **Halekin** - Grand Hotel Esplanade, Lützowufer 15, ✉ 10785, ✆ 25 47 88 58, Fax 2651171 – . MX e
closed Sunday - Monday – **Meals** (dinner only) 95/130 and à la carte 70/94.

XXXX **Hugenotten** - Hotel Inter-Continental, Budapester Str. 2, ✉ 10787, ✆ 26 02 12 63, Fax 260280760 – . MX a
closed Sunday – **Meals** (dinner only)(outstanding wine list) 109/152 and à la carte 83/100.

XXX **Opernpalais-Königin Luise**, Unter den Linden 5, ✉ 10117, ✆ 20 26 83, Fax 2004438 – 50. PZ e
closed Sunday - Monday and January – **Meals** (dinner only, booking essential) à la carte 51/80.

XXX ✿ **Bamberger Reiter**, Regensburger Str. 7, ✉ 10777, ✆ 2 18 42 82, Fax 2142348, – . MY b
closed Sunday - Monday, 1 to 14 January and 1 to 15 August – **Meals** (dinner only, booking essential) 145/185 and à la carte 92/113 – ***Bistro :*** **Meals** à la carte 66/76
Spec. Gebratene Bresse-Taube mit Trüffelsauce, Hummer und Jakobsmuscheln mit Zuckerschoten, Karamelisierter Haselnußschmarrn mit Mandelschaum.

XXX ✿ **Alt Luxemburg**, Windscheidtstr. 31, ✉ 10627, ✆ 3 23 87 30 – JX s
closed Sunday - Monday (September - April), Saturday - Sunday (May - August) – **Meals** (dinner only, booking essential) à la carte 95/135
Spec. Carpaccio von der Gänsestopfleber mit Trüffelvinaigrette, Mille-feuille von Tomaten und Hummer, Steinbutt im Reisblatt gebraten mit Currysauce.

XXX **Ristorante Anselmo**, Damaschkestr. 17, ✉ 10711, ✆ 3 23 30 94, Fax 3246228, , « Modern Italian rest. » – . JY z
closed Sunday – **Meals** à la carte 44/86.

XX **Ephraim - Palais**, Spreestr. 1, ✉ 10178, ☎ 2 42 51 08, Fax 3219292, « Elegant restaurant »
- AE ⓓ E VISA RZ
July - August dinner only - **Meals** à la carte 46/72.

XX **Ponte Vecchio** (Tuscan rest.), Spielhagenstr. 3, ✉ 10585, ☎ 3 42 19 99 - ⓓ JX
closed Tuesday and 4 weeks July - August - **Meals** (dinner only, booking essential) à la carte 55/93.

XX **Ana e Bruno** (Italian rest.), Sophie-Charlotten-Str. 101, ✉ 14059, ☎ 3 25 71 10, Fax 3226895
- AE E. ✻ EY
closed Sunday and Monday, 1 week January and 3 weeks June - July - **Meals** (dinner only, outstanding Italian wine list) à la carte 80/100.

XX **Borchardt**, Französische Str. 47, ✉ 10787, ☎ 2 29 31 44, Fax 20397150, « Courtyard-terrace » - AE VISA PZ
Meals à la carte 43/82.

XX **Il Sorriso** (Italian rest.), Kurfürstenstr. 76, ✉ 10787, ☎ 2 62 13 13, Fax 2650277, 斋 - AE ⓓ E VISA. ✻ MX
closed Sunday and 22 December - 5 January - **Meals** (booking essential for dinner) à la carte 58/73.

XX **Peppino** (Italian rest.), Fasanenstr. 65, ✉ 10719, ☎ 8 83 67 22 - AE LY
closed Sunday and 4 weeks July - August - **Meals** à la carte 63/77.

XX **Du Pont**, Budapester Str. 1, ✉ 10787, ☎ 2 61 88 11, Fax 2618811, 斋 - AE ⓓ E VISA MX
closed Saturday dinner, Sunday, Bank Holidays and 24 December - 2 January - **Meals** à la carte 65/88.

XX **Trio**, Klausenerplatz 14, ✉ 14059, ☎ 3 21 77 82 EY
closed Wednesday and Thursday - **Meals** (dinner only, booking essential) à la carte 47/69.

XX **Funkturm - Restaurant** (|‡|, DM 3), Messedamm 22, ✉ 14055, ☎ 30 38 29 96, Fax 30383915, ≤ Berlin - Ⓟ. AE ⓓ E VISA. ✻ EY
Meals (booking essential) à la carte 55/80.

X **Am Karlsbad** (modern restaurant in bistro style), Am Karlsbad 11, ✉ 10785, ☎ 2 64 53 49, Fax 2644240, 斋 NZ
Saturday dinner only, closed Sunday - **Meals** à la carte 37/61.

X **Daitokai** (Japanese rest.), Tauentzienstr. 9 (Europa Centre, 1st floor), ✉ 10789, ☎ 2 61 80 99, Fax 2616036 - AE ⓓ E VISA JCB. ✻ MX
closed Monday - **Meals** 54/94 and à la carte.

at Berlin-Britz by Karl-Marx-Straße HZ :

Park Hotel Blub without rest, Buschkrugallee 60, ✉ 12359, ☎ 60 00 36 00, Fax 60003777 - |‡| ⇔ TV ☎ ♿ ⇔ Ⓟ - 🏛 60. AE ⓓ E VISA
123 rm ☕ 204/223.

Britzer Hof without rest, Jahnstr. 13, ✉ 12347, ☎ 6 85 00 80, Fax 68500868 - |‡| ⇔ TV ☎ ⇔. AE ⓓ E VISA JCB
57 rm ☕ 155/250.

Buschkrugpark without rest, Buschkrugallee 107, ✉ 12359, ☎ 6 00 99 00, Fax 60099020 - |‡| TV ☎. AE ⓓ E VISA
closed 23 December - 1 January - **25 rm** ☕ 195/265.

at Berlin-Dahlem by Clayallee EZ :

Forsthaus Paulsborn ⛰, Am Grunewaldsee, ✉ 14193, ☎ 8 13 80 10, Fax 8141156, 斋 - TV ☎ Ⓟ - 🏛 80. AE ⓓ E VISA
Meals *(closed Monday)* à la carte 42/75 - **10 rm** ☕ 155/240.

XX **Alter Krug**, Königin-Luise-Str. 52, ✉ 14195, ☎ 8 32 50 89, Fax 8327749, « Garden terrace » - Ⓟ. AE ⓓ E VISA
closed Sunday lunch and Monday - **Meals** (weekdays dinner only) à la carte 47/79.

at Berlin-Grunewald :

Schloßhotel Vier Jahreszeiten, Brahmsstr. 6, ✉ 14193, ☎ 89 58 40, Fax 89584800, « Former Wilhelminian mansion », 🏋, ≘s, 🏊 - |‡| ▤ TV ☎ ⇔ Ⓟ - 🏛 40. AE ⓓ E VISA. ✻ rest EZ
Vivaldi *(dinner only)* **Meals** 104/168 - ***Le Jardin :*** **Meals** à la carte 56/83 - **52 rm** 578/757 - 10 suites.

XXXX ✿ **Grand Slam**, Gottfried-von-Cramm-Weg 47, ✉ 14193, ☎ 8 25 38 10, Fax 8266300, 斋 - AE ⓓ E VISA. ✻ by Königsallee EZ
closed Sunday, Monday, 2 weeks January and 3 weeks July - August - **Meals** (dinner only, booking essential) 135/175 à la carte 97/114
Spec. Apfel-Sellerie-Feuilleté mit Gänsestopfleber, Hummer-Couscous, Gebratener weißer Pfirsich mit Lavendelblüten-Eis (June - Sept.).

XXX Rockendorf im Grunewald, Hagenstr. 18, ✉ 14193, ☎ 8 25 45 71, Fax 8900670, 斋 - EZ
(dinner only, booking essential).

at Berlin-Kreuzberg :

Stuttgarter Hof, Anhalter Str. 9, 10963, 26 48 30, Fax 26483900, - rm - 25. NZ **e**
Meals à la carte 41/76 - **110 rm** 235/370.

Riehmers Hofgarten without rest, Yorckstr. 83, 10965, 78 10 11, Fax 7866059 - - 25. GZ **a**
21 rm 200/290.

at Berlin-Lichtenberg by Karl-Marx-Allee HY :

Ramada without rest, Frankfurter Allee 73a/corner Voigtstraße, 10247, 42 83 10, Fax 43831831 - - 25.
120 rm 169/213 - 4 suites.

Abacus - Am Tierpark, Franz-Mett-Str. 7, 10319, 5 16 20, Fax 5162400, - rm - 90.
Meals *(Monday - Friday dinner only)* (buffet only) 30/44 - **278 rm** 190/310.

at Berlin-Lichterfelde by Boelcke Straße GZ :

Villa Toscana without rest, Bahnhofstr. 19, 12207, 7 68 92 70, Fax 7734488, « Villa with elegant furnishings » - .
16 rm 178/276.

at Berlin-Neukölln :

Estrel Residence, Sonnenallee 225, 12057, 6 83 10, Fax 68312345, - rm - 1000. HZ **a**
Portofino (Italian rest.) **Meals** à la carte 33/57 - ***Sans Souci*** **Meals** à la carte 33/57 - **Sun Thai** (Thai rest.) **Meals** à la carte 34/63 - **1125 rm** 194/243 - 80 suites.

at Berlin-Mariendorf by Tempelhofer Damm GZ :

Landhaus Alpinia, Säntisstr. 32, 12107, 76 17 70 (Hotel) 7 41 99 98 (Rest.), Fax 7419835, « Garden-terrace », - - 20.
Säntisstuben : **Meals** à la carte 64/86 - **58 rm** 168/380.

at Berlin-Prenzlauerberg :

Sorat Hotel Gustavo without rest, Prenzlauer Allee 169, 10409, 44 66 10, Fax 44661661 - - 50. HX **b**
123 rm 190/310.

at Berlin-Reinickendorf by Sellerstr. GX :

Rheinsberg am See, Finsterwalder Str. 64, 13435, 4 02 10 02, Fax 4035057, « Lakeside garden terrace », , , , - - 60.
Meals à la carte 34/78 - **80 rm** 165/280.

at Berlin-Rudow :

Sorat Hotel u. Office without rest, Rudower Str. 90, 12351, 60 00 80, Fax 60008666, - - 35. by Karl-Marx-Straße HZ
96 rm 185/290.

at Berlin-Siemensstadt by Siemensdamm EX :

Holiday Inn Airport-Esplanade, Rohrdamm 80, 13629, 38 38 90, Fax 38389900, , , , - rm - 250. rest
Meals à la carte 46/70 - **336 rm** 255/410 - 4 suites.

Novotel, Ohmstr. 4, 13629, 3 80 30, Fax 3819403, - rm - 200.
Meals à la carte 34/58 - **119 rm** 207/272.

at Berlin-Steglitz by Hauptstr. FZ :

Steglitz International, Albrechtstr. 2 (corner Schloßstraße), 12120, 79 00 50, Telex 183545, Fax 79005530 - rm - 400. . rest
Meals à la carte 43/65 - **211 rm** 210/260 - 3 suites.

at Berlin-Tegel :

Sorat-Hotel Humboldt-Mühle, An der Mühle 5, 13507, 43 90 40, Fax 43904444, , , - rm - 50. by Müllerstraße FX
Meals à la carte 40/61 - **122 rm** 203/366.

Novotel Berlin Airport, Kurt-Schumacher-Damm 202 (by airport approach), 13405, 4 10 60, Telex 181605, Fax 4106700, , , (heated) - rm - 150. EX **r**
Meals à la carte 32/59 - **181 rm** 207/259.

at Berlin-Tiergarten :

Sorat Hotel Am Spreebogen , Alt Moabit 99, 10559, 39 92 00, Fax 39920999, , , - rm - 150. FY **b**
Meals à la carte 53/66 - **221 rm** 250/420.

at Berlin-Waidmannslust by Sellerstr. GX :

XXX ✿ **Rockendorf's Restaurant**, Düsterhauptstr. 1, ✉ 13469, ✆ 4 02 30 99, Fax 4022742, « Elegant installation » – P. AE ⓓ E VISA
closed Sunday - Monday, 22 December - 6 January and July – **Meals** *(booking essential)* 110/175 (lunch) 175/225 (dinner)
Spec. Chartreuse von Taubenbrust und Gänseleber, Loup de Mer und Langustinen auf Fenchelconfit, Rehrücken im Briocheteig mit geschmortem Spitzkohl.

COLOGNE (KÖLN) Nordrhein-Westfalen 987 ㉓ ㉔, 412 D 14 – pop. – alt. 65 m – ☎ 0221.

See : Cathedral (Dom)★★ (Magi's Shrine★★★, Gothic stained glass windows★ Cross of Gero (Gerokreuz)★, South chapel (Marienkapelle) : altarpiece★★★, stalls★, treasury★ GY – Roman-Germanic Museum (Römisch-Germanisches Museum)★★★ (Dionysos Mosaic) GY **M1** – Wallraf-Richartz-Museum and Museum Ludwig★★★ (Photo-Historama Agfa★) Gy **M2** – Diocesan Museum (Diözesean Museum)★ GY **M3** – Schnütgen-Museum★★ GZ **M4** – Museum of East-Asian Art (Museum für Ostasiatische Kunst)★★ by Hahnenstraßeand Richard Wagner Straße EV – Museum for Applied Art (Museum für Angewandte Kunst)★ GYZ **M6** – St. Maria Lyskirchen (frescoes★★) FX – St. Pantaleon (rood screen★) EV – St. Ursula : treasure★ (Goldene Kammer) FX – St. Kunibert (chancel : stained glass windows★) FU – St. Mary the Queen (St. Maria Königin) : wall of glass★ by Bonnerstraße FX – Old Town Hall (Altes Rathaus)★ GZ – Botanical garden Flora★ by Konrad-Adenauer-Ufer FU.

⛳9 Köln-Marienburg, Schillingsrotter Weg (T) ✆ 38 40 53 ; ⛳18 Bergisch Gladbach-Refrath (③ : 17km), (02204) 6 31 14.

✈ Köln-Bonn at Wahn (SE : 17 km) ✆ (02203) 4 01.

🚗 Köln-Deutz, Barmer Straße by Deutzer Brücke FV.

Exhibition Centre (Messegelände) by Deutzer Brücke FV, ✆ 82 11, Telex 8873426.

ℹ Tourist office (Verkehrsamt), Am Dom ✉ 5039, ✆ 2 21 33 40, Telex 8883421, Fax 2213320.

ADAC, Luxemburger Str. 169, ✉50963, ✆ 472747, Fax 4727452.

Düsseldorf 40 – Aachen 69 – Bonn 28 – Essen 68.

Plans on following pages

Excelsior Hotel Ernst, Domplatz, ✉ 50667, ✆ 27 01, Telex 8882645, Fax 135150, Massage, ≘s – |‡| ⇔ rm ▤ TV ☎ – 🏛 80. AE ⓓ E VISA. ✱ rest GY **a**
Meals à la carte 69/109 – **160 rm** ☐ 295/620 – 8 suites.

Maritim, Heumarkt 20, ✉ 50667, ✆ 2 02 70, Fax 2027826, Massage Ⅰ₆, ≘s, ☒ – |‡| ⇔ rm ▤ TV ☎ ♿ – 🏛 1300. AE ⓓ E VISA JCB. ✱ rest GZ **m**
Bellevue « Terrace with ≤ Cologne » *(closed Sunday lunch)* **Meals** à la carte 72/96 – ***La Gallerie*** *(dinner only, closed Sunday - Monday and July to August)* **Meals** à la carte 49/77 – **Rôtisserie : Meals** 49 (buffet lunch only) – **454 rm** ☐ 255/522 – 28 suites.

Hotel im Wasserturm ⛓ (former 19C water tower, elegant modern installation), Kaygasse 2, ✉ 50676, ✆ 2 00 80, Telex 8881109, Fax 2008888, ⛱, roof garden terrace with ≤ Cologne, ≘s – |‡| ⇔ rm ▤ rest TV ☎ 🚗 – 🏛 20. AE ⓓ E VISA JCB. ✱ rest FX **c**
Meals à la carte 68/93 – **90 rm** ☐ 419/548 – 42 suites.

Dom-Hotel ⛓, Domkloster 2a, ✉ 50667, ✆ 2 02 40, Telex 8882919, Fax 2024444, « Terrace with ≤ » – |‡| ⇔ rm TV ☎ – 🏛 60. AE ⓓ E VISA JCB GY **d**
Meals à la carte 65/92 – **126 rm** ☐ 370/770.

Köln Renaissance Hotel, Magnusstr. 20, ✉ 50672, ✆ 2 03 40, Fax 2034777, ⛱, Massage, ≘s, ☒ – |‡| ⇔ rm ▤ TV ☎ ♿ 🚗 – 🏛 200. AE ⓓ E VISA JCB. ✱ rest
Meals à la carte 62/84 – **236 rm** ☐ 298/674. EV **b**

Holiday Inn Crowne Plaza, Habsburger Ring 9, ✉ 50674, ✆ 2 09 50, Fax 251206, Massage, ≘s, ☒ – |‡| ⇔ rm ▤ TV ☎ ♿ 🚗 – 🏛 230. AE ⓓ E VISA JCB
Meals à la carte 40/60 – **299 rm** ☐ 323/656. by Hahnenstraße EV

Dorint Kongress-Hotel, Helenenstr. 14, ✉ 50667, ✆ 22 80, Fax 2281301, Massage, ≘s, ☒ – |‡| ⇔ rm ▤ TV ☎ 🚗 – 🏛 500. AE ⓓ E VISA. ✱ rest EV **p**
Meals à la carte 48/92 – **290 rm** ☐ 323/606 – 10 suites.

Consul, Belfortstr. 9, ✉ 50668, ✆ 7 72 10, Fax 7721259, Massage, ≘s, ☒ – |‡| ⇔ rm ▤ TV ☎ ♿ 🚗 P – 🏛 120. AE ⓓ E VISA JCB. ✱ rest FU **v**
Meals à la carte 46/78 – **120 rm** ☐ 230/395.

Sofitel Mondial am Dom, Kurt-Hackenberg-Platz 1, ✉ 50667, ✆ 2 06 30, Telex 8881932, Fax 2063522, ⛱ – |‡| ⇔ rm TV ☎ 🚗 – 🏛 180. AE ⓓ E VISA. ✱ rest GY **f**
Meals 28 (lunch) and à la carte 46/72 – **205 rm** ☐ 235/420.

Savoy without rest, Turiner Str. 9, ✉ 50668, ✆ 1 62 30, Fax 1623200, ≘s – |‡| ⇔ TV ☎ P – 🏛 70. AE ⓓ E VISA FU **s**
100 rm ☐ 175/475.

Haus Lyskirchen, Filzengraben 28, ✉ 50676, ✆ 2 09 70, Fax 2097718, ≘s, ☒ – |‡| ⇔ rm ▤ rest TV ☎ 🚗 – 🏛 60. AE ⓓ E VISA JCB. ✱ FX **u**
Meals *(closed Saturday lunch, Sunday and Bank Holidays)* à la carte 35/67 – **94 rm** ☐ 180/350.

Euro Plaza Cologne, Breslauer Platz 2, ✉ 50668, ✆ 1 65 10, Telex 8885123, Fax 1651333 – |‡| ⇔ rm ▤ TV ☎ – 🏛 20. AE ⓓ E VISA GY **c**
Meals à la carte 34/54 – **116 rm** ☐ 195/290 – 6 suites.

Ascot-Hotel without rest, Hohenzollernring 95, ✉ 50672, ☎ 52 10 76, Fax 521070, Fö, ≘s - |¢| ⇹ TV ☎ ⇔. AE ⓓ E VISA. ✻ EV **a**
closed 23 December - 2 January - **46 rm** ☐ 171/411.

Flandrischer Hof without rest, Flandrische Str. 3, ✉ 50674, ☎ 25 20 95, Fax 251052 - |¢| ⇹ TV ☎ P - 🏛 20. AE ⓓ E VISA by HahnenStraße EV
143 rm ☐ 115/370.

Senats Hotel without rest, Unter Goldschmied 9, ✉ 50667, ☎ 2 06 20, Fax 2062200 - |¢| ⇹ TV ☎ - 🏛 200. AE E VISA. ✻ GZ **b**
closed 20 December - 6 January - **59 rm** ☐ 275/385.

Dorint Hotel, Friesenstr. 44, ✉ 50670, ☎ 1 61 40, Fax 1614100, ☂ - |¢| ⇹ rm TV ☎ ♿ - 🏛 100. AE ⓓ E VISA. ✻ rest EV **n**
Meals à la carte 36/57 - **103 rm** ☐ 215/630.

Viktoria without rest, Worringer Str. 23, ✉ 50668, ☎ 72 04 76, Fax 727067 - |¢| TV ☎ P. AE ⓓ E VISA JCB. ✻ FU **t**
closed 24 December - 1 January - **47 rm** ☐ 175/460.

Mercure Severinshof, Severinstr. 199, ✉ 50676, ☎ 2 01 30, Telex 8881852, Fax 2013666, ☂, ≘s - |¢| ⇹ rm TV ☎ ⇔ - 🏛 140. AE ⓓ E VISA JCB. ✻ rest FX **a**
Meals à la carte 34/74 - **253 rm** ☐ 215/380 - 11 suites.

Coellner Hof, Hansaring 100, ✉ 50670, ☎ 12 20 75, Fax 135235 - |¢| ⇹ rm TV ☎ ⇔ - 🏛 30. AE ⓓ E VISA FU **k**
Meals *(closed Friday - Saturday)* à la carte 40/73 - **71 rm** ☐ 140/330.

CM Classica Hotel Europa am Dom without rest, Am Hof 38, ✉ 50667, ☎ 2 05 80, Fax 2582032 - |¢| ⇹ TV ☎ - 🏛 25. AE ⓓ E VISA JCB GYZ **z**
92 rm ☐ 290/390.

Cristall without rest, Ursulaplatz 9, ✉ 50668, ☎ 1 63 00, Fax 1630333, « Modern interior » - |¢| ⇹ TV ☎. AE ⓓ E VISA. ✻ FU **r**
85 rm ☐ 190/310.

Euro Garden Cologne without rest, Domstr. 10, ✉ 50668, ☎ 1 64 90, Fax 1649333, ≘s - |¢| ⇹ TV ☎ ⇔ - 🏛 30. AE ⓓ E VISA FU **a**
- **85 rm** ☐ 195/545.

Königshof without rest, Richartzstr. 14, ✉ 50667, ☎ 2 57 87 71, Telex 8881318, Fax 2578762 - |¢| TV ☎. AE ⓓ E VISA GY **n**
85 rm ☐ 155/395.

Kommerzhotel without rest, Breslauer Platz, ✉ 50668, ☎ 1 61 00, Fax 1610122, ≘s - |¢| TV ☎. AE ⓓ E VISA GY **r**
77 rm ☐ 185/380.

Antik Hotel Bristol without rest (antique furniture), Kaiser-Wilhelm-Ring 48, ✉ 50672, ☎ 12 01 95, Fax 131495 - |¢| TV ☎. AE ⓓ E VISA JCB EU **m**
closed 22 December - 2 January - **44 rm** ☐ 165/320.

Esplanade without rest, Hohenstaufenring 56, ✉ 50674, ☎ 21 03 11, Fax 216822 - |¢| TV ☎ ⇔. AE ⓓ E VISA EX **a**
closed 24 December - 2 January - **33 rm** ☐ 165/315.

CM Classica Hotel Residence without rest, Alter Markt 55, ✉ 50667, ☎ 2 57 69 91, Fax 2577659 - |¢| ⇹ TV ☎ - 🏛 15. AE ⓓ E VISA JCB GZ **c**
56 rm ☐ 230/330.

Astor without rest, Friesenwall 68, ✉ 50672, ☎ 25 31 01, Fax 253106 - |¢| ⇹ TV ☎ P. AE ⓓ E VISA. ✻ EV **y**
51 rm ☐ 174/340.

Conti without rest, Brüsseler Str. 40, ✉ 50674, ☎ 25 20 62, Fax 252107 - |¢| ⇹ ☎ ⇔. AE E VISA by Hahnenstraße EV
44 rm ☐ 125/260.

Merian-Hotel without rest, Allerheiligenstr. 1, ✉ 50668, ☎ 1 66 50, Fax 1665200 - |¢| TV ☎ ⇔ FU **c**
32 rm ☐ 110/220.

Metropol without rest, Hansaring 14, ✉ 50670, ☎ 13 33 77, Fax 138307 - |¢| TV ☎ - 🏛 25. AE ⓓ E VISA JCB EU **m**
closed 22 December - 2 January - **26 rm** ☐ 145/320.

Altstadt Hotel without rest, Salzgasse 7, ✉ 50667, ☎ 2 57 78 51, Fax 2577853, ≘s - |¢| TV ☎. AE ⓓ E GZ **p**
closed 20 December - 2 January - **28 rm** ☐ 95/180.

XXX **Ambiance am Dom** (in Excelsior Hotel Ernst), Trankgasse 1, ✉ 50667, ☎ 1 39 19 12 - AE ⓓ E VISA. ✻ GY **a**
closed Saturday - Sunday, Bank Holidays and 3 weeks August - **Meals** à la carte 79/104.

XXX ✿ **Rino Casati**, Ebertplatz 3, ✉ 50668, ☎ 72 11 08, Fax 728097 - AE ⓓ E VISA. ✻
closed Sunday - Monday (except exhibitions) - **Meals** (booking essential) 48 (lunch) and à la carte 79/104 FU **t**
Spec. Venezianische Fischsuppe, Tournedos vom Salm mit Sesamkruste und Rotweinsauce, Taubenbrust im Selleriemantel.

XXX **Die Bastei**, Konrad-Adenauer-Ufer 80, ✉ 50668, ☎ 12 28 25, Fax 1390187, ≤ Rhein - AE ⓓ E VISA. ✻ FU **b**
closed Saturday lunch - **Meals** à la carte 52/99.

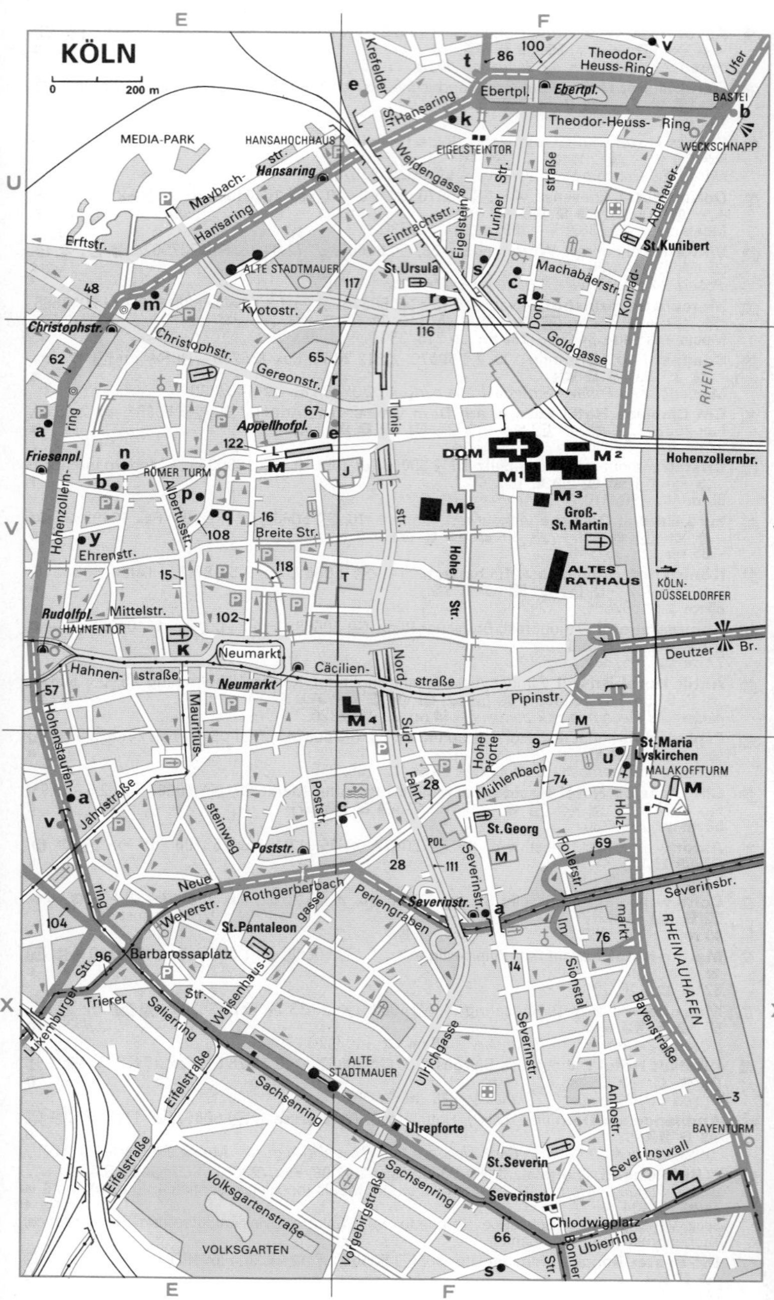
KÖLN
0
200 m
E
F
U
V
X
MEDIA-PARK
HANSAHOCHHAUS
Hansaring
Maybach-str.
Hansaring
Erftstr.
ALTE STADTMAUER
Kyotostr.
Christophstr.
Christophstr.
Gereonstr.
Appellhofpl.
Friesenpl.
Hohenzollern-ring
RÖMER TURM
Albertusstr.
Breite Str.
Ehrenstr.
Mittelstr.
Rudolfpl.
HAHNENTOR
Neumarkt
Cäcilien-
Hahnen-straße
Neumarkt
Mauritius-steinweg
Hohenstaufen-ring
Jahnstraße
Poststr.
Poststr.
Neue Weyerstr.
Rothgerberbach
Waisenhaus-gasse
St.Pantaleon
Barbarossaplatz
Luxemburger Str.
Trierer Str.
Salierring
Eifelstraße
Eifelstraße
Sachsenring
ALTE STADTMAUER
Ulrepforte
Sachsenring
Volksgartenstraße
VOLKSGARTEN
Vorgebirgstraße
Ulrichgasse
Perlengraben
Severinstr.
Severinstr.
Severinstr.
St.Severin
Severinstor
Chlodwigplatz
Bonner Str.
Ubierring
Severinswall
BAYENTURM
Annostr.
Bayenstraße
RHEINAUHAFEN
Im Sionstal
Severinsbr.
Follerstr.
markt
St.Georg
POL.
Holz-
Mühlenbach
Hohe Pforte
Süd-Fahrt
Nord-straße
Tunis-str.
Hohe Str.
Pipinstr.
St-Maria Lyskirchen
MALAKOFFTURM
Deutzer Br.
KÖLN-DÜSSELDORFER
ALTES RATHAUS
Groß-St. Martin
DOM
Hohenzollernbr.
RHEIN
Goldgasse
Domstr.
Machabäerstr.
Konrad-Adenauer-Ufer
St.Kunibert
St.Ursula
Eintrachtstr.
Eigelstein
Turiner Str.
straße
Weidengasse
Krefelder Str.
Hansaring
EIGELSTEINTOR
Ebertpl.
Ebertpl.
Theodor-Heuss-Ring
Theodor-Heuss-Ring
BASTEI
WECKSCHNAPP
Ufer

KÖLN

Breite Straße .... GZ
Ehrenstraße .... EV
Eigelstein .... FU
Gürzenichstraße .... GZ 55
Habsburgerring .... EV 57
Hahnenstraße .... EV
Hohenstaufenring .... EX
Hohenzollernring .... EV
Hohe Straße .... GYZ
Mittelstraße .... EV
Neumarkt .... EV
Richmodstraße .... EV 102
Schildergasse .... GZ
Severinstraße .... FX
Zeppelinstraße .... EV 118

Am Bayenturm .... FX 3
Am Leystapel .... GZ 4
Am Malzbüchel .... GZ 5
An den Dominikanern .. GY 8
An der Malzmühle .... FX 9
An St-Katharinen .... FX 14
Apostelnstraße .... EV 15
Auf dem Berlich .... EV 16
Augustinerstraße .... GZ 19
Bechergasse .... GZ 22
Bischofsgarten-Straße .. GY 26
Blaubach .... FX 28
Brückenstraße .... GZ 32
Dompropst-Ketzer-Straße .... GY 38
Drususgasse .... GY 39
Gladbacher Straße .... EU 48
Glockengasse .... GZ 50
Große Budengasse .... GZ 52
Große Neugasse .... GY 54
Heinrich-Böll-Platz .... GY 58
Kaiser-Wilhelm-Ring .... EV 62
Kardinal-Frings-Straße .... EV 65
Karolingerring .... FX 66
Kattenbug .... EV 67
Kleine Budengasse .... GZ 68
Kleine Witschgasse .... FX 69
Komödienstraße .... GY 71
Kurt-Hackenberg-Platz .. GY 72
Mathiasstraße .... FX 74
Mechtildisstraße .... FX 76
Minoritenstraße .... GZ 79
Neusser Straße .... FU 86
Offenbachplatz .... GZ 90
Pfälzer Straße .... EX 96
Quatermarkt .... GZ 99

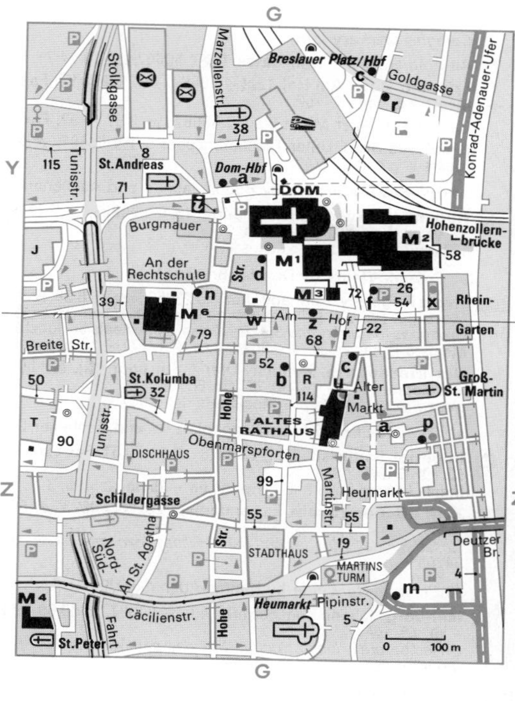

Riehler Straße .... FU 100
Roonstraße .... EX 104
Sankt-Apern-Straße .... EV 108
Tel-Aviv-Straße .... FX 111
Unter Goldschmied .... GZ 114
Unter Sachsenhausen .... GY 115
Ursulaßle .... FU 116
Victoriastraße .... FU 117
Zeughausstraße .... EV 122

XXX **Börsen-Restaurant Maître**, Unter Sachsenhausen 10, ✉ 50667, ☎ 13 30 21, Fax 133040 – ▤. AE ⓓ E VISA. ✂ EV **r**
closed Sunday, Bank Holidays and 4 weeks July - August – **Meals** à la carte 69/98 – ***Börsenstube :*** **Meals** à la carte 50/82.

XXX **Grande Milano**, Hohenstaufenring 37, ✉ 50674, ☎ 24 21 21, Fax 244846 – AE ⓓ E VISA EX **v**
closed Sunday and 3 weeks July - August – **Meals** à la carte 57/96 – ***Pinot di Pinot :*** **Meals** à la carte 38/54.

XX **Weinhaus im Walfisch** (17C timber framed house), Salzgasse 13, ✉ 50667, ☎ 2 57 78 79, Fax 2580861 – AE ⓓ E VISA GZ **p**
closed Saturday lunch, Sunday, Bank Holidays and 22 December - 6 January – **Meals** à la carte 63/92.

XX **Em Krützche**, Am Frankenturm 1, ✉ 50667, ☎ 2 58 08 39, Fax 253417, ☂ – AE ⓓ E VISA GY **x**
closed Monday – **Meals** *(booking essential)* 28 (lunch) and à la carte 56/85.

XX **Ratskeller**, Rathausplatz 1 (entrance Alter Markt), ✉ 50667, ☎ 2 57 69 29, Fax 2576946, « Courtyard » – ▤ ♿ – 🏟 80. AE ⓓ E VISA GZ **u**
Meals à la carte 38/75.

XX **Daitokai** (Japanese rest.), Kattenbug 2, ✉ 50667, ☎ 12 00 48, Fax 137503 – ▤. AE ⓓ E VISA JCB. ✂ EV **e**
closed Sunday – **Meals** à la carte 48/78.

X ✿ **Le Moissonnier** (Typical French bistro), Krefelder Str. 25, ✉ 50670, ☎ 72 94 79, Fax 7325461 FU **e**
closed Sunday - Monday, Bank Holidays dinner only – **Meals** à la carte 55/73
Spec. Petites ravioles à la tomate au basilic, Filet de lapin poêlé à la coriandre, Pavé de bœuf à la lie de vin.

Cologne brewery inns :

Alt Köln am Dom, Trankgasse 7, ✉ 50667, ☎ 13 74 71, Fax 136885 GY a

Früh am Dom, Am Hof 12, ✉ 50667, ☎ 2 58 03 97, Fax 256326, beer garden GY w
Meals à la carte 24/50.

Gaffel-Haus, Alter Markt 20, ✉ 50667, ☎ 2 57 76 92, Fax 253879, GZ a

Brauhaus Sion, Unter Taschenmacher 5, ✉ 50667, ☎ 2 57 85 40, Fax 2582081, GZ r
Meals à la carte 27/42.

at Cologne-Braunsfeld by Rudolfplatz EV and Aachener Str. :

Regent without rest, Melatengürtel 15, ✉ 50933, ☎ 5 49 90, Fax 5499998, – 80. AE VISA
171 rm 215/411 – 5 suites.

at Cologne-Deutz by Deutzer Brücke FV :

Hyatt Regency, Kennedy-Ufer 2a, ✉ 50679, ☎ 8 28 12 34, Fax 8281370, ≤, beer garden, Massage, – rm – 350. AE VISA JCB. rest
Graugans (Saturday and Sunday dinner only) **Meals** 56 (lunch) and à la carte 74/96 – ***Glashaus :*** **Meals** à la carte 55/74 – **307 rm** 321/777 – 18 suites.

Der Messeturm, Kennedy-Ufer (18th floor,), ✉ 50679, ☎ 88 10 08, Fax 818575, ≤ Cologne – – 30. AE VISA.
closed Saturday lunch – **Meals** à la carte 50/84.

at Cologne-Ehrenfeld by Rudolfplatz EV and Aachener Str. :

Imperial, Barthelstr. 93, ✉ 50823, ☎ 51 70 57, Fax 520993, – rest . AE VISA
Meals (dinner only) à la carte 39/63 – **35 rm** 198/340.

Zum offenen Kamin, Eichendorffstr. 25, ✉ 50823, ☎ 55 68 78, Fax 5502425 – AE VISA by Erftstraße EU
closed Sunday, Monday and Bank Holidays except exhibitions – **Meals** 48 (lunch) and à la carte 54/94.

at Cologne-Holweide by Konrad-Adenauer-Ufer FU :

Isenburg, Johann-Bensberg-Str. 49, ✉ 51067, ☎ 69 59 09, Fax 698703, « Garden terrace » – . AE VISA
closed Saturday lunch, Sunday, Monday, carnival, mid July - mid August and Christmas – **Meals** *(booking essential)* à la carte 64/92.

at Cologne-Junkersdorf by Rudolfplatz EV and Aachener Str. :

Brenner'scher Hof , Wilhelm-von-Capitaine-Str. 15, ✉ 50858, ☎ 9 48 60 00, Fax 94860010, , « Installation in country house style » – – 50. AE VISA
Meals *(closed Monday)* (dinner only) à la carte 56/79 – **40 rm** 225/410 – 7 suites.

at Cologne-Lindenthal by Rudolfplatz EV and B 264 :

Queens Hotel, Dürener Str. 287, ✉ 50935, ☎ 4 67 60, Fax 433765, « Garden terrace » – rm rest – 350. AE VISA. rest
Meals à la carte 44/78 – **147 rm** 260/554.

at Cologne-Marienburg by Bonner Straße FX :

Marienburger Bonotel, Bonner Str. 478, ✉ 50968, ☎ 3 70 20, Fax 3702132, , – – 40. AE VISA. rest
Meals à la carte 46/64 – **93 rm** 180/395 – 4 suites.

at Cologne-Marsdorf by Rudolfplatz EV and B 264 :

Novotel Köln-West, Horbeller Str. 1, ✉ 50858, ☎ (02234) 51 40, Telex 8886355, Fax 514106, , , (heated), – rm rest – 100. AE VISA
Meals à la carte 34/62 – **199 rm** 185/290.

at Cologne-Müngersdorf by Rudolfplatz EV and B 55 :

Landhaus Kuckuck, Olympiaweg 2, ✉ 50933, ☎ 49 23 23, Fax 4972847, – 120. AE VISA
closed Monday and 20 February - 2 March – **Meals** (booking essential) à la carte 62/85.

at Cologne - Porz-Grengel SE : 15 km by A 59 :

Holiday Inn, Waldstr. 255, ✉ 51147, ☎ (02203) 56 10, Telex 8874665, Fax 5619, , – rm – 90. AE VISA JCB
Meals à la carte 51/84 *(also vegetarian dishes)* – **177 rm** 330/560.

at Cologne - Porz-Wahnheide SE : 17 km by A 59 :

Quelle without rest, Heidestr. 246, ✉ 51147, ☎ (02203) 9 64 70, Fax 9647317 – – 30
95 rm 90/210.

at Cologne - Rodenkirchen by Bayen Straße FX :

Atrium Rheinhotel without rest, Karlstr. 2, ✉ 50996, ☎ 39 30 45, Fax 394054, – rm. **78 rm.** by Am Bayenturm FX

Laasphe, Bad Nordrhein-Westfalen 412 I 14, 987 ㉖ – pop. 16 000 – alt. 335 m – ☎ 02752 – Köln 144.

at Bad Laasphe-Hesselbach SW : 10 km :

XXX ✿✿ **L'ecole**, Hesselbacher Str. 23, ✉ 57334, ☎ 53 42, « Elegant installation » – P. AE E
closed Saturday lunch, Monday, Tuesday and January – **Meals** (booking essential) 140 and à la carte 72/100
Spec. Gebratene Gänseleber mit glacierten Apfelspalten, Das Beste vom Reh auf Spitzkohl mit Preiselbeerapfel, Moccacharlotte mit Mascarponesauce.

Wittlich Rheinland - Pfalz 987 ㉕ ㉖, 412 D 17 – pop. 17 300 – alt. 155 m – ☎ 06571.
Köln 130.

at Dreis SW : 8 km :

XXXX ✿✿ **Waldhotel Sonnora** with rm, Auf dem Eichelfeld, ✉ 54518, ☎ (06578) 4 06, Fax 1402, ≤, « Garden » – P. AE E VISA.
closed 6 January - 6 February – **Meals** *(closed Monday and Tuesday)* (booking essential) 125/158 and à la carte 85/120 – **18 rm** 70/140
Spec. Bretonischer Hummer in Curry-Korianderwürze mit grünen Äpfeln, Kroß gebratener Zander auf Rotwein- und Champagnersauce, Bluttaube mit Gänseleber im Wirsingblatt pochiert.

Prices For full details of the prices quoted in this Guide, consult the introduction.

DRESDEN L Sachsen 414 N 12, 984 ㉔, 987 ⑲ – pop. 480 000 – alt. 105 m – ☎ 0351.

See : Zwinger★★★ (Wall Pavilion★★, Nymphs' Bath★★, Porcelain Collection★★, National Mathematical-Physical Salon★★) AY – Semper Opera★★ AY – Former court church★★ (Hofkirche) BY – Palace (Schloß) : royal houses★ (Fürstenzug-Mosaik), Long Passage★ (Langer Gang) BY – Albertinum : Picture Gallery Old Masters★★★ (Gemäldegalerie Alte Meister), Picture Gallery New Masters★★★ (Gemäldegalerie Neue Meister), Green Vault★★★ (Grünes Gewölbe) BY – Prager Straße★ ABZ – Museum of History of Dresden★ (Museum für Geschichte der Stadt Dresden) BY L – Church of the Cross★ (Kreuzkirche) BY – Japanese Palace★ (Japanisches Palais) ABX – Museum of Folk Art★ (Museum für Volkskunst) BX **M 2** – Great Garden★ (Großer Garten) CDZ – Russian-Orthodox Church★ (Russisch-orthodoxe Kirche) (by Leningrader Str. BZ) – Brühl's Terrace ≤★ (Brühlsche Terrasse) BY – Equestrian statue of Augustus the Strong ★ (Reiterstandbild Augusts des Starken) BX **E**.

Envir. : Schloß (palace) Moritzburg★ (NW : 14 km by Hansastr. BX) – Schloß (palace) Pillnitz★ (SE : 15 km by Bautzener Str. CX) – Saxon Swiss★★★ (Sächsische Schweiz) : Bastei★★★, Festung (fortress) Königstein★★ ≤★★, Großsedlitz : Baroque Garden★.

18 Possendorf (S : 13 km) ☎ (035206) 33 76 51 11.

18 Herzogswalde (SW : 19 km) ☎ (0172) 3 57 68 88.

Dresden-Klotzsche (N : 13 km), ☎ 58 31 41. City Office, Rampische Str. 2, ☎ 4 95 60 13.

Dresden-Information, Prager Str. 10, ✉ 01069, ☎ 4 95 50 25, Fax 4951276.

Tourist-Information, Neustädter Narkt, ✉ 01097, ☎ 5 35 39.

ADAC, Schandauer Str. 46, ✉ 01277, ☎ 3 45 80, Fax 30214.

Berlin 198 – Chemnitz 70 – Görlitz 98 – Leipzig 111 – Praha 152.

Plans on following pages

Kempinski Hotel Taschenbergpalais, Am Taschenberg 3, ✉ 01067, ☎ 4 91 20, Fax 4912812, « Modern hotel in 18C Baroque palace », Massage, – rm – 320. AE E VISA JCB BY **a**
Meals à la carte 54/88 – **213 rm** 424/603 – 25 suites.

Maritim Hotel Bellevue, Große Meißner Str. 15, ✉ 01097, ☎ 5 66 20, Telex 329330, Fax 55997, ≤, « Courtyard terraces », – rm P – 260. AE E VISA JCB BX **a**
Meals *(closed Monday)* à la carte 45/78 – ***Canaletto*** *(dinner only, closed Sunday - Monday)*
Meals à la carte 70/91 – **340 rm** 260/448 – 16 suites.

Dresden Hilton, An der Frauenkirche 5, ✉ 01067, ☎ 8 64 20, Fax 8642725, – rm – 350. AE E VISA JCB BY **e**
– ***Rossini*** (Italian rest.) **Meals** à la carte 43/82 – ***Grüner Baum*** : **Meals** (buffet only) 45/49 – **333 rm** 325/515 – 4 suites.

Dorint Hotel, Grunauer Str. 14, ✉ 01069, ☎ 4 91 50, Fax 4915100, – – 160. AE E VISA CYZ **n**
Meals à la carte 37/62 – **244 rm** 240/340.

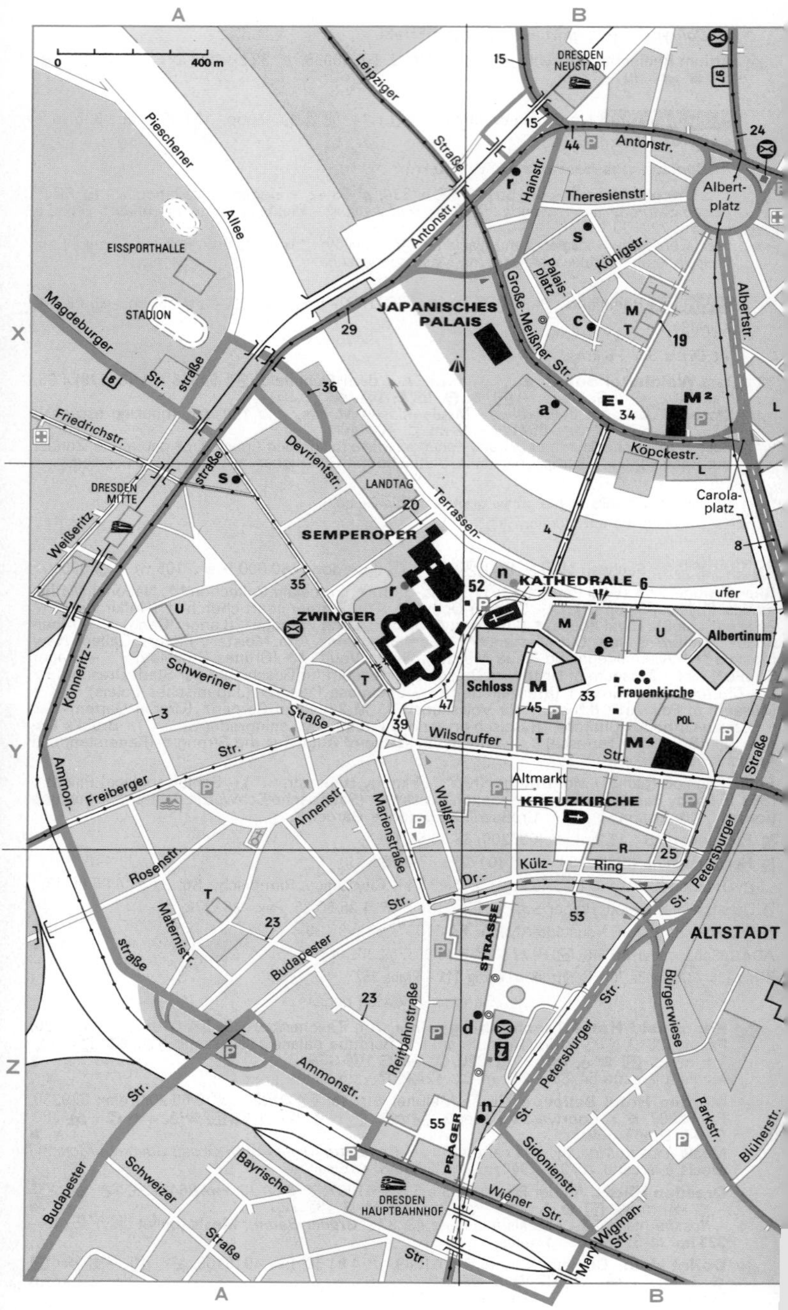

A
B
X
Y
Z
0
400 m
DRESDEN NEUSTADT
Leipziger Straße
Pieschener Allee
EISSPORTHALLE
STADION
Magdeburger Str.
straße
Antonstr.
Hainstr.
Theresienstr.
Albertplatz
Königstr.
Palaisplatz
Große Meißner Str.
JAPANISCHES PALAIS
Albertstr.
Köpckestr.
Carolaplatz
Friedrichstr.
DRESDEN MITTE
Weißeritz-
Devrientstr.
LANDTAG
Terrassenufer
SEMPEROPER
KATHEDRALE
ZWINGER
Schloss
Frauenkirche
Albertinum
POL.
Könneritz-
Ammon-
Schweriner Straße
Freiberger Str.
Wilsdruffer Str.
Altmarkt
KREUZKIRCHE
Annenstr.
Marienstraße
Wallstr.
Dr.-Külz-Ring
Rosenstr.
Maternistr.
straße
Budapester Str.
Reitbahnstraße
PRAGER STRASSE
St. Petersburger Str.
ALTSTADT
Bürgerwiese
Parkstr.
Blüherstr.
Sidonienstr.
Ammonstr.
Bayrische
Schweizer Straße
DRESDEN HAUPTBAHNHOF
Wiener Str.
Mary-Wigman-Str.

DRESDEN

Albertbrücke	CX	2
Alfred-Althus-Str.	AY	3
Augustusbrücke	BY	4
Brühlsche Terrasse	BY	6
Carolabrücke	BY	8
Elsasser Str.	CDY	13
Hansastr	BX	15
Hauptstr.	BX	19
Holländische Str.	AY	20
Josephinenstr.	AZ	23
Königsbrücker Str.	BX	24
Kreuzstr.	BYZ	25
Lessingstr.	CX	27
Marienbrücke	AX	29
Neumarkt	BY	33
Neustädter-Markt	BX	34
Ostra-Allee	AY	35
Ostra-Ufer	AX	36
Postplatz	AY	39
Reichpietschufer	CX	40
Rothenburger Straße	CX	42
Sachsenallee	CY	43
Schlesischer Pl.	BX	44
Schloßstr.	BY	45
Sophienstr	AY	47
Steinstr.	CY	49
Theaterplatz	BY	52
Waisenhausstr	BZ	53
Wiener Pl.	AZ	55

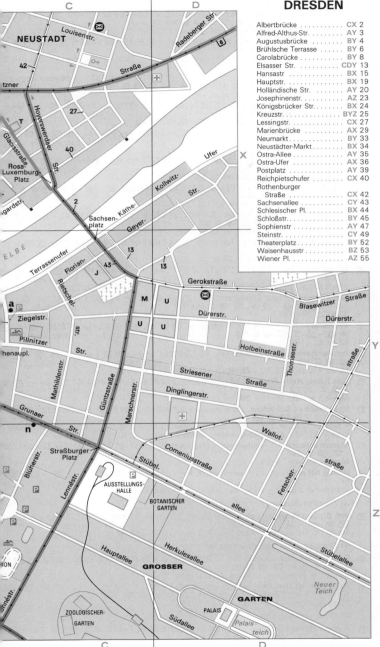

Bülow Residenz, Rähnitzgasse 19, ✉ 01097, ℰ 4 40 33, Fax 4403410, « Courty terrace » – 25. AE E VISA. rest BX
Meals (dinner only) à la carte 50/84 – **31 rm** 315/470.

Bayerischer Hof, Antonstr. 35, ✉ 01097, ℰ 5 02 41 93, Fax 570589, – 25. E VISA. rest BX
closed 22 - 31 December – **Meals** *(closed Saturday - Sunday)* (dinner only) à la carte 26/ – **23 rm** 195/290 – 3 suites.

Seidler art'otel, Ostra-Allee 33, ✉ 01067, ℰ 4 92 20, Fax 4922777, « Modern interior – rm – 350. AE E VISA AY
Meals à la carte 38/56 – **174 rm** 195/450.

Terrassenufer, Terrassenufer 12, ✉ 01069, ℰ 4 40 95 00, Fax 4409600, – – 20. AE E VISA JCB CY
Meals à la carte 27/49 – **196 rm** 295/440 – 6 suites.

Windsor, Roßmäßlerstr. 13, ✉ 01139, ℰ 8 49 01 41, Fax 8490144 – . AE VISA. rest by Leipziger Straße AX
Meals à la carte 22/45 – **25 rm** 185/298.

Astron, Hansastr. 37, ✉ 01097, ℰ 4 77 20, Fax 4772200, – rm – 250. AE E VISA JCB by Hansastraße BX
Meals à la carte 36/55 – **269 rm** 230/370.

Verde, Buchenstr. 10, ✉ 01097, ℰ 8 11 10, Fax 8111333, – rm – 25. AE E VISA JCB by Königsbrücker Str. BX
Meals à la carte 26/42 – **77 rm** 155/265.

Mercure Newa, Prager Straße, ✉ 01069, ℰ 5 67 60, Fax 53218, – rm – 220. AE E VISA BZ
Meals à la carte 33/61 – **315 rm** 210/440.

Martha Hospiz without rest, Nieritzstr. 11, ✉ 01097, ℰ 5 67 60, Fax 53218 – E VISA. BX
closed 21 to 27 December – **36 rm** 130/230.

Alpha, Fritz-Reuter-Str. 21, ✉ 01097, ℰ 5 02 24 41, Fax 571390, – . AE E VISA by Hansastr. BX
Meals *(closed Sunday)* (dinner only) à la carte 30/47 – **75 rm** 180/220.

Novalis without rest, Bärnsdorfer Str. 185, ✉ 01127, ℰ 8 21 30, Fax 8213180, – rm – 40. AE E VISA by Hansastraße BX
85 rm 160/195.

Wenotel without rest, Schlachthofring 24, ✉ 01067, ℰ 4 97 60, Fax 4976100 – – 20. AE E VISA by Pieschener Allee AX
82 rm 114/140.

An der Rennbahn, Winterbergstr. 96, ✉ 01237, ℰ 2 54 00 30, Fax 2522785, – . AE E VISA by Parkstraße and Tiergartenstraße BCZ
Meals à la carte 26/50 – **22 rm** 145/210.

Ibis Königstein, Prager Straße, ✉ 01069, ℰ 4 85 64 42, Fax 4954054 – rm – 30. AE E VISA BZ
Meals à la carte 30/46 – **306 rm** 170/250.

Italienisches Dörfchen, Theaterplatz 3, ✉ 01067, ℰ 49 81 60, Fax 4981688, « Terra with » – AE E VISA BY
– ***Erlwein :*** *(dinner only) (closed Monday)* **Meals** à la carte 68/112 – ***Weinzimmer :*** **Meals** la carte 37/58 – ***Kurfürstenzimmer :*** **Meals** à la carte 32/50.

Opernrestaurant, Theatherplatz 2 (1st floor), ✉ 01067, ℰ 4 91 15 21, Fax 4956097, – AE E VISA AY
Meals à la carte 38/68.

König Albert (bistro style restaurant), Königstr. 28, ✉ 01097, ℰ 5 48 83, – AE E BX
Saturday and Sunday dinner only – **Meals** à la carte 44/72.

at Dresden-Blasewitz :

Am Blauen Wunder, Loschwitzer Str. 48, ✉ 01309, ℰ 3 36 60, Fax 3366299 – – 35. AE E VISA by Blasewitzer Straße DY
Meals *(closed Sunday)* (Italian rest.) à la carte 32/72 – **40 rm** 190/260.

at Dresden-Cotta by Schweriner Str. AY :

Cotta-Hotel, Mobschatzer Str. 17, ✉ 01157, ℰ 4 28 60, Fax 4286333 – rm – 45. AE E VISA. rest
Meals à la carte 23/47 – **44 rm** 185/255.

Residenz Alt Dresden, Mobschatzerstr. 29, ✉ 01157, ℰ 4 28 10, Fax 4281988, – rm – 100. AE E VISA JCB.
Meals à la carte 37/61 – **124 rm** 190/250.

at Dresden-Klotzsche :

Airport Hotel, Karl-Marx-Str. 25, ✉ 01109, ℰ 8 83 30, Fax 8833333, – – 50. AE E VISA JCB by Königsbrücker Straße BX
Meals à la carte 33/67 – **100 rm** 196/310 – 6 suites.

at Dresden-Laubegast E : 9 km by Striesener Straße DY :

Prinz Eugen without rest, Gustav-Hartmann-Str. 4, ✉ 01279, ✆ 2 51 59 98, Fax 2515986 – AE E VISA
47 rm 190/240.

at Dresden-Leubnitz-Neuostra by Parkstr. BCZ and Teplitzer Str.

Treff Hotel Dresden, Wilhelm-Franke-Str. 90, ✉ 01219, ✆ 4 78 20, Fax 4782550, – rm – 370. AE E VISA
Meals à la carte 37/63 – **262 rm** 209/273.

at Dresden-Niedersedlitz SE : 10 km by Parkstraße BZ :

Ambiente without rest, Meusegaster Str. 23, ✉ 01259, ✆ 22 18 80, Fax 2218836 – E VISA
20 rm 158/265.

at Dresden-Reick by Parkstraße (B 172) BCZ :

Coventry, Hüßestr. 1, ✉ 01237, ✆ 2 81 63 11, Fax 2816310, – rm – 25. AE E VISA
Meals à la carte 33/60 – **51 rm** 220/330 – 3 suites.

at Dresden-Weißer Hirsch by Bautzner Straße CDX :

Villa Emma (modernized Art Deco villa), Stechgrundstr. 2 (corner of Bautzner Landstr.), ✉ 01324, ✆ 37 48 10, Fax 3748118, – rm AE E VISA
Meals *(closed Sunday)* (booking essential) à la carte 49/68 – **21 rm** 210/450.

Erholung, Rissweg 39, ✉ 01324, ✆ 37 79 93, Fax 377993 – AE E VISA
closed Sunday – **Meals** (dinner only) 77/123 and à la carte 65/83
Spec. Zander in der Kartoffelkruste mit Leipziger Allerlei, Grünes Filet vom Rind mit Rotweinsauce, Sächsische Quarkkeulchen mit Apfelmus.

at Radebeul NW : 7 km by Leipziger Straße AX :

Flamberg Parkhotel Hoflössnitz, Nizzastr. 55, ✉ 01445, ✆ (0351) 8 32 10, Fax 8321445, Massage, – rm – 170. AE E VISA JCB
– ***La Vigna :*** **Meals** à la carte 48/74 – ***Rienzi :*** **Meals** à la carte 39/56 – **202 rm** 285/430 – 13 suites.

DÜSSELDORF

Nordrhein-Westfalen 411 412 D 13, 987 ㉕ ㉖ – pop. 570 000 – alt. 40 m – ☎ 0211.

See : Königsallee★ EZ – Hofgarten★ DEY und Schloß Jägerhof (Goethemuseum★ EY **M1**) – Hetjensmuseum★ DZ **M4** – Land Economic Museum (Landesmuseum Volk u. Wirtschaft)★ DY **M5** – Museum of Art (Kunstmuseum)★ DY **M2** – Collection of Art (Kunstsammlung NRW)★ DY **M3** – Löbbecke-Museum und Aquazoo★ by Kaiserswerther Str. AU.

Envir. : Chateau of Benrath (Schloß Benrath) (Park★) S : 10 km by Siegburger Str. CX.

18 Ratingen-Hösel, NE : 16 km, ✆ (02102) 6 86 29 ; 18 Gut Rommeljans, NE : 12 km, ✆ (02102) 8 10 92 ; 18 Düsseldorf-Hubbelrath, E : 12 km, ✆ (02104) 7 21 78 ; 9 Düsseldorf-Hafen, Auf der Lausward, ✆ (0211) 39 65 98

18 Düsseldorf-Schmidtberg, NE : 12 km, ✆ (02104) 7 70 60.

Düsseldorf-Lohausen (N : 8 km), ✆ 42 10.

✆ 3 68 04 68.

Exhibition Centre (Messegelände), ✆ 4 56 01, Telex 8584853.

Tourist office, Heinrich-Heine-Allee 24, ✉ 40210, ✆ 17 20 20, Telex 8587785, Fax 161071.

ADAC, Himmelgeister Str. 63, ✉ 40225, ✆ 3 10 93 33.

Amsterdam 225 – Cologne 40 – Essen 31 – Rotterdam 237.

Plans on following pages

Breidenbacher Hof, Heinrich-Heine-Allee 36, ✉ 40213, ✆ 1 30 30, Fax 1303830, – rm – 60. AE E VISA JCB. EY **a**
Grill Royal *(Saturday, Sunday and Bank Holidays dinner only)* **Meals** à la carte 83/125 – ***Breidenbacher Eck :*** **Meals** à la carte 48/89 – ***Trader Vic's*** *(dinner only)* **Meals** à la carte 56/92 – **130 rm** 420/850 – 7 suites.

Steigenberger Parkhotel, Corneliusplatz 1, ✉ 40213, ✆ 1 38 10, Telex 8582331, Fax 131679, – rm rest – 200. AE E VISA JCB. rest EY **p**
Meals à la carte 64/100 – **160 rm** 330/590 – 9 suites.

Nikko, Immermannstr. 41, ✉ 40210, ✆ 83 40, Telex 8582080, Fax 161216, – rm – 450. AE E VISA JCB. rest BV **g**
Benkay (Japanese rest.) *(Saturday-Sunday dinner only)* **Meals** 28/48 (lunch) and à la carte 65/90 – ***Brasserie Nikkolette :*** **Meals** à la carte 39/71 – **301 rm** 334/683 – 5 suites.

Queens Hotel, Ludwig-Erhard-Allee 3, ✉ 40227, ✆ 7 77 10, Fax 7771777, – rm – 55. AE E VISA BV **s**
Meals (buffet lunch only) 39 – **120 rm** 295/620 – 5 suites.

Holiday Inn, Graf-Adolf-Platz 10, ✉ 40213, ✆ 3 84 80, Fax 3848390, – rm – 80. AE E VISA JCB. rest EZ **t**
Meals à la carte 51/72 – **177 rm** 259/543.

A
B
ADAC
GOLZHEIM
Reeser Pl.
Kaiserswerther Str.
Th.-Heuss-Brücke
THEODOR-HEUSS-BRÜCKE
Johannstr.
Heinrich-Ehrhardt-Str.
Grashofstr.
Rather Straße
Ulmenstr.
Roßstr.
Kennedydamm
Uerdinger Str.
DERENDORF
Münsterstr.
Brehmstr.
Cecilienallee
Golzheimer Platz
KÖLN-DÜSSELDORFER
RHEINPARK
Kennedydamm
Collenbachstr.
Gruner-str.
EIS-STADION
Klever Straße
Moltkestr.
S.-BAHN
Kaiser-Friedrich-Ring
Klever Str.
Nordstr.
Prinz-Georg-Str.
D.-ZOO
Rethelstr.
STADTHALLE
TONHALLE
RHEIN
Hofgartenufer
Schloßufer
Duisburger Str.
Kaiserstr.
Bagelstr.
Schinkelstr.
Schumannstr.
OBERKASSEL
Luegallee
Luegplatz
OBERKASSELER BRÜCKE
HOFGARTEN
Jägerhofstr.
Adlerstr.
Grafenberger Allee
Kaiser-Wilhelm-Ring
Schlossturm
ALTSTADT
D.-WEHRHAHN
Ackerstr.
Kölner Str.
Worringer Str.
Königsallee
Berliner Allee
Rheinufertunnel
RHEINKNIEBRÜCKE
Karl-Str.
Hauptbahnhof
Handelszentrum
Stahlwerkstr.
Graf-Adolf-Str.
Eisenstr.
HAFEN
Stromstr.
Reichsstr.
Fürstenwall
Hüttenstr.
Corneliusstr.
Ellerstr.
Lessingplatz
Oberbilker Markt
Kruppstraße
Kronprinzenstr.
Elisabethstr.
Bilker Allee
D.-FRIEDRICHSTADT
D.-VÖLKLINGER STR.
Bachstr.
D.-VOLKSGARTEN
Oberbilker Allee
S.-BAHN
D.-BILK
VOLKSGARTEN
Völklinger Str.
Volmerswerther Str.
Aachener Straße
Merowingerstr.
Mecumstraße
Hennekamp
Auf'm
Südring
Stoffeler Kapellenweg
U
V
X

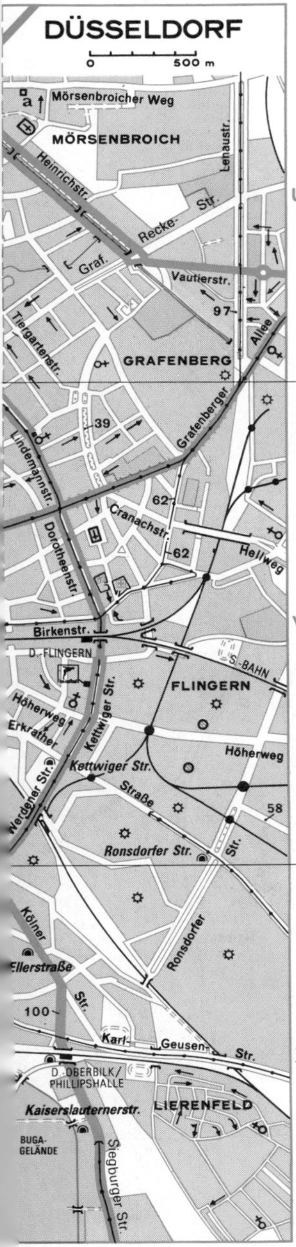

STREET INDEX

Am Wehrhahn EY 3
Berliner Allee EZ
Flinger Straße DY 28
Graf-Adolf-Straße EZ
Königsallee EZ
Schadowstraße EY 91

Aachener Straße AX
Achenbachstraße BV 2
Ackerstraße BV
Adlerstraße BV
Auf'm Hennekamp BX
Bachstraße AX
Bagelstraße BV
Bastionstraße DZ
Benrather Straße DZ
Benzenbergstraße AX 5
Berger Allee DZ
Bilker Allee AX
Bilker Straße DZ
Birkenstraße CV
Bismarckstraße EZ
Blumenstraße EZ 7
Bolkerstraße DY 8
Brehmplatz BU 9
Brehmstraße BU
Breite Straße EZ
Brunnenstraße BX 12
Burgplatz DY
Cecilienallee AU
Citadellstraße DZ 13
Collenbachstraße BU
Corneliusstraße EZ 15
Cranachstraße CV
Danziger Straße AU 16
Dorotheenstraße CV
Duisburger Straße EY
Eisenstraße BV
Elberfelder Straße EY 21
Elisabethstraße DZ
Ellerstraße BX
Erasmusstraße BX 22
Erkrather Straße CV
Ernst-Reuter-Pl. EZ 23
Eulerstraße BU 24
Fischerstraße EY 27
Friedrich-Ebert-Straße EZ 29
Friedrichstraße EZ
Fritz-Roeber-Straße DY
Fürstenplatz BX 30
Fürstenwall AX
Gartenstraße EY
Gladbacher Straße AX 31
Grabbeplatz DY 32
Graf-Adolf-Platz EZ 33
Grafenberger Allee BV
Graf-Recke-Str. CU
Grashofstraße BU
Grunerstraße BU
Hans-Sachs-Straße CV 39
Harkortstraße BV 40
Haroldstraße DZ
Heinr.-Ehrhardt-Straße BU
Heinr.-Heine-Allee EY 42
Heinrichstraße CU
Hellweg CV
Heresbachstraße BX 43
Herzogstraße BX 44
Höherweg CV
Hofgartenrampe DY 45
Hofgartenufer DY
Homberger Straße AU 46
Hubertusstraße DZ
Hüttenstraße BX
Immermannstraße EY
Inselstraße DY
Jacobistraße EY
Jägerhofstraße EY
Jan-Wellem-Platz EY 51
Johannstraße AU
Jülicher Straße BU 52
Jürgensplatz AX 54
Kaiser-Friedrich-Ring AU
Kaiserstraße EY
Kaiserwerther Straße AU
Kaiser-Wilhelm-Ring AV

Karl-Geusen-Straße CX
Karlplatz DZ
Karlstraße BV
Kasernenstraße DZ
Kavalleriestraße DZ
Kennedydamm AU
Kettwiger Straße CV
Klever Straße AU
Klosterstraße BV 56
Kölner Straße BV
Königsberger Straße CV 58
K.-Adenauer-Pl. BV 59
Kopernikusstr. AX 60
Kronprinzenstr. AX
Kruppstraße BX
Lenaustraße CU
Lessingplatz BX
Lichtstraße CV 62
Lindemannstr. CV
Lorettostraße AX 64
Luegallee AV
Luisenstraße EZ
Marktplatz DY 68
Martin-Luther-Platz EZ 69
Max.-Weyhe-Allee EY 70
Mecumstraße BX
Merowingerstr. AX
Mintropstraße BV 71
Mörsenbroicher Weg CU
Moltkestraße BU
Mühlenstraße DY 73
Münsterstraße BU
Nördl.Zubringer BU 77
Nordstraße EY
Oberbilker Allee BX
Oberbilker Markt BX 80
Oberkasseler Br. DY
Oststraße EZ
Pempelforter Str. BV 84
Plockstraße AX 86
Poststraße DZ
Prinz-Georg-Str. EY
Rather Straße BU
Ratinger Straße DY 88
Reichsstraße AX
Rethelstraße BV
Ronsdorfer Str. CX
Roßstraße BU
Schadowplatz EY 90
Scheurenstraße BV 92
Schillerplatz BV 93
Schinkelstraße BV
Schirmestraße BV 94
Schloßufer DY
Schneider-Wibbel-Gasse DY 95
Schulstraße DZ
Schumannstr. BV
Schwanenmarkt DZ 96
Siegburger Straße CX
Simrockstraße CU 97
Sonnenstraße BX 98
Steinstraße EZ
Sternstraße EY
Stoffeler Kapellenweg BX
Stoffeler Straße CX 100
Stresemannstr. EZ
Stromstraße AV
Südring AX
Th.-Heuss-Br. AU
Tiergartenstraße CU
Tonhallenstraße EY 101
Uerdinger Str. AU
Ulmenstraße BU
Vagedesstraße EY 104
Vautierstraße CU
Venloer Straße EY 105
Victoriaplatz DY
Völklinger Str. AX
Volmerswerther Straße AX
Werdener Straße CV
Witzelstraße BX 114
Worringer Platz BV 115
Worringer Straße BV

DÜSSELDORF

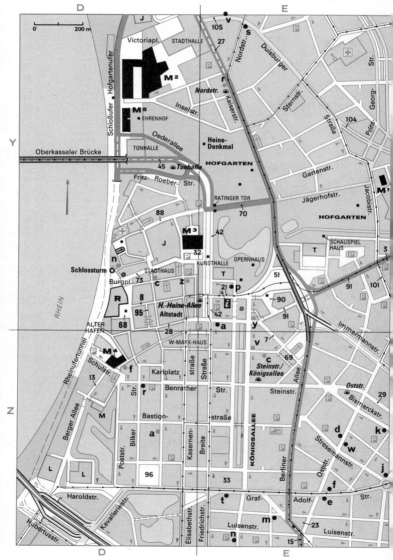

Am Wehrhahn	EY	3
Berliner Allee	EZ	
Flinger Str.	DY	28
Graf-Adolf-Str.	EZ	
Königsallee	EZ	
Schadowstraße	EY	91
Blumenstraße	EZ	7
Bolkerstraße	DY	8
Citadellstraße	DZ	13
Corneliusstraße	EZ	15
Elberfelder Str.	EY	21
Ernst-Reuter-Platz	EZ	23
Fischerstraße	EY	27
Friedrich-Ebert-Straße	EZ	29
Grabbeplatz	DY	32
Graf-Adolf-Platz	EZ	33
Heinrich-Heine-Allee	EY	42
Hofgartenrampe	DY	45
Jan-Wellem-Platz	EY	51
Marktplatz	DY	68
Martin-Luther-Platz	EZ	69
Maximilian-Weyhe-Allee	EY	70
Mühlenstraße	DY	73
Ratinger Str.	DY	88
Schadowplatz	EY	90
Schneider-Wibbel-Gasse	DY	95
Schwanenmarkt	DZ	96
Tonhallenstraße	EY	101
Vagedesstraße	EY	104
Venloer Str.	EY	105

Majestic (Italian rest.), Cantadorstr. 4, ✉ 40211, ☎ 36 70 30 (hotel) 35 72 92 (rest.), Fax 3670399, – rm – 30. AE E VISA JCB BV **a**
closed 21 December - 5 January – ***La Grappa*** (Italian rest.) *(closed Sunday and Bank Holidays except exhibitions)* **Meals** à la carte 60/82 – **52 rm** 245/460.

Esplanade, Fürstenplatz 17, ✉ 40215, ☎ 37 50 10, Fax 374032, – rm – 60. AE E VISA. BX **s**
Meals à la carte 42/70 – **81 rm** 159/448.

Madison I without rest, Graf-Adolf-Str. 94, ✉ 40210, ☎ 1 68 50, Fax 1685328, – – 50. AE E VISA JCB BV **n**
95 rm 165/275.

Eden without rest, Adersstr. 29, ✉ 40215, ☎ 3 89 70, Fax 3897777 – – 90. AE E VISA JCB EZ **m**
closed 22 December - 6 January – **121 rm** 175/472.

Dorint Hotel, Stresemannplatz 1, ✉ 40210, ☎ 3 55 40, Fax 354120 – rm – 50. AE E VISA EZ **j**
Meals *(closed Saturday and Sunday, except exhibitions)* (dinner only) à la carte 36/60 – **152 rm** 200/415 – 3 suites.

Madison II without rest, Graf-Adolf-Str. 47, ✉ 40210, ☎ 37 02 96, Fax 374311 – . AE E VISA JCB EZ **e**
closed July and 20 December - 8 January – **24 rm** 140/250.

Hotel An der Kö without rest, Talstr. 9, ✉ 40217, ☎ 37 10 48, Fax 370835 – . AE E VISA JCB EZ **n**
45 rm 158/320.

Astoria without rest, Jahnstr. 72, ✉ 40215, ☎ 38 51 30, Fax 372089 – . AE E VISA JCB. BX **b**
closed 22 December - 8 January – **26 rm** 149/350 – 4 suites.

Rema Hotel Savoy without rest, Oststr. 128, ✉ 40210, ☎ 36 03 36, Fax 356642, – – 100. AE E VISA JCB EZ **w**
123 rm 290/390.

Rema-Hotel Concorde without rest, Graf-Adolf-Str. 60, ✉ 40210, ☎ 36 98 25, Fax 354604 – . AE E VISA JCB EZ **f**
82 rm 170/340.

Carat Hotel without rest, Benrather Str. 7a, ✉ 40213, ☎ 1 30 50, Fax 322214, – – 25. AE E VISA DZ **r**
73 rm 210/395.

Rema-Hotel Monopol without rest, Oststr. 135, ✉ 40210, ☎ 8 42 08, Fax 328843 – . AE E VISA JCB EZ **d**
50 rm 170/340.

Uebachs without rest, Leopoldstr. 5, ✉ 40211, ☎ 36 05 66, Fax 358064 – rm – 30. AE E VISA BV **r**
82 rm 179/380.

Cornelius without rest, Corneliusstr. 82, ✉ 40215, ☎ 38 20 55, Fax 382050, – – 25. AE E VISA BX **s**
closed 20 December - 7 January – **48 rm** 130/250.

City without rest, Bismarckstr. 73, ✉ 40210, ☎ 36 50 23, Fax 365343 – . AE E VISA JCB EZ **k**
closed 23 December - 2 January – **54 rm** 140/298.

Terminus without rest, Am Wehrhahn 81, ✉ 40211, ☎ 35 05 91, Fax 358350, – . AE E VISA BV **f**
closed 23 December - 4 January – **45 rm** 170/480.

Prinz Anton without rest, Karl-Anton-Str. 11, ✉ 40211, ☎ 35 20 00, Fax 362010 – . AE E VISA JCB BV **k**
40 rm 160/398.

Residenz without rest, Worringer Str. 88, ✉ 40211, ☎ 36 08 54, Fax 364676 – . AE E VISA BV **z**
34 rm 148/390.

Ibis Hauptbahnhof without rest, Konrad-Adenauer-Platz 14, ✉ 40210, ☎ 1 67 20, Fax 1672101 – – 20. AE E VISA JCB BV **u**
166 rm 162/243.

Schumacher without rest, Worringer Str. 55, ✉ 40211, ☎ 36 78 50, Fax 3678570, – . AE E VISA JCB BV **d**
29 rm 150/380.

XXX ✿ **Victorian**, Königstr. 3a (1st floor), ✉ 40212, ☎ 32 02 22, Fax 131013 – . AE E VISA.
closed Sunday and Bank Holidays – **Meals** (booking essential) 55 (lunch) and à la carte 84/111 – ***Bistro im Victorian*** *(closed Sunday July and August)* **Meals** à la carte 34/78 EZ **c**
Spec. Terrine von Bresse-Taube und Gänseleber, Hummerbisque mit Hechtklösschen, Heide-Ente mit Orangen-Pfeffersauce.

XXX **La Scala** (Italian rest.), Königsallee 14 (1st floor), ✉ 40212, ☎ 32 68 32, Fax 328337 – AE E VISA JCB. EY **y**
closed Sunday except exhibitions and Christmas - New Year – **Meals** à la carte 63/98.

XX **Weinhaus Tante Anna** (former 16C house-chapel), Andreassstr. 2, ✉ 40213, ✆ 13 11 63, Fax 132974, « Antique pictures and furniture » - AE ⓓ E VISA JCB. ✻ DY c
closed Sunday (except exhibitions) - **Meals** (dinner only, booking essential, outstanding wine-list) à la carte 61/88.

XX **La Terrazza** (Italian rest.), Königsallee 30 (Kö-Centre, 2nd floor, |‡|), ✉ 40212, ✆ 32 75 40, Fax 320975 - AE ⓓ E VISA EZ v
Sunday and Bank Holidays dinner only, except exhibitions - **Meals** (booking essential) à la carte 61/86.

XX **Calvados**, Hohe Str. 33, ✉ 40213, ✆ 32 84 96, Fax 327877, ☂ - AE ⓓ E VISA DZ a
closed Sunday - **Meals** à la carte 54/78.

XX **Tse Yang** (Chinese rest.), Immermannstr. 65 (Immermannhof, entrance Konrad-Adenauer-Platz), ✉ 40210, ✆ 36 90 20, Fax 1649423 - AE ⓓ E VISA JCB BV v
Meals à la carte 43/83.

XX **Nippon Kan** (Japanese rest.), Immermannstr. 35, ✉ 40210, ✆ 35 31 35, Fax 3613625 - AE ⓓ E VISA JCB. ✻ BV g
closed Easter and Christmas - **Meals** (booking essential) à la carte 55/150.

XX **Daitokai** (Japanese rest.), Mutter-Ey-Str. 1, ✉ 40213, ✆ 32 50 54, Fax 325056 - ▤. AE ⓓ E VISA JCB. ✻ - **Meals** à la carte 47/80. DY z

Brewery-inns :

X **Zum Schiffchen**, Hafenstr. 5, ✉ 40213, ✆ 13 24 21, Fax 134596 - AE ⓓ E VISA DZ f
closed Christmas - New Year, Sunday and Bank Holidays - **Meals** à la carte 39/58.

X **Im Goldenen Ring**, Burgplatz 21, ✉ 40213, ✆ 13 31 61, Fax 324780, beer garden - AE ⓓ E VISA - *closed Christmas* - **Meals** à la carte 30/60. DY n

at Düsseldorf-Angermund N : 15 km by Danziger Straße AU :

🏨 **Haus Litzbrück**, Bahnhofstr. 33, ✉ 40489, ✆ (0203) 99 79 60, Fax 9979653, « Garden terrace », ≘s, 🏊, 🌳 - TV ☎ 🚗 P - 🎤 35. AE ⓓ E VISA. ✻
Meals à la carte 54/77 - **21 rm** ☐ 175/285.

at Düsseldorf-Benrath by Siegburger Str. CX :

🏨 **Rheinterrasse**, Benrather Schloßufer 39, ✉ 40597, ✆ 99 69 90, Fax 9969999, « Terrace with ⩤ » - TV ☎ P - 🎤 25. AE E VISA JCB
Meals à la carte 38/72 - **45 rm** ☐ 165/290.

XX **Giuseppe Verdi** (Italian rest.), Paulistr. 5 (1st floor), ✉ 40597, ✆ 7 18 49 44, Fax 7184944 - AE ⓓ E VISA
closed Saturday lunch, Monday and 2 weeks July - August - **Meals** à la carte 64/96.

XX **Lignano** (Italian rest.), Hildener Str. 43, ✉ 40597, ✆ 7 11 89 36, Fax 718959 - AE ⓓ E VISA. ✻ - *closed Sunday and 3 weeks July - August* - **Meals** (dinner only) à la carte 55/80.

at Düsseldorf-Bilk :

🏨 **Grand Hotel** without rest, Varnhagenstr. 37, ✉ 40225, ✆ 31 08 00, Fax 316667, ≘s - |‡| ⇎ TV ☎ ♿ 🚗 - 🎤 30. AE ⓓ E VISA JCB BX a
70 rm ☐ 175/295.

🏨 **Aida** without rest, Ubierstr. 36, ✉ 40223, ✆ 1 59 90, Fax 1599103, ≘s - |‡| TV ☎ ♿ P - 🎤 30. AE ⓓ E VISA. ✻ by Aachener Str. AX
93 rm ☐ 158/298.

at Düsseldorf-Derendorf by Prinz-Georg-Str. BU :

🏨 **Villa Viktoria** without rest, Blumenthalstr. 12, ✉ 40476, ✆ 46 90 00, Fax 46900601, « Elegant modern installation », ≘s, 🌳 - |‡| ⇎ TV ☎ 🚗. AE ⓓ E VISA JCB
40 suites ☐ 305/1140.

🏨 **Lindner Hotel Rhein Residence**, Kaiserswerther Str. 20, ✉ 40477, ✆ 4 99 90, Fax 4999499, ☂, Massage, 🚲, ≘s - |‡| ⇎ rm TV ☎ - 🎤 30. AE ⓓ E VISA JCB. ✻ rest
Meals à la carte 38/74 - **126 rm** ☐ 191/507. ABU f

🏨 **Gildors Hotel** without rest (with guest house), Collenbachstr. 51, ✉ 40476, ✆ 48 80 05, Fax 444844 - |‡| TV ☎ 🚗. AE ⓓ E VISA - **50 rm** ☐ 170/350. BU n

🏨 **Consul** without rest, Kaiserswerther Str. 59, ✉ 40477, ✆ 4 92 00 78, Fax 4982577 - |‡| TV ☎ 🚗. AE ⓓ E VISA - **29 rm** ☐ 150/280. AU c

XXX **Amalfi** (Italian rest.), Ulmenstr. 122, ✉ 40476, ✆ 43 38 09, Fax 4708112 - AE ⓓ E VISA
closed Saturday lunch, Sunday and 3 weeks August - **Meals** à la carte 46/76. BU r

XX **Gatto Verde** (Italian rest.), Rheinbabenstr. 5, ✉ 40476, ✆ 46 18 17, Fax 462933, ☂ - AE ⓓ E VISA JCB BU s
closed Saturday lunch, Sunday, Monday and 4 weeks July - August - **Meals** à la carte 57/89.

at Düsseldorf-Düsseltal :

🏨 **Haus am Zoo** 🐌 without rest, Sybelstr. 21, ✉ 40239, ✆ 62 63 33, Fax 626536, « Garden », ≘s, 🏊 (heated) - |‡| TV ☎ 🚗. AE E VISA. ✻ BU h
closed Christmas - early January - **23 rm** ☐ 180/280.

at Düsseldorf-Golzheim by Fischerstr. BV :

Radisson SAS Hotel, Karl-Arnold-Platz 5, ✉ 40474, ℘ 4 55 30, Fax 4553110, ... - ... rm ... - ... 400. AE ① E VISA JCB. ... rest AU **q**
Meals à la carte 46/80 - **309 rm** ... 345/692 - 15 suites.

Düsseldorf Hilton, Georg-Glock-Str. 20, ✉ 40474, ℘ 4 37 70, Telex 8584376, Fax 4377650, ..., Massage ... - ... rm ... - ... 1000. AE ① E VISA JCB. ... rest AU **r**
Meals à la carte 54/83 - **372 rm** ... 367/659 - 8 suites.

Ashley's Garden ..., Karl-Kleppe-Str. 20, ✉ 40474, ℘ 43 44 53(hotel) 4 70 83 05(rest.), Fax 453299, ..., ... - ... rm ... - ... 30. AE ① E VISA AU **e**
- ***Golzheimer Krug*** *(Saturday dinner only)* **Meals** à la carte 48/80 - **34 rm** ... 185/400.

Rosati (Italian rest.), Felix-Klein-Str. 1, ✉ 40474, ℘ 4 36 05 03, Fax 452963, ... - ... AE ① E VISA JCB. ... AU **s**
closed Saturday lunch and Sunday - **Meals** (booking essential) à la carte 65/85.

An'ne Bell, Rotterdamer Str. 11, ✉ 40474, ℘ 4 37 08 88, Fax 4380369, ... - E AU **a**
closed Saturday lunch, Thursday October to April, 1 week January, 1 to 8 April and 2 weeks October - **Meals** 68/82 and à la carte 67/100
Spec. Parmentier mit gebratener Gänsestopfleber und Trüffelmarinade, Hummerragout mit Kohlrabi, Beerentörtchen mit Vanilleeis.

at Düsseldorf-Kaiserswerth by Kaiserswerther Str. AU :

Im Schiffchen, Kaiserswerther Markt 9 (1st floor), ✉ 40489, ℘ 40 10 50, Fax 403667 - AE ① E VISA ...
closed Sunday-Monday - **Meals** (dinner only, booking essential) 164/196 and à la carte 120/160.
Spec. Bretonischer Hummer in Kamillenblüten gedämpft, Mit Kalbsbries gefüllte Canelloni in Trüffelbutter, Pochierte Williamsbirne und Pfirsich "Escoffier".

Aalschokker, Kaiserswerther Markt 9 (ground floor), ✉ 40489, ℘ 40 39 48, Fax 403667 - AE ① E VISA ...
closed Sunday-Monday - **Meals** (dinner only, booking essential) à la carte 72/94.
Spec. Sülze von Kartoffeln und Gänseleber mit Kümmeljus, "Himmel und Erde" mit gebratener Gänseleber, Eingelegter weißer Pfirsich auf Himbeercoulis.

at Düsseldorf-Lörick by Luegallee AV :

Fischerhaus ..., Bonifatiusstr. 35, ✉ 40547, ℘ 59 79 79, Telex 8584449, Fax 5979759 - ... AE ① E VISA
Meals (see **Hummerstübchen**) - **35 rm** ... 189/298.

Hummerstübchen, Bonifatiusstr. 35 (at Fischerhaus H.), ✉ 40547, ℘ 59 44 02, Fax 5979759 - ... - AE ① E VISA
closed Sunday, Monday and 8 to 24 January - **Meals** (dinner only, booking essential) 119/159 and à la carte 105/131.
Spec. Hummer-Menu, Steinbutt mit Kartoffelschuppen, Kalbsfilet im Reismantel mit Pfifferlingen.

at Düsseldorf-Lohausen by Danziger Str. AU :

Arabella Airport Hotel ..., at airport, ✉ 40474, ℘ 4 17 30, Telex 8584612, Fax 4173707 - ... rm ... - ... 180. AE ① E VISA
Meals 39 (buffet lunch) and à la carte 46/70 **200 rm** ... 210/330.

at Düsseldorf-Mörsenbroich by Rethelstr. DV :

Düsseldorf-Renaissance-Hotel, Nördlicher Zubringer 6, ✉ 40470, ℘ 6 21 60, Telex 172114001, Fax 6216666, ..., ... - ... rm ... - ... 300. AE ① E VISA ... rest BU **e**
Meals à la carte 54/84 - **245 rm** - ... 324/508 - 8 suites.

at Düsseldorf-Oberkassel by Luegallee AV :

Ramada, Am Seestern 16, ✉ 40547, ℘ 59 59 59, Telex 8585575, Fax 593569, ..., ... - ... rm ... - ... 120. AE ① E VISA
Meals à la carte 47/75 - **222 rm** ... 241/555.

Lindner-Hotel-Rheinstern, Emanuel-Leutze-Str. 17, ✉ 40547, ℘ 5 99 70, Telex 8584242, Fax 5997339, ..., ... - ... rm ... - ... 320. AE ① E VISA
Meals à la carte 34/53 - **254 rm** ... 251/447.

Hanseat without rest, Belsenstr. 6, ✉ 40545, ℘ 57 50 69, Telex 8581997, Fax 589662, « Elegant installation » - ... AE ① E VISA
closed Christmas - New Year - **37 rm** ... 175/280.

De' Medici (Italian rest.), Amboßstr. 3, ✉ 40547, ℘ 59 41 51, Fax 592612 - AE ① E VISA
closed Saturday lunch, Sunday and Bank Holidays except exhibitions - **Meals** (booking essential) à la carte 45/82.

Edo (Japanese restaurants : Teppan, Robata and Tatami), Am Seestern 3, ✉ 40547, ℘ 59 10 82, Fax 591394, « Japanese garden » - ... AE ① E VISA ...
closed Saturday lunch, Sunday and Bank Holiday - **Meals** à la carte 63/107.

at Düsseldorf-Unterbach SE : 11 km by Grafenberger Allee BV :

Landhotel Am Zault - Residenz, Gerresheimer Landstr. 40, ✉ 40627, ☎ 25 10 8
Fax 254718, , - ☎ - 80.
Meals *(closed Saturday lunch)* 32/46 (lunch) and à la carte 59/85 - **59 rm** 190/360.

at Düsseldorf-Unterbilk :

Sorat (elegant-modern installation), Volmerswerther Str. 35, ✉ 40221, ☎ 3 02 2
Fax 3027555 - rm ☎ - 130. AX
Meals à la carte 40/69 - **160 rm** 198/441.

XX **Savini**, Stromstr. 47, ✉ 40221, ☎ 39 39 31, Fax 391719 - AX
Meals (dinner only, booking essential) à la carte 54/70.

XX **Rheinturm Top 180** (revolving restaurant at 172 m), Stromstr. 20, ✉ 40221, ☎ 84 85 8
Fax 325619, Düsseldorf and Rhein (, DM 5,50) - - 60.
Meals à la carte 55/79. AV

at Düsseldorf-Unterrath by Ulmenstraße BU :

Lindner Hotel Airport, Unterrather Str. 108, ✉ 40468, ☎ 9 51 60, Fax 9516516, -
☎ - 120. rest
Meals à la carte 43/73 - **202 rm** 255/430.

at Meerbusch-Büderich by Luegallee AV - 02132 :

XXX **Landsknecht** with rm, Poststr. 70, ✉ 40667, ☎ 59 47, Fax 10978, - ☎ .
Meals *(closed Saturday lunch)* à la carte 55/75 - **8 rm** 160/280.

XXX **Landhaus Mönchenwerth**, Niederlöricker Str. 56 (at the boat landing stage), ✉ 4066
☎ 7 79 31, Fax 71899, ≤, « Garden terrace » - .
closed Friday - Saturday - **Meals** à la carte 59/98.

X **Lindenhof**, Dorfstr. 48, ✉ 40667, ☎ 26 64
closed Monday - **Meals** (dinner only, booking essential) à la carte 48/70.

Essen Nordrhein-Westfalen 411 412 E 12, 987 ⑭ - pop. 670 000 - alt. 120 m - 020
Düsseldorf 31.

at Essen-Kettwig S : 11 km :

XXXX ✿✿ **Résidence** with rm, Auf der Forst 1, ✉ 45219, ☎ (02054) 89 11, Fax 82501,
- rest ☎
closed 1 to 8 January and 3 weeks July-August - **Meals** *(closed Sunday-Monday) (dinner onl booking essential, outstanding wine list)* 135/178 and à la carte 97/125 - **18 rm** 210/55
Spec. Sülze von Ochsenschwanz und Gänsestopfleber mit Zuckerschotensalat, Zander und Hum mer im Zucchinimantel mit Artischocken, Lammrücken in Wirsing und geschmorte Lammhachs mit Schnippelbohnen.

Grevenbroich Nordrhein-Westfalen 412 C 13, 987 ㉓ - pop. 62 000 - alt. 60 m -
02181.
Düsseldorf 28.

XXXXX ✿✿ **Zur Traube** with rm, Bahnstr. 47, ✉ 41515, ☎ 6 87 67, Telex 8517193, Fax 61122 -
closed 29 March - 4 April, 19 July - 1 August and 24 December - 24 Juanuary - **Meals** *(close Sunday - Monday)* (booking essential, outstanding wine list) 78 (lunch) and à la carte 96/13 - **6 rm** 190/350.
Spec. Gänselebertorte mit Traubenconfit, Langustinen in Limonen-Ingwersauce, Taubenbrüst chen im Spitzkohlblatt mit schwarzen Trüffeln.

FRANKFURT ON MAIN Hessen 412 413 IJ 16, 987 ㉗ - pop. 660 000 - alt. 91 m - 069

See : Zoo★★★ FX - Goethe's House (Goethehaus)★ GZ **M2** - Cathedral (Dom)★ (Gothic Tower★★ Choir-stalls★, Museum★) HZ - Tropical Garden (Palmengarten)★ CV - Senckenberg Museum★ (Palaeontology department★★) CV **M9** - Städel Museum (Städelsches Museum an Städtische Galerie) ★★ GZ - Museum of Applied Arts (Museum für Kunsthandwerk)★ HZ - Germa Cinema Museum★ GZ **M7** - Henninger Turm ★ FX.

18 Frankfurt-Niederrad, by Kennedy-Allee CDX, ☎ 6 66 23 17.

Rhein-Main (SW : 12 km), ☎ 6 90 25 95.

at Neu-Isenburg (S : 7 km).

Exhibition Centre (Messegelände) (CX), ☎ 7 57 50, Telex 411558.

Tourist Information, Main Station (Hauptbahnhof), ✉ 60329, ☎ 21 23 88 49.

Tourist Information, im Römer, ✉ 60311, ☎ 21 23 87 08.

ADAC, Schumannstr. 4, ✉ 60325, ☎ 74 38 03 32, Fax 749254.

ADAC, Schillerstr. 12, ✉ 60313, ☎ 74 38 03 35, Fax 283597.

Wiesbaden 41 - Bonn 178 - Nürnberg 226 - Stuttgart 204.

Plans on following pages

Steigenberger Frankfurter Hof, Bethmannstr. 33, ✉ 60311, ℘ 2 15 02, Telex 411806, Fax 215900, Massage – rm – 120. AE VISA JCB. rest GZ e
Meals see **Restaurant Francais** below – ***Hofgarten*** *(closed Friday - Saturday)* **Meals** à la carte 62/85 – ***Frankfurter Stubb*** (booking essential) *(closed Saturday, Sunday, Bank Holidays and 4 weeks July - August)* **Meals** à la carte 39/63 – ***Kaiserbrunnen*** *(closed Sunday - Monday)* **Meals** à la carte 38/56 – **332 rm** 385/649 – 20 suites.

Hessischer Hof, Friedrich-Ebert-Anlage 40, ✉ 60325, ℘ 7 54 00, Telex 411776, Fax 7540924, « Rest. with collection of Sèvres porcelain » – rm – 120. AE VISA JCB. rest CX p
Meals 40 lunch and à la carte 55/88 – **117 rm** 268/661 – 11 suites.

Arabella Grand Hotel, Konrad-Adenauer-Str. 7, ✉ 60313, ℘ 2 98 10, Telex 4175926, Fax 2981810, Massage, – rm – 300. AE VISA JCB. rest HY c
– ***Premiere*** *(dinner only, closed Sunday, Bank Holidays and 4 weeks July - August)* **Meals** 90/136 and à la carte 76/107 – ***Brasserie :*** *(lunch only)* **Meals** à la carte 46/89 – ***Dynasty*** (Chinese rest.) **Meals** à la carte 47/84 – **378 rm** 395/684 – 11 suites.

Frankfurt Intercontinental, Wilhelm-Leuschner-Str. 43, ✉ 60329, ℘ 2 60 50, Telex 413639, Fax 252467, Massage, – rm – 600. AE VISA JCB GZ a
Meals à la carte 55/71 – **772 rm** 377/609 – 49 suites.

Frankfurt Marriott Hotel, Hamburger Allee 2, ✉ 60486, ℘ 7 95 50, Telex 416745, Fax 79552432, < Frankfurt, Massage, – rm – 600. AE VISA JCB. rest CV a
Meals à la carte 38/79 – **588 rm** 391/538 – 17 suites.

Le Meridien Parkhotel, Wiesenhüttenplatz 28, ✉ 60329, ℘ 2 69 70, Telex 412808, Fax 2697884, – rm – 160. AE VISA JCB CX k
Meals à la carte 50/75 – **296 rm** 323/644 – 11 suites.

Alexander am Zoo without rest, Waldschmidtstr. 59, ✉ 60316, ℘ 94 96 00, Fax 94960720, – – 40. AE VISA. FV c
closed 22 December - 2 January – **59 rm** 210/260 – 9 suites.

Palmenhof, Bockenheimer Landstr. 89, ✉ 60325, ℘ 7 53 00 60, Fax 75300666 – . AE VISA JCB CV m
closed 23 December - 2 January – **Meals** *(closed Saturday, Sunday and Bank Hollidays)* à la carte 59/72 – **47 rm** 195/310.

An der Messe without rest, Westendstr. 104, ✉ 60325, ℘ 74 79 79, Fax 748349 – . AE VISA CV e
46 rm 210/450.

Mercure, Voltastr. 29, ✉ 60486, ℘ 7 92 60, Telex 413791, Fax 79261606, – rm – 20. AE VISA JCB by Th.-Heuss-Allee CV
Meals à la carte 38/75 – **346 rm** 295/420 – 12 suites.

Scandic Crown Hotel, Wiesenhüttenstr. 42, ✉ 60329, ℘ 27 39 60, Telex 416394, Fax 27396795, Massage, – rm rest – 100. AE VISA CX s
Meals à la carte 44/66 – **144 rm** 250/440.

Imperial, Sophienstr. 40, ✉ 60487, ℘ 7 93 00 30, Telex 4189636, Fax 79300388 – . AE VISA JCB. rest CV t
Meals *(dinner only)* à la carte 40/66 – **60 rm** 190/450.

Novotel Frankfurt-Messe, Voltastr. 1 b, ✉ 60486, ℘ 79 30 30, Telex 412054, Fax 79303930, – rm – 140. AE VISA CV r
Meals à la carte 36/63 – **235 rm** 216/271.

Victoria Hotel without rest, Elbestr. 24, ✉ 60329, ℘ 27 30 60, Fax 27306100 – . AE VISA JCB CDX t
75 rm 160/365.

Bauer Hotel Domicil without rest, Karlstr. 14, ✉ 60329, ℘ 27 11 10, Fax 253266 – . AE VISA JCB CX d
closed Christmas - New Year – **70 rm** 179/289.

Rema-Hotel Bristol without rest, Ludwigstr. 13, ✉ 60327, ℘ 24 23 90, Fax 251539 – – 25. AE VISA JCB CX a
145 rm 170/360.

Turm-Hotel without rest, Eschersheimer Landstr. 20, ✉ 60322, ℘ 15 40 50, Fax 553578 – . AE VISA JCB GY b
closed 23 December - 8 January – **75 rm** 140/245.

Die Villa without rest, Emil-Sulzbach-Str. 14, ✉ 60486, ℘ 9 79 90 70, Fax 97990711 – . AE VISA JCB CV x
closed 20 December - 2 January – **22 rm** 230/390.

Intercity Hotel, Poststr. 8, ✉ 60329, ℘ 27 39 10, Telex 414709, Fax 27391999 – rm – 35. AE VISA CX e
Meals *(closed Saturday - Sunday)* à la carte 40/69 – **224 rm** 225/360.

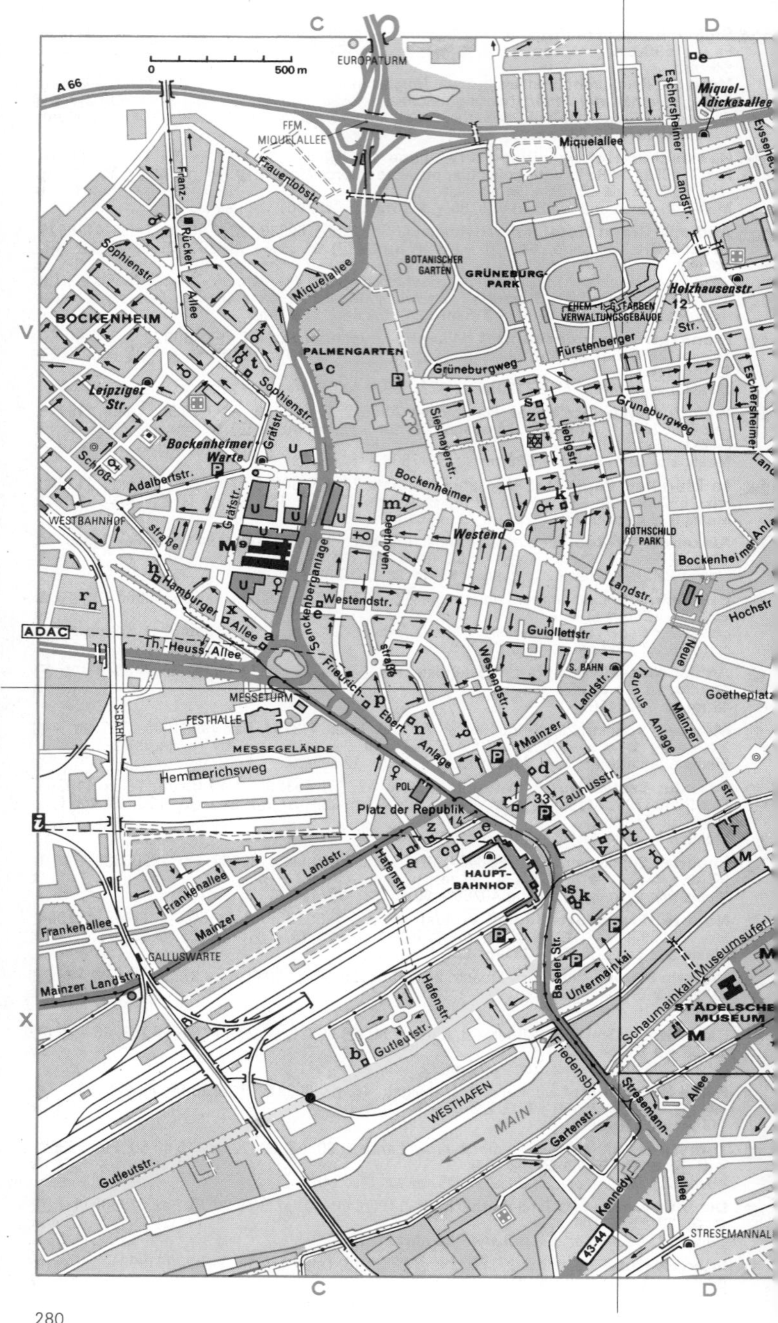
C
D
EUROPATURM
A 66
500 m
FFM. MIQUELALLEE
Miquel-Adickesallee
Miquelallee
Eschersheimer Landstr.
Frauenlobstr.
Franz-Rücker-Allee
Sophienstr.
Miquelallee
BOTANISCHER GARTEN
GRÜNEBURG-PARK
EHEM. I. G. FARBEN VERWALTUNGSGEBÄUDE
Holzhausenstr.
BOCKENHEIM
PALMENGARTEN
Fürstenberger Str.
Grüneburgweg
Leipziger Str.
Sophienstr.
Gräfstr.
Bockenheimer Warte
Siesmayerstr.
Liebigstr.
Schloß
Adalbertstr.
Bockenheimer Landstr.
WESTBAHNHOF
Beethovenstr.
Westend
ROTHSCHILD PARK
Senckenberganlage
Hamburger Allee
Westendstr.
ADAC
Th.-Heuss-Allee
Guiollettstr.
Westendstr.
S. BAHN
Neue Mainzer Str.
Taunus Anlage
Goetheplatz
Hochstr.
MESSETURM
FESTHALLE
Friedrich-Ebert-Anlage
MESSEGELÄNDE
Hemmerichsweg
Mainzer Landstr.
Taunusstr.
Platz der Republik
POL.
HAUPT-BAHNHOF
Hafenstr.
Frankenallee
Mainzer Landstr.
GALLUSWARTE
Baseler Str.
Untermainkai
Schaumainkai (Museumsufer)
STÄDELSCHE MUSEUM
Hafenstr.
Gutleutstr.
Friedensbr.
Stresemann-Allee
WESTHAFEN
MAIN
Gartenstr.
Gutleutstr.
Kennedy-allee
43-44
STRESEMANNALLEE
V
X

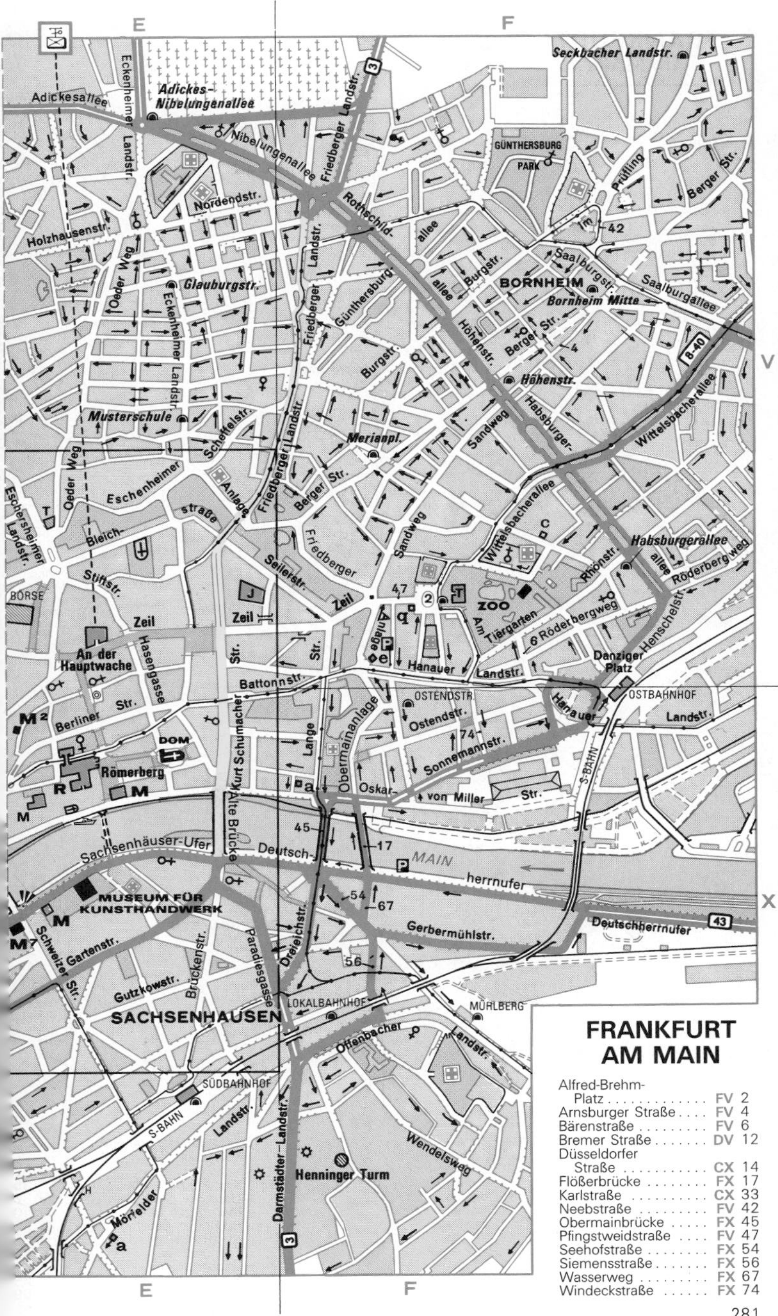

FRANKFURT AM MAIN

Alfred-Brehm-Platz	FV 2
Arnsburger Straße	FV 4
Bärenstraße	FV 6
Bremer Straße	DV 12
Düsseldorfer Straße	CX 14
Flößerbrücke	FX 17
Karlstraße	CX 33
Neebstraße	FV 42
Obermainbrücke	FX 45
Pfingstweidstraße	FV 47
Seehofstraße	FX 54
Siemensstraße	FX 56
Wasserweg	FX 67
Windeckstraße	FX 74

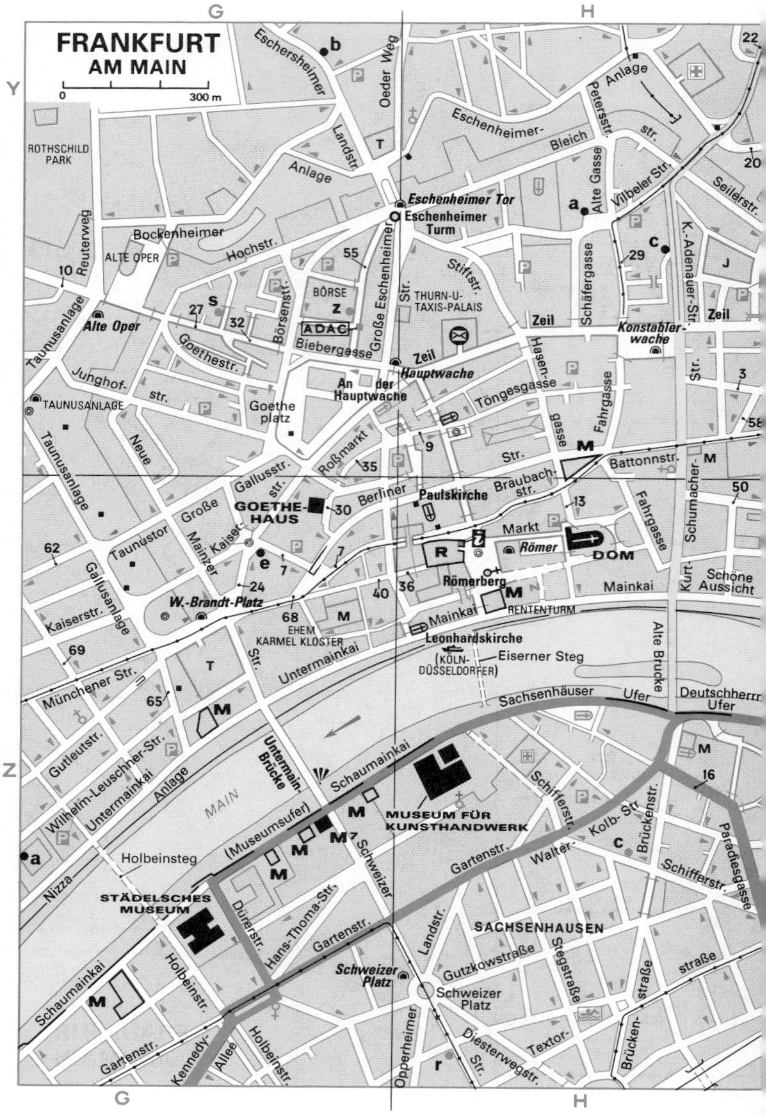

An der Hauptwache . . . GHY
Goethestraße . . . GY
Gr. Bockenheimer Straße . . . GY 27
Kaiserstraße . . . GZ
Münchener Straße . . . GZ
Roßmarkt . . . GY
Schillerstraße . . . GY 55
Zeil . . . HY

Allerheiligenstraße . . . HY 3
Bethmannstraße . . . GZ 7
Bleidenstraße . . . HY 9
Bockenheimer Landstr. . . . GY 10
Domstraße . . . HZ 13
Elisabethenstraße . . . HZ 16
Friedberger Anlage . . . HY 20
Friedberger Landstr. . . . HY 22
Friedensstraße . . . GZ 24
Große Friedberger Str. . . . HY 29
Großer Hirschgraben . . . GZ 30
Kalbächer Gasse . . . GY 32
Kleiner Hirchgraben . . . GY 35
Limpurgergasse . . . HZ 36
Münzgasse . . . GZ 40
Rechneigrabenstr. . . . HZ 50
Stoltzestraße . . . HY 58
Taunusstraße . . . GZ 62
Untermainanlage . . . GZ 65
Weißfrauenstraße . . . GZ 68
Weserstraße . . . GZ 69

Rhein-Main without rest, Heidelberger Str. 3, ✉ 60327, ☎ 25 00 35, Fax 252518 – CX b
50 rm ☐ 195/380.

Concorde without rest, Karlstr. 9, ✉ 60329, ☎ 23 32 30, Fax 237828 – CX r
closed 20 December - 2 January – **45 rm** ☐ 140/300.

Topas without rest, Niddastr. 88, ✉ 60329, ☎ 23 08 52, Fax 237228 – CX z
31 rm ☐ 105/210.

Cristall without rest, Ottostr. 3, ✉ 60329, ☎ 23 03 51, Telex 4170654, Fax 253368 – CX c
30 rm ☐ 105/210.

XXXXX ✿ **Restaurant Français** - Hotel Steigenberger Frankfurter Hof, Bethmannstr. 33, ✉ 60311, ☎ 2 15 02 – GZ e
closed Saturday lunch, Sunday - Monday and Bank Holidays except exhibitions and mid July - August – **Meals** (booking essential) à la carte 86/116
Spec. Salat von Hummer mit Mousse von der Brandade, Geschmortes Rindfleisch mit schwarzem Trüffel, Sisteron-Lammrücken mit Olivenkruste.

XXXXX ✿✿ **Weinhaus Brückenkeller**, Schützenstr. 6, ✉ 60311, ☎ 28 42 38, Fax 296068, « Vaulted cellar » – FX a
closed Sunday and Bank Holidays, except exhibitions, Christmas - early January and 2 weeks August – **Meals** (dinner only, booking essential) 98/145 and à la carte 90/133
Spec. Gebackenes Ei mit weißen Trüffeln (Oct.-Dec.), Schwarzfederhuhn mit Vanille gespickt, Neuseeland-Languste mit Haselnüssen.

XXX **Villa Leonhardi**, Zeppelinallee 18, ✉ 60325, ☎ 74 25 35, Fax 740476, « Terrace in park » – CV c
closed Saturday, Sunday, Bank Holidays and 23 December - early January – **Meals** 56 (lunch) and à la carte 68/88.

XX **Tse-Yang** (Chinese rest.), Kaiserstr. 67, ✉ 60329, ☎ 23 25 41, Fax 237825 – CX v
Meals à la carte 44/80.

XX **Gallo Nero** (Italian rest.), Kaiserhofstr. 7, ✉ 60313, ☎ 28 48 40, Fax 291645, – GY s
closed Sunday except exhibitions – **Meals** à la carte 57/85.

X **Gargantua** (Bistro style rest.), Liebigstr. 47, ✉ 60323, ☎ 72 07 18, Fax 720717, –
closed Saturday lunch, Sunday and late December - early January – **Meals** (booking essential) 38 (lunch) and à la carte 72/95. CV s

X **Ernos Bistro** (French rest.), Liebigstr. 15, ✉ 60323, ☎ 72 19 97, Fax 173838, – CV k
closed Saturday and Sunday except exhibitions, mid June - mid July and 24 December - early January – **Meals** (booking essential) 50 (lunch) à la carte 82/110.

X **Daitokai** (Japanese rest.), Friedberger Anlage 1 (Zoo-Passage), ✉ 60314, ☎ 4 99 00 21, Fax 447032 – FV e
Meals (booking essential) à la carte 53/70.

at Frankfurt-Bergen-Enkheim by Wittelsbacherallee FV – ✆ 06109 :

Amadeus, Röntgenstr. 5, ✉ 60338, ☎ 37 00, Fax 370720 – rm – 80.
Meals *(closed Saturday* à la carte 43/60 – **160 rm** ☐ 195/295.

at Frankfurt-Nieder-Erlenbach by Friedberger Landstr. FV and Homburger Landstr. N : 14 km :

XX **Erlenbach 33**, Alt Erlenbach 33, ✉ 60437, ☎ (06101) 4 80 98, Fax 48098 –
closed Tuesday and 3 weeks July - August – **Meals** (weekdays dinner only) à la carte 48/72.

at Frankfurt-Griesheim by Th.-Heuss-Allee CV :

Ramada, Oeserstr. 180, ✉ 65933, ☎ 3 90 50, Telex 416812, Fax 3808218, – rm rest – 220. rm
Meals à la carte 40/69 – **236 rm** ☐ 205/425.

at Frankfurt-Niederrad by Kennedy-Allee CDX :

Queens Hotel, Isenburger Schneise 40, ✉ 60528, ☎ 6 78 40, Telex 416717, Fax 6702634, – rm – 420.
Meals à la carte 46/86 – **277 rm** ☐ 301/482.

Arabella Congress Hotel, Lyoner Str. 44, ✉ 60528, ☎ 6 63 30, Telex 416760, Fax 6633666, – rm – 330. rest
Meals à la carte 42/72 – **393 rm** ☐ 228/436 – 8 suites.

Dorint, Hahnstr. 9, ✉ 60528, ☎ 66 30 60, Telex 4032180, Fax 66306600, – rm – 180.
Meals à la carte 42/66 – **191 rm** ☐ 217/469.

XX **Weidemann**, Kelsterbacher Str. 66, ✉ 60528, ☎ 67 59 96, Fax 673928, –
closed Saturday lunch, Sunday and Bank Holidays – **Meals** (booking essential) 51 (lunch) and à la carte 77/91. by Gartenstraße CX

at Frankfurt-Nordweststadt by Miquelallee (CV) :

Ramada Hotel Nordwest Zentrum without rest, Walter-Möller-Platz, ✉ 6043… ✆ 58 09 30, Fax 582447 – AE E VISA JCB
93 rm 175/218.

at Frankfurt-Rödelheim NW : 6 km by Theodor-Heuss-Allee (CV) and Ludwig-Landman… Str :

XX ✿ **Osteria Enoteca** (Italian rest.), Arnoldshainer Str. 2 (corner Lorcher Str.), ✉ 6048… ✆ 7 89 22 16, – AE E VISA.
closed Saturday dinner, Sunday and late December - early January – **Meals** (booking essentia… 95 and à la carte 71/90
Spec. Lauwarmer Polposalat mit Muscheln, Gebratener Seeteufel mit sizilianischen Kräuter… Kaninchen aus dem Ofen.

at Frankfurt-Sachsenhausen :

Holiday Inn Crowne Plaza, Mailänder Str. 1, ✉ 60598, ✆ 6 80 20, Telex 41180… Fax 6802333, – rm – 400. AE E VISA JCB. res…
Meals 45 and à la carte 53/99 – **404 rm** 325/589. by Darmstädter Landstr. (B 3) FX

XX **Bistrot 77**, Ziegelhüttenweg 1, ✉ 60598, ✆ 61 40 40, Fax 7240885, EX
closed Saturday lunch, Sunday, 3 weeks July - August and Christmas - early January – **Meal…** (outstanding wine list) 43 (lunch) and à la carte 65/97.

at Eschborn NW : 12 km :

Novotel, Philipp-Helfmann-Str. 10, ✉ 65760, ✆ (06196) 90 10, Telex 4072842, Fax 48211… (heated), – rm – 200. AE E VISA by A 66 CV
Meals à la carte 37/65 – **227 rm** 199/240.

at Neu-Isenburg - Gravenbruch SE : 11 km by Darmstädter Landstr. FX and B 459 :

Gravenbruch-Kempinski-Frankfurt, ✉ 63263, ✆ (06102) 50 50, Fax 505900, « Park », (heated), – rm – 350. AE E VISA JCB
Meals 46 (lunch) and à la carte 65/101 – **285 rm** 349/578 – 21 suites.

near Rhein-Main airport SW : 12 km by Kennedy-Allee CX – ✆ 069 :

Sheraton, at the airport (Central Terminal), ✉ 60549, ✆ 6 97 70, Telex 418929… Fax 69772209, – rm – 900. AE E VISA JCB. res… – ***Papillon*** (outstanding wine list) *(closed Saturday lunch, Sunday and Bank Holidays)* **Meal…** 58 (lunch) and à la carte 98/135 – ***Maxwell's Bistro :*** **Meals** à la carte 51/81 – **Taverne** *(close… Saturday and lunch Sunday)* **Meals** à la carte 43/75 – **1050 rm** 367/709 – 28 suites.

Steigenberger Avance Frankfurt Airport, Unterschweinstiege 16, ✉ 60549 Frankfur… ✆ 6 97 50, Telex 413112, Fax 69752505, Massage, – rm – 350. AE E VISA JCB. rest
Meals 46 (only buffet lunch) – **436 rm** 295/610 – 10 suites.

XX **5 Continents**, in the Airport, Ankunft Ausland B (Besucherhalle, Ebene 3), ✉ 60549 ✆ 69 05 39 01, Fax 694730, – – 30. AE E VISA JCB.
Meals à la carte 43/85.

XX **Waldrestaurant Unterschweinstiege**, Unterschweinstiege 16, ✉ 60549 Frankfurt ✆ 69 75 25 00, « Country house atmosphere, terrace » – AE E VISA JCB
Meals (booking essential) 46 (buffet) and à la carte 47/86.

Maintal Hessen 412 413 J 16 – pop. 40 000 – alt. 95 m – ✆ 06181.

Frankfurt am Main 13.

at Maintal-Dörnigheim :

XXX ✿ **Hessler** with rm, Am Bootshafen 4, ✉ 63477, ✆ (06181) 4 30 30, Fax 430333 – AE E VISA. rest
closed 3 weeks July – **Meals** *(closed Sunday - Monday)* (booking essential, outstanding win… list) 48 (lunch) and à la carte 88/116 – **7 rm** 180/395
Spec. Langustinen im Wan-Tan-Blatt, Lasagne von Fisch und Meeresfrüchten in Noilly-Prat Schaum, Taube im Blätterteig mit Wacholderrahm und Madeirabutter.

Mannheim Baden-Württemberg 987 ㉗, 412 413 I 18 – pop. 324 000 – alt. 95 m – ✆ 0621.

Frankfurt am Main 79.

XXX ✿✿ **Da Gianni** (elegant Italian rest.), R 7, 34 (Friedrichsring), ✉ 68161, ✆ 2 03 26 – AE E
closed Monday, Bank Holidays and 3 weeks July - August – **Meals** (booking essential) à la cart… 97/119
Spec. Steinbutt mit Meeresfrüchten, Wolfsbarsch und Jakobsmuscheln auf Artischocken, Ent… in Olivensauce.

Stromberg Kreis Kreuznach Rheinland-Pfalz 412 G 17, 987 ㉖ - pop. - alt. 235 m - ☏ 06724.

Frankfurt am Main 82.

XXXX ⊛⊛ **Le Val d'Or in Lafer's Stromburg** with rm, Schloßberg (E : 1,5km), ✉ 55442, ☏ 9 31 00, Fax 931090, ≤, beergarden - TV ☎ P - 100. AE ① E VISA
Meals *(Tuesday - Friday dinner only, closed Monday and 3 weeks January)* 145/179 and à la carte 103/134 - ***Deutscher Michel* : Meals** à la carte 52/73 - **13 rm** 160/350
Spec. Galette von zweierlei Lachs mit Caviar, Rehrücken in der Walnußkruste mit Petersilienwurzelpüree, Dessertimpressionen.

Wertheim Baden-Württemberg 987 ㉗, 412 413 L 17 - pop. 21 700 - alt. 142 m - ☏ 09342.

Frankfurt am Main 87.

at Wertheim-Bettingen E : 10 km :

⊛⊛ **Schweizer Stuben**, Geiselbrunnweg 11, ✉ 97877, ☏ 30 70, Fax 307155, « Hotel in a park », Massage, (heated), , , (indoor) - TV ☎ P - 30. AE ① E VISA
Meals *(closed Tuesday and January)* (Monday - Saturday dinner only, booking essential) 140/198 and à la carte 85/165 - **33 rm** 225/495 - 3 suites
Spec. Terrine von der Entenstopfleber mit gegrillten Äpfeln, Brandade vom Stockfisch mit Poutargue, Sisteron-Lamm mit Artischocken à la barigoule.

HAMBURG L Stadtstaat Hamburg 411 N 6, 987 ⑤ - pop. 1 650 000 - alt. 10 m - ☏ 040.

See : Jungfernstieg★ GY - Außenalster★★★ (trip by boat★★★) GHXY - Hagenbeck Zoo (Tierpark Hagenbeck)★★ by Schröderstiftstr. EX - Television Tower (Fernsehturm)★ (✻★★) EX - Fine Arts Museum (Kunsthalle)★★ HY **M1** - St. Michael's church (St. Michaelis)★ (tower ✻★) EFZ - Stintfang (≤★) EZ - Port (Hafen)★★ EZ - Decorative Arts and Crafts Museum (Museum für Kunst und Gewerbe)★ HY **M2** - Historical Museum (Museum für Hamburgische Geschichte)★ EYZ **M3** - Post-Museum★ FY **M4** - Planten un Blomen Park★ EFX - Museum of Ethnography (Hamburgisches Museum für Völkerkunde)★ by Rothenbaumchaussee FX.

Envir. : Altona and Northern Germany Museum (Norddeutsches Landesmuseum)★★ by Reeperbahn EZ - Altona Balcony (Altonaer Balkon) ≤★ by Reeperbahn EZ - Elbchaussee★ by Reeperbahn EZ.

18 Hamburg-Blankenese, In de Bargen 59 (W : 17 km), ☏ 81 21 77 ; 18 Ammersbek (NE : 15 km), ☏ (040) 6 05 13 37 ; 18 Hamburg-Wendlohe (N : 14 km), ☏ 5 50 50 14 ; 18 Wentorf, Golfstr. 2 (SE : 21 km), ☏ (040) 7 20 21 41.

✈ Hamburg-Fuhlsbüttel (N : 15 km), ☏ 50 80.

Hamburg-Altona, Sternschanze.

Exhibition Centre (Messegelände) (EFX), ☏ 3 56 91, Telex 212609.

i Tourismus-Zentrale Hamburg, Burchardstr. 14, ✉ 20095, ☏ 30 05 10, Fax 30051220.

i Tourist-Information, Harbour, Landungsbrücke 4-5, ✉ 20459, ☏ 30 05 12 00.

ADAC, Amsinckstr. 39, ✉ 20097, ☏ 23 91 90, Fax 23919271.

Berlin 289 - Bremen 120 - Hannover 151.

Plans on following pages

near Hauptbahnhof, at St. Georg, east of the Außenalster :

Kempinski Hotel Atlantic Hamburg, An der Alster 72, ✉ 20099, ☏ 2 88 80, Fax 247129, ≤ Außenalster, , Massage, , - rm TV ☎ - 300. AE ① E VISA JCB. rest HY **a**
Meals à la carte 58/105 - ***Atlantic-Mühle*** *(dinner only)* **Meals** à la carte 36/70 - **254 rm** 399/598 - 13 suites.

Holiday Inn Crowne Plaza, Graumannsweg 10, ✉ 22087, ☏ 22 80 60, Fax 2208704, Massage, , - rm TV ☎ - 120. AE ① E VISA JCB
- ***Lord Nelson*** *(Sunday and Monday lunch only)* **Meals** à la carte 42/81 - ***King George Pub* : Meals** à la carte 34/51 - **286 rm** 303/426. by Lange Reihe HX

Europäischer Hof, Kirchenallee 45, ✉ 20099, ☏ 24 82 48, Telex 2162493, Fax 24824799, , Massage, , , Squash - rm rest TV ☎ - 150. AE ① E VISA
Meals à la carte 35/58 - **320 rm** 180/420. HY **e**

Maritim Hotel Reichshof, Kirchenallee 34, ✉ 20099, ☏ 24 83 30, Fax 24833588, , - rm TV ☎ - 200. AE ① E VISA JCB. rest HY **d**
Meals à la carte 64/86 - **303 rm** 239/448 - 6 suites.

⊛ **Prem**, An der Alster 9, ✉ 20099, ☏ 24 17 26, Telex 2163115, Fax 2803851, « Antique furnishings, garden », - TV ☎ P. AE ① E VISA HX **c**
La mer *(Saturday - Sunday dinner only)* **Meals** à la carte 83/120 - **55 rm** 220/454 - 3 suites
Spec. Gänsestopfleberterrine mit Brioche, Loup de mer im Blätterteig, Karamelisiertes Kirschwasserparfait mit schwarzen Nüssen.

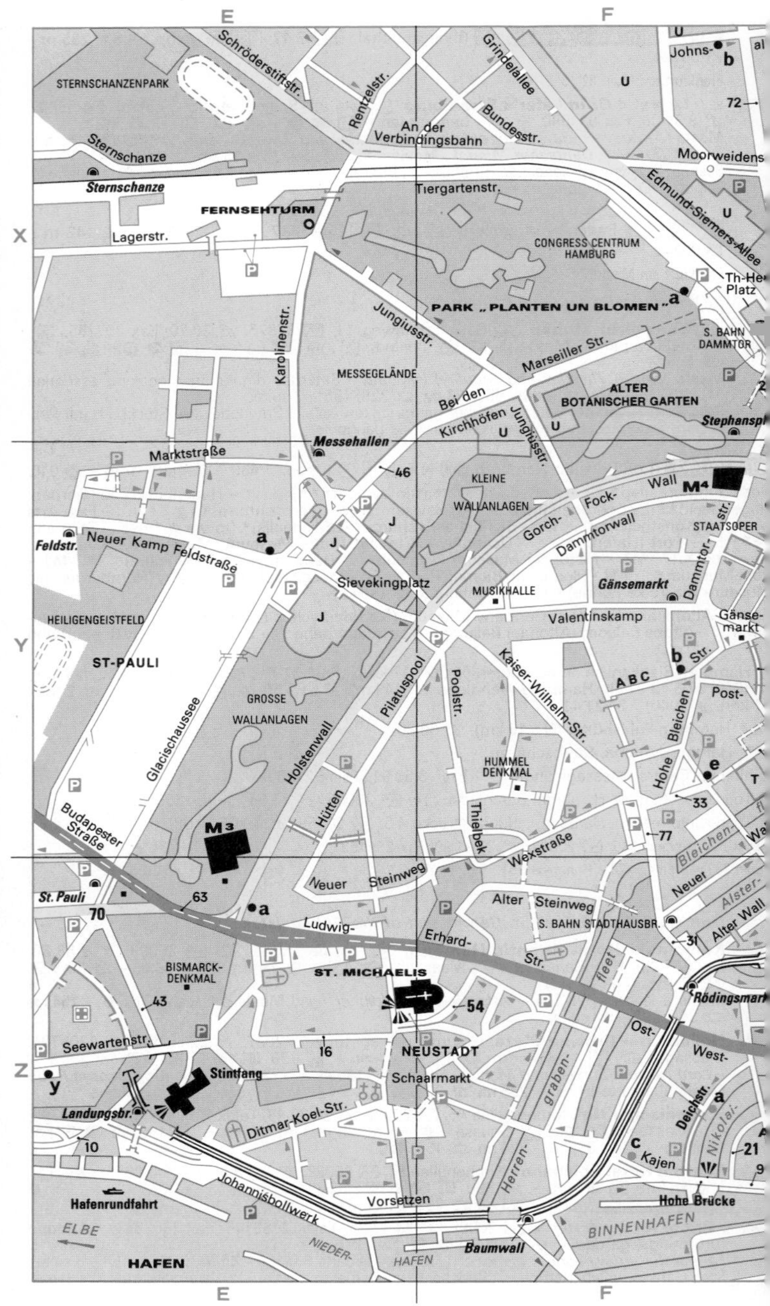

E
F
STERNSCHANZENPARK
Schröderstiftstr.
Rentzelstr.
Grindelallee
Bundesstr.
An der Verbindingsbahn
Johns-
b
72
Moorweidens
Sternschanze
Sternschanze
Tiergartenstr.
Edmund-Siemers-Allee
FERNSEHTURM
X
Lagerstr.
CONGRESS CENTRUM HAMBURG
Th-He Platz
PARK „PLANTEN UN BLOMEN"
a
Karolinenstr.
Jungiusstr.
S. BAHN DAMMTOR
MESSEGELÄNDE
Marseiller Str.
Bei den Kirchhöfen
ALTER BOTANISCHER GARTEN
Jungiusstr.
Stephanspl
Messehallen
Marktstraße
46
KLEINE WALLANLAGEN
Wall
M4
Fock-
Gorch-
Dammtorwall
STAATSOPER
Dammtor-str.
Feldstr.
Neuer Kamp
Feldstraße
a
Sievekingplatz
MUSIKHALLE
Gänsemarkt
Gänse-markt
Valentinskamp
HEILIGENGEISTFELD
Y
ST-PAULI
Kaiser-Wilhelm-Str.
b
Str.
ABC
Post-
Pilatuspool
Poolstr.
GROSSE WALLANLAGEN
Glacischaussee
Holstenwall
Bleichen
Hohe
e
HUMMEL DENKMAL
Hütten
33
Thielbek
77
Budapester Straße
M3
Wexstraße
Bleichen-
Neuer Steinweg
Neuer
St. Pauli
63
a
Alter Steinweg
S. BAHN STADTHAUSBR.
Alster-
70
Ludwig-Erhard-Str.
Alter Wall
31
BISMARCK-DENKMAL
ST. MICHAELIS
fleet
Rödingsmarkt
43
54
Ost-
West-
Seewartenstr.
16
NEUSTADT
Z
y
Stintfang
Schaarmarkt
Deichstr.
a
Landungsbr.
Ditmar-Koel-Str.
Herrengraben-
c
Kajen
Nikolai-
21
10
9
Johannisbollwerk
Hohe Brücke
Hafenrundfahrt
Vorsetzen
ELBE
NIEDER-
HAFEN
Baumwall
BINNENHAFEN
HAFEN
E
F

HAMBURG

Alsterarkaden . . . . . . GY 3
Bergstraße . . . . GY
Colonnaden . . . . FY
Dammtorstraße . . . . FY
Gerhofstraße . . . . . . FY 29
Große Bleichen . . . . FY 33
Großer Burstah . . . . FZ 35
Jungfernstieg . . . . . . GY
Mönckebergstraße . GHY
Neuer Wall . . . . FYZ
Poststraße . . . . FY
Spitalerstraße . . . GHY

Adenauerallee . . . . HY 2
Bei dem Neuen Krahn . FZ 9
Bei den St.-Pauli-Landungsbrücken . . EZ 10
Böhmkenstraße . . . . . . EZ 16
Börsenbrücke . . . . GZ 18
Cremon . . . . FZ 21
Dammtordamm . . . . . . FX 23
Graskeller . . . . FZ 31
Große Johannisstraße . . . . GZ 34
Große Reichenstraße . . . . . GZ 37
Hachmannplatz . . . . . . HY 39
Helgoländer Allee . . . . EZ 43

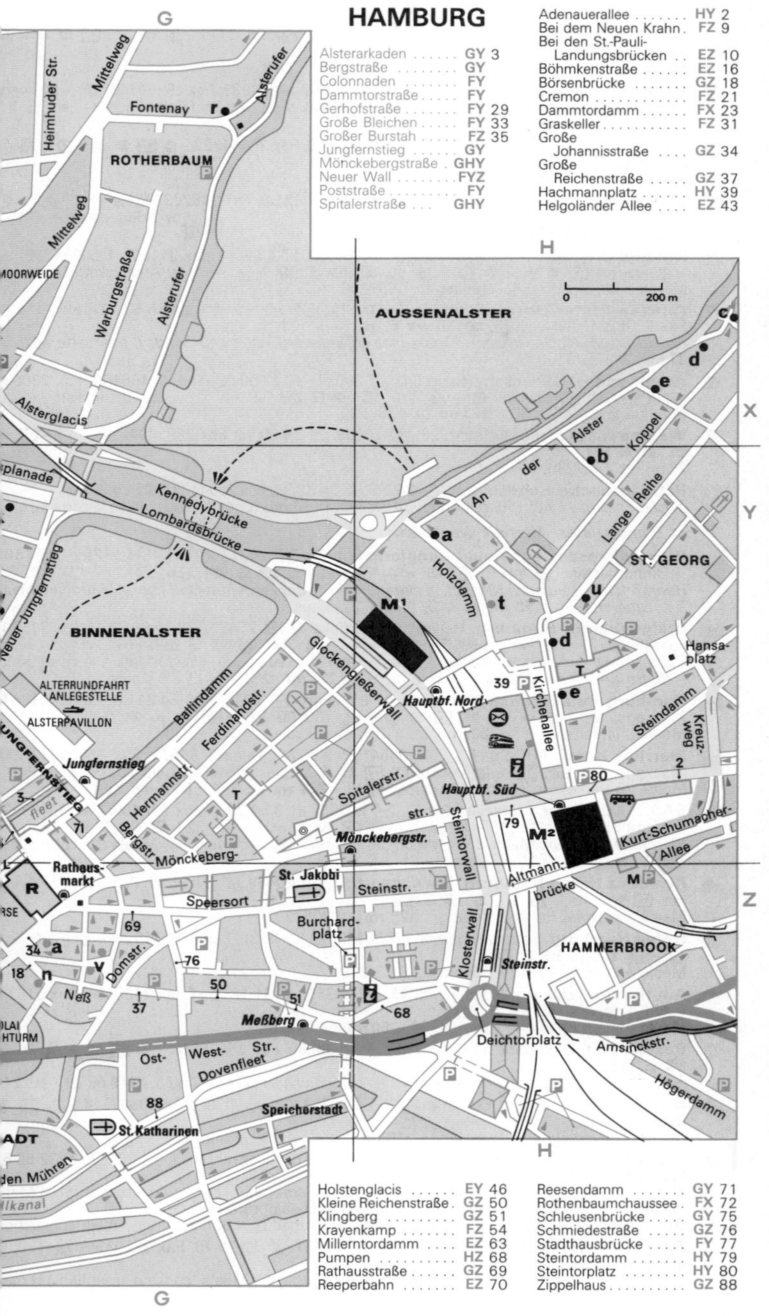

Holstenglacis . . . . . . EY 46
Kleine Reichenstraße . GZ 50
Klingberg . . . . GZ 51
Krayenkamp . . . . FZ 54
Millerntordamm . . . . EZ 63
Pumpen . . . . HZ 68
Rathausstraße . . . . . . GZ 69
Reeperbahn . . . . EZ 70

Reesendamm . . . . GY 71
Rothenbaumchaussee . FX 72
Schleusenbrücke . . . . . GY 75
Schmiedestraße . . . . . GZ 76
Stadthausbrücke . . . . . FY 77
Steintordamm . . . . HY 79
Steintorplatz . . . . HY 80
Zippelhaus . . . . GZ 88

Senator, Lange Reihe 18, ✉ 20099, ✆ 24 12 03, Fax 2803717 – rm. AE E VISA JCB HY
Meals (residents only)(dinner only) – **56 rm** 185/285.

Berlin, Borgfelder Str. 1, ✉ 20537, ✆ 25 16 40, Telex 213939, Fax 25164413, – rm rest – 30. AE E VISA. rest by Kurt-Schumacher-Allee HY
Meals à la carte 47/70 – **93 rm** 193/261.

Bellevue, An der Alster 14, ✉ 20099, ✆ 28 44 40, Fax 28444222 – – 40 AE E VISA JCB HX
Meals à la carte 48/63 – **78 rm** 190/330.

St. Raphael, Adenauerallee 41, ✉ 20097, ✆ 24 82 00, Fax 24820333, – rm – 40. AE E VISA. rest by Adenauerallee HY
Meals à la carte 42/59 – **130 rm** 190/300.

Novotel City Süd, Amsinckstr. 53, ✉ 20097, ✆ 23 63 80, Telex 211001, Fax 234230, – rm – 50. AE E VISA JCB by Amsinckstraße HZ
Meals à la carte 37/64 – **185 rm** 199/298.

Aussen-Alster-Hotel, Schmilinskystr. 11, ✉ 20099, ✆ 24 15 57, Telex 211278 Fax 2803231, – . AE E VISA JCB HX
closed 24 to 27 December – **Meals** *(closed Saturday lunch and Sunday)* à la carte 48/65 **27 rm** 180/310.

Ambassador, Heidenkampsweg 34, ✉ 20097, ✆ 23 00 02, Telex 2166100, Fax 230009 , – – 120. AE E VISA. by Amsinckstr. HZ
Meals à la carte 39/80 – **123 rm** 135/290.

Wedina without rest, Gurlittstr. 23, ✉ 20099, ✆ 24 30 11, Fax 2803894, , – AE E VISA HY
28 rm 145/230.

Peter Lembcke, Holzdamm 49, ✉ 20099, ✆ 24 32 90, Fax 2804123 – AE E VISA HY
closed Saturday lunch, Sunday and Bank Holidays – **Meals** (booking essential) à la carte 56/11

at Binnenalster, Altstadt, Neustadt :

Vier Jahreszeiten, Neuer Jungfernstieg 9, ✉ 20354, ✆ 3 49 40, Fax 3494602 ≤ Binnenalster – rm – 70. AE E VISA JCB. GY
Haerlin *(closed Sunday)* **Meals** à la carte 79/116 – ***Jahreszeiten-Grill*** *(closed Monday)* **Meal** à la carte 51/81 – **158 rm** 410/1000 – 12 suites.

Steigenberger Hamburg, Heiligengeistbrücke 4, ✉ 20459, ✆ 36 80 60, Telex 21530 Fax 36806777 – rm – 200. AE E VISA JCB FZ
Calla *(dinner only, closed Sunday - Monday and 4 weeks June - July)* **Meals** à la carte 60/8 – ***Bistro am Fleet :*** **Meals** à la carte 35/57 – **234 rm** 304/443 – 6 suites.

Hamburg Renaissance Hotel, Große Bleichen, ✉ 20354, ✆ 34 91 80, Fax 3491843 Massage, – rm – 130. AE E VISA JCB. rest FY
Meals à la carte 44/85 – **207 rm** 313/635 – 3 suites.

Marriott Hotel, ABC-Str. 52, ✉ 20354, ✆ 3 50 50, Telex 2165871, Fax 35051777, Massage, , , – rm – 160. AE E VISA JCB FY
Meals 25 (buffet lunch) and à la carte 45/69 – **277 rm** 380/554 – 4 suites.

SAS Plaza Hotel, Marseiller Str. 2, ✉ 20355, ✆ 3 50 20, Telex 214400, Fax 3502353 ≤ Hamburg, , , – rm – 320. AE E VISA. rest
Vierländer Stuben : **Meals** à la carte 36/56 – ***Trader Vic's*** *(dinner only)* **Meals** à la carte 50/8 – **560 rm** 312/514 – 7 suites. FX

Residenz Hafen Hamburg, Seewartenstr. 7, ✉ 20459, ✆ 31 11 90, Fax 314505, ≤ – – 60. AE E VISA EZ
Meals see Hotel Hafen Hamburg – **125 rm** 206/282.

Hafen Hamburg, Seewartenstr. 9, ✉ 20459, ✆ 31 11 30, Fax 3192736, ≤ – – 80. AE E VISA EZ
Meals à la carte 46/80 – **250 rm** 170/210.

Am Holstenwall, Am Holstenwall 19, ✉ 20355, ✆ 31 12 75, Telex 2165004, Fax 31626 – . AE E VISA EZ
Meals (dinner only) à la carte 54/86 – **50 rm** 196/340.

Baseler Hof, Esplanade 11, ✉ 20354, ✆ 35 90 60, Fax 35906918 – – 30. AE E VISA. GY
closed 23 to 29 December – **Meals** *(Sunday lunch only)* à la carte 47/65 – **149 rm** 140/21

Alster-Hof without rest, Esplanade 12, ✉ 20354, ✆ 35 00 70, Fax 35007514 – AE E VISA GY
closed 22 December - 4 January – **118 rm** 145/320 – 3 suites.

✿ **Cölln's Austernstuben** (private dining rooms), Brodschrangen 1, ✉ 20457, ✆ 32 60 5 Fax 326059 – AE E GZ
closed Saturday - January - August, Bank Holidays September - December and Sunday – **Meal** *(dinner only Saturday)* (booking essential) (mainly Seafood) à la carte 72/120
Spec. Krusten- und Schalentiere, "Feines vom Fischmarkt", Karamelisierter Apfelpfannkucher

Zum alten Rathaus, Börsenbrücke 10, ✉ 20457, ✆ 36 75 70, Fax 373093 – 130. AE E VISA JCB GZ
closed Saturday July - August, Sunday and Bank Holidays – **Meals** (booking essential) à la car 45/83.

XX **Deichgraf**, Deichstr. 23, ✉ 20459, ☎ 36 42 08, Fax 364268 – AE ⓓ E VISA FZ **a**
closed Saturday lunch, Sunday and Bank Holidays – **Meals** (booking essential) à la carte 55/110.

XX **il Ristorante** (Italian rest.), **Große Bleichen 16 (1st floor)**, ✉ 20354, ☎ 34 33 35, Fax 345748 – AE ⓓ E
Meals à la carte 54/90. FY **c**

XX **Ratsweinkeller**, **Große Johannisstr. 2**, ✉ 20457, ☎ 36 41 53, Fax 372201, « 1896 Hanseatic rest. » – 280. AE ⓓ E VISA
closed Sunday and Bank Holidays – **Meals** à la carte 38/85. GZ **R**

X **al Pincio** (Italian rest.), **Schauenburger Str. 59 (1st floor,** |‡|**)**, ✉ 20095, ☎ 36 52 55, Fax 362244 – AE ⓓ E VISA
closed Saturday lunch, Sunday, Bank Holidays and 4 weeks June - July – **Meals** (booking essential) à la carte 45/71. GZ **a**

at Hamburg-Alsterdorf by Grindelallee FX :

Alsterkrug-Hotel, Alsterkrugchaussee 277, ✉ 22297, ☎ 51 30 30, Fax 51303403, , – |‡| ⇔ rm TV ☎ – P – 50. AE ⓓ E VISA JCB.
Meals *(closed Sunday lunch)* à la carte 50/63 – **79 rm** ☐ 210/280.

at Hamburg-Altona by Reeperbahn EZ :

Rema-Hotel Domicil without rest, Stresemannstr. 62, ✉ 22769, ☎ 4 31 60 26, Telex 2164614, Fax 4397579 – |‡| ⇔ TV ☎ . AE ⓓ E VISA JCB
75 rm ☐ 200/360. by Budapester Straße EY

Intercityhotel, Paul-Nevermann-Platz 17, ✉ 22765, ☎ 38 03 40, Fax 38034999 – |‡| ⇔ rest TV ☎ & – 100. AE ⓓ E VISA JCB.
Meals *(closed Sunday)* à la carte 31/58 – **133 rm** ☐ 190/270.

XXXX ✿ **Landhaus Scherrer**, Elbchaussee 130, ✉ 22763, ☎ 8 80 13 25, Fax 8806260 – P. AE ⓓ E
closed Sunday and Bank Holidays – **Meals** (outstanding wine list) 159/186 and à la carte 87/125
Bistro-Restaurant *(lunch only)* **Meals** à la carte 71/92
Spec. Roulade von Lachs und Zander im Mangoldblatt, Kalbskopf in Barolosauce, Gratiniertes Limonenparfait mit Apfelkompott.

XXX ✿ **Le canard**, Elbchaussee 139, ✉ 22763, ☎ 8 80 50 57, Fax 472413, ←, – P. ⓓ E VISA.
closed Sunday – **Meals** (booking essential) (outstanding wine list) 135/189 and à la carte 90/120
Spec. Zander mit krosser Haut auf Rahmerbsen, Geschmortes und Crépinette vom Lamm mit Bohnenkernen und Thymianjus, Topfen-Mohn-Knödel mit eingelegten Zwetschgen.

XXX **Fischereihafen-Restaurant Hamburg** (Seafood only), **Große Elbstr. 143**, ✉ 22767, ☎ 38 18 16, Fax 3893021, ← – P. AE ⓓ E VISA
Meals (booking essential) (only Seafood) à la carte 53/111.

X **Rive Bistro**, Van-der Smissen-Str. 1 (Kreuzfahrt-Center), ✉ 22767, ☎ 3 80 59 19, Fax 3894775, ←, – AE
Meals (booking essential) à la carte 45/80.

at Hamburg-Bahrenfeld by Budapester Str. EY :

Novotel Hamburg West, Albert-Einstein-Ring 2, ✉ 22761, ☎ 89 95 20, Fax 89952333, , – |‡| ⇔ rm TV ☎ & P – 50. AE ⓓ E VISA
Meals à la carte 37/61 – **137 rm** ☐ 186/207 – 4 suites.

X ✿ **Tafelhaus**, Holstenkamp 71, ✉ 22525, ☎ 89 27 60, Fax 8993324, – P
closed Saturday lunch, Sunday, Monday, 2 weeks January and 3 weeks July – **Meals** (booking essential) 58 (lunch) and à la carte 73/83
Spec. Salat mit gebratenem Hummer in Koriander-Curryvinaigrette, Jakobsmuscheln im Speckmantel auf Spitzkohl, Crépinette vom Deichlamm aus dem Kräuterdampf.

at Hamburg-Barmbek by An der Alster HX :

Rema-Hotel Meridian without rest, Holsteinischer Kamp 59, ✉ 22081, ☎ 2 91 80 40, Fax 2983336, , – |‡| ⇔ TV ☎ & P – 30. AE ⓓ E VISA JCB
68 rm ☐ 200/360.

at Hamburg-Billbrook by Amsinckstr. HZ and Billstr. :

Böttcherhof, Wöhlerstr. 2, ✉ 22113, ☎ 73 18 70, Fax 73187899, , – |‡| ⇔ rm TV ☎ & P – 140. AE E VISA
Meals à la carte 42/73 – **155 rm** ☐ 200/370 – 6 suites.

at Hamburg-Billstedt by Kurt Schumacher-Allee and B 5 HY :

Panorama without rest, Billstedter Hauptstr. 44, ✉ 22111, ☎ 73 35 90, Fax 73359950, – |‡| ⇔ TV ☎ P – 150. AE ⓓ E VISA JCB
closed 23 - 30 December – **111 rm** ☐ 180/275 – 7 suites.

at Hamburg-Blankenese W : 16 km by Reeperbahn EZ :

Strandhotel , Strandweg 13, ✉ 22587, ☎ 86 13 44, Fax 864936, ←, , « Villa with elegant installation », – TV ☎ P. AE ⓓ E VISA
Meals *(closed Sunday)* (dinner only) (outstanding wine list) à la carte 54/87 – **16 rm** ☐ 198/376.

XX **Strandhof**, Strandweg 27, ✉ 22587, ☎ 86 52 36, Fax 863353, ←, – P. AE ⓓ E VISA
closed Monday, Tuesday and November – **Meals** à la carte 43/79.

at Hamburg-City Nord by Grindelallee FX :

Queens Hotel, Mexicoring 1, ✉ 22297, ✆ 63 29 40, Telex 2166503, Fax 6322472, – rm – 150. AE E VISA. rest
Meals à la carte 47/65 – **181 rm** 259/328.

at Hamburg-Duvenstedt by Grindelallee FX :

Le Relais de France, Poppenbütteler Chaussee 3, ✉ 22397, ✆ 6 07 07 50, Fax 6072673 – .
closed Sunday and Monday – **Meals** (dinner only, booking essential) à la carte 67/84 – ***Bistro*** *(lunch and dinner)* **Meals** à la carte 57/68.

at Hamburg-Eimsbüttel by Schröderstiftstraße EX :

Norge, Schäferkampsallee 49, ✉ 20357, ✆ 44 11 50, Fax 44115577 – rm rest – 80. AE E VISA JCB. rest
Meals 32 and à la carte 47/75 – **130 rm** 169/328.

at Hamburg-Eppendorf by Grindelallee FX :

Anna e Sebastiano (Italian rest.), Lehmweg 30, ✉ 20251, ✆ 4 22 25 95, Fax 4208008 – AE E VISA.
closed Sunday and Monday, 23 December - 16 January and 3 weeks June - July – **Meals** (dinner only, booking essential) 100/125 and à la carte 82/93
Spec. "Trofie" Kastaniennudeln mit Pesto, Risotto ai Frutti di Mare, Torta Gelato.

Il Gabbiano (Italian rest.), Eppendorfer Landstr. 145, ✉ 20251, ✆ 4 80 21 59, Fax 4807921, – AE E VISA
closed Saturday lunch, Sunday and 3 weeks July – **Meals** (booking essential) à la carte 53/75.

Sellmer (mainly Seafood), Ludolfstr. 50, ✉ 20249, ✆ 47 30 57, Fax 4601569 – . AE E VISA
Meals à la carte 48/104.

Österreich, Martinistr. 11, ✉ 20251, ✆ 4 60 48 30, Fax 472413, – AE
closed Sunday and Monday – **Meals** à la carte 50/71.

at Hamburg-Fuhlsbüttel by Grindelallee FX :

Airport Hotel, Flughafenstr. 47, ✉ 22415, ✆ 53 10 20, Telex 2166399, Fax 53102222, – rm rest – 170. AE E VISA
Meals à la carte 46/78 – **159 rm** 262/399 – 10 suites.

at Hamburg-Hamm by Kurt-Schumacher-Allee HY :

Hamburg International, Hammer Landstr. 200, ✉ 20537, ✆ 21 14 01, Fax 211409 – – 25. AE E VISA. rest
Meals *(closed Sunday)* à la carte 62/98 – **112 rm** 130/290.

at Hamburg-Harburg **2100** S : 15 km by Amsinckstr. HZ :

Lindtner, Heimfelder Str. 123, ✉ 21075, ✆ 79 00 90, Fax 79009482, « Elegant modern installation », – rm – 450. AE E VISA
Lilium : **Meals** 48 (lunch) and à la carte 68/84 – ***Hofgarten :*** **Meals** à la carte 46/79 – **115 rm** 245/355 – 6 suites.

Panorama, Harburger Ring 8, ✉ 21073, ✆ 76 69 50, Fax 76695183 – rm – 110. AE E VISA
Meals *(Sunday lunch only)* à la carte 38/65 – **98 rm** 180/250.

Marinas, Schellerdamm 26, ✉ 21079, ✆ 7 65 38 28, Fax 7651491, – AE E VISA
closed Saturday and Sunday lunch – **Meals** (booking essential for dinner) 44 (lunch) and à la carte 59/81
Spec. Krabben und Räucherlachs in Tomatengelee, Bouillabaisse von Nordseefischen, Gebratener Zander auf Ratatouille.

at Hamburg-Harvestehude :

Inter-Continental, Fontenay 10, ✉ 20354, ✆ 41 41 50, Telex 211099, Fax 41415186, ≤ Hamburg and Alster, , Massage, – rm – 350. AE E VISA JCB. rest GX r
– ***Fontenay-Grill*** *(dinner only)* **Meals** à la carte 65/117 – ***Orangerie :*** **Meals** à la carte 49/69 – **270 rm** 314/518 – 12 suites.

Garden Hotels Pöseldorf without rest, Magdalenenstr. 60, ✉ 20148, ✆ 41 40 40, Fax 4140420, « Elegant modern installation » – . AE E VISA
61 rm 200/450. by Mittelweg GX

Abtei, Abteistr. 14, ✉ 20149, ✆ 44 29 05, Fax 449820, – . AE E VISA. rest by Rothenbaumchaussee FX
closed 1 week January and July – **Meals** *(closed Sunday and Monday)* (dinner only, booking essential) à la carte 75/105 – **12 rm** 260/500
Spec. Gebratene Jakobsmuscheln mit Zuckerschotensalat, Steinbutt und Garnelen im Reisblat mit Koriandersauce, Crépinette vom Lammrücken.

Smolka, Isestr. 98, ✉ 20149, ✆ 48 09 80, Fax 4809811 – . AE E VISA JCB rest by Rothenbaumchaussee FX
Meals *(closed Sunday and Bank Holidays)* (dinner only) à la carte 45/68 – **40 rm** 165/320

at Hamburg-Langenhorn N : 8 km by B 433 :

Dorint-Hotel-Airport, Langenhorner Chaussee 183, ✉ 22404, ✆ 53 20 90, Fax 53209600, ≘s, 🏊 - |♦| ⇹ rm 📺 ☎ ♿ 🚗 - 🏃 80. AE ① E VISA. ✻ rest
Meals à la carte 41/72 - **147 rm** ☐ 243/408.

XX **Zum Wattkorn**, Tangstedter Landstr. 230, ✉ 22417, ✆ 5 20 37 97, Fax 472413, 🏡 - 🅟
closed Monday - **Meals** à la carte 57/77.

at Hamburg-Lemsahl-Mellingstedt by An der Alster NE : 16 km :

Treudelberg 🔇, Lemsahler Landstr. 45, ✉ 22397, ✆ 60 82 20, Fax 60822444, ≤, 🏡, 🏋, ≘s, 🏊, 🎾, ⛳ - |♦| ⇹ rm 📺 ☎ 🅟 - 🏃 125. AE ① E VISA JCB. ✻ rest
Meals à la carte 44/91 - **135 rm** ☐ 285/330.

XXX **Ristorante Dante** (Italian rest.), An der Alsterschleife 3, ✉ 22399, ✆ 6 02 00 43, Fax 6022826, 🏡 - 🅟. AE E
closed Monday, Tuesday - Friday dinner only - **Meals** (booking essential) à la carte 47/73.

at Hamburg-Rothenburgsort by Amsinkstr. HZ :

Forum Hotel, Billwerder Neuer Deich 14, ✉ 20539, ✆ 78 84 00, Fax 78841000, ≤, 🏡, 🏋, ≘s, 🏊 - |♦| ⇹ rm 📺 ☎ ♿ 🚗 🅟 - 🏃 90. AE ① E VISA JCB
Meals à la carte 45/54 - **385 rm** ☐ 198/310 - 12 suites.

at Hamburg-Rotherbaum :

Elysee 🔇, Rothenbaumchaussee 10, ✉ 20148, ✆ 41 41 20, Telex 212455, Fax 41412733, Massage, ≘s, 🏊 - |♦| ⇹ rm ▤ 📺 ☎ ♿ 🚗 - 🏃 350. AE ① E VISA FX **m**
Piazza Romana : **Meals** à la carte 52/83 - ***Brasserie :*** **Meals** à la carte 37/53 - **305 rm** ☐ 289/488 - 4 suites.

Vorbach without rest, Johnsallee 63, ✉ 20146, ✆ 44 18 20, Telex 213054, Fax 44182888 - |♦| 📺 ☎ 🚗 - 🏃 20. AE E VISA FX **b**
115 rm ☐ 170/280.

XX ✿ **L'auberge française** (French rest.), Rutschbahn 34, ✉ 20146, ✆ 4 10 25 32, Fax 4105857 - AE ① E VISA. ✻ by Grindelallee FX
closed Saturday June - August and Sunday - **Meals** *(dinner only Saturday)* (booking essential) à la carte 64/106
Spec. Gebratene Gänsestopfleber in Trüffelsauce, Seeteufel mit Safran-Knoblauch-Sauce, Früchtegratin mit Kirschsabayon.

at Hamburg-St. Pauli :

Astron Suite-Hotel without rest, Feldstr. 54, ✉ 20357, ✆ 43 23 20, Fax 43232300, ≘s - |♦| ⇹ 📺 ☎ ♿ 🚗 - 🏃 15. AE ① E VISA JCB EY **a**
119 rm ☐ 230/280.

at Hamburg-Stellingen by Grindelallee FX :

Holiday Inn, Kieler Str. 333, ✉ 22525, ✆ 54 74 00, Fax 54740100, ≘s - |♦| ⇹ rm 📺 ☎ 🚗 🅟 - 🏃 25. AE ① E VISA JCB
Meals à la carte 44/62 - **98 rm** 218/250.

Helgoland, Kieler Str. 177, ✉ 22525, ✆ 85 70 01, Fax 8511445 - |♦| ⇹ rm 📺 ☎ 🚗 🅟 - 🏃 25. AE ① E VISA. ✻
Meals (dinner only) à la carte 38/53 - **110 rm** ☐ 158/226.

at Hamburg-Stillhorn by Amsinckstr. HZ :

Forte Crest Hotel, Stillhorner Weg 40, ✉ 21109, ✆ 7 52 50, Telex 217940, Fax 7525444, ≘s, 🏊 - |♦| ⇹ rm ▤ rest 📺 ☎ ♿ 🅟 - 🏃 160. AE ① E VISA. ✻ rest
Meals à la carte 41/76 - **148 rm** ☐ 238/356.

at Hamburg-Uhlenhorst by An der Alster HX :

Parkhotel Alster-Ruh 🔇 without rest, Am Langenzug 6, ✉ 22085, ✆ 22 45 77, Fax 2278966 - 📺 ☎ 🚗. AE E VISA
23 rm ☐ 159/392.

Nippon (Japanese installation and rest.), Hofweg 75, ✉ 22085, ✆ 2 27 11 40, Telex 211081, Fax 22711490 - |♦| 📺 ☎ 🚗 - 🏃 20. AE ① E VISA. ✻
Meals *(closed Monday)* (dinner only) à la carte 45/68 - **42 rm** ☐ 194/303.

at Hamburg-Veddel by Amsinckstr. HZ :

Carat-Hotel, Sieldeich 9, ✉ 20539, ✆ 78 96 60, Fax 786196, ≘s - |♦| ⇹ rm 📺 ☎ 🅟 - 🏃 30. AE ① E VISA JCB
Meals *(closed Sunday lunch)* à la carte 35/60 - **91 rm** ☐ 190/250.

HANOVER (HANNOVER) Niedersachsen 411 412 LM 9, 987 ⑯ – pop. 510 000 – alt. 55 m – 0511.

See : Herrenhausen Gardens (Herrenhäuser Gärten)★★ (Großer Garten★★, Berggarten★) CV – Kestner-Museum★ DY **M1** – Market Church (Marktkirche) (Altarpiece★★) DY – Museum of Lower Saxony (Niedersächsisches Landesmuseum) (Prehistorical department★) EZ **M2** – Museum of Art (Kunstmuseum) (Collection Sprengel★) EZ.

Garbsen, Am Blauen See (W : 14 km), (05137) 7 30 68 ; Isernhagen FB, Gut Lohne (05139) 29 98 22. Langenhagen, Hainhang 22 (N : 12 km) (0511) 72 82 50.

Hanover-Langenhagen (N : 11 km), 9 77 12 23.

Raschplatz (EX).

Exhibition Centre (Messegelände) (by Bischofsholer Damm (FY) and Messe Schnellweg), 8 90 Telex 922728.

Tourist office, Ernst-August-Platz 2, ✉ 30159, 30 14 22, Fax 301414.

ADAC, Hindenburgstr. 37, ✉ 30175, 8 50 00, Fax 8500333.

Berlin 288 – Bremen 123 – Hamburg 151.

Plans on following pages

Kastens Hotel Luisenhof, Luisenstr. 1, ✉ 39159, 3 04 40, Telex 922325, Fax 304480 – rm rest – 160. AE E VISA JCB. rest EX
Meals *(closed Sunday July - August)* 35 lunch and à la carte 55/82 – **160 rm** 209/578 5 suites.

Maritim Grand Hotel, Friedrichswall 11, ✉ 30159, 3 67 70, Fax 325195 – rm rest – 250. AE E VISA JCB DY
– ***L'Adresse - Brasserie :*** **Meals** à la carte 50/96 – ***Wilhelm-Busch-Stube :*** *(dinner only closed Sunday and Bank Holidays)* **Meals** à la carte 30/48 – **285 rm** 255/588 14 suites.

Maritim Stadthotel, Hildesheimer Str. 34, ✉ 30169, 9 89 40, Fax 9894900, rm – 380. AE E VISA JCB. rest EZ
Meals à la carte 63/108 – **293 rm** 255/588.

Schweizerhof, Hinüberstr. 6, ✉ 30175, 3 49 50, Telex 923359, Fax 3495123 – rm – 250. AE E VISA JCB EX
Meals *(closed Sunday)* (dinner only) à la carte 65/97 – ***Gourmet's Buffet :*** **Meals** à la carte 43/6 – **200 rm** 269/459 – 3 suites.

Congress-Hotel am Stadtpark, Clausewitzstr. 6, ✉ 30175, 2 80 50, Telex 92126 Fax 814652, , Massage, , – rm – 1550. AE E VISA by Hans-Böckler Allee FY
Meals à la carte 44/69 *(also diet menu)* – **252 rm** 180/470 – 4 suites.

Grand Hotel Mussmann without rest, Ernst-August-Platz 7, ✉ 30159, 3 65 60 Fax 3656145 – – 50. AE E VISA EX
137 rm 178/498.

Königshof without rest, Königstr. 12, ✉ 30175, 31 20 71, Fax 312079 – – 30. AE E VISA EX
79 rm 158/188.

Plaza, Fernroder Str. 9, ✉ 30161, 3 38 80, Fax 3388488, – rm 100. AE E VISA EX
Meals à la carte 38/73 – **102 rm** 168/466.

Mercure, Am Maschpark 3, ✉ 30169, 8 00 80, Telex 921575, Fax 8093704, , rm rest – 130. AE E VISA EZ
Meals à la carte 35/60 – **145 rm** 215/275.

Am Funkturm, Hallerstr. 34, ✉ 30161, 3 39 80 (hotel) 33 23 09 (rest.), Fax 3398111 rm . AE E VISA EV
– ***Ristorante Milano :*** **Meals** à la carte 40/64 – **51 rm** 88/296.

Loccumer Hof, Kurt-Schumacher-Str. 16, ✉ 30159, 1 26 40, Fax 131192 – – 40. AE E VISA DX
Meals à la carte 44/74 *(vegetarian menu available)* – **78 rm** 135/360.

Körner, Körnerstr. 24, ✉ 30159, 1 63 60, Fax 18048, , – rm – 50. AE E VISA DX
closed Christmas - New Year – **Meals** *(closed Sunday)* 22 (lunch) and à la carte 33/67 – **75 rm** 140/240.

Am Rathaus, Friedrichswall 21, ✉ 30159, 32 62 68, Fax 328868, – . AE E VISA EY
Meals *(closed Saturday and Sunday)* à la carte 40/57 – **47 rm** 125/360.

Am Leineschloß without rest, Am Markte 12, ✉ 30159, 32 71 45, Fax 325502 – . AE E VISA. DY
81 rm 196/265.

Intercity-Hotel, Ernst-August-Platz 1, ✉ 30159, 3 02 60, Fax 3026499 – rest – 100. AE E VISA EX
Meals à la carte 29/55 – **57 rm** 125/380.

XXXX ✿ **Landhaus Ammann** with rm, Hildesheimer Str. 185, ✉ 30173, ✆ 83 08 18, Fax 8437749, « Elegant installation, patio with terrace », – |‡| ⇹ rm TV ☎ ♿ P – 50. AE ① E VISA. ✗ rest
by Hildesheimer Str. EFZ
Meals (outstanding wine list) 125/165 and à la carte 75/112 – **15 rm** ☐ 220/398
Spec. Tatar von Loup de mer auf Caviarsauce, Gänsestopfleber in Sauternes mit Apfelspalten, Perlhuhnbrust in Vin Jaune.

XXX ✿ **Bakkarat im Casino am Maschsee**, Arthur-Menge-Ufer 3 (1st floor), ✉ 30169, ✆ 88 40 57, Fax 885733, ←, – AE ① E VISA. ✗
DZ **a**
closed Sunday - Monday, Saturday lunch and 3 weeks January - February – **Meals** 49 (lunch) and à la carte 73/92
Spec. Gebeizter Lachs und Tatar von Nordseekrabben auf Reibekuchen, Heidschnuckenrücken in der Teigkruste, Rote Grütze mit Trestersabayon.

XXX **Feuchter's Lila Kranz** with rm, Kirchwender Str. 23, ✉ 30175, ✆ 85 89 21, Fax 854383, – TV ☎. AE ① VISA. ✗ rm
FX **b**
closed Saturday lunch – **Meals** 42 (lunch) and à la carte 62/87 – **5 rm** ☐ 180/240.

XXX ✿ **Romantik Hotel Georgenhof - Stern's Restaurant** with rm, Herrenhäuser Kirchweg 20, ✉ 30167, ✆ 70 22 44, Fax 708559, « Lower Saxony country house in a park, terrace » – TV ☎ P. AE ① E VISA
by Engelbosteler Damm CV
Meals (outstanding wine list) 36 (lunch) and à la carte 97/139 – **14 rm** ☐ 170/450
Spec. Trüffel-Gerichte (November - March), Ganze Ente aus dem Ofen (2 Pers.), Heidschnucken-Rücken (October - December).

XX **Clichy**, Weißekreuzstr. 31, ✉ 30161, ✆ 31 24 47, Fax 318283 – AE VISA
EV **d**
closed Saturday lunch and Sunday – **Meals** à la carte 74/89.

XX **Maritim Seeterrassen**, Arthur-Menge-Ufer 3, ✉ 30169, ✆ 88 40 57, Fax 887533, ←, – AE ① E VISA
DZ **a**
Meals à la carte 38/69.

XX **Gattopardo** (Italian rest.), Hainhölzer Str. 1 (Am Klagesmarkt), ✉ 30159, ✆ 1 43 75, Fax 318283, – AE E
DV **f**
Meals (dinner only) à la carte 46/58.

at Hannover-Bemerode by Bischofsholer Damm FY :

Treff Hotel Europa, Bergstr. 2, ✉ 30539, ✆ 9 52 80, Fax 9528488, – |‡| ⇹ rm TV ☎ ♿ P – 300. AE ① E VISA JCB. ✗ rest
Meals à la carte 41/75 – **183 rm** ☐ 165/265.

at Hanover-Buchholz by Bödekerstr. FV :

Pannonia Atrium Hotel, Karl-Wiechert-Allee 68, ✉ 30625, ✆ 5 40 70, Fax 572878, Massage, – |‡| ⇹ rm TV ☎ ♿ P – 180. AE ① E VISA
Meals à la carte 42/80 – **222rm** ☐ 220/290 – 6 suites.

XX **Gallo Nero**, Groß Buchholzer Kirchweg 72 b, ✉ 30655, ✆ 5 46 34 34, Fax 548283, « 18C farmhouse with contemporary interior design » – P. E VISA
closed Sunday, 1 week January and 3 weeks July - August – **Meals** à la carte 70/86.

at Hanover-Döhren :

XXX **Wichmann**, Hildesheimer Str. 230, ✉ 30519, ✆ 83 16 71, Fax 8379811, « Courtyard » – AE E VISA. ✗
by Hildesheimer Str. EFZ
Meals à la carte 62/110.

XX **Die Insel**, Rudolf-von-Bennigsen-Ufer 81, ✉ 30519, ✆ 83 12 14, Fax 831322, ←, – P
by Rudolf-von Benningsen-Ufer EZ
closed Monday and 2 weeks January – **Meals** (booking essential) à la carte 49/68.

at Hanover-Flughafen (Airport) N : 11 km :

Maritim Airport Hotel, Flughafenstr. 5, ✉ 30669, ✆ 9 73 70, Fax 9737590, – |‡| ⇹ rm TV ☎ – 800. AE ① E VISA JCB. ✗ rest
Meals 45 (buffet lunch) and à la carte 46/73 – **528 rm** ☐ 255/588 – 31 suites.

Holiday Inn Crowne Plaza, Petzelstr. 60, ✉ 30855 Langenhagen, ✆ (0511) 7 70 70, Telex 924030, Fax 737781, Massage, – |‡| ⇹ rm TV ☎ ♿ P – 150. AE ① E VISA JCB
Meals à la carte 44/77 – **210 rm** ☐ 215/535.

at Hanover-Kirchrode by Hans-Böckler Allee FY :

Queens Hotel Hannover, Tiergartenstr. 117, ✉ 30559, ✆ 5 10 30, Fax 526924, – |‡| ⇹ rm TV ☎ ♿ P – 300. AE ① E VISA
Meals à la carte 47/69 – **176 rm** ☐ 235/325 – 3 suites.

at Hanover-Kleefeld by Hans-Böckler Allee FY :

Kleefelder Hof without rest, Kleestr. 3a, ✉ 30625, ✆ 5 30 80, Fax 5308333 – |‡| TV ☎ ♿ P. AE ① E VISA JCB
86 rm ☐ 165/250.

at Hanover-Lahe by Hohenzollernstraße FV :

Holiday Inn Garden Court, Oldenburger Allee 1, ✉ 30659, ✆ 6 15 50, Fax 6155555 – |‡| ⇹ rm TV ☎ ♿ P – 280. AE ① E VISA
Meals à la carte 36/64 – **150 rm** ☐ 220/242.

8

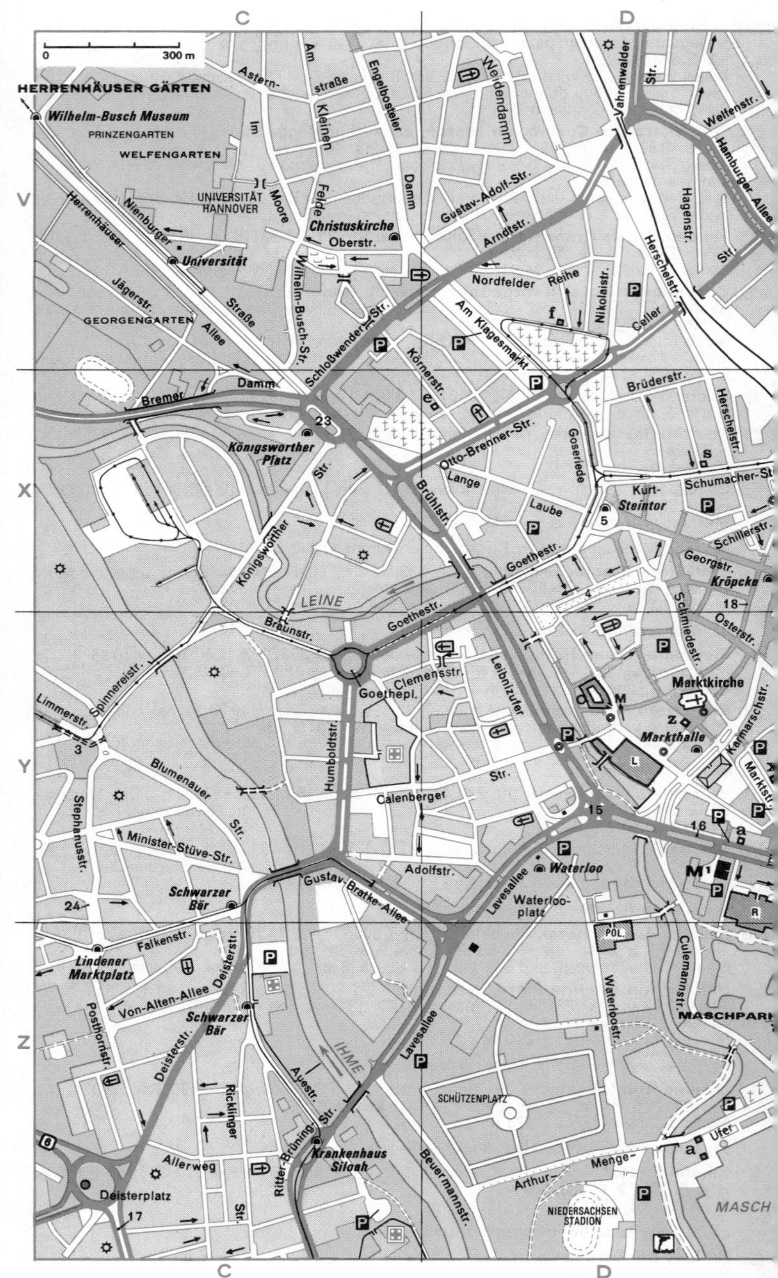

HERRENHÄUSER GÄRTEN
Wilhelm-Busch Museum
PRINZENGARTEN
WELFENGARTEN
UNIVERSITÄT HANNOVER
Christuskirche
Universität
GEORGENGARTEN
Königsworther Platz
LEINE
Kurt-Steintor
Kröpcke
Marktkirche
Markthalle
Waterloo
Schwarzer Bär
Lindener Marktplatz
Krankenhaus Siloah
IHME
SCHÜTZENPLATZ
NIEDERSACHSEN STADION
MASCHPARK
Deisterplatz
Goethepl.
Waterloo-platz

HANNOVER

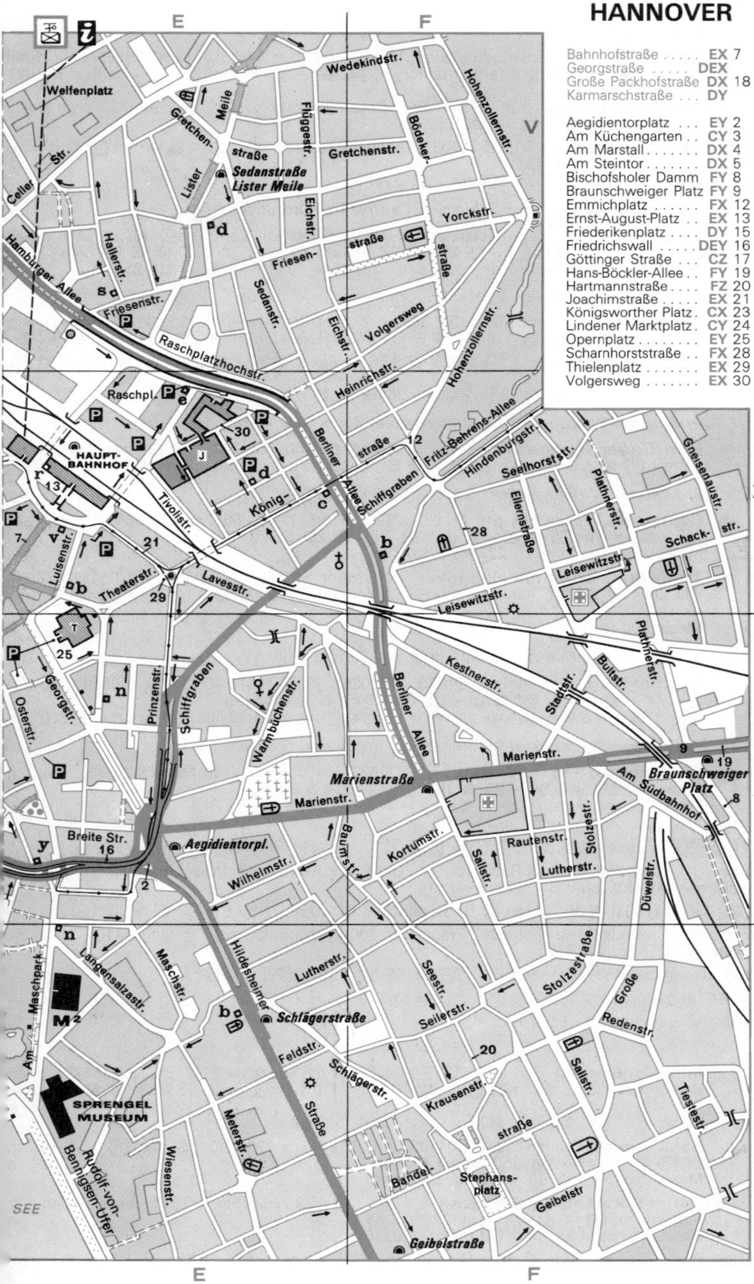

at Hannover-List by Hohenzollernstr. FV :

Seidler Hotel Pelikan, Podbielskistr. 145, ✉ 30177, ☎ 9 09 30, Fax 9093555, « Hotel with modern interior in a former factory », – rm – 140.
Signatur : **Meals** à la carte 41/63 – **Edo :** (Japanese rest.) *(dinner only, closed Sunday)* **Meals** à la carte 65/130 – **138 rm** 198/395.

Dorint, Podbielskistr. 21, ✉ 30163, ☎ 3 90 40, Fax 3904100, – rm – 250.
Meals à la carte 39/63 – **206 rm** 189/299.

at Hanover-Messe (near Exhibition Centre) by Hans-Böckler Allee FY :

Parkhotel Kronsberg, Laatzener Str. 18 (at Exhibition Centre), ✉ 30539, ☎ 8 74 00, Fax 867112, – rest – 200.
Meals *(closed 27 December - 2 January)* à la carte 40/71 – **169 rm** 185/330.

at Hanover-Roderbruch by Hans-Böckler Allee FY E : 7 km :

Novotel, Feodor-Lynen-Str. 1, ✉ 30625, ☎ 9 56 60, Fax 9566333, (heated) – rm – 110. **Meals** à la carte 39/63 – **112 rm** 175/225.

Ibis, Feodor-Lynen-Str. 1, ✉ 30625, ☎ 9 56 70, Fax 576128 – rm – 30.
Meals (dinner only) à la carte 28/46 – **96 rm** 130/199.

at Hanover-Vahrenwald by Vahrenwalder Str. DV N : 4km :

Fora, Großer Kolonnenweg 19, ✉ 30163, ☎ 6 70 60, Fax 7606111, – rm rest – 100. **Meals** à la carte 41/74 – **142 rm** 235/283.

at Laatzen by Hildesheimer Str. EFZ S : 9 km :

Copthorne, Würzburger Str. 21, ✉ 30880, ☎ (0511) 9 83 60, Fax 9836666, – rm – 280. rest
Meals à la carte 44/63 – **222 rm** 225/418.

Treff-Hotel Britannia Hannover, Karlsruher Str. 26, ✉ 30880, ☎ (0511) 8 78 20, Fax 863466, (covered court) – rm – 180. rest
Meals à la carte 44/80 – **100 rm** 180/235.

at Ronnenberg-Benthe by Bornumer Str. CZ and B 65, SW : 10 km :

Benther Berg, Vogelsangstr. 18, ✉ 30952, ☎ (05108) 6 40 60, Fax 640650, – rest – 60. rm
Meals *(closed dinner Sunday and Bank Holidays)* à la carte 60/95 – **70 rm** 145/280.

at Garbsen-Berenbostel by Bremer Damm CX and B 6, NW : 13 km :

Landhaus am See, Seeweg 27, ✉ 30827, ☎ (05131) 4 68 60, Fax 468666, ←, « Garden terrace », – – 30.
Meals *(closed Sunday dinner)* à la carte 41/65 – **37 rm** 95/260.

LEIPZIG

Sachsen 414 J 11, 984 ⑲, 987 ⑱ – pop. 480 000 – alt. 113 m – ☎ 0341.

See : Old Town Hall★ (Altes Rathaus) BY – Old Stock Exchange★ (Naschmarkt) BY – Museum of Fine Arts★ (Museum der Bildenden Künste) BZ.

Leipzig-Halle (NW : 13 km by Gerberstr. und Eutritzscher Str.BY), ☎ 22 40.

Exhibition Grounds (Messegelände), Prager Str. 200(by Windmühlenstr CZ), ✉ 04103, ☎ 22 30, Telex 312055, Fax 2232198.

Tourist-Information, Sachsenplatz 1, ✉ 04109, ☎ 7 10 40, Fax 281854.

ADAC, Augustusplatz 6, ✉ 04109, ☎ 2 11 05 51, Fax 2110540.

Berlin 165 – Dresden 109 – Erfurt 126.

Plans on following pages

Inter-Continental, Gerberstr. 15, ✉ 04105, ☎ 98 80, Telex 311245, Fax 9881229, beer-garden, Massage, – rm – 450. rest BY a
Meals à la carte 40/71 – **447 rm** 319/509 – 18 suites.

Renaissance, Querstr. 12, ✉ 04103, ☎ 1 29 20, Fax 1292800, – rm – 350. DY a
Meals à la carte 42/68 – **356 rm** 301/457.

Dorint Hotel Leipzig, Stephanstr. 6, ✉ 04103, ☎ 9 77 90, Fax 9779100, beer garden, – rm – 220. DZ n
Meals à la carte 39/64 – **179 rm** 220/300.

Parkhotel SeaSide, Richard-Wagner-Str. 7, ✉ 04109, ☎ 9 85 20, Fax 9852750 – rm – 80. rest CY s
Meals à la carte 37/54 – **288 rm** 230/295 – 12 suites.

Mercure Leipzig, Augustusplatz 5, ✉ 04109, ☎ 2 14 60, Fax 9604916 – ⬍ TV ☎ – 120. AE ⓓ E VISA JCB CZ **f**
Meals à la carte 35/64 – **283 rm** ☐ 190/335 – 10 suites.

Corum, Rudolf-Breitscheid-Str. 3, ✉ 04105, ☎ 1 25 10, Fax 1251100, – ⬍ rm TV ☎. AE ⓓ E VISA. rest CY **g**
Meals à la carte 33/59 – **121 rm** ☐ 159/250 – 6 suites.

Leipziger Hof, Hedwigstr. 3, ✉ 04315, ☎ 6 97 40, Fax 6974150, « Permanent exhibition of paintings », – ⬍ rm TV ☎. AE ⓓ E VISA. rest by Eisenbahnstraße DY
Meals *(closed Saturday - Sunday)* (dinner only) à la carte 35/52 – **73 rm** ☐ 155/240.

Deutscher Hof, Waldstr. 31, ✉ 04105, ☎ 7 11 00, Fax 7110222 – ⬍ TV ☎. AE ⓓ E VISA JCB by Gustav-Adolf-Str. AY
Meals *(closed Sunday, except exhibitions)* (dinner only) à la carte 29/65 – **39 rm** ☐ 170/215.

Leipziger Vereinshaus, Seeburgstr. 5, ✉ 04103, ☎ 2 17 01 00, Fax 2170222 – TV ☎ – 350. AE ⓓ E VISA JCB. CZ **d**
Meals (residents only) – **34 rm** ☐ 110/220.

Stadtpfeiffer, Augustusplatz 8 (Neues Gewandhaus), ✉ 04109, ☎ 9 60 51 86, Fax 2113594, – AE E VISA CZ
closed Sunday – **Meals** (outstanding wine-list) à la carte 42/67.

Apels Garten Kolonnadenstr. 2, ✉ 04109, ☎ 9 60 77 77, Fax 9607777, – ♿. AE E VISA AZ **q**
closed dinner Sunday and Bank Holidays – **Meals** à la carte 24/53.

Mövenpick, Naschmarkt 1, ✉ 04109, ☎ 2 11 77 22, Fax 2114810, – . AE ⓓ E VISA BY **r**
Meals à la carte 31/60.

at Leipzig-Eutritzsch by Eutritzscher Str. BY :

Prodomo, Gräfestr. 15a, ✉ 04129, ☎ 5 96 30, Fax 5963113 – ⬍ rm TV ☎ P – 40. AE ⓓ E VISA
Meals (dinner only) à la carte 32/53 – **83 rm** ☐ 145/235.

at Leipzig-Gohlis by Pfaffendorfer Str. BY :

De Saxe, Gohliser Str. 25, ✉ 01455, ☎ 5 93 80, Fax 5938299 – ⬍ TV ☎ P. AE ⓓ E VISA
Meals à la carte 31/49 – ***Bistro :*** **Meals** à la carte 29/39 – **33 rm** ☐ 150/230.

at Leipzig-Grosszschocher by Käthe-Kollwitz-Str. AZ and Erich-Zeigner-Allee :

Windorf, Gerhard-Ellrodt-Str. 21, ✉ 04249, ☎ 4 27 70, Fax 4277222, – ⬍ rm TV ☎ P – 30. AE E VISA
Meals (dinner only) à la carte 30/46 – **100 rm** ☐ 130/165.

at Leipzig-Leutzsch by Friedrich-Ebert-Str. AY :

Lindner Hotel, Hans-Driesch-Str. 27, ✉ 04179, ☎ 4 47 80, Fax 4478478, , , – ⬍ rm TV ☎ ♿ – 120. AE ⓓ E VISA JCB. rest
Meals à la carte 50/72 – **178 rm** ☐ 241/500 – 15 suites.

at Leipzig-Lindenau by Jahn-Allee AY :

Lindenau, Georg-Schwarz-Str. 33, ✉ 04177, ☎ 4 48 03 10, Fax 4480300, – ⬍ rm TV ☎ P. AE ⓓ E VISA JCB. rest
Meals *(closed Saturday - Sunday)* (dinner only) à la carte 31/50 – **52 rm** ☐ 185/260.

at Leipzig-Möckern by Eutritzscher Str. BY :

Silencium without rest, Georg-Schumann-Str. 268, ✉ 04159, ☎ 9 01 29 90, Fax 9012991 – ⬍ TV ☎ – 15. AE E VISA. rest
closed 24 December - 6 January – **34 rm** ☐ 97/180.

at Leipzig-Portitz by Berliner Str. CY :

Accento, Tauchaer Str. 260, ✉ 04349, ☎ 9 26 20, Fax 9262100, – ⬍ rm rest TV ☎ P – 60. AE E VISA JCB. rest
closed Christmas - 6 January – **Meals** (dinner only) à la carte 26/35 – **115 rm** ☐ 179/269.

at Leipzig-Reudnitz by Dresdner Str. DZ and Breite Str. :

Berlin without rest, Riebeckstr. 30, ✉ 04317, ☎ 2 67 30 00, Fax 2673280 – ⬍ TV ☎. AE ⓓ E VISA JCB
51 rm ☐ 150/199.

at Leipzig-Stötteritz by Prager Str. DZ :

Balance Hotel, Wasserturmstr. 33, ✉ 04299, ☎ 8 67 90, Fax 8679444, , – ⬍ rm rest TV ☎ ♿ – 35. AE ⓓ E VISA
Meals à la carte 40/60 – **134 rm** ☐ 180/245 – 3 suites.

at Lindenthal-Breitenfeld NW : 8 km, by Euritzscher Str. BX :

Breitenfelder Hof, Mitschurin Allee 8, ✉ 04466, ☎ (0341) 4 65 10, Fax 4651133, – rm TV ☎ P – 20. AE ⓓ E VISA. rest
Meals à la carte 33/45 – **73 rm** ☐ 175/225.

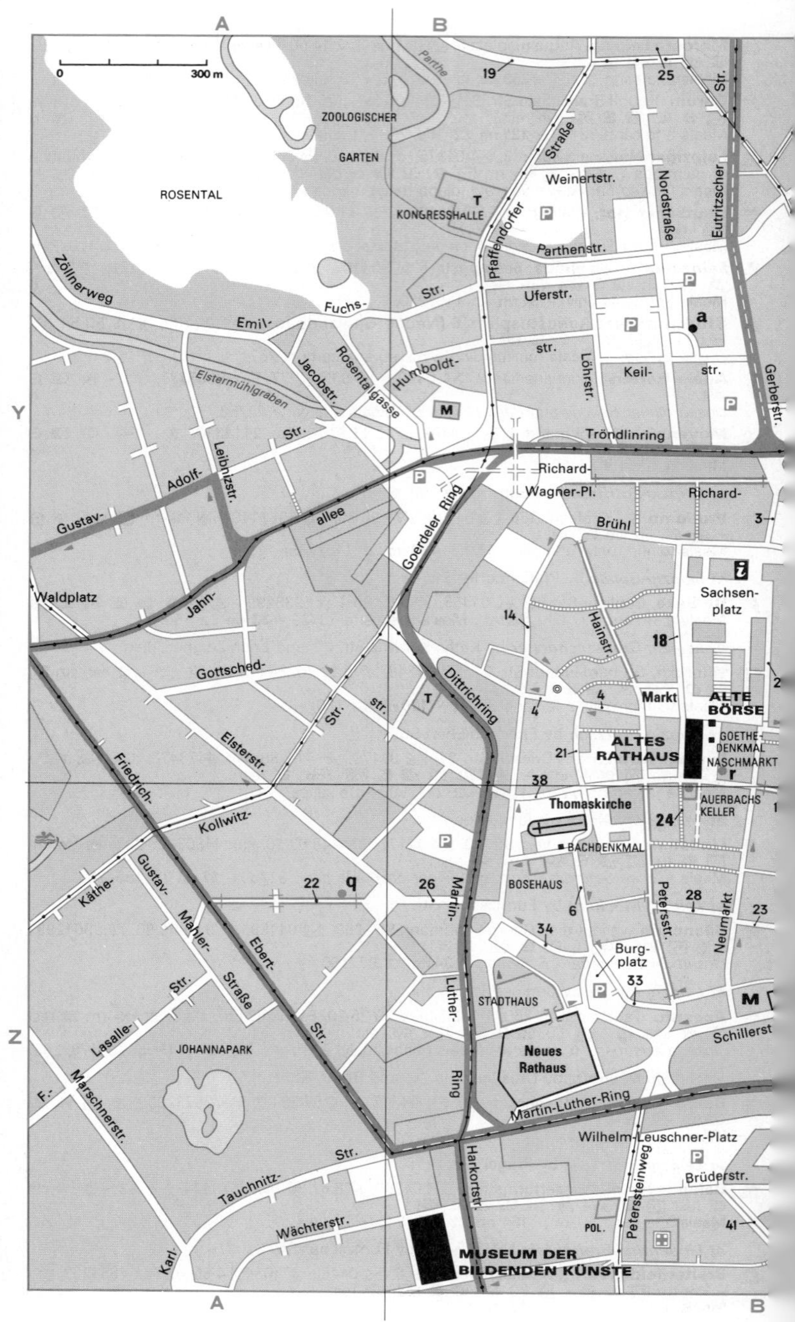
A
B
Y
Z
0
300 m
ROSENTAL
ZOOLOGISCHER
GARTEN
KONGRESSHALLE
T
Parthe
19
25
Straße
Weinertstr.
Nordstraße
Eutritzscher
Str.
Pfaffendorfer
Parthenstr.
Uferstr.
a
Zöllnerweg
Emil-
Fuchs-
Str.
Rosentalgasse
Jacobstr.
Humboldt-
str.
Löhrstr.
Keil-
str.
Gerberstr.
Elstermühlgraben
M
Tröndlinring
Leibnizstr.
Str.
Adolf-
Gustav-
allee
Goerdeler Ring
Richard-
Wagner-Pl.
Richard-
Brühl
3
Waldplatz
Jahn-
Sachsen-
platz
14
Hainstr.
18
Gottsched-
Dittrichring
str.
Str.
T
4
4
Markt
ALTE
BÖRSE
ALTES
RATHAUS
GOETHE-
DENKMAL
NASCHMARKT
r
21
Elsterstr.
Friedrich-
38
Thomaskirche
AUERBACHS
KELLER
24
Kollwitz-
BACHDENKMAL
Käthe-
Gustav-
22
q
26
Martin-
BOSEHAUS
6
Petersstr.
28
Neumarkt
23
Mahler-
Ebert-
34
Burg-
platz
Str.
Straße
Luther-
33
STADTHAUS
M
Schillerst
Lasalle-
Str.
JOHANNAPARK
Neues
Rathaus
F.-
Marschnerstr.
Ring
Martin-Luther-Ring
Wilhelm-Leuschner-Platz
Str.
Harkortstr.
Tauchnitz-
Peterssteinweg
Brüderstr.
Wächterstr.
POL.
41
Karl-
MUSEUM DER
BILDENDEN KÜNSTE
A
B

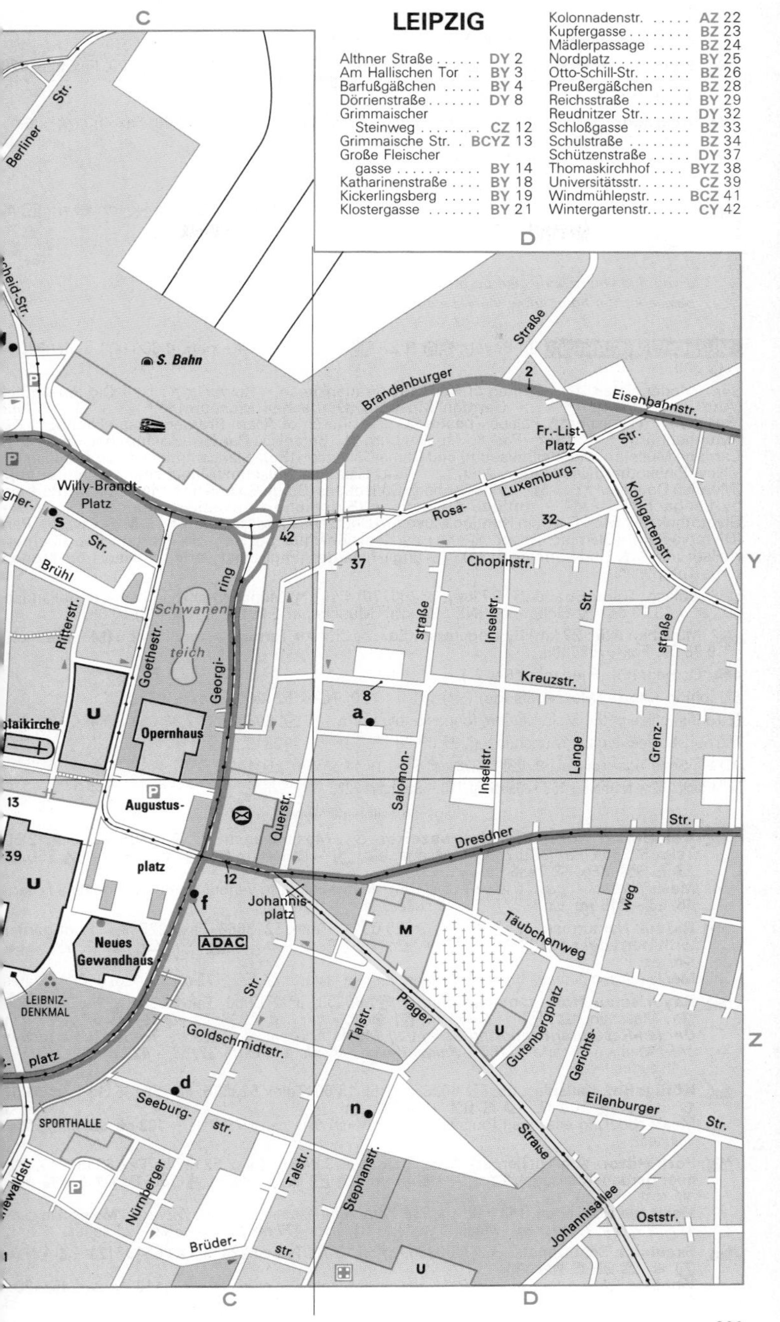
LEIPZIG
Althner Straße . . . . . . DY 2
Am Hallischen Tor . . BY 3
Barfußgäßchen . . . . BY 4
Dörrienstraße . . . . DY 8
Grimmaischer Steinweg . . . . CZ 12
Grimmaische Str. . BCYZ 13
Große Fleischer gasse . . . . BY 14
Katharinenstraße . . . . BY 18
Kickerlingsberg . . . . . BY 19
Klostergasse . . . . BY 21
Kolonnadenstr. . . . . . AZ 22
Kupfergasse . . . . BZ 23
Mädlerpassage . . . . . BZ 24
Nordplatz . . . . BY 25
Otto-Schill-Str. . . . . . . BZ 26
Preußergäßchen . . . . BZ 28
Reichsstraße . . . . BY 29
Reudnitzer Str. . . . . . . DY 32
Schloßgasse . . . . BZ 33
Schulstraße . . . . BZ 34
Schützenstraße . . . . . DY 37
Thomaskirchhof . . . . BYZ 38
Universitätsstr. . . . . . CZ 39
Windmühlenstr. . . . . BCZ 41
Wintergartenstr. . . . . . CY 42
C
D
Y
Z
Berliner Str.
S. Bahn
Brandenburger Straße
Eisenbahnstr.
Fr.-List-Platz
Rosa-Luxemburg-Str.
Kohlgartenstr.
Willy-Brandt-Platz
Brühl
Chopinstr.
Ritterstr.
Goethestr.
Schwanenteich
Georgiring
Opernhaus
Kreuzstr.
Salomonstraße
Inselstr.
Lange Str.
Grenzstraße
Augustusplatz
Querstr.
Dresdner Str.
Johannisplatz
ADAC
Neues Gewandhaus
LEIBNIZ-DENKMAL
Täubchenweg
Prager Straße
Talstr.
Goldschmidtstr.
Gutenbergplatz
Gerichtsweg
Eilenburger Str.
Seeburgstr.
SPORTHALLE
Nürnberger Str.
Stephanstr.
Johannisallee
Oststr.
Brüderstr.

at Seehausen N : 8 km, by B 2 BZ :

Hotel im Sachsenpark, Walther-Köhn-Str. 3, ✉ 04448, ☎ (0341) 5 25 20, Fax 52525 - rm rm - 60. AE E VISA
Meals à la carte 37/50 - **112 rm** 169/258.

Residenz, Residenzstr. 43 (Hohenheida), ✉ 04448, ☎ (034298) 4 50, Fax 450, - rm - 60. AE E VISA
Meals à la carte 34/67 - **53 rm** 150/250.

at Wachau SO : 8 km, by Prager Straße DZ :

Atlanta, Südring 21, ✉ 04445, ☎ (034297) 8 40, Fax 84999, - rm rm - 220. AE E VISA
Meals à la carte 39/57 - **197 rm** 195/245 - 6 suites.

If you find you cannot take up a hotel booking you have made, please let the hotel know immediately.

MUNICH (MÜNCHEN)

L Bayern 413 R 22, 987 ㊵, 426 G 4 - pop. 1 300 000 - alt. 520 - ☎ 089.

See : Marienplatz★ KZ - Church of Our Lady (Frauenkirche)★ (tower ★) KZ - Old Pinakoth (Alte Pinakothek)★★★ KY - German Museum (Deutsches Museum)★★★ LZ - The Pala (Residenz)★ (Treasury★★ Palace Theatre★) KY - Church of Asam Brothers (Asamkirche)★ KZ Nymphenburg★★ (Castle★, Park★, Amalienburg★★, Botanical Garden (Botanischer Garten)★ Carriage Museum (Marstallmuseum) and China-Collection (Porzellansammlung★) by Arnulfstr. - New Pinakothek (Neue Pinakothek)★ KY - City Historical Museum (Münchener Stadtmuseum (Moorish Dancers★★) KZ **M7** - Villa Lenbach Collections (Städt. Galerie im Lenbachhaus) (Portra by Lenbach★) JY **M4** - Antique Collections (Staatliche Antikensammlungen)★ JY **M3** Glyptothek★ JY **M2** - German Hunting Museum (Deutsches Jagdmuseum)★ KZ **M1** - Olympic Pa (Olympia-Park) (Olympic Tower ★★★) by Schleißheimer Str. FU - Hellabrunn Zoo (Tierpa Hellabrunn)★ by Lindwurmstr. (B 11) EX - English garden (Englischer Garten)★ (view from Mon teros Temple ★) LY.

18 Straßlach, Tölzer Straße (S : 17 km), ☎ (08170) 4 50 ; 9 München-Thalkirchen, Zentralländs 40, ☎ 7 23 13 04 ; 18 Eichenried (NE : 24 km), Münchener Str. 55, ☎ (08123) 10 05.

München (NE : 29 km) by Ungererstraße HU, City Air Terminal, Arnulfstraße (Main Statio ☎ 9 75 00, Fax 97557906.

Ostbahnhof, Friedenstraße(HX).

Exhibition Centre (Messegelände) (EX), ☎ 5 10 70, Telex 5212086, Fax 5107506.

Tourist office in the Main Station, (opposite plattform 11), ✉ 80335, ☎ 2 33 03 00, Fax 233302

Tourist-office, airport München, ☎ 97 59 28 15, Fax 975292813.

ADAC, Sendlinger-Tor-Platz 9, ✉ 80336, ☎ 5 40 19 44 56, Fax 5504449.

Innsbruck 162 - Nürnberg 165 - Salzburg 140 - Stuttgart 222.

Plans on following pages

Kempinski Hotel Vier Jahreszeiten, Maximilianstr. 17, ✉ 80539, ☎ 2 12 5 Telex 523859, Fax 21252000, Massage, - rm - 350. E VISA JCB. rest LZ
Meals *(closed August)* à la carte 65/106 - ***Bistro-Eck*** (also vegetarian dishes) **Meals** à la ca 46/66 - **316 rm** 395/770 - 45 suites.

Rafael, Neuturmstr. 1, ✉ 80331, ☎ 29 09 80, Telex 5213666, Fax 222539, « Roof gard with terrace and » - rm - 35. AE E VISA JC rest KZ
Meals *(closed Monday dinner)* 45 (lunch) and à la carte 64/98 - **73 rm** 420/950 - 7 suit

Bayerischer Hof, Promenadeplatz 6, ✉ 80333, ☎ 2 12 00, Telex 523409, Fax 21209 , Massage, - rm - 1200. AE E VISA JCB KY
Garden-Restaurant *(booking essential)* **Meals** à la carte 72/105 - ***Trader Vic's*** *(dinn only)* **Meals** à la carte 67/87 - ***Palais Keller : Meals*** à la carte 37/57 - **428 rm** 310/5 - 45 suites.

Königshof, Karlsplatz 25, ✉ 80335, ☎ 55 13 60, Telex 523616, Fax 55136113 - - 100. AE E VISA JCB. rest JY
Meals (booking essential) (outstanding wine list) à la carte 79/105 - **103 rm** 323/506 9 suites.

Park Hilton, Am Tucherpark 7, ✉ 80538, ☎ 3 84 50, Telex 5215740, Fax 38451845, beer garden, Massage, - rm - 780. AE E VISA JC rest HU
Meals see also **Hilton Grill** below - ***Tse Yang*** (Chinese rest.) *(closed Monday)* **Meals** à la ca 47/88 - ***Isar Terrassen : Meals*** à la carte 51/79 - **477 rm** 329/583 - 21 suites.

Excelsior, Schützenstr. 11, ✉ 80335, ☎ 55 13 70, Telex 522419, Fax 55137121 - . AE E VISA JCB JY
Vinothek *(closed Sunday and Bank Holidays)* **Meals** à la carte 44/57 - **113 rm** 245/420 4 suites.

Maritim, Goethestr. 7, ✉ 80336, ☎ 55 23 50, Fax 55235900, – rm – 280. AE ⓓ E VISA JCB. rest JZ **j**
Meals à la carte 50/86 – **352 rm** ☐ 302/492 – 5 suites.

Arabella Westpark Hotel, Garmischer Str. 2, ✉ 80339, ☎ 5 19 60, Telex 523680, Fax 5196649, – rm rest – 80. AE ⓓ E VISA JCB
closed 20 December - 6 January – **Meals** 42 (buffet lunch) and à la carte 41/64 – **258 rm** ☐ 220/445 – 6 suites. by Leopoldstr. GU

Trustee Parkhotel without rest, Parkstr. 31 (approach in Gollierstraße), ✉ 80339, ☎ 51 99 50, Fax 51995420 – – 25. AE ⓓ E VISA JCB EX **r**
closed 23 - 28 December – **35 rm** ☐ 245/476 – 6 suites.

King's Hotel without rest, Dachauer Str. 13, ✉ 80335, ☎ 55 18 70, Fax 55187300 – – 30. AE ⓓ E VISA JCB JY **f**
closed 23 December - 6 January – **96 rm** ☐ 195/265.

Eden-Hotel-Wolff, Arnulfstr. 4, ✉ 80335, ☎ 55 11 50, Fax 55115555 – rm – 150. AE ⓓ E VISA JCB JY **p**
Meals à la carte 35/68 – **211 rm** ☐ 210/450 – 4 suites.

Exquisit without rest, Pettenkoferstr. 3, ✉ 80336, ☎ 5 51 99 00, Fax 55199499, – – 30. AE ⓓ E VISA JZ **s**
50 rm ☐ 195/280 – 5 suites.

Drei Löwen, Schillerstr. 8, ✉ 80336, ☎ 55 10 40, Telex 523867, Fax 55104905 – rm – 20. AE ⓓ E VISA JCB. rest JZ **m**
Meals à la carte 33/54 – **130 rm** ☐ 182/250.

Platzl, Platzl 1 (Entrance Sparkassenstraße), ✉ 80331, ☎ 23 70 30, Telex 522910, Fax 23703800, – rm – 70. AE ⓓ E VISA. rest KZ **z**
Pfistermühle *(closed Saturday lunch, Sunday and mid July - mid August)* **Meals** 37 (lunch) and à la carte 42/67 – **167 rm** ☐ 220/398.

Krone without rest, Theresienhöhe 8, ✉ 80339, ☎ 50 40 52, Fax 506706 – . ⓓ E VISA EX **a**
30 rm ☐ 110/300.

Arabella-Central-Hotel without rest, Schwanthalerstr. 111, ✉ 80339, ☎ 51 08 30, Fax 51083249, – – 30. AE ⓓ E VISA EX **s**
closed 22 December - 8 January – **102 rm** ☐ 215/405.

Erzgießerei-Europe, Erzgießereistr. 15, ✉ 80335, ☎ 12 68 20, Fax 1236198 – rm – 50. AE ⓓ E VISA JY **a**
Meals *(closed Sunday lunch and Saturday)* à la carte 34/61 – **106 rm** ☐ 165/290.

Europa, Dachauer Str. 115, ✉ 80335, ☎ 54 24 20, Fax 54242500, – rm – 60. AE ⓓ E VISA FU **c**
Isola Bella (Italian rest.) **Meals** à la carte 30/56 – **180 rm** ☐ 180/350.

Domus without rest, St.-Anna-Str. 31, ✉ 80538, ☎ 22 17 04, Fax 2285359 – . AE ⓓ E VISA LY **b**
closed 23 to 28 December – **45 rm** ☐ 190/300.

Deutscher Kaiser without rest, Arnulfstr. 2, ✉ 80335, ☎ 5 45 30, Telex 522650, Fax 54532255 – – 80. AE ⓓ E VISA JY **r**
174 rm ☐ 190/320.

Carathotel without rest, Lindwurmstr. 13, ✉ 80337, ☎ 23 03 80, Fax 23038199 – . AE ⓓ E VISA JZ **f**
70 rm ☐ 195/295.

Intercityhotel, Bayerstr. 10, ✉ 80335, ☎ 54 55 60, Telex 523174, Fax 54556610 – rm – 100. AE ⓓ E VISA JCB JY **u**
Meals *(closed Sunday and 27 July - 11 August)* à la carte 36/55 – **203 rm** ☐ 195/398 – 4 suites.

Admiral without rest, Kohlstr. 9, ✉ 80469, ☎ 22 66 41, Fax 293674 – . AE ⓓ E VISA LZ **r**
33 rm ☐ 180/330.

Torbräu without rest, Tal 41, ✉ 80331, ☎ 22 50 16, Fax 225019 – Ⓟ. AE E VISA LZ **g**
closed Christmas - 6 January – **86 rm** ☐ 185/370 – 3 suites.

Mercure City without rest, Senefelder Str. 9, ✉ 80336, ☎ 55 13 20, Fax 596444 – – 50. AE ⓓ E VISA JCB JZ **r**
167 rm ☐ 168/310.

Kraft without rest, Schillerstr. 49, ✉ 80336, ☎ 59 48 23, Fax 5503856 – . AE ⓓ E VISA JZ **y**
closed 23 to 26 December – **40 rm** ☐ 140/240.

Sol Inn Hotel, Paul-Heyse-Str. 24, ✉ 80336, ☎ 51 49 00, Telex 522395, Fax 51490701, – rm – 35. AE ⓓ E VISA JCB. rest JZ **c**
Meals à la carte 35/66 – **182 rm** ☐ 172/410.

Atrium without rest, Landwehrstr. 59, ✉ 80336, ☎ 51 41 90, Fax 535066, – – 40. AE ⓓ E VISA JCB JZ **d**
162 rm ☐ 216/306.

STREET INDEX

Continued on following pages

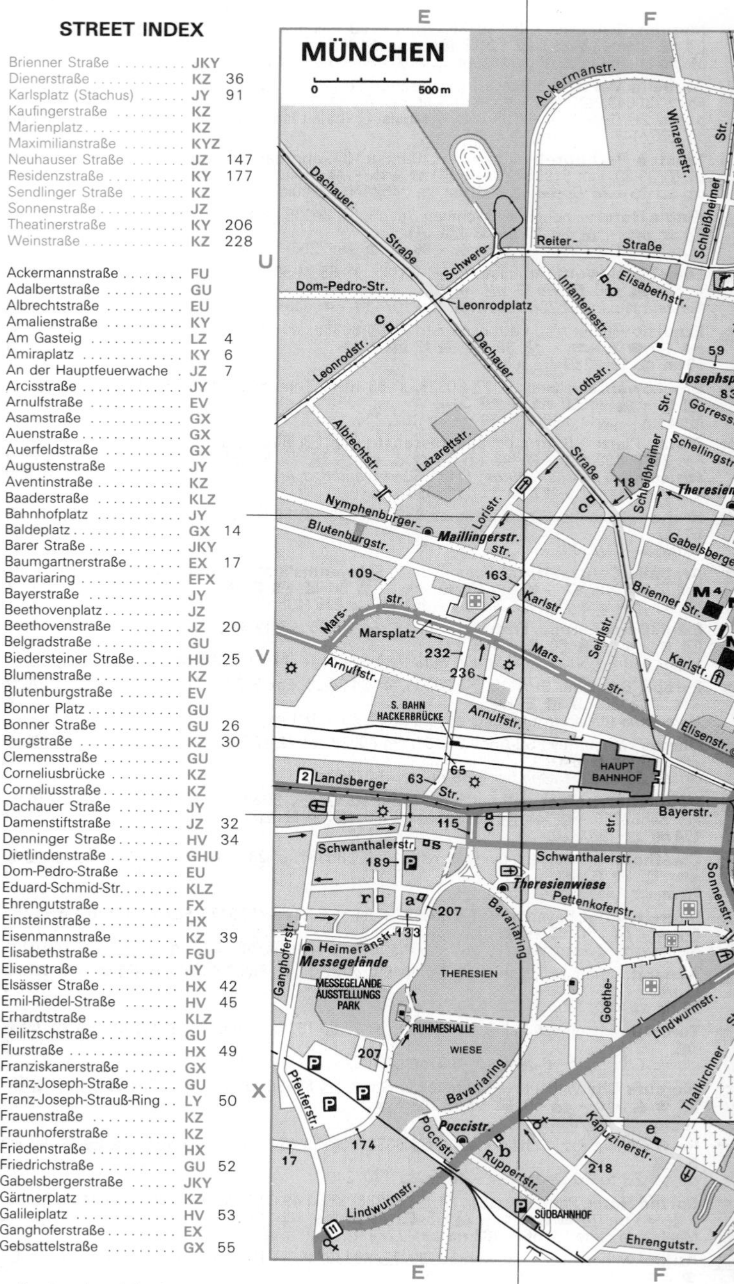

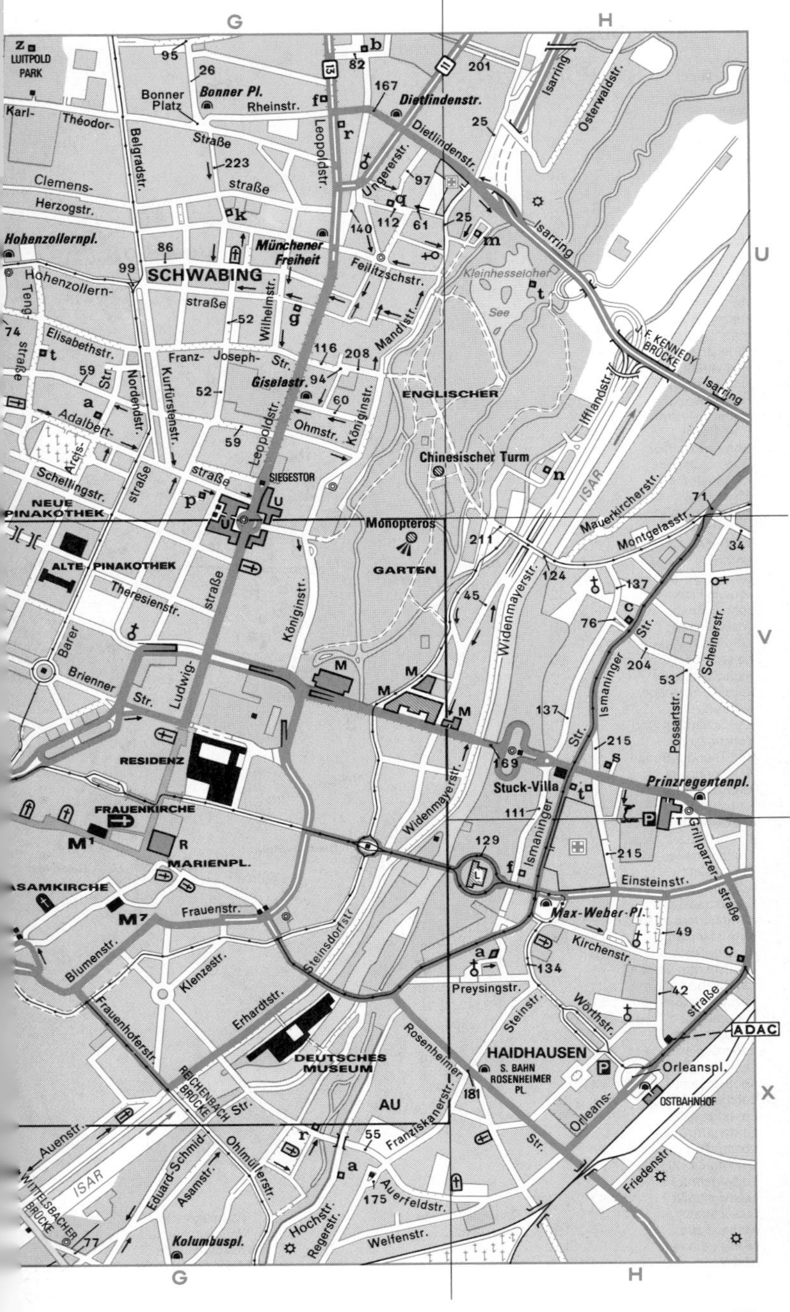
G
H
U
V
X
LUITPOLD PARK
Bonner Pl.
Bonner Platz
Rheinstr.
Leopoldstr.
Dietlindenstr.
Isarring
Osterwaldstr.
Karl-Theodor-Straße
Belgradstr.
Clemens-straße
Herzogstr.
Hohenzollernpl.
Münchener Freiheit
SCHWABING
Hohenzollern-straße
Feilitzschstr.
Kleinhesseloher See
J.-F.-KENNEDY BRÜCKE
Elisabethstr.
Franz-Joseph-Str.
Mandlstr.
Giselastr.
Kurfürstenstr.
Nordendstr.
ENGLISCHER
Adalbert-straße
Ohmstr.
Königinstr.
Ifflandstr.
Chinesischer Turm
Schellingstr.
SIEGESTOR
ISAR
Mauerkircherstr.
NEUE PINAKOTHEK
Monopteros
Montgelasstr.
ALTE PINAKOTHEK
GARTEN
Theresienstr.
Ludwigstraße
Widenmayerstr.
Ismaninger Str.
Scheinerstr.
Barer
Brienner Str.
Possartstr.
RESIDENZ
Stuck-Villa
Prinzregentenpl.
FRAUENKIRCHE
MARIENPL.
Grillparzerstraße
ASAMKIRCHE
Frauenstr.
Einsteinstr.
Max-Weber-Pl.
Steinsdorfstr.
Blumenstr.
Klenzestr.
Kirchenstr.
Preysingstr.
Erhardtstr.
Frauenhoferstr.
DEUTSCHES MUSEUM
Rosenheimer Str.
Steinstr.
Wörthstr.
ADAC
HAIDHAUSEN
S. BAHN ROSENHEIMER PL.
Orleanspl.
OSTBAHNHOF
REICHENBACH BRÜCKE
AU
Franziskanerstr.
Orleans-
Auenstr.
Ohlmüllerstr.
Eduard-Schmid-Str.
Asamstr.
Auerfeldstr.
Friedenstr.
WITTELSBACHER BRÜCKE
Hochstr.
Regerstr.
Welfenstr.
Kolumbuspl.

STREET INDEX

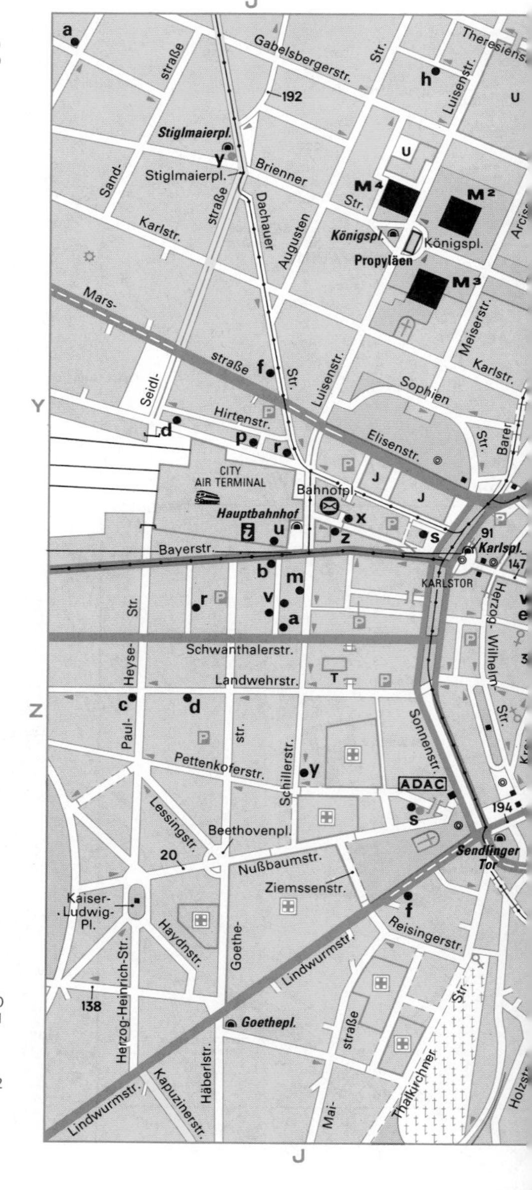

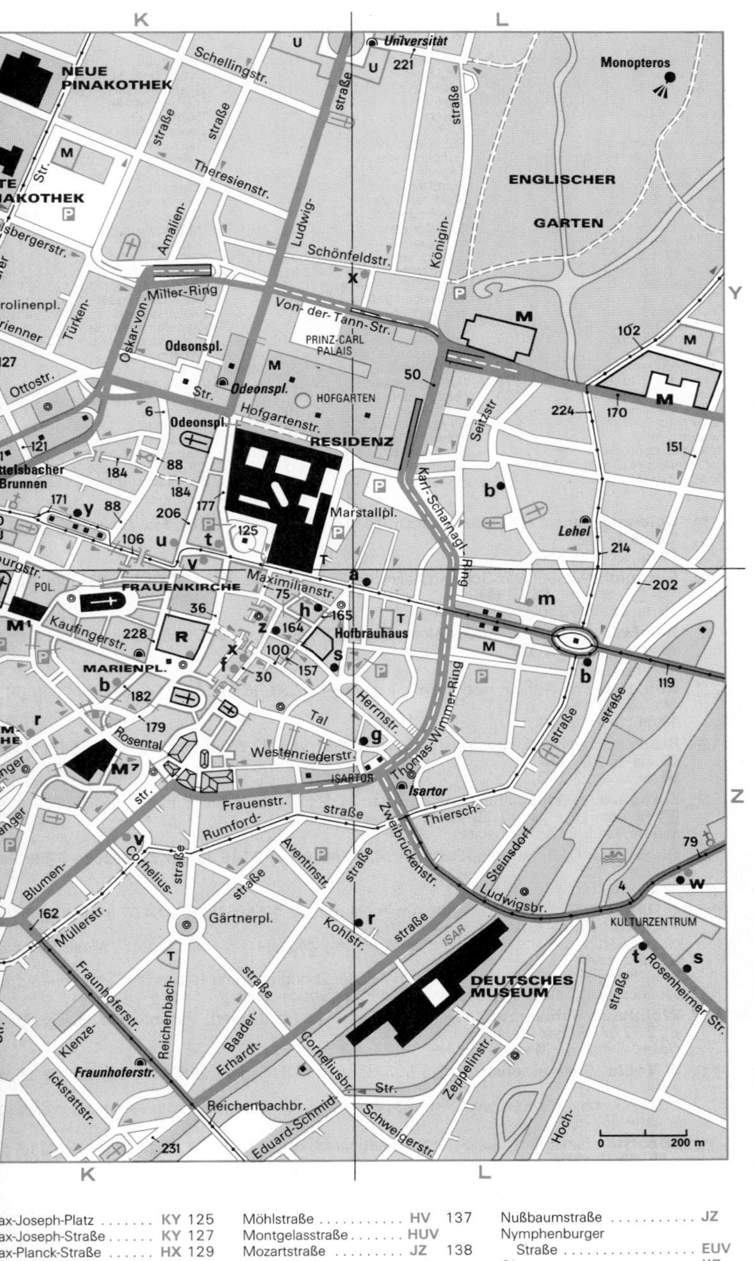

ax-Joseph-Platz .... KY 125
ax-Joseph-Straße ...... KY 127
ax-Planck-Straße ...... HX 129
eiserstraße .... JY
esseplatz .... EX 133
etzgerstraße .... HX 134

Möhlstraße .... HV 137
Montgelasstraße ...... HUV
Mozartstraße .... JZ 138
Müllerstraße .... KZ
Münchener Freiheit .... GU 140
Nordendstraße .... GU

Nußbaumstraße .... JZ
Nymphenburger Straße .... EUV
Oberanger .... KZ

Continued on following page

STREET INDEX TO MÜNCHEN TOWN PLANS (Concluded)

Odeonsplatz . . . . KY
Oettingenstraße . . . . LY 151
Ohlmüllerstraße . . . . GX
Ohmstraße . . . . GU
Orlandostraße . . . . KZ 157
Orleansplatz . . . . HX
Orleansstraße . . . . HX
Oskar-von-Miller-Ring . . . . KY
Osterwaldstraße . . . . HU
Ottostraße . . . . KY
Pacellistraße . . . . KY 160
Papa-Schmid-Straße . . . . . KZ 162
Pappenheimstraße . . . . . . EV 163
Paul-Heyse-Straße . . . . JZ
Pettenkoferstraße . . . . JZ
Pfeuferstraße . . . . EX
Pfisterstraße . . . . KZ 164
Platzl . . . . KZ 165
Poccistraße . . . . EX
Possartstraße . . . . HV
Potsdamer Straße . . . . . . GU 167
Preysingstraße . . . . HX
Prinzregentenbrücke . . . . HV 169
Prinzregentenstraße . . . . . LY 170
Promenadeplatz . . . . KY 171
Radlkoferstraße . . . . EX 174
Regerplatz . . . . GX 175
Regerstraße . . . . GX
Reichenbachbrücke . . . . . KZ
Reichenbachstraße . . . . . . KZ
Reisingerstraße . . . . JZ
Rheinstraße . . . . GU
Rindermarkt . . . . KZ 179
Rosenheimer Platz . . . . . HX 181
Rosenheimer Straße . . . LZ
Rosenstraße . . . . KZ 182
Rosental . . . . KZ
Rumfordstraße . . . . KZ
Ruppertstraße . . . . EFX
Salvatorstraße . . . . KY 184
Sandstraße . . . . JY
Scheinerstraße . . . . HV
Schellingstraße . . . . KY
Schießstättstraße . . . . . . EX 189
Schillerstraße . . . . JZ
Schleißheimer Str. . . . . . JY 192
Schönfeldstraße . . . . KLY
Schwanthalerstraße . . . . JZ
Schweigerstraße . . . . . . LZ
Schwere-Reiter-Straße . . . . EFU
Seidlstraße . . . . JY
Seitzstraße . . . . LY
Sendlinger-Tor-Platz . . . . JZ 194
Sophienstraße . . . . JY
Steinsdorfstraße . . . . LZ
Steinstraße . . . . HX
Stengelstraße . . . . HU 201
Sternstraße . . . . LZ 202
Sternwartstraße . . . . HV 204
Stiglmaierplatz . . . . JY
Tal . . . . KZ
Tengstraße . . . . GU
Thalkirchner Straße . . . . JZ
Theresienhöhe . . . . EX 20
Theresienstraße . . . . JK
Thiemestraße . . . . GU 20
Thierschstraße . . . . LZ
Thomas-Wimmer-Ring . . . . LZ
Tivolistraße . . . . HV 21
Triftstraße . . . . LY 21
Trogerstraße . . . . HVX 21
Türkenstraße . . . . KY
Tumblingerstraße . . . . . . FX 21
Ungererstraße . . . . GU
Veterinärstraße . . . . LY 22
Viktoriastraße . . . . GU 22
Von-der-Tann-Straße . . . . KLY
Wagmüllerstraße . . . . . . LY 22
Welfenstraße . . . . GX
Westenriederstraße . . . . KZ
Widenmayerstraße . . . . . GHV
Wilhelmstraße . . . . GU
Winzererstraße . . . . FU
Wittelsbacherbrücke . . . GX
Wittelsbacherstraße . . . . KZ 23
Wörthstraße . . . . HX
Wredestraße . . . . EV 23
Zeppelinstraße . . . . LZ
Ziemssenstraße . . . . JZ
Zirkus-Krone-Straße . . . . EV 23
Zweibrückenstraße . . . . . LZ

Splendid without rest, Maximilianstr. 54, ✉ 80538, ✆ 29 66 06, Fax 2913176 – AE E VISA
40 rm 100/350. LZ

Germania without rest, Schwanthaler Str. 28, ✉ 80336, ✆ 59 04 60, Fax 591171, – AE E VISA
95 rm 160/250. JZ

Reinbold without rest, Adolf-Kolping-Str. 11, ✉ 80336, ✆ 59 79 45, Fax 596272 – AE E VISA
63 rm 92/274. JZ

Königswache without rest, Steinheilstr. 7, ✉ 80333, ✆ 52 20 01, Fax 5232114 – AE E VISA
40 rm 140/290. JY

Brack without rest, Lindwurmstr. 153, ✉ 80337, ✆ 7 47 25 50, Fax 7250615 – AE E VISA JCB
50 rm 150/260. EX

Europäischer Hof without rest, Bayerstr. 31, ✉ 80335, ✆ 55 15 10, Fax 55151222 – 20. AE E VISA JCB
160 rm 135/280 – 7 suites. JZ

Olympic without rest, Hans-Sachs-Str. 4, ✉ 80469, ✆ 23 18 90, Fax 23189199 – AE E VISA
32 rm 155/280. KZ

XXXX ✿ **Hilton Grill** - Hotel Park Hilton, Am Tucherpark 7, ✉ 80538, ✆ 3 84 52 61, Fax 3845184 – AE E VISA JCB. HU
closed Saturday lunch, Monday, 2 to 14 January and late July - mid August – **Meals** 53 (lunch and à la carte 72/104
Spec. Hummermedaillons mit Zitronenmelisse, Zahnbrasse mit Ratatouille-Cannelloni auf Balsamicosauce, Gefülltes Entrecôte mit Fenchel-Zwiebelconfit.

XXX **Weinhaus Schwarzwälder** (Old Munich wine restaurant), Hartmannstr. 8, ✉ 80333, ✆ 2 12 09 79, Fax 2904172 – AE E VISA KYZ
closed Sunday – **Meals** à la carte 38/77.

XXX **El Toula**, Sparkassenstr. 5, ✉ 80331, ✆ 29 28 69, Fax 298043 – AE E VISA JCB KZ
closed Sunday, Monday, and 3 weeks July - August – **Meals** (booking essential for dinner) à la carte 66/78.

XX ✿ **Boettner** (small Old Munich rest.), Theatinerstr. 8, ✉ 80333, ✆ 22 12 10, Fax 221210, – AE E VISA KY
closed Saturday dinner, Sunday and Bank Holidays – **Meals** (booking essential) à la carte 73/14
Spec. Hechtsoufflé mit Sauce Nantua, Hummereintopf "Hartung", Rote Grütze.

XX ✿ **Gasthaus Glockenbach** (former old Bavarian pub), Kapuzinerstr. 29, ✉ 80337, ✆ 53 40 43, Fax 534043 – E VISA FX
closed Saturday lunch, Sunday - Monday and Bank Holidays – **Meals** (booking essential) à la carte 68/104
Spec. Blutwurstravioli mit Gänseleber, Variation vom Angus-Rind, Schokoladenpastete mit Früchten.

XX **Halali**, Schönfeldstr. 22, ✉ 80539, ☎ 28 59 09, Fax 282786 – AE E VISA LY x
closed Saturday lunch, Sunday, Bank Holidays and 2 weeks August – **Meals** (booking essential) à la carte 51/73.

XX **Weinhaus Neuner** (19C wine restaurant), Herzogspitalstr. 8, ✉ 80331, ☎ 2 60 39 54 – AE E VISA JZ e
closed Sunday, Bank Holidays and 2 weeks August – **Meals** à la carte 42/61.

XX **Galleria** (Italian rest.), Ledererstr. 2 (corner Sparkassenstr.), ✉ 80331, ☎ 29 79 95, Fax 2913653 – AE ⓓ E VISA KZ x
closed Sunday and 1 to 7 January – **Meals** (booking essential) à la carte 62/75.

X **Straubinger Hof** (Bavarian pub), Blumenstr. 5, ✉ 80331, ☎ 2 60 84 44, Fax 2608917, beer garden – AE E VISA. ⚘ KZ c
closed Saturday dinner, Sunday and Bank Holidays – **Meals** à la carte 24/52.

Brewery - inns :

X **Spatenhaus-Bräustuben**, Residenzstr. 12, ✉ 80333, ☎ 2 90 70 60, Fax 2913054, 🍽, « Furnished in traditional Alpine style » – AE ⓓ E VISA KY t
Meals à la carte 42/74.

X **Augustiner Gaststätten**, Neuhauser Str. 27, ✉ 80331, ☎ 55 19 92 57, Fax 2605379, « Beer garden » – AE ⓓ E VISA JZ w
Meals à la carte 29/59.

X **Altes Hackerhaus**, Sendlinger Str. 14, ✉ 80331, ☎ 2 60 50 26, Fax 2605027, 🍽 – AE ⓓ E VISA JCB KZ r
Meals à la carte 30/66.

X **Franziskaner Fuchsenstuben**, Perusastr. 5, ✉ 80333, ☎ 2 31 81 20, Fax 23181244, 🍽 – AE ⓓ E VISA JCB KY v
Meals à la carte 33/66.

X **Zum Spöckmeier**, Rosenstr. 9, ✉ 80331, ☎ 26 80 88, Fax 2605509, 🍽 – AE ⓓ E VISA
Meals à la carte 30/60. KZ b

X **Löwenbräukeller**, Nymphenburger Str. 2, ✉ 80335, ☎ 52 60 21, Fax 528933, beer garden – AE ⓓ E VISA JY y
Meals à la carte 35/54.

at Munich-Allach by Arnulfstr. EV :

🏠 **Lutter** without rest, Eversbuschstr. 109, ✉ 80999, ☎ 8 12 70 04, Fax 8129584 – TV ☎ P. E VISA. ⚘
closed 22 December - 2 January – **26 rm** ☕ 98/180.

at Munich-Bogenhausen :

🏨 **Sheraton**, Arabellastr. 6, ✉ 81925, ☎ 9 26 40, Telex 523754, Fax 916877, ≤ Munich, beer garden, Massage, ≘s, 🏊 – 🛗 ⚭ rm ▤ TV ☎ ♿ 🚗 – 🏛 650. AE ⓓ E VISA JCB. ⚘ rest
Meals à la carte 45/70 – **636 rm** ☕ 265/664 – 16 suites. by Isarring HU

🏨 **Palace**, Trogerstr. 21, ✉ 81675, ☎ 41 97 10, Fax 41971819, « Elegant installation with period furniture », ≘s, 🌳 – 🛗 ⚭ rm TV ☎ 🚗 – 🏛 40. AE ⓓ E VISA JCB HV t
Meals (residents only)(dinner only) – **71 rm** ☕ 264/568 – 6 suites.

🏨 **Arabella-Hotel**, Arabellastr. 5, ✉ 81925, ☎ 9 23 20, Telex 529987, Fax 92324449, ≤, 🍽, Massage, 🏋, ≘s, 🏊 – 🛗 ⚭ rm ▤ rest TV ☎ ♿ 🚗 P – 🏛 320. AE ⓓ E VISA. ⚘ rest
Meals à la carte 43/72 – **467 rm** ☕ 320/445 – 37 suites. by Isarring HU

🏨 **Prinzregent** without rest, Ismaninger Str. 42, ✉ 81675, ☎ 41 60 50, Fax 41605466, ≘s – 🛗 ⚭ TV ☎ 🚗 – 🏛 40. AE ⓓ E VISA HV t
closed 24 December - 11 January – **66 rm** ☕ 220/450.

🏨 **Rothof** without rest, Denniger Str. 114, ✉ 81925, ☎ 91 50 61, Fax 915066, 🌳 – 🛗 TV ☎ 🚗. AE ⓓ E VISA by Einsteinstr. HX
closed 24 December - 7 January – **37 rm** ☕ 198/330.

🏠 **Queens Hotel München**, Effnerstr. 99, ✉ 81925, ☎ 92 79 80, Telex 524757, Fax 983813 – 🛗 ⚭ rm ▤ rest TV ☎ 🚗 P – 🏛 200. AE ⓓ E VISA. ⚘ rest by Ismaninger Str. HV
Meals *(closed Sunday dinner)* à la carte 49/76 – **152 rm** ☕ 269/434.

XXX **Bogenhauser Hof** (1825 former hunting lodge), Ismaninger Str. 85, ✉ 81675, ☎ 98 55 86, Fax 9810221, « Garden terrace » – AE ⓓ VISA HV c
closed Sunday, Bank Holidays and Christmas - 6 January – **Meals** (booking essential) à la carte 67/90.

XXX **Acquarello** (Italian rest.), Mühlbaurstr. 36, ✉ 81677, ☎ 4 70 48 48, Fax 476464, 🍽 – AE E. ⚘ by Mühlbaurstr HV
closed Saturday and Sunday lunch – **Meals** à la carte 47/79.

XX **Käfer Schänke**, Schumannstr. 1, ✉ 81679, ☎ 4 16 82 47, Fax 4168623, 🍽, « Several rooms with elegant rustic installation » – AE ⓓ E VISA. ⚘ HV s
closed Sunday and Bank Holidays – **Meals** (booking essential) à la carte 57/100.

XX **Prielhof**, Oberföhringer Str. 44, ✉ 81925, ☎ 98 53 53, Fax 9827289, 🍽 – ⓓ E VISA
closed Saturday lunch, Sunday, Bank Holidays and 23 December - 6 January – **Meals** (booking essential) à la carte 58/75. by Ismaninger Str. HV

at Munich-Denning by Denninger Str. HV :

XXX **Casale** (Italian rest.), Ostpreußenstr. 42, ✉ 81927, ☎ 93 62 68, Fax 9306722, 帝 - AE ⓓ E VISA
Meals à la carte 45/75.

at Munich-Englschalking by Ismaninger Str. HU and Englschalkinger Str. :

XX ✿ **La Vigna** (Italian rest.), Wilhelm-Dieß-Weg 2, ✉ 81927, ☎ 93 14 16, 帝 - AE E VISA
closed Saturday, 23 December to 5 January and 1 week June – **Meals** à la carte 55/72
Spec. Linsensalat mit geräuchertem Schweinebäckchen, Ravioli von Tomaten und Mozzarella m Pesto, Rochenflügel mit Oliven-Thymiansauce.

at Munich-Haidhausen :

City Hilton, Rosenheimer Str. 15, ✉ 81667, ☎ 4 80 40, Telex 529437, Fax 48044804, 帝 - 劇 ⇔ rm ▤ TV ☎ ♿ ⇔ - 🔬 180. AE ⓓ E VISA JCB LZ
Meals 52 (buffet) and à la carte 61/96 – **479 rm** ☐ 470/600 – 4 suites.

Preysing, Preysingstr. 1, ✉ 81667, ☎ 45 84 50, Fax 45845444, ≘s, ⊠ - 劇 ▤ TV ☎ ⇔ - 🔬 50. AE ⓓ VISA LZ
closed 23 December - 6 January – **Meals** see **Preysing-Keller** below – **76 rm** ☐ 160/298 5 suites.

München Penta Hotel, Hochstr. 3, ✉ 81669, ☎ 4 80 30, Telex 529046, Fax 4488277 Massage, ≘s, ⊠ - 劇 ⇔ rm ▤ TV ☎ P - 🔬 360 LZ
582 rm – 6 suites.

XXX ✿ **Preysing-Keller** - Hotel Preysing, Innere-Wiener-Str. 6, ✉ 81667, ☎ 45 84 52 60 Fax 45845444, « Vaulted cellar, country house furniture » – ▤. AE ⓓ VISA LZ
closed Sunday, Bank Holidays and 23 December - 6 January – **Meals** (dinner only) (outstandin wine list) 89/125 and à la carte 52/87
Spec. Sautierte Garnelen auf Zucchini-Ricotta-Ravioli mit Minze, Kalbsfilet mit Pilzkruste un gerösteten Pinienkernen, Ananas-Crêpes mit Mandelschaum überbacken.

XX **Gallo Nero** (Italian rest.), Grillparzerstr. 1, ✉ 81675, ☎ 4 70 54 72, Fax 4701321, 帝 - AE E HX
closed Saturday lunch and Sunday – **Meals** à la carte 51/68.

X **Rue Des Halles** (Bistro), Steinstr. 18, ✉ 81667, ☎ 48 56 75 – E VISA HX
Meals (dinner only, booking essential) à la carte 52/82.

at Munich-Laim by Landsberger Str. (B 2) EV :

Transmar-Park-Hotel without rest, Zschokkestr. 55, ✉ 80686, ☎ 57 93 60, Fax 5793610C ≘s - 劇 TV ☎ ⇔ - 🔬 30. AE ⓓ E VISA JCB
68 rm ☐ 180/260.

at Munich-Langwied : NW : 13 km by Arnulfstr. EV

XX ✿ **Das kleine Restaurant im Gasthof Böswirth**, Waidachanger 9, ✉ 81249 ☎ 8 64 41 63, Fax 8643857, 帝 - P. AE
closed Sunday, Monday, Bank Holidays and 2 weeks late May - early June – **Meals** (dinner only (outstanding wine list) 85/125 – ***Gaststube*** *(also lunch, closed Monday)* Menu à la carte 44/6
Spec. Marinierte Milchkalbsschulter mit Trüffelöl, Gebratener Zander mit Steinpilzen, Topfen knödel mit Aprikosen.

at Munich-Neu Perlach by Rosenheimer Str. HX :

Mercure, Karl-Marx-Ring 87, ✉ 81735, ☎ 6 32 70, Telex 5213357, Fax 6327407, 帝, ≘s ⊠ - 劇 ⇔ rm ▤ rest TV ☎ ⇔ P - 🔬 140. AE ⓓ E VISA JCB
Meals 39 (buffet lunch) and à la carte 42/72 – **184 rm** ☐ 168/305 – 4 suites.

Villa Waldperlach without rest, Putzbrunner Str. 250(Waldperlach), ✉ 81739 ☎ 6 60 03 00, Fax 66003066 – 劇 ⇔ TV ☎ ⇔. AE ⓓ E VISA
21 rm ☐ 144/250.

at Munich-Schwabing :

Marriott-Hotel, Berliner Str. 93, ✉ 80805, ☎ 36 00 20, Telex 5216641, Fax 36002200, ≘s, ⊠ - 劇 ⇔ rm ▤ TV ☎ ♿ ⇔ - 🔬 320. AE ⓓ E VISA JCB. ⇔ rest
Meals à la carte 50/84 – **348 rm** ☐ 254/541 – 14 suites. by Ungererstr. (B 11) HU

Ramada Parkhotel, Theodor-Dombart-Str. 4 (corner of Berliner Straße), ✉ 80805 ☎ 36 09 90, Telex 5218720, Fax 36099684, 帝, Massage, ≘s – 劇 ⇔ rm TV ☎ ⇔ - 🔬 40 AE ⓓ E VISA JCB by Ungererstr. (B 11) HU
Meals à la carte 43/70 – **260 rm** ☐ 238/346 – 80 suites.

Holiday Inn Crowne Plaza, Leopoldstr. 194, ✉ 80804, ☎ 38 17 90, Telex 5215439 Fax 38179888, 帝, Massage, ≘s, ⊠ – 劇 ⇔ rm TV ☎ ⇔ – 🔬 320. AE ⓓ E VISA JCB
Meals à la carte 47/78 – **365 rm** ☐ 324/508 – 3 suites. by Leopoldstr. GU

Vitalis, Kathi-Kobus-Str. 24, ✉ 80797, ☎ 12 00 80, Telex 5215161, Fax 1298382, ⊠ – 劇 ⇔ rm TV ☎ ⇔ P – 🔬 60. AE ⓓ E VISA. ⇔ FU
Meals *(closed Saturday, Sunday and Bank Holidays)* à la carte 38/65 – **101 rm** ☐ 210/295

Cosmopolitan without rest, Hohenzollernstr. 5, ✉ 80801, ☎ 38 38 10, Fax 38381111 – 劇 TV ☎ ⇔. AE ⓓ E VISA JCB GU
71 rm ☐ 145/210.

Arabella - Olympiapark-Hotel, Helene-Mayer-Ring 12, ✉ 80809, ✆ 3 51 60 71, Fax 3543730, 🍽 – |‡| ⇎ rm 📺 ☎ 🅟 – 🏛 30. AE ⓓ E VISA by Schleißheimer Str. FU
closed 23 December - 8 January – **Meals** à la carte 38/65 – **105 rm** ☐ 231/352.

Residence, Artur-Kutscher-Platz 4, ✉ 80802, ✆ 38 17 80, Telex 529788, Fax 38178951, 🍽, 🏊 – |‡| ⇎ rm 📺 ☎ 🚗 – 🏛 60. AE ⓓ E VISA JCB GU q
Meals *(closed Saturday - Sunday)* à la carte 40/63 – **165 rm** ☐ 182/370.

Mercure without rest, Leopoldstr. 120, ✉ 80802, ✆ 39 05 50, Fax 349344 – |‡| 📺 ☎ 🚗. AE ⓓ E VISA JCB GU r
65 rm ☐ 190/305.

Leopold, Leopoldstr. 119, ✉ 80804, ✆ 36 70 61, Fax 36043150, 🍽 – |‡| 📺 ☎ 🚗 🅟. AE ⓓ E VISA GU f
closed 23 December - 1 January – **Meals** *(closed Saturday and 2 to 10 January)* à la carte 43/71 – **75 rm** ☐ 155/255.

Consul without rest, Viktoriastr. 10, ✉ 80803, ✆ 33 40 35, Fax 399266 – |‡| 📺 ☎ 🚗 🅟. AE E VISA GU k
25 rm ☐ 120/200.

Ibis München Nord, Ungererstr. 139, ✉ 80805, ✆ 36 08 30, Fax 363793, 🍽 – |‡| ⇎ 📺 ☎ ♿ 🚗 – 🏛 45. AE ⓓ E VISA by Ungererstraße GHU
Meals à la carte 34/51 – **138 rm** ☐ 186/201.

XXXX ✿✿ **Tantris**, Johann-Fichte-Str. 7, ✉ 80805, ✆ 36 20 61, Fax 3618469, 🍽 – ▤ 🅟. AE ⓓ E VISA. ✗ GU b
closed Sunday, Monday, Bank Holidays and 1 week January – **Meals** (booking essential) 188/218 and à la carte 87/129
Spec. Weißes Tomatenmousse mit sautiertem Octopus, Rehkotelett mit Aromaten und Apfel-Rotwein-Püree, Mangocrème und Passionsfrucht-Parfait im Schockoladenkegel.

XX **Savoy** (Italian rest.), Tengstr. 20, ✉ 80798, ✆ 2 71 14 45 – AE ⓓ E VISA GU t
closed Sunday – **Meals** (booking essential for dinner) à la carte 44/63.

XX **Spago** (Italian rest.), Neureutherstr. 15, ✉ 80799, ✆ 2 71 24 06, Fax 2780442, 🍽 – AE E
dinner only Saturday, Sunday and Bank Holidays – **Meals** à la carte 49/79. GU a

XX **Bistro Terrine**, Amalienstr. 89 (Amalien-Passage), ✉ 80799, ✆ 28 17 80, Fax 2809316, 🍽 – AE E VISA GU q
closed Saturday and Monday lunch, Sunday and Bank Holidays – **Meals** (booking essential for dinner) 43 (lunch) and à la carte 59/80.

XX **Seehaus**, Kleinhesselohe 3, ✉ 80802, ✆ 3 81 61 30, Fax 341803, ←, « Lakeside setting terrace » – 🅟. AE ⓓ E VISA HU t
Meals à la carte 41/74.

X **Bamberger Haus**, Brunnenstr. 2 (at Luitpoldpark), ✉ 80804, ✆ 3 08 89 66, Fax 3003304, « 18C palace with brewery and terrace » – 🅟. AE ⓓ E VISA GU z
Meals à la carte 36/69.

at Munich-Sendling by Lindwurmstr. (B 11) EX :

Holiday Inn München - Süd, Kistlerhofstr. 142, ✉ 81379, ✆ 78 00 20, Fax 78002672, beer garden, Massage, ≘s, 🏊 – |‡| ⇎ rm ▤ 📺 ☎ ♿ 🚗 – 🏛 90. AE ⓓ E VISA JCB. ✗ rest
closed 23 December - 6 January – **Meals** à la carte 42/78 – **320 rm** ☐ 285/442 – 7 suites.

Ambassador Parkhotel, Plinganserstr. 102, ✉ 81369, ✆ 72 48 90, Fax 72489100, beer garden – |‡| 📺 ☎ 🚗. AE ⓓ E VISA
closed 23 December - 7 January – **Meals** *(closed Saturday)* (Italian rest.) à la carte 38/67 – **42 rm** ☐ 175/275.

K u. K Hotel am Harras, Albert-Rosshaupter-Str. 4, ✉ 81369, ✆ 77 00 51, Telex 5213167, Fax 7212820 – |‡| 📺 ☎ 🚗. AE ⓓ E VISA JCB
Meals (residents only) (dinner only) – **129 rm** ☐ 199/335.

at Munich-Untermenzing by Arnulfstr. EV :

Romantik-Hotel Insel Mühle, von-Kahr-Str. 87, ✉ 80999, ✆ 8 10 10, Fax 8120571, 🍽, beer garden, « Converted 16C riverside mill » – 📺 ☎ ♿ 🚗 🅟 – 🏛 40. ⓓ E VISA
Meals *(closed Sunday and Bank Holidays)* à la carte 49/80 – **37 rm** ☐ 150/420.

at Unterhaching by Kapuzinerstr. GX :

Schrenkhof without rest, Leonhardsweg 6, ✉ 82008, ✆ 6 10 09 10, Fax 61009150, « Bavarian farmhouse furniture », ≘s – |‡| 📺 ☎ 🅟 – 🏛 40. AE ⓓ E VISA
closed 20 December - 8 January – **25 rm** ☐ 140/300.

Holiday Inn Garden Court, Inselkamer Str. 7, ✉ 82008, ✆ 66 69 10, Fax 66691600, beer garden, 🏋, ≘s – |‡| ⇎ rm 📺 ☎ ♿ 🚗 – 🏛 260. AE ⓓ E VISA JCB. ✗ rest
Meals à la carte 44/72 – **130 rm** ☐ 175/325 – 18 suites.

at Aschheim NE : 13 km by Riem :

Schreiberhof, Erdinger Str. 2, ✉ 85609, ✆ (089) 90 00 60, Fax 90006459, 🍽, Massage, 🏋, ≘s – |‡| ⇎ rm 📺 ☎ ♿ 🚗 🅟 – 🏛 90. AE ⓓ E VISA JCB
– ***Alte Gaststube :*** **Meals** à la carte 39/69 – **87 rm** ☐ 205/325.

at Grünwald S : 13 km by Wittelsbacher Brücke GX - ☎ 089 :

Tannenhof without rest, Marktplatz 3, ✉ 82031, ☎ 6 41 89 60, Fax 6415608, « Period house with elegant interior » - TV ☎ P. AE ⓓ E VISA. ✻
closed 20 December - 6 January - **21 rm** ☕ 150/220 - 3 suites.

at airport Franz-Josef-Strauß NE : 37km by A 9 and A 92 :

Kempinski Airport München, Terminalstraße/Mitte 20, ✉ 85356 München, ☎ (089) 9 78 20, Fax 97822610, Fб, ≘s, ⊠ - |‡| ⇔ rm ▤ TV ☎ ♿ ⇔ - 🏛 280. AE ⓓ E VISA JCB. ✻ rest
Meals à la carte 46/90 - **389 rm** ☕ 318/376 - 17 suites.

Il Mondo (Italian rest.), Bereich B - Ebene 07, ✉ 85356 München, ☎ (089) 97 59 28 70, Fax 97592856 - P. AE ⓓ E VISA
Meals à la carte 47/74.

Zirbelstube, Zentralgebäude - Ebene 04, ✉ 85356 Munich, ☎ (089) 97 59 28 60, Fax 97592856, « Original pine interior » - P. AE ⓓ E VISA
Meals à la carte 31/55.

Aschau im Chiemgau

Bayern 413 TU 23, 987 ㊵, 426 I 5 - pop. 5 200 - alt. 615 m - ☎ 08052.

Munich 82.

✿✿ **Residenz Heinz Winkler** ⛰, Kirchplatz 1, ✉ 83229, ☎ 1 79 90, Fax 179966, ≤ Kampenwand, 🏛, « Elegant hotel and renovated 17C inn », Massage, ≘s, 🌳 - |‡| ⇔ rm TV ☎ ⇔ P - 🏛 30. ⓓ E VISA. ✻ rest
Meals *(closed Monday lunch)* 165/198 and à la carte 87/134 - **32 rm** ☕ 210/450
Spec. Gnocchi in Schnittlauchsauce mit Kaviar, Seezungenfilet in Château Chalon, Crepinette vom Reh mit Portweinsauce.

STUTTGART

L Baden-Württemberg 413 KL 20, 987 ㊳ - pop. 559 000 - alt. 245 m - ☎ 0711.

See : Linden Museum ★★ KY **M1** - Park Wilhelma★ HT and Killesberg-Park★ GT - Television Tower (Fernsehturm) ✻★ HX - Stuttgart Gallery (Otto-Dix-Collection★) LY **M4** - Swabian Brewerymuseum (Schwäb. Brauereimuseum)★ by Böblinger Straße FX - Old Castle (Altes Schloß) (Renaissance courtyard★) - Württemberg Regional Museum★ (Sacred Statuary★★) LY **M3** - State Gallery★ (Old Masters Collection★★) LY **M2** - Collegiate church (Stiftskirche) (Commemorative monuments of dukes★) KY **A** - State Musem of Natural History (Staatl. Museum für Naturkunde)★ HT **M5** - Daimler-Benz Museum★ JV **M6** - Porsche Museum★ by Heilbronner Straße GT - Schloß Solitude★ by Rotenwaldstraße FX.

Envir. : Bad Cannstatt Spa Park (Kurpark)★ E : 4 km JT.

⛳ Kornwestheim, Aldinger Str. (N : 11 km), ☎ (07141) 87 13 19 ; ⛳18 Mönsheim (NW : 30 km by A 8), ☎ (07044) 69 09.

✈ Stuttgart-Echterdingen, by Obere Weinsteige (B 27) GX, ☎ 94 80, City Air Terminal, Stuttgart, Lautenschlagerstr. 14(LY), ☎ 20 12 68.

Exhibition Centre (Messegelände Killesberg) (GT), ☎ 2 58 91, Telex 722584, Fax 2589440.

ℹ Tourist-Info, Königstr. 1a, ✉ 70173, ☎ 2 22 82 40, Fax 2228253.

ADAC, Am Neckartor 2, ✉ 70190, ☎ 2 80 00, Fax 2800167.

Frankfurt am Main 204 - Karlsruhe 88 - Munich 222 - Strasbourg 156.

Plans on following pages

Maritim, Forststr. 2, ✉ 70174, ☎ 94 20, Fax 9421000, Massage, Fб, ≘s, ⊠ - |‡| ⇔ rm ▤ TV ☎ ♿ ⇔ - 🏛 800. AE ⓓ E VISA JCB. ✻ rest — FV **r**
Meals à la carte 56/87 - **555 rm** ☕ 257/408 - 50 suites.

Am Schloßgarten, Schillerstr. 23, ✉ 70173, ☎ 2 02 60, Telex 722936, Fax 2026888, « Terrace with ≤ » - |‡| ⇔ rm TV ☎ ⇔ - 🏛 100. AE ⓓ E VISA. ✻ rest — LY **u**
Meals 49 (lunch) and à la carte 64/104 - **118 rm** ☕ 255/470.

Inter-Continental, Willy-Brandt-Str. 30, ✉ 70173, ☎ 2 02 00, Telex 721996, Fax 202012, Massage, Fб, ≘s, ⊠ - |‡| ⇔ rm ▤ TV ☎ ♿ ⇔ - 🏛 250. AE ⓓ E VISA JCB. ✻ rest — HV **t**
Meals à la carte 48/70 - **277 rm** ☕ 348/546 - 24 suites.

Royal, Sophienstr. 35, ✉ 70178, ☎ 62 50 50, Telex 722449, Fax 628809 - |‡| ⇔ rm ▤ rest TV ☎ ⇔ P - 🏛 70. AE ⓓ E VISA JCB — KZ **b**
Meals *(closed Sunday and Bank Holidays)* à la carte 45/70 - **100 rm** ☕ 185/390 - 3 suites.

Parkhotel, Villastr. 21, ✉ 70190, ☎ 2 80 10, Telex 723405, Fax 2864353, 🏛 - |‡| ⇔ rm TV ☎ ⇔ - 🏛 80. AE ⓓ E VISA JCB. ✻ rest — HU **r**
Meals à la carte 55/79 - **72 rm** ☕ 180/330.

Ruff, Friedhofstr. 21, ✉ 70191, ☎ 2 58 70, Fax 2587404, ≘s, ⊠ - |‡| TV ☎ ⇔ P. AE ⓓ E VISA — GU **a**
closed 23 December - 1 January and 4 - 8 April - **Meals** *(closed Sunday lunch, Saturday and 12 - 27 August)* à la carte 36/65 - **81 rm** ☕ 145/208.

Rega Hotel, Ludwigstr. 18, ✉ 70176, ☎ 61 93 40, Fax 6193477 - |‡| TV ☎ ⇔ - 🏛 25. AE ⓓ E VISA — FV **a**
Meals *(Sunday lunch only)* à la carte 30/59 - **60 rm** ☕ 175/235.

Intercityhotel without rest, Arnulf-Klett-Platz 2, ✉ 70173, ☎ 2 25 00, Fax 2250499 – 🛗 ⇔ 📺 ☎ - 🏠 30. AE ⓓ E VISA LY p
112 rm ☕ 190/230.

Unger without rest, Kronenstr. 17, ✉ 70173, ☎ 2 09 90, Telex 723995, Fax 2099100 – 🛗 ⇔ 📺 ☎ 🚗 - 🏠 20. AE ⓓ E VISA LY a
97 rm ☕ 179/350.

Bergmeister without rest, Rotenbergstr. 16, ✉ 70190, ☎ 28 33 63, Fax 283719, ≘s – 🛗 ⇔ 📺 ☎ 🚗. AE ⓓ E VISA JCB HV r
47 rm ☕ 129/210.

Kronen-Hotel without rest, Kronenstr. 48, ✉ 70174, ☎ 2 25 10, Fax 2251404, ≘s – 🛗 ⇔ 📺 ☎ 🚗 - 🏠 20. AE ⓓ E VISA KY m
closed 22 December - 7 January – **83 rm** ☕ 160/320.

Wörtz zur Weinsteige, Hohenheimer Str. 30, ✉ 70184, ☎ 2 36 70 01, Fax 2367007, « Garden terrace » – ⇔ rm 📺 ☎ 🅿. AE ⓓ E VISA JCB LZ p
closed 20 December - 7 January – **Meals** *(closed Sunday, Monday and Bank Holidays)* à la carte 29/82 – **25 rm** ☕ 130/260.

Azenberg 🔇, Seestr. 114, ✉ 70174, ☎ 22 10 51, Fax 297426, ≘s, 🏊 – 🛗 ⇔ rm 📺 ☎ 🚗 🅿. AE ⓓ E VISA JCB. ✻ rest FU e
Meals (dinner only) (residents only) – **56 rm** ☕ 140/250.

Wartburg, Lange Str. 49, ✉ 70174, ☎ 2 04 50, Telex 721587, Fax 2045450 – 🛗 ▤ rest 📺 ☎ 🅿 - 🏠 45. AE ⓓ E VISA JCB KY g
closed Easter and 21 December - 2 January – **Meals** *(closed Saturday, Sunday and Bank Holidays)* (lunch only) à la carte 35/55 – **80 rm** ☕ 150/250.

Ketterer, Marienstr. 3, ✉ 70178, ☎ 2 03 90, Fax 2039600 – 🛗 ⇔ rm 📺 ☎ 🚗. AE ⓓ E VISA. ✻ rm KZ y
closed 22 December - 2 January – **Meals** *(closed Friday, Saturday and 15 July - 15 August)* à la carte 37/67 – **100 rm** ☕ 162/285.

Rieker without rest, Friedrichstr. 3, ✉ 70174, ☎ 22 13 11, Fax 293894 – 🛗 📺 ☎. AE E VISA LY d
61 rm ☕ 138/218.

Rema-Hotel Astoria without rest, Hospitalstr. 29, ✉ 70174, ☎ 29 93 01, Telex 722783, Fax 299307 – 🛗 ⇔ 📺 ☎ 🅿. AE ⓓ E VISA JCB KY r
50 rm ☕ 170/330.

City-Hotel without rest, Uhlandstr. 18, ✉ 70182, ☎ 21 08 10, Fax 2369772 – 📺 ☎ 🅿. AE ⓓ E VISA JCB. ✻ LZ a
31 rm ☕ 140/210.

Am Feuersee without rest, Johannesstr. 2, ✉ 70176, ☎ 61 95 40, Fax 61954160 – 🛗 📺 ☎. AE ⓓ E VISA FV t
closed 24 December - 2 January – **38 rm** ☕ 105/180.

Da Franco (Italian rest.), Calwer Str. 23, ✉ 70173, ☎ 29 15 81, Fax 294549 – ▤. AE ⓓ E VISA
closed Monday – **Meals** à la carte 47/76. KYZ c

La nuova Trattoria da Franco (Italian rest.), Calwer Str. 32 (1st floor), ✉ 70173, ☎ 29 47 44, Fax 294549 – AE ⓓ E VISA KYZ c
Meals à la carte 45/75.

Delice, Hauptstätter Str. 61, ✉ 70178, ☎ 6 40 32 22 – ✻ KZ a
(dinner only, booking essential, outstanding wine list).

Der Goldene Adler, Böheimstr. 38, ✉ 70178, ☎ 6 40 17 62, Fax 6492405 – 🅿. AE E VISA
closed Tuesday and Saturday lunch, Monday and August – **Meals** à la carte 38/84. FX e

La Scala (Italian rest.), Friedrichstr. 41 (1st floor, 🛗), ✉ 70174, ☎ 29 06 07, Fax 2991640 – ▤. AE E KY e
closed Sunday April - mid September and 3 weeks August – **Meals** 45/70 and à la carte.

Intercityrestaurant, Arnulf-Klett-Platz 2, ✉ 70173, ☎ 1 87 20, Fax 1872113 – AE E VISA
Meals à la carte 27/50. LY v

Krämer's Bürgerstuben, Gablenberger Hauptstr. 4, ✉ 70186, ☎ 46 54 81, Fax 486508 – AE ⓓ E VISA HV n
closed Saturday lunch, Sunday dinner, Monday and 3 weeks July - August – **Meals** (booking essential) à la carte 53/79.

Swabian wine taverns (Weinstuben) (mainly light meals only) :

Kachelofen, Eberhardstr. 10 (entrance in Töpferstraße), ✉ 70173, ☎ 24 23 78, 🍽 KZ x
closed Sunday and 22 December - 2 January – **Meals** (dinner only) à la carte 39/49.

Weinstube Schellenturm, Weberstr. 72, ✉ 70182, ☎ 2 36 48 88, Fax 2262699, 🍽 – AE. ✻ LZ u
closed Sunday and Bank Holidays – **Meals** (dinner only) à la carte 32/63.

Weinstube Träuble, Gablenberger Hauptstr. 66, ✉ 70186, ☎ 46 54 28, 🍽 – ✻ HV s
closed Sunday, Bank Holidays, 1 week April and late August - mid September – **Meals** (dinner only) à la carte 20/35.

Weinstube Klösterle (part of former monastery), Marktstr. 71 (Bad Cannstatt), ✉ 70372, ☎ 56 89 62, 🍽 – E VISA HT a
closed Sunday and Bank Holidays – **Meals** (dinner only) à la carte 35/61.

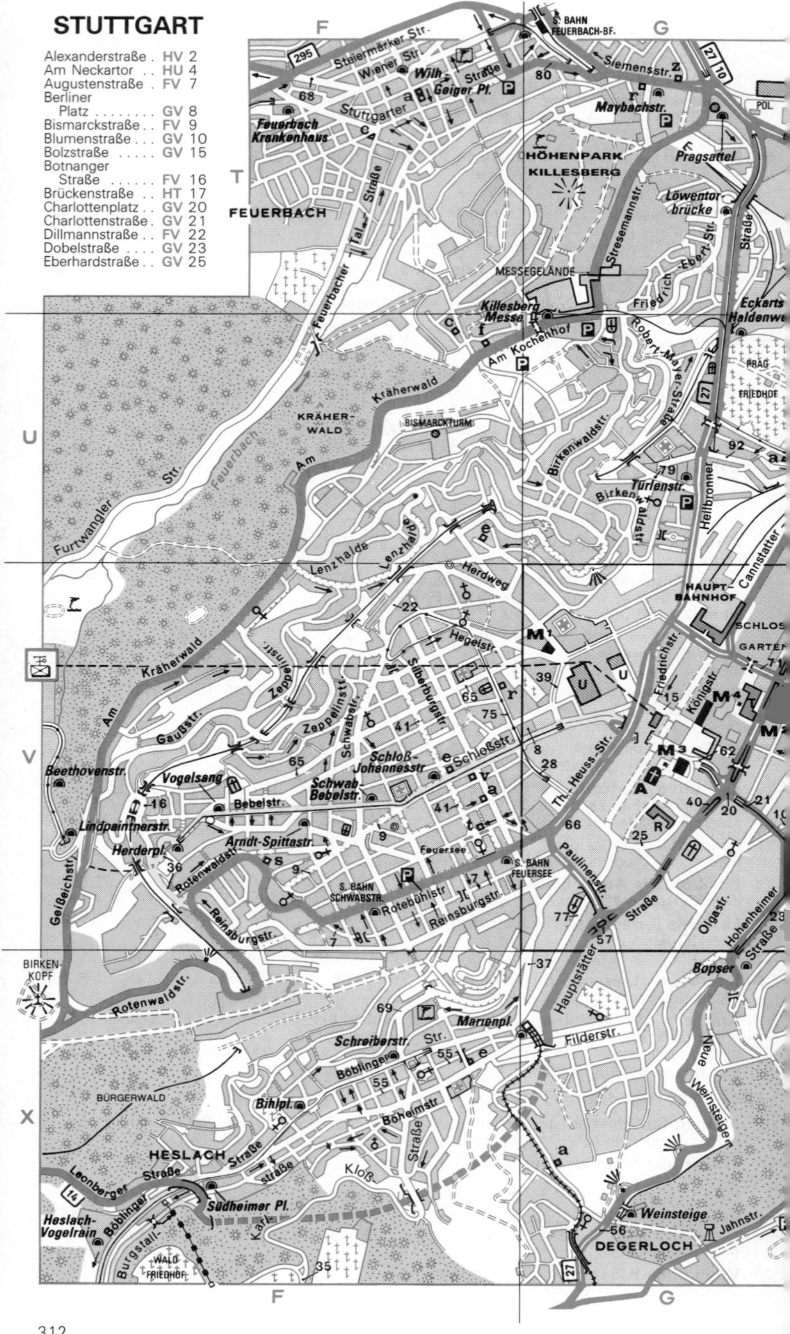
STUTTGART
Alexanderstraße . HV 2
Am Neckartor . . HU 4
Augustenstraße . FV 7
Berliner Platz . . . . GV 8
Bismarckstraße . . FV 9
Blumenstraße . . . GV 10
Bolzstraße . . . . . GV 15
Botnanger Straße . . . . . . FV 16
Brückenstraße . . HT 17
Charlottenplatz . . GV 20
Charlottenstraße . GV 21
Dillmannstraße . . FV 22
Dobelstraße . . . . GV 23
Eberhardstraße . . GV 25
F
G
T
U
V
X
S. BAHN FEUERBACH-BF.
FEUERBACH
Feuerbach Krankenhaus
Wilh.-Geiger Pl.
Maybachstr.
Pragsattel
HÖHENPARK KILLESBERG
Löwentorbrücke
MESSEGELÄNDE
Killesberg Messe
KRÄHERWALD
BISMARCKTURM
Türlenstr.
HAUPTBAHNHOF
Vogelsang
Beethovenstr.
Lindpaintnerstr.
Herderpl.
Schloß-Johannesstr.
Schwab-Bebelstr.
Arndt-Spittastr.
S. BAHN SCHWABSTR.
S. BAHN FEUERSEE
BIRKENKOPF
Bopser
Marienpl.
Schreiberstr.
Böblinger
Bihlpl.
BÜRGERWALD
HESLACH
Südheimer Pl.
Heslach-Vogelrain
WALDFRIEDHOF
Weinsteige
DEGERLOCH
PRAG FRIEDHOF
SCHLOSSGARTEN

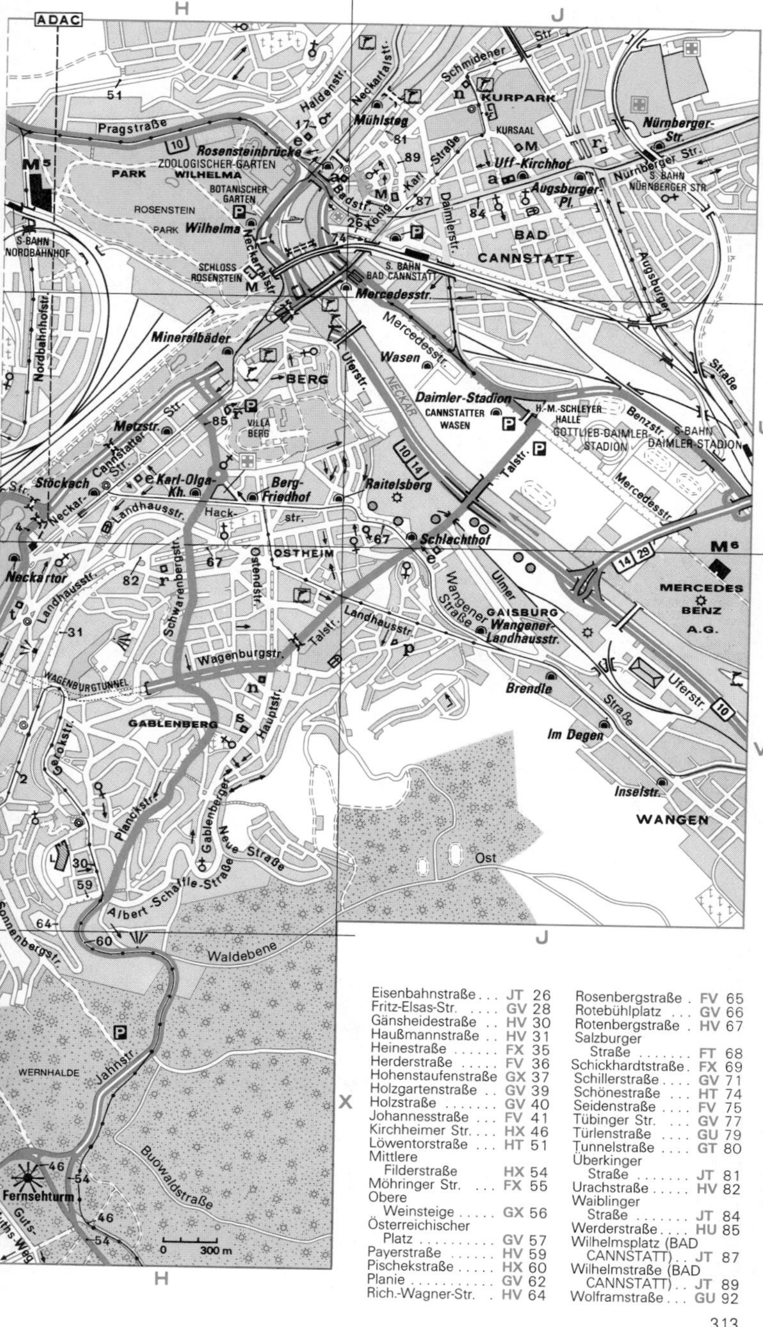

ADAC
H
J
T
U
V
X
Pragstraße
PARK WILHELMA
ZOOLOGISCHER GARTEN
BOTANISCHER GARTEN
ROSENSTEIN PARK
Wilhelma
Rosensteinbrücke
SCHLOSS ROSENSTEIN
S-BAHN NORDBAHNHOF
Nordbahnhofstr.
Haldenstr.
Neckartalstr.
Mühlsteg
Schmidener Str.
KURPARK
KURSAAL
Uff-Kirchhof
Augsburger-Pl.
Nürnberger-Str.
Nürnberger Str.
S. BAHN NÜRNBERGER STR.
Badstr.
König-Karl-Straße
Daimlerstr.
BAD CANNSTATT
S. BAHN BAD CANNSTATT
Mercedesstr.
Augsburger Straße
Mineralbäder
BERG
VILLA BERG
Uferstr.
NECKAR
Wasen
Daimler-Stadion
CANNSTATTER WASEN
H.-M.-SCHLEYER-HALLE
GOTTLIEB-DAIMLER-STADION
Benzstr.
S-BAHN DAIMLER-STADION
Talstr.
Metzstr.
Cannstatter Str.
Stöckach
Neckar-Str.
Karl-Olga-Kh.
Berg-Friedhof
Raitelsberg
Landhausstr.
Hack-str.
OSTHEIM
Schlachthof
Ostendstr.
Neckartor
Schwarenbergstr.
Wangener Straße
Ulmer Straße
GAISBURG
Wangener-Landhausstr.
MERCEDES BENZ A.G.
Wagenburgstr.
WAGENBURGTUNNEL
GABLENBERG
Hauptstr.
Gerokstr.
Brendle
Im Degen
Inselstr.
WANGEN
Plankstr.
Gablenberger
Neue Straße
Albert-Schäffle-Straße
Ost
Sonnenbergstr.
Waldebene
WERNHALDE
Jahnstr.
Buowaldstraße
Fernsehturm
Guts-Muths-Weg
0 300 m

STUTTGART

Charlottenplatz . . . . LZ 20
Eberhardstraße . . . . KLZ 25
Königstraße . . . . KLYZ
Schulstraße . . . . KZ 75
Theodor- Heuss- Str. . . . . KYZ 80

Arnulf-Klett-Platz . . . . LY 6
Augustenstraße . . . . KZ 7
Blumenstraße . . . . LZ 10
Bolzstraße . . . . LY 15
Calwer Str. . . . . KYZ 18

Dorotheenstraße . . . . LZ 24
Friedrichsplatz . . . . KY 27
Hauptstätter Str. . . . . KZ 30
Hegelplatz . . . . KY 32
Heilbronner Str. . . . . LY 34
Holzstraße . . . . LZ 40
Karlsplatz . . . . LY 43
Karlstraße . . . . LZ 44
Katharinenplatz . . . . LZ 45
Kirchstraße . . . . LZ 46
Konrad- Adenauer- Str. . . . . LY 47
Kronenstraße . . . . KLY 48
Kronprinzstraße . . . . KYZ 49
Leonhardsplatz . . . . LZ 50

Marktplatz . . . . KLZ 52
Marktstraße . . . . LZ 53
Österreichischer Platz . . . . KZ 57
Pfarrstraße . . . . LZ 61
Rotebühlplatz . . . . KZ 66
Rotebühlstraße . . . . KZ 70
Schloßplatz . . . . LY 72
Silberburgstraße . . . . KZ 76
Sophienstraße . . . . KZ 78
Torstraße . . . . KZ 82
Ulrichstraße . . . . LY 83
Wilhelmsplatz . . . . LZ 86
Wilhelmstraße . . . . LZ 88
Willi- Bleicher- Str. . . . . . . KY 91

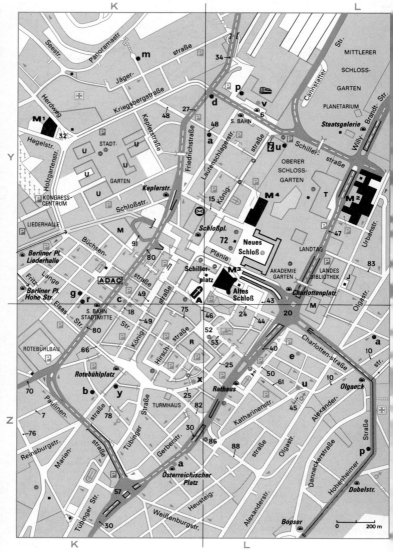

✗ **Bäcka-Metzger**, Aachener Str. 20 (Bad Cannstatt), ✉ 70376, ✆ 54 41 08, Fax 557655 *closed Sunday, Monday, Bank Holidays and August* – **Meals** (dinner only) à la carte 35/50. HT e

✗ **Weinhaus Stetter**, Rosenstr. 32, ✉ 70182, ✆ 24 01 63, 余 LZ e *closed Monday to Friday until 3 p.m., Saturday dinner, Sunday, Bank Holidays and 24 December - 8 January* – **Meals** (mainly cold dishes, outstanding wine list) 15/25 ♨.

at Stuttgart-Botnang by Botnanger Str. FV :

Hirsch, Eltinger Str. 2, ✉ 70195, ✆ 69 29 17, Fax 6990788, beer garden – |‡| TV ☎ ⇔ P – 🏃 140. AE ◑ E VISA
Meals *(closed Sunday dinner and Monday)* à la carte 36/70 – **44 rm** ☐ 96/150.

XX **La Fenice**, Beethovenstr. 9, ✉ 70195, ✆ 6 99 07 03, Fax 6990703, 余 – AE E. ✻ rest *closed Monday* – **Meals** (booking essential for dinner) à la carte 66/88.

at Stuttgart-Büsnau by Rotenwaldstraße FX :

Relexa Waldhotel Schatten, Magstadter Straße (Solitudering), ✉ 70569, ✆ 6 86 70, Fax 6867999, 余, ≘s – |‡| ⇔ rm TV ☎ ♿ ⇔ P – 🏃 80. AE ◑ E VISA. ✻ rest
Meals à la carte 43/90 – **136 rm** ☐ 255/390 – 7 suites.

at Stuttgart-Bad Cannstatt :

Pannonia Hotel Stuttgart, Teinacher Str. 20, ✉ 70372, ✆ 9 54 00, Fax 9540630, 余, ≘s – |‡| ⇔ rm ▤ rest TV ☎ P – 🏃 110. AE ◑ E VISA. ✻ rest JT n
Meals à la carte 46/72 – **156 rm** ☐ 165/255 – 6 suites.

Krehl's Linde, Obere Waiblinger Str. 113, ✉ 70374, ✆ 52 75 67, Fax 5286370, 余 – TV ☎ ⇔ JT r
Meals *(closed Sunday - Monday)* à la carte 43/88 – **18 rm** 100/220.

at Stuttgart-Degerloch :

Waldhotel Degerloch ⛰, Guts-Muths-Weg 18, ✉ 70597, ✆ 76 50 17, Fax 7653762, 余, ≘s, ✗ – |‡| TV ☎ ♿ P – 🏃 100. AE ◑ E VISA by Guts-Muths-Weg HX
Meals à la carte 42/73 – **50 rm** ☐ 155/290.

XXXX ✿ **Wielandshöhe**, Alte Weinsteige 71, ✉ 70597, ✆ 6 40 88 48, Fax 6409408, ≤ Stuttgart, 余 – AE ◑ E VISA GX a
closed Sunday, Monday and Bank Holidays – **Meals** (booking essential) 98/168 and à la carte 88/130
Spec. Gänseleber en cocotte, Gratinierter Hummer mit Basilikum-Kartoffelsalat, Kaninchenrücken mit schwarzen Oliven.

XXX **Skyline-Restaurant** (in TV-tower at 144 m, |‡|), Jahnstr. 120, ✉ 70597, ✆ 24 61 04, Fax 2360633, ✳ Stuttgart and surroundings – AE ◑ E VISA
closed Monday – **Meals** (booking essential for dinner) à la carte 68/95.

XX **Das Fässle**, Löwenstr. 51, ✉ 70597, ✆ 76 01 00, Fax 764432, 余 – AE ◑ E VISA
closed Sunday – **Meals** à la carte 48/79. by Jahnstraße GX

at Stuttgart-Fasanenhof by Obere Weinsteige (B 27) GX :

Mercure, Eichwiesenring 1, ✉ 70567, ✆ 7 26 60, Fax 7266444, 余, ≘s – |‡| ⇔ rm ▤ TV ☎ ♿ ⇔ P – 🏃 120. AE ◑ E VISA
Meals à la carte 42/75 – **148 rm** ☐ 207/294.

Fora Hotel, Vor dem Lauch 20 (Businesspark), ✉ 70567, ✆ 7 25 50, Fax 7255666, 余, ≘s – |‡| ⇔ rm ▤ rest TV ☎ ⇔ – 🏃 80. AE ◑ E VISA. ✻ rest
Meals à la carte 36/60 – **101 rm** ☐ 190/220.

at Stuttgart-Feuerbach :

Messehotel Europe without rest, Siemensstr. 33, ✉ 70469, ✆ 81 48 30, Fax 8148348 – |‡| ⇔ ▤ TV ☎ ⇔. AE ◑ E VISA GT r
114 rm ☐ 210/280.

Kongresshotel Europe, Siemensstr. 26, ✉ 70469, ✆ 81 00 40, Fax 854082, ≘s – |‡| ⇔ rm ▤ TV ☎ ⇔ – 🏃 130. AE ◑ E VISA GT z
Meals *(closed Saturday and Sunday lunch)* à la carte 53/90 – **150 rm** ☐ 150/280.

Weinsberg (Rest. Bistro style), Grazer Str. 32, ✉ 70469, ✆ 13 54 60, Fax 1354666 – |‡| ⇔ rm TV ☎ ⇔ – 🏃 30. AE ◑ E VISA. ✻ rest FT a
closed 1 - 25 August – **Meals** *(closed Saturday dinner and Sunday)* à la carte 30/75 – **37 rm** ☐ 165/260.

at Stuttgart-Flughafen (Airport) S : 15 km by Obere Weinsteige (B 27) GX :

Airport Mövenpick-Hotel, Randstr. 7, ✉ 70629, ✆ 7 90 70, Telex 7245677, Fax 793585, 余, ≘s – |‡| ⇔ rm ▤ rest TV ☎ ♿ P – 🏃 45. AE ◑ E VISA JCB
Meals à la carte 46/80 – **230 rm** ☐ 280/382.

XXX ✿ **top air**, Randstraße (in the airport) Terminal 1, ✉ 70621, ✆ 9 48 21 37, Fax 7979210 – ▤ – 🏃 170. AE ◑ E VISA
closed Saturday lunch – **Meals** 52 (lunch) and à la carte 72/104
Spec. Lauwarmer Salat von Hummer mit Liliengemüse und Curry, Steinbutt mit Sardellen in Estragon-Gemüsenage, Rücken vom Salzgras-Lamm mit Barolosauce, in 2 Gängen serviert (2 Pers.).

at Stuttgart-Hoheheim by Mittlere Filderstraße HX :

XXXX ✿ **Speisemeisterei**, Am Schloß Hohenheim, ✉ 70599, ✆ 4 56 00 37, Fax 4560038, –
closed Sunday dinner, Monday and 1 to 15 January – **Meals** (weekdays dinner only, booking essential) à la carte 70/107
Spec. Seeteufel mit Nudeln und Tomaten-Zucchinigemüse, Taubenbrust mit Gänseleber in Blätterteig, Rhabarberkompott mit Topfenknödel.

at Stuttgart-Möhringen SW : 7 km by Obere Weinsteige GX :

Copthorne Hotel (with Stuttgart International), Plienienger Str. 100, ✉ 70567, ✆ 72 10, Fax 7212009, , (direct entrance to the recreation centre Schwaben Quelle) – rm – 80. AE E VISA
Don Giovanni (Italian rest.) *(closed Monday, weekdays dinner only)* **Meals** à la carte 44/67 ***Time Square :*** **Meals** à la carte 44/70 – **454 rm** 248/528.

Gloria, Sigmaringer Str. 59, ✉ 70567, ✆ 7 18 50 (hotel) 7 18 51 17 (rest.), Fax 7185121, , – – 50. AE VISA
– ***Möhringer Hexle :*** **Meals** à la carte 28/66 – **84 rm** 129/194.

at Stuttgart-Obertürkheim by Augsburger Straße JU :

Brita Hotel, Augsburger Str. 671, ✉ 70329, ✆ 32 02 30, Fax 324440 – rm rest – 80. AE E VISA. rest
closed 24 December - 1 January – ***Post*** *(closed Sunday and Bank Holidays lunch, Saturday and 5 to 25 August* **Meals** à la carte 34/63 – **70 rm** 143/254.

at Stuttgart-Plieningen S : 14 km by Mittlere Filderstraße HX :

Fissler-Post, Schoellstr. 4, ✉ 70599, ✆ 4 58 40, Fax 4584333, – rm – 80. AE E VISA.
Meals (booking essential) à la carte 45/74 *(vegetarian menu available)* – **60 rm** 88/190.

Romantik Hotel Traube, Brabandtgasse 2, ✉ 70599, ✆ 45 89 20, Fax 4589220, – rm . AE E VISA
closed 23 December - 3 January – **Meals** *(closed Saturday and Sunday)* (booking essential) à la carte 44/95 – **20 rm** 140/280.

at Stuttgart-Stammheim by Heilbronner Straße GT :

Novotel-Nord, Korntaler Str. 207, ✉ 70439, ✆ 98 06 20, Fax 803673, , (heated) – rm – 150. AE E VISA
Meals à la carte 30/57 – **117 rm** 130/195.

at Stuttgart-Vaihingen by Böblinger Str. FX :

Fontana Stuttgart, Vollmöllerstr. 5, ✉ 70563, ✆ 73 00, Telex 7255763, Fax 7302525, Massage, , , , , – rm – 250. AE E VISA. rest
Meals à la carte 42/95 – **250 rm** 55/395 – 5 suites.

at Stuttgart-Weilimdorf by B 295 FT :

Holiday Inn Garden Court, Mittlerer Pfad 27, ✉ 70499, ✆ 98 88 80, Fax 988889, , – rm – 200. AE E VISA JCB
Meals 28/34 buffet and à la carte 38/66 – **202 rm** 167/364 – 7 suites.

at Stuttgart-Zuffenhausen by Heilbronner Straße GT :

Fora Hotel Residence, Schützenbühlstr. 16, ✉ 70435, ✆ 8 20 01 00, Fax 8200101, – rm rest – 40. AE E VISA
Meals à la carte 39/65 – **120 rm** 175/200.

at Fellbach NE : 8 km by Nürnberger Straße (B 14) JT – ✆ 0711 :

Classic Congress Hotel, Tainer Str. 7, ✉ 70734, ✆ 5 85 90, Telex 7254900, Fax 5859304, – rm – 60. AE E VISA JCB
closed 23 December - 6 January – **Meals** see **Alt Württemberg** below – **148 rm** 195/350.

XX **Alt Württemberg**, Tainer Str. 7 (Schwabenlandhalle), ✉ 70734, ✆ 58 00 88, Fax 581927 – . AE E VISA
Meals à la carte 43/83.

X **Aldinger's Weinstube Germania** with rm, Schmerstr. 6, ✉ 70734, ✆ 58 20 37, Fax 582077, – .
closed 2 weeks February - March and 3 weeks July - August – **Meals** *(closed Sunday, Monday and Bank Holidays)* à la carte 38/69 – **7 rm** 75/135.

at Fellbach-Schmiden NE : 8,5 km by Nürnberger Straße (B 14) JT :

Hirsch, Fellbacher Str. 2, ✉ 70736, ✆ (0711) 9 51 30, Fax 5181065, , – – 25. AE E VISA JCB
Meals *(closed Friday, Sunday and 2 weeks July - August)* à la carte 40/65 – **116 rm** 90/200.

at Gerlingen W : 10 km by Rotenwaldstraße FX – ✆ 07156 :

Krone, Hauptstr. 28, ✉ 70839, ✆ 4 31 10, Fax 4311100 – rm – 60. AE E VISA
Meals *(closed Sunday, Monday, Bank Holidays, Easter and Christmas)* (booking essential) à la carte 45/89 *(vegetarian menu available)* – **56 rm** 138/248.

at Korntal-Münchingen NW : 9 km, by Heilbronner Str. GT :

Mercure, Siemensstr. 50, ✉ 70825, ✆ (07150) 1 30, Fax 13266, beer garden, ≘s, ▣ - |‡| ⇝ rm ▤ ▣ ☎ ♿ Ⓟ - 🏂 160. AE ⓓ E VISA
Meals à la carte 49/78 - **208 rm** ⊐ 182/214.

at Leinfelden-Echterdingen S : 11 km by Obere Weinsteige (B 27) GX :

Filderland without rest, Tübinger Str. 16 (Echterdingen), ✉ 70771, ✆ (0711) 9 49 46, Fax 9494888 - |‡| ▣ ☎ ⇔ - 🏂 20. AE ⓓ E VISA. ✗
closed 24 December - 2 January - **48 rm** ⊐ 135/190.

Baiersbronn Baden-Württemberg 413 HI 21, 987 ㊳ - pop. 16 000 - alt. 550 m - ☎ 07442.
Stuttgart 100.

XXXX ✿✿✿ **Schwarzwaldstube** (French rest.), Tonbachstr. 237 (at Kur- and Sporthotel Traube Tonbach), ✉ 72270, ✆ 49 26 65, Fax 492692, ← - ▤ Ⓟ. AE ⓓ E VISA. ✗
closed Monday, Tuesday, 8 to 30 January and 29 July - 20 August - **Meals** (booking essential) 158/202 and à la carte 105/144
Spec. Salat von bretonischem Hummer, Langustinen und Seppioline, Sankt-Petersfisch im Lauchmantel, Gemüsecharlotte mit Kompott von Kalbsschwanz.

XXXX ✿✿ **Restaurant Bareiss**, Gärtenbühlweg 14 (at Hotel Bareiss), ✉ 72270, ✆ 4 70, Fax 47320, ← - ▤ Ⓟ. AE ⓓ E VISA
closed Monday, Tuesday, 28 May - 21 June and 25 November - 24 December - **Meals** (booking essential, outstanding wine list) 140/180 and à la carte 92/118 - ***Kaminstube* : Meals** à la carte 59/77
Spec. Suprême vom Bressetäubchen mit Risotto und Sommertrüffel, Ganzer Saint-Pierre in der Folie mit Ingwersauce, Variation von schwarzer Valrhona-Schokolade.

Öhringen Baden-Württemberg 413 L 19, 987 ㉗ - pop. 20 000 - alt. 230 m - ☎ 07941.
Stuttgart 68.

at Friedrichsruhe N : 6 km :

✿✿ **Wald- und Schloßhotel Friedrichsruhe** ⛰, ✉ 74639 Zweiflingen, ✆ (07941) 6 08 70, Telex 74498, Fax 61468, 🍽, « Garden, park », ≘s, ⛱, ▣, ✗, 18 - |‡| ▣ ☎ ⇔ Ⓟ - 🏂 60. AE ⓓ E VISA
Meals *(closed Monday - Tuesday)* (outstanding wine list) 130/195 and à la carte 96/131 - ***Jägerstube* : Meals** à la carte 53/77 - **48 rm** ⊐ 165/395 - 12 suites
Spec. Rouget mit Basilikum gefüllt auf gegrilltem Fenchel, Sautierter bretonischer Hummer mit geschmortem Zwiebellauch, Navarin vom Lamm und Lammkotelette im Kartoffelrösti.

Greece

Hellás

ATHENS

PRACTICAL INFORMATION

LOCAL CURRENCY

Greek Drachma: 100 GRD = 0.42 USD ($) (Jan. 96)

TOURIST INFORMATION

National Tourist Organisation (EOT): 2 Kar. Servias, ☎ 322 25 45 (information). Hotel reservation: Hellenic Chamber of Hotels, 24 Stadiou, ☎ 323 71 93, Telex: 214 269. Fax 322 54 49, also at East Airport ☎ 961 27 22 - Tourist Police: 4 Stadiou ☎ 171.

FOREIGN EXCHANGE

Banks are usually open on weekdays from 8am to 2pm. A branch of the National Bank of Greece is open daily from 8am to 2pm (from 9am to 1pm at weekends) at 2 Karageorgi Servias (Sindagma). East Airport offices operate a 24-hour service.

AIRLINES

OLYMPIC AIRWAYS: 96 Singrou 117 41 Athens, ☎ 926 73 33/926 91 11-3, 2 Kotopouli (Omonia), ☎ 926 72 16-9, reservations only ☎ 966 66 66.
All following Companies are located near Sindagma Square:
AIR FRANCE: 18 Vouliagmenis Avenue 166 75 Athens, ☎ 960 11 00.
BRITISH AIRWAYS: 10 Othonos 105 57 Athens, ☎ 325 06 01.
JAPAN AIRLINES: 22 Voulis 105 57 Athens, ☎ 325 20 75.
LUFTHANSA: 11 Vas. Sofias 106 71 Athens, ☎ 771 60 02.
SABENA: 41 c, Vouliagmenis Avenue, ☎ 960 00 21-4.
SWISSAIR: 4 Othonos 105 57 Athens, ☎ 323 75 81.
TWA: 8 Xenofondos 105 57 Athens, ☎ 322 64 51.

TRANSPORT IN ATHENS

Taxis: may be hailed in the street even when already engaged: it is advised to always pay by the meter.
Bus: good for sightseeing and practical for short distances: 75 GRD.
Metro: one single line crossing the city from North (Kifissia) to South (Pireas) : 100 GRD.

POSTAL SERVICES

General Post Office: 100 Eolou (Omonia) with poste restante, and also at Sindagma.
Telephone (OTE): 15 Stadiou and 85 Patission (all services).

SHOPPING IN ATHENS

In summer, shops are usually open from 8am to 1.30pm, and 5.30 to 8.30pm. They close on Sunday, and at 2.30pm on Monday, Wednesday and Saturday. In winter they open from 9am to 5pm on Monday and Wednesday, from 10am to 7pm on Tuesday, Thursday and Friday, from 8.30am to 3.30pm on Saturday. Department Stores in Patission and Eolou are open fron 8.30 am to 8 pm on weekdays and 3 pm on Saturdays. The main shopping streets are to be found in Sindagma, Kolonaki, Monastiraki and Omonia areas. Flea Market (generally open on Sunday) and Greek Handicraft in Plaka and Monastiraki.

TIPPING

Service is generally included in the bills but it is usual to tip employees.

SPEED LIMITS

The speed limit in built up areas is 50 km/h (31 mph); on motorways the maximum permitted speed is 100 km/h (62 mph) and 80 km/h (50 mph) on others roads.

SEAT BELTS

The wearing of seat belts is compulsory for drivers and front seat passengers.

BREAKDOWN SERVICE

The ELPA (Automobile and Touring Club of Greece) operate a 24 hour breakdown service: phone 174.

Athens

(ATHÍNA) Atikí 980 ㉚ - Pop. 3 076 786 (Athens and Piraeus area) - ✆ 01.

SIGHTS :

Views of Athens : Lycabettos (Likavitós) ☀★★★ DX - Philopappos Hill (Lófos Filopápou) ≤★★★ AY.

ANCIENT ATHENS

Acropolis★★★ (Akrópoli) ABY - Theseion★★ (Thissío) AY and Agora★ (Arhéa Agorá) AY - Theatre of Dionysos★★ (Théatro Dionissou) BY and Odeon of Herod Atticus★ (Odío Iródou Atikoú) AY - Olympieion★★ (Naós Olimbíou Diós) BY and Hadrian's Arch★ (Píli Adrianoú) BY - Tower of the Winds★ BY **G** in the Roman Forum (Romaïkí Agorá).

OLD ATHENS AND THE TURKISH PERIOD

Pláka★★ : Old Metropolitan★★ BY **A2** - Monastiráki★ (Old Bazaar) : Kapnikaréa (Church) BY **A6**, Odós Pandróssou★ BY **29**, Monastiráki Square★ BY.

MODERN ATHENS

Sindagma Square★ CY : Greek guard on sentry duty - Academy, University and Library Buildings★ (Akadimía CX, Panepistímio CX, Ethnikí Vivliothíki BX) - National Garden★ (Ethnikós Kípos) CY.

MUSEUMS

National Archaelogical Museum★★★ (Ethnikó Arheologikó Moussío) BX - Acropolis Museum★★★ BY **M1** - Museum of Cycladic and Ancient Greek Art★★ DY **M15** - Byzantine Museum★★ (Vizandinó Moussío) DY - Benaki Museum★★ (Moussío Benáki, private collection of antiquities and traditional art) CDY - Museum of Traditional Greek Art★ BY **M2** - National Historical Museum★ BY **M7** - Jewish Museum of Greece★ BY **M16** - National Gallery and Soutzos Museum★ (painting and sculpture) DY **M8**.

EXCURSIONS

Cape Sounion★★★ (Soúnio) SE : 71 km BY - Kessariani Monastery★★, E : 9 km DY - Daphne Monastery★★ (Dafní) NW : 10 km AX - Aigina Island★ (Égina) : Temple of Aphaia★★, 3 hours Return.

18 Glifáda (near airport) ✆ 894 68 20, Fax 894 37 21.

✈ S : 15 km, East Airport ✆ 969 41 11 (International Airport - All companies except Olympic Airways), West Airport ✆ 966 66 66 (Elinikó Airport - Olympic Airways only).

🚘 1 Karolou ✆ 524 06 01.

ℹ Tourist Information (EOT), 2 Amerikis ✆ 322 31 11, Information center (at National Bank), Stadiou ✆ 322 25 45 and East Airport ✆ 961 27 22.
ELPA (Automobile and Touring Club of Greece), 2 Messogion ✆ 779 16 15.

Igoumenítsa 581 - Pátra 215 - Thessaloníki 479.

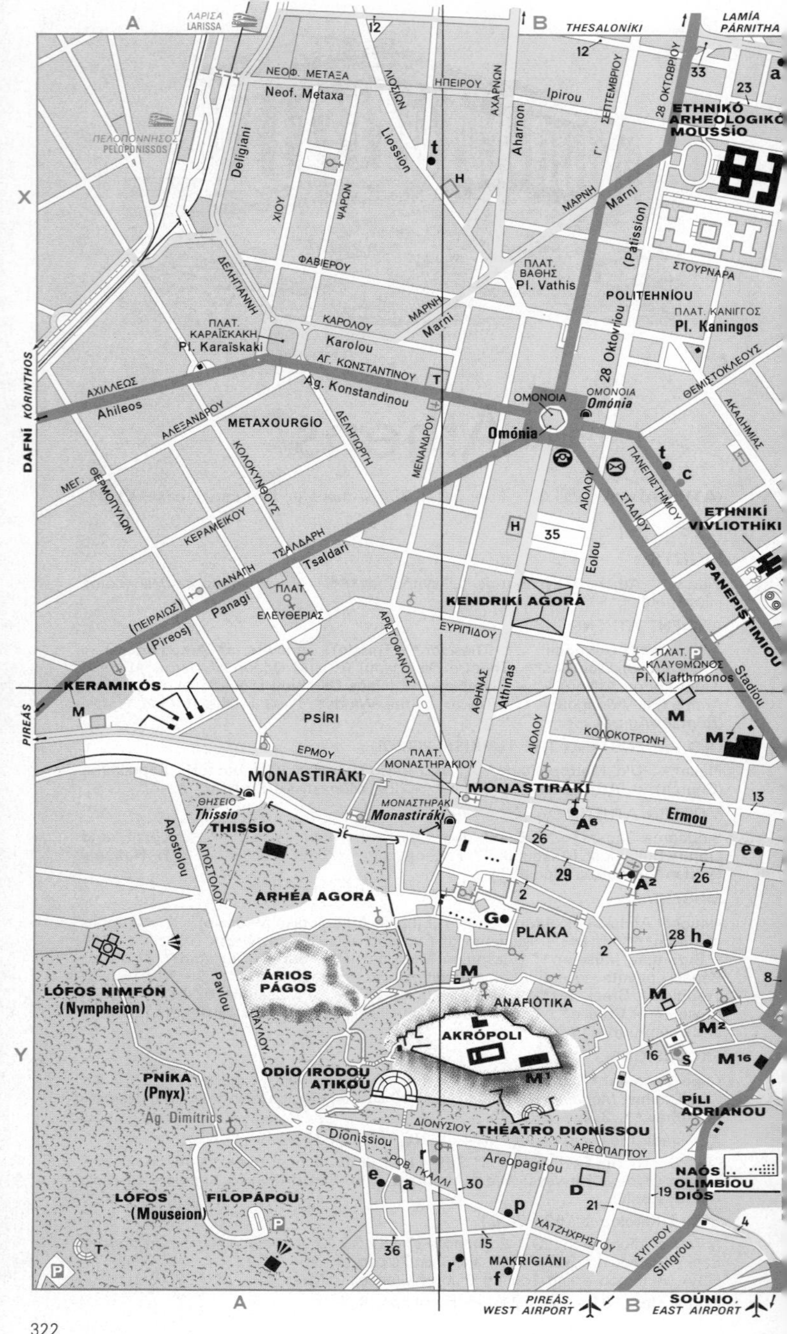
ΛΑΡΙΣΑ
LARISSA
THESALONÍKI
LAMÍA
PÁRNITHA
ΠΕΛΟΠΟΝΝΗΣΟΣ
PELOPONISSOS
ΝΕΟΦ. ΜΕΤΑΞΑ
Neof. Metaxa
ΗΠΕΙΡΟΥ
Ipirou
ΑΧΑΡΝΩΝ
Aharnon
ΛΙΟΣΙΩΝ
Liossion
28 ΟΚΤΩΒΡΙΟΥ
ETHNIKÓ ARHEOLOGIKÓ MOUSSÍO
Deligiani
ΧΙΟΥ
ΨΑΡΩΝ
ΜΑΡΝΗ
Marni
(Patission)
ΦΑΒΙΕΡΟΥ
ΔΕΛΗΓΙΑΝΝΗ
ΠΛΑΤ. ΒΑΘΗΣ
Pl. Vathis
ΣΤΟΥΡΝΑΡΑ
POLITEHNÍOU
ΠΛΑΤ. ΚΑΝΙΓΓΟΣ
Pl. Kaningos
ΠΛΑΤ. ΚΑΡΑΪΣΚΑΚΗ
Pl. Karaïskaki
ΚΑΡΟΛΟΥ
Karolou
ΑΓ. ΚΩΝΣΤΑΝΤΙΝΟΥ
Ag. Konstandinou
28 Oktovriou
ΘΕΜΙΣΤΟΚΛΕΟΥΣ
DAFNÍ KÓRINTHOS
ΑΧΙΛΛΕΩΣ
Ahileos
ΑΛΕΞΑΝΔΡΟΥ
METAXOURGÍO
ΟΜΟΝΟΙΑ
Omónia
ΑΚΑΔΗΜΙΑΣ
ΜΕΝΑΝΔΡΟΥ
ΔΕΛΗΓΙΩΡΓΗ
ΚΟΛΟΚΥΝΘΟΥΣ
ΜΕΓ.
ΘΕΡΜΟΠΥΛΩΝ
ΚΕΡΑΜΕΙΚΟΥ
ΑΙΟΛΟΥ
ΠΑΝΕΠΙΣΤΗΜΙΟΥ
ΣΤΑΔΙΟΥ
ETHNIKÍ VIVLIOTHÍKI
ΤΣΑΛΔΑΡΗ
Tsaldari
35
Eolou
PANEPISTIMIOU
ΠΑΝΑΓΗ
Panagi
ΠΛΑΤ. ΕΛΕΥΘΕΡΙΑΣ
KENDRIKÍ AGORÁ
(ΠΕΙΡΑΙΩΣ)
(Pireos)
ΑΡΙΣΤΟΦΑΝΟΥΣ
ΕΥΡΙΠΙΔΟΥ
ΑΘΗΝΑΣ
Athinas
ΠΛΑΤ. ΚΛΑΥΘΜΩΝΟΣ
Pl. Klafthmonos
Stadiou
KERAMIKÓS
PSÍRI
PIREÁS
ΚΟΛΟΚΟΤΡΩΝΗ
ΕΡΜΟΥ
ΠΛΑΤ. ΜΟΝΑΣΤΗΡΑΚΙΟΥ
MONASTIRÁKI
ΘΗΣΕΙΟ
Thissío
THISSÍO
ΜΟΝΑΣΤΗΡΑΚΙ
Monastiráki
Ermou
Apostolou
ΑΠΟΣΤΟΛΟΥ
ARHÉA AGORÁ
PLÁKA
LÓFOS NIMFÓN
(Nympheion)
Pavlou
ÁRIOS PÁGOS
ΠΑΥΛΟΥ
ANAFIÓTIKA
AKRÓPOLI
PNÍKA
(Pnyx)
ODÍO IRODOU ATIKOÚ
Ag. Dimítrios
ΔΙΟΝΥΣΙΟΥ
THÉATRO DIONÍSSOU
PÍLI ADRIANOU
Dionissiou
ΑΡΕΟΠΑΓΙΤΟΥ
Areopagitou
ΡΟΒ. ΓΚΑΛΛΙ
NAÓS OLIMBÍOU DIÓS
LÓFOS FILOPÁPOU
(Mouseion)
ΧΑΤΖΗΧΡΗΣΤΟΥ
ΣΥΓΓΡΟΥ
Singrou
MAKRIGIÁNI
PIREÁS, WEST AIRPORT
SOÚNIO, EAST AIRPORT

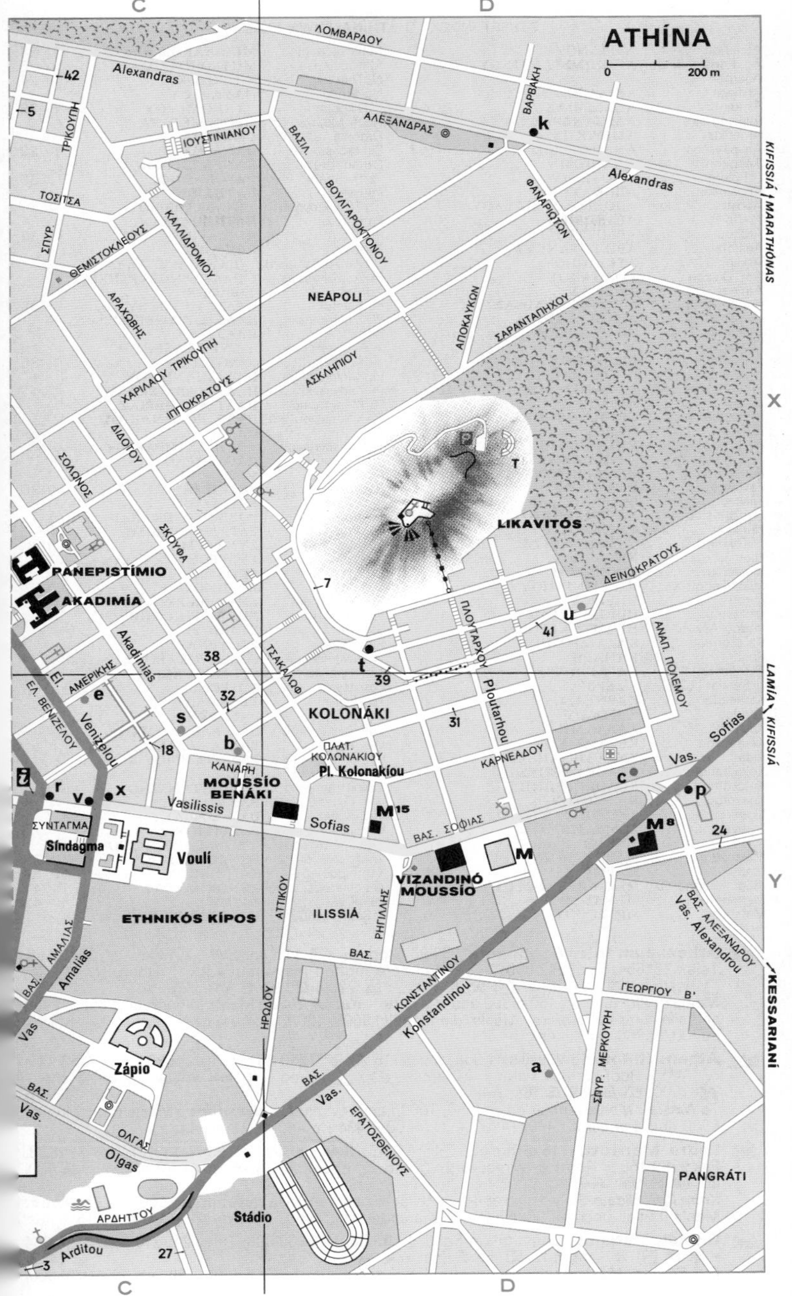

ATHÍNA
0
200 m
C
D
X
Y
Alexandras
ΛΟΜΒΑΡΔΟΥ
ΑΛΕΞΑΝΔΡΑΣ
ΒΑΡΒΑΚΗ
ΙΟΥΣΤΙΝΙΑΝΟΥ
ΤΡΙΚΟΥΠΗ
ΤΟΣΙΤΣΑ
ΣΠΥΡ.
ΘΕΜΙΣΤΟΚΛΕΟΥΣ
ΚΑΛΛΙΔΡΟΜΙΟΥ
ΒΑΣΙΛ
ΒΟΥΛΓΑΡΟΚΤΟΝΟΥ
ΦΑΝΑΡΙΩΤΩΝ
KIFISSIÁ
MARATHÓNAS
ΑΡΑΧΩΒΗΣ
NEÁPOLI
ΑΠΟΚΑΥΚΩΝ
ΣΑΡΑΝΤΑΠΗΧΟΥ
ΧΑΡΙΛΑΟΥ ΤΡΙΚΟΥΠΗ
ΙΠΠΟΚΡΑΤΟΥΣ
ΑΣΚΛΗΠΙΟΥ
ΔΙΔΟΤΟΥ
ΣΟΛΩΝΟΣ
ΣΚΟΥΦΑ
LIKAVITÓS
PANEPISTÍMIO
AKADIMÍA
ΔΕΙΝΟΚΡΑΤΟΥΣ
ΑΝΑΠ. ΠΟΛΕΜΟΥ
ΠΛΟΥΤΑΡΧΟΥ
Ploutarhou
ΤΣΑΚΑΛΩΦ
Akadimias
ΑΜΕΡΙΚΗΣ
ΕΛ. ΒΕΝΙΖΕΛΟΥ
Venizélou
KOLONÁKI
LAMÍA
KIFISSIÁ
ΠΛΑΤ. ΚΟΛΩΝΑΚΙΟΥ
Pl. Kolonakíou
ΚΑΝΑΡΗ
MOUSSÍO BENÁKI
ΚΑΡΝΕΑΔΟΥ
Vas. Sofias
Vasilissis Sofias
ΒΑΣ. ΣΟΦΙΑΣ
ΣΥΝΤΑΓΜΑ
Síndagma
Voulí
VIZANDINÓ MOUSSÍO
ΒΑΣ. ΑΛΕΞΑΝΔΡΟΥ
Vas. Alexandrou
ETHNIKÓS KÍPOS
ΑΤΤΙΚΟΥ
ILISSIÁ
ΡΗΓΙΛΛΗΣ
ΒΑΣ. ΚΩΝΣΤΑΝΤΙΝΟΥ
Konstandinou
ΓΕΩΡΓΙΟΥ Β'
KESSARIANÍ
ΒΑΣ. ΑΜΑΛΙΑΣ
Amalias
ΗΡΩΔΟΥ
Vas.
Zápio
ΣΠΥΡ. ΜΕΡΚΟΥΡΗ
ΕΡΑΤΟΣΘΕΝΟΥΣ
ΒΑΣ. ΟΛΓΑΣ
Vas. Olgas
PANGRÁTI
ΑΡΔΗΤΤΟΥ
Arditou
Stádio

STREET INDEX TO ATHÍNA TOWN PLAN

Street		Grid	No.
Adrianou	ΑΔΡΙΑΝΟΥ	BY	2
Ag. Konstandinou	ΑΓ. ΚΩΝΣΤΑΝΤΙΝΟΥ	AX	
Aharnon	ΑΧΑΡΝΩΝ	BX	
Ahilleos	ΑΧΙΛΛΕΩΣ	AX	
Akadimias	ΑΚΑΔΙΜΙΑΣ	BCX	
Alexandras	ΑΛΕΞΑΝΔΡΑΣ	CDX	
Amerikis	ΑΜΕΡΙΚΗΣ	CXY	
Anapavseos	ΑΝΑΠΑΥΣΕΩΣ	CY	3
Anapiron Polemou	ΑΝΑΠΗΡΩΝ ΠΟΛΕΜΟΥ	DXY	
Apokafkon	ΑΠΟΚΑΥΚΩΝ	DX	
Apostolou Pavlou	ΑΠΟΣΤΟΛΟΥ ΠΑΥΛΟΥ	AY	
Arahovis	ΑΡΑΧΩΒΗΣ	CX	
Arditou	ΑΡΔΗΤΤΟΥ	CY	
Aristofanous	ΑΡΙΣΤΟΦΑΝΟΥΣ	AX	
Asklipiou	ΑΣΚΛΗΠΙΟΥ	DX	
Ath. Diakou	ΑΘ. ΔΙΑΚΟΥ	BY	4
Athinas	ΑΘΗΝΑΣ	BXY	
Bouboulinas	ΜΠΟΥΜΠΟΥΛΙΝΑΣ	CX	5
Deligiani	ΔΕΛΗΓΙΑΝΝΗ	AX	
Deligiorgi	ΔΕΛΗΓΙΩΡΓΗ	AX	
Didotou	ΔΙΔΟΤΟΥ	CX	
Dionissiou Areopagitou	ΔΙΟΝΥΣΙΟΥ ΑΡΕΟΠΑΓΙΤΟΥ	ABY	
El. Venizelou	ΕΛ ΒΕΝΙΖΕΛΟΥ	CXY	
Eolou	ΑΙΟΛΟΥ	BXY	
Eratosthenous	ΕΡΑΤΟΣΘΕΝΟΥΣ	DY	
Ermou	ΕΡΜΟΥ	ABY	
Evelpidos Rongakou	ΕΥΕΛΠΙΔΟΣ ΡΟΓΚΑΚΟΥ	DX	7
Fanarioton	ΘΑΝΑΡΙΩΤΩΝ	DX	
Favierou	ΘΑΒΙΕΡΟΥ	AX	
Filelinon	ΘΙΛΕΛΛΗΝΩΝ	BY	8
Hadzihristou	ΧΑΤΖΗΧΡΗΣΤΟΥ	BY	
Harilaou Trikoupi	ΧΑΡΙΛΑΟΥ ΤΡΙΚΟΥΠΗ	CX	
Hiou	ΧΙΟΥ	AX	
Ioulianou	ΙΟΥΛΙΑΝΟΥ	AX	12
Ioustinianou	ΙΟΥΣΤΙΝΙΑΝΟΥ	CX	
Ipirou	ΗΠΕΙΡΟΥ	ABX	
Ipokratous	ΙΠΠΟΚΡΑΤΟΥΣ	CX	
Irodou Atikou	ΗΡΩΔΟΥ ΑΤΤΙΚΟΥ	DY	
Kalidromiou	ΚΑΛΛΙΔΡΟΜΙΟΥ	CX	
Kanari	ΚΑΝΑΡΗ	CY	
Karageorgi Servias	ΚΑΡΑΓΙΩΡΓΗ ΣΕΡΒΙΑΣ	BY	13
Karneadou	ΚΑΡΝΕΑΔΟΥ	DY	
Karolou	ΚΑΡΟΛΟΥ	AX	
Kavaloti	ΚΑΒΑΛΛΟΤΙ	BY	15
Keramikou	ΚΕΡΑΜΕΙΚΟΥ	AX	
Kidathineon	ΚΥΔΑΘΗΝΑΙΩΝ	BY	16
Kolokinthous	ΚΟΛΟΚΥΝΘΟΥΣ	AX	
Kolokotroni	ΚΟΛΟΚΟΤΡΩΝΗ	BY	
Kriezotou	ΚΡΙΕΖΩΤΟΥ	CY	18
Liossion	ΛΙΟΣΙΩΝ	AX	
Lomvardou	ΛΟΜΒΑΡΔΟΥ	DX	
Makri	ΜΑΚΡΗ	BY	19
Makrigiani	ΜΑΚΡΥΓΙΑΝΝΗ	BY	21
Marni	ΜΑΡΝΗ	ABX	
Meg. Alexandrou	ΜΕΓ. ΑΛΕΞΑΝΔΡΟΥ	AX	
Menandrou	ΜΕΝΑΝΔΡΟΥ	AX	
Metsovou	ΜΕΤΣΟΒΟΥ	BX	23
Mihalakopoulou	ΜΙΧΑΛΑΚΟΠΟΥΛΟΥ	DY	24
Mitropoleos	ΜΗΤΡΟΠΟΛΕΩΣ	BY	26
N. Theotoki	Ν. ΘΕΟΤΟΚΗ	CY	27
Navarhou Nikodimou	ΝΑΥΑΡΧΟΥ ΝΙΚΟΔΗΜΟΥ	BY	28
Neof. Metaxa	ΝΕΟΦ. ΜΕΤΑΞΑ	AX	
Omonia	ΟΜΟΝΟΙΑ	BX	
Pandrossou	ΠΑΝΔΡΟΣΟΥ	BY	29
Panepistimiou	ΠΑΝΕΜΙΣΤΗΜΙΟΥ	BX	
Parthenonos	ΠΑΡΘΕΝΩΝΟΣ	BY	30
Patission (28 Oktovriou)	ΠΑΤΗΣΙΩΝ (28 ΟΚΤΩΒΡΙΟΥ)	BX	
Patr. Ioakim	ΠΑΤΡ. ΙΩΑΚΕΙΜ	DY	31
Pindarou	ΠΙΝΔΑΡΟΥ	CY	32
Pireos (Panagi Tsaldari)	ΠΕΙΡΑΙΩΣ (ΠΑΝΑΓΗ ΤΣΑΛΔΑΡΗ)	AX	
Pl. Anexartissias (Vathis)	ΠΛΑΤ. ΑΝΕΞΑΡΤΗΣΙΑΣ (ΒΑΘΗΣ)	BX	
Pl. Egiptou	ΠΛΑΤ. ΑΙΓΥΠΤΟΥ	BX	33
Pl. Eleftherias	ΠΛΑΤ. ΕΛΕΥΘΕΡΙΑΣ	AX	
Pl. Eth. Andistasseos (Kodzia)	ΠΛΑΤ. ΕΘΝ. ΑΝΤΙΣΤΑΣΕΩΣ (ΚΟΤΖΙΑ)	BX	35
Pl. Kaningos	ΠΛΑΤ. ΚΑΝΙΓΓΟΣ	BX	
Pl. Karaïskaki	ΠΛΑΤ. ΚΑΡΑΙΣΚΑΚΗ	AX	
Pl. Klafthmonos	ΠΛΑΤ. ΛΑΥΘΕΡΙΑΖ	BX	
Pl. Kolonakiou	ΠΛΑΤ. ΚΟΛΩΝΑΚΙΟΥ	DY	
Pl. Monastirakiou	ΠΛΑΤ. ΜΟΝΑΣΤΗΡΑΚΙΟΥ	ABY	
Ploutarhou	ΠΛΟΥΤΑΡΧΟΥ	DX	
Psaron	ΨΑΡΩΝ	AX	
Radzieri	ΡΑΤΖΙΕΡΗ	AY	36
Rigilis	ΡΗΓΙΛΛΗΣ	DY	
Rovertou Gali	ΡΟΒΕΡΤΟΥ ΓΚΑΛΛΙ	AY	
Sarandapihou	ΣΑΡΑΝΤΑΠΗΧΟΥ	DX	
Sindagma	ΣΥΝΤΑΓΜΑ	CY	
Singrou	ΣΥΓΓΡΟΥ	BY	
Skoufa	ΣΚΟΥΦΑ	CX	
Solonos	ΣΟΛΩΝΟΣ	CX	
Spir. Merkouri	ΣΗΥΡ. ΜΕΡΚΟΥΡΗ	DY	
Spir. Trikoupi	ΣΗΥΡ. ΤΡΙΚΟΥΠΗ	CX	
Stadiou	ΣΤΑΔΙΟΥ	BXY	
Stournara	ΣΤΟΥΡΝΑΡΑ	BX	
Themistokleous	ΘΕΜΙΣΤΟΚΛΕΟΥΣ	BCX	
Thermopilon	ΘΕΡΜΟΠΥΛΩΝ	AX	
Tossitsa	ΤΟΣΙΤΖΑ	CX	
Tsakalof	ΤΣΑΚΑΛΩΦ	DXY	
Varvaki	ΒΑΡΒΑΚΗ	DX	
Vas. Alexandrou	ΒΑΣ. ΑΛΕΞΑΝΔΡΟΥ	DY	
Vas. Amalias	ΒΑΣ. ΑΜΑΛΙΑΣ	CY	
Vas. Georgiou B'	ΒΑΣ. ΓΕΩΡΓΙΟΥ Β	DY	
Vas. Konstandinou	ΒΑΣ. ΚΩΝΣΤΑΝΤΙΝΟΥ	DY	
Vas. Olgas	ΒΑΣ. ΟΛΓΑΣ	CY	
Vas. Sofias	ΒΑΣ. ΣΟΦΙΑΣ	CDY	
Vassiliou Voulgaroktonou	ΒΑΣΙΛΕΙΟΥ ΒΟΥΛΓΑΡΟΚΤΟΝΟΥ	DX	
Voukourestiou	ΒΟΥΚΟΥΡΕΣΤΙΟΥ	CX	38
Xanthipou	ΞΑΝΘΙΠΠΟΥ	DXY	39
Xenokratous	ΞΕΝΟΚΠΑΤΟΥΣ	DX	41
Zaïmi	ΖΑΙΜΗ	CX	42
3 Septemvriou	Γ'ΣΕΠΤΕΜΒΡΙΟΥ	BX	

Athenaeum Inter-Continental, 89-93 Singrou, ✉ 117 45, SW : 2 ¾ km ✆ 9023 666, Telex 221554, Fax 9243 000, « Première rooftop restaurant with ≤ Athens », heated – rm – 2200. AE ① E VISA JCB.
Meals (buffet lunch) 5450/9300 and a la carte – ***Kublai Khan :*** **Meals** (dinner only) 6950/7750 and a la carte – ***Première :*** **Meals** (dinner only) 9000/13000 and a la carte – 4800 – **515 rm** 58700/86700, 44 suites.

Athens Hilton, 46 Vassilissis Sofias, ✉ 115 28, ✆ 7250 201, Telex 215808, Fax 7253 110, ≤, « Roof terrace with ≤ Athens », heated – rm – 1000. AE ① E VISA JCB DY **p**
Ta Nissia : **Meals** (dinner only) 8750/10000 and a la carte – ***Byzantine :*** **Meals** (buffet lunch) 5900 and a la carte 5400/14200 – 4500 – **434 rm** 46000, 19 suites.

Ledra Marriott, 115 Singrou, ✉ 117 45, SW : 3 km ✆ 9347 711, Telex 221833, Fax 9359 153, « Rooftop terrace with and ✻ Athens » – rm – 400. AE ① E VISA JCB.
Kona Kai : **Meals** - Polynesian and Japanese - (dinner only) a la carte approx. 20000 – ***Zephyros :*** **Meals** (buffet lunch) 4000/6700 and a la carte – 4450 – **241 rm** 41300/60320, 15 suites.

Grande Bretagne, Constitution Sq., ✉ 105 63, ✆ 3330 000, Telex 215346, Fax 3328 064 – – 500. AE ① E VISA JCB. CY **v**
G B Corner : **Meals** (buffet lunch) 3700/7900 and a la carte – 5200 – **291 rm** 60000/95000, 23 suites.

Divani Palace Acropolis, 19-25 Parthenonos, ✉ 117 42, ☎ 9222 945, Telex 218306, Fax 9214 993, « Ancient ruins of Themistocles wall in basement », – 🛗 ▤ TV ☎ – 300. AE ⓓ E VISA JCB. ※ BY r
Aspassia : **Meals** 5800 and a la carte – ***Roof Garden :*** **Meals** *(closed Tuesday and November-May)* (live music) (dinner only) 8500 – **246 rm** ☕ 39000/60000, 7 suites.

Le NJV Meridien, 2 King George I, Sindagma Sq., ✉ 105 64, ☎ 325 5301, Telex 210568, Fax 323 5856 – 🛗 rm ▤ TV ☎ – 300. AE ⓓ E VISA JCB. ※ CY r
Meals a la carte 7500/10000 – ☕ 3900 – **152 rm** 54186, 25 suites.

Novotel Athens, 4-6 Mihail Voda, ✉ 104 39, ☎ 8250 422, Telex 226264, Fax 8837 816, « Roof garden with and ✻ Athens » – 🛗 ▤ TV ☎ – 600. AE ⓓ E VISA JCB AX t
Meals 4500/7000 and a la carte – ☕ 3300 – **190 rm** 28000/34800, 5 suites.

St. George Lycabettus, 2 Kleomenous, ✉ 106 75, ☎ 7290 711, Telex 214253, Fax 7290 439, , « ≤ Athens from rooftop restaurant », – 🛗 ▤ TV ☎ – 280. AE ⓓ E VISA JCB. ※ DX t
Grand Balcon : **Meals** (dinner only) 11000 and a la carte – ***Mediterraneo :*** **Meals** 5200/6500 and a la carte – **162 rm** ☕ 46100/53600.

Holiday Inn, 50 Mihalakopoulou, ✉ 115 28, ☎ 7248 322, Telex 2188, Fax 7248 187, – 🛗 rm ▤ TV ☎ – 500. AE ⓓ E VISA JCB. ※ DY
Meals (buffet lunch) 4900 and a la carte – ☕ 3200 – **187 rm** 41000/54700, 4 suites.

Zafolia, 87-89 Alexandras, ✉ 114 74, ☎ 6449 002, Telex 214468, Fax 6442 042, « Rooftop terrace with and ≤ Athens » – 🛗 ▤ TV ☎ – 200. AE ⓓ E VISA JCB. ※ DX k
Meals 4400 and a la carte – **191 rm** ☕ 19700/24200.

Electra, 5 Ermou, ✉ 105 63, ☎ 3223 223, Telex 216896, Group Telex 216896, Fax 3220 310 – 🛗 ▤ TV ☎. AE ⓓ E VISA JCB. ※ BY e
Meals 3900/4800 and a la carte – **110 rm** ☕ 27800/35000.

Herodion, 4 Rovertou Galli, ✉ 117 42, ☎ 9236 832, Telex 219423, Fax 9235 851, « Roof garden with ≤ Acropolis » – 🛗 ▤ TV ☎ – 50. AE ⓓ E VISA JCB. ※ BY p
Meals 4500 and a la carte – **90 rm** ☕ 27250/36000.

Electra Palace, 18 Nikodimou, ✉ 105 57, ☎ 3241 401, Telex 216896, Group Telex 216896, Fax 3241 875, « Terrace with and ≤ Athens » – 🛗 rm ▤ TV ☎ – 180. AE ⓓ E VISA JCB. ※ BY h
Meals 3900/4800 and a la carte – **101 rm** ☕ 27800/35000, 5 suites.

Philippos without rest., 3 Mitseon, ✉ 117 42, ☎ 9223 611, Telex 219423, Group Telex 219423, Fax 9223 615 – 🛗 ▤ rm TV ☎. AE ⓓ E VISA JCB. ※ BY f
48 rm ☕ 18500/23000.

Acropolis View without rest., 10 Webster, off Rovertou Galli, ✉ 117 42, ☎ 9217 303, Telex 219936, Fax 9230 705, « Roof terrace with ≤ Acropolis » – 🛗 ▤ ☎. AE E AY e
32 rm ☕ 14900/19900.

XXX **Athenaeum,** 8 Amerikis, ✉ 106 71, ☎ 3631 125, Fax 3635 957, « Elegant classic decor » – ▤. AE ⓓ E VISA JCB CY e
closed Sunday, June-August and Bank Holidays – **Meals** (dinner only) a la carte 7900/11400.

XXX **Boschetto,** Evangelismou, off Vas. Sofias, ✉ 106 75, ☎ 7210 893, Fax 7223 598, , « Summerhouse in small park » – ▤. AE VISA DY c
closed Sunday, 1 week Easter, 10 to 20 August and 1-2 January – **Meals** - Italian - (dinner only except 15 April-15 October) a la carte 5000/13000.

XXX **Symposio,** 46 Erehthiou, ✉ 117 42, ☎ 9225 321, Fax 9232 780, « Conservatory in winter, in summer » – AE ⓓ E VISA JCB AY r
closed Sunday, Easter, 15 August and 1 January – **Meals** (booking essential) (dinner only) 8000/15000 and a la carte 9500/15800.

XX **L'Abreuvoir,** 51 Xenokratous, Kolonaki, ✉ 106 76, ☎ 7229 106, Fax 7253 009, , « Outdoor summer service » – ▤. AE ⓓ E VISA JCB DX u
closed 19 February – **Meals** - French - 4150/8700 and a la carte.

XX Dodeka Apostoloi, Kanari 17, Kolonaki, ✉ 106 71, ☎ 3619 358, « Tasteful decor » – ▤
Meals - French, Greek, Italian rest. CY b

XX **Ideal,** 46 Panepistimiou, (El. Venizelou), ✉ 106 78, ☎ 330 3000, Fax 330 3003 – ▤. AE ⓓ E VISA JCB BX c
closed Sunday and Christmas – **Meals** a la carte 4950/8470.

XX Bajazzo, 14 Anapavseos, ✉ 116 36, ☎ 7291420, Fax 7291420. DX a

XX **Dioscuri,** 16 Dimitriou Vassiliou, N. Psihiko, ✉ 154 51, NE : 7 km by Kifissia Rd turning at A.B. supermarket ☎ 6476 546, Fax 6713 997, – ▤. AE ⓓ E VISA
closed July-August lunch and Sunday – **Meals** (booking essential) 6000/6600 and a la carte.

X **Strofi,** 25 Rovertou Galli, ✉ 117 42, ☎ 9214 130, , « ≤ Acropolis from rooftop terrace » – ▤. AE ⓓ E VISA AY a
closed Sunday and 1 week Easter – **Meals** (dinner only) 4500/5500 and a la carte.

X Kidathineon, 3 Filomoussou, Eterias, ✉ 105 58, ☎ 3234 281, BY s

"The Tavernas"

Typical Greek restaurants, generally very modest, where it is pleasant to spend the evening, surrounded by noisy but friendly locals, sometimes with guitar or bouzouki entertainment. These restaurants are usually open for dinner only.

XX **Myrtia,** 32 Trivonianou, ✉ 116 36, ✆ 7012 276, Fax 9247 181 – ▤. AE ⓓ E VISA
closed Sunday and 15 July-30 August – **Meals** (music) (booking essential) (dinner only) 8000/10000. by Anapavseos Rd CY

X O Anthropos, 13 Arhelaou, Pangrati, ✉ 116 35, ✆ 7235 914 DY a
Meals - Seafood rest.

Environs

at Kifissia NE : 15 km by Vas. Sofias – DY :

Pentelikon, 66 Diligianni, Kefalari, ✉ 145 62, off Harilaou Trikoupi follow signs to Politia, ✆ 8080 311, Fax 8019 223, terrace, pool, garden – lift ▤ TV ☎ P – 150. AE ⓓ E VISA JCB.
Vardis : **Meals** - French - *(closed Sunday)* (dinner only) a la carte approx. 13000 – ***La Terrasse*** : **Meals** (buffet lunch) 1950 and a la carte 4200/11000 – ☕ 4200 – **33 rm** 61000/73000, 6 suites.

at Pireas SW : 10 km by Singrou – BY :

XX **Aglamer,** 54-56 Akti Koumoundourou, Mikrolimano, ✉ 185 33, ✆ 4115 511, Fax 4530 335, ≤ Harbour, terrace – ▤. AE ⓓ E VISA
closed Easter Sunday and 1 December – **Meals** - Seafood - 4500 (lunch) and a la carte 5800/9650.

X Durambeis, 29 Athinas Dilaveri, ✉ 185 33, ✆ 4122 092, terrace
Meals - Seafood rest.

Hungary

Magyarország

BUDAPEST

PRACTICAL INFORMATION

LOCAL CURRENCY

Forint : 100 UF = 0.72 US $ (Jan. 96)

PRICES

Prices may change if goods and service costs in Hungary are revised and it is therefore always advisable to confirm rates with the hotelier when making a reservation.

FOREIGN EXCHANGE

It is strongly advised against changing money other than in banks, exchange offices or authorised offices such as large hotels, tourist offices, etc... Banks are usually open on weekdays from 8.30am to 4pm.

HOTEL RESERVATIONS

In case of difficulties in finding a room through our hotel selection, it is always possible to apply to IBUSZ Hotel Service, Apaci ut. 1, Budapest 5th ✆ (1) 118 57 76, Fax 117 90 99. This office offers a 24-hour assistance to the visitor.

POSTAL SERVICES

Post offices are open from 8am to 8pm on weekdays and 8am to 3pm on Saturdays.
General Post Office : Városház ut. 19, Budapest 5th, ✆ (1) 117 69 94.

SHOPPING IN BUDAPEST

In the index of street names, those printed in red are where the principal shops are found. Typical goods to be bought include embroidery, lace, china, leather goods, paprika, salami, Tokay, palinka, foie-gras... Shops are generally open from 10am to 6pm on weekdays (8pm on Thursday) and 9am to 1pm on Saturday.

TIPPING

Hotel, restaurant and café bills include service in the total charge but it is usual to leave the staff a gratuity which will vary depending upon the service given.

CAR HIRE

The international car hire companies have branches in Budapest. Your hotel porter should be able to give details and help you with your arrangements.

BREAKDOWN SERVICE

A breakdown service is operated by SARGA ANGYAL (Yellow Angel), ✆ (02) 52 80 00.

SPEED LIMIT

On motorways, the maximum permitted speed is 120 km/h – 74 mph, 100 km/h – 62 mph on other roads and 50 km/h – 31 mph in built up areas.

SEAT BELTS

In Hungary, the wearing of seat belts is compulsory for drivers and front seat passengers.

Budapest

Hungary 970 N 6 - Pop. 2 172 000 - ✪ 1.

Views of Budapest

St. Gellert Monument and Citadel (Szt. Gellért-szobor, Citadella) ≤★★★ EX - Fishermen's Bastion (Halászbástya) ≤★★ DU.

BUDA

Matthias Church★★ (Mátyás-templom) DU - Attractive Streets★★ (Tancsics Mihaly utca - Fortuna utca - Uri utca) CDU - Royal Palace★★ (Budavári palota) DV - Hungarian National Gallery★★ (Magyar Nemzeti Galéria) DV **M1** - Budapest Historical Museum★ (Budapesti Történeti Múzeum) DV **M1** - Vienna Gate★ (Bécsi kapu) CU **D** - War History Museum★ (Hadtörténety Múzeum) CU **M2**.

PEST

Parliament Building★★★ (Országház) EU - Museum of Fine Arts★★★ (Szepmüveszeti Múzeum) BY **M3** - Hungarian National Museum★★ (Magyar Nemzeti Múzeum) FVX **M4** - Museum of Applied Arts★★ (Iparmüvészeti Múzeum) BZ **M5** - Szechenyi Thermal Baths★★ (Széchenyi Gyógyés Strandfürdö) BY **D** - Hungarian State Opera House★ (Magyar Állami Operaház) FU **B** - Liszt Conservatory : foyer★ (Liszt Ferenc Zenemüvészeti Föiskola) FU **D** - Chinese Art Museum★ (Kína Muzéum) BYZ **M6** - St. Stephen's Basilica★ (Szt. István-bazilika) EU **E** - City Parish Church★ (Belvárosi plébániatemplom) EV **K** - University Church★ (Egyetemi Templom) FX **R** - Franciscan Church★ (Ferences templom) FV **L** - Municipal Concert Hall★ (Vigadó) EV **F** - Town Hall★ (Fövárosi Tanács) EFV **H** - Paris Arcade★ (Párizsi udvar) EV **P** - Vaci Street★ (Váci utca) EV - Hungaria Restaurant★ (Hungaria Ettermek) BZ **N** - Budapest West Station★ (Nyugati pályaudvar) AY - Millenary Monument★ (Millenniumi emlékmu) BY **F** - City Park★ (Városliget) BYZ - Vajdahunyad Castle★ (Vajdahunyad vára) BY **B** - Hungarian Transport Museum★ (Magyar Közlekedesi Múzeum) BY **M7**.

ADDITIONAL SIGHTS

Chain Bridge★★ (Széchenyi Lánchíd) DEV - Margaret Island★ (Margitsziget) AY - Aquincum Museum★ (Aquincumi Muzéum) N : 12 km by Szentendrei út AY - Gellert Thermal Baths★ (Gellért gyógyfürdö) EX - St. Ann's Church★ (Szent Anna templom) DU.

Envir.

Szentendre★ N : 20 km - Visegrad N : 42 km : Citadel, view★★

✈ Ferihegy SE : 16 km by Üllοї FX, ✆ 157 71 55 (information), Bus to airport : from International Bus station, Elisabeth tér, Station 6 Budapest 5th and Airport Bus Service CRI - MALEV, Roosevelt tér 2, Budapest 5th ✆ 118 90 33

ℹ Tourinform, Sütő u. 2, ✉ H 1052 ✆ 117 98 00 - IBUSZ Head Office, Ferenciek tér 5, Budapest 5th ✆ 118 68 66.

Munich 678 - Prague 533 - Venice 740 - Vienna 243 - Zagreb 350

Kempinski H. Corvinus Budapest M, Erzsébet Tér 7-8, ✉ 1051, ℘ 266 1000, Telex 22 22 99, Fax 266 2000, Fö, ≘s, ⊡ - |‡| ⇎ rm ▤ TV ☎ ♿ ⇔ - 🏛 450. AE ⓓ E VISA JCB. ⚘ rest EV a
Corvinus : **Meals** *(closed Saturday, Sunday and Bank Holidays)* 3000/6000 and dinner a la carte *Bistro Jardin* : **Meals** (buffet lunch) 2200 and a la carte 2600/4100 - ⊒ 2717 - **345 rm** 29047/44039, 22 suites.

Hilton ⛰, Hess András Tér 1-3, ✉ 1014, ℘ 175 1000, Telex 22 5984, Fax 156 0285, ≤ Danube and city, « Remains of a 13C Dominican church » - |‡| ⇎ rm ▤ TV ☎ ♿ ⇔ - 🏛 500. AE ⓓ E VISA JCB. ⚘ rest DU a
Dominican : **Meals** a la carte 2310/10250 - *Kalocsa* : **Meals** (dinner only) a la carte 2470/6100 - ⊒ 2717 - **295 rm** 24362/45445, 28 suites.

Budapest Marriott M, Apáczai Csere János Utca 4, ✉ 1364, ℘ 266 7000, Telex 22 5277, Fax 266 5000, ≤ Danube and Buda, 斎, Fö, ≘s - |‡| ⇎ rm ▤ TV ☎ ⇔ - 🏛 500. AE ⓓ E VISA JCB. ⚘ EV r
Csarda : **Meals** *(closed Sunday)* (dinner only) a la carte 2200/4500 - *Duna Grill* : **Meals** (buffet lunch) 1874 and a la carte 2000/3500 - ⊒ 2811 - **342 rm** 29512, 20 suites.

Forum, Apáczai Csere János Utca 12-14, Box 231 H-1368, ✉ 1052, ℘ 117 9111, Telex 22 4178, Fax 117 9808, ≤ Danube and Buda, Fö, ≘s, ⊡ - |‡| ⇎ rm ▤ TV ☎ ♿ ⇔ - 🏛 200. AE ⓓ E VISA JCB. ⚘ EV n
Silhouette : **Meals** a la carte 3280/5622 - *Grill* : **Meals** a la carte 2811/3748 - ⊒ 2343 - **385 rm** 29984/39354, 15 suites.

Atrium Hyatt M, Roosevelt Tér 2, ✉ 1051, ℘ 266 1234, Telex 22 5485, Fax 266 9101, ≤, Fö, ≘s, ⊡ - |‡| ⇎ rm ▤ TV ☎ ♿ ⇔ - 🏛 350. AE ⓓ E VISA JCB EV e
Old Timer : **Meals** a la carte 2300/5600 - *Atrium Terrace* : **Meals** (buffet lunch) 1780 and a la carte 1350/2700 - *Clark Brasserie* : **Meals** a la carte 1250/1800 - ⊒ 2530 - **319 rm** 29047/46850, 26 suites.

Radisson Béke, Teréz Körut 43, ✉ 1067, ℘ 132 3300, Telex 22 5748, Fax 153 3380, ≘s, ⊡ - |‡| ⇎ rm ▤ TV ☎ ⇔ - 🏛 150. AE ⓓ E VISA JCB FU a
Shakespeare : **Meals** (lunch only) 1950 and a la carte - *Szondi* : **Meals** (dinner only) a la carte 3748/5622 - **238 rm** ⊒ 24362/29984, 8 suites.

Aquincum M ⛰, Árpád Fejedelem Utja 94, ✉ 1036, ℘ 250 33 60, Telex 222160, Fax 250 46 72, ≤, Therapy centre, Fö, ≘s, ⊡ - |‡| ▤ TV ☎ ♿ ⇔ Ⓟ - 🏛 280. AE ⓓ E VISA JCB
Ambrosia : **Meals** a la carte 1440/4900 - *Apicins* : **Meals** a la carte 1130/4280 - **304 rm** ⊒ 25299/30921, 8 suites. AY d

Gellért, Gellért Tér 1, ✉ 1111, ℘ 185 22 00, Telex 224363, Fax 166 66 31, « Art Nouveau decor », Direct entrance to the Therapeutic bath, ≘s, ⛱ heated, ⊡ - |‡| ▤ TV ☎ ♿ ⇔ - 🏛 320. AE ⓓ E VISA. ⚘ rest EX n
Meals 3000/5000 and a la carte - **226 rm** 14805/32608, 13 suites.

Ramada Grand Hotel ⛰, Margitsziget, ✉ 1138, ℘ 132 1100, Telex 22 6682, Fax 153 3029, ≤, 斎, Direct entrance to Thermal Hotel, ≘s, ⊡ - |‡| ⇎ rm TV ☎ ♿ ⇔ Ⓟ - 🏛 85. AE ⓓ E VISA JCB AY b
Meals (buffet lunch) 2000 and a la carte - **157 rm** ⊒ 14992/30921, 10 suites.

Thermal H. Helia, Kárpát Utca 62-64, ✉ 1133, ℘ 270 3277, Telex 20 2539, Fax 270 2262, ≤, Therapy centre, Fö, ≘s, ⊡ - |‡| ⇎ rm ▤ TV ☎ ♿ Ⓟ - 🏛 340. AE ⓓ E VISA JCB. ⚘ rest AY c
Meals (buffet lunch) 2343/6091 and dinner a la carte - **254 rm** ⊒ 18740/29984, 8 suites.

K + K Hotel Opera M ⛰ without rest., Revay Utca 24, ✉ 1065, ℘ 269 0222, Telex 22 2653, Fax 269 0230 - |‡| ⇎ rm ▤ TV ☎ ⇔ - 🏛 50. AE ⓓ E VISA FU f
113 rm ⊒ 17803/29047, 2 suites.

Mercure Korona M, Kecskeméti Utca 14, ✉ 1053, ℘ 117 4111, Telex 22 3622, Fax 118 3867, ≘s, ⊡ - |‡| ⇎ rm ▤ TV ☎ ♿ ⇔ - 🏛 80. AE ⓓ E VISA JCB. ⚘ rest FX s
Meals (buffet lunch) 1874/9370 and a la carte - **422 rm** ⊒ 17803/24362, 10 suites.

Astoria, Kossuth Lajos Utca 19, ✉ 1053, ℘ 117 34 11, Telex 224205, Fax 118 67 98, « Art Nouveau decor » - TV ☎ - 🏛 30. AE ⓓ E VISA JCB. ⚘ rest FV q
Meals 1800/3000 and a la carte - **124 rm** ⊒ 15000/20000, 5 suites.

Grand H. Hungaria, Rákóczi Utca 90, ✉ 1074, ℘ 322 90 50, Telex 22 4987, Fax 268 19 99, Fö, ≘s - |‡| ▤ TV ☎ ⇔ - 🏛 380. AE ⓓ E VISA JCB BZ f
Meals 2343/4685 and a la carte - **503 rm** ⊒ 20614/25299, 8 suites.

Flamenco, Tas Vezér Utca 7, ✉ 1113, ℘ 161 22 52, Telex 22 4647, Fax 165 80 07, 斎, ≘s, ⊡ - |‡| ⇎ rm ▤ TV ☎ ⇔ Ⓟ - 🏛 200. AE ⓓ E VISA JCB. ⚘ rest AZ p
Meals 2500/5500 and a la carte - **330 rm** ⊒ 14992/23425, 8 suites.

Alba without rest., Apor Péter Utca 3, ✉ 1011, ℘ 175 92 44, Telex 22 5671, Fax 175 98 99 - |‡| ⇎ TV ☎ ⇔ - 🏛 25. AE ⓓ E VISA DV e
95 rm ⊒ 14055/18740.

Novotel Budapest Centrum, Alkotás Utca 63-67, ✉ 1444, ℘ 186 95 88, Telex 22 5495, Fax 166 56 36, ≘s, ⊡ - |‡| ▤ TV ☎ Ⓟ. AE ⓓ E VISA JCB. ⚘ rest CX h
Meals 1000/2500 and a la carte - **318 rm** ⊒ 14055/20614, 6 suites.

Mercure Buda, Krisztina Körut 41-43, ✉ 1013, ℘ 156 63 33, Telex 22 5495, Fax 155 69 64, ≘s, ⊡ - |‡| ⇎ rm ▤ TV ☎ ⇔ Ⓟ - 🏛 80. AE ⓓ E VISA JCB CV f
Meals 1312/2061 and a la carte - **388 rm** ⊒ 14055/20614, 6 suites.

BUDAPEST

Bécsi u. . . . . EV
Deák Ferenc u. . . . . EV 8
Haris Köz . . . . EV 21
Párizsi u. . . . . EV 53
Petőfi
  Sándor u. . . . . EV 55
Régi posta u. . . . . EV 58
Váci u. . . . . EFV
Vörösmarty Tér . . . . EV

Apáczai Csere
  János u. . . . . EV 2
Árpád Fejedelem
  útja . . . . AY 3
Bárczy István u. . . . . EV 4
Batthyány u. . . . . CDU 5
Erzsébet Krt . . . . BZ 6
Fehérvári út. . . . . AZ 11
Ferenciek Tér . . . . EFV 12
Ferenc Krt. . . . . BZ 14
Fortuna u. . . . . CDU 15
Fö u. . . . . DUV 17
Gerlóczy u. . . . . FV 19
Groza Péter
  Rakpart . . . . EVX 20
Hattyú u. . . . . CU 22
Hunfalvy u. . . . . CDU 24
Irányi u. . . . . EX 26
Irinyi József u. . . . . AZ 27
Kálmán Imre u. . . . . EU 29
Karinthy
  Frigyes út. . . . . AZ 31
Karolina út. . . . . AZ 32
Károlyi Mihály u. . . . . FVX 33
Kecskeméti u. . . . . FX 35
Kosciuszko
  Tádé u. . . . . CV 37
Kuny Domokos u. . . . . CV 39
Lajos u. . . . . AY 40
Logodi u. . . . . CU 42
Magyar u. . . . . FVX 44
Moszkva Tér . . . . AZ 45
Nagyenyed u. . . . . CV 46
Nagyszölös u. . . . . AZ 47
Naphegy u. . . . . CDV 48
Országház u. . . . . CDU 50
Pacsirtamezö u. . . . . AY 52
Reáltanoda u. . . . . FV 57
Rumbach
  Sebestyén u. . . . . FV 60
Schönherz
  Zoltán u. . . . . AZ 62
Szabó Ilonka u. . . . . CDU 64
Szentendrei út. . . . . AY 65
Szerb u. . . . . FX 66
Szt. István Krt. . . . . AY 67
Tábor u. . . . . CDV 70
Táncsics Mihály u. . . . . . . CDV 71
Városház u. . . . . EFV 73
Vörösvári út. . . . . AY 75

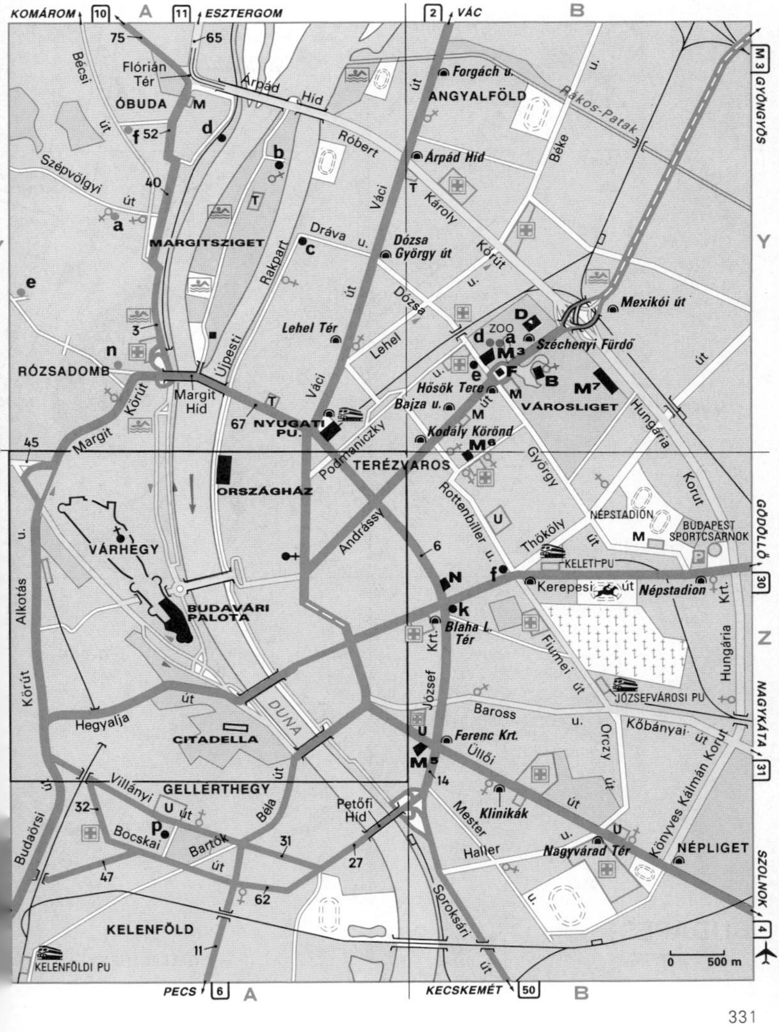

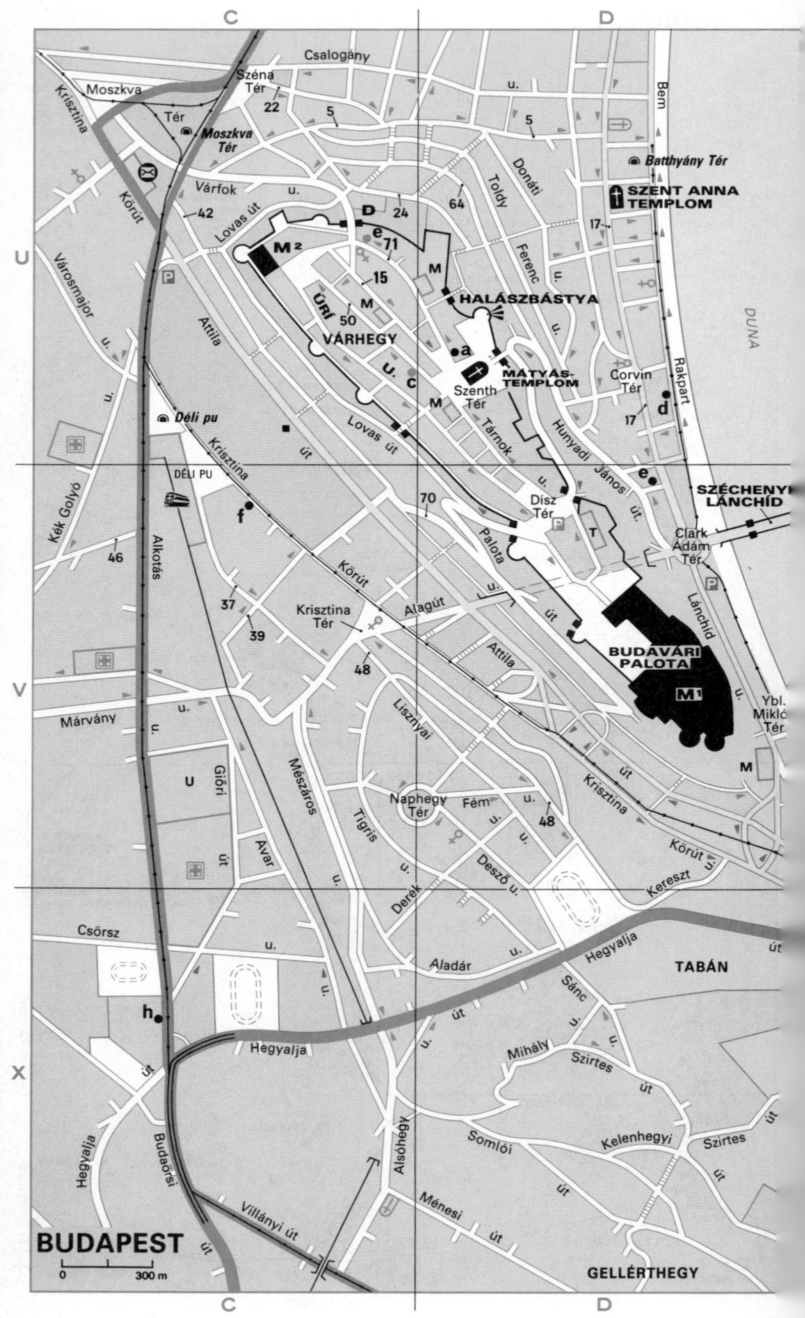
BUDAPEST
0
300 m
C
D
U
V
X
Csalogány
Széna Tér
Moszkva Tér
Moszkva Tér
Krisztina
Batthyány Tér
SZENT ANNA TEMPLOM
Bem
Donáti
Toldy
Várfok u.
Lovas út
Körút
Városmajor u.
Attila
VÁRHEGY
ÚRI u.
HALÁSZBÁSTYA
MÁTYÁS-TEMPLOM
Szenth Tér
Ferenc u.
Corvin Tér
Rakpart
DUNA
Déli pu
DÉLI PU
Krisztina
Tárnok
Hunyadi János út
Dísz Tér
SZÉCHENYI LÁNCHÍD
Clark Ádám Tér
Kék Golyó
Alkotás
Palota út
Krisztina Tér
Alagút
Attila
BUDAVÁRI PALOTA
Lánchíd u.
Ybl. Mikló Tér
Márvány u.
Győri út
Mészáros u.
Lisznyai
Naphegy Tér
Fém u.
Tigris u.
Avar
Derék u.
Desző u.
Krisztina Körút
Kereszt
Csörsz u.
Aladár u.
Hegyalja út
TABÁN
Sánc u.
Hegyalja
Mihály u.
Szirtes út
Alsóhegy
Somlói út
Kelenhegyi út
Szirtes út
Budaörsi út
Ménesi út
Villányi út
GELLÉRTHEGY

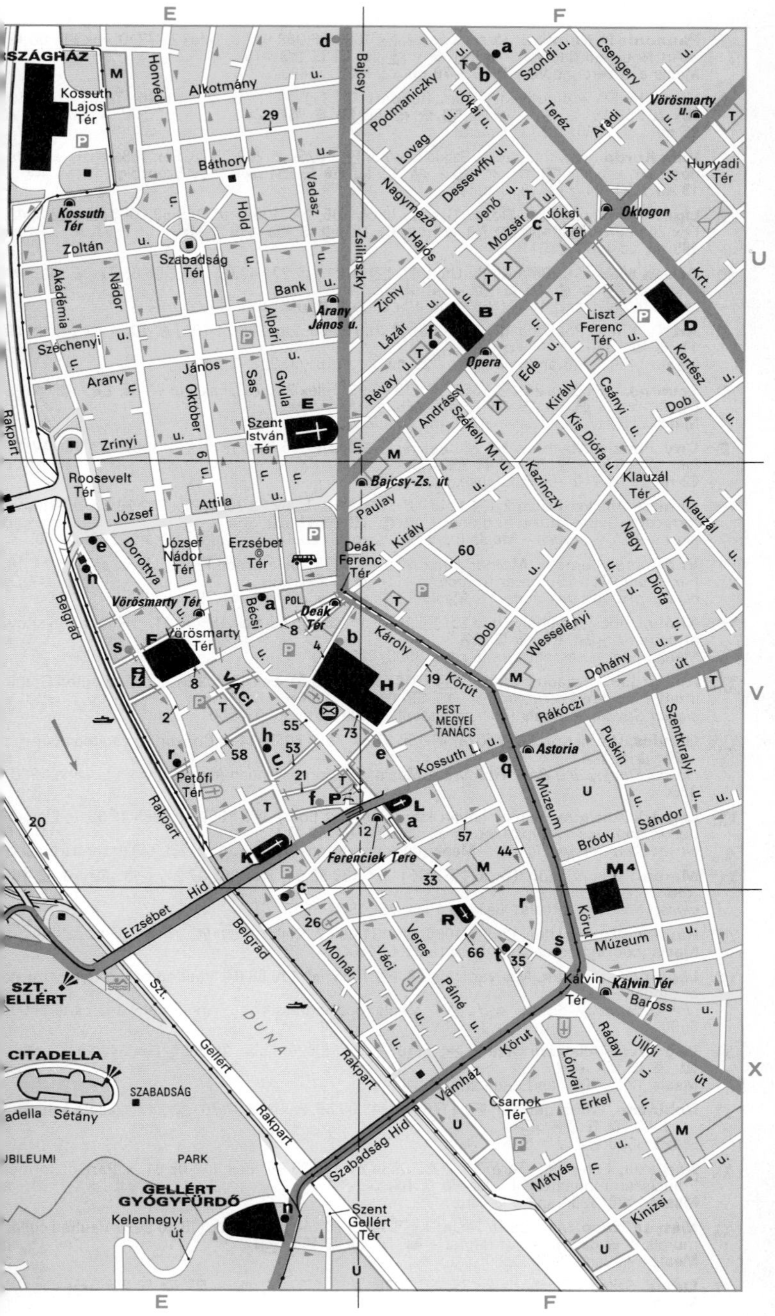

E
F
Kossuth Lajos Tér
Alkotmány
Honvéd
Báthory
Kossuth Tér
Zoltán
Szabadság Tér
Akadémia
Nádor
Hold
Vadasz
Bank
Arany János u.
Alpári
Széchenyi
Arany
János
Október 6 u.
Sas
Gyula
Szent István Tér
Zrínyi
Roosevelt Tér
Attila
József
József Nádor Tér
Erzsébet Tér
Deák Ferenc Tér
Deák Tér
Dorottya
Vörösmarty Tér
Bécsi
VÁCI
Petőfi Tér
Belgrád Rakpart
Erzsébet Híd
Ferenciek Tere
Bajcsy-Zsilinszky út
Bajcsy-Zs. út
Podmaniczky
Lovag
Jókai u.
Szondi u.
Csengery
Teréz
Aradi
Vörösmarty u.
Hunyadi Tér
Dessewffy u.
Nagymező
Hajós
Jenő u.
Mozsár
Jókai Tér
Oktogon
Zichy
Lázár
Opera
Liszt Ferenc Tér
Krt.
Kertész
Révay u.
Andrássy
Székely M. u.
Ede
Király
Kis Diófa u.
Csányi
Dob
Kazinczy
Klauzál Tér
Klauzál
Paulay
Nagy Diófa
Wesselényi
Károly Körút
Dohány
PEST MEGYEI TANÁCS
Rákóczi
Kossuth L. u.
Astoria
Puskin
Szentkirályi
Múzeum Körút
Sándor
Bródy
Múzeum
Kálvin Tér
Baross
Ráday
Üllői út
Molnár
Váci
Veres Pálné u.
Vámház Körút
Lónyai
Csarnok Tér
Erkel
Mátyás
Kinizsi
Szabadság Híd
Szent Gellért Tér
Szt. Gellért Rakpart
DUNA
SZT. GELLÉRT
CITADELLA
Citadella Sétány
SZABADSÁG
JUBILEUMI PARK
GELLÉRT GYÓGYFÜRDŐ
Kelenhegyi út
U
V
X

Pannonia H. Nemzeti, József Körut 4, ✉ 1088, ✆ 269 93 10, Telex 22 7710, Fax 114 00 19, « Art Nouveau decor » – 🛗 TV ☎ – 🏛 25. AE E VISA JCB. ✈ BZ **k**
Meals a la carte approx. 1950 – **76 rm** ☐ 10307/14992.

Victoria M without rest., Bem Rakpart 11, ✉ 1011, ✆ 201 86 44, Telex 20 2650, Fax 201 58 16, ≤, ≘s – 🛗 ▤ TV ☎ P. AE ⓓ E VISA JCB DU **d**
26 rm ☐ 17335/18272, 1 suite.

Villa Korda 🐚 without rest., Szikla Utca 9, ✉ 1025, ✆ 269 73 26, Fax 168 40 01, ≤ Budapest, 🌳 – 🛗 ▤ TV ☎ 🚗 P – 🏛 40. AE ⓓ E VISA JCB by Szépvölgyi Utca AY
18 rm ☐ 11244/13118, 3 suites.

Liget M without rest., Dózsa György Utca 106, ✉ 1068, ✆ 269 53 00, Telex 22 3648, Fax 269 53 29, ≘s – 🛗 ▤ TV ☎ 🚗 P. AE ⓓ E VISA JCB BY **e**
139 rm ☐ 17803/19115.

Queen Mary 🐚, Béla Király Utca 47, ✉ 1121, ✆ 274 40 00, Fax 156 83 77, ≤, ≘s, 🌳 – ▤ rest TV ☎ P. AE E VISA JCB. ✈
Meals (dinner only) 1124/1687 and a la carte – **22 rm** ☐ 10307/11244.

Art M, Királyi Pál Utca 12, ✉ 1053, ✆ 266 21 66, Fax 266 21 70, Fő, ≘s – ▤ TV ☎. AE ⓓ E VISA JCB FX **t**
Meals 1406/3748 and a la carte – **29 rm** ☐ 12181/15929, 3 suites.

Taverna, Váci Utca 20, ✉ 1052, ✆ 138 49 99, Telex 22 7707, Fax 118 71 88, ≘s – 🛗 ▤ rest TV ☎ 🚗 – 🏛 50. AE ⓓ E VISA JCB. ✈ rest EV **h**
Meals 2530 and a la carte – **224 rm** ☐ 17897/23144.

City Panzio Mathias M without rest., Március 15 Tér, n° 8, ✉ 1056, ✆ 138 47 11, Fax 117 90 86 – 🛗. AE ⓓ E VISA JCB EX **c**
22 rm ☐ 14617/20895, 3 suites.

XXXX **Gundel,** Állatkerti Utca 2, ✉ 1146, ✆ 321 35 50, Telex 22 7024, Fax 342 29 17, « Summer terrace », Gypsy music at dinner – ▤ P. AE ⓓ E VISA JCB BY **d**
closed 24 December – **Meals** (booking essential) 2000/8500 and a la carte 2600/6100.

XXX **Vadrózsa,** Pentelei Molnár Utca 15, ✉ 1025, by Rómer Flóris Utca ✆ 135 11 18, Fax 115 00 44, « Summer terrace » – AE ⓓ E VISA JCB AY **e**
closed mid July-mid August – **Meals** 5520/6480 and a la carte 2940/4500.

XXX **Király,** Táncsics Mihály Utca 25, ✉ 1014, ✆ 156 85 65, Fax 156 98 91, « Hungarian show at dinner » – ▤. AE ⓓ E VISA CU **e**
Meals (booking essential) a la carte 3900/6200.

XXX **Alabárdos,** Országház Utca 2, ✉ 1014, ✆ 156 08 51, Fax 156 08 51, 🍽, « Vaulted Gothic interior, covered courtyard » – ▤. AE ⓓ E VISA JCB CU **c**
closed Sunday – **Meals** (booking essential) a la carte 3000/6500.

XXX **Garvics,** Urömí Köz 2, ✉ 1025, ✆ 168 32 54, Fax 250 73 14, « Converted vaulted chapel » – AE ⓓ E VISA AY **a**
closed Sunday and Bank Holidays – **Meals** (booking essential) (dinner only) a la carte 1900/3800.

XXX **Légrádi Antique,** Bárczy István Utca 3-5 (first floor), ✉ 1052, ✆ 266 49 93, « Elegant decor, antiques », Gypsy music at dinner – AE ⓓ VISA EV **b**
closed Saturday and Sunday – **Meals** (booking essential) (buffet lunch) 2300/9200 and a la carte.

XXX **Marco Polo,** Vigadó Tér 3, ✉ 1051, ✆ 138 33 54, Fax 266 27 27 – ▤. AE ⓓ E VISA JCB EV **s**
closed Sunday – **Meals** - Italian - a la carte 1800/3600.

XXX **Barokk,** Mozsár Utca 12, ✉ 1066, ✆ 131 89 42, Cellar – ▤. AE FU **c**
Meals (booking essential) a la carte 2200/4300.

XXX **Légrádi Testvérek,** Magyar Utca 23, ✉ 1053, ✆ 118 68 04, Vaulted cellar, Gypsy music at dinner – AE FX **r**
closed Saturday, Sunday and July – **Meals** (booking essential) (dinner only) a la carte 2500/3500.

XX **Bagolyvár,** Állatkerti Utca 2, ✉ 1146, ✆ 351 63 95, Telex 22 7024, Fax 342 29 17, 🍽 – AE ⓓ E VISA JCB BY **d**
Meals 1300/2000 and a la carte.

XX **Robinson,** Városligeti Tér, ✉ 1146, ✆ 343 09 55, Fax 343 37 76, 🍽, « Lakeside setting » – ▤. AE ⓓ E VISA JCB BY **a**
Meals 6000 and a la carte.

XX **Kárpátia,** Ferenciek Tere 7-8, ✉ 1053, ✆ 117 35 96, Fax 118 05 91, « Part of former Franciscan monastery » – AE ⓓ E VISA JCB FV **a**
Meals 1406/3280 and a la carte.

XX **Mátyás Pince,** Március 15 Tér, n° 7, ✉ 1056, ✆ 118 05 95, Fax 118 16 50, « Vaulted cellar, murals », Gypsy music at dinner – ▤. AE ⓓ E VISA JCB EX **c**
Meals a la carte 2600/5200.

XX **Lugas,** Szilágyí Erzsbetfasor 77, ✉ 1026, ✆ 212 37 34, 🍽 – AE ⓓ E VISA JCB
Meals a la carte 2100/5300. by Moszkva Tér AZ

✗ **Kisbuda Gyöngye,** Kenyeres Utca 34, ✉ 1034, ✆ 168 64 02, Fax 168 92 27 – ▤. AE
closed Sunday except dinner October-May – **Meals** (booking essential) a la carte 2300/3200. AY f

✗ **Apostolok,** Kigyó Utca 4, ✉ 1052, ✆ 267 02 90, Fax 118 36 58, « Old chapel decor, wood carving » – AE ⊕ E VISA
Meals a la carte 870/2970. EV f

✗ **Aranymókus,** Istenhegyi Utca 25, ✉ 1126, ✆ 155 67 28, Fax 155 95 94, ☂ – AE ⊕ E VISA JCB
Meals a la carte 2000/5000. CV

at the Motorway M 1/M 7, South 8 km – BZ – ✉ – ☎ 06 Budaörs :

Forte Agip M, Agip Utca 2, ✉ 2040, ✆ 23 313 500, Fax 23 313 505, ☂, ≘s – |‡| ⇆ rm ▤ TV ☎ ⇔ P – 🏛 300. AE ⊕ E VISA JCB
Meals (buffet lunch) 1312/3748 and a la carte – **158 rm** ☐ 15461/18272, 3 suites.

Republic of

Ireland

DUBLIN

The town plans in the Republic of Ireland Section of this Guide are based upon the Ordnance Survey of Ireland by permission of the Government of the Republic, Permit number 6124.

PRACTICAL INFORMATION

LOCAL CURRENCY

Punt (Irish Pound): 1 IEP = 1.60 USD ($) (Jan. 96)

TOURIST INFORMATION

The telephone number and address of the Tourist Information office is given in the text under ℹ.

FOREIGN EXCHANGE

Banks are open between 10am and 4pm on weekdays only.

Banks in Dublin stay open to 5pm on Thursdays and banks at Dublin and Shannon airports are open on Saturdays and Sundays.

SHOPPING IN DUBLIN

In the index of street names those printed in red are where the principal shops are found.

CAR HIRE

The international car hire companies have branches in each major city. Your hotel porter should be able to give details and help you with your arrangements.

TIPPING

Many hotels and restaurants include a service charge but where this is not the case an amount equivalent to between 10 and 15 per cent of the bill is customary. Additionally doormen, baggage porters and cloakroom attendants are generally given a gratuity.

Taxi drivers are tipped between 10 and 15 per cent of the amount shown on the meter in addition to the fare.

SPEED LIMITS

The maximum permitted speed in the Republic is 60 mph (97 km/h) except where a lower speed limit is indicated.

SEAT BELTS

The wearing of seat belts is compulsory if fitted for drivers and front seat passengers. Additionaly, children under 12 are not allowed in front seats unless in a suitable safety restraint.

ANIMALS

It is forbildden to bring domestic animals (dogs, cats...) into the Republic of Ireland.

Dublin

(Baile Átha Cliath) Dublin 405 N 7 – pop. 859 976 – ☎ 01.

See : City★★★ – Trinity College★★★ (Library★★★) JY – Chester Beatty Library★★★ – Phoenix Park★★★ – Dublin Castle★★ HY – Christ Church Cathedral★★ HY – St. Patrick's Cathedral★★ HZ – Marsh's Library★★ HZ – National Museum★★ (Treasury★★), KZ – National Gallery★★ KZ – Merrion Square★★ KZ – Rotunda Hospital Chapel★★ JX – Kilmainham Hospital★★ – Kilmainham Gaol Museum★★ – National Botanic Gardens★★ – Nº 29★ KZ **D** – Liffey Bridge★ JY – Taylors' Hall★ HY – City Hall★ HY – St. Audoen's Gate★ HY **B** – St. Stephen's Green★ JZ – Grafton Street★ JZ – Powerscourt Centre★ JY – Civic Museum★ JY **M1** – Bank of Ireland★ JY – O'Connell Street★ (Anna Livia Fountain★), JX – St. Michan's Church★ HY **E** – Hush Lane Municipal Gallery of Modern Art★ JX **M4** – Pro-Cathedral★ JX – Garden of remembrance★ JX – Custom House★ KX – Bluecoat school★ – Guiness Museum★ – Marino Casino★ – Zoological Gardens★ – Newman House JZ.

Envir. : Powerscourt★★ (Waterfall★★★) S : 14 m by N 11 and R 117 Russborough House★★★, SW : 22 m by N 81.

18 Edmondstown, Rathfarnham ☎ 4932461, S : 3 m by N 81 – 18 Elm Park, G & S.C., Nutley House, Donnybrook ☎ 2693438, SE : 3 m by N 11 – 18 Milltown, Lower Churchtown Rd, ☎ 977060, S : by R 117 – 18 Royal Dublin, North Bull Island Dollimont, ☎ 336346 NE : by R 105 – 18 Forrest Little ☎ 840118 – 18 Lucan ☎ 6280246.

✈ Dublin Airport ☎ 8444900, N : 5 ½ m. by N 1 – Terminal : Busaras (Central Bus Station) Store St.

⛴ to Holyhead (B & I Line) 2 daily – to the Isle of Man : (Douglas) (Isle of Man Steam Packet Co Ltd.) (4 h 30 mn).

ℹ 14 Upper O'Connell St. ☎ 874 77 33 – Dublin Airport ☎ 284 47 68 – Baggot Street Bridge ☎ 284 47 68.

Belfast 103 – Cork 154 – Londonderry 146.

DUBLIN
CENTRE

Street	Grid	No.
Anne Street South	JYZ	6
Dawson Street	JYZ	
Duke Street	JY	58
Grafton Street	JYZ	
Henry Street	JX	
Ilac Centre	HJX	
Irish Life Mall Centre	JKX	
O'Connell Street	JX	
Brunswick Street North	HX	24
Buckingham Street	KX	25
Bull Alley	HZ	27
Chancery Street	HY	33
Clanbrassil Street	HZ	40
College Green	JY	45
College Street	JY	46
Cornmarket	HY	49
D'Olier Street	JY	51
Earlsfort Terrace	JZ	60
Essex Quay	HY	66
Fishamble Street	HY	67
George's Quay	KY	69
Golden Lane	HZ	70
Henrietta Street	HX	75
High Street	HY	78
Kevin Street Upper	HZ	85
Kildare Street	JKZ	87
King Street South	JZ	88
Marlborough Street	JX	100
Merchants Quay	HY	103
Montague Street	JZ	106
Mount Street Upper	KZ	112
Nicholas Street	HY	118
Parnell Square East	JX	126
Parnell Square North	JX	127
Parnell Square West	HJX	129
St Mary's Abbey Street	HY	148
St Patrick Close	HZ	150
Stephen Street	HJY	165
Tara Street	KY	171
Wellington Quay	HJY	181
Werburgh Street	HY	183
Westland Row	KY	186
Westmoreland Street	JY	187
Wexford Street	HZ	189
Winetavern Street	HY	193
Wood Quay	HY	196

Town plans:
roads most used by traffic
and those on which guide-
listed hotels and restaurants
stand are fully drawn;
the beginning only
of lesser roads is indicated.

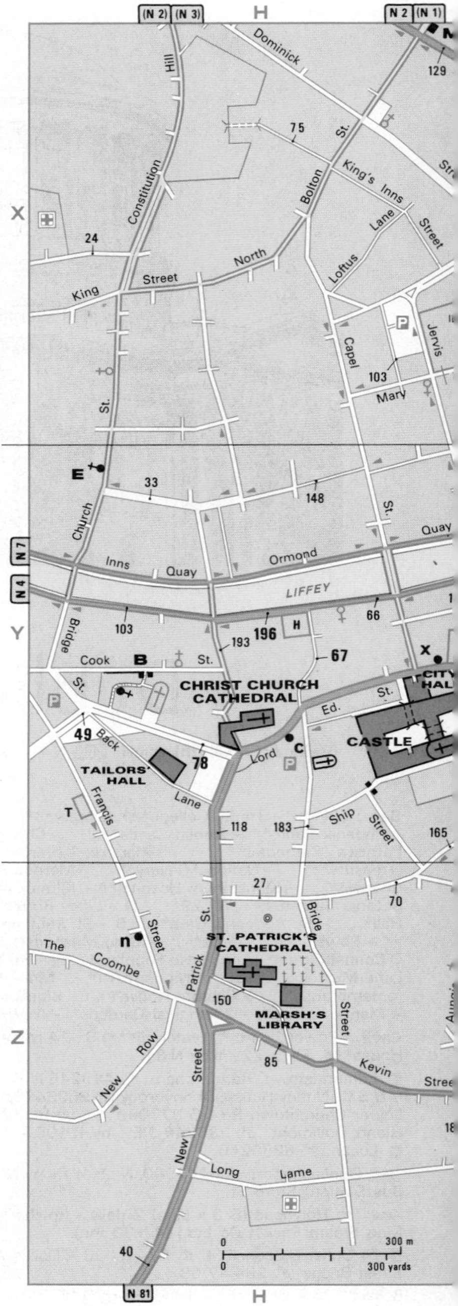

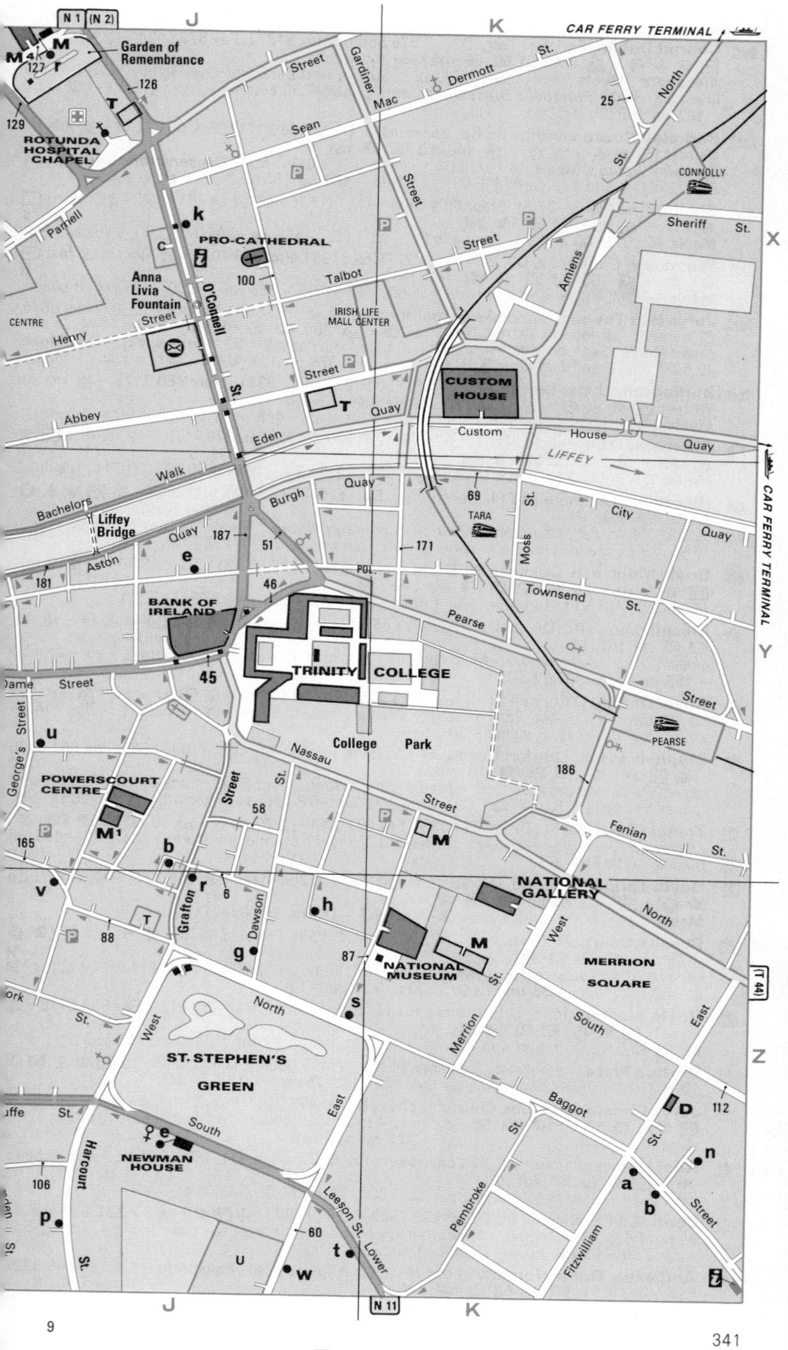

N 1
(N 2)
J
K
CAR FERRY TERMINAL
Garden of Remembrance
ROTUNDA HOSPITAL CHAPEL
PRO-CATHEDRAL
Anna Livia Fountain
IRISH LIFE MALL CENTER
CONNOLLY
CUSTOM HOUSE
LIFFEY
Liffey Bridge
TARA
BANK OF IRELAND
TRINITY COLLEGE
College Park
PEARSE
POWERSCOURT CENTRE
NATIONAL GALLERY
NATIONAL MUSEUM
MERRION SQUARE
ST. STEPHEN'S GREEN
NEWMAN HOUSE
X
Y
Z
T 44
N 11

Conrad Dublin, Earlsfort Terr., D2, ✆ 676 5555, Telex 91872, Fax 676 5424 – |‡| ⇔ rm ▤ TV ☎ ♿ 🅿 – 🏛 300. AE ① VISA JCB. ✗ JZ w
Alexandra : **Meals** *(closed Saturday lunch, Sunday and Bank Holidays)* 18.50/27.50 **t.** and a la carte 🍷 6.50 – ***Plurabelle Brasserie :*** **Meals** 14.50/15.50 **t.** and a la carte 🍷 6.50 – ☕ 11.50 – **182 rm** 165.00/190.00 **t.**, 9 suites.

Berkeley Court, Lansdowne Rd, Ballsbridge, D4, ✆ 660 1711, Fax 661 7238 – |‡| ⇔ rm ▤ rest TV ☎ ♿ 🚗 🅿 – 🏛 440. AE ① VISA. ✗ by T44 KZ
Berkeley Room : **Meals** 14.75/26.00 **t.** and a la carte 🍷 5.60 – ***Conservatory Grill :*** **Meals** 9.75/15.00 **t.** and a la carte 🍷 5.60 – ☕ 9.95 – **181 rm** 155.00/175.00 **st.**, 5 suites.

Shelbourne (Forte), 27 St. Stephen's Green, D2, ✆ 676 6471, Fax 661 6006 – |‡| ⇔ rm TV ☎ 🚗 – 🏛 400. AE ① VISA JZ s
Meals 15.50/26.00 and a la carte 🍷 5.65 – ☕ 11.50 – **155 rm** 130.00/172.00, 9 suites – SB .

Westbury, Grafton St., D2, ✆ 679 1122, Telex 91091, Fax 679 7078 – |‡| ⇔ rm ▤ rest TV ☎ 🚗 – 🏛 150. AE ① VISA JCB. ✗ JY b
Meals 16.50/24.00 **t.** and a la carte 🍷 5.60 – ☕ 10.00 – **195 rm** 155.00/175.00 **t.**, 8 suites.

Jurys H. & Towers, Pembroke Rd, Ballsbridge, D4, ✆ 660 5000, Telex 93723, Fax 660 5540, heated – |‡| ⇔ rm ▤ rest TV ☎ ♿ 🅿 – 🏛 850. AE ① VISA. ✗ by T44 KZ
Kish : **Meals** - Seafood - (dinner only) 25.00 **t.** and a la carte 🍷 6.00 – ***Embassy Garden :*** **Meals** 12.50/21.00 **t.** and a la carte 🍷 6.00 – ☕ 9.75 – **378 rm** 121.00/180.00 **t.**, 6 suites – SB .

Burlington, Upper Leeson St., D4, ✆ 660 5222, Telex 93815, Fax 660 3172 – |‡| ⇔ rm ▤ rest TV ☎ ♿ 🅿 – 🏛 1000. AE ① VISA JCB. ✗ by N11 KZ
Meals 14.50/17.50 **t.** and a la carte 🍷 5.50 – ☕ 9.35 – **448 rm** 115.00/135.00 **t.**, 4 suites.

Gresham, O'Connell St., D1, ✆ 874 6881, Telex 32473, Fax 878 7175 – |‡| ▤ rest TV ☎ ♿ 🚗 – 🏛 250. AE ① VISA. ✗ JX k
Meals 12.50/24.20 **st.** and a la carte 🍷 7.90 – ☕ 11.00 – **194 rm** 80.00/160.00 **t.**, 6 suites.

Hibernian, Eastmoreland Pl., Ballsbridge, D4, ✆ 668 7666, Fax 660 2655 – |‡| TV ☎ ♿ 🅿. AE ① VISA. ✗ by Baggot Street KZ
closed 24 to 29 December – ***Patrick Kavanagh Room :*** **Meals** *(closed Saturday lunch)* 13.95/29.95 **t.** and dinner a la carte 🍷 5.95 – **29 rm** ☕ 90.00/157.00 **st.** – SB .

Doyle Montrose, Stillorgan Rd, D4, SE : 4 m. by N 11 ✆ 269 3311, Fax 269 1164 – |‡| ▤ rest TV ☎ ♿ 🅿 – 🏛 80. AE ① VISA JCB. ✗ by N11 KZ
Meals 9.35/16.50 **t.** and a la carte 🍷 5.80 – ☕ 7.40 – **179 rm** 83.00/143.00 **t.**

Mespil, Mespil Rd, D4, ✆ 667 1222, Fax 667 1244 – |‡| ⇔ rm ▤ rest. TV ☎ ♿ 🅿 – 🏛 40. AE ① VISA ✗ by Baggot Street KZ
closed 24 to 26 December – **Meals** (bar lunch)/dinner 17.95 **t.** and a la carte 🍷 5.25 – ☕ 6.50 – **153 rm** 65.00/80.00 **t.** – SB.

Royal Dublin, O'Connell St., D1, ✆ 873 3666, Fax 873 3120 – |‡| TV ☎ 🚗 – 🏛 220. AE ① VISA. ✗ – *closed 25 December* – **Meals** 11.50/18.95 **st.** and a la carte 🍷 4.75 – **114 rm** ☕ 83.00/104.00 **st.**, 3 suites – SB . JX m

Stephen's Hall, Earlsfort Centre, 14-17 Lower Leeson St., D2, ✆ 661 0585, Fax 661 0606 – |‡| TV ☎ 🚗. AE ① VISA. ✗ JZ
closed 24 December-4 January – **Meals** *(closed Sunday and Bank Holidays)* 9.50/15.00 **t.** and dinner a la carte 🍷 5.00 – ☕ 8.00 – **3 rm** 100.00/140.00 **st.**, **34 suites** 140.00/200.00 **t.** – SB .

Temple Bar, Fleet St., D2, ✆ 677 3333, Fax 677 3088 – |‡| TV ☎ ♿ – 🏛 30. AE ① VISA. ✗ *closed 23 December-4 January* – **Meals** 8.25/18.00 **st.** and a la carte – ☕ 6.00 – **108 rm** 85.00/110.00 **st.** – SB . JY e

Doyle Tara, Merrion Rd, D4, SE : 4 m. on T 44 ✆ 269 4666, Fax 269 1027 – |‡| ▤ rest TV ☎ 🅿 – 🏛 300. AE ① VISA. ✗ KZ
Meals 8.90/14.00 **t.** and a la carte – ☕ 6.50 – **113 rm** 76.00/99.00 **t.**

Russell Court, 21-25 Harcourt St., D2, ✆ 478 4066, Fax 478 1576 – |‡| ⇔ rm TV ☎ 🅿 – 🏛 150. AE ① VISA. ✗ JZ p
closed 24 to 29 December – **Meals** (bar meals Sunday) 12.50/16.00 **t.** and dinner a la carte 🍷 6.50 – ☕ 6.50 – **36 rm** 60.00/90.00 **t.**, 6 suites – SB .

Doyle Skylon, Upper Drumcondra Rd, N : 2 ½ m. on N 1 ✆ 837 9121, Fax 837 2778 – |‡| ▤ rest TV ☎ 🅿. AE ① VISA. ✗
Meals 9.50/13.25 **t.** and a la carte 🍷 4.60 – ☕ 6.50 – **92 rm** 76.00/99.00 **t.** – SB .

Grafton Plaza without rest., Johnsons Pl., D2, ✆ 475 0888, Fax 475 0908 – |‡| TV ☎ ♿. AE ① VISA. ✗ – *closed 24 to 26 December* – ☕ 7.50 – **75 rm** 70.00/95.00 **st.** JZ v

Jurys Christchurch Inn, Christchurch Pl., D8, ✆ 475 0111, Fax 475 0488 – |‡| ⇔ rm ▤ rest TV ☎ ♿ 🅿. AE ① VISA. ✗ – *closed 24 to 26 December* – **Meals** (bar lunch)/dinner 13.50 **st.** and a la carte 🍷 4.95 – ☕ 6.00 – **182 rm** 51.00 **st.** HY c

Ariel House without rest., 52 Lansdowne Rd, Ballsbridge, D4, ✆ 668 5512, Fax 668 5845 – TV ☎ 🅿. VISA. ✗ by T44 KZ
closed 24 December-14 January – ☕ 7.50 – **28 rm** 60.00/140.00 **t.**

Central, 1-5 Exchequer St., D2, ✆ 679 7302, Fax 679 7303 – |‡| TV ☎ – 🏛 80. AE ① VISA. ✗ *closed 24 to 27 December* – **Meals** (bar lunch Monday to Friday) a la carte 13.90/17.65 **t.** 🍷 5.95 – ☕ 7.50 – **69 rm** 60.00/110.00 **t.**, 1 suite. JY u

Anglesea Town House without rest., 63 Anglesea Rd, Ballsbridge, D4, ✆ 668 3877, Fax 668 3461 – TV ☎. AE VISA. ✗ by T44 KZ
closed 20 December-4 January – **7 rm** ☕ 45.00/90.00 **t.**

XXX ✿✿ **Patrick Guilbaud,** 46 James' Pl., James' St., off Lower Baggot St., D2, ✆ 676 4192, Fax 661 0052 – ▤. AE VISA KZ **n**
closed Sunday, Monday, 1 to 10 January and Bank Holidays – **Meals** - French - 18.50/30.00 **t.** and a la carte 32.00/38.00 **t.** 8.00
Spec. Cassolette of Dublin Bay prawns with lemon butter, Crubeens (pigs trotters) served with a mushroom pudding, Croustade aux pommes.

XXX ✿ **The Commons,** Newman House, 85-86 St. Stephen's Green, D2, ✆ 475 2597, Fax 478 0551, « Contemporary collection of James Joyce inspired Irish Art » – AE VISA JZ **e**
closed Saturday lunch, Sunday, 2 weeks Christmas and Bank Holidays – **Meals** 18.00/30.00 **t.** and a la carte 30.50/43.50 **t.** 7.00
Spec. Pan fried slices of duck foie gras with grilled Clonakilty black pudding, Grilled turbot fillet, pea and smoked bacon confit, beluga caviar sauce, Braised loin of lamb with parsley dumplings, fennel, thyme and Parmesan.

XXX **Ernie's,** Mulberry Gdns, off Morehampton Rd, Donnybrook, D4, ✆ 269 3300, Fax 269 3260, « Contemporary Irish Art collection » – ▤. AE VISA by N11 KZ
closed Saturday lunch, Sunday, Monday and 1 week Christmas – **Meals** 10.00/25.00 **t.** and dinner a la carte 24.00/33.50 **t.** 7.50.

XXX **Viking at Clontarf Castle,** Castle Av., Clontarf, D3, NE : 3½ m. ✆ 833 2271, Fax 833 4549 – ▤ P. AE VISA KX
closed Sunday, Monday, Good Friday and 24 to 26 December – **Meals** (dinner only) 14.50 **t.** and a la carte 5.50.

XXX **Le Coq Hardi,** 35 Pembroke Rd, D4, ✆ 668 9070, Fax 668 9887 – P. AE VISA JCB
closed Saturday lunch, Sunday, 2 weeks August, 2 weeks Christmas and Bank Holidays – **Meals** 18.00/30.00 **t.** and a la carte 8.00. by Baggot Street KZ

XX **Chapter One,** The Dublin Writers Museum, 18-19 Parnell Sq., D1, ✆ 873 2266, Fax 873 2330 – ▤ P. AE VISA JX **r**
closed Saturday lunch, Monday dinner, Sunday, 25 to 26 December and Bank Holidays – **Meals** 12.50/22.50 **t.** and dinner a la carte 18.25/23.75 **t.** 6.00.

XX ✿ **Thornton's,** (Thornton), I Portobello Rd, D8, ✆ 454 9067, Fax 454 9067 – ▤. AE VISA
closed Sunday and Monday – **Meals** (booking essential) (dinner only) 28.50 **t.** and a la carte 26.50/32.45 **t.** 6.75. by N81 HZ
Spec. Marinated wild Atlantic salmon with cucumber jelly, Sautéed loin of lamb with courgette clafoutis and thyme jus, Nougat pyramid with glazed fruit and orange sauce.

XX **Locks,** 1 Windsor Terr., Portobello, ✆ 4543391, Fax 4538352 – AE VISA
closed Saturday lunch, Sunday, last week July-first week August and 1 week Christmas – **Meals** 13.95/22.00 **t.** and a la carte 5.95. by N81 HZ

XX **Polo One,** 5-6 Molesworth Pl., off Molesworth St., D2, ✆ 662 2233, Fax 678 9593 AE VISA
closed Sunday – **Meals** 10.00/17.50 **t.** and a la carte 5.50. JZ **h**

XX **Zen,** 89 Upper Rathmines Rd, D6, ✆ 4979428 – ▤. AE VISA
closed lunch Monday, Tuesday, Wednesday, Saturday and 25 to 26 December – **Meals** - Chinese (Szechuan) - 8.00/18.00 **st.** and a la carte 5.00. by Camden Street JZ

XX **Les Frères Jacques,** 74 Dame St., D2, ✆ 679 4555, Fax 679 4725 – AE VISA HY **x**
closed Saturday lunch, Sunday, 25-30 December and Bank Holidays – **Meals** - French - 13.00/20.00 **t.** and dinner a la carte 5.50.

XX **L'Ecrivain,** 109 Lower Baggot St., D2, ✆ 661 1919, Fax 661 0617, – ▤. AE VISA
closed Saturday lunch, Sunday, 25 to 27 December and Bank Holidays– **Meals** (booking essential) 11.00/25.00 **t.** and dinner a la carte 6.50. KZ **b**

XX **La Stampa,** 35 Dawson St., D2, ✆ 677 8611, Fax 677 3336 – AE VISA JZ **g**
closed lunch Saturday and Sunday, Good Friday and 25 December – **Meals** 10.50 **t.** (lunch) and dinner a la carte 17.40/27.40 **t.** 6.00.

XX **Peacock Alley,** 112 Lower Baggot St., ✆ 662 0760, Fax 662 0776 AE VISA KZ **a**
closed Saturday lunch, Sunday, 23 December to lunch 31 December and Bank Holidays – **Meals** (booking essential) 15.95/35.00 **t.**

XX **Old Dublin,** 90-91 Francis St., D8, ✆ 4542028, Fax 4541406 – AE VISA HZ **n**
closed Saturday lunch, Sunday and Bank Holidays – **Meals** - Russian-Scandinavian - 12.50/19.50 **t.** and dinner a la carte 5.95.

XX **Chandni,** 174 Pembroke Rd, Ballsbridge, D4, ✆ 668 1458 – ▤. AE VISA
closed Sunday lunch – **Meals** - Indian - 7.95/39.95 **st.** and dinner a la carte. by T44 KZ

XX **Fitzers Café,** RDS, Merrion Rd, Ballsbridge, D4, ✆ 667 1301, Fax 667 1299 – P. AE VISA by T44 KZ
closed 25-26 December, January and Good Friday – **Meals** (booking essential) 10.50/35.95 **t.** and a la carte 6.95.

X **Dobbin's,** 15 Stephen's Lane, off Lower Mount St., D2, ✆ 676 4679, Fax 661 3331 – ▤ P. AE VISA by T44 KZ **s**
closed Saturday lunch, Monday dinner, Sunday and Bank Holidays – **Meals** - Bistro - 14.50/23.00 **st.** and a la carte 6.25.

X **Roly's Bistro,** 7 Ballsbridge Terr., Ballsbridge, D4, ✆ 668 2611, Fax 660 8535 – ▤. AE VISA by T44 KZ
closed Good Friday and 25 to 26 December – **Meals** 9.50 **t.** (lunch) and dinner a la carte 14.40/20.95 **t.** 4.50.

Italy

Italia

ROME – FLORENCE – MILAN – NAPLES
PALERMO – TAORMINA – TURIN – VENICE

PRACTICAL INFORMATION

LOCAL CURRENCY

Italian Lire: 1000 ITL = 0.06 USD ($) (Jan. 96)

TOURIST INFORMATION

Welcome Office (Ente Provinciale per il Turismo):
– Via Parigi 11 - 00185 ROMA (closed Sunday), ✆ 06/488991, Fax 481 93 16
– Via Marconi 1 - 20123 MILANO, ✆ 02/861287, Fax 720 22 432
See also telephone number and address of other Tourist Information offices in the text of the towns under ℹ.
American Express:
– Piazza di Spagna 38 - 00187 ROMA, ✆ 06/67641, Fax 678 24 56
– Via Brera 3 - 20121 MILANO, ✆ 02/80 94 11, Fax 86 10 28

AIRLINES

ALITALIA: Via Bissolati 20 - 00187 ROMA, ✆ 06/65621, Fax 656 28 310
Via Albricci 5 - 20122 MILANO, ✆ 02/62811, Fax 805 67 57
AIR FRANCE: Via Sardegna 40 - 00187 ROMA, ✆ 06/48187911, Fax 488 45 03
Piazza Cavour 2 - 20121 MILANO, ✆ 02/760731, Fax 760 73 333
DELTA AIRLINES: Via Bissolati 46 - 00187 ROMA, ✆ 06/4773, Fax 481 70 79
Via Melchiorre Gioia 66 - 20125 MILANO, ✆ 02/67 07 00 77, Fax 67 07 31 82
TWA: Via Barberini 59 - 00187 ROMA, ✆ 06/47241, Fax 474 61 25
Corso Europa 11 - 20122 MILANO, ✆ 02/77961, Fax 76 01 45 83

FOREIGN EXCHANGE

Money can be changed at the Banca d'Italia, other banks and authorised exchange offices (Banks close at 1.30pm and at weekends).

POSTAL SERVICES

Local post offices: open Monday to Saturday 8.30am to 2.00pm
General Post Office (open 24 hours only for telegrams):
– Piazza San Silvestro 00187 ROMA – Piazza Cordusio 20123 MILANO

SHOPPING

In the index of street names those printed in red are where the principal shops are found. In Rome, the main shopping streets are: Via del Babuino, Via Condotti, Via Frattina, Via Vittorio Veneto; in Milan: Via Dante, Via Manzoni, Via Monte Napoleone, Corso Vittorio Emanuele.

BREAKDOWN SERVICE

Certain garages in the centre and outskirts of towns operate a 24 hour breakdown service. If you break down the police are usually able to help by indicating the nearest one.
A free car breakdown service (a tax is levied) is operated by the A.C.I. for foreign motorists carrying the fuel card (Carta Carburante). The A.C.I. also offers telephone information in English (24 hours a day) for road and weather conditions and tourist events: 06/4477.

TIPPING

As well as the service charge, it is the custom to tip employees. The amount can vary depending upon the region and the service given.

SPEED LIMITS

On motorways, the maximum permitted speed is 130 km/h - 80 mph for vehicles over 1000 cc, 110 km/h - 68 mph for all other vehicles. On other roads, the speed limit is 90 km/h - 56 mph.

Rome

(ROMA) 00100 988 ㉖ 430 Q 19 - Pop. 2 687 881 - alt. 20 - ☎ 06.

9 18 Parco de' Medici (closed Tuesday) ✉ 00148 Roma SW : 4,5 km ☎ 655 34 77 - Fax 655 33 44.

18 (closed Monday) at Acquasanta ✉ 00178 Roma SE : 12 km. ☎ 780 34 07, Fax 78 34 62 19.

18 and 18 Marco Simone (closed Tuesday) at Guidonia Montecelio ✉ 00012 Roma W : 7 km ☎ (0774) 366 469, Fax 366 476.

9 Arco di Costantino (closed Tuesday) ✉ 00188 Roma N : 15 km ☎ 33 62 44 40, Fax 33 61 29 19

9 Fioranello (closed Wednesday) at Santa Maria delle Mole ✉ 00040 Roma SE : 19 km ☎ 713 80 80, Fax 713 82 12.

9 and 18 (closed Monday) at Olgiata ✉ 00123 Roma NW : 19 km ☎ 308 89 141, Fax 308 89 968.

✈ Ciampino SW : 15 km ☎ 794941 and Leonardo da Vinci di Fiumicino SE : 26 km ☎ 65951 - Alitalia, via Bissolati 13 ✉ 00187 ☎ 46881 and via della Magliana 886 ✉ 00148 ☎ 65643.

🚗 Termini ☎ 4775 - Tiburtina ☎ 47301.

ℹ via Parigi 5 ✉ 00185 ☎ 48 89 92 00, Fax 481 93 16 ; at Termini Station ☎ 4871270 ; at Fiumicino Airport ☎ 65010255.

A.C.I. via Cristoforo Colombo 261 ✉ 00147 ☎ 514 971 and via Marsala 8 ✉ 00185 ☎ 49981, Telex 610686, Fax 499 82 34.

Distances from Rome are indicated in the text of the other towns listed in this Guide.

SIGHTS

Rome's most famous sights are indicated on the town plans pp. 2 to 9. For a more complete visit use the Michelin Green Guide to Rome.

ROMA
NORTH CENTRE
Traffic restricted
in the town center

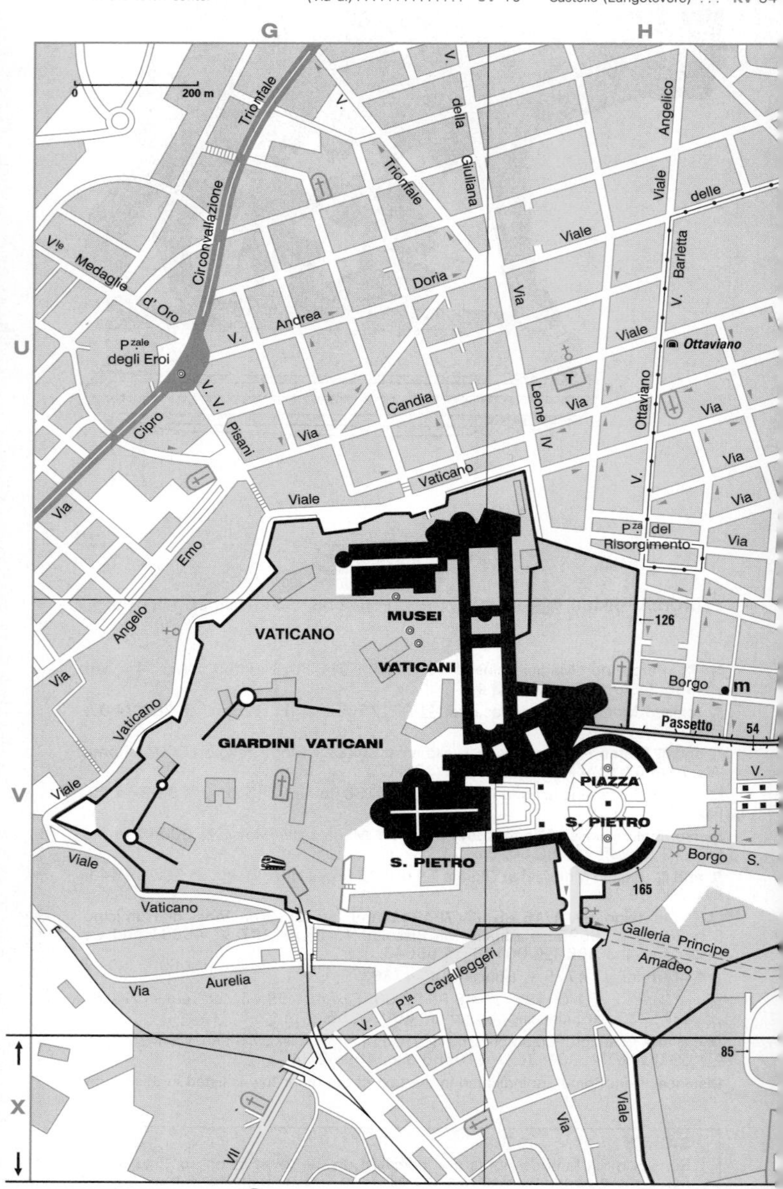

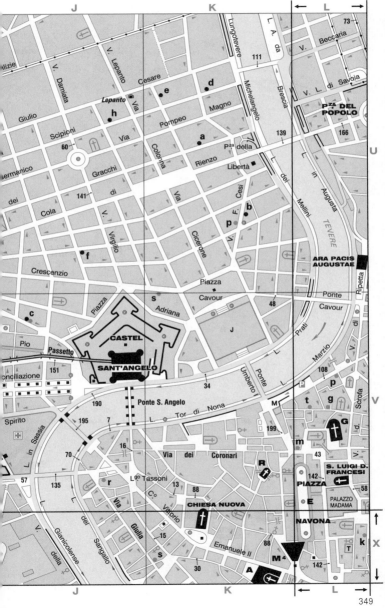

Street	Grid	No.
Governo Vecchio (Via d.)	KVX	88
Lucania (Via)	PU	94
Monte Brianzo (Via di)	LV	108
Nenni (Ponte P.)	KU	111
Porta Angelica (Via di)	HV	126
Prinicpe A. Savoia Aosta (Ponte	JV	135
Quirinale (Via d.)	OV	138
Regina Margherita (Ponte)	KU	139
Regolo (Via A.)	JU	14
Rinascimento (Corso d.)	LVX	14
Rotonda (Via)	MX	14
S. Angelo (Borgo)	JV	15
S. Chiara (Via)	MX	15

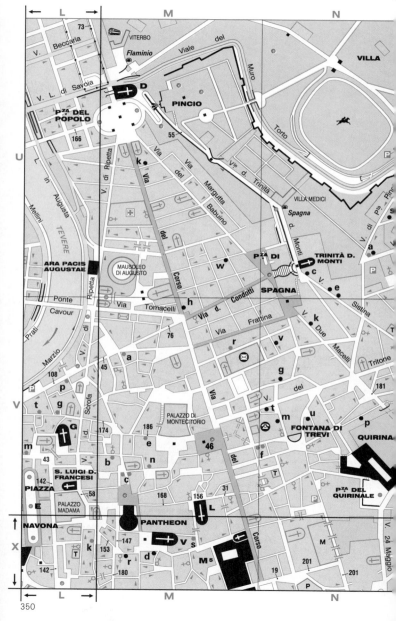

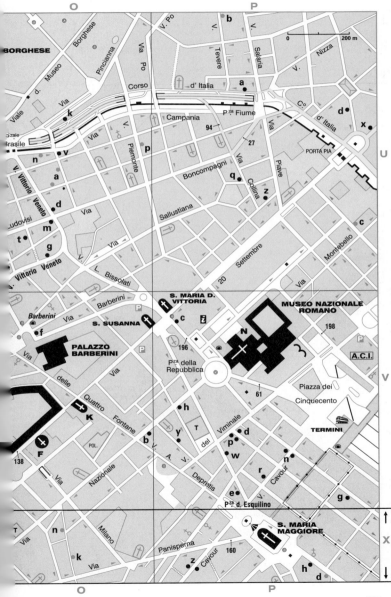

ROMA

SOUTH CENTRE

Traffic restricted in the town center

Alberteschi (Lungotevere) . . . . MZ 6
Anguillara (Lungotevere d.) . . . . . . LY 10
Banchi Vecchi (Via d.) . . . . JKX 15
Battisti (Via C.) . . . . NX 19
Belli (Piazza G. G.) . . . . LYZ 21
Botteghe Oscure Via d.) . . . . MY 22
Busiri-Vici (Via A.) . . . . HZ 25

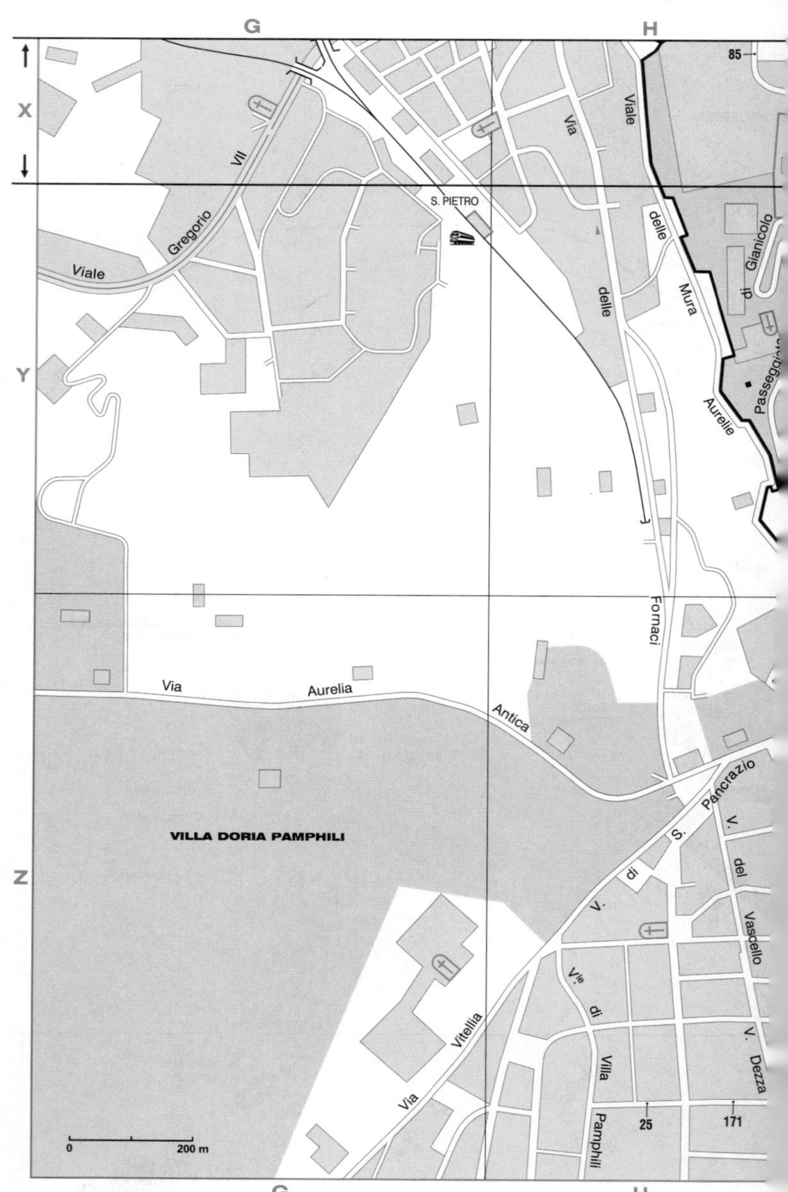

J K L

NAVONA

PAL. FARNESE

VILLA FARNESINA

PAL. SPADA

GIANICOLO

S. PIETRO IN MONTORIO

TRASTEVERE

J K L

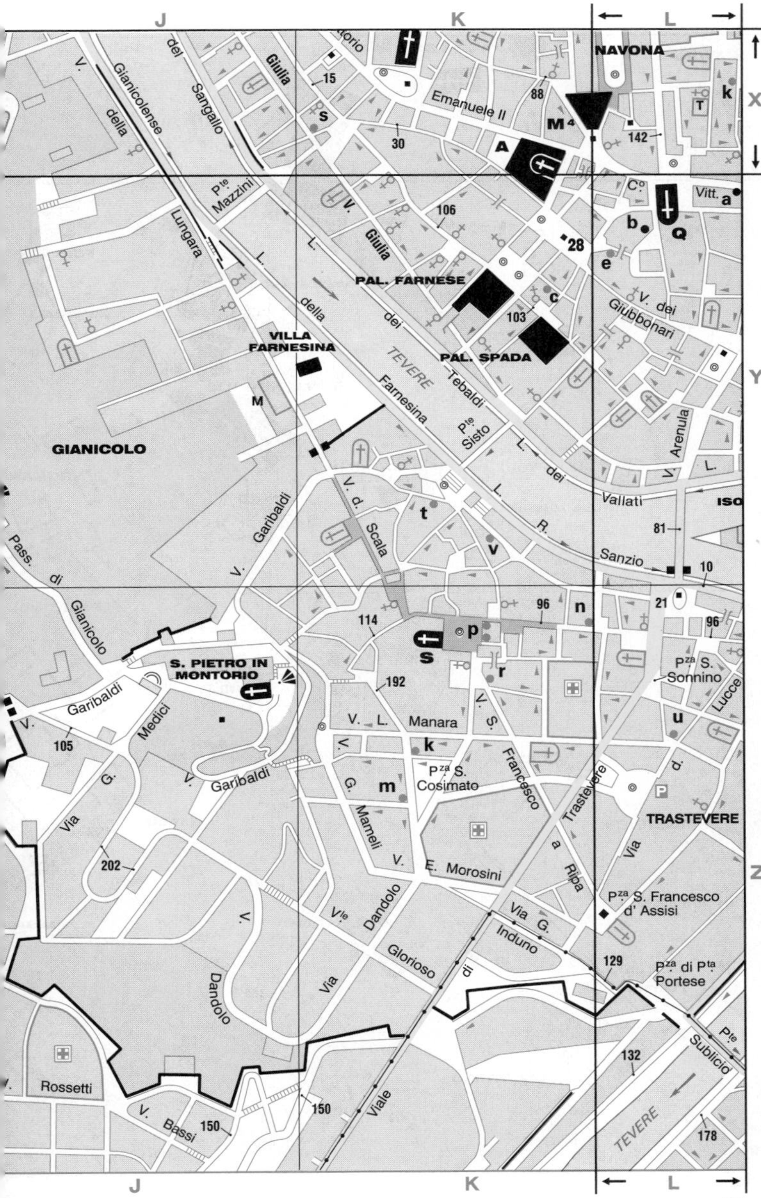

Monserrato (Via) .... KY 106
Paglia (Via d.) .... KZ 114
Pierleoni (Lungotevere d.) ...... MZ 117
Plebiscito (Via d.) .... MY 121
Porta Lavernale (Via) .... MZ 127
Porta Portese (Via di) ... LZ 129
Portico d'Ottavia (Via) ... MY 130
Portuense (Lungotevere) .... LZ 132
Publicii (Clivo d.) .... NZ 136
Rinascimento (Corso d.) .... LVX 142
Rotonda (Via) .... MX 147
Saffi (Viale A.) .... JKZ 150

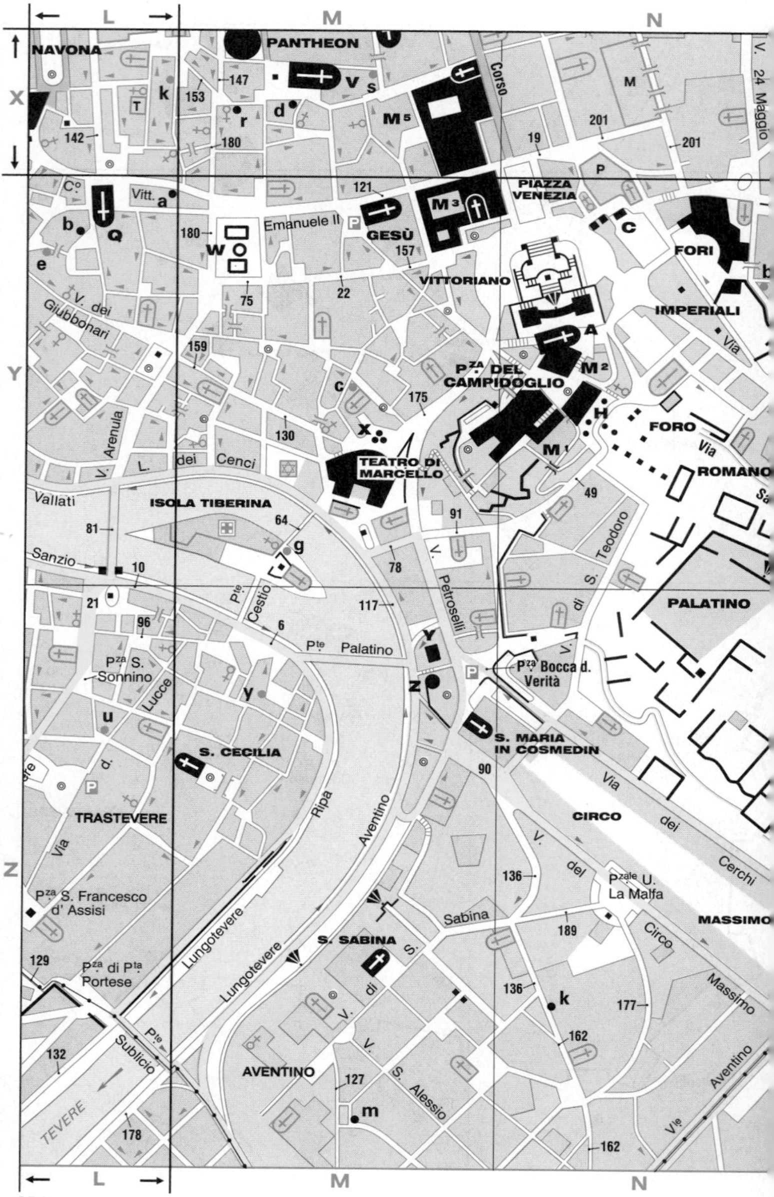

O P

X Y Z

S. MARIA MAGGIORE
Via Panisperna
Via Cavour
160
Via Milano
Cavour
Via G. Lanza
V. d. Statuto
Via Merulana
Via Mecenate
S. PIETRO IN VINCOLI
Fori Imperiali
DOMUS AUREA
COLOSSEO
V. Domus Aurea
V. R. Bonghi
Via Labicana
V. di S. Giovanni in Laterano
S. CLEMENTE
ARCO DI COSTANTINO
V. di San Gregorio
V. Claudia
V. di S. Stefano Rotondo
Pza di Porta Capena
Vle d. Terme di Caracalla
V. d. Navicella
Via Amba Aradam
V. d. Ferratella
V. Ipponio
Pza di Porta Metronia
V. Gallia
0 200 m

O P

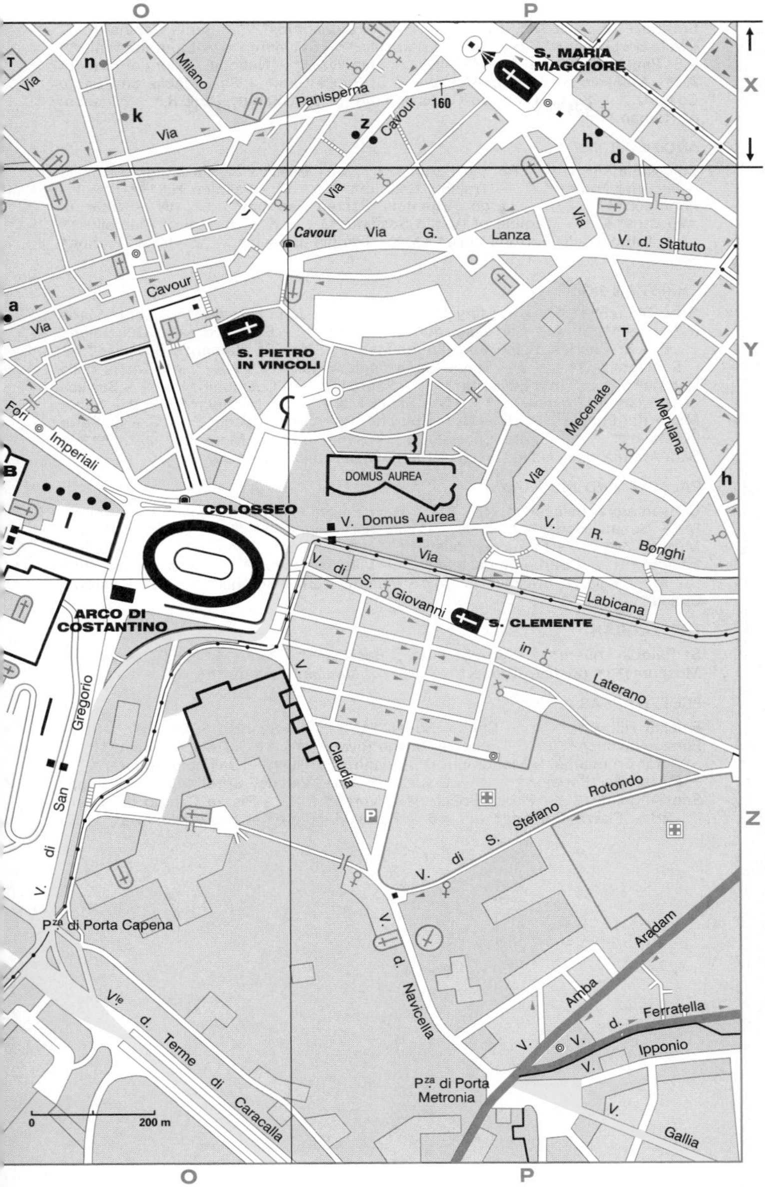

Sights

How to make the most of a trip to Rome - some ideas :

Borghese Museum★★★ - Villa Giulia★★★ - Catacombs★★★ - Santa Sabina★★ MZ - Villa Borghese★★ NOU - Baths of Caracalla★★ - St Lawrence Without the Walls★★ - St Paul Without the Walls★★ - Old Appian Way★★ - National Gallery of Modern Art★- Mausoleum of Caius Cestius★ - St Paul's Gate★ - San'Agnese and Santa Costanza★ - Santa Croce in Gerusalemme★ - San Saba★ - E.U.R.★ - Museum of Roman Civilisation.

ANCIENT ROME

Colosseum★★★ OYZ - Roman Forum★★★ NOY - Basilica of Maxentius★★★ OY **B** - Imperial Fora★★★ NY - Trajan's Column★★★ NY **C** - Palatine Hill★★★ NOYZ - Pantheon★★★ MVX - Largo Argentina Sacred Precinct★★ MY **W** - Altar of Augustus★★ LU - Temple of Apollo Sosianus★★ MY **X** - Theatre of Marcellus★★ MY - Tempio della Fortuna Virile★ MZ **Y** - Tempio di Vesta★ MZ **Z** - Isola Tiberina★ MY.

CHRISTIAN ROME

Gesù Church★★★ MY - St Mary Major★★★ PX - St John Lateran★★★ - Santa Maria d'Aracoeli★★ NY **A** - San Luigi dei Francesi★★ LV - Sant'Andrea al Quirinale★★ OV **F** - St Charles at the Four Fountains★★ OV **K** - St Clement's Basilica★★ PZ - Sant'Ignazio★★ MV **L** - Santa Maria degli Angeli★★ PV **N** - Santa Maria della Vittoria★★ PV - Santa Susanna★★ OV - Santa Maria in Cosmedin★★ MNZ - Basilica of St Mary in Trastevere★★ KZ **S** - Santa Maria sopra Minerva★★ MX **V** - Santa Maria del Popolo★ MU **D** - New Church★ KX - Sant'Agostino★ LV **G** - St Peter in Chains★ OY - Santa Cecilia★ MZ - San Pietro in Montorio★ JZ ⋞★★★ - Sant'Andrea della Valle★ LY **Q** - Santa Maria della Pace★ KV **R**.

PALACES AND MUSEUMS

Conservators' Palace★★★ MNY **M¹** - New Palace★★★ (Capitoline Museum★★) NY **M¹** - Senate House★★★ NY **H** - Castel Sant'Angelo★★★ JKV - National Roman Museum★★★ PV - Chancery Palace★★ KX **A** - Palazzo Farnese★★ KY - Quirinal Palace★★ NOV - Barberini Palace★★ OV - Villa Farnesina★★ KY - Palazzo Venezia★ MY **M³** - Palazzo Braschi★ KX **M⁴** - Palazzo Doria Pamphili★ MX **M⁵** - Palazzo Spada★ KY.

THE VATICAN

St Peter's Square★★★ HV - St Peter's Basilica★★★ (Dome ⋞★★★) GV - Vatican Museums★★★ (Sistine Chapel★★★) GHUV - Vatican Gardens★★★ GV.

PRETTY AREAS

Pincian Hill ⋞★★★ MU - Capitol Square★★★ MNY - Spanish Square★★★ MNU - Piazza Navona★★★ LVX - Fountain of the Rivers★★★ LV **E** - Trevi Fountain★★★ NV - Victor Emmanuel II Monument (Vittoriano) ⋞★★ MNY - Quirinale Square★★ NV - Piazza del Popolo★★ MU - Gianicolo★ JY - Via dei Coronari★ KV - Ponte Sant'Angelo★ JKV - Piazza Bocca della Verità★ MNZ - Piazza Campo dei Fiori★ KY **28** - Piazza Colonna★ MV **46** - Porta Maggiore★ - Piazza Venezia★ MNY.

North area Monte Mario, Stadio Olimpico, via Flaminia-Parioli, Villa Borghese, via Salaria, via Nomentana (Plans : Rome pp. 2 to 5) :

Cavalieri Hilton, via Cadlolo 101 ✉ 00136 ☏ 35091, Telex 625337, Fax 3509224, ≤ city, « Terraces and park », – ▤ TV ☎ ♿ – P – 25-2100. AE ⓢ ⓓ E VISA JCB. by via Trionfale GU
Meals *La Pergola* Rest. a la carte 86/137000 – ☕ 30000 – **359 rm** 399/540000, 17 suites.

Lord Byron ⊛, via De Notaris 5 ✉ 00197 ☏ 3220404, Telex 611217, Fax 3220405 – ▤ TV ☎. AE ⓢ ⓓ E VISA JCB. by lungotevere A. da Brescia KU
Meals (see rest. **Relais le Jardin** below) – **28 rm** ☕ 410/550000, 9 suites.

Aldrovandi Palace Hotel, via Aldrovandi 15 ✉ 00197 ☏ 3223993, Telex 616141, Fax 3221435, « Small shaded park » – ▤ TV ☎ P – 50-350. AE ⓢ ⓓ E VISA JCB. by via Flaminia LU
Meals (see rest. **Relais La Piscine** below) – **128 rm** ☕ 500/550000, 10 suites.

Parco dei Principi, via Gerolamo Frescobaldi 5 ✉ 00198 ☏ 854421, Telex 610517, Fax 8845104, ≤, « Small park with », – ▤ TV ☎ – 1000. AE ⓢ ⓓ E VISA. rest by via Pinciana OU
Meals 65/70000 – **165 rm** ☕ 290/430000, 15 suites.

Polo without rest., piazza Gastaldi 4 ✉ 00197 ☏ 3221041, Telex 623107, Fax 3221359 – ▤ TV ☎ – 70. AE ⓢ ⓓ E VISA. by lungotevere A. da Brescia KU
66 rm ☕ 320/360000.

Degli Aranci, via Oriani 11 ✉ 00197 ☏ 8070202, Fax 8070704 – ▤ TV ☎ – 40. AE ⓢ ⓓ E VISA. by lungotevere A. da Brescia KU
Meals 33000 – ☕ 15000 – **54 rm** 225/320000.

Clodio without rest., via di Santa Lucia 10 ✉ 00195 ☏ 3721122, Telex 625050, Fax 3250745 – ▤ TV ☎ – 30. AE ⓢ ⓓ E VISA JCB. by Circonvallazione Trionfale GU
114 rm ☕ 180/250000.

Santa Costanza without rest., viale 21 Aprile 4 ✉ 00162 ☏ 8600602, Fax 8602786, – TV ☎ ♿ – 50. AE ⓢ E VISA by via 20 Settembre PU
50 rm ☕ 150/200000.

XXXX ✿ **Relais le Jardin** - Hotel Lord Byron, via De Notaris 5 ✉ 00197 ☏ 3220404, Fax 3220405, Elegant rest. – ▤. AE ⓢ ⓓ E VISA JCB. by lungotevere A. da Brescia KU
closed Sunday and August – **Meals** (booking essential) a la carte 70/136000
Spec. Gnocchi di semolino con trota salmonata e zucchine, Lombatina di vitello farcita con spugnole e carciofi in crosta di tagliolini (spring), Tulipano di croccante con spuma di agrumi e noci.

XXX **Relais la Piscine** - Hotel Aldrovandi Palace, via Mangili 6 ✉ 00197 ☏ 3216126, « Outdoor summer service » – ▤ P. AE ⓢ ⓓ E VISA JCB.
Meals 60/80000 (lunch) 80/100000 (dinner) and a la carte 78/122000. by lungotevere A. da Brescia KU

XX **Al Ceppo,** via Panama 2 ✉ 00198 ☏ 8419696 – AE ⓢ ⓓ E VISA by via Salaria PU
closed Monday and 8 to 30 August – **Meals** (booking essential for dinner) a la carte 53/77000.

XX **Il Caminetto,** viale dei Parioli 89 ✉ 00197 ☏ 8083946, – ▤. AE ⓢ ⓓ VISA.
Meals a la carte 49/66000. by lungotevere A. da Brescia KU

XX **La Scala,** viale dei Parioli 79/d ✉ 00197 ☏ 8083978, – ▤. AE ⓢ ⓓ E VISA.
closed Wednesday and 2 to 25 August – **Meals** a la carte 40/62000. by lungotevere A. da Brescia KU

XX **Al Fogher,** via Tevere 13/b ✉ 00198 ☏ 8417032, Typical Venetian rest. – ▤. AE ⓢ ⓓ E VISA. PU **b**
closed Saturday lunch, Sunday and August – **Meals** a la carte 56/80000.

X **Delle Vittorie,** via Monte Santo 62/64 ✉ 00195 ☏ 3252776, – AE ⓢ ⓓ E VISA JCB. by via Lepanto JU
closed Sunday, 1 to 20 August and 23 December-3 January – **Meals** a la carte 46/65000.

X **A Tutta Birra,** piazza Callistio 5 ✉ 00199 ☏ 86208791, Fax 86208778, Judaic-Roman rest. – AE ⓢ E VISA. by via Salaria PU
closed Monday and 15 August – **Meals** a la carte 40/50000.

X **Nuraghe Sardo,** viale Medaglie d'Oro 50 ✉ 00136 ☏ 39736584, Sardinian and seafood specialities – ▤. AE ⓓ. by via le Medaglie d'Oro GU
closed Wednesday, 16 to 22 April, August and 23 to 31 December – **Meals** a la carte 34/60000.

Middle-western area San Pietro (Vatican City), Gianicolo, corso Vittorio Emanuele, piazza Venezia, Pantheon and Quirinale, Pincio and Villa Medici, piazza di Spagna, Palatino and Fori (Plans : Rome pp. 2 and 3) :

Hassler, piazza Trinità dei Monti 6 ✉ 00187 ☏ 6782651, Telex 610208, Fax 6789991, ≤ City from roof-garden rest. – ▤ TV ☎ – 70. AE ⓓ VISA JCB. NU **c**
Meals *(closed Sunday dinner)* a la carte 135/191000 – ☕ 30000 – **100 rm** 450/900000, 14 suites.

Eden, via Ludovisi 49 ✉ 00187 ☏ 478121, Telex 610567, Fax 4821584 – ▤ TV ☎ – 60. AE ⓢ ⓓ E VISA JCB. NU **a**
Meals (see rest. **La Terrazza** below) – ☕ 28000 – **101 rm** 450/700000, 11 suites.

Holiday Inn Minerva, piazza della Minerva 69 00186 69941888, Telex 620091, Fax 6794165 – rm – 80. AE E VISA JCB. MX **d**
Meals a la carte 62/105000 – 32000 – **131 rm** 415/590000, 3 suites.

De la Ville Inter-Continental, via Sistina 69 00187 67331, Telex 620836, Fax 6784213 – – 40-120. AE E VISA JCB. NU **e**
Meals 70/100000 – **169 rm** 533/641000, 23 suites.

Jolly Leonardo da Vinci, via dei Gracchi 324 00192 32499, Telex 611182, Fax 3610138 – rm – 30-220. AE E VISA JCB. rest KU **a**
Meals 60000 – **256 rm** 340/390000.

Dei Borgognoni without rest., via del Bufalo 126 00187 69941505, Telex 623074, Fax 69941501 – – 25-70. AE E VISA JCB. NV **g**
20000 – **50 rm** 390/470000.

Visconti Palace without rest., via Federico Cesi 37 00193 3684, Telex 622489, Fax 3200551 – – 25-150. AE E VISA. KU **b**
234 rm 280/400000, 13 suites.

Plaza without rest., via del Corso 126 00186 69921111, Telex 624669, Fax 69941575 – – 60. AE E VISA JCB MV **h**
37000 – **196 rm** 343/490000, 5 suites.

Atlante Star, via Vitelleschi 34 00193 6873233, Telex 622355, Fax 6872300 – – 50. AE E VISA JCB JV **c**
Meals (see rest. **Les Etoiles** below) – **61 rm** 390/490000, 3 suites.

Valadier, via della Fontanella 15 00187 3611998, Telex 620873, Fax 3201558 – – 35. AE E VISA JCB. MU **k**
Meals a la carte 55/71000 – **35 rm** 330/450000, 3 suites.

Delle Nazioni without rest., via Poli 7 00187 6792441, Telex 614193, Fax 6782400 – . AE E VISA. NV **m**
83 rm 305/385000, 4 suites.

Giulio Cesare without rest., via degli Scipioni 287 00192 3210751, Telex 613010, Fax 3211736, – – 40. AE E VISA JCB. KU **d**
80 rm 280/380000.

Farnese without rest., via Alessandro Farnese 30 00192 3212553, Fax 3215129 – . AE E VISA. KU **e**
22 rm 240/350000.

White without rest., via Arcione 77 00187 6991242, Telex 626065, Fax 6788451 – – 40. AE E VISA. NV **p**
40 rm 250/300000.

Santa Chiara without rest., via Santa Chiara 21 00186 6872979, Fax 6873144 – – 40. AE E VISA JCB. MX **r**
93 rm 230/320000, 3 suites.

Internazionale without rest., via Sistina 79 00187 69941823, Fax 6784764 – . AE E VISA JCB NU **e**
40 rm 210/295000, 2 suites.

Arcangelo without rest., via Boezio 15 00192 6874143, Fax 6893050 – . AE E VISA. JU **f**
33 rm 185/250000.

Della Torre Argentina without rest., corso Vittorio Emanuele 102 00186 6833886, Fax 68801641 – . AE E VISA JCB. LY **a**
52 rm 205/290000, suite.

Tritone without rest., via del Tritone 210 00187 69922575, Telex 614254, Fax 6782624 – . AE VISA. NV **t**
43 rm 220/270000.

Olympic without rest., via Properzio 2/a 00193 6896650, Telex 623368, Fax 68308255 – . AE E VISA JCB JU **g**
52 rm 190/260000.

Gerber without rest., via degli Scipioni 241 00192 3216485, Fax 3217048 – . AE E VISA. JU **h**
27 rm 160/200000.

Columbus, via della Conciliazione 33 00193 6865435, Telex 620096, Fax 6864874, « 15C building, period decor », – – 30-200. AE E VISA JCB. JV **k**
Meals a la carte 65/100000 – **105 rm** 205/270000.

Sant'Anna without rest., borgo Pio 133 00193 68801602, Fax 68308717 – . AE E VISA. HV **m**
20 rm 170/240000.

Accademia without rest., piazza Accademia di San Luca 75 00187 69922607, Fax 6785897 – . AE VISA. NV **u**
58 rm 220/270000.

Madrid without rest., via Mario de' Fiori 95 00187 6991511, Fax 6791653 – . AE E VISA JCB. NV **v**
19 rm 185/260000, 7 suites.

Condotti without rest., via Mario de' Fiori 37 ✉ 00187 ☎ 6794661, Fax 6790457 – 🛗 ▤ 📺 ☎. AE 🅂 ⓓ E VISA JCB. ✻ MU **w**
16 rm ☕ 270/350000.

City without rest., via Due Macelli 97 ✉ 00187 ☎ 6784037, Fax 6797972 – 🛗 ⇔ ▤ 📺 ☎. AE 🅂 ⓓ E VISA JCB. ✻ NV **k**
29 rm ☕ 220/280000.

Teatro di Pompeo without rest., largo del Pallaro 8 ✉ 00186 ☎ 68300170, Fax 68805531, « Vaults of Pompeius' theatre » – 🛗 ▤ 📺 ☎ – 🏛 30. AE 🅂 ⓓ E VISA. ✻ LY **b**
12 rm ☕ 200/260000.

XXXX ✿ **La Terrazza** - Hotel Eden, via Ludovisi 49 ✉ 00187 ☎ 478121, Fax 4821584, « Roof-garden with ≤ town » – ▤. AE 🅂 ⓓ E VISA JCB. ✻ NU **a**
Meals a la carte 95/145000
Spec. Carpaccio tiepido con funghi e rucola, Lasagnette gratinate con legumi e pesto, Scaloppa di orata in agrodolce con cipollotti.

XXX **El Toulà,** via della Lupa 29/b ✉ 00186 ☎ 6873498, Fax 6871115, Elegant rest. – ▤. AE 🅂 ⓓ E VISA JCB. ✻ MV **a**
closed Saturday lunch, Sunday, August and 24 to 26 December – **Meals** (booking essential) a la carte 66/104000 (15 %).

XXX **Les Etoiles** - Atlante Star, via dei Bastioni 1 ✉ 00193 ☎ 6893434, « Roof-garden and summer service on terrace with ≤ St. Peter's Basilica » – ▤. AE 🅂 ⓓ E VISA JCB. ✻ JV **c**
Meals 70/120000 (lunch) 90/170000 (dinner) and a la carte 105/155000.

XXX **Enoteca Capranica,** piazza Capranica 100 ✉ 00186 ☎ 69940992, Fax 69940989 – ▤. AE 🅂 ⓓ VISA JCB. ✻ MV **n**
closed Saturday lunch and Sunday – **Meals** 40000 (lunch only) and a la carte 55/70000.

XXX **Camponeschi,** piazza Farnese 50 ✉ 00186 ☎ 6874927, Fax 6865244, « Summer service with ≤ Farnese palace » – ▤. AE 🅂 ⓓ E VISA. ✻ KY **c**
closed Sunday and 13 to 22 August – **Meals** (dinner only) (booking essential) a la carte 62/110000 (13 %).

XX ✿ **Quinzi Gabrieli,** via delle Coppelle 6 ✉ 00186 ☎ 6879389, Fax 6874940, Seafood – AE 🅂 ⓓ E VISA. ✻ MV **b**
closed Sunday and August – **Meals** (dinner only) (booking essential) a la carte 80/120000 (10 %)
Spec. Insalata di aragosta ai sapori mediterranei, Spaghetti alla Gregoriana, Moscardini alla diavola.

XX **La Rosetta,** via della Rosetta 9 ✉ 00187 ☎ 6861002, Fax 6872852, Seafood – ▤. AE 🅂 ⓓ E VISA JCB MV **c**
closed Saturday lunch, Sunday and 5 to 25 August – **Meals** (booking essential) a la carte 95/140000.

XX **Vecchia Roma,** via della Tribuna di Campitelli 18 ✉ 00186 ☎ 6864604, ☂, Typical Roman rest. with local and seafood specialities – ▤. AE ⓓ MY **c**
closed Wednesday and 10 to 25 August – **Meals** a la carte 51/87000 (12 %).

XX ✿ **Il Convivio,** via dell'Orso 44 ✉ 00186 ☎ 6869432, Fax 6869432 – ▤. AE 🅂 ⓓ E VISA
closed Sunday – **Meals** (booking essential) a la carte 73/109000 (12 %) LV **g**
Spec. Gamberi con passatina di canellini e peperone dolce, Mezze maniche alla gricia con fave, Piccione in casseruola al rosmarino e salsa di vino cotto.

XX **Lo Squalo Bianco,** via Federico Cesi 36 ✉ 00193 ☎ 3214700, Seafood – ▤. AE 🅂 ⓓ E VISA. ✻ KU **p**
closed Sunday and August – **Meals** (booking essential) a la carte 50/80000.

XX **Piccola Roma,** via Uffici del Vicario 36 ✉ 00186 ☎ 6798606 – ▤. AE 🅂 ⓓ E VISA. ✻
closed Sunday and August – **Meals** a la carte 42/63000. MV **e**

XX **Eau Vive,** via Monterone 85 ✉ 00186 ☎ 68801095, Fax 68802571, Catholic missionaries, international cuisine, « 16C building » – ▤. AE 🅂 E VISA. ✻ LX **k**
closed Sunday and August – **Meals** (booking essential for dinner) a la carte 58/73000.

XX **Taverna Giulia,** vicolo dell'Oro 23 ✉ 00186 ☎ 6869768, Fax 6893720, Ligurian rest. – ▤. AE 🅂 ⓓ E VISA JCB. ✻ JV **r**
closed Sunday and August – **Meals** (booking essential for dinner) a la carte 47/68000.

XX **Passetto,** via Zanardelli 14 ✉ 00186 ☎ 68806569, Fax 68806569 – AE 🅂 ⓓ E VISA JCB. ✻ LV **m**
closed Sunday except June-September – **Meals** a la carte 68/101000.

XX **Il Drappo,** vicolo del Malpasso 9 ✉ 00186 ☎ 6877365, ☂, Sardinian rest. – ▤. AE 🅂 E VISA. ✻ KX **s**
closed Sunday and August – **Meals** (booking essential) 60000 b.i..

XX **Da Pancrazio,** piazza del Biscione 92 ✉ 00186 ☎ 6861246, Fax 6861246, « Inn rebuilt on the remains of Pompeius' theatre » – ⇔. AE 🅂 ⓓ E VISA JCB. ✻ LY **e**
closed Wednesday, 1 to 20 August and Christmas – **Meals** a la carte 46/82000.

XX **Quirino,** via delle Muratte 84 ✉ 00187 ☎ 6794108 – 🅂 E VISA NV **f**
closed Sunday and August – **Meals** a la carte 44/70000.

XX **Da Mario,** via della Vite 55 ✉ 00187 ☎ 6783818, Fax 6798419, Tuscan rest. – ▤. AE 🅂 ⓓ E VISA. ✻ MV **r**
closed Sunday and August – **Meals** a la carte 42/59000.

XX **Campana,** vicolo della Campana 18 ✉ 00186 ✆ 6867820, Habitués trattoria – ▤. AE Ⓢ ⓞ VISA LV **p**
closed Monday and August – **Meals** a la carte 48/55000.

XX **Sora Lella,** via di Ponte Quattro Capi 16 (Isola Tiberina) ✉ 00186 ✆ 6861601, Traditional Roman rest. – ▤. AE Ⓢ E VISA. ✻ MY **g**
closed Sunday and August – **Meals** a la carte 46/84000.

X **Hostaria da Cesare,** via Crescenzio 13 ✉ 00193 ✆ 6861227, Trattoria-pizzeria, Seafood – ▤. AE Ⓢ ⓞ E VISA. ✻ KUV **s**
closed Sunday dinner, Monday, Easter, August and Christmas – **Meals** a la carte 50/75000.

X **L'Orso 80,** via dell'Orso 33 ✉ 00186 ✆ 6864904 – ▤. AE Ⓢ ⓞ E VISA. ✻ LV **t**
closed Monday and August – **Meals** carta 45/67000.

X **Al Moro,** vicolo delle Bollette 13 ✉ 00187 ✆ 6783495, Roman trattoria – ▤. ✻ NV **f**
closed Sunday and August – **Meals** (booking essential) a la carte 49/80000.

X **Il Buco,** via Sant'Ignazio 8 ✉ 00186 ✆ 6793298, Tuscan rest. – ▤. AE Ⓢ ⓞ. ✻ MX **s**
closed Monday and 15 to 31 August – **Meals** a la carte 37/58000.

Central eastern area via Vittorio Veneto, via Nazionale, Viminale, Santa Maria Maggiore, Colosseum, Porta Pia, via Nomentana, Stazione Termini, Porta San Giovanni (**Plans : Rome pp. 4 and 5**) :

Excelsior, via Vittorio Veneto 125 ✉ 00187 ✆ 4708, Telex 610232, Fax 4826205 – |‡| ▤ TV ☎ – 🏛 25-600. AE Ⓢ ⓞ E VISA JCB. ✻ rest OU **d**
Meals (residents only) a la carte 87/144000 – ☕ 31000 – **272 rm** 418/649000, 44 suites.

Le Grand Hotel, via Vittorio Emanuele Orlando 3 ✉ 00185 ✆ 4709, Telex 610210, Fax 4747307 – |‡| ▤ TV ☎ – 🏛 40-300. AE Ⓢ ⓞ E VISA JCB. ✻ PV **c**
Meals a la carte 100/140000 – ☕ 31000 – **134 rm** 429/638000, 35 suites 990/1760000.

Majestic, via Vittorio Veneto 50 ✉ 00187 ✆ 486841, Telex 622262, Fax 4880984 – |‡| ▤ TV ☎ ♿ – 🏛 150. AE Ⓢ ⓞ VISA JCB. ✻ OU **e**
Meals a la carte 65/100000 – **88 rm** ☕ 450/540000, 6 suites.

Bernini Bristol, piazza Barberini 23 ✉ 00187 ✆ 4883051, Telex 610554, Fax 4824266 – |‡| ⇆ rm ▤ TV ☎ – 🏛 40-100. AE Ⓢ ⓞ E VISA JCB. ✻ OV **f**
Meals a la carte 62/105000 – ☕ 27500 – **110 rm** 385/506000, 14 suites.

Ambasciatori Palace, via Vittorio Veneto 62 ✉ 00187 ✆ 47493, Telex 610241, Fax 4743601, ≘s – |‡| ▤ TV ☎ ♿ – 🏛 50-200. AE Ⓢ ⓞ E VISA JCB. ✻ rest OU **g**
Meals a la carte 73/111000 – ☕ 25000 – **100 rm** 350/500000, 8 suites.

Quirinale, via Nazionale 7 ✉ 00184 ✆ 4707, Telex 610332, Fax 4820099, « Summer service in garden » – |‡| ▤ TV ☎ – 🏛 25-250. AE Ⓢ ⓞ E VISA JCB. ✻ PV **h**
Meals a la carte 68/102000 – **189 rm** ☕ 280/400000, 3 suites.

Artemide without rest., via Nazionale 22 ✉ 00184 ✆ 489911, Telex 623061, Fax 48991700 – |‡| ▤ TV ☎ ♿ – 🏛 60-120. AE Ⓢ ⓞ E VISA. ✻ OV **b**
82 rm ☕ 300/430000, 5 suites.

Jolly Vittorio Veneto, corso d'Italia 1 ✉ 00198 ✆ 8495, Telex 612293, Fax 8841104 – |‡| ⇆ rm ▤ TV ☎ – 🏛 35-400. AE Ⓢ ⓞ E VISA. ✻ rest OU **k**
Meals *(closed Sunday dinner and August)* a la carte 74/111000 – **200 rm** ☕ 340/425000, 3 suites.

Regina Baglioni, via Vittorio Veneto 72 ✉ 00187 ✆ 476851, Telex 620863, Fax 485483 – |‡| ⇆ rm ▤ TV ☎ – 🏛 50. AE Ⓢ ⓞ E VISA JCB. ✻ OU **m**
Meals a la carte 50/120000 – **130 rm** ☕ 360/520000, 7 suites.

Mecenate Palace Hotel without rest., via Carlo Alberto 3 ✉ 00185 ✆ 4461354, Fax 4461354 – |‡| ⇆ ▤ TV ☎ ♿ – 🏛 25-30. AE Ⓢ ⓞ E VISA. ✻ PX **h**
59 rm ☕ 310/420000, 3 suites.

Mediterraneo, via Cavour 15 ✉ 00184 ✆ 4884051, Fax 4744105 – |‡| ▤ TV ☎ – 🏛 25-90. AE Ⓢ ⓞ E VISA JCB. ✻ PV **n**
Meals *(closed Saturday)* 33/43000 – **257 rm** ☕ 325/435000, 10 suites.

Starhotel Metropole, via Principe Amedeo 3 ✉ 00185 ✆ 4774, Telex 611061, Fax 4740413 – |‡| ▤ TV ☎ 🚗 – 🏛 40-200. AE Ⓢ ⓞ E VISA JCB. ✻ rest PV **p**
Meals a la carte 50/75000 – **268 rm** ☕ 330/430000.

Forum, via Tor de' Conti 25 ✉ 00184 ✆ 6792446, Telex 622549, Fax 6786479, « Roof-garden rest. with ≤ Imperial Forum » – |‡| ▤ TV ☎ 🚗 – 🏛 100. AE Ⓢ ⓞ E VISA JCB. ✻ OY **a**
Meals *(closed Sunday)* a la carte 78/129000 – **81 rm** ☕ 280/420000.

Londra e Cargill, piazza Sallustio 18 ✉ 00187 ✆ 473871, Telex 622227, Fax 4746674 – |‡| ▤ TV ☎ 🚗 – 🏛 25-200. AE Ⓢ ⓞ E VISA. ✻ PU **q**
Meals *(closed August and Saturday-Sunday lunch)* a la carte 60/70000 – **105 rm** ☕ 250/320000, 4 suites.

Genova without rest., via Cavour 33 ✉ 00184 ✆ 476951, Telex 621599, Fax 4827580 – |‡| ▤ TV ☎. AE Ⓢ ⓞ E VISA JCB. ✻ PV **r**
91 rm ☕ 245/360000.

Universo, via Principe Amedeo 5 ✉ 00185 ℘ 476811, Telex 610342, Fax 4745125 – 🛗 ▤ 📺 ☎ ♿ – 🧑‍🏫 25-300. AE 🅂 ◑ E VISA JCB. ✗ rest PV p
Meals 50000 – **198 rm** ☕ 242/353000.

Sofitel, via Lombardia 47 ✉ 00187 ℘ 478021 and rest. 4818965, Telex 622247, Fax 4821019 – 🛗 ⇹ rm ▤ 📺 ☎ – 🧑‍🏫 25-90 NU s
124 rm.

La Residenza without rest., via Emilia 22 ✉ 00187 ℘ 4880789, Fax 485721 – 🛗 ▤ 📺 ☎. AE 🅂 E VISA. ✗ OU t
27 rm ☕ 130/270000.

Massimo D'Azeglio, via Cavour 18 ✉ 00184 ℘ 4870270, Telex 610556, Fax 4827386 – 🛗 ▤ 📺 ☎ – 🧑‍🏫 200. AE 🅂 ◑ E VISA JCB. ✗ PV n
Meals *(closed Sunday)* 43000 – **205 rm** ☕ 285/385000.

Eliseo without rest., via di Porta Pinciana 30 ✉ 00187 ℘ 4870456, Telex 610693, Fax 4819629 – 🛗 ▤ 📺 ☎ – 🧑‍🏫 25. AE 🅂 ◑ E VISA JCB. ✗ OU u
51 rm ☕ 250/400000, 7 suites.

Victoria, via Campania 41 ✉ 00187 ℘ 473931, Telex 610212, Fax 4871890, « Terrace roof-garden » – 🛗 ▤ 📺 ☎ – 🧑‍🏫 30. AE 🅂 ◑ E VISA. ✗ rest OU v
Meals 40000 – **110 rm** ☕ 250/350000.

Britannia without rest., via Napoli 64 ✉ 00184 ℘ 4883153, Telex 611292, Fax 4882343 – 🛗 ▤ 📺 ☎ Ⓟ. AE 🅂 ◑ E VISA JCB PV y
32 rm ☕ 230/290000.

Napoleon, piazza Vittorio Emanuele 105 ✉ 00185 ℘ 4467264, Telex 611069, Fax 4467282 – 🛗 ▤ 📺 ☎ – 🧑‍🏫 25-80. AE 🅂 ◑ E VISA. ✗ by via Cavour PVX
Meals (residents only) (dinner only) 36000 – **79 rm** ☕ 220/320000.

Imperiale, via Vittorio Veneto 24 ✉ 00187 ℘ 4826351, Telex 621071, Fax 4826351 – 🛗 ▤ 📺 ☎. AE 🅂 ◑ E VISA. ✗ OV s
Meals 58000 – **95 rm** ☕ 330/460000.

Rex without rest., via Torino 149 ✉ 00184 ℘ 4824828, Telex 620522, Fax 4882743 – 🛗 ▤ 📺 ☎ – 🧑‍🏫 30-50. AE 🅂 ◑ E VISA JCB PV w
46 rm ☕ 250/320000, 2 suites.

Executive without rest., via Aniene 3 ✉ 00198 ℘ 8552030, Telex 620415, Fax 8414078 – 🛗 ▤ 📺 ☎ ♿. AE 🅂 ◑ E VISA JCB PU a
54 rm ☕ 200/250000.

Turner without rest., via Nomentana 29 ✉ 00161 ℘ 44250077, Fax 44250165 – 🛗 ▤ 📺 ☎. AE 🅂 ◑ E VISA JCB. ✗ PU x
37 rm ☕ 190/230000.

Borromeo without rest., via Cavour 117 ✉ 00184 ℘ 485856, Fax 4882541 – 🛗 ▤ 📺 ☎ ♿. AE 🅂 ◑ E VISA JCB. ✗ PX z
28 rm ☕ 190/270000, suite.

Venezia without rest., via Varese 18 ✉ 00185 ℘ 4457101, Telex 616038, Fax 4957687 – 🛗 ▤ 📺 ☎. AE 🅂 ◑ E VISA JCB. ✗ by corso d'Italia PU
59 rm ☕ 164/222000.

Diana, via Principe Amedeo 4 ✉ 00185 ℘ 4827541, Telex 611198, Fax 486998 – 🛗 ▤ 📺 ☎ – 🧑‍🏫 25. AE 🅂 ◑ E VISA JCB. ✗ PV d
Meals 38000 – ☕ 18000 – **187 rm** 190/270000, 2 suites.

Commodore without rest., via Torino 1 ✉ 00184 ℘ 485656, Telex 612170, Fax 4747562 – 🛗 ▤ 📺 ☎. AE 🅂 ◑ E VISA. ✗ PV e
60 rm ☕ 265/395000.

Barocco without rest., via della Purificazione 4 angolo piazza Barberini ✉ 00187 ℘ 4872001, Fax 485994 – 🛗 ▤ 📺 ☎. AE 🅂 ◑ E VISA JCB OV a
28 rm ☕ 280/380000.

Marcella without rest., via Flavia 106 ✉ 00187 ℘ 4746451, Telex 621351, Fax 4815832 – 🛗 ▤ 📺 ☎. AE 🅂 ◑ E VISA JCB. ✗ PU z
68 rm ☕ 180/260000.

Valle without rest., via Cavour 134 ✉ 00184 ℘ 4815736, Fax 4885837 – 🛗 ▤ 📺 ☎. AE 🅂 ◑ E VISA JCB. ✗ PX z
28 rm ☕ 198/275000.

Ariston without rest., via Turati 16 ✉ 00185 ℘ 4465399, Telex 614479, Fax 4465396 – 🛗 ▤ 📺 ☎ – 🧑‍🏫 100. AE 🅂 ◑ E VISA JCB. ✗ PV g
97 rm ☕ 155/205000, 4 suites.

Canada without rest., via Vicenza 58 ✉ 00185 ℘ 4457770, Telex 613037, Fax 4450749 – 🛗 ▤ 📺 ☎. AE 🅂 ◑ E VISA JCB. ✗ by corso d'Italia PU
74 rm ☕ 165/220000.

XXXX **Sans Souci,** via Sicilia 20/24 ✉ 00187 ℘ 4821814, Fax 4821771, Elegant tavernlate night dinners – ▤. AE 🅂 ◑ E VISA JCB. ✗ OU a
closed Monday and 6 August-3 September – **Meals** (dinner only) (booking essential) a la carte 96/150000.

XXX **Grappolo d'Oro,** via Palestro 4/10 ✉ 00185 ℘ 4941441, Fax 4452350 – ▤. AE 🅂 ◑ E VISA JCB PU c
closed Sunday and August – **Meals** 30/50000 (lunch) and a la carte 45/65000.

XX **Coriolano,** via Ancona 14 ✉ 00198 ℘ 44249863, Elegant trattoria – ▤. AE ⓢ ⓓ E VISA JCB PU **d**
closed 5 to 30 August, Sunday and Saturday in July – **Meals** (booking essential) a la carte 54/91000 (15 %).

XX **Agata e Romeo,** via Carlo Alberto 45 ✉ 00185 ℘ 4466115, Fax 4465842 – ▤. AE ⓢ ⓓ E VISA JCB. ✻ PX **d**
closed Sunday, August and Christmas – **Meals** (booking essential) a la carte 62/85000.

XX **Giovanni,** via Marche 64 ✉ 00187 ℘ 4821834, Fax 4817366, Habitués rest. – ▤. AE ⓢ E VISA OU **a**
closed Friday dinner, Saturday and August – **Meals** a la carte 53/99000.

XX **Girarrosto Toscano,** via Campania 29 ✉ 00187 ℘ 4823835, Fax 4821899 – ▤. AE ⓢ ⓓ E VISA JCB. ✻ OU **n**
closed Wednesday – **Meals** a la carte 52/87000.

XX **Mario's Hostaria,** piazza del Grillo 9 ✉ 00184 ℘ 6793725, 斎 – ▤. AE ⓢ ⓓ E VISA. ✻ NY **b**
closed Sunday – **Meals** (booking essential) a la carte 37/69000.

XX **Cesarina,** via Piemonte 109 ✉ 00187 ℘ 4880073, Bolognese rest. – ▤. AE ⓢ ⓓ E VISA. ✻ OU **p**
closed Sunday – **Meals** a la carte 44/77000.

XX **Bonne Nouvelle,** via del Boschetto 73 ✉ 00184 ℘ 486781, Seafood – ▤. AE ⓢ ⓓ E VISA JCB. ✻ OX **k**
closed Sunday and 10 to 31 August – **Meals** (booking essential) a la carte 47/72000.

XX **Dai Toscani,** via Forlì 41 ✉ 00161 ℘ 44231302, Tuscan rest. – ▤. AE ⓢ ⓓ E VISA
closed Sunday and August – **Meals** a la carte 48/70000 (10 %). by via 20 Settembre PU

X **Hostaria Costa Balena,** via Messina 5/7 ✉ 00198 ℘ 8417686, Seafood trattoria – ▤. AE ⓢ ⓓ E VISA. ✻ by via 20 Settembre PU
closed Saturday lunch, Sunday and 10 to 29 August – **Meals** a la carte 37/65000.

X **Crisciotti-al Boschetto,** via del Boschetto 30 ✉ 00184 ℘ 4744770, Rustic trattoria, « Summer service under pergola » – ⓢ E VISA OX **n**
closed Friday dinner, Saturday, August and Christmas – **Meals** a la carte 31/48000 (10 %).

X **Colline Emiliane,** via degli Avignonesi 22 ✉ 00187 ℘ 4817538, Emilian rest. – ▤
closed Friday and August – **Meals** (booking essential) a la carte 45/62000. NV **d**

X **La Tana del Grillo,** via Alfieri 4/8 ✉ 00185 ℘ 70453517, Ferrarese rest. – AE ⓢ ⓓ E VISA PY **h**
closed Sunday and Monday lunch – **Meals** (booking essential) a la carte 46/73000.

Southern area Aventino, Porta San Paolo, Terme di Caracalla, via Appia Nuova (**Plans : Rome** pp. 2 to 5) :

🏨 **Domus Aventina** ⛰ without rest., via Santa Prisca 11/b ✉ 00153 ℘ 5746135, Fax 57300044 – ▤ 📺 ☎. AE ⓢ ⓓ E VISA JCB. ✻ NZ **k**
26 rm ☕ 170/260000.

🏨 **Piccadilly** without rest., via Magna Grecia 122 ✉ 00183 ℘ 77207017, Fax 70476686 – ▤ 📺 ☎. AE ⓢ ⓓ E VISA. ✻ by via Gallia PZ
55 rm ☕ 150/205000.

🏨 **Sant'Anselmo** ⛰ without rest., piazza Sant'Anselmo 2 ✉ 00153 ℘ 5748119, Fax 5783604, 🌳 – 📺 ☎. AE ⓢ ⓓ E VISA. ✻ MZ **m**
45 rm ☕ 140/195000.

XX ✿ **Checchino dal 1887,** via Monte Testaccio 30 ✉ 00153 ℘ 5743816, Fax 5743816, Historical building, typical Roman cuisine – AE ⓢ ⓓ E VISA. ✻ by lungotevere Aventino MZ
closed August, 24 December-3 January, Sunday dinner and Monday, Sunday lunch June-September – **Meals** (booking essential) a la carte 60/97000 (15 %)
Spec. Rigatoni con la paiata, Coda alla vaccinara, Abbacchio alla cacciatora.

XX **Da Severino,** piazza Zama 5/c ✉ 00183 ℘ 7000872 – ▤. AE ⓢ ⓓ E VISA
closed Monday and 1 to 28 August – **Meals** a la carte 50/60000.
by via dell'Amba Aradam PZ

XX **Il Cortile,** via Alberto Mario 26 ✉ 00152 ℘ 5803433 – AE ⓢ ⓓ VISA. ✻
closed Sunday dinner and Monday – **Meals** a la carte 44/61000. by viale Trastevere KZ

Trastevere area (typical district) (**Plans : Rome p. 3**) :

XXX **Alberto Ciarla,** piazza San Cosimato 40 ✉ 00153 ℘ 5818668, Fax 5884377, 斎, Seafood – ▤. AE ⓢ ⓓ E VISA JCB. ✻ KZ **k**
closed Sunday, 1 to 15 August and 1 to 13 January – **Meals** (dinner only) (booking essential) 70/95000 and a la carte 71/116000.

XX **Corsetti-il Galeone,** piazza San Cosimato 27 ✉ 00153 ℘ 5816311, Fax 5896255, 斎, Roman seafood rest., « Typical atmosphere » – ▤. AE ⓢ ⓓ E VISA JCB KZ **m**
Meals a la carte 46/80000.

XX **Carlo Menta,** via della Lungaretta 101 ✉ 00153 ℘ 5884450, 斎, Seafood – ▤. AE ⓢ ⓓ E VISA. ✻ KZ **n**
closed Monday and 16 July-10 August – **Meals** (dinner only) (booking essential) a la carte 58/82000 (15 %).

XX **Galeassi,** piazza di Santa Maria in Trastevere 3 ✉ 00153 ☎ 5803775, ☂, Roman seafood rest. – AE ⓢ ⓞ E VISA. ✻ KZ **q**
closed Monday and 20 December-20 January – **Meals** a la carte 46/78000.

XX **Paris,** piazza San Callisto 7/a ✉ 00153 ☎ 5815378, ☂ – ▤. AE ⓢ ⓞ E VISA. ✻ KZ **r**
closed Sunday dinner, Monday and August – **Meals** a la carte 54/87000.

XX **Checco er Carettiere,** via Benedetta 10 ✉ 00153 ☎ 5817018, ☂, Roman seafood rest. – ▤. AE ⓢ ⓞ E VISA KY **t**
closed Sunday dinner, Monday, 10 to 30 August and 2 to 10 January – **Meals** a la carte 52/78000.

XX **Pastarellaro,** via di San Crisogono 33 ✉ 00153 ☎ 5810871, Roman seafood rest. – ▤. AE ⓢ ⓞ E VISA LZ **u**
closed Wednesday and August – **Meals** a la carte 45/80000 (12 %).

XX **Taverna Trilussa,** via del Politeama 23 ✉ 00153 ☎ 5818918, Fax 5811064, ☂, Typical Roman rest. – ▤. AE ⓢ ⓞ VISA JCB KY **v**
closed Sunday dinner, Monday and 30 July-28 August – **Meals** a la carte 36/57000.

X **Peccati di Gola,** piazza dei Ponziani 7/a ✉ 00153 ☎ 5814529, Fax 5816840, ☂ – AE ⓢ ⓞ E VISA. ✻ MZ **y**
closed Monday, 4 to 18 September and 2 to 16 January – **Meals** a la carte 56/88000.

Outskirts of Rome

on national road 1 - Aurelia :

Jolly Hotel Midas, via Aurelia al km 8 ✉ 00165 ☎ 66396, Telex 622821, Fax 66418457, ⛱, ⛱, ✂ – |‡| ▤ TV ☎ P – 🚣 650. AE ⓢ ⓞ E VISA. ✻ by via Aurelia GV
Meals a la carte 56/90000 – **342 rm** ☕ 220/240000, 5 suites.

Villa Pamphili, via della Nocetta 105 ✉ 00164 ☎ 5862, Telex 626539, Fax 66157747, 🏋, ⛱, ⛱ (covered in winter), ⛱, ✂ – |‡| ▤ TV ☎ ♿ P – 🚣 25-500. AE ⓢ ⓞ E VISA JCB. ✻ rest by via Garibaldi JZ
Meals a la carte 55/82000 – **238 rm** ☕ 290/340000.

Holiday Inn St. Peter's, via Aurelia Antica 415 ✉ 00165 ☎ 6642, Telex 625434, Fax 6637190, ⛱, ⛱, ⛱, ✂ – |‡| ⇸ rm ▤ TV ☎ ♿ P – 🚣 25-220. AE ⓢ ⓞ E VISA JCB. ✻ by via Garibaldi JZ
Meals a la carte 58/88000 – ☕ 25000 – **321 rm** 310/430000.

Forte Agip, via Aurelia al km 8 ✉ 00165 ☎ 66411200, Telex 613699, Fax 66414437, ⛱ – |‡| ▤ TV ☎ P – 🚣 25-150. AE ⓢ ⓞ E VISA. ✻ rest by via Aurelia GV
Meals a la carte 39/64000 – **213 rm** ☕ 194/234000.

on national road 6 - Casilina :

Myosotis, piazza Pupinia 2 ✉ 00133 ☎ 2054470, Fax 2053671, ⛱ heated – ▤ TV ☎ P – 🚣 35. AE ⓢ ⓞ E VISA. ✻ by via Merulana PY
Meals (see rest. **Villa Marsili** below) – **18 rm** ☕ 180/220000.

XX **Villa Marsili,** via Casilina 1604 ✉ 00133 ☎ 2050200, Fax 2055176 – ▤ P. AE ⓢ ⓞ E VISA. ✻ by via Merulana PY
closed Wednesday – **Meals** a la carte 37/49000.

on the Ancient Appian way :

XX **Cecilia Metella,** via Appia Antica 125/129 ✉ 00179 ☎ 5136743, Fax 5136743, ☂, « Shaded garden » – P. AE ⓢ ⓞ E VISA by viale delle Terme di Caracalla OZ
closed Monday and 12 to 30 August – **Meals** a la carte 42/66000.

to E.U.R. Garden City :

Sheraton, viale del Pattinaggio ✉ 00144 ☎ 5453, Telex 626074, Fax 5940689, ⛱, ⛱, ✂ – |‡| ▤ TV ☎ ♿ 🚗 P – 🚣 25-1800. AE ⓢ ⓞ E VISA JCB. ✻
Meals a la carte 54/86000 – **609 rm** ☕ 390/470000, 14 suites. by viale Aventino NZ

Shangri Là-Corsetti, viale Algeria 141 ✉ 00144 ☎ 5916441, Telex 614664, Fax 5413813, ⛱ heated, ⛱ – ▤ TV ☎ P – 🚣 25-80. AE ⓢ ⓞ E VISA. ✻ by viale Aventino NZ
Meals *(closed 11 to 25 August)* a la carte 50/86000 - **52 rm** ☕ 266/330000, 11 suites.

XX **Vecchia America-Corsetti,** piazza Marconi 32 ✉ 00144 ☎ 5926601, Fax 5922284, ☂, Typical rest. and ale house – AE ⓢ ⓞ E VISA by viale Aventino NZ
Meals a la carte 45/76000.

on the motorway to Fiumicino close to the ring-road :

Sheraton Golf, viale Parco de Medici 22 ✉ 00148 ☎ 522408, Telex 620297, Fax 52240742 – ▤ TV ☎ P – 🚣 25-630. AE ⓢ ⓞ E VISA JCB. ✻ by viale Trastevere KZ
Meals 72/90000 – ☕ 20000 – **248 rm** 420/490000, 14 suites.

Holiday Inn-Parco Medici, viale Castello della Magliana 65 ✉ 00148 ☎ 65581, Telex 613302, Fax 6557005, ⛱, ⛱, ✂ – |‡| ▤ TV ☎ ♿ P – 🚣 650. AE ⓢ ⓞ E VISA JCB. ✻ by viale Trastevere KZ
Meals a la carte 70/90000 – ☕ 16000 – **316 rm** 300/415000.

on the Tiburtina way :

XX **Gabriele,** via Ottoboni 74 ✉ 00159 ☎ 4393498, Rest. and pizzeria – AE ⓢ ⓞ E VISA. ✻
closed Saturday and August – **Meals** carta 48/65000. by corso d'Italia PU

Baschi **05023** Terni 988 ㉕, 430 N 18 - pop. 2 741 alt. 165 - ☎ 0744.

Roma 118 - Orvieto 10 - Terni 70 - Viterbo 46.

XXX ✿✿ **Vissani,** N : 12 km ✉ 05020 Civitella del Lago ☎ 950396, Fax 950396 - ≡ Ⓟ. AE Ⓢ ⓞ E VISA. ✻
closed Sunday dinner and Wednesday - **Meals** (booking essential) 100/140000 (lunch) 140000 (dinner) and a la carte 130/205000 (15 %)
Spec. Insalata di scampi al profumo di senape cinese e pomodori secchi, Risotto con zucca gialla e moscardini salsa di cardi gobbi e mozzarella di bufala, Pernice rossa con gnocchi di fegatini allo zibibbo con salsa di olive nere e mentuccia.

When driving through towns
use the plans in the ***MICHELIN*** *Red Guide.*

Features indicated include :
throughroutes and by passes,
traffic junctions and major squares,
new streets, car parks, pedestrian streets...
All this information is revised annually.

FLORENCE **(FIRENZE) 50100** Ⓟ 988 ⑮, 429 430 K 15 - pop. 392 800 alt. 49 - ☎ 055.

See : Cathedral★★★ (Duomo) Y : east end★★★, dome★★★ (✻★★) Campanile★★★ YB : ✻★★ Baptistry★★★ YC : doors★★★, mosaics★★★ Cathedral Museum★★ Y **M1** - Piazza della Signoria★★ Z Loggia della Signoria★★ Z **D** : Perseus★★★ by B. Cellini Palazzo Vecchio★★★ Z **H** **Uffizi Gallery**★★★ Z - Bargello Palace and Museum★★★ Z San Lorenzo★★★ Y : Church★★, Laurentian Library★★, Medici Tombs★★★ in Medicee Chapels★★ - Medici-Riccardi Palace★★ Y : Chapel★★★, Luca Giordano Gallery★★ - Church of Santa Maria Novella★★ Y : frescoes★★★ by Ghirlandaio - Ponte Vecchio★★ Z Pitti Palace★★ DV : Palatine Gallery★★★, Silver Museum★★, Works★★ by Macchiaioli in Modern Art Gallery★ - Boboli Garden★ DV : ✻★★ from the Citadel Belvedere Porcelain Museum★ DV Monastery and Museum of St. Mark★★ ET : works★★★ by Beato Angelico - Academy Gallery★★ ET : Michelangelo gallery★★★ Piazza della Santissima Annunziata★ ET **168** : frescoes★ in the church, portico★★ with corners decorated with terracotta Medallions★★ in the Foundling Hospital★ - Church of Santa Croce★★ EU : Pazzi Chapel★★ Excursion to the hills★★ : ✻★★★ from Michelangiolo Square EFV, Church of San Miniato al Monte★★ EFV Strozzi Palace★★ Z - Rucellai Palace★★ Z Santa Maria del Carmine★★ DUV Last Supper of San Salvi★ BS **G** Orsanmichele★ ZN : tabernacle★★ by Orcagna - La Badia Z : campanile★, delicate relief sculpture in marble★★, tombs★, Virgin appearing to St. Bernard★ by Filippino Lippi - Sassetti Chapel★★ and the Chapel of the Annunciation★ in the Holy Trinity Church Z Church of the Holy Spirit★ DUV - Last Supper★ of Sant'Apollonia ET All Saints' Church DU : Last Supper★ by Ghirlandaio-Davanzanti Palace★ Z **M2** New Market Loggia★ Z **K** - Museums : Archaeological★★ (Chimera from Arezzo★★)ET, Science★ Z **M6** Semi- precious Stone Workshop★ ET **M4.**

Envir. : Medicee Villas★ : villa della Pietraia★ - Villa di Castello★ - Villa di Poggio a Caiano★★ by via P. Toselli CT : 17 km Galluzzo Carthusian Monastery★★ by via Senese CV.

18 Dell'Ugolino (closed Monday), to Grassina ✉ 50015 ☎ 2301009, Fax 2301141, S : 12 km BS.

✈ of Peretola NW : 4 km by via P. Todelli CT ☎ 373498 - Alitalia, lungarno Acciaiuoli 10/12 r, ✉ 50123 ☎ 27888.

ℹ via Cavour 1 r ✉ 50129 ☎ 290832, Fax 2760383.

A.C.I. viale Amendola 36 ✉ 50121 ☎ 24861.

Roma 277 - Bologna 105 - Milano 298.

Plans on following pages

Excelsior, piazza Ognissanti 3 ✉ 50123 ☎ 264201, Telex 570022, Fax 210278 - ≡ TV ☎ ♿ - 🔺 300. AE Ⓢ ⓞ E VISA JCB. ✻ rest DU **b**
Meals a la carte 90/132000 - ☕ 47500 - **190 rm** 396/605000, 4 suites.

Grand Hotel Ciga, piazza Ognissanti 1 ✉ 50123 ☎ 288781, Telex 570055, Fax 217400 - ≡ TV ☎ ♿ - 🔺 25-220. AE Ⓢ ⓞ E VISA JCB. ✻ rest DU **a**
Meals a la carte 94/151000 - ☕ 47500 - **102 rm** 473/682000, 17 suites.

Savoy, piazza della Repubblica 7 ✉ 50123 ☎ 283313, Telex 570220, Fax 284840 - ≡ TV ☎ ♿ - 🔺 150. AE Ⓢ ⓞ E VISA. ✻ rest Z **a**
Meals a la carte 75/120000 - **101 rm** ☕ 350/530000, suite.

Villa Medici, via Il Prato 42 ✉ 50123 ☎ 2381331, Telex 570179, Fax 2381336, ≡ TV ☎ - 🔺 30-90. AE Ⓢ ⓞ E VISA JCB. ✻ CT **c**
Meals 70/85000 and ***Lorenzo de' Medici Rest.*** a la carte 57/106000 - ☕ 25000 - **88 rm** 382/543000, 13 suites.

Regency, piazza Massimo D'Azeglio 3 ✉ 50121 ☎ 245247, Telex 571058, Fax 2346735, - ≡ TV ☎. AE Ⓢ ⓞ E VISA JCB. ✻ rest FU **a**
Meals ***Relais le Jardin*** Rest. *(closed Sunday)* (booking essential) a la carte 70/110000 - **34 rm** ☕ 370/550000, 5 suites.

Helvetia e Bristol, via dei Pescioni 2 ✉ 50123 ☎ 287814, Telex 572696, Fax 288353 - ≡ TV ☎. AE Ⓢ ⓞ E VISA. ✻ Z **b**
Meals a la carte 62/104000 - ☕ 30500 - **52 rm** 363/545000, 15 suites.

Brunelleschi, piazza Santa Elisabetta 3 ⊠ 50122 ✆ 562068, Telex 575805, Fax 219653, ≤, « Small private museum » – rm – 100. AE E VISA JCB
Z c
Meals (residents only) a la carte 60/90000 – **94 rm** 330/440000, suite.

Plaza Hotel Lucchesi, lungarno della Zecca Vecchia 38 ⊠ 50122 ✆ 26236, Telex 570302, Fax 2480921, ≤ – rm – 70-160. AE E VISA JCB. rest
EV b
Meals *(closed Sunday)* (residents only) a la carte 56/90000 – **97 rm** 310/440000, 10 suites.

Grand Hotel Baglioni, piazza Unità Italiana 6 ⊠ 50123 ✆ 23580, Telex 570225, Fax 2358895, « Roof-garden rest. with ≤ » – – 25-200. AE E VISA JCB. rest
Y d
Meals a la carte 55/85000 – **193 rm** 275/380000, suite.

Majestic, via del Melarancio 1 ⊠ 50123 ✆ 264021, Telex 570628, Fax 268428 – – 80. AE E VISA JCB. rest
Y e
Meals 50/55000 – **103 rm** 310/440000, suite.

Berchielli without rest., piazza del Limbo 6 r ⊠ 50123 ✆ 264061, Telex 575582, Fax 218636, ≤ – – 100. AE E VISA JCB.
Z h
73 rm 370/400000, 3 suites.

Bernini Palace without rest., piazza San Firenze 29 ⊠ 50122 ✆ 288621, Telex 573616, Fax 268272 – – 40. AE E VISA.
Z k
83 rm 300/420000, 3 suites.

Montebello Splendid, via Montebello 60 ⊠ 50123 ✆ 2398051, Telex 574009, Fax 211867, – – 100. AE E VISA JCB. rest
CU e
Meals *(closed Sunday)* a la carte 52/95000 – **53 rm** 300/410000, suite.

Sofitel, via de' Cerretani 10 ⊠ 50123 ✆ 2381301, Telex 580515, Fax 2381312 – rm. AE E VISA JCB. rest
Y r
Meals a la carte 48/83000 – **84 rm** 300/360000.

Rivoli without rest., via della Scala 33 ⊠ 50123 ✆ 282853, Telex 571004, Fax 294041, – – 100. AE E VISA JCB.
DU m
65 rm 270/350000.

Continental without rest., lungarno Acciaiuoli 2 ⊠ 50123 ✆ 282392, Telex 580525, Fax 283139, « Floral terrace with ≤ » – . AE E VISA JCB
Z m
25000 – **47 rm** 290/370000, suite.

Lungarno without rest., borgo Sant'Jacopo 14 ⊠ 50125 ✆ 264211, Telex 570129, Fax 268437, ≤, « Collection of modern pictures » – – 30. AE E VISA JCB
Z s
25000 – **54 rm** 270/360000, 6 suites.

De la Ville, piazza Antinori 1 ⊠ 50123 ✆ 2381805, Telex 570518, Fax 2381809 – – 60. AE E VISA JCB
Y f
Meals (residents only) a la carte 51/64000 – **75 rm** 328/448000, 4 suites.

Jolly, piazza Vittorio Veneto 4/a ⊠ 50123 ✆ 2770, Telex 570191, Fax 294794, « on panoramic terrace » – – 30-100. AE E VISA. rest
CTU d
Meals a la carte 43/98000 – **167 rm** 260/360000.

Holiday Inn, viale Europa 205 ⊠ 50126 ✆ 6531841, Telex 570376, Fax 6531806, – rm – 50-120
by via Orsini FV
92 rm.

Londra, via Jacopo da Diacceto 18 ⊠ 50123 ✆ 2382791, Telex 571152, Fax 210682, – – 200. AE E VISA. rest
DT h
Meals a la carte 55/80000 – **158 rm** 280/380000.

Croce di Malta, via della Scala 7 ⊠ 50123 ✆ 218351, Telex 570540, Fax 287121, – – 50. AE E VISA JCB. rest
DU n
Meals 35/50000 (lunch) and ***Al Coccodrillo*** Rest. *(closed Sunday and Monday lunch)* a la carte 45/75000 – **83 rm** 270/360000, 15 suites.

Augustus without rest., piazzetta dell'Oro 5 ⊠ 50123 ✆ 283054, Telex 570110, Fax 268557 – – 70. AE E VISA JCB
Z m
54 rm 350/410000, 2 suites.

Kraft, via Solferino 2 ⊠ 50123 ✆ 284273, Telex 571523, Fax 2398267, « Roof garden rest. with ≤ », – – 40-50. AE E VISA JCB. rest
CU g
Meals a la carte 52/86000 – **77 rm** 280/410000.

Pierre without rest., via de' Lamberti 5 ⊠ 50123 ✆ 217512, Telex 573175, Fax 2396573 – . AE E VISA JCB
Z t
25000 – **39 rm** 240/290000.

Starhotel Michelangelo, viale Fratelli Rosselli 2 ⊠ 50123 ✆ 2784, Telex 571113, Fax 2382232 – – 50-250. AE E VISA JCB. rest
CT f
Meals (residents only) – **138 rm** 250/340000.

Gd H. Minerva, piazza Santa Maria Novella 16 ⊠ 50123 ✆ 284555, Telex 570414, Fax 268281, – – 30-90. AE E VISA JCB. rest
Y n
Meals a la carte 45/72000 – **96 rm** 320/440000, 3 suites.

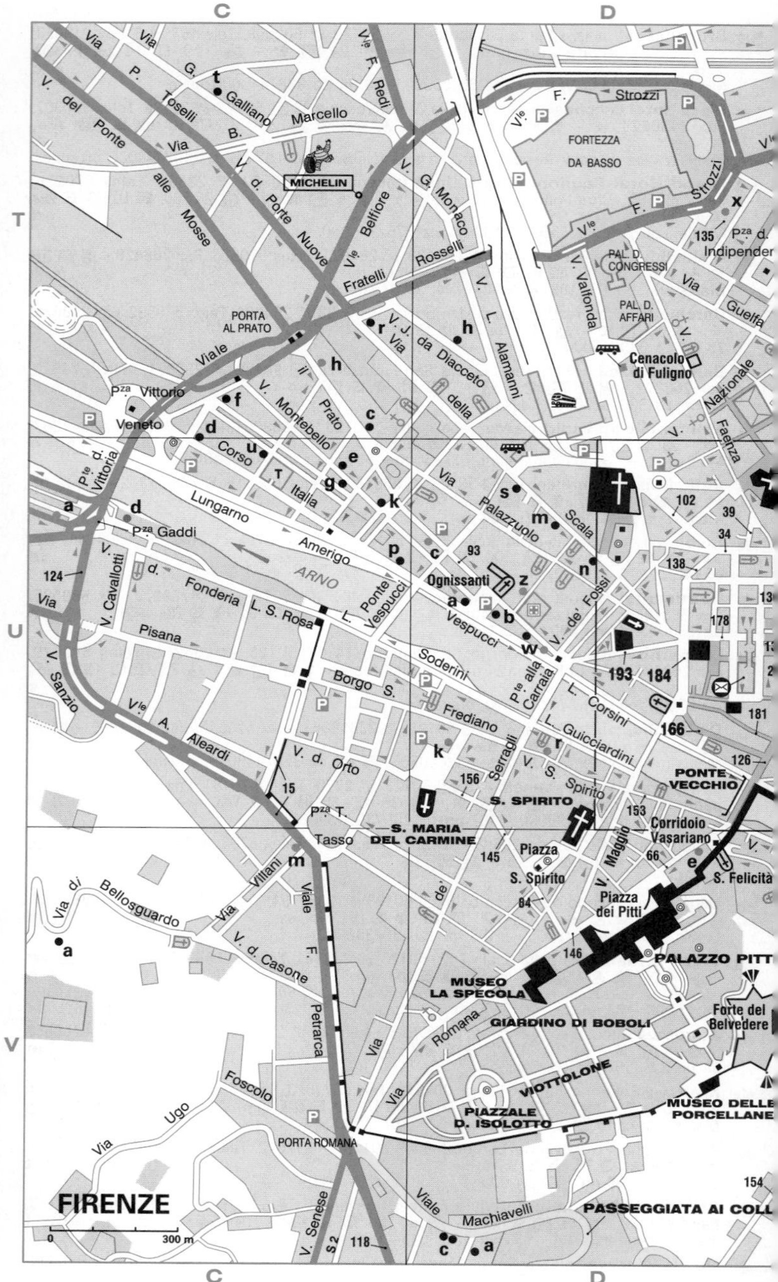

Traffic restricted

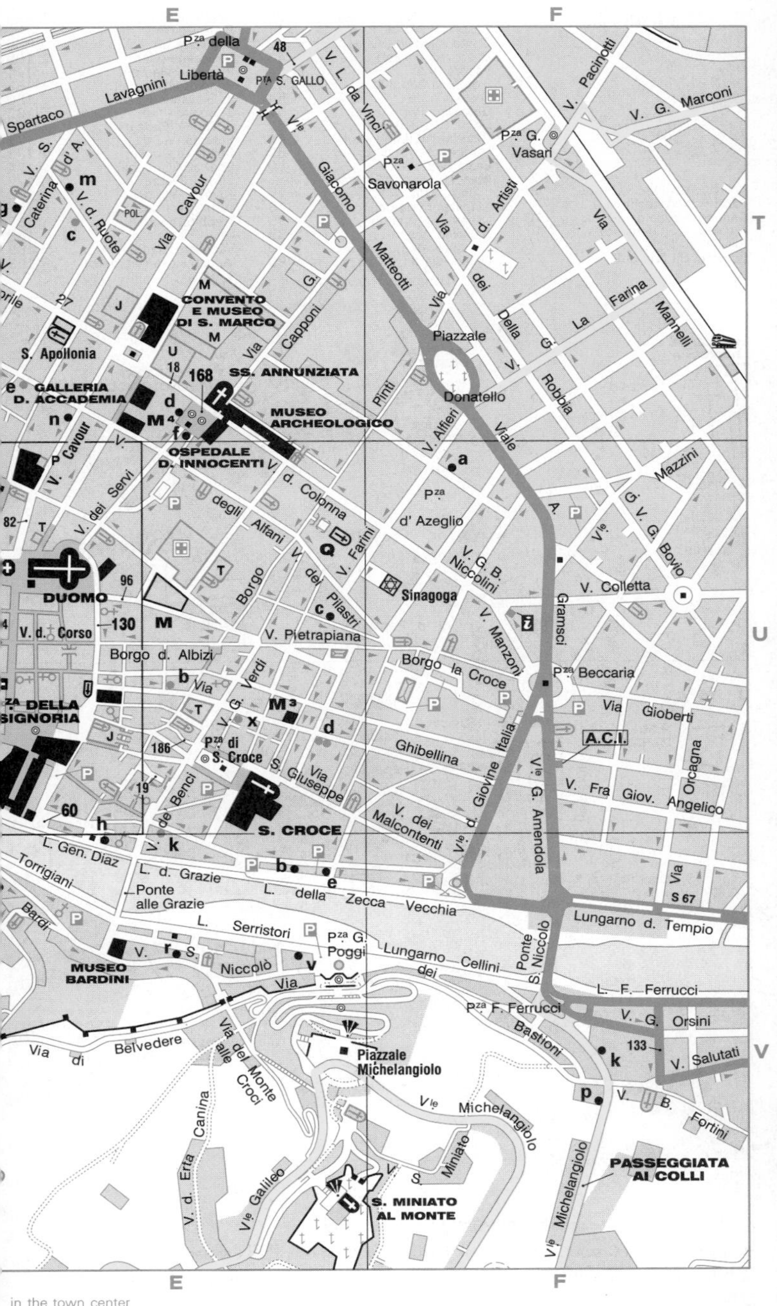

in the town center

FIRENZE

Calimala	Z 24
Calzaiuoli (Via dei)	YZ
Por S. Maria (Via)	Z 126
Porta Rossa (Via)	Z
Roma (Via)	YZ
S. Jacopo (Borgo)	Z
Strozzi (Via degli)	Z
Tornabuoni (Via)	Z
Vecchio (Ponte)	Z
Agli (Via degli)	Y 3
Albizi (Vorgo degli)	Z 7
Antinori (Piazza degli)	Y 10
Archibusieri (Lungamo)	Z 12
Avelli (Via degli)	Y 16
Brunelleschi (Via de)	YZ 22
Canto de' Nelli (Via del)	T 27
Castellani (Via de')	Z 31
Dante Alighieri (Via)	Z 42
Davanzati (Piazza)	Z 43
Faenza (Via)	Y 51
Fiordalisa (Via del)	Z 52
Fossi (Via de')	Y 54
Ghibellina (Via)	Z 57
Gondi (Via dei)	Z 61
Guicciardini (Lungarno)	Z 64
Lambertesca (Via)	Z 69
Leoni (Via dei)	Z 70
Madonna degli Aldobrandini (Piazza di)	Y 75
Magazzini (Via dei)	Z 76
Melarancio (Via del)	Y 85
Monalda (Via)	Z 88
Nazionale (Via)	Y 90
Oriulo (Via d.)	Y 96
Orsanmichele (Via)	Z 99
Parte Guelfa (Piazza di)	Z 106
Pelliccena (Via)	Z 109
Pescioni (Via de')	YZ 111
Rondinelli (Via de')	Y 138
S. Giovanni (Piazza)	Y 150
S. Spinto (Via)	Z 162
S. Trinità (Piazza)	Z 163
Sassetti (Via de')	Z 171
Spada (Via della)	Z 173
Speziali (Via degli)	174
Strozzi (Piazza)	Z 177
Tavolini (Via dei)	180
Terme (Via delle)	181
Trebbio (Via del)	Y 187
Uffizi (Piazzale degli)	188
Vaccherecia (Via)	Z 189
Vigna Nuova (Via della)	Z 193

Traffic restricted in the town centre

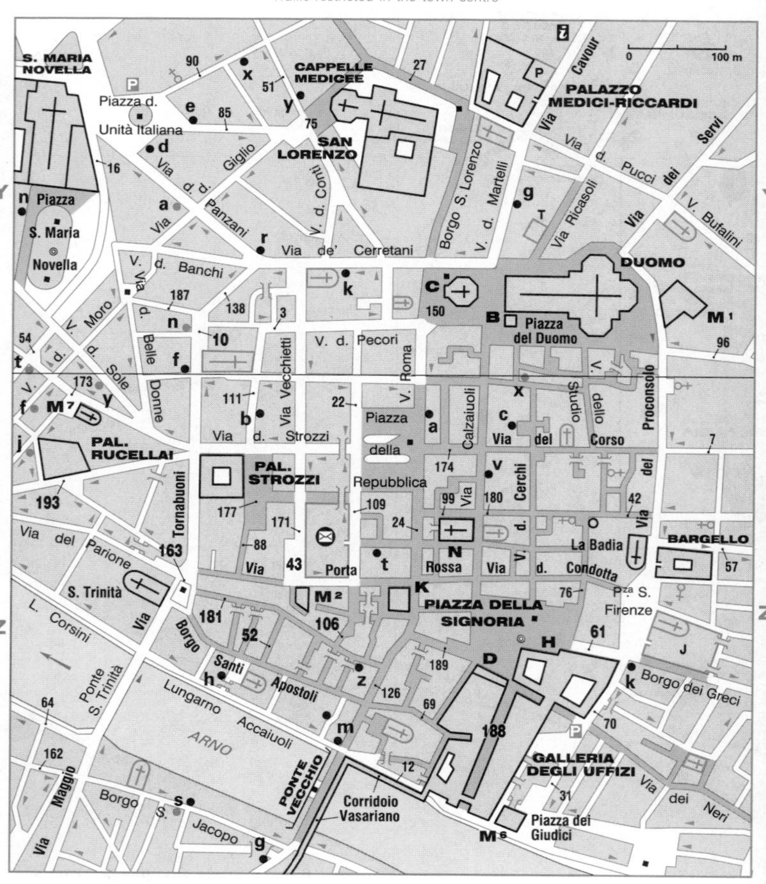

For the quickest route use the MICHELIN Main Road Maps :

970 Europe, 976 Czech Republic-Slovak Republic, 980 Greece, 984 Germany, 985 Scandinavia-Finland, 986 Great Britain and Ireland, 987 Germany-Austria-Benelux, 988 Italy, 989 France, 990 Spain-Portugal *and* 991 Yugoslavia.

STREET INDEX TO FIRENZE TOWN PLAN

Executive without rest., via Curtatone 5 ✉ 50123 ☎ 217451, Telex 574522, Fax 268346, – |‡| ▤ TV ☎ – 🏛 50. AE ⑤ ⓪ E VISA JCB CU **k**
☕ 30000 – **38 rm** 260/340000.

Principe without rest., lungarno Vespucci 34 ✉ 50123 ☎ 284848, Telex 571400, Fax 283458, ≤, – |‡| ▤ TV ☎. AE ⑤ ⓪ E VISA JCB. ✂ CU **p**
16 rm ☕ 300/405000.

Alexander, viale Guidoni 101 ✉ 50127 ☎ 4378951, Telex 574026, Fax 416818 – |‡| ▤ TV ☎ ♿ P – 🏛 50-300. AE ⑤ ⓪ E VISA by viale F. Redi CT
Meals a la carte 36/74000 – **88 rm** ☕ 190/260000.

J and J without rest., via di Mezzo 20 ✉ 50121 ☎ 2345005, Telex 570554, Fax 240282 – ▤ TV ☎. AE ⑤ ⓪ E VISA JCB. ✂ EU **c**
19 rm ☕ 350/395000, 2 suites.

Il Guelfo Bianco without rest., via Cavour 29 ✉ 50129 ☎ 288330, Fax 295203 – |‡| ▤ TV ☎ ♿. AE ⑤ E VISA. ✂ ET **n**
29 rm ☕ 170/240000.

Malaspina without rest., piazza dell'Indipendenza 24 ✉ 50129 ☎ 489869, Fax 474809 – |‡| ▤ TV ☎. AE ⑤ ⓪ E VISA. ✂ ET **g**
31 rm ☕ 154/242000.

Palazzo Benci without rest., piazza Madonna degli Aldobrandini 3 ✉ 50123 ☎ 2382821, Fax 288308 – |‡| ▤ TV ☎ – 🏛 30. AE ⑤ ⓪ E VISA JCB. ✂ Y **y**
34 rm ☕ 150/220000.

Le Due Fontane without rest., piazza della SS. Annunziata 14 ✉ 50122 ☎ 280086, Telex 575550, Fax 294461 – |‡| ▤ TV ☎ – 🏛 40. AE ⑤ ⓪ E VISA. ✂ ETU **f**
56 rm ☕ 135/245000.

Royal without rest., via delle Ruote 52 ✉ 50129 ☎ 483287, Fax 490976, « Garden » – |‡| ▤ TV ☎ P. AE ⑤ E VISA ET **m**
39 rm ☕ 150/240000.

Villa Azalee without rest., viale Fratelli Rosselli 44 ✉ 50123 ☎ 214242, Fax 268264, – ▤ TV ☎. AE ⑤ ⓪ E VISA CT **r**
24 rm ☕ 145/218000.

Calzaiuoli without rest., via Calzaiuoli 6 ✉ 50122 ☎ 212456, Telex 580589, Fax 268310 – |‡| ▤ TV ☎ ♿. AE ⑤ ⓪ E VISA Z **v**
45 rm ☕ 180/209000.

Fenice Palace without rest., via dei Martelli 10 ✉ 50129 ☎ 289942, Telex 575580, Fax 210087 – |‡| ▤ TV ☎. AE ⑤ ⓪ E VISA. ✂ Y **g**
72 rm ☕ 243/319000.

Select without rest., via Giuseppe Galliano 24 ✉ 50144 ☎ 330342, Telex 572626, Fax 351506 – |‡| ▤ TV ☎. AE ⑤ ⓪ E VISA CT **t**
☕ 10000 – **36 rm** 135/160000.

David without rest., viale Michelangiolo 1 ✉ 50125 ☎ 6811695, Fax 680602, – |‡| ▤ TV ☎ ♿ P. AE ⑤ ⓪ E VISA. ✂ FV **k**
☕ 15000 – **26 rm** 110/180000.

Villa Liberty without rest., viale Michelangiolo 40 ✉ 50125 ☎ 6810581, Fax 6812595, – |‡| ▤ TV ☎ P. AE ⑤ ⓪ E VISA FV **p**
14 rm ☕ 180/210000, 2 suites.

Goldoni without rest., via Borgo Ognissanti 8 ✉ 50123 ☎ 284080, Fax 282576 – |‡| ▤ TV ☎. AE ⑤ ⓪ E VISA DU **w**
20 rm ☕ 130/200000.

Balestri without rest., piazza Mentana 7 ✉ 50122 ☎ 214743, Fax 2398042 – |‡| ▤ TV ☎ – 🏛 50. AE ⑤ ⓪ E VISA. ✂ EUV **h**
49 rm ☕ 170/230000, suite.

City without rest., via Sant'Antonino 18 ✉ 50123 ☎ 211543, Fax 295451 – |‡| ▤ TV ☎. AE ⑤ ⓪ E VISA Y **x**
18 rm ☕ 160/210000.

Privilege without rest., lungarno della Zecca Vecchia 26 ✉ 50122 ☎ 2341221, Fax 243287 – ▤ TV ☎. AE ⑤ ⓪ E VISA EV **e**
18 rm ☕ 150/200000.

Loggiato dei Serviti without rest., piazza SS. Annunziata 3 ✉ 50122 ☎ 289592, Fax 289595 – |‡| ▤ TV ☎. AE ⑤ ⓪ E VISA JCB ET **d**
29 rm ☕ 185/255000, 4 suites.

Della Signoria without rest., via delle Terme 1 ✉ 50123 ☎ 214530, Fax 216101 – |‡| ▤ TV ☎. AE ⑤ ⓪ E VISA JCB Z **z**
27 rm ☕ 215/280000.

Byron without rest., via della Scala 49 ✉ 50123 ☎ 280852, Telex 570278, Fax 213273 – |‡| TV ☎ P. AE ⑤ ⓪ E VISA JCB DU **s**
45 rm ☕ 140/210000.

Silla without rest., via dei Renai 5 ✉ 50125 ☎ 2342888, Fax 2341437 – |‡| ▤ TV ☎. AE ⑤ ⓪ E VISA EV **r**
32 rm ☕ 150/200000.

Pitti Palace without rest., via Barbadori 2 ✉ 50125 ℘ 2398711, Fax 2398867 – |‡| ▤ TV ☎. AE ⑤ ⓓ E VISA. ✻ Z g
72 rm ☕ 165/260000.

Laurus without rest., via de' Cerretani 8 ✉ 50123 ℘ 2381752, Fax 268308 – |‡| ▤ TV ☎. AE ⑤ ⓓ E VISA. ✻ Y k
59 rm ☕ 180/260000.

Rapallo, via di Santa Caterina d'Alessandria 7 ✉ 50129 ℘ 472412, Telex 574251, Fax 470385 – |‡| ▤ TV ☎. AE ⑤ ⓓ E VISA. ✻ rest ET g
Meals (residents only) 33000 – ☕ 16000 – **30 rm** 105/160000.

Ariele without rest., via Magenta 11 ✉ 50123 ℘ 211509, Fax 268521, – |‡| TV ☎ P. AE ⑤ ⓓ E VISA JCB CU u
☕ 18000 – **39 rm** 130/155000.

Sanremo without rest., lungarno Serristori 13 ✉ 50125 ℘ 2342823, Fax 2342269 – |‡| ▤ TV ☎. AE ⑤ ⓓ E VISA EV v
closed 15 January-15 February – **20 rm** ☕ 130/170000.

XXXX ✿✿ **Enoteca Pinchiorri,** via Ghibellina 87 ✉ 50122 ℘ 242777, Fax 244983, « Summer service in a cool courtyard » – ▤. AE ⑤ E VISA JCB EU x
closed Sunday, Monday-Wednesday lunch, 4 to 28 August and 18 to 27 December – **Meals** (booking essential) 90/150000 (lunch) 150000 (dinner) and a la carte 125/210000
Spec. Filetto di coniglio marinato al rosmarino con crema di fagioli e fegato grasso, Garganelli con farina di grano farro saltati con porri rucola e ceci, Triglie impanate alle erbe con cavolfiore gratinato.

XXXX **Sabatini,** via de' Panzani 9/a ✉ 50123 ℘ 211559, Fax 210293, Elegant traditional decor – ▤. AE ⑤ ⓓ E VISA JCB. ✻ Y a
closed Monday – **Meals** a la carte 59/96000 (13 %).

XXX **Harry's Bar,** lungarno Vespucci 22 r ✉ 50123 ℘ 2396700, Fax 2396700 – ▤. AE ⑤ E VISA
closed Sunday and 15 December-5 January – **Meals** (booking essential) a la carte 54/82000 (16 %). DU w

XXX ✿ **Don Chisciotte,** via Ridolfi 4 r ✉ 50129 ℘ 475430, Fax 485305 – ▤. AE ⑤ ⓓ E VISA JCB DT x
closed Sunday, Monday lunch and August – **Meals** (booking essential) a la carte 62/98000
Spec. Carpaccio di gamberoni con arance e olio d'oliva, Taglierini verdi con scampi in mantello di zucchine, Filetto di vitello in crosta di pane e salsa al Brunello.

XX **Osteria n. 1,** via del Moro 20 r ✉ 50123 ℘ 284897 – AE ⑤ ⓓ E VISA Z f
closed Sunday and 3 to 26 August – **Meals** a la carte 54/80000 (10 %).

XX **Dino,** via Ghibellina 51 r ✉ 50122 ℘ 241452, Fax 241378 – ▤. AE ⑤ ⓓ E VISA. ✻
closed Sunday dinner and Monday – **Meals** a la carte 45/68000. EU d

XX **Taverna del Bronzino,** via delle Ruote 25/27 r ✉ 50129 ℘ 495220 – ▤. AE ⑤ ⓓ E VISA
closed Sunday and August – **Meals** a la carte 53/76000. ET c

XX **Cantinetta Antinori,** piazza Antinori 3 ✉ 50123 ℘ 292234, Tuscan Rest. – ▤. AE ⑤ ⓓ VISA JCB. ✻ Y n
closed Saturday, Sunday, August and Christmas – **Meals** a la carte 54/79000 (10 %).

XX **Acquerello,** via Ghibellina 156 r ✉ 50122 ℘ 2340554, Fax 2340554 – ▤. AE ⑤ ⓓ E VISA
closed Thursday – **Meals** a la carte 41/59000 (12 %). EU b

XX **Mamma Gina,** borgo Sant'Jacopo 37 r ✉ 50125 ℘ 2396009 – ▤. AE ⑤ ⓓ E VISA JCB Z s
closed Sunday and 7 to 21 August – **Meals** a la carte 41/71000 (12 %).

XX **Ottorino,** via delle Oche 12/16 r ✉ 50122 ℘ 215151, Fax 287140 – ▤. AE ⑤ ⓓ E VISA JCB YZ x
closed Sunday – **Meals** a la carte 52/73000.

XX **Buca Mario,** piazza Ottaviani 16 r ✉ 50123 ℘ 214179, Fax 214179, Typical trattoria – ▤. AE ⑤ ⓓ E VISA. ✻ YZ t
closed Wednesday, Thursday lunch and August – **Meals** a la carte 42/76000 (12 %).

X **La Baraonda,** via Ghibellina 67 r ✉ 50122 ℘ 2341171, Fax 2341171 – AE ⓓ EU d
closed Sunday, Monday lunch and August – **Meals** a la carte 31/53000 (10 %).

X **Il Latini,** via dei Palchetti 6 r ✉ 50123 ℘ 210916, Typical trattoria – AE ⑤ ⓓ E VISA. ✻ Z j
closed Monday, July or August and 24 December-1 January – **Meals** a la carte 39/55000.

X **Il Cigno,** via Varlungo 3 r ✉ 50136 ℘ 691762, Fax 691762, – P. ⑤ E VISA. ✻
closed Monday and November – **Meals** a la carte 38/60000. by lungarno del Tempio FV

X **Il Profeta,** borgo Ognissanti 93 r ✉ 50123 ℘ 212265 – ▤. AE ⑤ ⓓ VISA. ✻ DU c
closed Sunday and 15 to 31 August – **Meals** a la carte 38/58000 (12 %).

X **Baldini,** via il Prato 96 r ✉ 50123 ℘ 287663, Fax 287663 – ▤. AE ⑤ ⓓ E VISA. ✻
closed Saturday, Sunday dinner, 1 to 20 August and 24 December-3 January – **Meals** a la carte 35/50000. CT h

X **La Martinicca,** via del Sole 27 r ✉ 50123 ℘ 218928 – ▤. AE ⑤ ⓓ E VISA Z y
closed Sunday and August – **Meals** a la carte 40/58000.

X **Cafaggi,** via Guelfa 35 r ✉ 50129 ☎ 294989 – ▤. AE ⓢ E VISA — ET e
closed Sunday and 15 July-15 August – **Meals** a la carte 35/76000.

X **Del Carmine,** piazza del Carmine 18 r ✉ 50124 ☎ 218601 – AE ⓢ ⓞ E VISA — DU k
closed Sunday and 7 to 21 August – **Meals** a la carte 29/41000.

X **Trattoria Vittoria,** via della Fonderia 52 r ✉ 50142 ☎ 225657, Seafood – ▤. AE ⓢ ⓞ E VISA — CU d
closed Wednesday – **Meals** a la carte 58/74000.

X **Angiolino,** via Santo Spirito 36 r ✉ 50125 ☎ 2398976, Typical trattoria – ✻ — DU r
closed Sunday dinner, Monday and 27 June-25 July – **Meals** a la carte 34/47000.

X **Del Fagioli,** corso Tintori 47 r ✉ 50122 ☎ 244285, Typical tuscan trattoria — EV k
closed August, Sunday and Saturday June-September – **Meals** a la carte 37/48000.

X **Alla Vecchia Bettola,** viale Ludovico Ariosto 32 r ✉ 50124 ☎ 224158, « Typical atmosphere » – ✻ — CV m
closed Sunday, Monday, August and 23 December-2 January – **Meals** a la carte 32/58000.

on the hills S : 3 km :

Gd H. Villa Cora ⛰, viale Machiavelli 18 ✉ 50125 ☎ 2298451, Telex 570604, Fax 229086, 🏖, « Floral park with ⛲ » – |ǂ| ▤ TV ☎ P – 🎪 50-150. AE ⓢ ⓞ E VISA JCB — DV c
Meals ***Taverna Machiavelli*** Rest. a la carte 70/100000 – **32 rm** ☕ 420/750000, 10 suites 900/1500000.

Torre di Bellosguardo ⛰ without rest., via Roti Michelozzi 2 ✉ 50124 ☎ 2298145, Fax 229008, ✳ town and hills, « Park and terrace with ⛲ » – |ǂ| ☎ P. AE ⓢ ⓞ E VISA — CV a
☕ 25000 – **10 rm** 290/390000, 6 suites 490/590000.

Villa Belvedere ⛰ without rest., via Benedetto Castelli 3 ✉ 50124 ☎ 222501, Fax 223163, ≤ town and hills, « Garden-Park with ⛲ », ✂ – |ǂ| ▤ TV ☎ ♿ P. AE ⓢ ⓞ E VISA. ✻ — by via Senese CV
March-November – **23 rm** ☕ 250/290000, 3 suites.

Villa Carlotta ⛰, via Michele di Lando 3 ✉ 50125 ☎ 2336134, Telex 573485, Fax 2336147, 🌳 – |ǂ| ▤ TV ☎ P. AE ⓢ ⓞ E VISA JCB. ✻ rest — DV a
Meals (residents only) a la carte 44/77000 – **27 rm** ☕ 250/350000.

Classic without rest., viale Machiavelli 25 ✉ 50125 ☎ 229351, Fax 229353, 🌳 – |ǂ| TV ☎ P. AE ⓢ E VISA — DV c
☕ 10000 – **19 rm** 120/180000, 3 suites.

at Arcetri S : 5 km – ✉ **50125** Firenze :

X **Omero,** via Pian de' Giullari 11 r ☎ 220053, Country trattoria with ≤, « Summer service on terrace » – AE ⓢ ⓞ E VISA. ✻ — by viale Galileo DZ
closed Tuesday and August – **Meals** a la carte 39/59000 (13 %).

at Galluzzo S : 6,5 km – ✉ **50124** Firenze :

Relais Certosa, via Colle Ramole 2 ☎ 2047171, Telex 574332, Fax 268575, ≤, « Garden-Park », ✂ – |ǂ| ▤ TV ☎ P – 🎪 35-70. AE ⓢ ⓞ E VISA JCB. ✻
Meals 45000 – **63 rm** ☕ 297/340000, 6 suites. — by via Senese CV

X **Trattoria Bibe,** via delle Bagnese 15 ☎ 2049085, Fax 2047167, 🏖 – P. AE ⓢ VISA
closed Wednesday, Thursday lunch, 15 to 28 February and 10 to 20 November – **Meals** a la carte 35/50000. — by via Senese CV

at Candeli E : 7 km – ✉ **50010** :

Villa La Massa ⛰, via La Massa 24 ☎ 6510101, Fax 6510109, ≤, 🏖, « 17C house and furnishings », ⛲, 🌳, ✂ – |ǂ| ▤ TV ☎ ♿ P – 🎪 120. AE ⓢ ⓞ E VISA. ✻ rest
25 March-October – **Meals** ***Il Verrocchio*** Rest. *(closed Monday)* a la carte 65/98000 – ☕ 25000 – **33 rm** 283/450000, 5 suites.

towards Trespiano N : 7 km :

Villa le Rondini ⛰, via Bolognese Vecchia 224 ✉ 50139 Firenze ☎ 400081, Fax 268212, ≤ town, « Among the olive trees », ⛲, 🌳, ✂ – TV ☎ P – 🎪 200. AE ⓢ ⓞ E VISA. ✻ rest
Meals 45/130000 – **31 rm** ☕ 170/250000, 2 suites.

on the motorway at ring-road A1-A11 NW : 10 km :

Forte Agip, ✉ 50013 Campi Bisenzio ☎ 4205081, Fax 4219015 – |ǂ| ▤ TV ☎ ♿ P – 🎪 40-200. AE ⓢ ⓞ E VISA. ✻ rest
Meals a la carte 39/64000 – **163 rm** ☕ 184/224000.

close to motorway station A1 Florence South SE : 6 km :

Sheraton Firenze Hotel, ✉ 50126 ☎ 64901, Telex 575860, Fax 680747, ⛲, ✂ – |ǂ| ⇔ rm ▤ TV ☎ ♿ 🚗 P – 🎪 30-1500. AE ⓢ ⓞ E VISA JCB. ✻
Meals a la carte 52/82000 – **307 rm** ☕ 340/360000, 6 suites.

MILAN 20100 **P** 988 ③, 428 F 9 – pop. 1 334 171 alt. 122 – ☎ 02.

See: Cathedral★★★ (Duomo) MZ – Cathedral Museum★★ MZ **M1** – Via and Piazza Mercanti★ MZ **155** La Scala Opera House★★ MZ Manzoni House★ MZ **M7** Brera Art Gallery★★★ KV – Castle of the Sforzas★★★ JV – Ambrosian Library★★ MZ : portraits★★★ of Gaffurio and Isabella d'Este, Raphael's cartoons★★★ – Poldi-Pezzoli Museum★★ KV **M2** : portrait of a woman★★★ (in profile) by Pollaiolo – Natural Story Museum★ LV **M6** – Leonardo da Vinci Museum of Science and Technology★ HX **M4** – Church of St. Mary of Grace★ HX : Leonardo da Vinci's Last Supper★★★ – Basilica of St. Ambrose★★ HJX : altar front★★ – Church of St. Eustorgius★ JY : Portinari Chapel★★ – General Hospital★ KXY – Church of St. Satiro★ : dome★ MZ – Church of St. Maurice★★ JX – Church of St. Lawrence Major★ JY.

Envir.: Chiaravalle Abbey★ SE : 7 km by corso Lodi LY.

18, 9 (closed Monday) at Monza Park ✉ 20052 Monza ☎ (039) 303081, Fax 304427, by N : 20 km;

18 Molinetto (closed Monday) at Cernusco sul Naviglio ✉ 20063 ☎ 92105128, Fax 92106635, by NE : 14 km;

18 Barlassina (closed Monday) at Birago di Camnago ✉ 20030 ☎ (0362) 560621, Fax 560934, by N : 26 km;

18 (closed Monday) ta Zoate di Tribiano ✉ 20067 ☎ 90632183, Fax 90631861, SE : 20 km;

18 Le Rovedine (closed Monday) at Noverasco di Opera ✉ 20090 ☎ 57606420, Fax 57606405, by via Ripamonti BP.

Motor-Racing circuit at Monza Park by N : 20 km, ☎ (039) 22366.

✈ Forlanini of Linate E : 8 km ☎ 74852200 and Malpensa by NW : 45 km ☎ 74852200 – Alitalia, corso Como 15 ✉ 20154 ☎ 62818 and via Albricci 5 ✉ 20122 ☎ 62817.

☎ 675001.

i via Marconi 1 ✉ 20123 ☎ 809662, Fax 72022432 – Central Station ✉ 20124 ☎ 6690532.

A.C.I. corso Venezia 43 ✉ 20121 ☎ 77451.

Roma 572 – Genève 323 – Genova 142 – Torino 140.

Plans on following pages

Historical centre Duomo, Scala, Sforza Castle, corso Magenta, via Torino, corso Vittorio Emanuele, via Manzoni

Four Seasons, via Gesù 8 ✉ 20121 ☎ 77088, Fax 77085000, – 280. AE VISA JCB. rest — KV **a**
Meals *Il Teatro Rest. (closed lunch, Sunday and August)* a la carte 76/118000 and *La Veranda Rest.* a la carte 62/94000 – 33000 – **77 rm** 737/913000, 16 suites.

Grand Hotel et de Milan, via Manzoni 29 ✉ 20121 ☎ 723141, Fax 86460861 – – 40-100. AE VISA JCB. — KV **g**
Meals *Caruso Rest. (closed dinner except Sunday)* 90/120000 and a la carte 76/101000 see also rest **Don Carlos** below – 30000 – **87 rm** 550/693000, 8 suites.

Jolly Hotel President, largo Augusto 10 ✉ 20122 ☎ 7746, Telex 312054, Fax 783449 – rm – 30-100. AE VISA JCB. rest — NZ **q**
Meals a la carte 63/106000 – **220 rm** 425/505000.

Brunelleschi, via Baracchini 12 ✉ 20123 ☎ 8843, Telex 312256, Fax 804924 – – 40. AE VISA JCB. — MZ **z**
Meals *(closed Saturday and August)* (residents only) a la carte 60/83000 – **128 rm** 330/450000, 5 suites.

Dei Cavalieri, piazza Missori 1 ✉ 20123 ☎ 8857, Telex 312040, Fax 72021683 – – 40-60. AE VISA JCB. rest — MZ **m**
Meals 45/50000 – **177 rm** 290/340000, 7 suites.

Bonaparte Hotel, via Cusani 13 ✉ 20121 ☎ 8560, Fax 8693601 – – 25. AE VISA. rest — JV **a**
Meals a la carte 50/85000 – **43 rm** 360/440000, 13 suites.

Grand Hotel Duomo, via San Raffaele 1 ✉ 20121 ☎ 8833, Telex 312086, Fax 86462027 – AE VISA. rest — MZ **u**
Meals a la carte 66/96000 – **153 rm** 385/525000, 18 suites.

Galileo without rest., corso Europa 9 ✉ 20122 ☎ 7743, Telex 322095, Fax 76020584 – AE VISA JCB. — NZ **x**
89 rm 310/410000, 6 suites.

Spadari al Duomo without rest., via Spadari 11 ✉ 20123 ☎ 72002371, Fax 861184, « Collection of modern art » – AE VISA. — MZ **f**
38 rm 360/420000.

Sir Edward without rest., via Mazzini 4 ✉ 20123 ☎ 877877, Fax 877844, – AE VISA. — MZ **h**
38 rm 290/390000, suite.

Regina without rest., via Cesare Correnti 13 ✉ 20123 ☎ 58106913, Fax 58107033 – – 40. AE VISA — JY **a**
closed August and 24 December-2 January – **43 rm** 250/320000.

MILANO

Street	Grid	No.
Aurispa (V.)	JY	14
Battisti (V. C.)	KLX	20
Bocchetto (V.)	JX	30
Borgogna (V.)	KX	36
Borgonuovo (V.)	KV	38
Calatafimi (V.)	JY	45
Caradosso (V.)	HX	49
Ceresio (V.)	JU	59
Circo (V.)	JX	63
Col di Lana (Via)	JY	65
Col Moschin (V.)	JY	66
Conça del Naviglio (V.)	JY	69
Copernico (V.)	LT	72
Cordusio (Pza)	KX	73
Cune (Vie P.M.)	HV	77
Dugnani (V.)	HY	80
Fatebenefratelli (V.)	KV	92
Gangliano (V.)	KT	98
Generale Fara (V.)	KT	100
Ghislen (V. A.)	HY	101
Giardini (V. dei)	KV	102
Gran S. Bernardo (V.)	HT	105
Guastalla (V.)	KX	110
Induno (V. Fratelli)	HT	116
Lambertenghi (V.P.)	KT	122

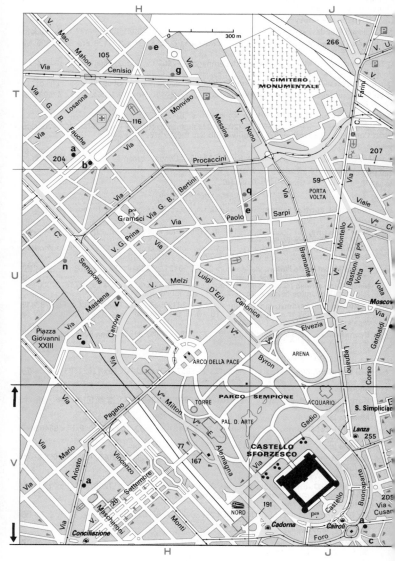

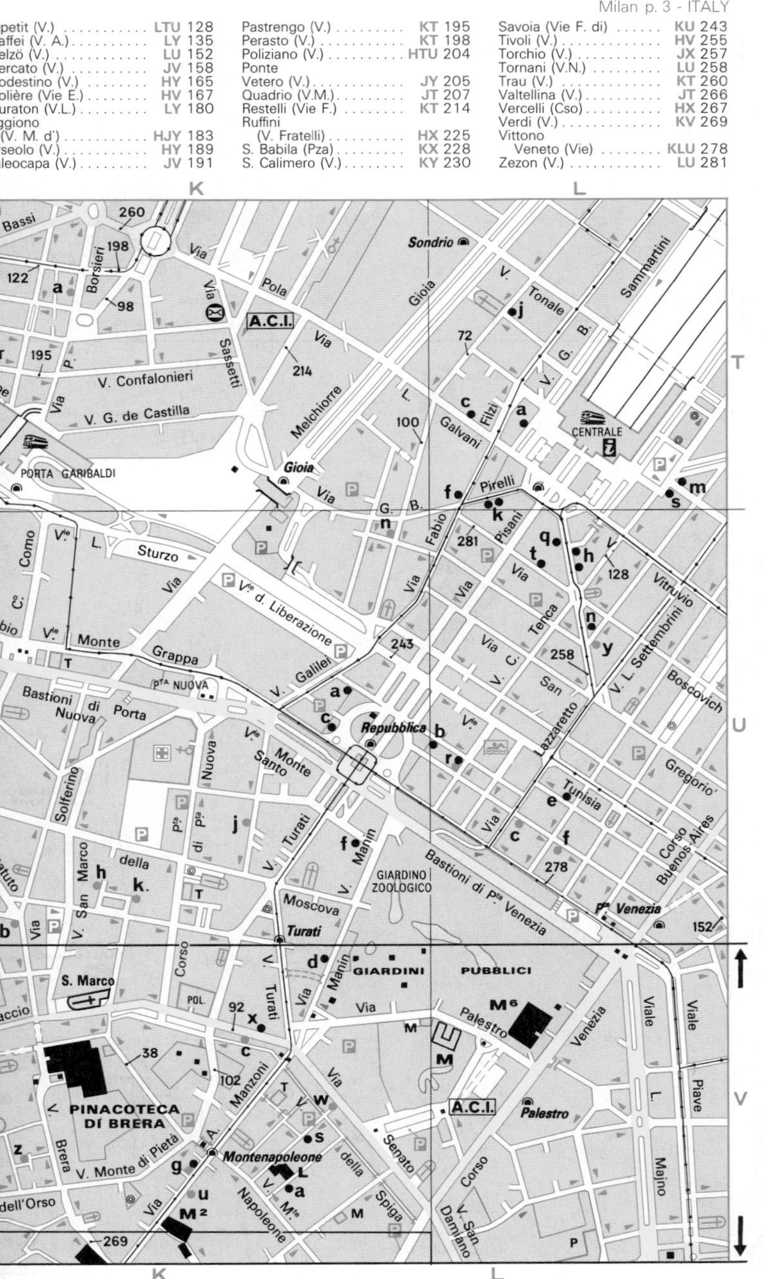

K
L
T
U
V
Sondrio
V. Tonale
Sammartini
Via Pola
Via Gioia
A.C.I.
Via Sassetti
Via Melchiorre
V. Confalonieri
V. G. de Castilla
V. G. B.
Galvani
Filzi
CENTRALE
PORTA GARIBALDI
Gioia
Via G. B. Pirelli
Via Fabio
Pisani
Via Tenca
V.le L. Sturzo
V.le d. Liberazione
C.o Como
V.le Monte Grappa
PTA NUOVA
Bastioni di Porta Nuova
V. Galilei
Republica
V.le Monte Santo
Via C. San
Lazzaretto
V. L. Settembrini
Vitruvio
Boscovich
Gregorio
Tunisia
Corso Buenos Aires
Via Solferino
Via San Marco
della
V. Turati
V. Manin
GIARDINO ZOOLOGICO
Bastioni di Pta Venezia
Pta Venezia
Moscova
Turati
GIARDINI PUBBLICI
Via Palestro
Corso Venezia
Viale L. Majno
Viale Piave
S. Marco
POL.
PINACOTECA DI BRERA
V. Brera
V. Monte di Pietà
A. Manzoni
Montenapoleone
Via Napoleone
V. Mte
Via della Spiga
Via Senato
Palestro
Corso V. San Damiano
dell'Orso
M6
M2

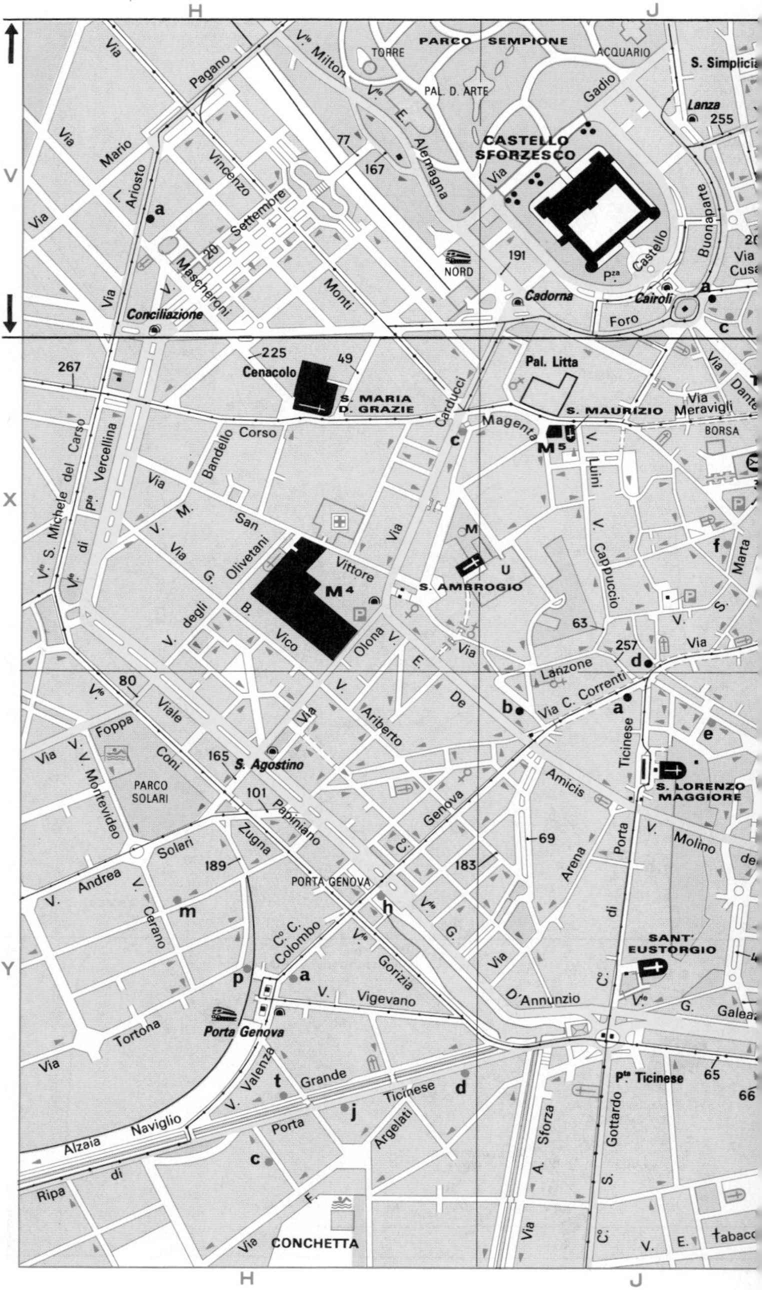

PARCO SEMPIONE
CASTELLO SFORZESCO
S. MARIA D. GRAZIE
S. MAURIZIO
S. AMBROGIO
S. LORENZO MAGGIORE
SANT' EUSTORGIO
CONCHETTA
PARCO SOLARI
PORTA GENOVA
Cenacolo
Pal. Litta
Conciliazione
Cadorna
Cairoli
Lanza
S. Agostino
Porta Genova
Pta Ticinese
NORD
TORRE
ACQUARIO
PAL. D. ARTE
BORSA

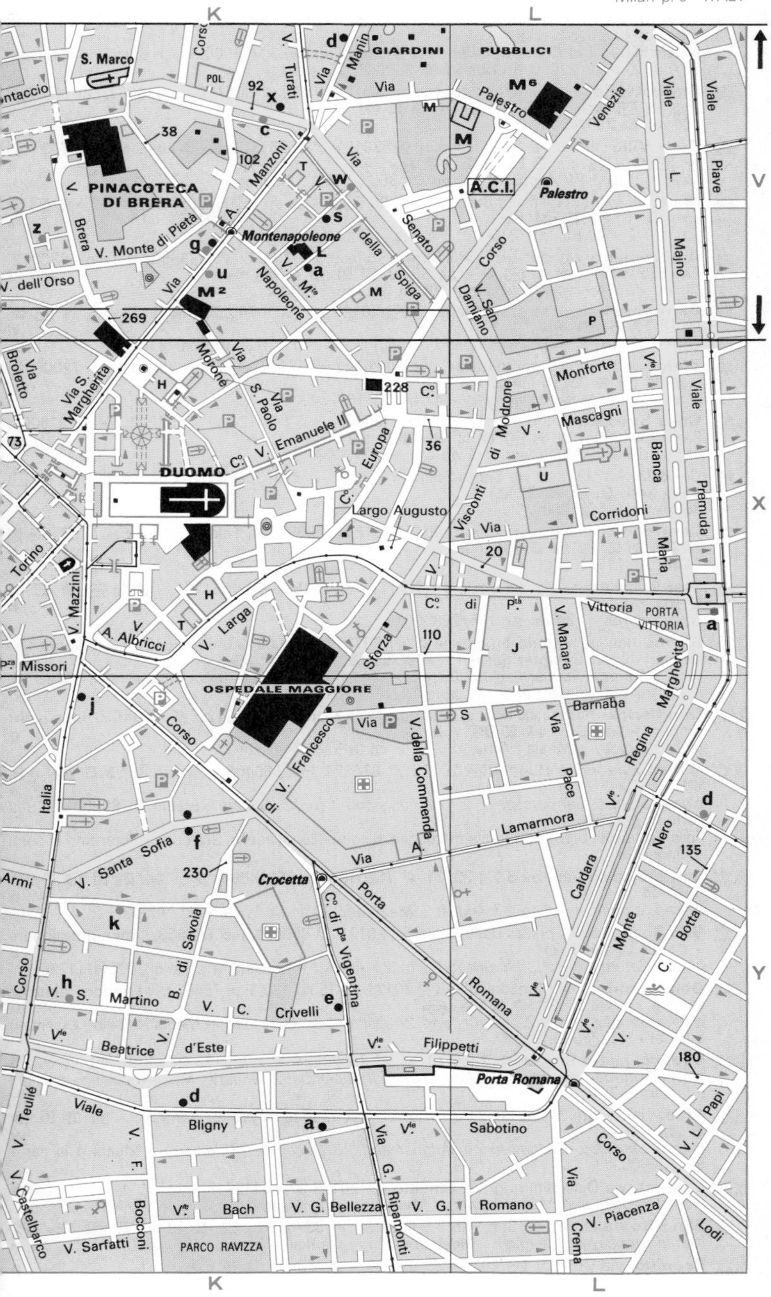

GIARDINI PUBBLICI
S. Marco
PINACOTECA DI BRERA
Montenapoleone
Palestro
A.C.I.
DUOMO
Largo Augusto
OSPEDALE MAGGIORE
PORTA VITTORIA
Crocetta
Porta Romana
PARCO RAVIZZA
V. Manzoni
Via Turati
Via Manin
Via Palestro
Viale Venezia
Viale Piave
Viale L. Majno
Via della Spiga
Via Senato
Corso Venezia
V. Brera
V. Monte di Pietà
V. dell'Orso
Via Napoleone
Via Morone
Via S. Paolo
C° V. Emanuele II
C° Europa
Via Monforte
V. Mascagni
V. San Damiano
Via Visconti di Modrone
Via Corridoni
Viale Bianca Maria
Viale Premuda
Via Broletto
Via S. Margherita
Torino
V. Mazzini
P za Missori
V. Larga
A. Albricci
C° di P ta Vittoria
V. Sforza
V. Manara
Via Barnaba
Via Pace
Via Francesco Sforza
V. della Commenda
Via Lamarmora
Viale Regina Margherita
Via Porta Romana
Corso Italia
V. Santa Sofia
Armi
Via Nero
Monte
Botta
Caldara
Corso Italia
C° di P ta Vigentina
V. S. Martino
V. B. di Savoia
V. C. Crivelli
V le Beatrice d'Este
V le Filippetti
Viale Bligny
V le Sabotino
Corso Lodi
V. Teulié
V. Castelbarco
V. F. Bocconi
V le Bach
V. G. Bellezza
Via G. Ripamonti
V. G. Romano
Via Crema
V. Piacenza
V. L. Papi
V. Sarfatti
Viale Montenero
Viale Caldara
Via Torino
Corso di Porta Romana
POL.
K
L
V
X
Y

Cavour, via Fatebenefratelli 21 ✉ 20121 ✆ 6572051, Fax 6592263 – |♦| ▤ TV ☎. AE ⓢ ⓓ E VISA JCB. ✻ rest KV **x**
Meals 55000 and ***Conte Camillo Rest.*** *(closed Sunday)* 30/35000 (lunch only) and a la carte 65/80000 – ☐ 22000 – **113 rm** 240/300000, 2 suites.

Starhotel Rosa without rest., piazza Fontana ✉ 20122 ✆ 8831, Telex 316067, Fax 8057964 – |♦| ▤ TV ☎ – 🔺 30-120. AE ⓢ ⓓ E VISA JCB NZ **v**
184 rm ☐ 340/450000.

De la Ville without rest., via Hoepli 6 ✉ 20121 ✆ 867651, Telex 312642, Fax 866609 – |♦| ▤ TV ☎ – 🔺 60. AE ⓢ ⓓ E VISA JCB. ✻ NZ **h**
closed 29 July-29 August – **102 rm** ☐ 350/450000, 2 suites.

Manzoni without rest., via Santo Spirito 20 ✉ 20121 ✆ 76005700, Fax 784212 – |♦| TV ☎ 🚗. AE ⓢ ⓓ E VISA. ✻ KV **s**
☐ 19000 – **49 rm** 160/210000, 3 suites.

Ambrosiano without rest., via Santa Sofia 9 ✉ 20122 ✆ 58306044, Telex 333872, Fax 58305067 – |♦| ▤ TV ☎ – 🔺 35-60. AE ⓢ ⓓ E VISA. ✻ KY **f**
closed 23 December-1 January – **78 rm** ☐ 155/230000.

Carrobbio without rest., via Medici 3 ✉ 20123 ✆ 89010740, Fax 8053334 – |♦| ▤ TV ☎. AE ⓢ ⓓ E VISA JCB JX **d**
closed August and 22 December-6 January – ☐ 21000 – **35 rm** 220/310000.

Zurigo without rest., corso Italia 11/a ✉ 20122 ✆ 72022260, Telex 353091, Fax 72000013 – |♦| ▤ TV ☎. AE ⓢ ⓓ E VISA JCB KY **j**
closed 24 December-7 January – **41 rm** ☐ 167/249000.

Casa Svizzera without rest., via San Raffaele 3 ✉ 20121 ✆ 8692246, Telex 316064, Fax 72004690 – |♦| ▤ TV ☎. AE ⓢ ⓓ E VISA MZ **u**
closed 28 July-24 August – **45 rm** ☐ 198/240000.

Canada without rest., via Santa Sofia 16 ✉ 20122 ✆ 58304844, Fax 58300282 – |♦| ▤ TV ☎ ♿ 🚗. AE ⓢ ⓓ E VISA KY **f**
35 rm ☐ 175/260000.

Centro without rest., via Broletto 46 ✉ 20121 ✆ 8692821, Telex 332632, Fax 875578 – |♦| ▤ TV ☎. AE ⓢ ⓓ E VISA JCB MZ **a**
54 rm ☐ 145/200000.

Star without rest., via dei Bossi 5 ✉ 20121 ✆ 801501, Fax 861787 – |♦| ▤ TV ☎. AE ⓢ E VISA. ✻ MZ **b**
closed August – **30 rm** ☐ 135/208000.

XXXXX **Savini,** galleria Vittorio Emanuele II ✉ 20121 ✆ 72003433, Fax 86461060, Elegant traditional decor, « Winter garden » – ▤. AE ⓢ ⓓ E VISA JCB MZ **s**
closed Sunday, August and 23 December-6 January – **Meals** (booking essential) 65000 b.i. (lunch) 80000 (dinner) and a la carte 72/130000 (12 %).

XXXX **Don Carlos** - Hotel Grand Hotel et de Milan, vicolo Manzoni ✉ 20121 ✆ 72314640, Late night dinners – ▤. AE ⓢ ⓓ E VISA JCB KV **g**
closed Sunday – **Meals** *(dinner only)* a la carte 57/87000.

XXX ✿ **Peck,** via Victor Hugo 4 ✉ 20123 ✆ 876774, Fax 860408 – ▤. AE ⓢ ⓓ E VISA JCB. ✻ MZ **e**
closed Sunday, Bank Holidays, 2 to 23 July and 1 to 10 January – **Meals** 60/80000 and a la carte 71/115000
Spec. Tartare di branzino e uova di quaglia, Risotto alla milanese, Scaloppa di branzino ai semi di finocchio.

XXX **Santini,** corso Venezia 3 ✉ 20121 ✆ 782010, Fax 76014691, 🏠 – ▤. AE ⓢ ⓓ E VISA JCB. ✻ NZ **n**
closed Sunday and 4 to 27 August – **Meals** 55000 and a la carte 72/96000.

XXX **Biffi Scala-Toulà,** piazza della Scala ✉ 20121 ✆ 866651, Fax 866653, Late night dinners – ▤. AE ⓢ ⓓ E VISA MZ **c**
closed Saturday lunch, Sunday and 2 to 28 August – **Meals** a la carte 63/97000 (12 %).

XXX **Don Lisander,** via Manzoni 12/a ✉ 20121 ✆ 76020130, Fax 784573, « Outdoor summer service » – ▤. AE ⓢ ⓓ E VISA JCB KV **u**
closed Sunday, 12 to 22 August and 24 December-10 January – **Meals** (booking essential) a la carte 64/98000.

XXX **Boeucc,** piazza Belgioioso 2 ✉ 20121 ✆ 76020224, Fax 796173, 🏠 – ▤. AE. ✻ NZ **j**
closed Saturday, Sunday lunch, August and 24 December-2 January – **Meals** (booking essential) a la carte 63/101000.

XXX **Alfio,** via Senato 31 ✉ 20121 ✆ 780731, Fax 783446, « Winter garden » – ▤. AE ⓢ ⓓ E VISA JCB KV **w**
closed Saturday, Sunday lunch, August and 23 December-3 January – **Meals** a la carte 61/101000.

XXX **L'Ulmet,** via Disciplini ang. via Olmetto ✉ 20123 ✆ 86452718 – ▤ JY **d**
closed Sunday and Monday lunch – **Meals** (booking essential) a la carte 65/104000.

XXX **San Vito da Nino,** via San Vito 5 ✉ 20123 ✆ 8376586 – ▤. AE ⓢ ⓓ E VISA JCB. ✻
closed Monday and August – **Meals** (booking essential) a la carte 53/74000. JY **e**

XXX **Peppino,** via Durini 7 ✉ 20122 ✆ 781729 – ▤. AE ⓢ ⓓ E VISA NZ **p**
closed Friday, Saturday lunch and 10 to 31 July – **Meals** a la carte 52/71000.

MILANO

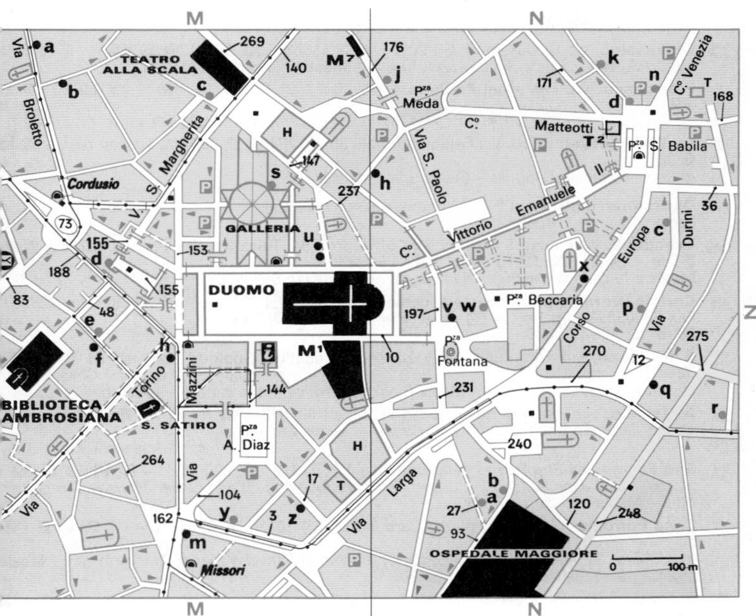

XX **La Dolce Vita,** via Bergamini 11 ✉ 20122 ☎ 58307418 – ▤. AE ⓢ ◑ E VISA. ✈ NZ **a**
closed Saturday lunch, Sunday and August – **Meals** (booking essential for dinner) 20/30000 (lunch) 50000 (dinner) and a la carte 40/50000 b.i.

XX **Bagutta,** via Bagutta 14 ✉ 20121 ☎ 76002767, Fax 799613, 余, Meeting place for artists, « Original paintings and caricatures » – AE ⓢ ◑ E VISA. ✈ NZ **k**
closed Sunday and 23 December-5 January – **Meals** a la carte 71/112000.

XX **Franco il Contadino,** via Fiori Chiari 20 ✉ 20121 ☎ 86463446, Typical rest. and meeting place for artists – ▤. AE ⓢ ◑ E VISA KV **y**
closed Tuesday, Wednesday lunch and July – **Meals** 40/55000 (lunch) 55/70000 (dinner) and a la carte 55/77000.

XX **Rovello,** via Rovello 18 ✉ 20121 ☎ 864396 – ▤. AE ◑ E VISA. ✈ JV **c**
closed Saturday except dinner September-June and Sunday – **Meals** a la carte 50/70000.

XX **Akasaka,** via Durini 23 ✉ 20122 ☎ 76023679, Fax 76020338, Japanese rest. – ▤. AE ⓢ ◑ E VISA JCB. ✈ NZ **c**
closed Monday and 15 to 23 August – **Meals** 25/70000 (10 %) lunch 70/150000 (10 %) dinner and a la carte 61/143000 (10 %).

XX **Al Mercante,** piazza Mercanti 17 ✉ 20123 ☎ 8052198, Fax 86465250, « Outdoor summer service » – AE ⓢ ◑ E VISA MZ **d**
closed Sunday and 1 to 25 August – **Meals** a la carte 48/68000.

XX **Moon Fish,** via Bagutta 2 ✉ 20121 ☎ 76005780, 余, Seafood – ▤. ⓢ NZ **d**
closed Sunday – **Meals** a la carte 57/87000.

XX **Albric,** via Albricci 3 ✉ 20122 ☎ 86461329, Fax 86461329 – ▤. AE ⓢ ⓓ E VISA JCB. ✻ MZ y
closed Saturday lunch, Sunday and 14 to 28 August – **Meals** 50/60000 (lunch) 60/80000 (dinner) and a la carte 60/83000.

XX **Boccondivino,** via Carducci 17 ✉ 20123 ☎ 866040, Specialities salumi, cheese and regional wines – ▤. ⓢ E VISA HX c
closed Sunday and August – **Meals** (dinner only) (booking essential) 50/80000.

XX **Santa Marta,** via Santa Marta 6 ✉ 20123 ☎ 8052090, Fax 8052090 – AE ⓢ ⓓ E VISA
closed Sunday, August and Christmas – **Meals** a la carte 57/71000. JX f

XX **Da Marino-al Conte Ugolino,** piazza Beccaria 6 ✉ 20122 ☎ 876134 – ▤. AE ⓢ ⓓ E VISA NZ w
closed Sunday and August – **Meals** a la carte 53/70000 (11 %).

XX **Ciovassino,** via Ciovassino 5 ✉ 20121 ☎ 8053868 – ▤. AE ⓢ ⓓ E VISA KV z
closed Saturday lunch, Sunday and August – **Meals** a la carte 49/77000.

X **Francesco,** via Festa del Perdono 4 ✉ 20122 ☎ 58307404, 🏡 – ▤. AE ⓢ ⓓ E VISA NZ b
closed Sunday, 12 to 24 August and 23 to 31 December – **Meals** a la carte 41/66000.

X **La Tavernetta-da Elio,** via Fatebenefratelli 30 ✉ 20121 ☎ 653441, Tuscan rest. – AE ⓢ E VISA KV c
closed Sunday and August – **Meals** a la carte 48/68000.

Directional centre via della Moscova, via Solferino, via Melchiorre Gioia, viale Zara, via Carlo Farini

🏨 **Executive,** viale Luigi Sturzo 45 ✉ 20154 ☎ 6294, Telex 310191, Fax 29010238 – 🛗 ▤ TV ☎ – 🚹 25-800. AE ⓢ ⓓ E VISA JCB. ✻ KTU e
Meals a la carte 63/96000 – **414 rm** ☕ 180/220000, 6 suites.

🏨 **Carlyle Brera Hotel** without rest., corso Garibaldi 84 ✉ 20121 ☎ 29003888, Telex 323357, Fax 29003993 – 🛗 ⇔ ▤ TV ☎ ♿ 🚗. AE ⓢ ⓓ VISA JCB. ✻ JU u
98 rm ☕ 355/395000.

XX **A Riccione,** via Taramelli 70 ✉ 20124 ☎ 6686807, Seafood – ▤. AE ⓢ ⓓ E VISA JCB by via Melchiorre Gioia KLT
closed Monday and August – **Meals** (booking essential) a la carte 65/106000.

XX **Al Tronco,** via Thaon di Revel 10 ✉ 20159 ☎ 606072 – ▤. AE ⓢ ⓓ E VISA
closed Saturday lunch, Sunday and August – **Meals** a la carte 38/62000.
by via Melchiorre Gioia KLT

XX **San Fermo,** via San Fermo della Battaglia 1 ✉ 20121 ☎ 29000901 – AE ⓢ ⓓ E VISA
closed 1 to 7 January, Sunday, dinner Saturday June-August and dinner Monday September-May – **Meals** a la carte 44/68000. KU h

XX **Casa Fontana-23 Risotti,** piazza Carbonari 5 ✉ 20125 ☎ 6704710 – ▤. AE ⓢ E VISA. ✻ by via M. Gioia LT
closed 5 to 27 August, Monday, Saturday lunch and Saturday dinner-Sunday in July – **Meals** (booking essential) a la carte 59/88000.

XX **Il Verdi,** piazza Mirabello 5 ✉ 20121 ☎ 6590797 – ▤ KU k
Meals 18/30000 (lunch) and a la carte 40/62000.

XX **Da Fumino,** via Bernina 43 ✉ 20158 ☎ 606872, 🏡, Tuscan trattoria – ▤. AE ⓢ ⓓ E VISA by via C. Farini JT
closed Saturday lunch, Sunday and August – **Meals** a la carte 42/73000.

XX **Rigolo,** via Solferino 11 ang. largo Treves ✉ 20121 ☎ 86463220, Fax 86463220, Habitués rest. – ▤. AE ⓢ ⓓ E VISA. ✻ KU b
closed Monday and August – **Meals** a la carte 39/63000.

X **Osteria de l'Isula,** via Borsieri 27 ✉ 20159 ☎ 6080785, 🏡 – AE ⓓ KT a
closed Sunday and 10 to 25 August – **Meals** (booking essential) a la carte 45/65000.

Central Station corso Buenos Aires, via Vittor Pisani, piazza della Repubblica

🏨 **Principe di Savoia,** piazza della Repubblica 17 ✉ 20124 ☎ 6230 and rest 29090026, Telex 310052, Fax 6595838, 🏋 – 🛗 ▤ TV ☎ ♿ 🚗 – 🚹 700. AE ⓢ ⓓ E VISA JCB. ✻ KU a
Meals 90/110000 and ***Galleria Rest.*** a la carte 95/145000 – ☕ 48500 – **235 rm** 506/693000, 47 suites 1045/2200000.

🏨 **Palace,** piazza della Repubblica 20 ✉ 20124 ☎ 6336 and rest ☎ 29000803, Telex 311026, Fax 654485 – 🛗 ⇔ rm ▤ TV ☎ ♿ 🚗 Ⓟ – 🚹 25-250. AE ⓢ ⓓ E VISA JCB. ✻ rest LU b
Meals ***Casanova Grill Rest.*** (booking essential) 100000 – ☕ 27500 – **208 rm** 424/605000, 8 suites.

🏨 **Excelsior Gallia,** piazza Duca d'Aosta 9 ✉ 20124 ☎ 6785, Telex 311160, Fax 66713239, 🏋, ≘s – 🛗 ⇔ rm ▤ TV ☎ – 🚹 40-500. AE ⓢ ⓓ E VISA JCB. ✻ LT a
Meals a la carte 57/125000 – ☕ 35000 – **239 rm** 390/440000, 9 suites.

🏨 **Milano Hilton,** via Galvani 12 ✉ 20124 ☎ 69831, Telex 330433, Fax 66710810 – 🛗 ⇔ rm ▤ TV ☎ ♿ 🚗 – 🚹 30-250. AE ⓢ ⓓ E VISA JCB. ✻ rest LT c
Meals 60/65000 – ☕ 35000 – **321 rm** 407/514000.

Duca di Milano, piazza della Repubblica 13 ✉ 20124 ✆ 6284, Telex 325026, Fax 6555966 – 40-60. AE VISA JCB. rest
closed August – **Meals** a la carte 80/110000 – 31000 – 99 suites 451/616000. KU **c**

Michelangelo, piazza Luigi di Savoia ang. via Scarlatti ✉ 20124 ✆ 6755, Telex 340330, Fax 6694232 – rm – 25-450. AE VISA JCB
closed August – **Meals** a la carte 85/115000 – **300 rm** 360/500000, 7 suites. LTU **s**

Century Tower Hotel, via Fabio Filzi 25/b ✉ 20124 ✆ 67504, Telex 330557, Fax 66980602 – 40-60. AE VISA JCB.
Meals 48/55000 b.i. – 148 suites 290/360000. LT **f**

Jolly Hotel Touring, via Tarchetti 2 ✉ 20121 ✆ 6335, Telex 320118, Fax 6592209 – 25-120. AE VISA JCB. rest
Meals 65000 and ***Amadeus Rest.*** a la carte 49/80000 – **317 rm** 350/430000. KU **f**

Starhotel Ritz, via Spallanzani 40 ✉ 20129 ✆ 2055, Telex 333116, Fax 29518679 – 25-160. AE VISA JCB. rest by Corso Buenos Aires LU
Meals (residents only) – **206 rm** 340/450000.

Doria Grand Hotel, viale Andrea Doria 22 ✉ 20124 ✆ 6696696, Telex 360173, Fax 6696669 – 25-70. AE VISA JCB. rest by corso Buenos Aires LU
Meals *(closed August)* a la carte 60/114000 – **118 rm** 340/390000, 2 suites.

Bristol without rest., via Scarlatti 32 ✉ 20124 ✆ 6694141, Fax 6702942 – – 50. AE VISA
closed August – **68 rm** 203/270000. LT **m**

Atlantic without rest., via Napo Torriani 24 ✉ 20124 ✆ 6691941, Telex 321451, Fax 6706533 – 25. AE VISA JCB
62 rm 260/360000. LU **h**

Manin, via Manin 7 ✉ 20121 ✆ 6596511, Telex 320385, Fax 6552160, – – 25-100. AE VISA JCB. rest
closed 3 to 18 August and 24 December-7 January – **Meals** *(closed Saturday)* a la carte 53/91000 – 23000 – **112 rm** 240/310000, 6 suites. KV **d**

Augustus without rest., via Napo Torriani 29 ✉ 20124 ✆ 66988271, Fax 6703096 – . AE VISA JCB
closed 25 July-25 August and 23 December-5 January – **56 rm** 141/201000. LU **q**

Mediolanum without rest., via Mauro Macchi 1 ✉ 20124 ✆ 6705312, Telex 310448, Fax 66981921 – . AE VISA JCB
52 rm 200/303000. LU **n**

Sanpi without rest., via Lazzaro Palazzi 18 ✉ 20124 ✆ 29513341, Fax 29402451 – – 30. AE VISA.
closed August and 23 December-8 January – **61 rm** 241/310000, 2 suites. LU **e**

Berna without rest., via Napo Torriani 18 ✉ 20124 ✆ 6691441, Telex 334695, Fax 6693892 – – 30-60. AE VISA JCB.
115 rm 170/250000. LU **h**

Auriga without rest., via Pirelli 7 ✉ 20124 ✆ 66985851, Fax 66980698 – – 25. AE VISA JCB
closed August – **65 rm** 175/200000. LTU **k**

Madison without rest., via Gasparotto 8 ✉ 20124 ✆ 67074150, Telex 326543, Fax 67075059 – – 100. AE VISA
92 rm 205/305000, 8 suites. LT **j**

Galles, via Ozanam 1 ang. corso Buenos Aires ✉ 20129 ✆ 204841, Telex 322091, Fax 2048422, – – 25-150. AE VISA JCB.
Meals *(closed Sunday)* a la carte 40/64000 – 14000 – **105 rm** 240/340000.
by corso Buenos Aires LU

Albert without rest., via Tonale 2 ang. via Sammartini ✉ 20125 ✆ 66985446, Fax 66985624 – – 35. AE VISA by via Sammartini LT
62 rm 150/230000.

Demidoff without rest., via Plinio 2 ✉ 20129 ✆ 29513889, Fax 29405816 – . AE VISA JCB by via Vitruvio LU
closed 2 to 30 August and 24 December-2 January – **36 rm** 140/200000.

New York without rest., via Pirelli 5 ✉ 20124 ✆ 66985551, Fax 6697267 – . AE VISA
closed 1 to 28 August and 24 December-5 January – **69 rm** 141/210000. LTU **k**

Bolzano without rest., via Boscovich 21 ✉ 20124 ✆ 6691451, Fax 6691455, – . AE VISA JCB.
15000 – **35 rm** 130/190000. LU **t**

Sempione, via Finocchiaro Aprile 11 ✉ 20124 ✆ 6570323, Telex 340498, Fax 6575379 – . AE VISA JCB
Meals (see rest. **Piazza Repubblica** below) – **39 rm** 170/230000. LU **r**

XXX **Nino Arnaldo,** via Poerio 3 ✉ 20129 ☎ 76005981 – ▤. AE ⑤ ⓓ E VISA
closed Saturday lunch, Sunday and August – **Meals** (booking essential)50/60000 (lunch) 60/80000 (dinner) and a la carte 67/107000. by corso Monforte LX

XX ⚘ **Joia,** via Panfilo Castaldi 18 ✉ 20124 ☎ 29522124, Vegetarian cuisine – ⅓ ▤. AE ⑤ ⓓ E VISA JCB LU c
closed Saturday lunch, Sunday, August and 26 December-3 January – **Meals** (booking essential) 20/65000 (lunch) 45/65000 (dinner) and a la carte 54/80000
Spec. Bavarese di formaggio dolce con funghi al timo, Maccheroncini con dadolata di melanzane pinoli fave e code di scampi al finocchietto selvatico, Fritto leggero vegetariano o vegano.

XX **Cavallini,** via Mauro Macchi 2 ✉ 20124 ☎ 6693771, Fax 6693174, « Outdoor summer service » – AE ⑤ ⓓ E VISA LU y
closed Saturday, Sunday, 3 to 23 August and 22 to 26 December – **Meals** 42000 and ***Enoteca il Vigneto Rest.*** a la carte 48/79000.

XX **Calajunco,** via Stoppani 5 ✉ 20129 ☎ 2046003 – ▤. ⑤ ⓓ E VISA. ✻
closed Saturday lunch, Sunday, 10 to 31 August and 23 December-4 January – **Meals** (booking essential) 40/55000 (lunch) 100/120000 (dinner) and a la carte 76/110000. by corso Buenos Aires LU

XX **13 Giugno,** via Goldoni 44 ang. via Uberti ✉ 20129 ☎ 719654, 㖈, Sicilian rest. – ▤. AE ⑤ ⓓ E VISA JCB by via Mascagni LX
closed Sunday – **Meals** (booking essential) 40/55000 (lunch only) and 55/60000 (dinner only)

XX **Le 5 Terre,** via Appiani 9 ✉ 20121 ☎ 6575177, Fax 653034, Seafood – ▤. AE ⑤ ⓓ E VISA
closed Saturday lunch, Sunday and 8 to 22 August – **Meals** a lal carte 52/87000. KU

XX **Piazza Repubblica** - Hotel Sempione, via Manuzio 11 ✉ 20124 ☎ 6552715 – ▤. AE ⑤ ⓓ VISA
closed Saturday lunch, Sunday and 8 to 31 August – **Meals** a la carte 40/63000. LU

XX **Altopascio,** via Gustavo Fara 17 ✉ 20124 ☎ 6702458, Tuscan rest. – ▤. AE ⑤ ⓓ E VISA
closed Saturday, Sunday lunch and August – **Meals** a la carte 42/61000. KU n

XX **Osteria la Risacca 2,** viale Regina Giovanna 14 ✉ 20129 ☎ 29531801, Seafood – ▤. AE ⑤ E VISA. ✻ by corso Buenos Aires LU
closed Saturday lunch, Sunday and 1 to 25 August – **Meals** a la carte 35/82000.

XX **Sukrity,** via Panfilo Castaldi 22 ✉ 20124 ☎ 201315, Indian rest. – AE ⑤ ⓓ E VISA. ✻
closed Monday – **Meals** (booking essential for dinner) 18/28000 lunch 34/40000 (10 %) dinner and a la carte 38/46000 (10 %). LU

Romana-Vittoria corso Porta Romana, corso Lodi, corso XXII Marzo, corso Porta Vittoria

XX **Mauro,** via Colonnetta 5 ✉ 20122 ☎ 5461380 – ▤ NZ
closed Saturday lunch, Monday, August and 24 December-2 January – **Meals** a la carte 50/87000.

XX **Hosteria del Cenacolo,** via Archimede 12 ✉ 20129 ☎ 5455536, « Summer service in garden » – AE ⑤ E VISA. ✻ by corso di Porta Vittoria LX
closed Saturday lunch, Sunday and August – **Meals** a la carte 49/71000.

XX **I Matteoni,** piazzale 5 Giornate 6 ✉ 20129 ☎ 55188293, Habitués rest. – ▤. AE ⑤ ⓓ E VISA – *closed Sunday and August* – **Meals** a la carte 40/60000. LX a

XX **Seiperseo,** via Andrea Maffei 12 ✉ 20135 ☎ 55184212 – ▤. AE ⑤ E VISA. ✻ LY d
closed Saturday lunch, Sunday and lunch August – **Meals** 20/35000 (lunch only) and a la carte 54/66000.

XX **Da Giacomo,** via B. Cellini ang. via Sottocorno 6 ✉ 20129 ☎ 76023313 – ▤. AE ⑤ ⓓ E VISA by corso di Porta Vittoria LX
closed Monday, August and 24 December-2 January – **Meals** (booking essential) a la carte 63/103000.

XX **La Risacca 6,** via Marcona 6 ✉ 20129 ☎ 55181658, Fax 55017796, 㖈, Seafood – ▤ AE ⑤ ⓓ E VISA by corso di Porta Vittoria LX
closed Sunday, Monday lunch, August and Christmas – **Meals** a la carte 59/90000.

XX **Gazebo,** via Cadore 2 ✉ 20135 ☎ 59900029, Rest. and pizzeria – ▤. AE ⑤ ⓓ E VISA. ✻
closed Saturday, Sunday lunch, 3 August-1 September and 30 December-7 January – **Meals** a la carte 41/56000. by corso di Porta Vittoria LX

X **Masuelli San Marco,** viale Umbria 80 ✉ 20135 ☎ 55184138, Fax 55184138 – ▤. AE ⑤ E VISA by corso di Porta Vittoria LX
closed Sunday, Monday lunch, 16 August-10 September and 25 December-6 January – **Meals** (booking essential for dinner) a la carte 45/68000.

Navigli via Solari, Ripa di Porta Ticinese, viale Bligny, piazza XXIV Maggio

D'Este without rest., viale Bligny 23 ✉ 20136 ☎ 58321001, Telex 324216, Fax 58321136 – |‡| ▤ TV ☎ – 🚶 40-80. AE ⑤ ⓓ E VISA. ✻ KY d
79 rm ☕ 230/318000.

Crivi's without rest., corso Porta Vigentina 46 ✉ 20122 ☎ 582891, Telex 313255, Fax 58318182 – |‡| ▤ TV ☎ 🚗 – 🚶 30-120. AE ⑤ ⓓ E VISA JCB KY e
closed August – **83 rm** ☕ 210/280000, 3 suites.

Liberty without rest., viale Bligny 56 ✉ 20136 ☎ 58318562, Fax 58319061 – |‡| ▤ TV ☎ 🚗. AE ⑤ E VISA. ✻ KY a
closed 10 to 25 August – ☕ 20000 – **52 rm** 160/230000.

XXX ✿ **Sadler,** via Ettore Troilo 14 ang. via Conchetta ✉ 20136 ☎ 58104451, Fax 58112343, 🏡 - ▤. AE 🅂 ⓓ E VISA JCB by corso S. Gottardo JY
closed Sunday, 5 to 30 August and 1 to 10 January - **Meals** *(dinner only)* 80/120000 and a la carte 78/129000
Spec. Frittelle di fiori di zucchina farciti di mozzarella (spring-summer), Maccheroni al torchio al ragù d'astice, Involtini di pescatrice farciti ai gamberi e avvolti nella melanzana (spring-autumn).

XXX **Yar,** via Mercalli 22 ✉ 20122 ☎ 58309603, Typical Russian cuisine - ▤. AE 🅂 E VISA
closed Sunday - **Meals** (booking essential) 20000 (lunch) 50/90000 (dinner) and a la carte 50/68000. KY **k**

XX **Al Porto,** piazzale Generale Cantore ✉ 20123 ☎ 89407425, Fax 8321481, Seafood - ▤. AE 🅂 ⓓ E VISA HY **h**
closed Sunday, Monday lunch, August and 24 December-3 January - **Meals** (booking essential) a la carte 58/83000.

XX **Osteria di Porta Cicca,** ripa di Porta Ticinese 51 ✉ 20143 ☎ 8372763, Fax 8372763 - ▤. 🅂 ⓓ E VISA. ✻ HY **j**
closed Sunday and 7 to 20 July - **Meals** (booking essential) 35000 (lunch) 50/70000 (dinner) and a la carte 42/76000.

XX **Tornavento,** Alzaia Naviglio Grande 36 ✉ 20144 ☎ 89406068, Rest. and piano bar - ▤. AE 🅂 ⓓ E VISA. ✻ HY **b**
closed Sunday and 10 to 31 August - **Meals** *(dinner only)* a la carte 46/70000.

XX **Trattoria Aurora,** via Savona 23 ✉ 20144 ☎ 89404978, 🏡, Piedmontese rest. - AE 🅂 ⓓ E VISA HY **m**
closed Monday - **Meals** 30000 (lunch) and 55000 b.i. (dinner).

XX **Osteria del Binari,** via Tortona 1 ✉ 20144 ☎ 89409428, Fax 89407470, 🏡, Old Milan atmosphere - ▤. AE 🅂 ⓓ E VISA HY **p**
closed Sunday and 10 to 17 August - **Meals** (dinner only) (booking essential) 59000.

XX **Le Buone Cose,** via San Martino 8 ✉ 20122 ☎ 58310589, Seafood - ▤. AE 🅂 E VISA
closed Saturday lunch, Sunday and August - **Meals** (booking essential) 40000 (lunch) and a la carte 49/95000. KY **h**

XX **Il Torchietto,** via Ascanio Sforza 47 ✉ 20136 ☎ 8372910, Mantuan rest. - ▤. AE 🅂 ⓓ E VISA. ✻ by via A. Sforza JY
closed Monday, August and 26 December-3 January - **Meals** 35000 (lunch only) and a la carte 51/71000.

XX **Al Capriccio,** via Washington 106 ✉ 20146 ☎ 48950655, Seafood - ▤. AE 🅂 E VISA. ✻
closed Monday and August - **Meals** a la carte 61/88000. by via Foppa JY

XX **Shri Ganesh,** via Lombardini 8 ✉ 20143 ☎ 58110933, Indian rest. - ▤. AE 🅂 ⓓ E VISA
closed Sunday and 6 to 21 August - **Meals** *(dinner only)* a la carte 30/45000. HY **c**

X **Asso di Fiori-Osteria dei Formaggi,** Alzaia Naviglio Grande 54 ✉ 20144 ☎ 89409415 - AE 🅂 ⓓ VISA HY **t**
closed Sunday and 10 to 25 August - **Meals** *(dinner only)* a la carte 41/61000.

X **Ponte Rosso,** Ripa di Porta Ticinese 23 ✉ 20143 ☎ 8373132, Trattoria-bistrot with Triestine and Lombardy specialities HY **d**
closed Sunday and dinner except Thursday and Saturday - **Meals** 30/40000 (lunch) and 50/60000 (dinner).

Fiera-Sempione corso Sempione, piazzale Carlo Magno, via Monte Rosa, via Washington

🏨 **Hermitage,** via Messina 10 ✉ 20154 ☎ 33107700, Fax 33107399, 🏋 - 🛗 ▤ 📺 ☎ ♿ 🚗 - 🏛 30-240. AE 🅂 ⓓ E VISA. ✻ HJU **q**
Meals (see rest. **Il Sambuco** below) - **123 rm** ☕ 270/380000, 7 suites.

🏨 **Grand Hotel Fieramilano,** viale Boezio 20 ✉ 20145 ☎ 336221, Telex 331426, Fax 314119, 🏡 - 🛗 ▤ 📺 ☎ ♿ - 🏛 60. AE 🅂 ⓓ E VISA. ✻ rest by via Vincenzo Monti HV
Meals a la carte 34/58000 - **238 rm** ☕ 280/350000.

🏨 **Grand Hotel Ramada,** via Washington 66 ✉ 20146 ☎ 48521, Fax 4818925 - 🛗 ⚡ rm ▤ 📺 ☎ 🚗 - 🏛 1200. AE 🅂 ⓓ E VISA JCB. ✻ by corso Magenta HX
Meals 55000 and ***La Brasserie Rest.*** a la carte 50/79000 - **321 rm** ☕ 460/590000, suite.

🏨 **Regency** without rest., via Arimondi 12 ✉ 20155 ☎ 39216021, Fax 39217734, « In an early 20C noble mansion » - 🛗 ⚡ ▤ 📺 ☎ - 🏛 50. AE 🅂 ⓓ E VISA. ✻
closed August - **52 rm** ☕ 235/320000, 2 suites. by corso Sempione HU

🏨 **Poliziano** without rest., via Poliziano 11 ✉ 20154 ☎ 33602494, Fax 33106410 - 🛗 ▤ 📺 ☎ 🚗 - 🏛 70. AE 🅂 ⓓ E VISA JCB HT **a**
closed 8 to 28 August - **98 rm** ☕ 195/300000, 2 suites.

🏨 **Capitol** without rest., via Cimarosa 6 ✉ 20144 ☎ 48003050, Telex 316150, Fax 4694724 - 🛗 ▤ 📺 ☎ - 🏛 60. AE 🅂 ⓓ E VISA JCB by corso Magenta HX
96 rm ☕ 245/315000.

🏨 **Ariosto** without rest., via Ariosto 22 ✉ 20145 ☎ 4817844, Fax 4980516 - 🛗 ▤ 📺 ☎ - 🏛 40. AE 🅂 ⓓ E VISA HV **a**
☕ 15000 - **53 rm** 138/198000.

🏨 **Domenichino** without rest., via Domenichino 41 ✉ 20149 ☎ 48009692, Fax 48003953 - 🛗 ▤ 📺 ☎ 🚗 🅟 - 🏛 50. AE 🅂 ⓓ E VISA JCB. ✻ by corso Sempione HU
closed 2 to 25 August and 20 December-6 January - **62 rm** ☕ 160/230000, 4 suites.

Mozart without rest., piazza Gerusalemme 6 ✉ 20154 ✆ 33104215, Fax 33103231 – AE E VISA. HT **b**
closed 8 to 28 August – **88 rm** ☕ 170/240000, 3 suites.

Metrò without rest., corso Vercelli 61 ✉ 20144 ✆ 468704, Fax 48010295 – 35. AE E VISA JCB by via Ariosto HV
34 rm ☕ 160/220000.

Admiral without rest., via Domodossola 16 ✉ 20145 ✆ 3492151, Fax 33106660 – 65. AE E VISA by via Procaccini HTU
closed 23 July-28 August – **60 rm** ☕ 130/170000.

Lancaster without rest., via Abbondio Sangiorgio 16 ✉ 20145 ✆ 344705, Fax 344649 – AE E VISA HU **c**
closed August – **30 rm** ☕ 155/240000.

Berlino without rest., via Plana 33 ✉ 20155 ✆ 324141, Telex 312609, Fax 39210611 – AE E VISA JCB by corso Sempione HU
closed 26 July-25 August and 24 December-3 January – **47 rm** ☕ 160/230000.

XXX ✿ **Il Sambuco** - Hotel Hermitage, via Messina 10 ✉ 20154 ✆ 33610333, Fax 3319425 – AE E VISA JCB. HU **q**
closed Saturday lunch, Sunday, 1 to 20 August and 27 December-3 January – **Meals** a la carte 59/96000
Spec. Piatto di pesce e verdure alla ligure, Tagliolini con calamaretti e pomodoro fresco, Fritto di calamaretti zanchette acquadelle gamberi di laguna e merluzzetti.

XXX ✿ **Alfredo-Gran San Bernardo,** via Borgese 14 ✉ 20154 ✆ 3319000, Fax 6555413, Milanese rest. – AE VISA HT **e**
closed August, 23 December-9 January, Sunday and Saturday June-July – **Meals** (booking essential) a la carte 73/103000
Spec. Risotto alla milanese ed al salto, Stracotto al Barbaresco, Costoletta alla milanese.

XXX **Trattoria del Ruzante,** via Massena 1 ✉ 20145 ✆ 316102 – AE E VISA. HU **v**
closed Saturday lunch, Sunday and August – **Meals** (booking essential) 38/50000 (lunch) 60/90000 (dinner) and a la carte 54/93000.

XXX **Raffaello,** via Monte Amiata 4 ✉ 20149 ✆ 4814227 – AE E VISA
closed Wednesday and 1 to 24 August – **Meals** a la carte 48/78000. by via Vincenzo Monti HV

XXX **Dall'Antonio,** via Cenisio 8 ✉ 20154 ✆ 33101511 – AE E VISA. HT **g**
closed Sunday and August – **Meals** (booking essential) a la carte 60/85000.

XX **Taverna della Trisa,** via Francesco Ferruccio 1 ✉ 20145 ✆ 341304, Trentine rest. – VISA HU **n**
closed Monday and August – **Meals** a la carte 45/65000.

X **Al Vecchio Porco,** via Messina 8 ✉ 20154 ✆ 313862, Rest. and pizzeria – AE E VISA HU **e**
closed Sunday lunch and Monday – **Meals** a la carte 50/70000.

X **Trattoria del Previati,** via Gaetano Previati 21 ✉ 20149 ✆ 48000064 – AE E VISA. by via Vincenzo Monti HV
closed 10 to 31 August – **Meals** a la carte 36/61000.

X **Al Vöttantott,** corso Sempione 88 ✉ 20154 ✆ 33603114 – AE E VISA
closed Sunday and August – **Meals** a la carte 31/64000. by corso Sempione HU

Zone periferiche

North-Western area viale Fulvio Testi, Niguarda, viale Fermi, viale Certosa, San Siro, via Novara

Grand Hotel Brun, via Caldera 21 ✉ 20153 ✆ 45271 and rest ✆ 48203791, Telex 315370, Fax 48204746 – 25-500. AE E VISA. rest
Meals 55000 and ***Don Giovanni Rest.*** *(closed Sunday)* a la carte 74/104000 – **330 rm** ☕ 250/300000, 24 suites. by corso Sempione HU

Accademia without rest., viale Certosa 68 ✉ 20155 ✆ 39211122, Telex 315550, Fax 33103878, « Rooms with fresco murals » – AE E VISA JCB by corso Sempione HU
67 rm ☕ 250/370000.

Raffaello without rest., viale Certosa 108 ✉ 20156 ✆ 3270146, Telex 315499, Fax 327044 – 180. AE E VISA JCB. by corso Sempione HU
143 rm ☕ 200/300000, 2 suites.

Novotel Milano Nord, viale Suzzani 13 ✉ 20162 ✆ 66101861, Telex 331292 Fax 66101961, – rm 25-500. AE E VISA rest by via Valtellina JT
Meals a la carte 40/83000 – **172 rm** ☕ 215/260000.

Rubens without rest., via Rubens 21 ✉ 20148 ✆ 40302, Telex 353617, Fax 48193114 « Rooms with fresco murals » – 25. AE E VISA by corso Magenta HX
closed 1 to 21 August – **87 rm** ☕ 270/385000.

Ibis without rest., viale Suzzani 13/15 ✉ 20162 ✆ 66103000, Telex 360141, Fax 66102797 – 🛗 ⇔ rm ▤ TV ☎ ♿ P – 🎤 50. AE 🄱 ⦿ E VISA by via Valtellina JT
132 rm ☕ 135/160000.

Mirage without rest., via Casella 61 angolo viale Certosa ✉ 20156 ✆ 39210471, Fax 39210589 – 🛗 ▤ TV ☎ ♿ – 🎤 30-60. AE 🄱 ⦿ VISA by corso Sempione HU
50 rm ☕ 200/265000, 5 suites.

XX **La Pobbia,** via Gallarate 92 ✉ 20151 ✆ 38006641, Fax 38006641, Modern rustic rest., « Outdoor summer service » – 🎤 40. AE 🄱 ⦿ E VISA. ✗ by corso Sempione HU
closed Sunday and August – **Meals** a la carte 52/79000 (12 %).

XX **Ribot,** via Cremosano 41 ✉ 20148 ✆ 33001646, « Summer service in garden » – P. AE 🄱 ⦿ VISA by corso Sempione HU
closed Monday and 10 to 25 August – **Meals** a la carte 48/60000.

XX **Al Bimbo,** via Marcantonio dal Re 38 ang. via Certosa ✉ 20156 ✆ 3272290, Fax 39216365 – ▤. AE 🄱 ⦿ E VISA by corso Sempione HU
closed Saturday lunch, Sunday and August – **Meals** a la carte 46/74000.

Northern-Eastern area viale Monza, via Padova, via Porpora, viale Romagna, viale Argonne, viale Forlanini

Concorde without rest., via Petrocchi 1 ang. viale Monza ✉ 20125 ✆ 26112020, Telex 315805, Fax 26147879 – 🛗 ▤ TV ☎ 🚗. AE 🄱 ⦿ E VISA. ✗
closed 1 to 24 August – **120 rm** ☕ 270/385000. by corso Buenos Aires LU

Starhotel Tourist, viale Fulvio Testi 300 ✉ 20126 ✆ 6437777, Telex 326852, Fax 6472516, 🏋 – 🛗 ⇔ rm ▤ TV ☎ 🚗 P – 🎤 30-170. AE 🄱 ⦿ E VISA JCB. ✗ rest
Meals a la carte 45/60000 – **139 rm** ☕ 250/340000. by corso Buenos Aires LU

Lombardia, viale Lombardia 74 ✉ 20131 ✆ 2824938, Fax 2893430 – 🛗 ▤ TV ☎ 🚗 – 🎤 30-100. AE 🄱 ⦿ E VISA JCB. ✗ rest by corso Buenos Aires LU
closed 7 to 21 August – **Meals** *(closed Saturday dinner and Sunday)* a la carte 31/66000 – **78 rm** ☕ 143/219000, 6 suites.

Zefiro without rest., via Gallina 12 ✉ 20129 ✆ 7384253, Fax 713811 – 🛗 ▤ TV ☎ – 🎤 30. 🄱 E VISA. ✗ by via Mascagni LX
closed August and 23 December-3 January – **55 rm** ☕ 140/210000.

XXX ✿ **L'Ami Berton,** via Nullo 14 angolo via Goldoni ✉ 20129 ✆ 713669 – ▤. AE 🄱 E VISA. ✗
closed Saturday lunch, Sunday, August and Christmas – **Meals** (booking essential) 70/90000 (lunch) 85/100000 (dinner) and a la carte 63/106000 by via Mascagni LX
Spec. Insalatina di calamaretti e lenticchie, Bavette ai filetti di triglia e cipollotto fresco, Filetto di rombo con finferli e zafferano.

XX **Osteria Corte Regina,** via Rottole 60 ✉ 20132 ✆ 2593377, 🍽, Elegant rustic rest. with Lombardy specialities by corso Buenos Aires LU
closed Saturday lunch, Sunday and August – **Meals** a la carte 60/80000.

XX **Hostaria Mamma Lina,** viale Monza 256 ✉ 20128 ✆ 2574770, Fax 2550311, 🍽, Rest. and piano-bar with Apulian specialities – AE 🄱 ⦿ E VISA JCB by corso Buenos Aires LU
closed Easter, Christmas and Monday except August – **Meals** a la carte 56/81000.

XX **Baia Chia,** via Bazzini 37 ✉ 20131 ✆ 2361131, 🍽, Seafood – ▤. 🄱 E VISA. ✗
closed Sunday, Easter, August and Christmas – **Meals** (booking essential) a la carte 40/81000. by corso Buenos Aires LU

X **La Paranza,** via Padova 3 ✉ 20127 ✆ 2613224, Seafood – ▤. AE 🄱 E VISA
closed Monday and August – **Meals** (booking essential) a la carte 41/62000 (10 %).
by corso Buenos Aires LU

X **I Ricordi,** via Ricordi 8 ✉ 20131 ✆ 29516987, 🍽, Seafood – AE 🄱 ⦿ E VISA
closed Saturday lunch, Sunday, 1 to 23 August and 1 to 7 January – **Meals** a la carte 46/78000. by corso Buenos Aires LU

X **Doge di Amalfi,** via Sangallo 41 ✉ 20133 ✆ 730286, 🍽, Rest. and pizzeria – ▤. AE 🄱 ⦿ E VISA JCB by via Mascagni LX
closed Monday and August – **Meals** a la carte 31/60000.

X **Mykonos,** via Tofane 5 ✉ 20125 ✆ 2610209, Taverna with Greek cuisine
closed Tuesday and August – **Meals** (dinner only) (booking essential) a la carte 33/43000. by corso Buenos Aires LU

Southern-Eastern area viale Molise, corso Lodi, via Ripamonti, corso San Gottardo

Quark, via Lampedusa 11/a ✉ 20141 ✆ 84431, Telex 353448, Fax 8464190, 🍽, 🏊 – 🛗 ⇔ rm ▤ TV ☎ 🚗 P – 🎤 25-1100. AE 🄱 ⦿ E VISA JCB. ✗ rest
closed 22 July-25 August – **Meals** 59000 – **285 rm** ☕ 320/360000. by corso Italia KY

Novotel Milano Est Aeroporto, via Mecenate 121 ✉ 20138 ✆ 58011085, Telex 331237, Fax 58011086, 🏊 – 🛗 ⇔ rm ▤ TV ☎ ♿ P – 🎤 25-350. AE 🄱 ⦿ E VISA. ✗ rest
Meals a la carte 52/79000 – **206 rm** ☕ 260/350000. by corso di Porta Vittoria LX

XX **Antica Trattoria Monluè,** via Monluè 75 ✉ 20143 ✆ 7610246, Country trattoria with summer service – ▤ P. AE 🄱 ⦿ E VISA. ✗ by corso di Porta Vittoria LX
closed Saturday lunch, Sunday and 4 to 20 August – **Meals** a la carte 47/70000.

XX **La Plancia,** via Cassinis 13 ✉ 20139 ✆ 5390558, Seafood pizzeria – ▤. AE 🄱 ⦿ E VISA
closed Sunday and August – **Meals** a la carte 41/66000. by corso Lodi LY

X **Taverna Calabiana,** via Calabiana 3 ✉ 20139 ✆ 55213075, Rest. and pizzeria – ▤. AE 🄱 VISA. ✗ by corso Lodi LY
closed Sunday, Monday, 16 to 21 April, August and 24 December-5 January – **Meals** a la carte 43/62000.

Southern-Western area viale Famagosta, viale Liguria, via Lorenteggio, viale Forze Armate, via Novara

Holiday Inn, via Lorenteggio 278 ✉ 20152 ☎ 410014, Fax 48304729 – rm TV – 70. AE VISA JCB. rest by via Foppa HY
Meals ***L'Univers Gourmand Rest.*** a la carte 48/60000 – 33500 – **119 rm** 305/375000.

Green House without rest., viale Famagosta 50 ✉ 20142 ☎ 8132451, Fax 816624 – TV. AE VISA. by Ripa di Porta Ticinese HY
15000 – **45 rm** 130/180000.

XXX ✿✿ **Aimo e Nadia,** via Montecuccoli 6 ✉ 20147 ☎ 416886, Fax 48302005 – . AE VISA. by via Foppa HY
closed Saturday lunch, Sunday, August and 1 to 6 January – **Meals** (booking essential) 55/95000 (lunch) 95000 (dinner) and a la carte 95/130000
Spec. Fonduta di fiori di zucca e ricotta al sapore di tartufo (spring-autumn), Bucatini in insalata di pomodorini pugliesi (spring-summer), Petto di faraona al vino cotto e nocciole con fagottino di melanzane al rognone.

at Chiaravalle Milanese by Corso Lodi LY : 7 km :

XX **Antica Trattoria San Bernardo,** via San Bernardo 36 ✉ 20139 Milano ☎ 57409831, Rustic elegant rest., « Outdoor summer service » – . AE VISA.
closed Sunday dinner, Monday and August – **Meals** a la carte 63/91000.

on national road 35-Milanofiori by via Francesco Sforza JY : 10 km :

Jolly Hotel Milanofiori, Strada 2 ✉ 20090 Assago ☎ 82221, Telex 325314, Fax 89200946, – rm TV – 120. AE VISA. rest
closed August and 22 December 7 January – **Meals** 52000 – **255 rm** 285/345000.

on road New Vigevanese-Zingone by via Foppa HY : 11 km :

Eur without rest., via Leonardo da Vinci 36 A ✉ 20090 Trezzano sul Naviglio ☎ 4451951, Fax 4451075 – TV – 70. AE VISA JCB
41 rm 140/180000.

on national road West-Assago by via Foppa HY : 11 km :

Forte Agip, ✉ 20090 Assago ☎ 4880441, Telex 325191, Fax 48843958, – rm TV – 300. AE VISA. rest
Meals 30/64000 – **219 rm** 184/224000.

Abbiategrasso 20081 Milano 988 ③, 428 F 8 – pop. 27 501 alt. 120 – ☎ 02.

Roma 590 – Alessandria 80 – Milano 24 – Novara 29 – Pavia 33.

at Cassinetta di Lugagnano N : 3 km – ✉ **20081** :

XXXX ✿✿✿ **Antica Osteria del Ponte,** ☎ 9420034, Fax 9420610, – . AE VISA JCB.
closed Sunday, Monday, August and 25 December-12 January – **Meals** (booking essential) 75000 (lunch) 150000 (dinner) and a la carte 98/153000
Spec. Lasagnetta ai cipollotti e tartufi neri (January-April), Brandade di stoccafisso, Crépinette di carne di capretto alle mandorle (November-June).

Bergamo 24100 P 988 ③, 428 E 11 – pop. 115 899 alt. 249 – ☎ 035.

9, 9 and 9 L'Albenza (closed Monday) at Almenno San Bartolomeo ✉ 24030 ☎ 640028, Fax 643066;

9 La Rossera (closed Tuesday) at Chiuduno ✉ 24060 ☎ 838600, Fax 4427047.

Orio al Serio ☎ 326323, Fax 313432 – Alitalia, via Casalino 5 ☎ 224425, Fax 235127.

Roma 601 – Brescia 52 – Milano 47.

XXX ✿✿ **Da Vittorio,** viale Papa Giovanni XXIII 21 ✉ 24121 ☎ 218060, Fax 218060 – . AE VISA
closed Wednesday and 5 to 25 August – **Meals** 60/95000 (lunch) 95/130000 (dinner) and a la carte 80/120000
Spec. Lasagnetta aperta con scampi e insalata trevisana brasata, Filetto di branzino al basilico fritto e salsa al timo, Soufflé caldo al frutto della passione.

Canneto sull'Oglio 46013 Mantova 428 429 G 13 – pop. 4 591 alt. 35 – ☎ 0376.

Roma 493 – Brescia 51 – Cremona 32 – Mantova 38 – Milano 123 – Parma 44.

towards Carzaghetto NW : 3 km :

XXXX ✿✿✿ **Dal Pescatore,** ✉ 46013 ☎ 723001, Fax 70304, « Outdoor dinner summer service » – . AE VISA JCB.
closed Monday, Tuesday, 12 August-1 September, Christmas and 2 to 17 January – **Meals** (booking essential) 120000 and a la carte 86/129000
Spec. Tortelli di pecorino ricotta e parmigiano, Piedini di maiale con verze e legumi (November-March), Anatra all'aceto balsamico.

Erbusco 25030 Brescia 428 429 F 11 – pop. 6 412 alt. 251 – ☎ 030.
Roma 578 – Bergamo 35 – Brescia 22 – Milano 69.

XXXX ✿✿✿ **Gualtiero Marchesi,** località Bellavista N : 1,5 km ☎ 7760562, Fax 7760573, ≤ lake and mountains, Elegant installation – ▤ P. AE ⑤ ⊙ E VISA. ✻
closed Sunday dinner, Monday, August and 1 to 26 January – **Meals** (booking essential) 65000 (lunch) 100/150000 (dinner) and a la carte 85/135000
Spec. Raviolo aperto, Filetto di vitello alla Rossini secondo Gualtiero Marchesi, Cotoletta di vitello alla milanese.

Ranco 21020 Varese 428 E 7, 219 ⑦ – pop. 1 029 alt. 214 – ☎ 0331.
Roma 644 – Laveno Mombello 21 – Milano 67 – Novara 51 – Sesto Calende 12 – Stresa 37 – Varese 27.

XXX ✿✿ **Il Sole** with rm, ☎ 976507, Fax 976620, ≤, « Summer service under pergola », – ▤ rm TV ☎ P. AE ⑤ ⊙ E VISA. ✻
closed December and January – **Meals** (booking essential) *(closed Monday dinner except June-September and Tuesday)* 85/100000 (10 %) lunch 100/135000 (10 %) dinner and a la carte 85/135000 (10 %) – ☐ 15000 – **4 rm** 210/300000, 4 suites 340/360000
Spec. Biscotto di sardine marinate, Lasagna multicolore con scampi e salsa al Sauternes, Rostin negàa.

Soriso 28018 Novara 428 E 7, 219 ⑯ – pop. 745 alt. 452 – ☎ 0322.
Roma 654 – Arona 20 – Milano 78 – Novara 40 – Stresa 35 – Torino 114 – Varese 46.

XXXX ✿✿ **Al Sorriso** with rm, ☎ 983228, Fax 983328 – ▤ rest TV ☎. AE ⑤ ⊙ E VISA. ✻
closed 5 to 22 August and 8 to 22 January – **Meals** (booking essential) *(closed Monday and Tuesday lunch)* a la carte 97/132000 – **8 rm** ☐ 150/210000
Spec. Sfogliata di patate gratinata con pesce persico al prezzemolo (March-December), Filetto di rombo laccato al miele con porcini e piselli (March-November), Piccione rosolato all'aceto balsamico e finferli (June-November).

NAPLES (NAPOLI) 80100 P 988 ㉗, 431 E 24 – pop. 1 061 583 – High Season : April-October – ☎ 081.

See : National Archaeological Museum★★★ KY – New Castle★★ KZ – Port of Santa Lucia★★ BU : ≤★★ of Vesuvius and bay – ≤★★★ at night from via Partenope of the Vomero and Posillipo FX – San Carlo Theatre★ KZ **T1** – Piazza del Plebiscito★ JKZ – Royal Palace★ KZ – Carthusian Monastery of St. Martin★★ JZ : ≤★★★ ofthe Bay of Naples from gallery 25.
Spacca-Napoli quarter★★ KY – Tomb★★ of King Robert the wise in Church of Santa Chiara★ KY – Caryatids★ by Tino da Camaino in Church of St. Dominic Major KY – Sculptures★ in Chapel of St. Severo KY – Arch★, Tomb★ of Catherine of Austria, apse★ in Church of St. Lawrence Major LY – Capodimonte Palace and National Gallery★★.
Mergellina★ : ≤★★ of the bay – Villa Floridiana★ EVX : ≤★ – Catacombs of St. Gennaro★★ – Church of Santa Maria Donnaregina★ LY – Church of St. Giovanni a Carbonara★ LY – Capuan Gate★ LMY – Cuomo Palace★ LY – Sculptures★ in the Church of St. Anne of the Lombards KYZ – Posillipo★ – Marechiaro★ – ≤★★ of the Bay from Virgiliano Park (or Rimembranza Park).

Exc. : Bay of Naples★★★ road to Campi Flegrei★★, to Sorrento Penisula Island of Capri★★★ Island of Ischia★★★.

⛳9 (closed Monday and Tuesday) at Arco Felice ✉ 80072 ☎ 5264296, W : 19 km.

✈ Ugo Niutta of Capodichino NE : 6 km (except Saturday and Sunday) ☎ 5425333 – Alitalia, via Medina 41 ✉ 80133 ☎ 5425222.

⛴ to Capri (1 h 15 mn), Ischia (1 h 15 mn) e Procida (1 h), daily – Caremar-Travel and Holidays, molo Beverello ✉ 80133 ☎ 5513882, Fax 5522011; to Cagliari 19 June-17 September Thursday and Saturday, Thursday October-May (15 h 45 mn) and Palermo daily (11 h) – Tirrenia Navigazione, Stazione Marittima, molo Angioino ✉ 80133 ☎ 7613688, Telex 710030, Fax 7201567 to Ischia daily (1 h 15 mn) – Alilauro and Linee Lauro, molo Beverello ✉ 80133 ☎ 5522838, Fax 5513236 ; to Aeolian Island Wednesday and Friday, 15 June-15 September Monday, Tuesday, Thursday, Friday, Saturday and Sunday (14 h) – Siremar-Genovese Agency, via De Petris 78 ✉ 80133 ☎ 5512112, Telex 710196, Fax 5512114.

⛴ to Capri (45 mn), Ischia (45 mn) and Procida (35 mn), daily – Caremar-Travel and Holidays, molo Beverello ✉ 80133 ☎ 5513882, Fax 5522011; to Ischia (30 mn) and Capri (40 mn), daily – Alilauro, via Caracciolo 11 ✉ 80122 ☎ 7611004, Fax 7614250; to Capri daily (40 mn)Navigazione Libera del Golfo, molo Beverello ✉ 80133 ☎ 5520763, Telex 722661, Fax 5525589 to Capri (45 mn), to Aeolian Island June-September (4 h) and Procida-Ischia daily (35 mn) – Aliscafi SNAV, via Caracciolo 10 ✉ 80122 ☎ 7612348, Telex 720446, Fax 7612141.

ℹ piazza dei Martiri 58 ✉ 80121 ☎ 405311 – piazza del Plebiscito (Royal Palace) ✉ 80132 ☎ 418744, Fax 418619 – Central Station ✉ 80142 ☎ 268779 - Capodichino Airport ✉ 80133 ☎ 7805761 – piazza del Gesù Nuovo 7 ✉ 80135 ☎ 5523328 - Passaggio Castel dell'Ovo ✉ 80132 ☎ 7645688.

A.C.I. piazzale Tecchio 49/d ✉ 80125 ☎ 2394511.

Roma 219 – Bari 261

Plans on following pages

NAPOLI

Giordano (Via L.) . . . . **EV** 64
Scarlatti (Via Alessandro) . . . . . . **EV** 153

Arcoleo (Via G.) . . . . **FX** 5
Arena della Sanità (Via) . . . **GU** 6
Artisti (Piazza degli) . . . . . . **EV** 9
Bernini (Via G. L.) . . . . **EV** 12
Bonito (Via G.) . . . . **FV** 13
Carducci (Via G.) . . . . **FX** 20
Chiatamone (Via) . . . . **FX** 25

Cirillo (Via D.) . . . . **GU** 27
Colonna (Via Vittoria) . . . . . **FX** 29
Crocelle (Via) . . . . **GU** 35
D'Auria (Via G.) . . . . **FV** 40
Ferraris (Via Galileo) . . . . . . **HV** 54
Fontana (Via Domenico) . . **EU** 58
Gen. Pignatelli (Via) . . . . . . **HU** 62

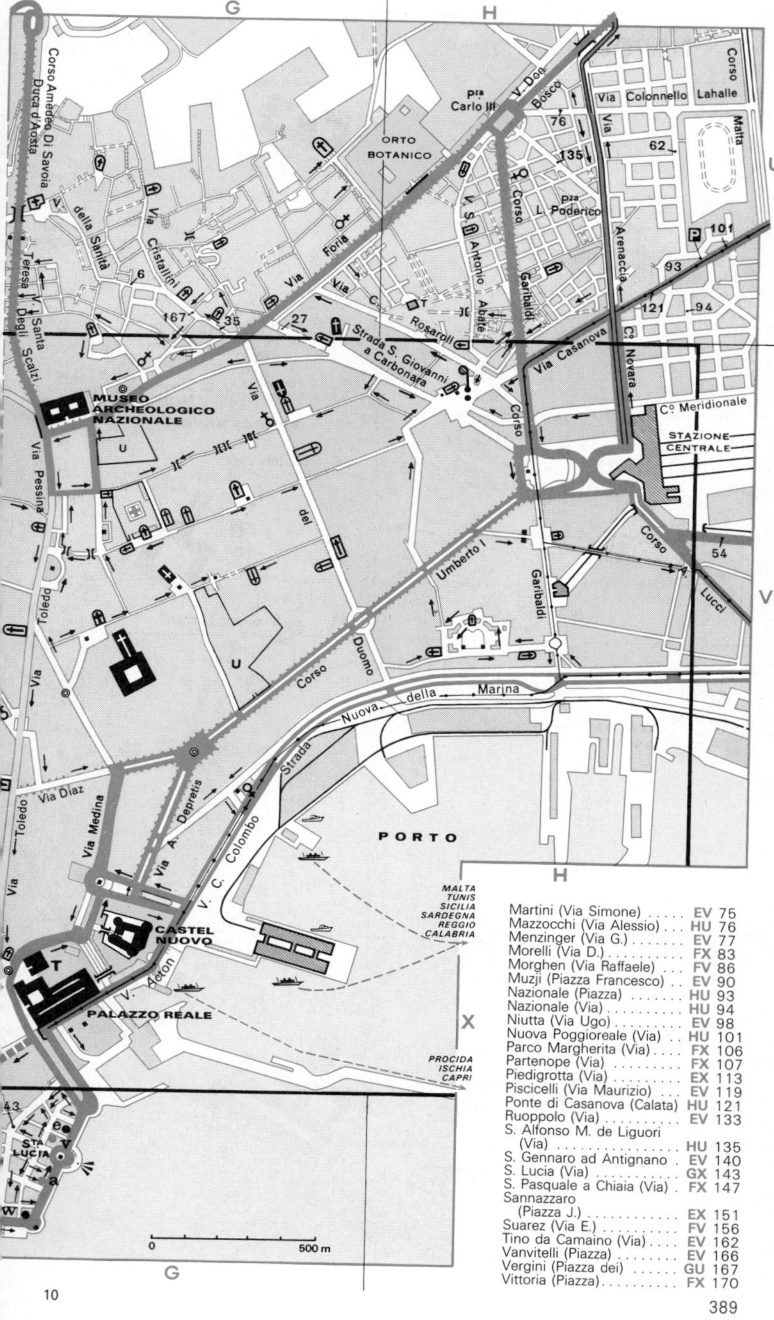

Martini (Via Simone) ..... EV 75
Mazzocchi (Via Alessio) ... HU 76
Menzinger (Via G.) .... EV 77
Morelli (Via D.) .... FX 83
Morghen (Via Raffaele) ... FV 86
Muzji (Piazza Francesco) .. EV 90
Nazionale (Piazza) .... HU 93
Nazionale (Via) .... HU 94
Niutta (Via Ugo) .... EV 98
Nuova Poggioreale (Via) .. HU 101
Parco Margherita (Via) .... FX 106
Partenope (Via) .... FX 107
Piedigrotta (Via) .... EX 113
Piscicelli (Via Maurizio) ... EV 119
Ponte di Casanova (Calata) HU 121
Ruoppolo (Via) .... EV 133
S. Alfonso M. de Liguori (Via) .... HU 135
S. Gennaro ad Antignano . EV 140
S. Lucia (Via) .... GX 143
S. Pasquale a Chiaia (Via) . FX 147
Sannazzaro (Piazza J.) .... EX 151
Suarez (Via E.) .... FV 156
Tino da Camaino (Via) .... EV 162
Vanvitelli (Piazza) .... EV 166
Vergini (Piazza dei) ...... GU 167
Vittoria (Piazza) .... FX 170

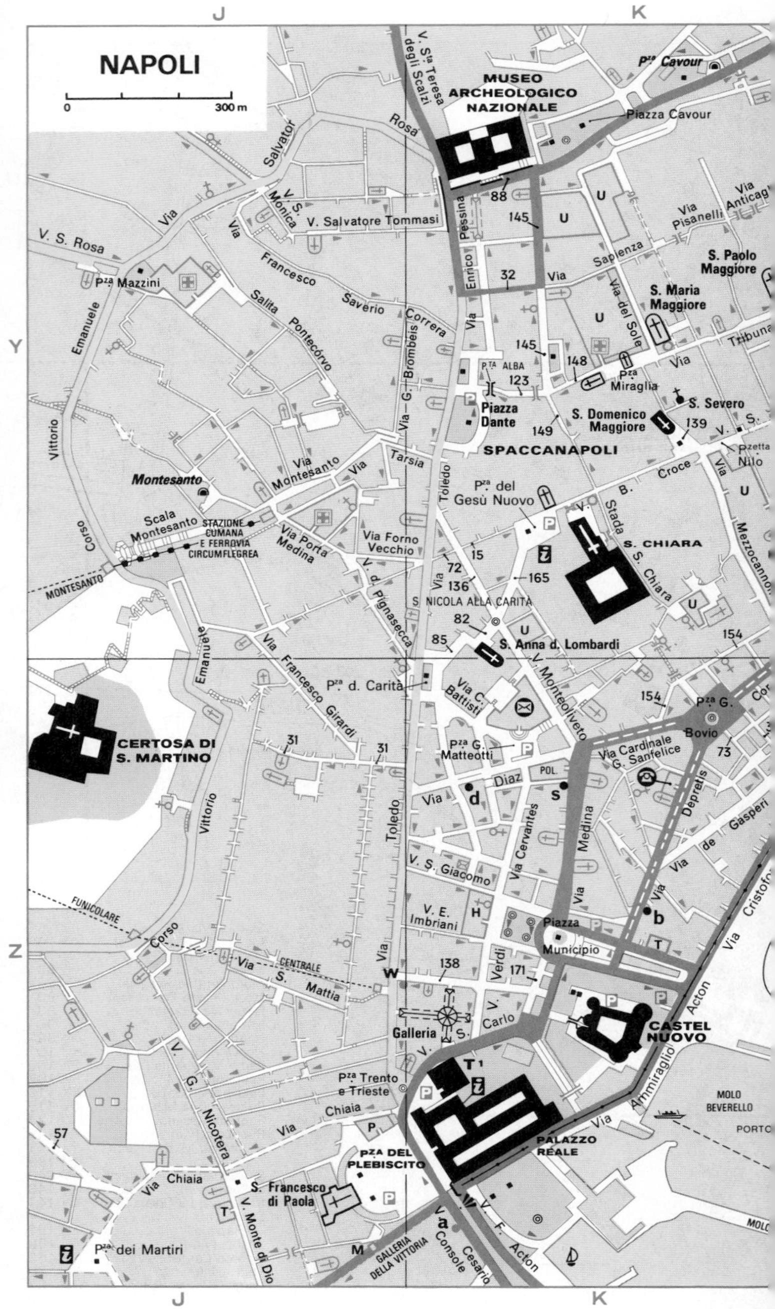
NAPOLI
0
300 m
MUSEO ARCHEOLOGICO NAZIONALE
Piazza Cavour
Pza Cavour
SPACCANAPOLI
S. CHIARA
CERTOSA DI S. MARTINO
CASTEL NUOVO
PALAZZO REALE
S. Paolo Maggiore
S. Maria Maggiore
S. Domenico Maggiore
S. Severo
Piazza Dante
Pza del Gesù Nuovo
S. NICOLA ALLA CARITÀ
S. Anna d. Lombardi
Pza d. Carità
Pza G. Matteotti
Pza G. Bovio
Piazza Municipio
Galleria
Pza Trento e Trieste
PZA DEL PLEBISCITO
S. Francesco di Paola
Pza dei Martiri
Pza Mazzini
Montesanto
STAZIONE CUMANA E FERROVIA CIRCUMFLEGREA
MONTESANTO
FUNICOLARE
CENTRALE
MOLO BEVERELLO
PORTO
Via Toledo
Corso Vittorio Emanuele
Via Chiaia
Via Medina
Via Depretis
Via Acton
Via Ammiraglio
Via Cristoforo
GALLERIA DELLA VITTORIA
J
K
Y
Z

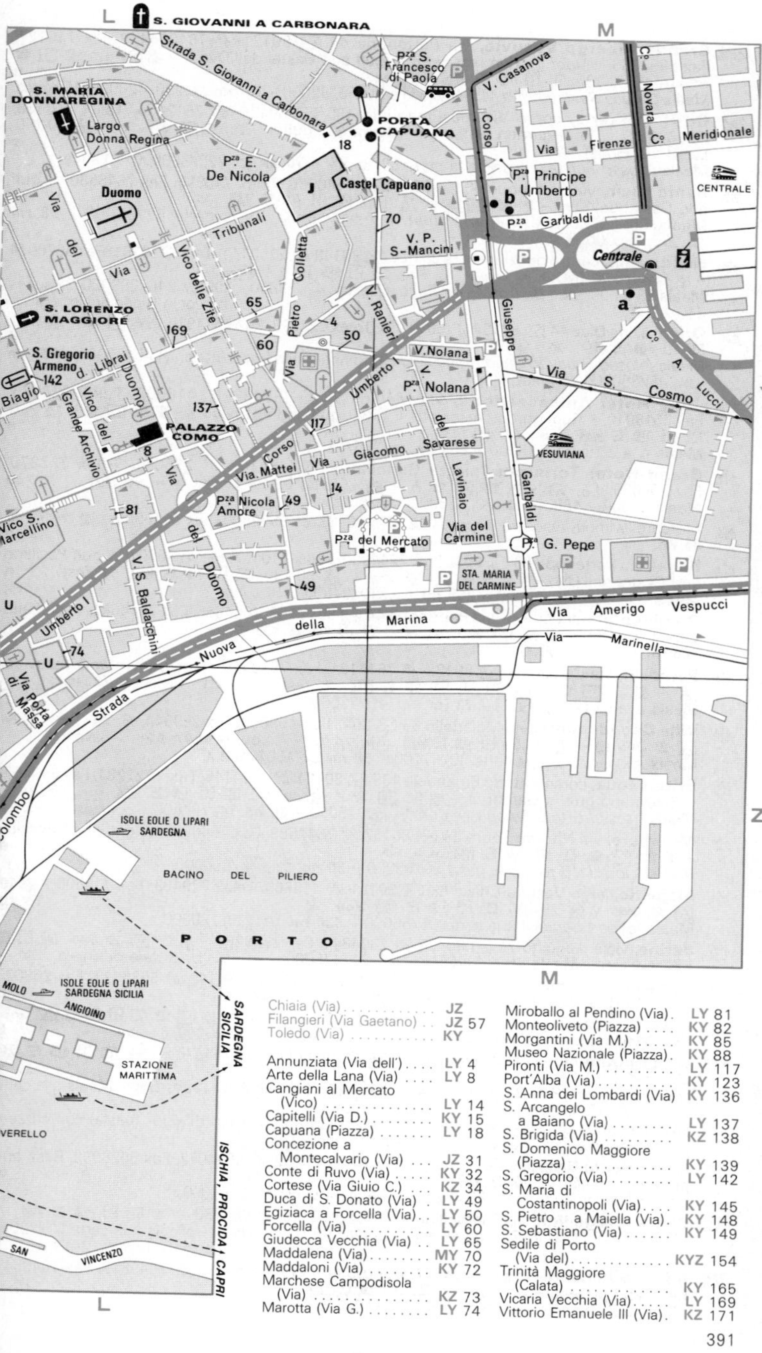

Chiaia (Via)	JZ	
Filangieri (Via Gaetano)	JZ	57
Toledo (Via)	KY	
Annunziata (Via dell')	LY	4
Arte della Lana (Via)	LY	8
Cangiani al Mercato (Vico)	LY	14
Capitelli (Via D.)	KY	15
Capuana (Piazza)	LY	18
Concezione a Montecalvario (Via)	JZ	31
Conte di Ruvo (Via)	KY	32
Cortese (Via Giuio C.)	KZ	34
Duca di S. Donato (Via)	LY	49
Egiziaca a Forcella (Via)	LY	50
Forcella (Via)	LY	60
Giudecca Vecchia (Via)	LY	65
Maddalena (Via)	MY	70
Maddaloni (Via)	KY	72
Marchese Campodisola (Via)	KZ	73
Marotta (Via G.)	LY	74
Miroballo al Pendino (Via)	LY	81
Monteoliveto (Piazza)	KY	82
Morgantini (Via M.)	KY	85
Museo Nazionale (Piazza)	KY	88
Pironti (Via M.)	LY	117
Port'Alba (Via)	KY	123
S. Anna dei Lombardi (Via)	KY	136
S. Arcangelo a Baiano (Via)	LY	137
S. Brigida (Via)	KZ	138
S. Domenico Maggiore (Piazza)	KY	139
S. Gregorio (Via)	LY	142
S. Maria di Costantinopoli (Via)	KY	145
S. Pietro a Maiella (Via)	KY	148
S. Sebastiano (Via)	KY	149
Sedile di Porto (Via del)	KYZ	154
Trinità Maggiore (Calata)	KY	165
Vicaria Vecchia (Via)	LY	169
Vittorio Emanuele III (Via)	KZ	171

Grande Albergo Vesuvio, via Partenope 45 ✉ 80121 ✆ 7640044, Telex 710127 Fax 5890380, « Roof garden rest. with ≤ gulf and Castel dell'Ovo » – |‡| ⇹ rm ▤ TV ☎ ⇔ – 🏛 40-400. AE ⓢ ◑ E VISA. ✻ rest FX
Meals ***Caruso Rest.*** *(closed Monday)* a la carte 59/82000 – **167 rm** ☐ 290/420000, 16 suites

Gd H. Parker's, corso Vittorio Emanuele 135 ✉ 80121 ✆ 7612474, Telex 710578 Fax 663527, « Roof garden rest. with ≤ town and gulf » – |‡| ▤ TV ☎ ⇔ – 🏛 50-250 AE ⓢ ◑ E VISA. ✻ EX
Meals *(closed Sunday dinner)* a la carte 56/86000 – **70 rm** ☐ 220/330000, 10 suites.

Santa Lucia, via Partenope 46 ✉ 80121 ✆ 7640666, Telex 710595, Fax 7648580, ≤ gulf and Castel dell'Ovo – |‡| ▤ TV ☎ – 🏛 110. AE ⓢ ◑ E VISA. ✻ GX
Meals 60/80000 and ***Megaris Rest.*** *(closed Sunday)* a la carte 62/96000 – **98 rm** ☐ 270/390000, 3 suites.

Holiday Inn, centro direzionale Isola e/6 ✉ 80143 ✆ 2250111, Telex 720161, Fax 562807 – |‡| ⇹ rm ▤ TV ☎ ♿ ⇔ – 🏛 150. AE ⓢ ◑ E VISA JCB. ✻
Meals 28/50000 and ***Bistrot Victor Rest.*** a la carte 47/69000 – **298** ☐ 240/280000, 32 suites 340/380000. by corso Meridionale MY

Oriente, via Diaz 44 ✉ 80134 ✆ 5512133, Telex 722398, Fax 5514915 – ▤ TV ☎ – 🏛 300 AE ⓢ ◑ E VISA. ✻ KZ
Meals *(closed Friday to Sunday and August)* (dinner only) (residents only) 45/60000 – **130 rm** ☐ 245/360000, 2 suites.

Jolly Hotel Ambassador's, via Medina 70 ✉ 80133 ✆ 416000, Telex 720335 Fax 5518010, « Roof garden rest. with ≤ town, gulf and Vesuvius » – |‡| ▤ TV ☎ – 🏛 250 AE ⓢ ◑ E VISA JCB. ✻ rest KZ
Meals a la carte 71/113000 – **251 rm** ☐ 245/290000.

Grand Hotel Terminus, piazza Garibaldi 91 ✉ 80142 ✆ 286011, Telex 722270 Fax 206689, Fδ, ≘s – |‡| ▤ TV ☎ ♿ – 🏛 300. AE ⓢ ◑ E VISA JCB. ✻ rest MY
Meals 32000 – **188 rm** ☐ 200/280000, 6 suites.

Mercure, without rest., via Depretis 123 ✉ 80133 ✆ 5529500, Fax 5529509 – |‡| ▤ TV ☎ **85 rm**. KZ

Royal, via Partenope 38 ✉ 80121 ✆ 7644800, Telex 710167, Fax 7645707, ≤ gulf Posillipo and Castel dell'Ovo, ⛱ – |‡| ▤ TV ☎ ⇔ – 🏛 50-180. AE ⓢ ◑ E VISA. ✻ rest FX
Meals a la carte 70/90000 – **269 rm** ☐ 210/340000, 16 suites.

Continental without rest., via Partenope 44 ✉ 80121 ✆ 7644636, Fax 7644661, ≤ gulf and Castel dell'Ovo – |‡| ▤ TV ☎ – 🏛 600. AE ⓢ ◑ E VISA. ✻ FX
166 rm ☐ 210/340000.

Paradiso, via Catullo 11 ✉ 80122 ✆ 7614161, Fax 7613449, ≤ gulf, town and Vesuvius – |‡| ▤ TV ☎ – 🏛 80. AE ⓢ ◑ E VISA. ✻ rest by Riviera di Chiaia EFX
Meals a la carte 44/68000 – **71 rm** ☐ 170/270000.

Villa Capodimonte, via Moiariello 66 ✉ 80131 ✆ 459000, Fax 299344, ≤, ⛲, ✂ – |‡| ▤ TV ☎ ⇔ Ⓟ – 🏛 50. AE ⓢ ◑ E VISA JCB. ✻ rest by corso Amedes di Savoia GU
Meals *(dinner only)* a la carte 45/57000 – **58 rm** ☐ 150/240000.

Britannique, corso Vittorio Emanuele 133 ✉ 80121 ✆ 7614145, Telex 722281, Fax 660457 ≤ town and gulf, « Garden » – |‡| ▤ TV ☎ – 🏛 25-100. AE ⓢ ◑ E VISA JCB. ✻ rest
Meals *(closed 5 to 27 August)* 40000 – ☐ 15000 – **80 rm** 142/215000, 8 suites. EX

Miramare, via Nazario Sauro 24 ✉ 80132 ✆ 7647589, Fax 7640775, ≤ gulf and Vesuvius – |‡| ▤ TV ☎. AE ⓢ ◑ E VISA JCB. ✻ GX
Meals *(closed 16 to 31 August)* 50/65000 – **30 rm** ☐ 240/350000.

Majestic, largo Vasto a Chiaia 68 ✉ 80121 ✆ 416500, Telex 720408, Fax 416500 – |‡| ▤ TV ☎ ⇔ – 🏛 25-100. AE ⓢ ◑ E VISA JCB. ✻ FX
Meals *(closed Sunday)* a la carte 35/55000 – **130 rm** ☐ 190/280000.

Serius, viale Augusto 74 ✉ 80125 ✆ 2394844, Fax 2399251 – |‡| ▤ TV ☎ ⇔. AE ⓢ E VISA. ✻ rest – **Meals** 45000 – **69 rm** ☐ 120/175000. by Riviera di Chiaia EFX

Nuovo Rebecchino without rest., corso Garibaldi 356 ✉ 80142 ✆ 5535327, Fax 268026 – |‡| ▤ TV ☎. AE ⓢ ◑ E VISA JCB – **58 rm** ☐ 160/200000. MY

Cavour, piazza Garibaldi 32 ✉ 80142 ✆ 283122, Fax 287488 – |‡| TV ☎. AE ⓢ ◑ E VISA JCB ✻ – **Meals** (see rest. **Cavour** below) – ☐ 10000 – **86 rm** 150/190000, 6 suites. MY

✻ **La Cantinella,** via Cuma 42 ✉ 80132 ✆ 7648684, Fax 7648769 – ▤. AE ⓢ ◑ E VISA JCB. ✻ GX
closed Sunday, 13 to 31 August, 24 to 26 December and New Year's Day – **Meals** a la carte 46/86000 (12 %)
Spec. Fagottino di pesce spada affumicato con scampi, "Occhio di lupo" (pasta) con cozze e piccoli fiori di zucca, Nodino di vitello alla "Cantinella".

Ciro a Santa Brigida, via Santa Brigida 73 ✉ 80132 ✆ 5524072, Fax 5528992, Rest. and pizzeria – ▤. AE ⓢ ◑ E VISA JZ
closed Sunday and 14 to 29 August – **Meals** a la carte 43/64000.

Ciro a Mergellina, via Mergellina 18/23 ✉ 80122 ✆ 681780 – ▤. AE ⓢ ◑ E VISA
closed Friday 15 July-25 August and Monday September-June – **Meals** a la carte 51/72000 (12 %). by Riviera di Chiaia EFX

Il Posto Accanto-Rosolino, via Nazario Sauro 2/7 ✉ 80132 ✆ 7649873, Fax 7640547 Rest. and pizzeria – ▤ – 🏛 70. AE ⓢ ◑ E VISA. ✻ GX
closed Sunday dinner – **Meals** a la carte 40/66000 (15 %).

XX **San Carlo,** via Cesario Console 18/19 ✉ 80132 ☏ 7649757 – AE 🅢 ◑ E VISA. ✂ KZ **a**
closed Sunday and 3 August-3 September – **Meals** (booking essential) a la carte 60/87000.

XX **Don Salvatore,** strada Mergellina 4 A ✉ 80122 ☏ 681817, Fax 7614329, Rest. and pizzeria – ▤. AE 🅢 ◑ E VISA by Riviera di Chiaia EFX
closed Wednesday – **Meals** a la carte 42/65000.

XX **Cavour,** piazza Garibaldi 34 ✉ 80142 ☏ 264730 – ▤. AE 🅢 ◑ E VISA JCB. ✂ MY **b**
Meals a la carte 36/60000.

X **Sbrescia,** rampe Sant'Antonio a Posillipo 109 ✉ 80122 ☏ 669140, Typical rest. with ≤ town and gulf. AE 🅢 E VISA by Riviera di Chiaia EFX
closed Monday and 15 to 28 August – **Meals** a la carte 37/60000 (13 %).

Island of Capri **80073** Napoli 988 ㉗, 431 F 24 – pop. 12 416 alt. from ø to 589 (monte Solaro) – High Season : Easter and June-September – ☎ 081.
The limitation of motor-vehicles' access is regulated by legislative rules.

Gd H. Quisisana, via Camerelle 2 ☏ 8370788, Telex 710520, Fax 8376080, ≤ sea and Certosa, 余, « Garden with ⛱ », Fø, ≘s, ⛱, ✗ – 🛗 ▤ TV ☎ – 🔬 25-550. AE 🅢 ◑ E VISA. ✂ – *Easter-October* – **Meals** ***La Colombaia Rest.*** a la carte 55/87000 and ***Quisy Rest.*** (dinner only) a la carte 75/148000 – **150 rm** ☐ 350/650000, 14 suites.

Scalinatella 🔇 without rest., via Tragara 8 ☏ 8370633, Fax 8378291, ≤ sea and Certosa, ⛱ heated – 🛗 ▤ TV ☎. AE 🅢 VISA – *15 March-5 November* – **28 rm** ☐ 450/630000.

Punta Tragara 🔇, via Tragara 57 ☏ 8370844, Telex 710261, Fax 8377790, ≤ Faraglioni and coast, 余, « Panoramic terrace with ⛱ heated » – 🛗 ▤ TV ☎. AE 🅢 ◑ E VISA JCB. ✂
Easter-October – **Meals** a la carte 54/79000 (15 %) – **10 rm** ☐ 300/420000, 30 suites ☐ 400/550000.

Luna 🔇, viale Matteotti 3 ☏ 8370433, Fax 8377459, ≤ sea, Faraglioni and Certosa, 余, « Terraces and garden with ⛱ » – 🛗 ▤ TV ☎. AE 🅢 ◑ E VISA. ✂ rest
April-October – **Meals** a la carte 57/70000 – **50 rm** ☐ 300/450000, 4 suites.

La Palma, via Vittorio Emanuele 39 ☏ 8370133, Telex 722015, Fax 8376966, 余, ≘s – 🛗 ▤ TV ☎ – 🔬 25-200. AE 🅢 ◑ E VISA. ✂ rest
Meals 40000 and ***Relais La Palma Rest.*** *(April-October)* a la carte 43/68000 – **74 rm** ☐ 250/420000.

La Pazziella 🔇 without rest., via Fuorlovado 36 ☏ 8370044, Fax 8370085, « Floral garden » – ▤ TV ☎. AE 🅢 ◑ E VISA. ✂
15 March-15 October and New Year – **19 rm** ☐ 220/320000, suite.

Flora 🔇, via Serena 26 ☏ 8370211, Fax 8378949, ≤ sea and Certosa, 余, « Floral terrace » – ▤ TV ☎. AE 🅢 ◑ E VISA. ✂ rest
closed 9 January-1 March – **Meals** 40/60000 and ***La Certosa di San Giacomo Rest.*** *(closed October-15 December)* a la carte 50/70000 – **10 rm** ☐ 350000.

Villa Brunella 🔇, via Tragara 24 ☏ 8370122, Fax 8370430, ≤ sea and coast, 余, « Floral terraces », ⛱ heated – ▤ rm TV ☎. AE 🅢 ◑ E VISA. ✂
19 March-5 November – **Meals** a la carte 33/66000 (12 %) – **18 rm** ☐ 345000.

Villa delle Sirene, via Camerelle 51 ☏ 8370102, Fax 8370957, ≤, 余, « Lemon grove with ⛱ » – 🛗 ▤ TV ☎. AE 🅢 ◑ E VISA JCB. ✂
April-October – **Meals** *(closed Tuesday except June-September)* a la carte 45/56000 – **35 rm** ☐ 260/340000.

XX **La Capannina,** via Le Botteghe 14 ☏ 8370732, Fax 8376990 – ▤. AE 🅢 ◑ E VISA. ✂
15 March-10 November ; closed Wednesday except August – **Meals** (booking essential for dinner) a la carte 52/80000 (15 %).

XX **Casanova,** via Le Botteghe 46 ☏ 8377642 – AE 🅢 ◑ E VISA
closed 3 January-March and Thursday except July-September – **Meals** a la carte 36/76000 (12 %).

at Anacapri alt. 275 – ✉ **80071** :

Europa Palace, via Capodimonte 2 ☏ 8373800, Telex 710397, Fax 8373191, ≤, 余, « Floral terraces with ⛱ », Fø, ≘s, ⛱ – 🛗 ▤ TV ☎ – 🔬 30-200. AE 🅢 ◑ E VISA JCB. ✂
April-October – **Meals** a la carte 69/98000 – **90 rm** ☐ 250/480000, suite.

at Marina Piccola – ✉ **80073** Capri :

XXX **Canzone del Mare,** ☏ 8370104, Fax 8370541, ≤ Faraglioni and sea, 余, « Bathing establishment with ⛱ » – AE 🅢 VISA. ✂
Easter-October – **Meals** *(lunch only)* 70/80000 and a la carte 70/105000.

Sant'Agata sui due Golfi **80064** Napoli 431 F 25 – alt. 391 – High Season : April-September – ☎ 081.
Roma 266 – Castellammare di Stabia 28 – Napoli 55 – Salerno 56 – Sorrento 9.

XXX ✿✿ **Don Alfonso 1890** with rm, ☏ 8780026, Fax 5330226, 余 – 🅟. AE ◑ E VISA. ✂
closed 10 January-25 February – **Meals** *(closed Monday June-September and Tuesday October-May)* (booking essential) a la carte 80/125000 – 3 suites ☐ 160/240000
Spec. Astice in crosta di patate con maggiorana e cetrioli. Linguine alle vongole e zucchine. Casseruola di pesci di scoglio crostacei e frutti di mare.

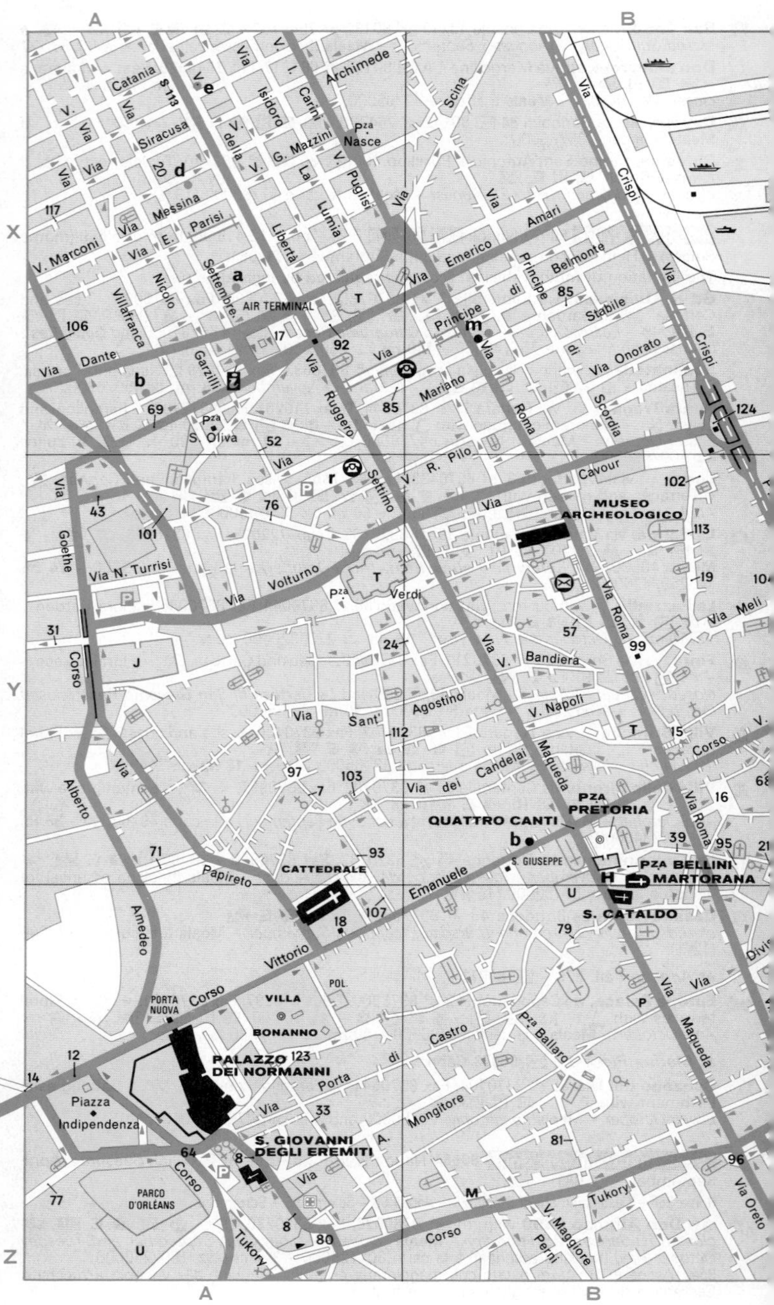

MUSEO ARCHEOLOGICO
QUATTRO CANTI
PZA PRETORIA
PZA BELLINI
MARTORANA
S. CATALDO
CATTEDRALE
VILLA BONANNO
PALAZZO DEI NORMANNI
S. GIOVANNI DEGLI EREMITI
PARCO D'ORLÉANS
Piazza Indipendenza
PORTA NUOVA
AIR TERMINAL
S. GIUSEPPE

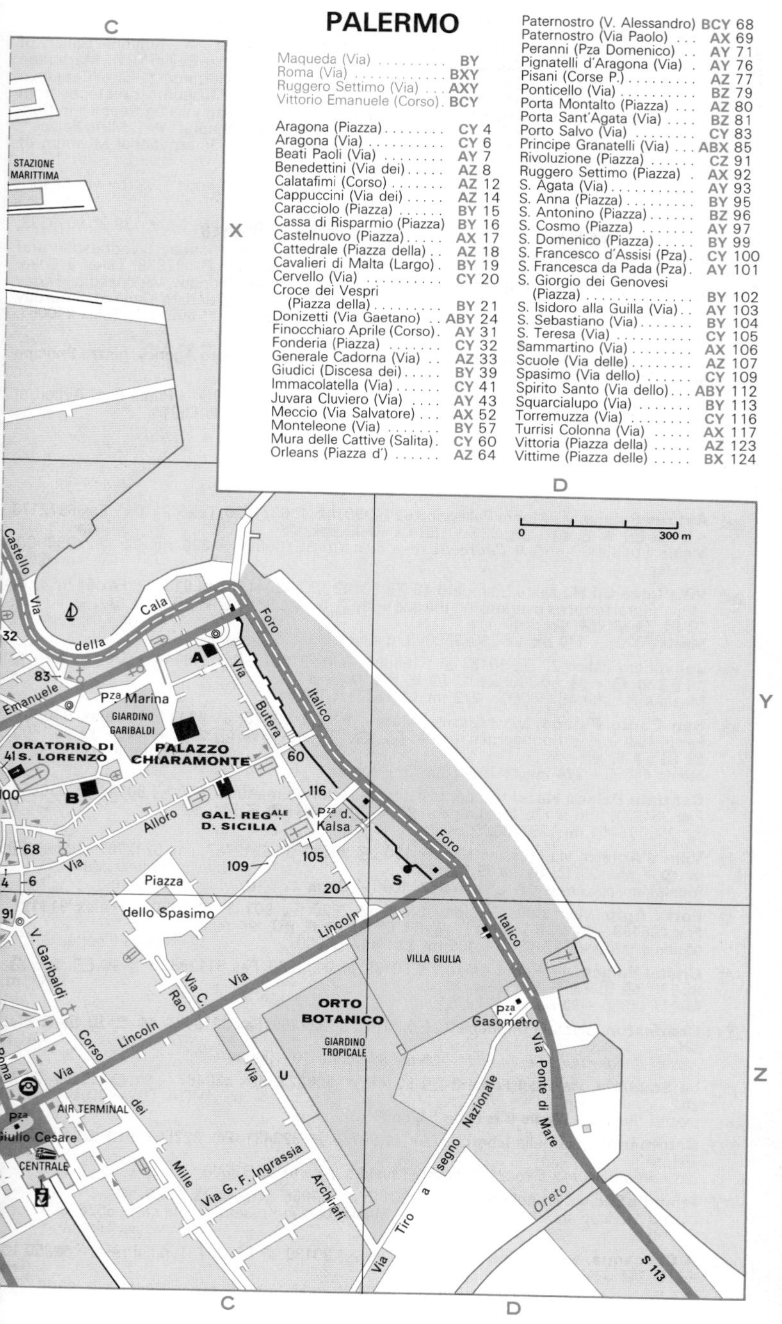
PALERMO
Maqueda (Via) . . . . BY
Roma (Via) . . . . BXY
Ruggero Settimo (Via) . . . AXY
Vittorio Emanuele (Corso) . BCY
Aragona (Piazza) . . . . CY 4
Aragona (Via) . . . . CY 6
Beati Paoli (Via) . . . . AY 7
Benedettini (Via dei) . . . . . AZ 8
Calatafimi (Corso) . . . . AZ 12
Cappuccini (Via dei) . . . . . AZ 14
Caracciolo (Piazza) . . . . . . BY 15
Cassa di Risparmio (Piazza) BY 16
Castelnuovo (Piazza) . . . . . AX 17
Cattedrale (Piazza della) . . AZ 18
Cavalieri di Malta (Largo) . BY 19
Cervello (Via) . . . . CY 20
Croce dei Vespri (Piazza della) . . . . BY 21
Donizetti (Via Gaetano) . . ABY 24
Finocchiaro Aprile (Corso) . AY 31
Fonderia (Piazza) . . . . CY 32
Generale Cadorna (Via) . . AZ 33
Giudici (Discesa dei) . . . . . BY 39
Immacolatella (Via) . . . . . . CY 41
Juvara Cluviero (Via) . . . . AY 43
Meccio (Via Salvatore) . . . AX 52
Monteleone (Via) . . . . BY 57
Mura delle Cattive (Salita) . CY 60
Orleans (Piazza d') . . . . . . AZ 64
Paternostro (V. Alessandro) BCY 68
Paternostro (Via Paolo) . . . AX 69
Peranni (Pza Domenico) . . AY 71
Pignatelli d'Aragona (Via) . AY 76
Pisani (Corse P.) . . . . AZ 77
Ponticello (Via) . . . . BZ 79
Porta Montalto (Piazza) . . . AZ 80
Porta Sant'Agata (Via) . . . . BZ 81
Porto Salvo (Via) . . . . CY 83
Principe Granatelli (Via) . . . ABX 85
Rivoluzione (Piazza) . . . . . . CZ 91
Ruggero Settimo (Piazza) . AX 92
S. Agata (Via) . . . . AY 93
S. Anna (Piazza) . . . . BY 95
S. Antonino (Piazza) . . . . . BZ 96
S. Cosmo (Piazza) . . . . AY 97
S. Domenico (Piazza) . . . . . BY 99
S. Francesco d'Assisi (Pza) . CY 100
S. Francesca da Pada (Pza) . AY 101
S. Giorgio dei Genovesi (Piazza) . . . . BY 102
S. Isidoro alla Guilla (Via) . . AY 103
S. Sebastiano (Via) . . . . BY 104
S. Teresa (Via) . . . . CY 105
Sammartino (Via) . . . . AX 106
Scuole (Via delle) . . . . AZ 107
Spasimo (Via dello) . . . . . . CY 109
Spirito Santo (Via dello) . . . ABY 112
Squarcialupo (Via) . . . . BY 113
Torremuzza (Via) . . . . CY 116
Turrisi Colonna (Via) . . . . . AX 117
Vittoria (Piazza della) . . . . AZ 123
Vittime (Piazza delle) . . . . . BX 124
C
D
X
Y
Z
0
300 m
STAZIONE MARITTIMA
Via Castello
Cala
della
Foro Italico
Via Butera
Emanuele
Pza Marina
GIARDINO GARIBALDI
ORATORIO DI S. LORENZO
PALAZZO CHIARAMONTE
GAL. REGALE D. SICILIA
Pza d. Kalsa
Via Alloro
Piazza dello Spasimo
V. Garibaldi
Via Lincoln
Corso Via Lincoln
Via C. Rao
VILLA GIULIA
ORTO BOTANICO
GIARDINO TROPICALE
Pza Gasometro
Via Ponte di Mare
Via Tiro a segno Nazionale
Oreto
S 113
AIR TERMINAL
Pza Giulio Cesare
CENTRALE
Via dei Mille
Via G. F. Ingrassia
Archirafi
Roma
A
B
S
U
32
83
41
100
68
4
6
91
60
116
105
109
20

PALERMO (Sicily) 90100 P 988 (35), 432 M 22 – pop. 694 749 – ☎ 091.

See : Palace of the Normans★★ : the palatine Chapel★★★, mosaics★★★ AZ – Regional Gallery of Sicily★★ in Abbatellis Palace★ : Death Triumphant frescoe★★★ CY – Piazza Bellini★ BY : Martorana Church★★, Church of St. Cataldo★★ – Church of St. John of the Hermits★★ AZ – Capuchin Catacombs★★ – Piazza Pretoria★ BY : fountain★★ – Archaeological Museum★ : metopes from the temples at Selinus★★, the Ram★★ BY – Chiaramonte Palace★ : magnolia fig trees★★ in Garibaldi Gardens CY – St. Lawrence Oratory★ CY Quattro Canti★ BY – Cathedral★ AYZ Mirto Palace★ CY **B** Villa Bonanno★ AZ Zisa Palace★ – Botanical garden★ CDZ – International Museum of Marionettes★ CY **A** Sicilian carts★ in Ethnographic Museum **M.**

Envir. : Monreale★★★ AZ by Corso Calatafimi : 8 km – Monte Pellegrino★★ BX by via Crispi : 14 km.

✈ Punta Raisi E : 30 km ☎ 591690, Fax 595030 – Alitalia, via Mazzini 59 ✉ 90139 ☎ 6019333.

⛴ to Genova Monday and Wednesday (22 h) and to Livorno Monday, Wednesday and Friday (19 h) – Grandi Traghetti, via Mariano Stabile 53 ✉ 90141 ☎ 587939, Telex 910098, Fax 589629; to Napoli daily (11 h), to Genova 18 June-31 December, Monday, Wednesday, Friday and Sunday, Monday, Wednesday and Friday (24 h) January-May and to Cagliari Saturday (14 h 30 mn) – Tirrenia Navigazione, calata Marinai d'Italia ✉ 90133 ☎ 6021213, Telex 910057, Fax 6021221.

⛴; to Aeolian Island June-September daily (1 h 50 mn) – SNAV Barbaro Agency, piazza Principe di Belmonte 51/55 ✉ 90139 ☎ 586533, Fax 584830.

ℹ piazza Castelnuovo 34 ✉ 90141 ☎ 583847, Telex 910179, Fax 331854 – Punta Raisi Airport at Cinisi ☎ 591698 – piazza Giulio Cesare (Central Station) ✉ 90127 ☎ 6165914.

A.C.I. via delle Alpi 6 ✉ 90144 ☎ 300468.

Messina 235.

Plans on preceding pages

🏨 **Astoria Palace,** via Monte Pellegrino 62 ✉ 90142 ☎ 6371820, Telex 911045, Fax 6372178 – 🛗 ▤ TV ☎ ♿ P – 🏛 30-800. AE 🅂 ⊙ E VISA. ✈ by via Crispi BX
Meals 50/85000 and ***Il Cedro Rest.*** a la carte 50/85000 – **326 rm** ☐ 182/256000, 8 suites.

🏨 **Villa Igiea Gd H.,** salita Belmonte 43 ✉ 90142 ☎ 543744, Telex 910092, Fax 547654, ≤, ☂, « Floral terraces overlooking the sea with 🏊 », 🎾, ✂ – 🛗 ▤ TV ☎ ♿ P – 🏛 50-400. AE 🅂 ⊙ E VISA. ✈ rest by via Crispi BX
Meals 70000 – **110 rm** ☐ 230/350000, 6 suites.

🏨 **Jolly,** Foro Italico 22 ✉ 90133 ☎ 6165090, Telex 910076, Fax 6161441, ☂, 🏊, 🎾 – 🛗 ▤ TV ☎ P – 🏛 50-300. AE 🅂 ⊙ E VISA. ✈ rest DY **s**
Meals a la carte 49/76000 – **272 rm** ☐ 177/225000.

🏨 **San Paolo Palace,** via Messina Marine 91 ✉ 90123 ☎ 6211112, Telex 910069, Fax 6215300, ≤, « Roof-garden rest. », 🏋, ♨, 🏊, ✂ – 🛗 ▤ TV ☎ ♿ 🚗 P – 🏛 50-1500. AE 🅂 ⊙ E VISA. ✈ by via Ponte di Mare DZ
Meals 45000 – **274 rm** ☐ 160/207000, 9 suites.

🏨 **Centrale Palace Hotel** without rest., corso Vittorio Emanuele 327 ✉ 90134 ☎ 336666, Fax 334881, « In a 17C building » – 🛗 ▤ TV ☎. AE ⊙ E VISA. ✈ BY **b**
☐ 20000 – **61 rm** 130/200000, suite. –

🏨 **Villa d'Amato,** via Messina Marine 180 ✉ 90123 ☎ 6212767, Fax 6212767 – 🛗 ▤ TV ☎ P – 🏛 100. AE 🅂 ⊙ E VISA. ✈ by via Ponte di Mare DZ
Meals *(closed Sunday)* a la carte 45/64000 – **25 rm** ☐ 110/160000, 12 suites.

🏨 **Forte Agip,** viale della Regione Siciliana 2620 ✉ 90145 ☎ 552033, Telex 911196, Fax 408198 – 🛗 ▤ TV ☎ P – 🏛 90. AE 🅂 ⊙ E VISA. ✈ rest
Meals a la carte 39/64000 – **105 rm** ☐ 164/204000. by via della Libertà AX

🏨 **Cristal Palace,** via Roma 477/d ✉ 90139 ☎ 6112580, Fax 6112589 – 🛗 ▤ TV ☎ – 🏛 30-130. AE 🅂 ⊙ E VISA JCB. ✈ BX **m**
Meals 45000 – **90 rm** ☐ 127/181000.

XXXX **Charleston,** piazzale Ungheria 30 ✉ 90141 ☎ 321366, Fax 321347 – ▤. AE 🅂 ⊙ E VISA. ✈ AY **r**
closed Sunday June-September – **Meals** a la carte 70/100000.

XXX **La Scuderia,** viale del Fante 9 ✉ 90146 ☎ 520323, Fax 520467 – ▤ P. AE 🅂 ⊙ E VISA by via C.A. Dalla Chiesa AX
closed Sunday – **Meals** a la carte 54/85000.

XXX **Gourmand's,** via della Libertà 37/e ✉ 90139 ☎ 323431, Fax 322507 – ▤. AE 🅂 ⊙ E VISA. ✈ AX **e**
closed Sunday and 5 to 25 August – **Meals** a la carte 50/75000.

XX **Friend's Bar,** via Brunelleschi 138 ✉ 90145 ☎ 201066, ☂ – ▤. AE 🅂 ⊙. ✈
closed Monday and 16 to 31 August – **Meals** (booking essential) a la carte 50/67000. by via della Libertà AX

XX **A Cuccagna,** via Principe Granatelli 21/a ✉ 90139 ☎ 587267, Typical rest. – ▤. AE 🅂 ⊙ E VISA JCB. ✈ BX **m**
closed 14 to 31 August and Friday (except June-September) – **Meals** a la carte 35/60000.

XX **Il Ristorantino,** piazza De Gasperi 19 ✉ 90146 ☎ 512861, Fax 6702999, 🏨 – ▤. AE 🅂 ◑ E VISA — by via C.A. Dalla Chiesa AX
closed Monday and August – **Meals** a la carte 44/78000.

XX **Regine,** via Trapani 4/a ✉ 90141 ☎ 586566 – ▤. AE 🅂 ◑ E VISA. ✻ — AX **d**
closed Sunday and August – **Meals** a la carte 41/58000.

X **Trattoria Biondo,** via Carducci 15 ✉ 90141 ☎ 583662 – ▤. AE 🅂 E VISA. ✻ — AX **a**
closed Wednesday and 15 July-15 September – **Meals** a la carte 34/47000 (15 %).

X **Il Vespro,** via B. D'Acquisto 9 ✉ 90141 ☎ 589932, Rest. and pizzeria – ▤. AE 🅂 ◑ E VISA. ✻ — AX **b**
closed Monday and August – **Meals** a la carte 37/49000.

TAORMINA (Sicily) 98039 Messina 988 ㊲, 432 N 27 – pop. 10 115 alt. 250 – ☎ 0942.
See : Site★★★ – Greek Theatre★★ : ≤★★★ B – Public garden★★ B – ✻★★ from the Square 9 Aprile A 13 – Corso Umberto★ A – Belvedere★ B – Castle★ : ≤★ A.
Exc. : Etna★★★, SW : for Linguaglossa.
18 Picciolo, contrada Rovitello ✉ 95012 Castiglione di Sicilia ☎ 986171, W : 25 km.
ℹ piazza Santa Caterina (Corvaja palace) ☎ 23243, Fax 24941.
Catania 52 ② – Enna 135 ② – Messina 52 ① – Palermo 255 ② – Siracusa 111 ② – Trapani 359 ②.

TAORMINA

Umberto (Corso) . . . . A
Cappuccini (Via) . . . . A 2
Crocifisso (Via) . . . . A 3
Dionisio (Via) . . . . A 5
Duomo (Piazza) . . . . A 6
S. Antonio (Piazza) . . . . A 9
Vinci (V. Leonardo da) . . . . A 10
Vittorio Emanuele II (Pza) . . B 12
9 Aprile (Piazza) . . . . A 13

Traffic restricted in the town centre from June to September

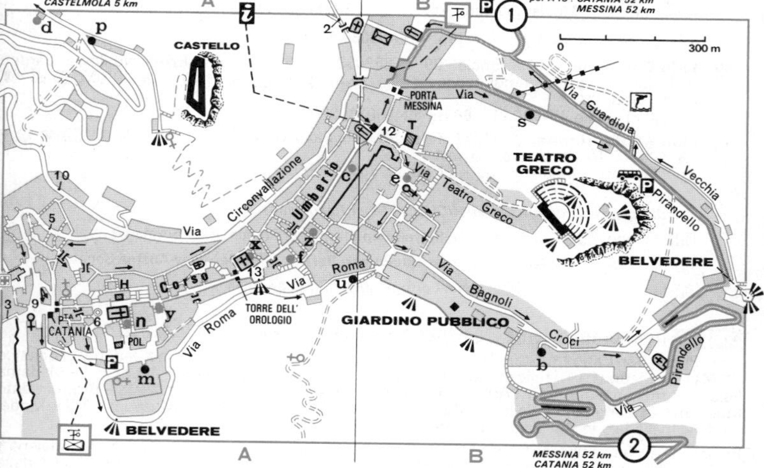

🏨 **San Domenico Palace** ⛵, piazza San Domenico 5 ☎ 23701, Telex 980013, Fax 625506, 🏨, « 15C monastery with floral garden, ≤ sea, coast and Etna », ⛱ heated – 🛗 ▤ TV ☎ – 🏛 400. AE 🅂 ◑ E VISA. ✻ — A **m**
Meals 95000 – **111 rm** ☕ 350/620000, 6 suites.

🏨 **Monte Tauro** ⛵, via Madonna delle Grazie 3 ☎ 24402, Telex 980048, Fax 24403, ≤ sea and coast, ⛱ – 🛗 ▤ TV ☎ 🅟 – 🏛 100. AE 🅂 ◑ E VISA JCB. ✻ — AB **u**
Meals 35000 – **70 rm** ☕ 210/280000.

🏨 **Villa Ducale** ⛵, without rest., via Leonardo da Vinci 60 ☎ 28153, Fax 28710, ≤ sea, coast and Etna – ▤ TV ☎ 🅟. AE 🅂 E VISA — A **p**
closed 10 January-20 February – **10 rm** ☕ 190/300000.

🏨 **Villa Fiorita** without rest., via Pirandello 39 ☎ 24122, Fax 625967, ≤ sea and coast, ⛱, ⛱, 🌳 – 🛗 ▤ TV ☎ 🚗. AE 🅂 E VISA — B **s**
24 rm ☕ 140/150000.

🏨 **Villa Belvedere** without rest., via Bagnoli Croci 79 ☎ 23791, Fax 625830, ≤ gardens, sea and Etna, « ⛱ on terrace with panoramic view », 🌳 – 🛗 ☎ 🅟. 🅂 E VISA — B **b**
closed 16 January-February and 11 November-14 December – **44 rm** ☕ 144/225000.

🏨 **Villa Sirina,** contrada Sirina ☎ 51776, Fax 51671, ⛱, 🌳 – ▤ TV ☎ 🅟. AE 🅂 ◑ E VISA. ✻ — 2 km by via Crocifisso A
closed November-20 December – **Meals** (residents only) (dinner only) – **15 rm** ☕ 150/180000.

XXXX **La Giara,** vico La Floresta 1 ☎ 23360, Fax 23233, « Rest. and piano bar » – ▤. AE ⓢ ⓞ E VISA JCB. ✗ A
closed Monday except June-September – **Meals** *(dinner only)* a la carte 53/81000.

XX **La Griglia,** corso Umberto 54 ☎ 23980, Fax 626047 – ▤. AE ⓢ ⓞ E VISA. ✗ A
closed Tuesday and 20 November-20 December – **Meals** a la carte 40/60000.

XX **A' Zammara,** via Fratelli Bandiera 15 ☎ 24408, Fax 24408, « Summer service in a sma shaded garden » – AE ⓢ ⓞ E VISA JCB. ✗ A
closed 5 to 20 January and Wednesday except June-September – **Meals** a la carte 32/6200

XX **Da Lorenzo,** via Michele Amari 4 ☎ 23480, ☂ – AE ⓢ ⓞ E VISA A
closed 1 to 15 November and Wednesday except June to September – **Meals** a la cart 36/61000.

X **Il Ciclope,** corso Umberto ☎ 23263, Fax 625910, ☂ – ▤. AE ⓢ E VISA JCB. ✗ A
closed Wednesday and 10 to 31 January – **Meals** a la carte 32/46000.

X **Il Baccanale,** piazzetta Filea 1 ☎ 625390, ☂ – ▤. ⓢ E VISA. ✗ B
closed Thursday except July-September – **Meals** a la carte 30/52000.

X **La Chioccia d'Oro,** via Leonardo da Vinci ☎ 28066, ⋞ A
closed Thursday and November – **Meals** a la carte 27/47000.

X **Vicolo Stretto,** via Vicolo Stretto ☎ 23849, ☂ – ▤. ⓢ E VISA. ✗ A
closed 8 January-8 February and Monday except 15 July-September – **Meals** a la cart 32/53000.

at Mazzarò by ② : 5,5 km – ✉ **98030** :

Mazzarò Sea Palace, ☎ 24004, Fax 626237, ⋞ small bay, ☂, ⛱, 🏊 – |‡| ▤ TV ☎ ⇐ – 🏛 90. AE ⓢ ⓞ E VISA. ✗
April-October – **Meals** a la carte 75/90000 – **84 rm** ⊐ 185/310000, 3 suites.

at Lido di Spisone by ① : 7 km – ✉ **98030** Mazzarò :

Lido Caparena, via Nazionale 189 ☎ 652033, Fax 652033, ⋞, « Extensive flower garde with outdoor rest. summer service », ⛱, 🏊 – |‡| ▤ TV ☎ ♿ P – 🏛 40-200. AE ⓢ ⓞ E VISA JCB. ✗
Meals a la carte 45/74000 – **88 rm** ⊐ 230/300000.

Lido Mediterranée, ☎ 24422, Telex 980175, Fax 24774, ⋞, ☂, 🏊 – |‡| ▤ TV ☎ P 🏛 100. AE ⓢ ⓞ E VISA. ✗ rest
April-October – **Meals** 60000 – **72 rm** ⊐ 250/350000.

For the quickest route use the MICHELIN Main Road Maps :

970 Europe, 976 Czech Republic-Slovak Republic, 980 Greece, 984 Germany,

985 Scandinavia-Finland, 986 Great Britain and Ireland, 987 Germany-Austria-Benelux,

988 Italy, 989 France, 990 Spain-Portugal *and* 991 Yugoslavia.

TURIN (TORINO) 10100 P 988 ⑫, 428 G 5 – pop. 945 551 alt. 239 – ☎ 011.

See : Piazza San Carlo★★ CXY – Egyptian Museum★★, Sabauda Gallery★★ in Academy of Scienc CX **M1** – Cathedral★ VX : relic of the Holy Shroud★★★ – Mole Antonelliana★ : ✳★★ DX – Madam Palace★ : museum of Ancient Art★ CX **A** – Royal Palace★ : Royal Armoury★ CDVX – Risorgiment Museum★ in Carignano Palace CX **M2** – Carlo Biscaretti di Ruffia Motor Museum★ **M5** – Mode medieval village★ in the Valentino Park CDZ.

Envir. : Basilica of Superga★ : ⋞★★★, royal tombs★ – Tour to the pass, Colle della Maddalena★ : ⋞★★ of the city from the route Superga-Pino Torinese, ⋞★ of the city from the route Colle dell Maddalena-Cavoretto.

18, 9 I Roveri (March-November ; closed Monday) at La Mandria ✉ 10070 Fiano ☎ 9235719 Fax 9235669, N : 18 km;

18, 18 (closed Monday, January and February), at Fiano Torinese ✉ 10070 ☎ 9235440 Fax 9235886, N : 20 km;

18 Le Fronde (closed Tuesday, January and February) at Avigliana ✉ 10051 ☎ 935083 Fax 930928, W : 24 km;

9 Stupinigi (closed Monday), ☎ 3472640, Fax 3978038;

9 (closed Monday and 21 December-9 January) at Vinovo ✉ 10048 ☎ 9653880, Fax 9623748

✈ Turin Airport of Caselle N : 15 km ☎ 5676361, Telex 225119, Fax 5676420 – Alitalia, via Lagrange 35 ✉ 10123 ☎ 57698.

🚘 ☎ 6651111-int. 2611.

ℹ via Roma 226 (piazza C.L.N.) ✉ 10121 ☎ 535901, Fax 530070 – Porta Nuova Railway station ✉ 10125 ☎ 531327.

A.C.I. via Giovanni Giolitti 15 ✉ 10123 ☎ 57791.

Roma 669 – Briançon 108 – Chambéry 209 – Genève 252 – Genova 170 – Grenoble 224 – Milano 140 – Nice 220

Plans on following pages

Turin Palace Hotel, via Sacchi 8 ✉ 10128 ✆ 5625511, Fax 5612187 – ▤ TV ☎ ♿ – 30-200. AE ⓢ ⓓ E VISA. ✻ rest CY **u**
Meals *(closed August)* a la carte 65/105000 – ▭ 28000 – **122 rm** 280/330000, 2 suites.

Jolly Principi di Piemonte, via Gobetti 15 ✉ 10123 ✆ 5629693, Telex 221120, Fax 5620270 – |♦| ▤ TV ☎ – 30-300. AE ⓢ ⓓ E VISA JCB. ✻ rest CY **z**
Meals 65/75000 – **107 rm** ▭ 408/430000, 8 suites.

Le Meridien Lingotto, via Nizza 262 ✉ 10126 ✆ 6642000, Fax 6642001 – |♦| ⇆ rm ▤ TV ☎ ♿ – 35. AE ⓢ ⓓ E VISA. ✻ by via Nizza CZ
Meals a la carte 63/128000 – **244 rm** ▭ 350000.

Gd H. Sitea, via Carlo Alberto 35 ✉ 10123 ✆ 5170171, Fax 548090 – |♦| ▤ TV ☎ – 30-100. AE ⓢ ⓓ E VISA JCB. ✻ rest CY **t**
Meals a la carte 65/90000 – **117 rm** ▭ 270/360000.

Jolly Ambasciatori, corso Vittorio Emanuele II 104 ✉ 10121 ✆ 5752, Telex 221296, Fax 544978 – |♦| ⇆ rm ▤ TV ☎ – 25-400. AE ⓢ ⓓ E VISA JCB. ✻ rest BX **a**
Meals 50/60000 – **199 rm** ▭ 295/360000, 4 suites.

Diplomatic, via Cernaia 42 ✉ 10122 ✆ 5612444, Telex 225445, Fax 540472 – |♦| ▤ TV ☎ – 50-200 BX **g**
126 rm.

Jolly Hotel Ligure, piazza Carlo Felice 85 ✉ 10123 ✆ 55641, Telex 220167, Fax 535438 – |♦| ▤ TV ☎ – 50-200. AE ⓢ ⓓ E VISA. ✻ rest CY **b**
Meals a la carte 59/94000 – **169 rm** ▭ 310/370000, 2 suites.

City, via Juvarra 25 ✉ 10122 ✆ 540546, Fax 548188 – |♦| ▤ TV ☎. AE ⓢ ⓓ E VISA BV **e**
Meals (residents only) 40/80000 – ▭ 15000 – **57 rm** 240/320000.

Starhotel Majestic without rest., corso Vittorio Emanuele II 54 ✉ 10123 ✆ 539153, Telex 216260, Fax 534963 – |♦| ▤ TV ☎. AE ⓢ ⓓ E VISA JCB CY **e**
152 rm ▭ 290/340000.

Concord, via Lagrange 47 ✉ 10123 ✆ 5176756, Telex 221323, Fax 5176305 – |♦| ▤ TV ☎ ♿ – 180. AE ⓢ ⓓ E VISA. ✻ rest CY **s**
Meals 58000 – **135 rm** ▭ 260/335000, 3 suites.

Victoria without rest., via Nino Costa 4 ✉ 10123 ✆ 5611909, Fax 5611806 – |♦| ▤ TV ☎. AE ⓢ E VISA. ✻ CY **v**
90 rm ▭ 180/230000.

Holiday Inn Turin City Centre without rest., via Assietta 3 ✉ 10121 ✆ 5167111, Fax 5167699 – |♦| ⇆ ▤ TV ☎ ♿ Ⓟ – 50. AE ⓢ ⓓ E VISA JCB CY **a**
57 rm ▭ 250/350000.

Genio without rest., corso Vittorio Emanuele II 47 ✉ 10125 ✆ 6505771, Fax 6508264 – |♦| ▤ TV ☎ – 25. AE ⓢ ⓓ E VISA JCB CYZ **w**
90 rm ▭ 150/200000, ▤ 10000.

Royal, corso Regina Margherita 249 ✉ 10144 ✆ 4376777, Telex 220259, Fax 4376393 – |♦| ▤ TV ☎ ♿ – 25-600. AE ⓢ ⓓ E VISA BV **u**
closed 1 to 28 August – **Meals** a la carte 35/57000 – **73 rm** ▭ 180/250000.

Boston without rest., via Massena 70 ✉ 10128 ✆ 500359, Fax 599358, – |♦| ▤ TV ☎. AE ⓢ ⓓ E VISA BZ **c**
51 rm ▭ 150/200000, 2 suites, ▤ 10000.

Luxor without rest., corso Stati Uniti 7 ✉ 10128 ✆ 5620777, Fax 5628324 – |♦| ▤ TV ☎. AE ⓢ ⓓ E VISA CZ **s**
71 rm ▭ 170/220000, 2 suites.

Genova e Stazione without rest., via Sacchi 14/b ✉ 10128 ✆ 5629400, Fax 5629896 – |♦| ▤ TV ☎ ♿ – 40-60. AE ⓢ ⓓ E VISA. ✻ CZ **b**
closed 1 to 18 August – **58 rm** ▭ 145/200000, ▤ 10000.

President without rest., via Cecchi 67 ✉ 10152 ✆ 859555, Fax 2480465 – |♦| ▤ TV ☎. AE ⓢ ⓓ E VISA CV **s**
72 rm ▭ 130/170000.

Alexandra without rest., lungo Doria Napoli 14 ✉ 10152 ✆ 858327, Fax 2483805 – |♦| ▤ TV ☎. AE ⓢ ⓓ E VISA CV **c**
56 rm ▭ 155/200000.

Crimea without rest., via Mentana 3 ✉ 10133 ✆ 6604700, Fax 6604912 – |♦| TV ☎. AE ⓢ ⓓ E VISA JCB. ✻ DZ **e**
49 rm ▭ 170/210000.

Gran Mogol without rest., via Guarini 2 ✉ 10123 ✆ 5612120, Fax 5623160 – |♦| ▤ TV ☎. AE ⓢ ⓓ E VISA JCB CY **r**
closed August – **45 rm** ▭ 150/200000, ▤ 10000.

Piemontese without rest., via Berthollet 21 ✉ 10125 ✆ 6698101, Fax 6690571 – |♦| ▤ TV ☎ Ⓟ. AE ⓢ ⓓ E VISA JCB. ✻ CZ **x**
35 rm ▭ 145/190000.

TORINO

Carlo Felice (Piazza)	CY	16
Roma (Via)	CXY	
S. Carlo (Piazza)	CXY	
Alfieri (Via)	CY	6
Cadorna (Lungo Po L.)	DY	10
Carignano (Piazza)	CX	12
Carlo Emanuele II (Pza)	DY	13
Casale (Corso)	DY	18
Castello (Piazza)	CX	19
Cesare Augusto (Piazza)	CV	23
Consolata (Via della)	CV	27
Diaz (Lungo Po A.)	DY	32
Gran Madre di Dio (Piazza)	DY	38
Milano (Via)	CV	46
Ponte Vittorio Emanuele I	DY	55
Repubblica (Piazza della)	CV	62
S. Francesco d'Assisi (Via)	CX	66
Solferino (Piazza)	CX	75
Vitt. Emanuele II (Lgo)	BCY	90
4 Marzo (Via)	CX	93
20 Settembre (Via)	CXY	96

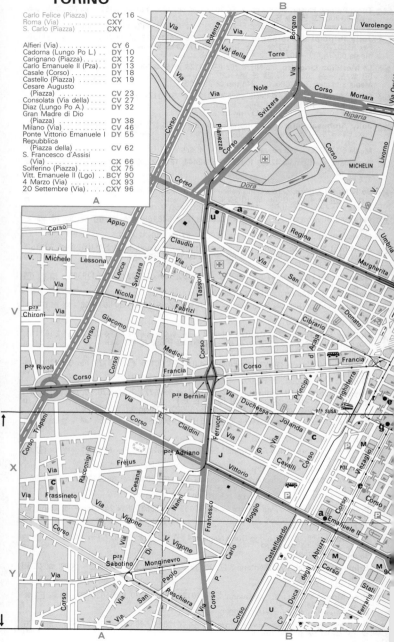

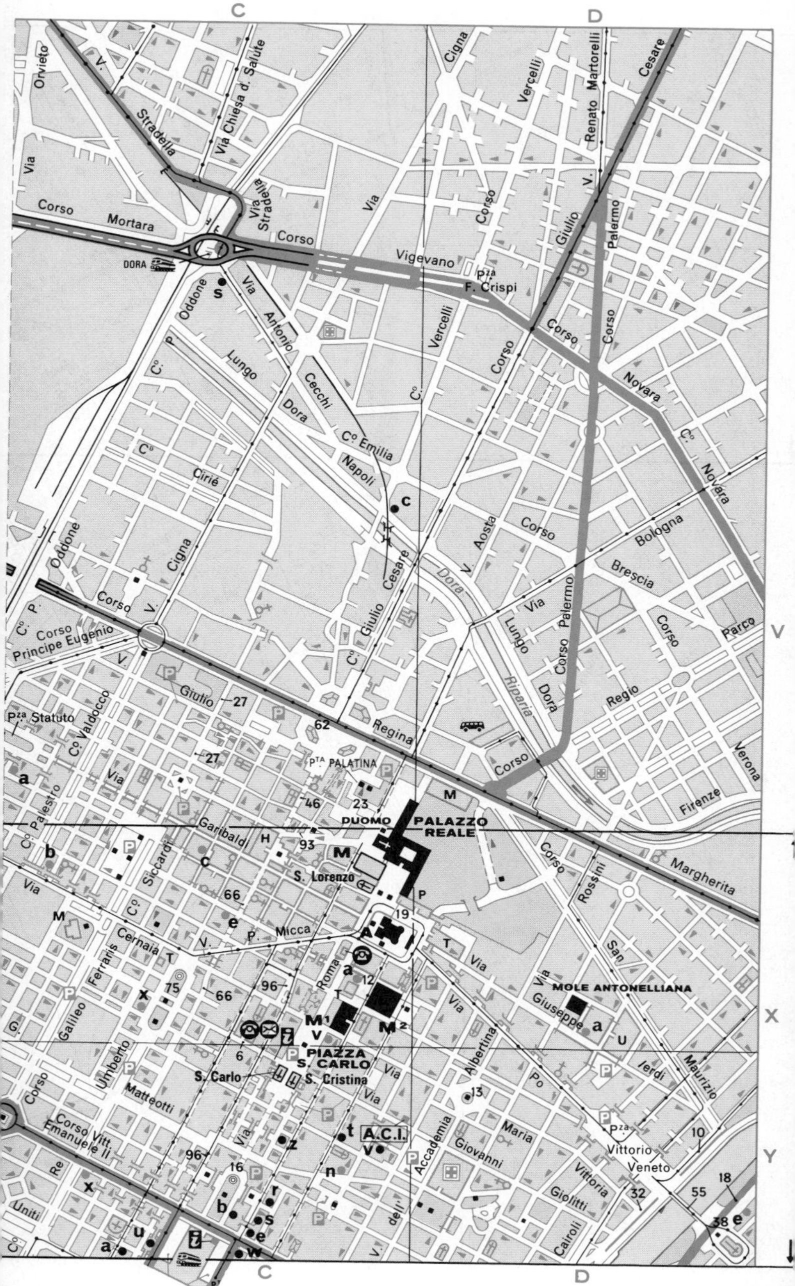
C
D
Orvieto
Via
Stradella
Via Chiesa d. Salute
Corso
Mortara
Via Stradella
Corso
Vigevano
Cigna
Vercelli
Renato Martorelli
Cesare
Via
Corso
Giulio
V.
Palermo
DORA
Pza F. Crispi
Oddone
Via Antonio
Vercelli
Corso
Corso
Novara
Lungo
Dora
Cecchi
Cº Emilia
Napoli
Cº
Cº Cirié
Cº Novara
Corso
Bologna
Brescia
V. Aosta
Dora
Oddone
Cigna
Corso
V.
Cesare
Giulio
Cº
Via
Lungo
Corso Palermo
Corso
Parco
V
Cº P.
Corso Principe Eugenio
V.
Giulio
27
62
Regina
Riparia
Dora
Regio
Verona
Pza Statuto
Cº Valdocco
27
PTA PALATINA
Corso
a
Via
46
23
M
Firenze
Cº Palestro
Garibaldi
H
93
DUOMO
PALAZZO REALE
Corso
Rossini
Margherita
b
c
M
S. Lorenzo
P
Via
Siccardi
Cº
66
19
M
e
Micca
San
Cernaia
V.
P.
T
Via
Ferraris
T
a
12
Via
MOLE ANTONELLIANA
75
96
Roma
X
Galileo
x
66
Via
Giuseppe
a
M1
M2
U
G.
V
Umberto
6
PIAZZA S. CARLO
Via
Albertina
Verdi
Maurizio
S. Carlo
S. Cristina
Po
Corso
Matteotti
Via
13
Maria
Corso Vitt. Emanuele II
Via
t
A.C.I.
Accademia
Pza Vittorio Veneto
10
Y
96
z
v
Giovanni
Re
16
n
Vittoria
18
x
r
Giolitti
32
55
b
s
dell'
Cairoli
38
e
Uniti
u
e
V.
Cº
a
w
C
D

A
B
X
Y
Z
Corso Trapani
Corso Cialdini
Pza Adriano
Ferrucci
Via Jolanda
Via G. Cavalli
Corso Vittorio Emanuele II
Fréjus
Via Racconigi
Via Frassineto
Cesana
Nanni
Francesco
Corso Vigone
Via Boggio
Via Di Nanni
V. Vigone
Corso P. Carlo
Castelfidardo
Pza Sabotino
Monginevro
Via San Paolo
Peschiera
Corso Duca degli Abruzzi
Corso Stati
Ferraris
Vinzaglio
POL
Corso
Via Lancia
Via Paolo Braccini
Corso Duca d'Aosta
Via Luigi Einaudi
Galileo
Via Umberto
Via Duca degli Abruzzi
Cristoforo Colombo
Corso Re
Via Rivalta
Corso Racconigi
Cº Mediterraneo
Via Rosselli
Corso de Gasperi
Caboto
Carle
Largo Orbassano
Corso de Nicola
Ferraris
Rosselli
Filippo Turati
Tripoli
Orbassano
Corso 4 Novembre
Via G. Pascoli
Pza Costantino il Grande
OSPEDALE MILITARE
Lepanto
Cº
Galileo
Sovietica
Corso Bramante
Corso Sebastopoli
Corso Agnelli
STADIO COMUNALE
Corso Unione
Pza G. Carducci
Via

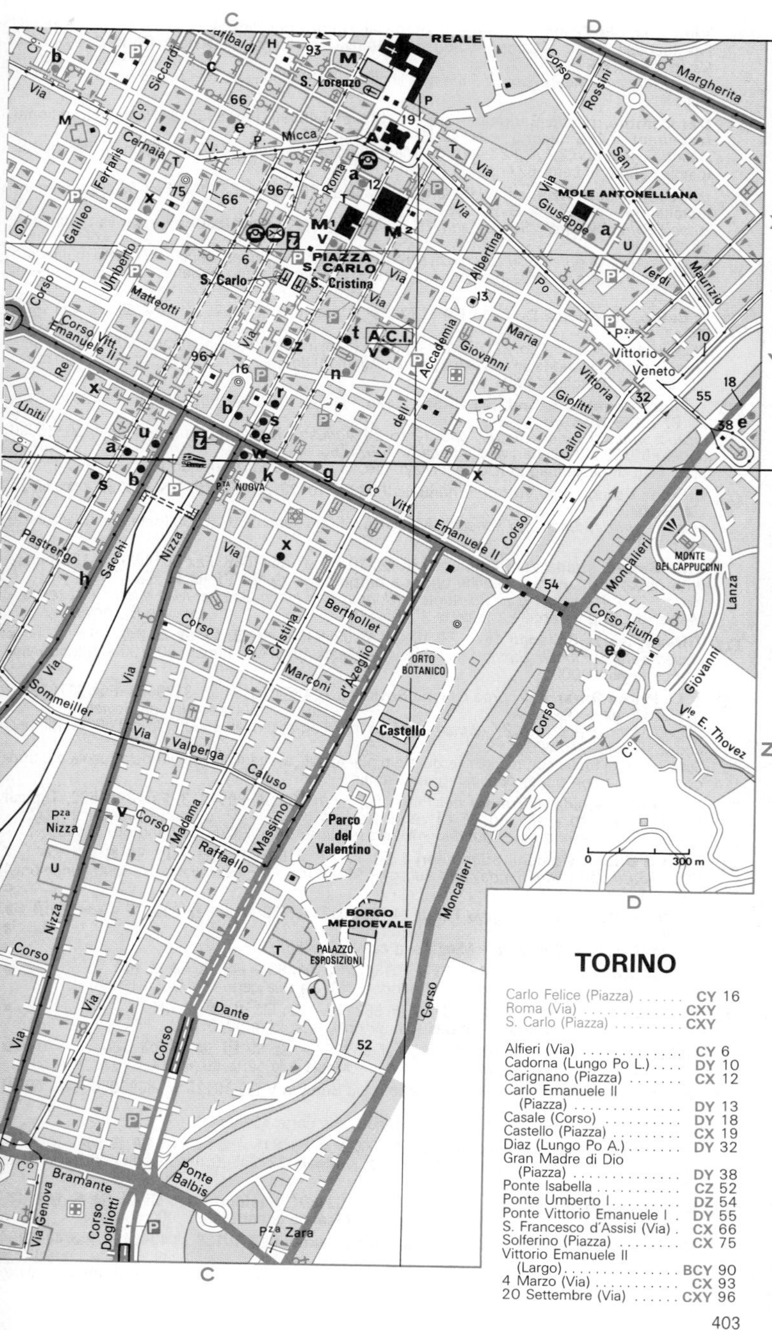

TORINO

Carlo Felice (Piazza)	CY	16
Roma (Via)	CXY	
S. Carlo (Piazza)	CXY	
Alfieri (Via)	CY	6
Cadorna (Lungo Po L.)	DY	10
Carignano (Piazza)	CX	12
Carlo Emanuele II (Piazza)	DY	13
Casale (Corso)	DY	18
Castello (Piazza)	CX	19
Diaz (Lungo Po A.)	DY	32
Gran Madre di Dio (Piazza)	DY	38
Ponte Isabella	CZ	52
Ponte Umberto I	DZ	54
Ponte Vittorio Emanuele I	DY	55
S. Francesco d'Assisi (Via)	CX	66
Solferino (Piazza)	CX	75
Vittorio Emanuele II (Largo)	BCY	90
4 Marzo (Via)	CX	93
20 Settembre (Via)	CXY	96

XXXX **Villa Sassi-El Toulà** with rm, strada al Traforo del Pino 47 ⊠ 10132 ✆ 8980556, Fax 8980095, , « 18C country house in extensive parkland » – | rm – 200. AE VISA. by corso Casale DY
closed August – **Meals** *(closed Sunday)* a la carte 75/109000 – 20000 – **15 rm** 270/400000, suite.

XXXX **Del Cambio,** piazza Carignano 2 ⊠ 10123 ✆ 546690, Fax 535282, Historic traditional restaurant, « 19C decor » – . AE VISA. CX **a**
closed Sunday and 27 July-27 August – **Meals** (booking essential) 65/95000 (lunch) 85/105000 (dinner) and a la carte 62/108000 (15 %).

XXX ✿ **Vecchia Lanterna,** corso Re Umberto 21 ⊠ 10128 ✆ 537047, Fax 530391, Elegant installation – . VISA. CY **x**
closed Saturday lunch, Sunday and 10 to 20 August – **Meals** (booking essential) a la carte 65/110000
Spec. Cappella di porcino su zoccolo di semolino farcito di fonduta, Timballo di risotto mantecato al fegato d'anatra in salsa piemontese, Carrè d'agnello all'aceto balsamico con croccante di basilico.

XXX ✿ **Balbo,** via Andrea Doria 11 ⊠ 10123 ✆ 8125566, Fax 8127524 – . AE VISA JCB. CY **n**
closed Monday and 1 to 22 August – **Meals** (booking essential) a la carte 60/110000
Spec. Tortino di storione all'olio extravergine, Agnolotti del "plin" ai profumi dell'orto, Fritto misto alla torinese (October-April).

XXX ✿ **Neuv Caval 'd Brôns,** piazza San Carlo 151 ⊠ 10123 ✆ 5627483, Fax 543610 – . AE VISA JCB. CXY **v**
closed Saturday lunch, Sunday and 10 to 24 August – **Meals** (booking essential) 50/80000 (lunch) 60/80000 (dinner) and a la carte 105/155000
Spec. Flan di Castelmagno (October-May), Riso al Barolo, Manzo di Carrù.

XXX **Rendez Vous,** corso Vittorio Emanuele II 38 ⊠ 10123 ✆ 887666, Fax 889362 – . AE VISA. CZ **g**
closed Saturday lunch and Sunday – **Meals** 35/80000 (lunch) 60/90000 (dinner) and a la carte 52/82000.

XXX **Villa Somis,** strada Val Pattonera 138 ⊠ 10133 ✆ 6613086, Fax 6614626, « 18C house with park ; and summer service under a pergola » – . AE VISA
closed 2 to 9 January, 5 to 26 August, Monday and lunch October-May except weekends – **Meals** (booking essential) a la carte 40/65000. by viale E. Thovez DZ

XXX **Tiffany,** piazza Solferino 16/h ⊠ 10121 ✆ 535948 – . AE VISA. CX **x**
closed Saturday lunch, Sunday and August – **Meals** 40/50000 (lunch) 50/70000 (dinner) and a la carte 56/92000.

XXX ✿ **La Prima Smarrita,** corso Unione Sovietica 244 ⊠ 10134 ✆ 3179657, Fax 3179191 – . AE VISA. by corso Unione Sovietica BZ
closed Monday and 3 to 27 August – **Meals** (booking essential) 45000 (lunch) 60000 (dinner) and a la carte 60/89000
Spec. Filetti di triglia con piccole verdure e pinoli tostati, Maltagliati con vongole rucola e pomodoro, Rombo con punte di asparagi e calamari.

XXX **La Cloche,** strada al Traforo del Pino 106 ⊠ 10132 ✆ 8994213, Fax 8981522, Typical atmosphere – – 100. AE VISA. by corso Moncalieri CDZ
closed Sunday dinner and Monday – **Meals** (surprise menu)30/50000 and 60/120000.

XXX **Trait d'Union,** via degli Stampatori 4 ⊠ 10122 ✆ 541979, – VISA.
closed Saturday lunch, Sunday and August – **Meals** (booking essential) 25/38000 (lunch only) and a la carte 43/64000. CX **c**

XXX **Al Gatto Nero,** corso Filippo Turati 14 ⊠ 10128 ✆ 590414, Fax 590477 – . AE VISA. BZ **z**
closed Sunday and August – **Meals** a la carte 60/80000.

XX **Al Bue Rosso,** corso Casale 10 ⊠ 10131 ✆ 8191393 – . AE VISA DY **e**
closed Saturday lunch, Monday and August – **Meals** a la carte 57/78000 (10 %).

XX **Perbacco,** via Mazzini 31 ⊠ 10123 ✆ 882110 – . AE VISA DZ **x**
closed Sunday and August – **Meals** (dinner only) a la carte 47/67000.

XX **Galante,** corso Palestro 15 ⊠ 10122 ✆ 537757 – . AE VISA JCB BV **u**
closed Saturday lunch, Sunday and August – **Meals** a la carte 50/80000.

XX **Due Mondi-da Ilio,** via Saluzzo 3 angolo via San Pio V ⊠ 10125 ✆ 6692056 – . AE VISA CZ **k**
closed Monday and 1 to 15 August – **Meals** a la carte 40/83000.

XX **Porta Rossa,** via Passalacqua 3/b ⊠ 10122 ✆ 530816 – . AE VISA CV **a**
closed Saturday lunch, Sunday and August – **Meals** 22/25000 (lunch only) and a la carte 35/79000.

XX **Il Porticciolo,** via Barletta 58 ⊠ 10136 ✆ 321601, Seafood – . AE VISA.
closed Saturday lunch, Sunday and August – **Meals** a la carte 48/78000. AZ **a**

XX **Duchesse,** via Duchessa Jolanda 7 ang. via Beaumont ⊠ 10138 ✆ 4346494, Fax 4346494 – . AE VISA JCB BX **c**
closed Sunday dinner, Monday, August and 25 December-3 January – **Meals** a la carte 42/73000.

X **Trômlin,** a Cavoretto, via alla Parrocchia 7 ✉ 10133 ☎ 6613050
closed lunch except Bank Holidays, Monday and August – **Meals** (booking essential) (surprise menu) 50000 b.i.. by corso Moncalieri DZ

X **C'era una volta,** corso Vittorio Emanuele II 41 ✉ 10125 ☎ 655498, Piedmontese rest. – ▤. AE ⓢ ⓓ E VISA CZ **k**
closed Sunday and August – **Meals** (dinner only) (booking essential) 35/45000.

Costigliole d'Asti 14055 Asti 988 ⑫, 428 H 6 – pop. 5 932 alt. 242 – ☎ 0141.
Roma 629 – Acqui Terme 34 – Alessandria 51 – Asti 15 – Genova 108 – Torino – 77.

XXX ✿✿ **Guido,** piazza Umberto I 27 ☎ 966012, Fax 966012 – AE ⓢ ⓓ E VISA
closed Sunday, Bank Holidays, 1 to 20 August and 23 December-10 January – **Meals** (dinner only) (booking essential) 110000
Spec. Zuppa di porcini (autumn), Agnolotti al sugo di stinco, Stracotto di bue al Barolo (winter).

VENICE (VENEZIA) 30100 P 988 ⑤, 429 F 19 – pop. 309 041 – ☎ 041.

See : St. Marks Square★★★ FGZ :.
Basilica★★★ GZ – Doges Palace★★★ GZ – Campanile★★ : ※★★ FGZ **F** – Procuratie★★ FZ – Libreria Vecchia★ GZ – Correr Museum★★ FZ **M1** – Clock Tower★ FZ **K** – Bridge of Sighs★★ GZ.
Grand Canal★★★ :
Rialto Bridge★★ FY – Right bank : Cà d'Oro★★★ EX – Vendramin-Calergi Palace★ BT – Cà Loredan★★ EY **H** – Grimani Palace★★ EY Corner-Spinelli Palace★★ BTU Grassi Palace★ BU – Left bank : Academy of Fine Arts★★★ BV Dario Palace★ BV **S** – Peggy Guggenheim Collection★ in Palace Venier dei Leoni BV **M2** – Rezzonico Palace★★ : museum on 18C Venice★★ AU Querini-Stampalia Palace★ GY – Giustinian Palace★★ AU **X** – Cà Foscari★★ AU **Y** Bernardo Palace★★ BT – Camerlenghi Palace★★ FX **A** – Cà Pesaro★ EX.
Churches :
Santa Maria della Salute★★ BV – St. Giorgio Maggiore★★ : ※★★★ from campanile★★ CV – St. Zanipolo★★ GX – Santa Maria Gloriosa dei Frari★★★ AT – St. Zaccaria★★ GZ – Interior decoration★★ by Veronese in the Church of St. Sebastiano AU – Paintings★ by Guardi in the Church of Angelo Raffaele AU – Ceiling★ of the Church of St. Pantaleone AT – Santa Maria dei Miracoli★ GX – St. Francesco della Vigna★ DT – Redentore★ (Giudecca Island) AV – Ghetto★★ ABT.
Scuola di St. Rocco★★★ AT – Scuola di St. Giorgio degli Schiavoni★★★ DT – Scuola dei Carmini★ AU – Rio dei Mendicanti★ GX – Facade★ of the Scuola di St. Marco GX – Palazzo Labia★★ AT.
The Lido★★ – Murano★★ : Glass Museum★, Church of Santi Maria e Donato★★ – Burano★★ – Torcello★★ : mosaics★★ in the Cathedral of Santa Maria Assunta.

18 (closed Monday) at Lido Alberoni ✉ 30011 ☎ 731333, Fax 731339 15 mn by boat and 9 km;

18, 9 Cà della Nave (closed Tuesday), at Martellago ✉ 30030 ☎ 5401555, Fax 5401926, NW : 12 km;

18, 9 Villa Condulmer (closed Monday), at Zerman ✉ 31020 ☎ 457062, Fax 457202, N : 17 km.

✈ Marco Polo of Tessera, NE : 13 km ☎ 2609260 – Alitalia, San Marco-Bacino Orseolo 1166 ✉ 30124 ☎ 5216333.

⛴ to Lido - San Nicolò from piazzale Roma (Tronchetto) daily (35 mn); to island of Pellestrina-Santa Maria del Mare from Lido Alberoni daily (15 mn).

⛴ to Punta Sabbioni from Riva degli Schiavoni daily (40 mn) ; to islands of Burano (30 mn), Torcello (40 mn), Murano (1 h 10 mn) from Punta Sabbioni daily ; to islands of Murano (10 mn), Burano (50 mn), Torcello (50 mn) from Fondamenta Nuove daily; to Treporti-Cavallino from Fondamenta Nuove daily (1 h 10 mn); to Venezia-Fondamenta Nuove from Treporti-Cavallino (1 h 10 mn), to islands of Murano (1 h), Burano (20 mn), Torcello (25 mn) daily – Information : ACTV-Venetian Trasport Union, piazzale Roma ✉ 30135 ☎ 5287886, Fax 5207135.

ℹ Palazzetto Selva-Molo di San Marco 71/c ✉ 30124 ☎ 5226356 – Santa Lucia Railway station ✉ 30121 ☎ 719078.

Roma 528 ① – Bologna 152 ① – Milano 267 ① – Trieste 158 ①

Plans on following pages

🏨 **Cipriani** ⛰, isola della Giudecca 10 ✉ 30133 ☎ 5207744, Telex 410162, Fax 5203930, ≤, ☂, « Floral garden with heated 🏊 », ≘s, 🎾 – |♦| ▤ TV ☎ – 🏛 80. AE ⓢ ⓓ E VISA. ✈
closed 9 January-24 February – **Meals** *(closed until 15 March)* a la carte 120/170000 – **92 rm** ☕ 1000/1200000, 5 suites (**Palazzo Vendramin** 7 apartments). CV **h**

🏨 **Danieli,** riva degli Schiavoni 4196 ✉ 30122 ☎ 5226480, Telex 410077, Fax 5200208, ≤ San Marco Canal, « Hall in a small Venetian style courtyard and summer rest. service on terrace with panoramic view » – |♦| ▤ TV ☎ – 🏛 70-150. AE ⓢ ⓓ E VISA JCB. ✈ rest GZ **a**
Meals a la carte 123/202000 – ☕ 53000 – **221 rm** 396/759000, 9 suites.

🏨 **Gritti Palace,** campo Santa Maria del Giglio 2467 ✉ 30124 ☎ 794611, Telex 410125, Fax 5200942, ≤ Grand Canal, « Outdoor rest. summer service on the Grand Canal » – |♦| ✈ rm ▤ TV ☎ ♿ – 🏛 50. AE ⓢ ⓓ E VISA JCB. ✈ EZ **a**
Meals *(closed Monday)* a la carte 96/140000 – **93 rm** ☕ 554/898000, 2 suites.

🏨 **Bauer Grünwald,** campo San Moisè 1459 ✉ 30124 ☎ 5207022, Telex 410075, Fax 5207557, ≤ Grand Canal, ☂ – |♦| ▤ TV ☎ – 🏛 25-150. AE ⓢ ⓓ E VISA. ✈ rest
Meals a la carte 90/140000 – **214 rm** ☕ 350/650000, 3 suites. FZ **h**

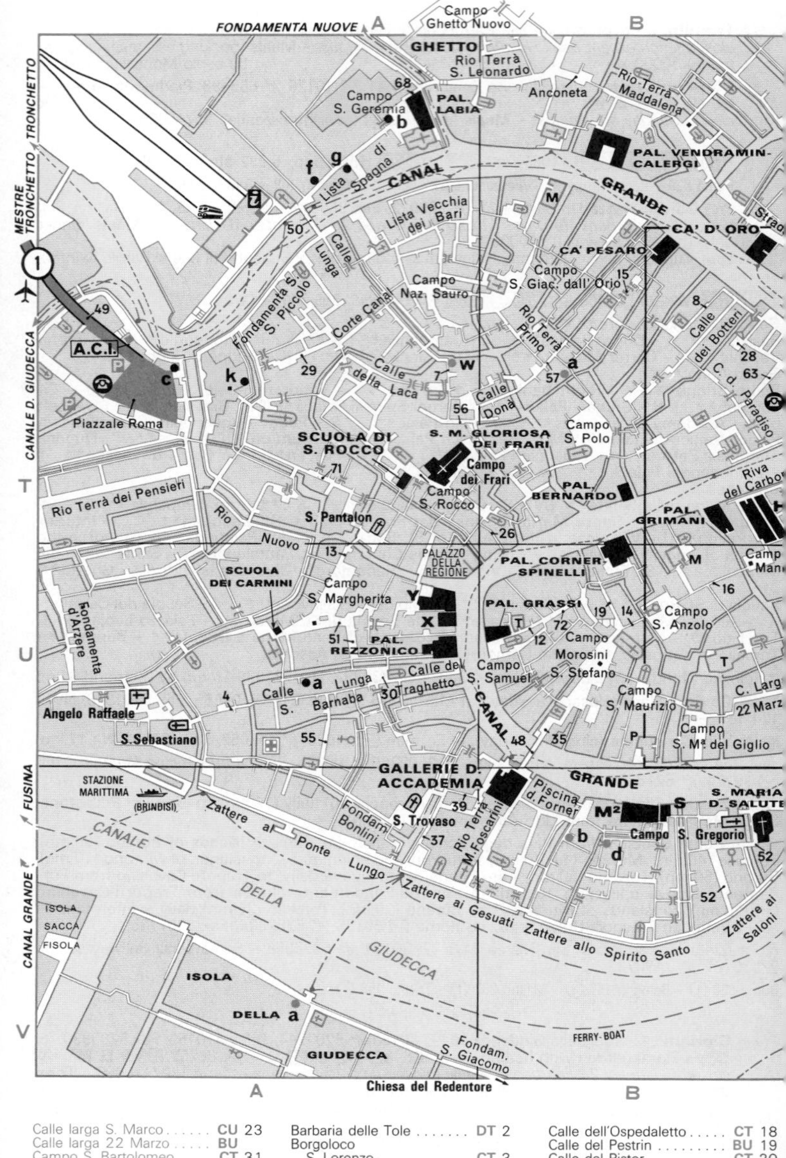

Calle larga S. Marco . . . . . CU 23
Calle larga 22 Marzo . . . . . BU
Campo S. Bartolomeo . . . . CT 31
Frezzeria . . . . CU 40
Merceria del Capitello . . . . CT 41
Merceria dell'Orologio . . . . CU 42
Merceria S. Salvador . . . . . CT 43
Merceria S. Zulian . . . . CT 44
Piazza S. Marco . . . . CU
Ponte di Rialto . . . . CT
Ruga degli Orefici . . . . CT 62
Salizzada S. Moisé . . . . CU 70
Via 2 Aprile . . . . CT 74

Barbaria delle Tole . . . . DT 2
Borgoloco
S. Lorenzo . . . . CT 3
Calle Avogaria . . . . AU 4
Calle del Caffettier . . . . AT 7
Calle del Campanile . . . . BT 8
Calle di Canonica . . . . CU 9
Calle delle Carrozze . . . . . . BU 12
Calle della Chiesa . . . . AU 13
Calle dei Frati . . . . BU 14
Calle Longo . . . . BT 15
Calle della Mandola . . . . BU 16
Calle Larga Mazzini . . . . CT 17

Calle dell'Ospedaletto . . . . . CT 18
Calle del Pestrin . . . . BU 19
Calle del Pistor . . . . CT 20
Calle delle Rasse . . . . CU 22
Calle lunga
S. M. Formosa . . . . CT 24
Calle del Te Deum . . . . DT 25
Calle del Traghetto
Vecchio . . . . BT 26
Campo Bandiera e Moro . . DU 27
Campo delle Beccarie . . . . BT 28
Campo della Lana . . . . AT 29
Campo S. Barnaba . . . . AU 30

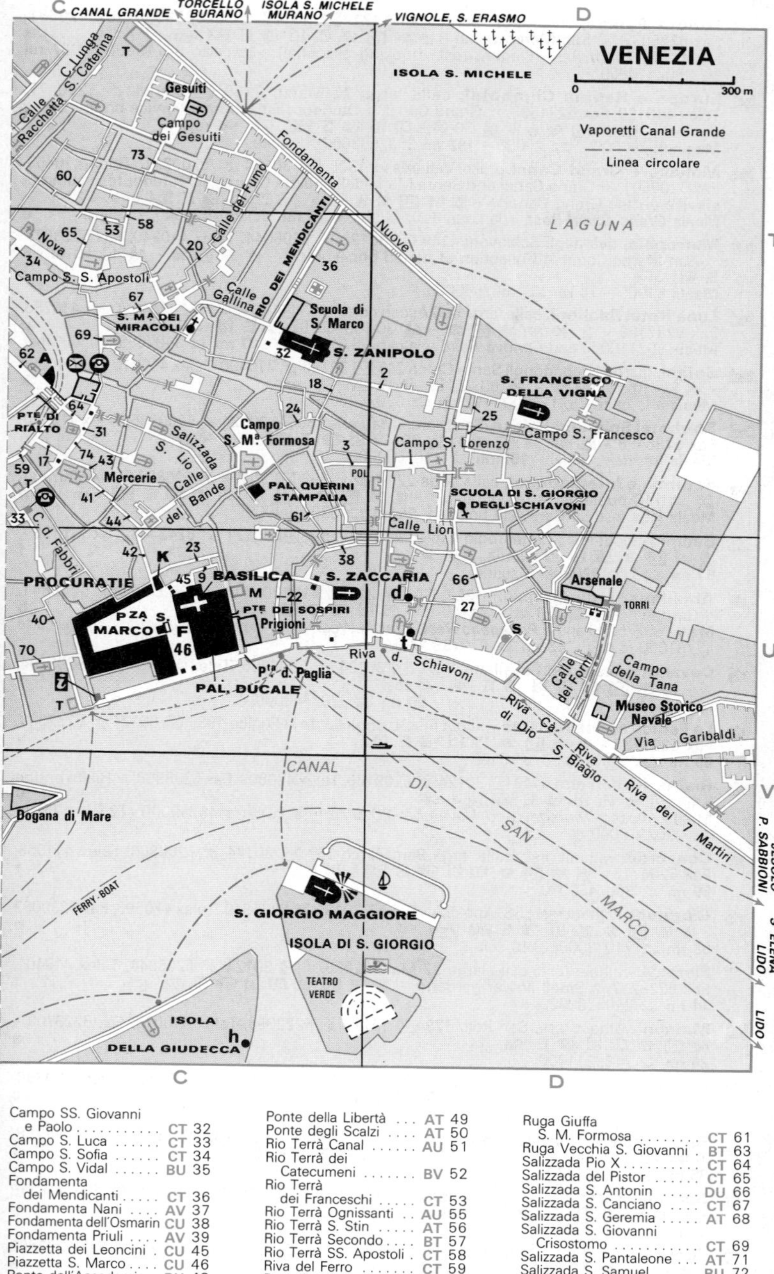
VENEZIA
0
300 m
Vaporetti Canal Grande
Linea circolare
CANAL GRANDE
TORCELLO BURANO
ISOLA S. MICHELE MURANO
VIGNOLE, S. ERASMO
ISOLA S. MICHELE
LAGUNA
Gesuiti
Campo dei Gesuiti
Calle Racchetta
C. Lunga S. Caterina
Fondamenta Nuove
Calle del Fumo
RIO DEI MENDICANTI
Nova
Campo S. S. Apostoli
Calle Gallina
Scuola di S. Marco
S. ZANIPOLO
S. Mª DEI MIRACOLI
S. FRANCESCO DELLA VIGNA
Campo S. Francesco
PTE DI RIALTO
Salizzada S. Lio
Calle del Bande
Campo S. Mª Formosa
Campo S. Lorenzo
Mercerie
PAL. QUERINI STAMPALIA
SCUOLA DI S. GIORGIO DEGLI SCHIAVONI
C. d. Fabbri
Calle Lion
PROCURATIE
BASILICA
S. ZACCARIA
Arsenale
TORRI
PZA S. MARCO
PTE DEI SOSPIRI
Prigioni
Riva d. Schiavoni
Pta d. Paglia
PAL. DUCALE
Calle dei Forni
Campo della Tana
Museo Storico Navale
Via Garibaldi
Riva di Dio
Riva Cà
Riva S. Biagio
Riva dei 7 Martiri
CANAL DI SAN MARCO
Dogana di Mare
FERRY-BOAT
S. GIORGIO MAGGIORE
ISOLA DI S. GIORGIO
TEATRO VERDE
ISOLA DELLA GIUDECCA
JESOLO P. SABBIONI
S. ELENA LIDO
LIDO

Londra Palace, riva degli Schiavoni 4171 ✉ 30122 ✆ 5200533, Telex 420681, Fax 5225032, ≤ San Marco Canal – |‡| ▤ TV ☎. AE ⑤ ⓓ E VISA JCB GZ **t**
Meals ***Do Leoni*** Rest (Elegant rest., booking essential) a la carte 84/136000 – **57 rm** ☑ 350/410000.

Europa e Regina Cigahotel, calle larga 22 Marzo 2159 ✉ 30124 ✆ 5200477, Telex 410123, Fax 5231533, ≤ Grand Canal, « Outdoor rest. summer service on the Grand Canal » – |‡| ▤ TV ☎ ♿ – 🏛 30-140. AE ⑤ ⓓ E VISA JCB. ✻ rest FZ **d**
Meals 85/90000 – ☑ 26000 – **192 rm** 363/583000, 13 suites.

Monaco e Grand Canal, calle Vallaresso 1325 ✉ 30124 ✆ 5200211, Telex 410450, Fax 5200501, ≤ Grand Canal and Santa Maria della Salute Church, « Outdoor rest. summer service on the Grand Canal » – |‡| ▤ TV ☎ ♿ – 🏛 40. AE ⑤ ⓓ E VISA JCB. ✻ rm
Meals ***Grand Canal Rest.*** a la carte 100/145000 – **70 rm** ☑ 350/520000, 2 suites. FZ **e**

Metropole, riva degli Schiavoni 4149 ✉ 30122 ✆ 5205044, Telex 410340, Fax 5223679, ≤ San Marco Canal, « Collection of period bric-a-brac » – |‡| ▤ TV ☎ – 🏛 40. AE ⑤ ⓓ E VISA JCB DU **t**
Meals 51000 – **74 rm** ☑ 450/540000.

Luna Hotel Baglioni, calle larga dell'Ascensione 1243 ✉ 30124 ✆ 5289840, Telex 410236, Fax 5287160 – |‡| ⇄ rm ▤ TV ☎ – 🏛 30-150. AE ⑤ ⓓ E VISA JCB. ✻ rest FZ **p**
Meals 90/110000 and ***Canova Rest.*** a la carte 67/115000 – **87 rm** ☑ 340/595000, 6 suites.

Sofitel, giardini Papadopoli Santa Croce 245 ✉ 30135 ✆ 710400, Telex 410310, Fax 710394 – |‡| ⇄ rm ▤ TV ☎ – 🏛 60. AE ⑤ ⓓ E VISA. ✻ rest AT **k**
Meals a la carte 75/115000 – **92 rm** ☑ 380/480000.

Starhotel Splendid-Suisse, San Marco-Mercerie 760 ✉ 30124 ✆ 5200755, Telex 410590, Fax 5286498 – |‡| ⇄ ▤ TV ☎ – 🏛 80. AE ⑤ ⓓ E VISA JCB. ✻ rest FY **n**
Meals (residents only) – **157 rm** ☑ 410/600000.

Saturnia e International, calle larga 22 Marzo 2398 ✉ 30124 ✆ 5208377, Fax 5207131, ⛱, « 14C nobleman's townhouse » – |‡| ▤ TV ☎ – 🏛 60. AE ⑤ ⓓ E VISA JCB EZ **n**
Meals (see rest. **La Caravella** below) – **95 rm** ☑ 380/494000.

Bellini without rest., Cannaregio 116-Lista di Spagna ✉ 30121 ✆ 5242488, Fax 715193 – |‡| ▤ TV ☎. AE ⑤ ⓓ E VISA JCB. ✻ AT **f**
67 rm ☑ 270/390000, 3 suites.

Amadeus, Lista di Spagna 227 ✉ 30121 ✆ 715300, Telex 420811, Fax 5240841, « Garden » – |‡| ▤ TV ☎ – 🏛 40-150. AE ⑤ ⓓ E VISA JCB AT **b**
Meals 55/75000 and ***Il Papageno Rest.*** *(closed Wednesday except May-September)* a la carte 47/81000 (12 %) – **63 rm** ☑ 270/380000.

Cavalletto, calle del Cavalletto 1107 ✉ 30124 ✆ 5200955, Telex 410684, Fax 5238184, ≤ – |‡| ▤ TV ☎. AE ⑤ ⓓ E VISA. ✻ rest FZ **f**
Meals a la carte 63/129000 (12 %) – **96 rm** ☑ 330/440000.

La Fenice et des Artistes without rest., campiello de la Fenice 1936 ✉ 30124 ✆ 5232333, Fax 5203721 – |‡| ▤ TV ☎. AE ⑤ ⓓ E VISA EZ **v**
65 rm ☑ 190/300000, 3 suites.

Rialto, riva del Ferro 5149 ✉ 30124 ✆ 5209166, Telex 420809, Fax 5238958, ≤ Rialto bridge – ▤ TV ☎. AE ⑤ ⓓ E VISA JCB. ✻ FY **v**
Meals *(closed Thursday and November-20 March)* a la carte 45/69000 (12 %) – **71 rm** ☑ 220/310000.

Concordia without rest., calle larga San Marco 367 ✉ 30124 ✆ 5206866, Telex 411069, Fax 5206775 – |‡| ▤ TV ☎. AE ⑤ ⓓ E VISA JCB GZ **r**
55 rm ☑ 300/450000.

Giorgione without rest., SS. Apostoli 4587 ✉ 30131 ✆ 5225810, Telex 420598, Fax 5239092 – |‡| ▤ TV ☎. AE ⑤ ⓓ E VISA JCB. ✻ FX **b**
58 rm ☑ 210/300000, 10 suites.

Flora 🕭 without rest., calle larga 22 Marzo 2283/a ✉ 30124 ✆ 5205844, Telex 410401, Fax 5228217, « Small flower garden » – |‡| ▤ TV ☎. AE ⑤ ⓓ E VISA JCB EZ **t**
44 rm ☑ 210/280000.

Marconi without rest., San Polo 729 ✉ 30125 ✆ 5222068, Telex 410073, Fax 5229700 – ▤ TV ☎. AE ⑤ ⓓ E VISA JCB FY **a**
26 rm ☑ 218/311000.

Santa Chiara without rest., Santa Croce 548 ✉ 30125 ✆ 5206955, Telex 420690, Fax 5228799 – |‡| ▤ TV ☎ Ⓟ. AE ⑤ ⓓ E VISA. ✻ AT **c**
☑ 20000 – **28 rm** 270/295000.

San Cassiano-Cà Favretto without rest., Santa Croce 2232 ✉ 30135 ✆ 5241768, Telex 420810, Fax 721033, ≤ – ▤ TV ☎. AE ⑤ E VISA JCB EX **f**
35 rm ☑ 218/311000.

Spagna without rest., lista di Spagna 184 ✉ 30121 ✆ 715011, Telex 420360, Fax 715318 – |‡| ▤ TV ☎. AE ⑤ ⓓ E VISA JCB AT **g**
19 rm ☑ 190/270000.

Firenze without rest., San Marco 1490 ✉ 30124 ✆ 5222858, Telex 410627, Fax 5202668 – |‡| ▤ TV ☎. AE ⑤ E VISA JCB. ✻ FZ **a**
25 rm ☑ 210/305000.

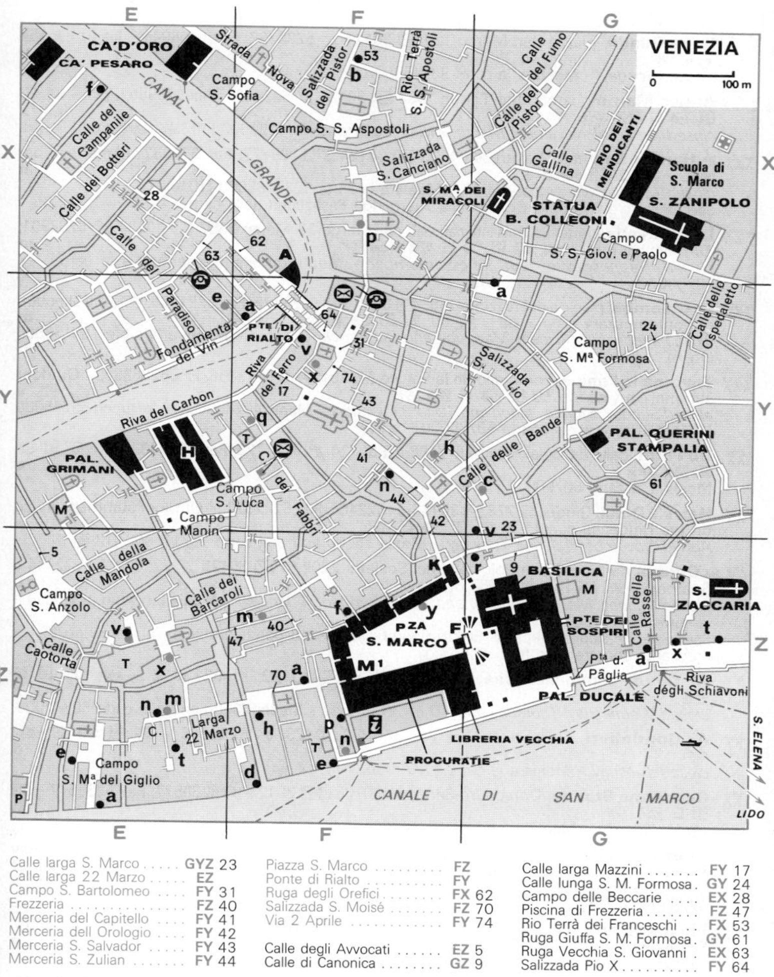

Calle larga S. Marco ..... GYZ 23	Piazza S. Marco .... FZ	Calle larga Mazzini .... FY 17
Calle larga 22 Marzo ..... EZ	Ponte di Rialto .... FY	Calle lunga S. M. Formosa . GY 24
Campo S. Bartolomeo .... FY 31	Ruga degli Orefici .... FX 62	Campo delle Beccarie .... EX 28
Frezzeria .... FZ 40	Salizzada S. Moisé .... FZ 70	Piscina di Frezzeria .... FZ 47
Merceria del Capitello .... FY 41	Via 2 Aprile .... FY 74	Rio Terrà dei Franceschi .. FX 53
Merceria dell Orologio .... FY 42		Ruga Giuffa S. M. Formosa . GY 61
Merceria S. Salvador ..... FY 43	Calle degli Avvocati ...... EZ 5	Ruga Vecchia S. Giovanni . EX 63
Merceria S. Zulian .... FY 44	Calle di Canonica .... GZ 9	Salizzada Pio X .... FY 64

Ala without rest., campo Santa Maria del Giglio 2494 ✉ 30124 ☎ 5208333, Telex 410275, Fax 5206390 – |‡| ▤ TV ☎. AE ⑤ ① E VISA JCB. ✻ EZ **e**
85 rm ☕ 180/250000.

Panada without rest., San Marco-calle dei Specchieri 646 ✉ 30124 ☎ 5209088, Telex 410153, Fax 5209619 – |‡| ▤ TV ☎. AE ⑤ ① E VISA JCB GY **v**
48 rm ☕ 200/300000.

Pausania without rest., Dorsoduro 2824-fondamenta Gherardini ✉ 30123 ☎ 5222083, Telex 420178, Fax 5222989 – ▤ TV ☎. AE ⑤ E VISA JCB – **23 rm** ☕ 190/280000. AU **a**

Savoia e Jolanda, riva degli Schiavoni 4187 ✉ 30122 ☎ 5206644, Telex 410620, Fax 5207494, ← San Marco Canal, ☂ – |‡| ▤ ☎. AE ⑤ ① E VISA. ✻ rest GZ **x**
Meals *(closed Tuesday)* 45000 – **80 rm** ☕ 210/290000.

Bisanzio ⑤ without rest., calle della Pietà 3651 ✉ 30122 ☎ 5203100, Telex 420099, Fax 5204114 – |‡| ▤ TV ☎. AE ⑤ ① E VISA JCB DU **d**
39 rm ☕ 200/280000.

Santa Marina without rest., campo Santa Marina 6068 ✉ 30122 ☎ 5239202, Fax 5200907 – ▤ TV ☎. AE ⑤ ① E VISA JCB. ✻ GXY **a**
16 rm ☕ 200/300000.

XXXX **Caffè Quadri,** piazza San Marco 120 ✉ 30124 ✆ 5289299, Fax 5208041 – AE $ ⓓ VISA JCB. ✻ FZ **y**
closed Monday – **Meals** a la carte 93/150000.

XXXX **Antico Martini,** campo San Fantin 1983 ✉ 30124 ✆ 5224121, Fax 5289857, ☂ – ▤. AE $ ⓓ E VISA JCB. ✻ EZ **x**
closed lunch 24 November-March – **Meals** a la carte 74/120000 (15 %).

XXX ✿ **Harry's Bar,** calle Vallaresso 1323 ✉ 30124 ✆ 5285777, Fax 5208822, American bar rest. – ▤. AE $ ⓓ E VISA FZ **n**
closed Monday November-March – **Meals** a la carte 123/188000 (10 %)
Spec. Risotto alle seppie, Scampi alla Thermidor, Pasticceria della casa.

XXX **La Caravella** - Hotel Saturnia-International, calle larga 22 Marzo 2397 ✉ 30124 ✆ 5208901, ☂, Typical rest. – ▤. AE $ ⓓ E VISA JCB. ✻ EZ **m**
closed Wednesday except June-September – **Meals** (booking essential) a la carte 75/132000.

XXX **La Colomba,** piscina di Frezzeria 1665 ✉ 30124 ✆ 5221175, Fax 5221468, ☂, « Collection of contemporary art » – ▤ – 🏛 60. AE $ ⓓ E VISA JCB. ✻ FZ **m**
closed Wednesday except May-June and September-October – **Meals** a la carte 78/133000 (15 %).

XXX **Taverna la Fenice,** campiello de la Fenice ✉ 30124 ✆ 5223856, Fax 5236866, « Outdoor summer service » – AE $ ⓓ E VISA. ✻ EZ **v**
closed Sunday, Monday lunch and 10 to 31 January – **Meals** 40/60000 (15 %) lunch 55/75000 (15 %) dinner and a la carte 53/86000 (15 %).

XX **Do Forni,** calle dei Specchieri 457/468 ✉ 30124 ✆ 5237729, Fax 5288132 – ▤. AE $ ⓓ E VISA JCB GY **c**
Meals a la carte 60/90000 (12 %).

XX **Harry's Dolci,** Giudecca 773 ✉ 30133 ✆ 522484, Fax 5222322, « Outdoor summer service on the Giudecca canal » – ▤. AE ⓓ E VISA AV **a**
April-6 November ; closed Tuesday – **Meals** 75000 and a la carte 70/119000 (12 %).

XX ✿ **Osteria da Fiore,** San Polo-calle del Scaleter 2202/A ✉ 30125 ✆ 721308, Fax 721343, Seafood – ▤. AE $ ⓓ E VISA BT **a**
closed Sunday, Monday, August and 23 December-11 January – **Meals** (booking essential) a la carte 66/111000
Spec. Spaghetti coi caparossoli, Filetto di rombo in crosta di patate profumate al rosmarino, Cialda croccante con crema e frutti di bosco.

XX **Al Covo,** campiello della Pescaria 3968 ✉ 30122 ✆ 5223812 – ⚹. AE $ E VISA DU **s**
closed Wednesday, Thursday and 10 to 20 August – **Meals** 40000 and a la carte 60/87000.

XX **Ai Gondolieri,** Dorsoduro-San Vio 366 ✉ 30123 ✆ 5286396 – AE $ ⓓ E VISA. ✻ BV **d**
closed Tuesday – **Meals** a la carte 47/71000 (10 %).

XX **Cantinone Storico,** Dorsoduro-San Vio 660/661 ✉ 30123 ✆ 5239577, Fax 5239577 – AE $ E VISA. ✻ BV **b**
closed Sunday – **Meals** a la carte 40/60000.

XX **Al Graspo de Ua,** calle dei Bombaseri 5094 ✉ 30124 ✆ 5200150, Fax 5233917, Typical taverna – ▤. AE $ ⓓ E VISA FY **x**
closed Monday, Tuesday, 1 to 18 August and 20 December-13 January – **Meals** a la carte 52/83000 (16 %).

XX **Fiaschetteria Toscana,** San Giovanni Crisostomo 5719 ✉ 30121 ✆ 5285281, Fax 5285521, ☂ – ▤. AE $ ⓓ E VISA FX **p**
closed Tuesday and 6 July-2 August – **Meals** a la carte 43/70000 (12 %).

XX **Caffè Orientale,** San Polo-calle del Caffettier 2426 ✉ 30125 ✆ 719804, Fax 715167, ☂ – AE $ ⓓ E VISA AT **w**
closed Sunday dinner and Monday – **Meals** a la carte 45/76000.

XX **Vini da Gigio,** Cannaregio 3628/a-Fondamenta San Felice ✉ 30131 ✆ 5285140 – AE $ ⓓ E VISA BT
closed Monday, 7 to 21 August and 7 to 21 January – **Meals** (booking essential) a la carte 39/73000.

X **Trattoria alla Madonna,** calle della Madonna 594 ✉ 30125 ✆ 5223824, Fax 5210167, Venetian trattoria – AE $ E VISA JCB. ✻ EY **e**
closed Wednesday, 4 to 17 August and 24 December-January – **Meals** a la carte 38/59000 (12 %).

X **Al Conte Pescaor,** piscina San Zulian 544 ✉ 30124 ✆ 5221483, Rustic rest. – ▤ FY **h**
closed Sunday and 7 January-7 February – **Meals** a la carte 42/71000.

X **Antica Carbonera,** calle Bembo 4648 ✉ 30124 ✆ 5225479, Venetian trattoria – ▤. AE $ ⓓ E VISA JCB FY **q**
closed 20 July-10 August, 8 January-2 February, Sunday July-August and Tuesday September-June – **Meals** a la carte 43/80000 (12 %).

in Lido : 15 mn by boat from San Marco FZ – ✉ **30126** Venezia Lido.
ℹ Gran Viale S. M. Elisabetta 6 ☏ 5265721 :

Excelsior, lungomare Marconi 41 ☏ 5260201, Telex 410023, Fax 5267276, ≤, ⛱, ⛱, 🎾, 18 – |♦| ▤ TV ☎ ♿ 🚗 P – 🚶 40-600
seasonal – **197 rm.**

Des Bains, lungomare Marconi 17 ☏ 5265921, Telex 410142, Fax 5260113, ≤, ⛱, « Floral park with heated ⛱ and 🎾 », ≋, 🎾 – |♦| ▤ TV ☎ P – 🚶 90-380. AE ⓢ ◑ E VISA. ✗ rest
April-October – **Meals** 90/120000 – ☕ 29500 – **191 rm** 412/495000, suite.

Villa Mabapa, riviera San Nicolò 16 ☏ 5260590, Telex 410357, Fax 5269441, « Summer rest. in garden » – |♦| ▤ TV ☎ ♿ – 🚶 85. AE ⓢ ◑ E VISA JCB. ✗ rest
closed 9 January-9 February – **Meals** a la carte 50/76000 – **61 rm** ☕ 260/380000.

Quattro Fontane ⛳, via 4 Fontane 16 ☏ 5260227, Telex 411006, Fax 5260726, « Summer service rest. in garden », 🎾 – ▤ TV ☎ P – 🚶 40. AE ⓢ ◑ E VISA. ✗ rest
5 April-October – **Meals** a la carte 85/131000 – **62 rm** ☕ 250/400000.

Le Boulevard without rest., Gran Viale S. M. Elisabetta 41 ☏ 5261990, Telex 410185, Fax 5261917 – |♦| ▤ TV ☎ P – 🚶 60. AE ⓢ ◑ E VISA JCB. ✗
45 rm ☕ 310/420000.

Trattoria Favorita, via Francesco Duodo 33 ☏ 5261626, Fax 5267296, « Outdoor summer service » – AE ⓢ ◑ E VISA
closed Monday and 15 January-15 February – **Meals** a la carte 46/74000.

in Burano 50 mn by boat from Fondamenta Nuove CT and 32 mn by boat from Punta Sabbioni – ✉ **30012** :

Al Gatto Nero-da Ruggero, ☏ 730120, Fax 735570, ⛱, Typical trattoria – AE ⓢ ◑ E VISA
closed Monday, 30 October-15 November and 30 January-10 February – **Meals** a la carte 43/75000.

in Torcello 50 mn by boat from Fondamenta Nuove CT and 37 mn by boat from Punta Sabbioni – ✉ **30012** Burano :

Locanda Cipriani, ☏ 730150, Fax 735433, « Summer service in garden » – ▤. AE ⓢ ◑ E VISA
closed Tuesday and January-18 February – **Meals** a la carte 82/115000 (15 %).

Ostaria al Ponte del Diavolo, ☏ 730401, Fax 730250, « Outdoor summer service », ⛱ – AE ⓢ E VISA JCB
closed January, February, Thursday and dinner except Saturday – **Meals** a la carte 57/89000 (10 %).

Norway

Norge

OSLO

PRACTICAL INFORMATION

LOCAL CURRENCY

Norwegian Kroner: 100 NOK = 15.81 USD ($) (Jan. 96)

TOURIST INFORMATION

The telephone number and address of the Tourist Information office is given in the text under ℹ.

FOREIGN EXCHANGE

In the Oslo area banks are usually open between 8.15am and 3.30pm, but in summertime, 15.5 - 31/8, they close at 3pm. Thursdays they are open till 5pm. Saturdays and Sundays closed.
Most large hotels, main airports and railway stations have exchange facilities. At Fornebu Airport the bank is open from 6.30am to 10.30pm on weekdays and 7.00am to 10pm on Sundays, all the year round.

MEALS

At lunchtime, follow the custom of the country and try the typical buffets of Scandinavian specialities.
At dinner, the a la carte and set menus will offer you more conventional cooking.

SHOPPING IN OSLO

(Knitware - Silver ware)

Your hotel porter should be able to help you with information.

CAR HIRE

The international car hire companies have branches in each major city. Your hotel porter should be able to give details and help you with your arrangements.

TIPPING IN NORWAY

A service charge is included in hotel and restaurant bills and it is up to the customer to give something in addition if he wants to.
The cloakroom is sometimes included in the bill, sometimes an extra charge is made.
Taxi drivers and baggage porters don't expect to be tipped. It is up to you if you want to give a gratuity.

SPEED LIMITS

The maximum permitted speed within built-up areas is 50 km/h - 31mph. Outside these areas it is 80 km/h - 50mph. Where there are other speed limits (lower or higher) they are signposted.

SEAT BELTS

The wearing of seat belts in Norway is compulsory for drivers and all passengers.

ANIMALS

Very strict quarantine regulations for animals exist from all countries except Sweden. NO dispensations.

Oslo

Norge 985 M 7 - pop. 458 364.

See : Bygdøy AZ : Viking Ships★★★ (Vikingeskipene), Folk Museum (Norsk Folkemuseum), Kon-Tiki and RA Museum★ (Kon-Tiki Museet), Polarship Fram★ (Fram Museet), Maritime Museum★ (Norsk Sjøfartsmuseum) – Frognerparken★ (Vigeland Sculptures★★) AX – City-Hall★ (Rådhuset) BY **H** – Munch Museum★ (Munchmuseet) CY – National Gallery★ (Nasjonalgalleriet) BY **M1** – Akershus Castle★ (Akershus Festning) BZ – Historical Museum★ (Historisk Museum) BY **M2**.

Outskirts : Holmenkollen★★ (NW : 10 km) : Ski Jump★, Ski Museum★ AX – Tryvann Tower★★ (Tryvannstårnet) (NW : 14 km) : ☼★★ AX – Sonja Henie-Onstad Art Centre★ (Henie-Onstads Kultursenter) (W : 12 km) AY.

18 Oslo Golfklubb ☎ 22 50 44 02.

✈ Fornebu SW : 8 km ☎ 67 59 67 16 – SAS : Oslo City, Stenersg. 1 a ☎ Business travel : 22 17 00 10 (Europe and Overseas) 22 17 00 20 (Domestics and Scandinavia), Vacation travel : 22 42 77 60 – Air Terminal : Havnegata, main railway station, seaside.

⛴ Copenhagen, Frederikshavn, Kiel, Hirtshals : contact tourist information centre (see below).

ℹ Norwegian Information Centre Vestbaneplassen 1 ☎ 22 83 00 50, Fax 22 83 81 50, and main railway station ☎ 22 17 11 24 – KNA (Kongelig Norsk Automobilklub) Royal Norwegian Automobile Club, Drammensveien 20C ☎ 22 56 19 00 – NAF (Norges Automobil Forbund), Storg. 2 ☎ 22 34 14 00.

Hamburg 888 – København 583 – Stockholm 522.

OSLO

Street	Grid	No.
Karl Johans gate	BCY	
Grensen	CY	
Lille Grensen	CY	37
Torggata	CY	
Apotekergata	CY	2
Biskop Gunnerus' gate	CY	8
Bygdøy kappellvei	AZ	9
Christian Frederiks plass	CY	10
Christiania torv	CY	13
Dronningens gate	CYZ	14
Dronning Mauds gate	BY	16
Edvard Storms gate	BX	17
Elisenbergveien	AX	19
Fredriksborgveien	AZ	20
Fridtjof Nansens plass	BY	21
Frimanns gate	CX	23
Gimleveien	AX	24
Grubbegata	CY	27
Haakon VII's gate	BY	28
Hammersborgtunnelen	CY	30
Jernbanetorget	CY	31
Josefines gate	ABX	32
Kristian Augusts gate	BCY	33
Langés gate	CX	34
Lapsetorvet	AY	35
Lassons gate	AY	36
Løchenveien	AZ	38
Løkkeveien	ABY	39
Munchs gate	CY	41
Munkedamsveien	ABY	42
Nedre Slottsgate	CYZ	44
Nedre Vollgate	BY	45
Nygata	CY	47
Pløens gate	CY	48
Professor Aschehougs pl.	CY	49
Professor Dahls gate	AX	51
Riddervolds gate	AX	52
Roald Amundsens gate	BY	53
Rosteds gate	CX	54
Ruseløkkveien	ABY	55
Rådhusplassen	BY	56
Schives gate	AX	57
Skillebekk	AY	59
Skovveien	AXY	60
Stortingsgata	BY	62
Stortorvet	CY	63
Strandgata	CZ	64
Sven Bruns gate	BX	65
Thor Olsens gate	CX	67
Tullins gate	BX	68
Uelands gate	CX	69
Vaterlandtunnelen	CY	71
Youngstorget	CY	72
Øvre Slottsgate	CY	73

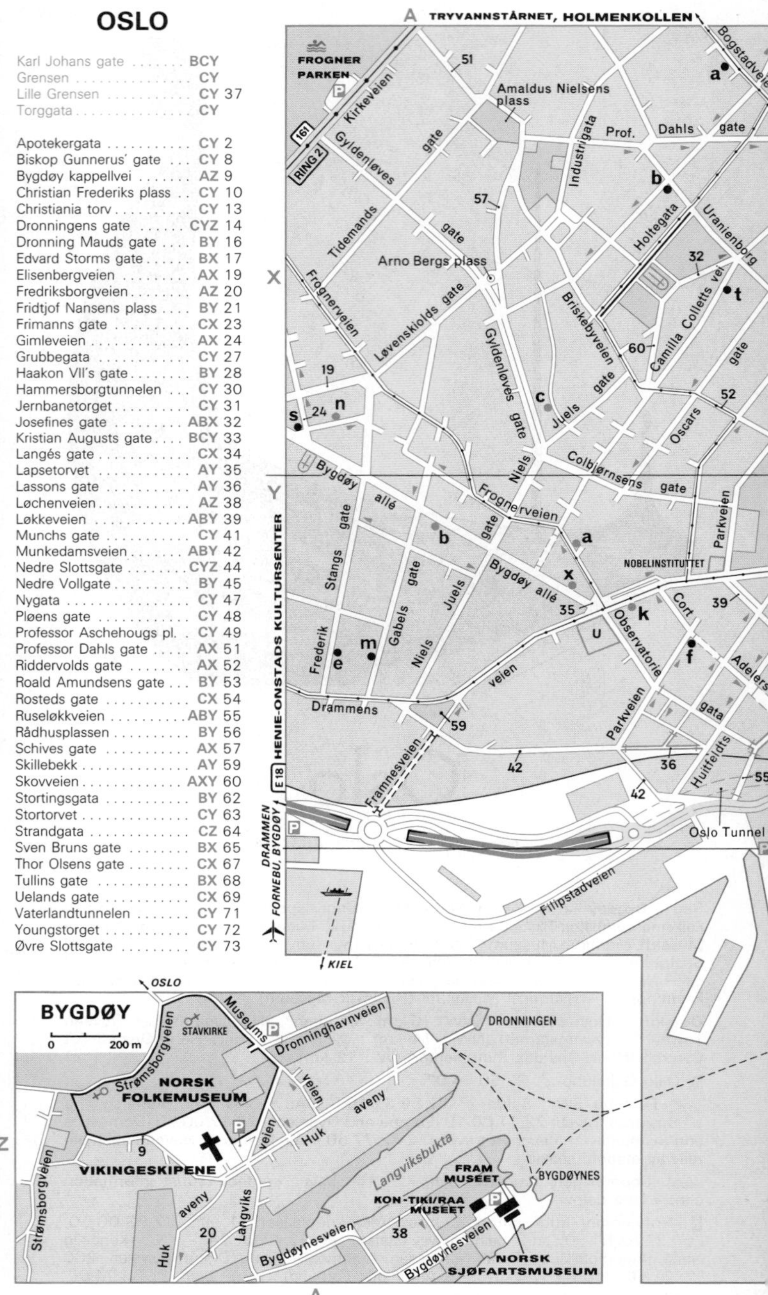

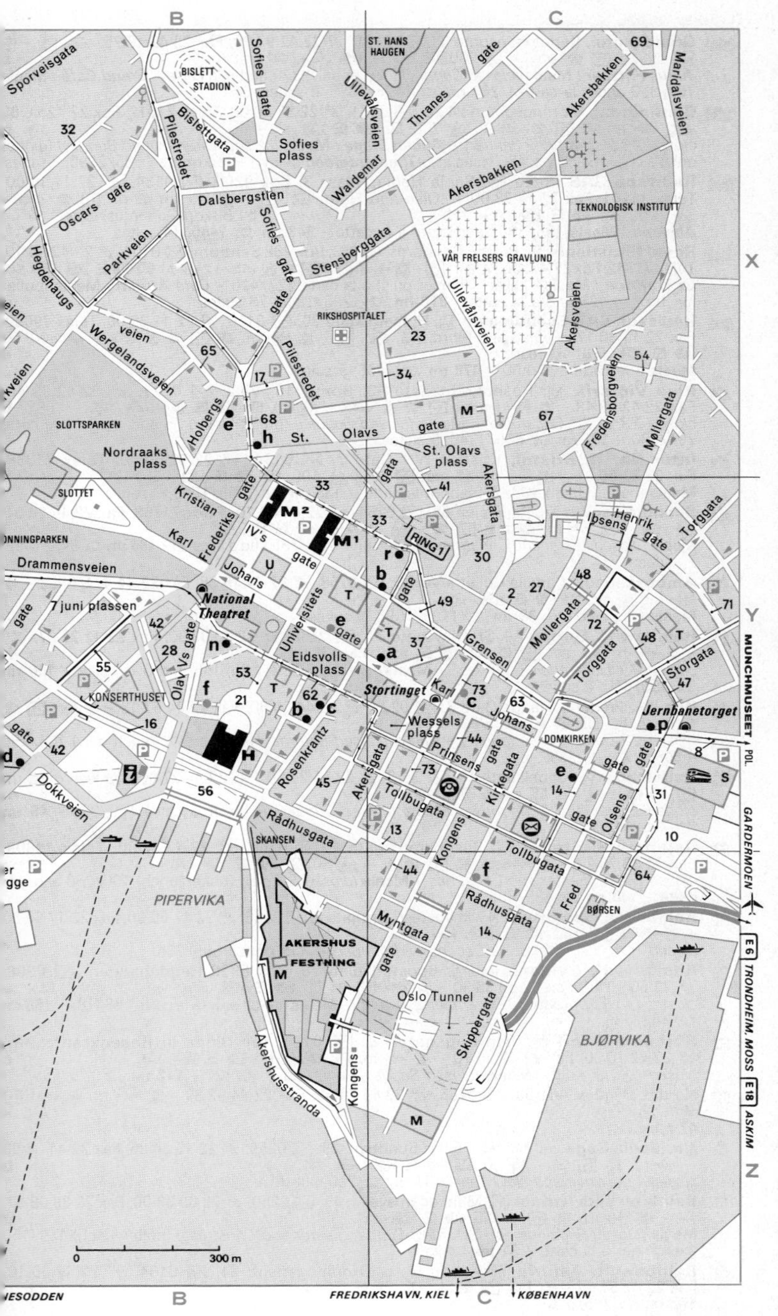

B
C
X
Y
N
ST. HANS HAUGEN
BISLETT STADION
Sporveisgata
Sofies gate
Sofies plass
Bislettgata
Pilestredet
Ullevålsveien
Thranes gate
Akersbakken
Maridalsveien
Waldemar
Dalsbergstien
Oscars gate
Parkveien
Heggedehaugs
Stensberggata
TEKNOLOGISK INSTITUTT
VÅR FRELSERS GRAVLUND
RIKSHOSPITALET
Akersveien
Wergelandsveien
Fredensborgveien
Møllergata
SLOTTSPARKEN
Holbergs
St. Olavs gate
St. Olavs plass
Nordraaks plass
Akersgata
SLOTTET
Kristian Frederiks gate
Karl Johans gate
IV's gate
Henrik Ibsens gate
Torggata
RING 1
Drammensveien
Universitets gate
National Theatret
7 juni plassen
Olav Vs gate
Eidsvolls plass
Grensen
KONSERTHUSET
Stortinget
Storgata
Jernbanetorget
Wessels plass
Prinsens gate
Kirkegata
DOMKIRKEN
Rosenkrantz
Tollbugata
Olsens
Dokkveien
Rådhusgata
SKANSEN
Kongens gate
PIPERVIKA
Myntgata
Fred
BØRSEN
AKERSHUS FESTNING
Oslo Tunnel
Skippergata
BJØRVIKA
Akershusstranda
MUNCHMUSEET
POL.
GARDERMOEN
E 6
TRONDHEIM, MOSS
E 18
ASKIM
0
300 m
NESODDEN
FREDRIKSHAVN, KIEL
KØBENHAVN

Grand Hotel, Karl Johansgate 31, ✉ 0101, ☎ 22 42 93 90, Fax 22 42 12 25, ≘s, ▢ - |‡| ⇔ rm ▤ TV ☎ ⇔ - 🏋 700. AE ① E VISA JCB. ✗ rest CY a
Julius Fritzner : **Meals** *(closed Sunday)* (dinner only) 370 and a la carte - *Grand Café :* **Meals** 167/350 and a la carte - **269 rm** ☐ 1475/1875, 6 suites.

Continental, Stortingsgaten 24-26, ✉ 0161, ☎ 22 82 40 00, Telex 71012, Fax 22 42 96 89 - |‡| ⇔ rm ▤ TV ☎ ⇔ - 🏋 200. AE ① E VISA. ✗ BY n
closed 23 December-2 January - Annen Etage : **Meals** *(closed Saturday and Sunday)* (dinner only) a la carte approx. 450 - (see also *Theatercaféen* below) - **150 rm** ☐ 1585/2290, 8 suites.

Radisson SAS Plaza M, Sonja Henies Plass 3, Box 9206, ✉ 0134, ☎ 22 17 10 00, Telex 11241, Fax 22 17 73 00, ≤ Olso and Fjord, ≘s, ▢ - |‡| ⇔ rm ▤ rm TV ☎ ⇔ - 🏋 1000. AE ① E VISA JCB. ✗ by Biskop Gunnerus' Gate CY
Abelone : **Meals** 155/390 and dinner a la carte - **648 rm** ☐ 1465, 14 suites.

Royal Christiania M, Biskop Gunnerus' Gate 3, Box 768 Sentrum, ✉ 0106, ☎ 22 42 94 10, Telex 71342, Fax 22 42 46 22, ≘s, ▢ - |‡| ⇔ rm ▤ TV ☎ ♿ ⇔ - 🏋 400. AE ① E VISA JCB. ✗
La Trattoria : **Meals** - Italian - (dinner only) a la carte 227/410 - *Café Atrium :* **Meals** (buffet lunch only) 198 and a la carte - **378 rm** ☐ 1295/1945, 73 suites. CY p

Radisson SAS Scandinavia M, Holbergsgate 30, ✉ 0166, ☎ 22 11 30 00, Telex 79090, Fax 22 11 30 17, ≤ Olso and Fjord, Lδ, ≘s, ▢ - |‡| ⇔ rm ▤ TV ☎ ♿ ⇔ - 🏋 800. AE ① E VISA JCB. ✗ rest BX e
Meals a la carte 225/400 - **479 rm** ☐ 1465, 9 suites.

Rica Victoria M, Rosenkrantzgate 13, Box 1718, Vika, ✉ 0121, ☎ 22 42 99 40, Fax 22 42 99 43 - |‡| ⇔ rm ▤ TV ☎ ♿ ⇔ - 🏋 50. AE ① E VISA JCB. ✗ BY b
closed 23 to 26 December - **Meals** *(closed Sunday)* (buffet lunch) 75 and dinner a la carte 294/380 - **192 rm** ☐ 815/1240, 5 suites.

Inter Nor H. Bristol, Kristian IV's Gate 7, ✉ 0164, ☎ 22 82 60 00, Telex 71668, Fax 22 82 60 01 - |‡| ⇔ rm ▤ rest TV ☎ - 🏋 100. AE ① E VISA JCB. ✗ CY b
Meals (buffet lunch) 137/275 and a la carte - **138 rm** ☐ 1095/1595, 3 suites.

Scandic Crown M, Parkveien 68, ✉ 0254, ☎ 22 44 69 70, Telex 71763, Fax 22 44 26 01, Lδ, ≘s - |‡| ⇔ rm ▤ rest TV ☎ - 🏋 100. AE ① E VISA. ✗ AY f
Meals *(closed Easter and Christmas)* (buffet lunch) 85/395 and a la carte - **183 rm** ☐ 845/1495, 2 suites.

Ambassadeur, Camilla Colletts Vei 15, ✉ 0258, ☎ 22 44 18 35, Fax 22 44 47 91, ≘s - |‡| ⇔ rm TV ☎. AE ① E VISA. ✗ AX t
Meals (see below) - **33 rm** ☐ 1195/1395, 8 suites.

Rainbow H. Europa M, St. Olavsgate 31, ✉ 0166, ☎ 22 20 99 90, Fax 22 11 27 27, ⛱ - |‡| ⇔ rm ▤ rest TV ☎. AE ① E VISA JCB. ✗ BX h
closed 19 December-2 January - **Meals** *(closed Sunday)* 35/155 and a la carte - **160 rm** ☐ 450/650, 4 suites.

Ritz ⛺, Frederik Stangs Gate 3, ✉ 0272, ☎ 22 44 39 60, Fax 22 44 67 13 - |‡| ⇔ TV ☎ P - 🏋 60. AE ① E VISA JCB. ✗ rest AY e
closed 23 December-2 January - **Meals** *(closed Saturday and Sunday)* (lunch only) 100/150 - **50 rm** ☐ 790/990.

Gabelshus ⛺, Gabelsgate 16, ✉ 0272, ☎ 22 55 22 60, Fax 22 44 27 30 - |‡| ⇔ rm ▤ rm TV ☎ P - 🏋 70. AE ① E VISA. ✗ AY m
closed Easter and Christmas - **Meals** *(closed Sunday lunch)* a la carte 160/385 - **45 rm** ☐ 790/1050.

Rainbow H. Stefan M, Rosenkrantzgate 1, ✉ 0159, ☎ 22 42 92 50, Telex 19809, Fax 22 33 70 22 - |‡| ⇔ rm ▤ TV ☎ ♿ - 🏋 50. AE ① E VISA. ✗ CY r
closed 5 days Easter and Christmas - **Meals** *(closed Sunday)* (buffet lunch) 100/250 and a la carte - **138 rm** ☐ 485/895.

Rainbow H. Spectrum M without rest., Brugate 7, ✉ 0186, ☎ 22 17 60 30, Fax 22 17 60 80 - |‡| ⇔ TV ♿. AE ① E VISA JCB. ✗
closed 3 to 8 April and 22 December-1 January - **119 rm** ☐ 585/785.

Rainbow H. Gyldenløve M, Bogstadveien 20, Box 5920 Hegdehaugen, ✉ 0308, ☎ 22 60 10 90, Fax 22 60 33 90 - |‡| ⇔ TV ☎. AE ① E VISA JCB. ✗ AX a
closed 4 to 9 April and 20 December-2 January - **Meals** (lunch only) a la carte 118/184 - **168 rm** ☐ 485/785.

Rainbow Cecil M, Stortingsgaten 8, ✉ 0161, (entrance in Rosenkrantzgate) ☎ 22 42 70 00, Fax 22 42 26 70 - |‡| ⇔ rm TV ☎ ♿. AE ① E VISA. ✗ BY c
closed 3 to 9 April - **Meals** *(closed Sunday)* (lunch only) 40/130 - **112 rm** ☐ 775/995.

Norum, Bygdøy Allé 53, ✉ 0265, ☎ 22 44 79 90, Fax 22 44 92 39 - |‡| ⇔ rm ▤ rest TV ☎ - 🏋 30 AX s
47 rm.

Norlandia Saga without rest., Eilert Sundtsgt. 39, ✉ 0259, ☎ 22 43 04 85, Fax 22 44 08 63 - ⇔ rm ▤ TV ☎ - 🏋 30. AE ① E VISA JCB. ✗ AX b
closed Christmas and New Year - **37 rm** ☐ 780/998.

Rainbow Vika Atrium M, Munkedamsveien 45, ✉ 0250, ☎ 22 83 33 00, Fax 22 83 09 57, Lδ - |‡| ⇔ rm ▤ TV ☎. AE ① E VISA. ✗ BY d
Meals *(closed Friday dinner, Saturday, Sunday, Easter and Christmas)* (buffet lunch) 110/150 and dinner a la carte - **91 rm** ☐ 965.

Rainbow H. Astoria M without rest., Dronningensgt. 21, ✉ 0154, ☎ 22 42 00 10, Fax 22 42 57 65 - |‡| ⇔ TV ☎ ♿. AE ① E VISA JCB. ✗ CY e
132 rm ☐ 395/620.

XXX ✿ **Bagatelle** (Hellstrøm), Bygdøy Allé 3, ✉ 0257, ☎ 22 44 63 97, Fax 22 43 64 20 – AE ⓓ E VISA AY x
closed Sunday, Easter and Christmas – **Meals** (booking essential) (dinner only) 450/780 and a la carte 450/650
Spec. Coquillages, crustacés et poissons, Perdrix de neige et chevreuil, "Norvégienne" aux mures jaunes.

XXX ✿ **Le Canard,** President Harbitz Gate 4, ✉ 0259, ☎ 22 42 40 28, Fax 22 55 65 65, « Tastefully decorated 1900 villa » – AE ⓓ E VISA AX c
closed Sunday and 4, 5 and 8 April – **Meals** (dinner only) 395/475 and a la carte 372/605
Spec. Parfait de foie de canard à la gelée de truffe, Magret de canard parfumé de raifort, sauce au cognac, Crème brûlée au miel d'acacia.

XXX **Statholdergaarden,** Rådhusgate 11, (entrance by Kirkegate) 1st floor, ✉ 0151, ☎ 22 41 88 00, Fax 22 41 22 24 – ▤. AE ⓓ E VISA CZ f
closed Sunday, 31 March-8 April, 3 weeks summer, Christmas-New Year and Bank Holidays – **Meals** (booking essential) (dinner only) 495 and a la carte.

XXX **Ambassadeur** (at Ambassadeur H.), Camilla Colletts Vei 15, ✉ 0258, ☎ 22 44 18 35, Fax 22 44 47 91, « Antique paintings » – ▤. AE ⓓ E VISA. ✻ AX t
closed Saturday and Sunday – **Meals** (dinner only) 375/595 and a la carte.

XXX **D'Artagnan,** Øvre Slottsgate 16 (1st floor), ✉ 0157, ☎ 22 41 50 62, Fax 22 42 77 41 – ▤. AE ⓓ E VISA JCB CY c
closed Saturday except September-January, Sunday, 8 July-5 August and 22 December-6 January – **Meals** (dinner only) 450/595 and a la carte.

XX ✿ **Spisestedet Feinschmecker,** Balchensgate 5, ✉ 0265, ☎ 22 44 17 77, Fax 22 56 11 39, « Tasteful decor » – ▤. AE ⓓ E VISA JCB AX n
closed Sunday, Easter and last 3 weeks July – **Meals** (booking essential) (dinner only) 385/475 and a la carte 428/498
Spec. Baked or grilled scallops, Sautéed breast of duck with braised endive, Crème brûlée flavoured with basil.

XX **Det Blå Kjøkken,** Drammensveien 30, ✉ 0255, ☎ 22 44 26 50, Fax 22 55 71 56 – ▤. AE ⓓ E VISA JCB AY k
closed Sunday and Bank Holidays – **Meals** (dinner only) 398/545 and a la carte.

XX **Blom,** Paléet, Karl Johansgate 41b, ✉ 0162, ☎ 22 42 73 00, Fax 22 42 04 28, « Collection of heraldic shields and paintings » – AE ⓓ E VISA BY e
closed Saturday lunch, Sunday, 1 week Easter, Christmas-New Year and Bank Holidays – **Meals** (buffet lunch) 165/395 and a la carte.

XX **Babette's Gjestehus,** 1 Rådhuspassagen, Fridtjof Nansens Pl. 2, ✉ 0160, ☎ 22 41 64 64, Fax 22 44 25 07, « Attractive decor » – ▤. AE ⓓ E VISA BY f
closed Sunday, 3 to 8 April, 24 to 27 and 31 December – **Meals** (booking essential) (dinner only) a la carte 343/419.

XX **Kastanjen,** Bygdøy Allé 18, ✉ 0262, ☎ 22 43 44 67, Fax 22 55 48 72 – AE ⓓ E VISA JCB AY b
closed Sunday, Easter and 2 weeks mid July – **Meals** (dinner only) 335/425 and a la carte.

XX **Theatercaféen** (at Continental H.), Stortingsgaten 24-26, ✉ 0161, ☎ 22 82 40 50, Telex 71012, Fax 22 41 20 94 – ⅍. AE ⓓ E VISA BY n
closed 25 December – **Meals** (booking essential) (buffet lunch) 30 and a la carte 242/428.

X **A Touch of France,** Øvre Slottsgate 16, ✉ 0157, ☎ 22 42 56 97, Fax 22 42 77 41 – ▤. AE ⓓ E VISA JCB CY c
closed Sunday and Monday lunch and 22 December-2 January – **Meals** - French style brasserie - 195/250 and a la carte.

at Fornebu Airport SW : 8 km by E 18 – AY – and Snarøyveien – ☎ 02 Oslo :

Radisson SAS Park, Fornebuparken, Box 185, ✉ 1324 Lysaker, ☎ 67 12 02 20, Telex 78745, Fax 67 12 00 11, « Private beach and park », Fδ, ≘s, ✻ – |‡| ⅍ rm ▤ rm TV ☎ ♿ P – 🔬 150. AE ⓓ E VISA JCB. ✻
Meals (buffet lunch) 175/230 and a la carte – **254 rm** ☐ 1315/1655.

at Sandvika SW : 14 km by E 18 – AY – exit E 68 – ☎ 02 Oslo :

Rica H. Oslofjord M, Sandviksveien 184, Box 160, ✉ 1300 Sandvika, ☎ 67 54 57 00, Fax 67 54 27 33, Fδ, ≘s – |‡| ⅍ rm ▤ TV ☎ ♿ ⟹ P – 🔬 400. AE ⓓ E VISA. ✻ rest
Orchidee : **Meals** (buffet lunch) 190 and a la carte 269/438 – ***Fontaine :*** **Meals** (buffet lunch) 190 and a la carte 282/542 – **228 rm** ☐ 1080/1315, 15 suites.

at Holmenkollen NW : 10 km by Bogstadveien – AX – Sørkedalsveien and Holmenkollveien – ☎ 02 Oslo :

Holmenkollen Park H. Rica M ⛷, Kongeveien 26, ✉ 0391, ☎ 22 92 20 00, Telex 72094, Fax 22 14 61 92, ≤ Oslo and Fjord, ≘s, ⛆ – |‡| ⅍ ▤ TV ☎ ♿ ⟹ P – 🔬 100. AE ⓓ E VISA JCB. ✻ rest
De Fem Stuer : **Meals** (buffet lunch) 275/450 and dinner a la carte – ***Galleriet :*** **Meals** (buffet lunch) 205/450 and a la carte – **221 rm** ☐ 795/1795, 11 suites.

Portugal

LISBON

PRACTICAL INFORMATION

LOCAL CURRENCY

Escudo: 100 PTE = 0.67 USD ($) (Jan. 96).

FOREIGN EXCHANGE

Hotels, restaurants and shops do not always accept foreign currencies and the tourist is therefore advised to change cheques and currency at banks, saving banks and exchange offices - The general opening times are as follows: banks 8.30am to noon and 1 to 2.45pm (closed on Saturdays), money changers 9.30am to 6pm (usually closed on Saturday afternoons and Sundays).

TRANSPORT

Taxis may be hailed when showing the green light or sign "Livre" on the windscreen.
Metro (subway) network. In each station complete information and plans will be found.

SHOPPING IN LISBON

Shops and boutiques are generally open from 9am to 1pm and 3 to 7pm - In Lisbon, the main shopping streets are: Rua Augusta, Rua do Carmo, Rua Garrett (Chiado), Rua do Ouro, Rua da Prata, Av. de Roma.

TIPPING

A service charge is added to all bills in hotels, restaurants and cafés; it is usual, however, to give an additional tip for personal service; 10 % of the fare or ticket price is also the usual amount given to taxi drivers and cinema and theatre usherettes.

SPEED LIMITS

The speed limit on motorways is 120 km/h - 74 mph, on other roads 90 km/h - 56 mph and in built up areas 50 km/h - 37 mph.

SEAT BELTS

The wearing of seat belts is compulsory for drivers and passengers.

THE FADO

The Lisbon Fado (songs) can be heard in restaurants in old parts of the town such as the Alfama, the Bairro Alto and the Mouraria. A selection of fado cabarets will be found at the end of the Lisbon restaurant list.

Lisbon

(LISBOA) 1100 P 440 P 2 - Pop. 662 782 - alt. 111 - ✆ 01.

SEE :

View over the city : ★★ from the Suspension Bridge (Ponte de 25 Abril), ★★ from Christ in Majesty (Cristo-Rei) S : 3,5 km.

CENTRE :

Pombaline Lisbon ★ (A Baixa Pombalina)

See : Rossio (square)★ KX - Praça do Comércio★★ KZ - Santa Justa lift (Elevador de Santa Justa ⋞★) KY.

Chiado and Up town **(Bairro Alto★)**

See : Do Carmo Church (Archeological Museum)★ KY **M1** - Rua Garret★ KY - São Roque Church★ (São João Baptista chappel★★) JX : São Roque Arte Sacra Museum★ (priestly ornaments★) JKX **M2** - São Pedro de Alcântara Belvedere★ ⋞★ (Miradouro de São Pedro de Alcântara) JX **A**.

Medieval Lisbon★★

See : Cathedral★★ (Sé : gothic tumulos★, grill★, tresor★) LY - Santa Luzia Belvedere★ (Miradouro de Santa Luzia) LY C - Decorative Arts Museum (Museu de Artes Decorativas★ : Fundação Ricardo do Espírito Santo Silva) LY **M3** - St. Georges Castle (Castelo de São Jorge)★★ (⋞★★) LX - Alfama★ LY.

Modern Lisbon

Avenida da Liberdade★ JV - Edward VII Park★ (Cold Greenhouse★) FS.

BELÉM★★ W : by Av. 24 de Julho EU.

See : Hieronymite Monastery★★ (Mosteiro dos Jerónimos) : Santa Maria Church★★★ (Igreja de Santa Maria : crypt★★, cloister★★★, tresor★) - Belém Tower★★ (Torre de Belém) - Monument to the Discoveries★ (Padrão dos Descobrimentos).

MUSEUMS

See : Museum of Ancient Art★★★ (Museu Nacional de Arte Antiga : polyptych da Adoração de São Vicente★★★, Anunciação★, Tentações de Santo Antão★★★, Twelve Apostles★, japanese folding screens★★, chapel★) EU **M7** - Calouste Gulbenkian Museum★★★ (Art collection) FR - Modern Art Center★ FR **M4** - Maritime Museum★★ (Museu da Marinha) W : by Av. 24 de Julho EU - Coach Museum★★ (Museu Nacional dos Coches) W : by Av. 24 de Julho EU - Azulejo Museum★★ NE : by Av. Infante D. Henrique MX - Water Museum da EPAL★ (Museu da Água da EPAL) NE : by Av. Infante D. Henrique MX - Costume Museum★ (Museu Nacional do Traje) N : by Av. da Liberdade - Military Museum (ceilings★) MY **M10**.

OTHER CURIOSITIES

See : Church of Mother of God★★ (Igreja da Madre de Deus : capítulo room★) NE : by Av. Infante D. Henrique MX - Marquis Fronteira Palace★★ (Palácio dos Marqueses de Fronteira : azulejos★★) ER - Zoologic Garden★ ER - São Vicente de Fora Church (azulejos★) MX - Free Waters Aqueduct★ (Aqueduto das Águas Livres) ES - Botanic Garden★ JV - Our Lady Fátima Church (Igreja de Nossa Senhora de Fátima : windows★) N : by Av. de Berna FR - Estrela Basílica (Basílica da Estrela : dome★, garden★) EU L - Old Conception Church (Igreja da Conceição Velha : south front★) LZ **V** - Monsanto Park★ (Parque florestal da Monsanto) ER - Campo de Santa Clara★ MX.

9, 18 Estoril Golf Club W : 25 km ✆ 468 01 76 - 18 Lisbon Sports Club NW : 20 km ✆ 431 00 77 - 18 Club de Campo de Lisboa S : 15 km ✆ 297 13 14

✈ Lisbon Airport N : 8 km from city centre ✆ 848 11 01 - T.A.P., Praça Marquês de Pombal 3, ✉ 1200, ✆ 386 40 80 and airport ✆ 841 50 00.

🚗 ✆ 887 75 09.

⛴ to Madeira : E.N.M., Rua de São Julião 5-1º, ✉ 1100, ✆ 887 01 21 and Cais Rocha Conde de Óbidos, ✉ 1350 ✆ 396 25 47.

ℹ Palácio Foz, Praça dos Restaudores ✆ 346 63 07, Fax 346 87 72 and airport ✆ 849 36 89 - **A.C.P.** Rua Rosa Araújo 24, ✉ 1200, ✆ 356 39 31, Telex 12581, Fax 57 47 32.

Madrid 658 - Bilbao/Bilbo 907 - Paris 1820 - Porto 314 - Sevilla 417.

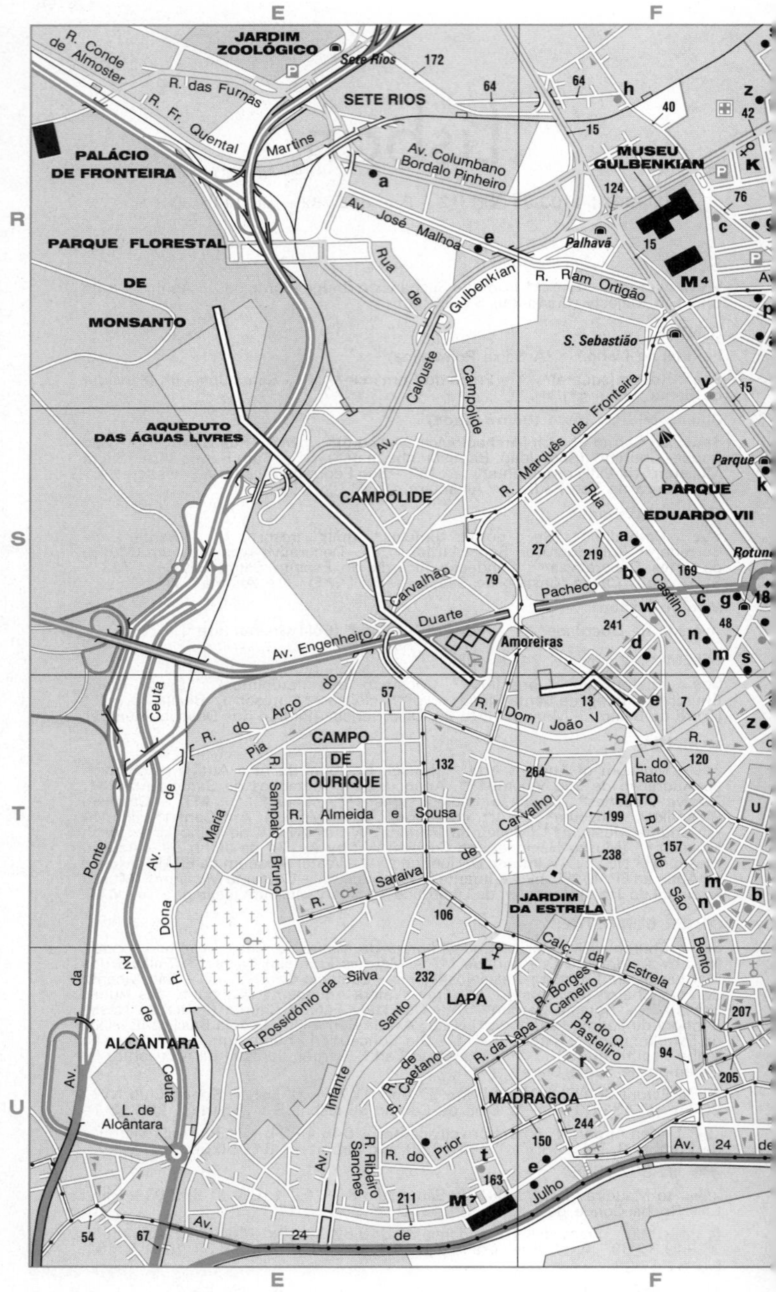
E
F
R
S
T
U
JARDIM ZOOLÓGICO
Sete Rios
SETE RIOS
R. Conde de Almoster
R. das Furnas
R. Fr. Quental
Martins
PALÁCIO DE FRONTEIRA
PARQUE FLORESTAL DE MONSANTO
Av. Columbano Bordalo Pinheiro
Av. José Malhoa
Rua de
Calouste Gulbenkian
Campolide
R. Ram Ortigão
MUSEU GULBENKIAN
Palhavã
S. Sebastião
AQUEDUTO DAS ÁGUAS LIVRES
CAMPOLIDE
R. Marquês da Fronteira
Rua Castilho
PARQUE EDUARDO VII
Parque
Carvalhão
Duarte
Pacheco
Av. Engenheiro
Amoreiras
R. Dom João V
L. do Rato
RATO
Av. Ceuta
Ponte
R. do Arco do
Pia
CAMPO DE OURIQUE
R. Sampaio Bruno
R. Almeida e Sousa
R. Saraiva de Carvalho
Maria
Av. Dona
R. de São Bento
JARDIM DA ESTRELA
Calç. da Estrela
R. Borges Carneiro
R. do Q. Pastelero
R. Possidónio da Silva
Santo
LAPA
R. da Lapa
R. de S. Caetano
Infante
MADRAGOA
Av. da
ALCÂNTARA
L. de Alcântara
Av. de Ceuta
R. Ribeiro Sanches
R. do Prior
Av.
Av. 24 de Julho
M 4
M 7
Rotun

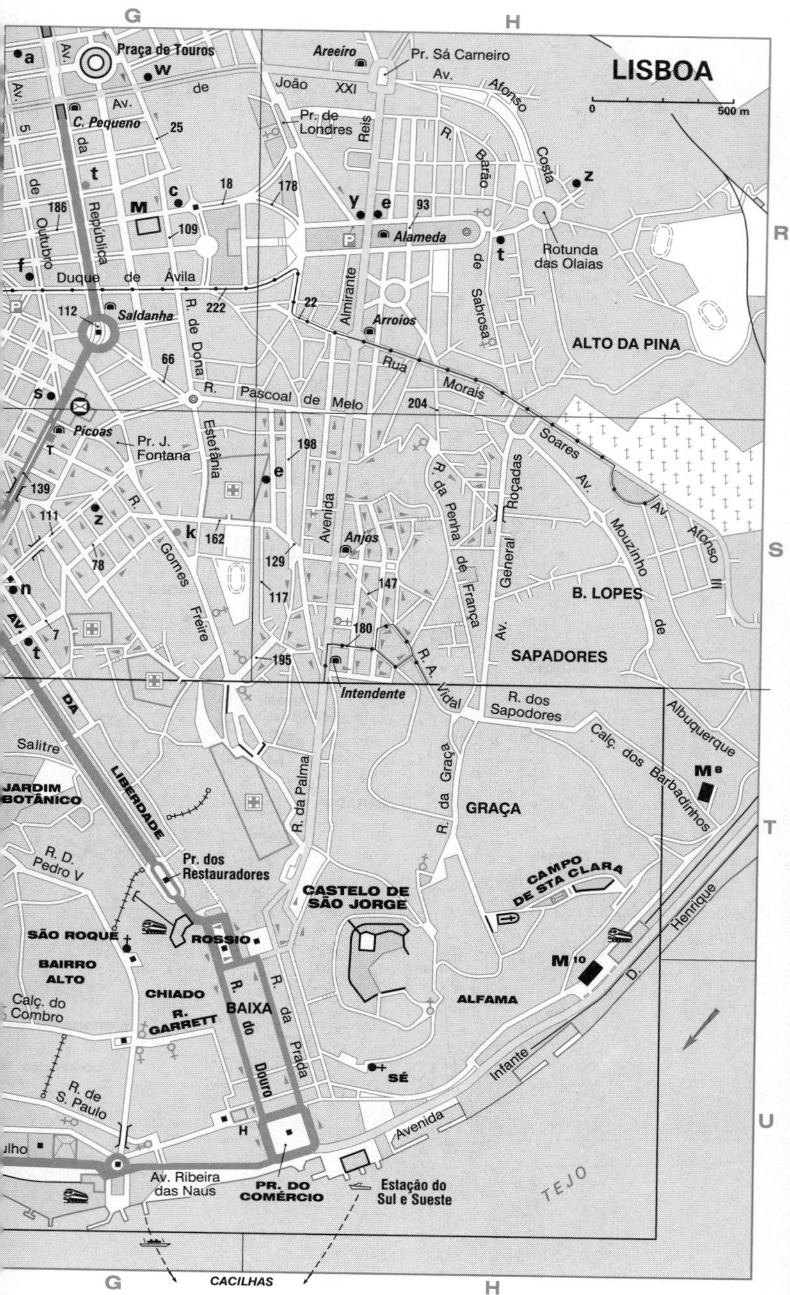
LISBOA
0
500 m
G
H
R
S
T
U
Praça de Touros
Areeiro
Pr. Sá Carneiro
C. Pequeno
Pr. de Londres
Alameda
Rotunda das Olaias
Duque de Ávila
Saldanha
Arroios
ALTO DA PINA
R. Pascoal de Melo
Picoas
Pr. J. Fontana
Estefânia
Anjos
Intendente
B. LOPES
SAPADORES
R. dos Sapadores
Calç. dos Barbadinhos
GRAÇA
JARDIM BOTÂNICO
Salitre
LIBERDADE
R. da Palma
Pr. dos Restauradores
CASTELO DE SÃO JORGE
CAMPO DE STA CLARA
SÃO ROQUE
ROSSIO
BAIRRO ALTO
CHIADO
R. GARRETT
BAIXA
R. do Douro
R. da Prada
ALFAMA
SÉ
Infante
D. Henrique
Avenida
Av. Ribeira das Naus
PR. DO COMÉRCIO
Estação do Sul e Sueste
TEJO
CACILHAS
R. D. Pedro V
Calç. do Combro
R. de S. Paulo
R. de Sabrosa
R. Barão
Av. Almirante Reis
Av. João XXI
Av. Afonso Costa
Rua Morais Soares
Av. General Roçadas
R. da Penha de França
R. A. Vidal
R. da Graça
Av. Mouzinho de Albuquerque
Av. Afonso III
R. Gomes Freire
Av. 5 de Outubro
Av. da República
R. de Dona
Av. da Liberdade

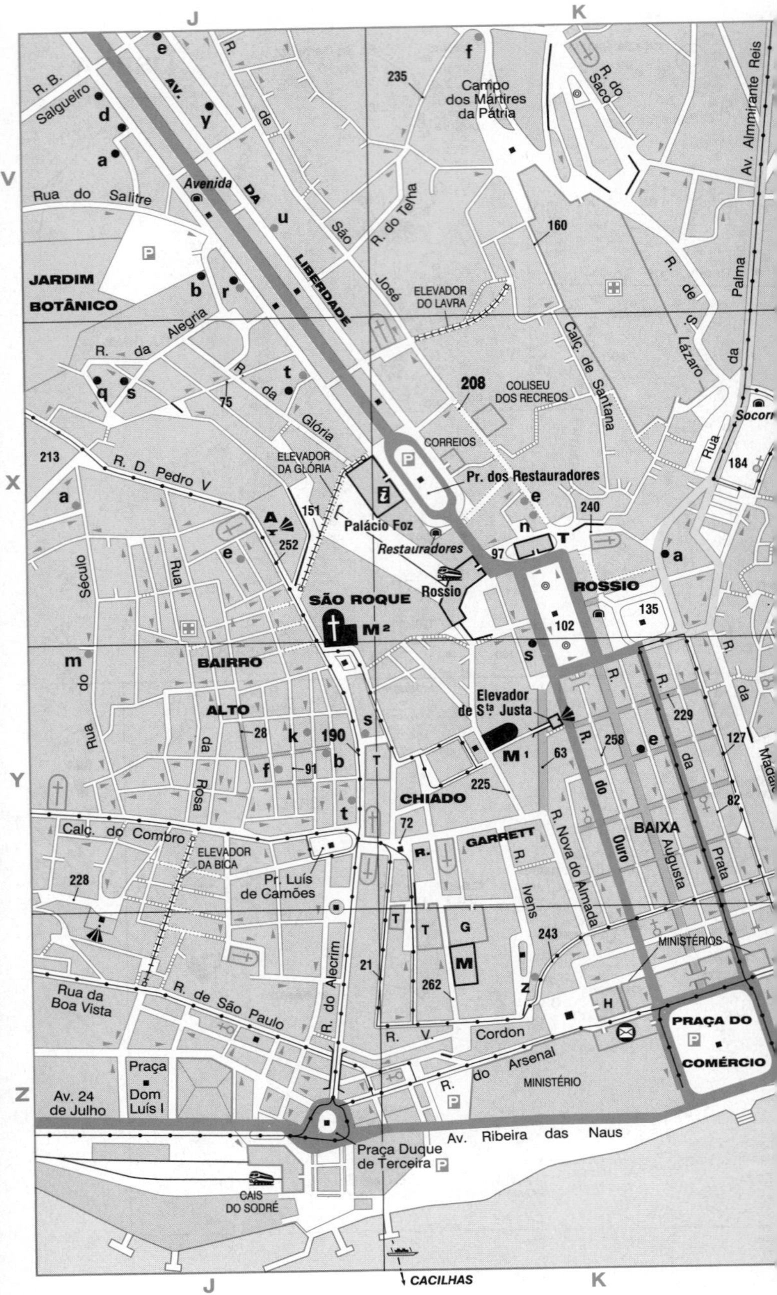
J
K
V
X
Y
Z
Campo dos Mártires da Pátria
R. do Saco
Av. Almirante Reis
Av. da Liberdade
Avenida
Rua do Salitre
R. B. Salgueiro
JARDIM BOTÂNICO
R. da Alegria
R. de São José
R. do Telha
ELEVADOR DO LAVRA
Calç. de Santana
R. de S. Lázaro
Rua da Palma
COLISEU DOS RECREIOS
CORREIOS
Pr. dos Restauradores
R. da Glória
ELEVADOR DA GLÓRIA
R. D. Pedro V
Palácio Foz
Restauradores
Rossio
ROSSIO
SÃO ROQUE
BAIRRO ALTO
Rua do Século
Rua da Rosa
Elevador de Sta. Justa
CHIADO
R. Garrett
R. Nova do Almada
R. do Ouro
R. Augusta
R. da Prata
BAIXA
Calç. do Combro
ELEVADOR DA BICA
Pr. Luís de Camões
R. Ivens
MINISTÉRIOS
Rua da Boa Vista
R. de São Paulo
R. do Alecrim
R. V. Cordon
R. do Arsenal
MINISTÉRIO
PRAÇA DO COMÉRCIO
Praça Dom Luís I
Av. 24 de Julho
Praça Duque de Terceira
Av. Ribeira das Naus
CAIS DO SODRÉ
CACILHAS
Socorro
Rua da Madalena

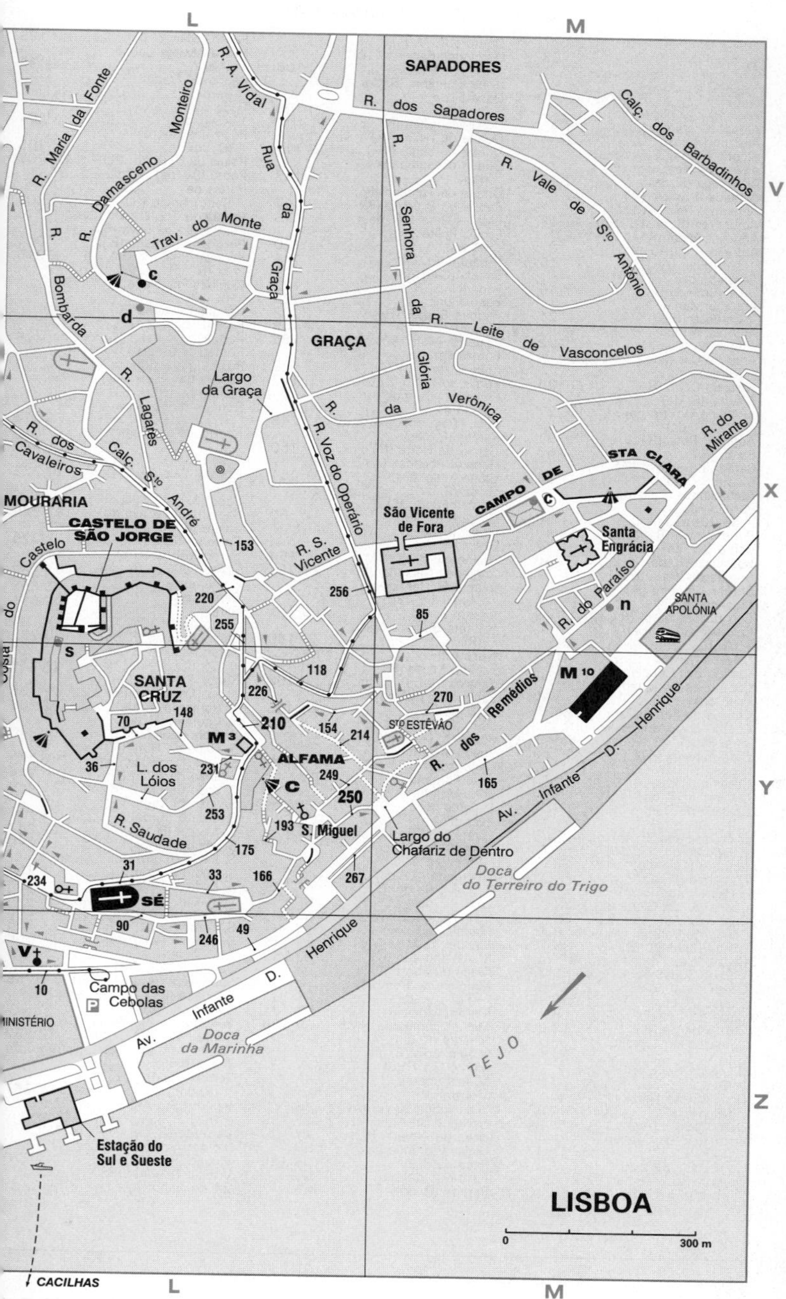

L
M
SAPADORES
R. dos Sapadores
Calç. dos Barbadinhos
R. Vale de Sto António
R. Senhora da Glória
R. A. Vidal
Rua da Graça
R. Maria da Fonte
Monteiro
R. Damasceno
Trav. do Monte
R. Bombarda
c
d
GRAÇA
R. Leite de Vasconcelos
Largo da Graça
R. Lagares
R. da Verónica
R. do Mirante
R. dos Cavaleiros
Calç. Sto André
R. Voz do Operário
MOURARIA
CASTELO DE SÃO JORGE
Castelo
R. S. Vicente
São Vicente de Fora
CAMPO DE STA CLARA
C
Santa Engrácia
R. do Paraíso
n
SANTA APOLÓNIA
153
220
256
85
255
S
SANTA CRUZ
118
226
270
M 10
R. dos Remédios
154
214
STO ESTÊVÃO
210
M 3
148
70
36
L. dos Lóios
231
ALFAMA
249
C
250
253
193
S. Miguel
R. Saudade
175
Largo do Chafariz de Dentro
165
Av. Infante D. Henrique
31
33
166
267
234
SÉ
Doca do Terreiro do Trigo
90
246
49
V
10
Campo das Cebolas
INISTÉRIO
Doca da Marinha
TEJO
Estação do Sul e Sueste
CACILHAS
V
X
Y
Z
LISBOA
0
300 m

STREET INDEX TO LISBOA TOWN PLANS

Centre : Av. da Liberdade, Rua Augusta, Rua do Ouro, Praça do Comércio, Praça Dom Pedro IV (Rossio), Praça dos Restauradores

Tivoli Lisboa, Av. da Liberdade 185, ✉ 1200, ☎ 353 01 81, Telex 12588, Fax 57 94 61, « Terrace with ≤ town », heated, - ▮ ▤ TV ☎ - 40/200. AE ⓓ E VISA. Meals 4800 - ***Grill Terraço :*** **Meals** a la carte 5650/8450 - ***Zodíaco :*** **Meals** a la carte 4550/6050 - **298 rm** ☐ 31000/35000, 29 suites. JV **d**

Sofitel Lisboa, Av. da Liberdade 125, ✉ 1250, ☎ 342 92 02, Telex 42557, Fax 342 92 22 - ▮ ▤ TV ☎ ♿ - 25/300. AE ⓓ E VISA JCB JV **r**
Meals (see rest. ***Cais da Avenida*** below) - ☐ 2000 - **166 rm** 33000, 4 suites.

Lisboa Plaza, Travessa do Salitre 7, ✉ 1200, ☎ 346 39 22, Telex 16402, Fax 347 16 30 - ▮ ▤ TV ☎ - 25/140. AE ⓓ E VISA JCB. JV **b**
Meals 3800 - **94 rm** ☐ 24000/29500, 12 suites.

Tivoli Jardim, Rua Julio Cesar Machado 7, ✉ 1200, ☎ 353 99 71, Telex 12172, Fax 355 65 66, heated, - ▮ ▤ TV ☎ P. AE ⓓ E VISA. JV **a**
Meals 4600 - **119 rm** ☐ 23500/29000.

Mundial, Rua D. Duarte 4, ✉ 1100, ☎ 886 31 01, Telex 12308, Fax 887 91 29, ≤ - ▮ ▤ TV ☎ P - 25/120. AE ⓓ E VISA JCB. KX **a**
Meals 3950 - **141 rm** ☐ 15750/19000, 6 suites.

Lisboa coffee shop only, Rua Barata Salgueiro 5, ✉ 1150, ☎ 355 41 31, Telex 60228, Fax 355 41 39 - ▮ ▤ TV ☎. AE ⓓ E VISA JCB. JV **e**
55 rm ☐ 15750/18750, 6 suites.

Veneza without rest, Av. da Liberdade 189, ✉ 1250, ☎ 352 26 18, Fax 352 66 78, « Old palace » - ▮ ▤ TV ☎ P. AE ⓓ E VISA JCB. JV **d**
36 rm ☐ 13000/16000.

Príncipe Real, Rua da Alegria 53, ✉ 1250, ☎ 346 01 16, Fax 342 21 04 - ▮ ▤ TV ☎. AE ⓓ E VISA JCB. JX **q**
Meals 2750 - **24 rm** ☐ 17500/21000.

Britânia without rest, Rua Rodrigues Sampaio 17, ✉ 1150, ☎ 315 50 16, Telex 13733, Fax 315 50 21 - ▮ ▤ TV ☎. AE ⓓ E VISA JCB. JV **y**
30 rm ☐ 16500/18500.

Metropole without rest, Praça do Rossio 30, ✉ 1100, ☎ 346 91 64, Fax 346 91 66 - ▮ ▤ TV ☎. AE ⓓ E VISA JCB KY **s**
36 rm ☐ 17000/19000.

Botánico without rest, Rua Mãe de Água 16, ✉ 1250, ☎ 342 03 92, Fax 342 01 25 - ▮ ▤ TV ☎. AE ⓓ E VISA. JX **s**
30 rm ☐ 10500/12000.

Albergaria Senhora do Monte without rest, Calçada do Monte 39, ✉ 1100, ☎ 886 60 02, Fax 887 77 83, ≤ São Jorge castle, town and river Tejo - ▮ ▤ TV ☎. AE ⓓ E VISA. LV **c**
28 rm ☐ 14500/17500.

Insulana without rest, Rua da Assunção 52, ✉ 1100, ☎ 342 76 25 - ▮ ▤ TV ☎. AE ⓓ E VISA. KY **e**
32 rm ☐ 7800/9000.

XXXX **Tágide,** Largo da Académia Nacional de Belas Artes 18, ✉ 1200, ☎ 342 07 20, Fax 347 18 80, ≤ - ▤. AE ⓓ E VISA JCB. KZ **z**
closed Saturday lunch and Sunday - **Meals** a la carte 6900/8000.

XXXX **Clara,** Campo dos Mártires da Pátria 49, ✉ 1150, ☎ 885 30 53, Fax 885 20 82, Garden-terrace - ▤. AE ⓓ E VISA. KV **f**
closed Saturday lunch, Sunday and 1 to 15 August - **Meals** a la carte 5000/6200.

XXXX **Tavares,** Rua da Misericórdia 37, ✉ 1200, ☎ 342 11 12, Fax 347 81 25, Late 19C decor - ▤. AE ⓓ E VISA JCB. JY **t**
closed Saturday and Sunday lunch - **Meals** a la carte 7100/9100.

XXX **Bachus,** Largo da Trindade 9, ✉ 1200, ☎ 342 28 28, Fax 342 12 60 - ▤. AE ⓓ E VISA JCB. JY **s**
closed Sunday - **Meals** a la carte approx. 6800.

XXX **Gambrinus,** Rua das Portas de Santo Antão 25, ✉ 1100, ☎ 342 14 66, Fax 346 50 32 - ▤. AE VISA. KX **n**
Meals a la carte 10000/13000.

XXX **Escorial,** Rua das Portas de Santo Antão 47, ✉ 1100, ☎ 346 44 29, Fax 346 37 58 - ▤. AE ⓓ E VISA JCB. KX **e**
Meals a la carte approx. 5840.

XXX **Cais da Avenida,** Av. da Liberdade 123, ✉ 1250, ☎ 342 92 24, Fax 342 92 22 - ▤. AE ⓓ E VISA JCB. JV **r**
Meals a la carte approx. 5100.

XXX **Jardim Tropical** with self-service, Av. da Liberdade 144, ✉ 1200, ☎ 342 20 70, Fax 342 31 24, « Tropical conservatory » - ▤. AE ⓓ E VISA JCB JV **u**
closed Sunday - **Meals** a la carte 4200/5750.

XXX **Casa do Leão,** Castelo de São Jorge, ✉ 1100, ☎ 887 59 62, Fax 887 63 29, ≤ - ▤. AE ⓓ E VISA. LXY **s**
Meals a la carte 4450/6950.

XX **Consenso,** Rua da Académia das Ciências 1, ✉ 1200, ☎ 343 13 13, Fax 343 13 12, « Modern decor in a rustic style » - ▤. AE ⓓ E VISA. ✻ JY **m**
closed Saturday lunch and Sunday - **Meals** a la carte 3800/7200.

XX **Via Graça,** Rua Damasceno Monteiro 9 B, ✉ 1100, ☎ 887 08 30, Fax 887 03 05, ← São Jorge castle, town and river Tejo - ▤. AE ⓓ E VISA JCB. ✻ LV **d**
closed Saturday lunch, Sunday lunch, and 15 to 30 August - **Meals** a la carte 3300/5600.

XX **O Faz Figura,** Rua do Paraíso 15 B, ✉ 1100, ☎ 886 89 81, ←, 籥 - ▤. AE ⓓ E VISA. ✻
closed Sunday - **Meals** a la carte 4500/6100. MX **n**

XX **Sancho,** Travessa da Glória 14, ✉ 1250, ☎ 346 97 80 - ▤. AE E VISA. ✻ JX **t**
closed Sunday - **Meals** a la carte 2500/4450.

X **Porta Branca,** Rua do Teixeira 35, ✉ 1250, ☎ 342 10 24, Fax 347 92 57 - ▤. AE ⓓ E VISA. ✻ JX **e**
closed Saturday lunch and Sunday - **Meals** a la carte approx. 3800.

X **Mercado de Santa Clara,** Campo de Santa Clara (at market), ✉ 1170, ☎ 887 39 86, Fax 887 39 86, ← - ▤. AE ⓓ E VISA. ✻ MX **c**
closed Sunday dinner, Monday and August - **Meals** a la carte approx. 4450.

East : Av. da Liberdade, Av. Almirante Reis, Av. Estados Unidos de América, Av. de Roma, Av. João XXI, Av. da República, Praça Marquês de Pombal

Holiday Inn Crowne Plaza, Av. Marechal Craveiro Lopes 390, ✉ 1700, ☎ 759 96 39, Telex 61170, Fax 758 66 05, Fö - |♦| ▤ TV ☎ ♿ ⇔ - 🏛 25/200. AE ⓓ E VISA JCB. ✻ N : by Av. da República GR
Meals a la carte 6250/8500 - ☕ 1600 - **205 rm** 19500, 16 suites.

Holiday Inn Lisboa, Av. António José de Almeida 28 A, ✉ 1000, ☎ 793 52 22, Telex 60330, Fax 793 66 72, Fö - |♦| ▤ TV ☎ ♿ ⇔ - 🏛 25/250. AE ⓓ E VISA JCB. ✻ GR **c**
Meals 3850 - ☕ 1500 - **161 rm** 29000/34000, 8 suites.

Altis Park H., Av. Engenheiro Arantes e Oliveira 9, ✉ 1900, ☎ 846 08 66, Fax 846 08 38 - |♦| ▤ TV ☎ ♿ ⇔ - 🏛 25/400. AE ⓓ E VISA. ✻ rest HR **z**
Meals 3650 - **285 rm** ☕ 20000/22000, 15 suites.

Lutécia, Av. Frei Miguel Contreiras 52, ✉ 1700, ☎ 80 31 21, Telex 12457, Fax 80 78 18, ← - |♦| ▤ TV ☎ - 🏛 25/100. AE ⓓ E VISA JCB. ✻ N : by Av. Almirante Reis HR
Meals a la carte approx. 4500 - **142 rm** ☕ 18000/21000, 8 suites.

Lisboa Alif H. without rest, Campo Pequeno 51, ✉ 1000, ☎ 795 24 64, Telex 64460, Fax 795 41 16 - |♦| ▤ TV ☎ ♿ ⇔ - 🏛 25/40. AE ⓓ E VISA. ✻ GR **w**
107 rm ☕ 9900/11500, 8 suites.

Sol Lisboa, Av. Duque de Loulé 41, ✉ 1050, ☎ 353 21 08, Telex 65522, Fax 353 18 65, ⛱ - |♦| ▤ TV ☎ ♿ ⇔. AE ⓓ E VISA. ✻ GS **z**
Meals *(closed Sunday)* a la carte approx. 5000 - ☕ 1200 - **80 rm** 23000/25000, 4 suites.

A. S. Lisboa without rest, Av. Almirante Reis 188, ✉ 1000, ☎ 847 30 25, Telex 44257, Fax 847 30 34 - |♦| ▤ TV ☎ - 🏛 25/80. AE ⓓ E VISA. ✻ HR **e**
75 rm ☕ 7900.

Presidente coffee shop only, Rua Alexandre Herculano 13, ✉ 1150, ☎ 353 95 01, Fax 352 02 72 - |♦| ▤ TV ☎ - 🏛 25/40. AE ⓓ E VISA. ✻ GS **t**
59 rm ☕ 13000/15000.

Dom Carlos without rest, Av. Duque de Loulé 121, ✉ 1050, ☎ 353 90 71, Fax 352 07 28 - |♦| ▤ TV ☎ - 🏛 25/40. AE ⓓ E VISA JCB. ✻ GS **n**
76 rm ☕ 14000/18000.

Roma, Av. de Roma 33, ✉ 1700, ☎ 796 77 61, Telex 16586, Fax 793 29 81, ←, ⛱ - |♦| ▤ TV ☎ - 🏛 25/230. AE ⓓ E VISA JCB. ✻ N : by Av. Almirante Reis HR
Meals 3000 - **263 rm** ☕ 12000/15000.

Fonte Luminosa without rest, Alameda D. Afonso Enriques 70 - 6°, ✉ 1000, ☎ 80 48 96, Fax 80 90 03 - |♦| ▤ TV ☎. E VISA. ✻ HR **y**
37 rm ☕ 6000/7500.

Dom João without rest, Rua José Estêvão 43, ✉ 1100, ☎ 52 41 71, Fax 352 45 69 - |♦| ▤ TV ☎. AE ⓓ E VISA. ✻ - **18 rm** ☕ 7500/8500. HS **e**

XXXX **Antonio Clara - Clube de Empresários,** Av. da República 38, ✉ 1050, ☎ 796 63 80, Fax 797 41 44, « Former old palace » - ▤ Ⓟ. AE ⓓ E VISA JCB. ✻ GR **t**
closed Sunday and 15 to 31 August - **Meals** a la carte approx. 6100.

X **Celta,** Rua Gomes Freire 148, ✉ 1150, ☎ 57 30 69 - ▤. AE ⓓ E VISA GS **k**
closed Sunday - **Meals** a la carte 2870/3930.

West : Av. da Liberdade, Av. 24 de Julho, Av. da India, Av. Infante Santo, Av. de Berna, Av. António Augusto de Aguiar, Largo de Alcântara, Praça Marquês de Pombal, Praça de Espanha.

Ritz Inter-Continental, Rua Rodrigo da Fonseca 88, ✉ 1093, ☎ 69 20 20, Telex 12589, Fax 69 17 83, ←, 籥 - |♦| ▤ TV ☎ ♿ ⇔ Ⓟ - 🏛 25/600. AE ⓓ E VISA JCB. ✻ FS **b**
Varanda : **Meals** a la carte 5500/8100 - ☕ 2500 - **265 rm** 42000/48000, 20 suites.

Sheraton Lisboa H., Rua Latino Coelho 1, ✉ 1097, ☎ 57 57 57, Telex 12774, Fax 54 71 64, ←, Fö, ⛱ heated - |♦| ▤ TV ☎ ♿ ⇔ - 🏛 25/550. AE ⓓ E VISA JCB. ✻ GR **s**
Alfama Grill *(closed Saturday, Sunday and August)* **Meals** a la carte 6400/8700 - ***Caravela :*** **Meals** a la carte 5450/6750 - ☕ 2000 - **377 rm** 35000/38000, 7 suites.

Da Lapa, Rua do Pau de Bandeira 4, 1200, 395 00 05, Fax 395 06 65, « Park with waterfall and » – 25/225. AE E VISA. EU **a**
Meals a la carte 5750/7600 – 2750 – **78 rm** 32000/35000, 8 suites.

Le Meridien Lisboa, Rua Castilho 149, 1000, 69 09 00, Telex 64315, Fax 69 32 31, – – 25/550. AE E VISA. FS **a**
Meals 4500 - ***Brasserie des Amis* : Meals** a la carte 6200/7200 – 2300 – **313 rm** 38500/42500, 17 suites.

Alfa Lisboa, Av. Columbano Bordalo Pinheiro, 1000, 726 21 21, Telex 18477, Fax 726 30 31, – – 25/600. AE E VISA. ER **a**
A Aldeia* : Meals** a la carte 3850/4150 - ***Grill Pombalino *(closed Saturday, Sunday, Bank Holidays and August)* **Meals** a la carte 5100/5300 – **440 rm** 25000/30000.

Altis, Rua Castilho 11, 1200, 357 92 62, Telex 13314, Fax 354 86 96, – – 25/700. AE E VISA. FT **z**
Girasol *(lunch only except Sunday)* **Meals** a la carte 4000/5600 - ***Grill Dom Fernando*** *(closed Sunday)* **Meals** a la carte 4850/5700 – **290 rm** 28000/32000, 13 suites.

Novotel Lisboa, Av. José Malhoa 1642, 1000, 726 60 22, Telex 40114, Fax 726 64 96, – – 25/300. AE E VISA ER **e**
Meals a la carte approx. 4100 – 1100 – **246 rm** 13800/14800.

Continental, Rua Laura Alves 9, 1000, 793 50 05, Telex 65632, Fax 797 36 69 – – 25/180. AE E VISA JCB. FR **z**
D. Miguel *(closed Saturday and Sunday)* **Meals** a la carte approx. 5700 - ***Coffee Shop Continental* : Meals** a la carte approx. 4300 – **210 rm** 21500/24500, 10 suites.

Real Parque, Av. Luís Bívar 67, 1050, 57 01 01, Fax 57 07 50 – – 25/100. AE E VISA. FR **a**
Meals 4500 -***Cozinha do Real* : Meals** a la carte 4900/6300 – **147 rm** 25000/28000, 6 suites.

Lisboa Penta, Av. dos Combatentes, 1600, 726 40 54, Telex 18437, Fax 726 42 81, – – 25/600. AE E VISA JCB. rest
***Grill Passarola* : Meals** a la carte approx. 7210 - ***Verde Pino* : Meals** a la carte approx. 3500 – **584 rm** 20000/24000, 4 suites. NW : by Av. A. Augusto de Aguiar FR

Fénix, Praça Marquês de Pombal 8, 1200, 386 21 21, Telex 12170, Fax 386 01 31 – – 25/100. AE E VISA JCB. FS **g**
***Bodegón* : Meals** a la carte 4200/6350 – **119 rm** 18500/20500, 4 suites.

Zurique, Rua Ivone Silva 18, 1050, 793 71 11, Telex 65349, Fax 793 72 90, – – 25/150. AE E VISA. FR **s**
Meals 3000 – **248 rm** 13000/15000, 4 suites.

Diplomático, Rua Castilho 74, 1200, 386 20 41, Telex 13713, Fax 386 21 55 – – 25/60. AE E VISA JCB. FS **c**
Meals *(closed Saturday, Sunday and Bank Holidays)* a la carte 2900/4100 – **73 rm** 15000/17500, 17 suites.

Flórida without rest, Rua Duque de Palmela 32, 1200, 57 61 45, Telex 12256, Fax 54 35 84 – – 25/100. AE E VISA JCB. FS **x**
108 rm 16000/19200.

Barcelona without rest, Rua Laura Alves 10, 1000, 795 42 73, Fax 795 42 81, – – 25/230. AE E VISA JCB. FR **q**
120 rm 15500/18500, 5 suites.

Quality H., Campo Grande 7, 1700, 795 75 55, Fax 795 75 00 – – 25/50. AE E VISA. N : by Av. da República GR
Meals 3000 – **80 rm** 20000/23000, 2 suites.

Executive Inn without rest, Av. Conde Valbom 56, 1050, 795 11 57, Telex 65618, Fax 795 11 66 – . AE E VISA JCB. FR **g**
72 rm 12000/14000.

Amazónia H. coffee shop only, Travessa Fábrica dos Pentes 12, 1250, 387 70 06, Telex 66361, Fax 387 90 90, heated – – 25/200. AE E VISA. FS **d**
192 rm 11250/12800.

Dom Manuel I without rest, Av. Duque de Ávila 189, 1050, 57 61 60, Telex 43558, Fax 57 69 85, « Tasteful decor » – . AE E VISA JCB. FR **p**
64 rm 11500/13000.

Dom Rodrigo Suite H. coffee shop only, Rua Rodrigo da Fonseca 44, 1200, 386 38 00, Fax 386 30 00, – . AE E VISA. FS **m**
800 – **57 suites** 19000/23000.

Nacional without rest, Rua Castilho 34, 1250, 355 44 33, Fax 356 11 22 – . AE E VISA. FST **s**
59 rm 13200/15400, 2 suites.

York House, Rua das Janelas Verdes 32, 1200, 396 25 44, Telex 16791, Fax 397 27 93, « Former 16C convent. Portuguese decor » – . AE E VISA JCB. FU **e**
Meals a la carte approx. 4500 – **31 rm** 25200/31500, 3 suites.

Miraparque, Av. Sidónio Pais 12, 1000, 352 42 86, Telex 16745, Fax 57 89 20 – . AE E VISA. FS **k**
Meals 3000 – **101 rm** 10500/12000.

As Janelas Verdes without rest, Rua das Janelas Verdes 47, ⊠ 1200, ☎ 396 81 43, Fax 396 81 44, Late 18C house with attractive courtyard – ▤ TV ☎. AE ⓓ E VISA JCB. ✻
17 rm ☕ 25000/27000. FU **e**

Da Torre, Rua dos Jerónimos 8, ⊠ 1400, ☎ 363 62 62, Fax 364 59 95 – |♦| ▤ TV ☎ – 🏛 25/50. AE ⓓ E VISA JCB W : by Av. 24 de Julho EU
Meals (see rest. ***São Jerónimo*** below) – **50 rm** ☕ 11850/14700.

Flamingo, Rua Castilho 41, ⊠ 1250, ☎ 386 21 91, Fax 386 12 16 – |♦| ▤ TV ☎. AE ⓓ E VISA. ✻ FS **n**
Meals 3000 – **39 rm** ☕ 13500/16500.

Berna without rest, Av. António Serpa 13, ⊠ 1050, ☎ 793 67 67, Telex 62516, Fax 793 62 78 – |♦| ▤ TV ☎ 🚗 – 🏛 25/140. AE ⓓ E VISA. ✻ GR **a**
240 rm ☕ 9000/10000.

Eduardo VII, Av. Fontes Pereira de Melo 5, ⊠ 1050, ☎ 353 01 41, Telex 18340, Fax 353 38 79, ≤ – |♦| ▤ TV ☎ – 🏛 25/60. AE ⓓ E VISA. ✻ FS **p**
Meals 3600 – **119 rm** ☕ 12500/14700, 2 suites.

Imperador without rest, Av. 5 de Outubro 55, ⊠ 1050, ☎ 352 48 84, Fax 352 65 37 – |♦| ▤ TV ☎. AE ⓓ E VISA. ✻ GR **f**
☕ 500 – **43 rm** 8000/9000.

XXX **Casa da Comida,** Travessa das Amoreiras 1, ⊠ 1200, ☎ 388 53 76, Fax 387 51 32, « Patio with plants » – ▤. AE ⓓ E VISA. ✻ FT **e**
closed Saturday lunch and Sunday – **Meals** a la carte 6000/10900.

XXX **Pabe,** Rua Duque de Palmela 27 A, ⊠ 1250, ☎ 353 74 84, Fax 353 64 37, English pub style – ▤. AE ⓓ E VISA. ✻ FS **x**
Meals a la carte 4800/7500.

XXX ✿ **Conventual,** Praça das Flores 45, ⊠ 1200, ☎ 60 91 96, Fax 60 91 96 – ▤. AE ⓓ E VISA
closed Saturday lunch, Bank Holidays lunch and Sunday – **Meals** a la carte 3800/6300
Spec. Concha de mariscos gratinada. Lombo de linguado com molho de marisco. Pato com champagne e pimenta rosa. FT **m**

XXX **São Jerónimo,** Rua dos Jerónimos 12, ⊠ 1400, ☎ 364 87 97, Fax 363 26 92, Modern decor – ▤. AE ⓓ E VISA. ✻ W : by Av. 24 de Julho EU
closed Saturday lunch and Sunday – **Meals** a la carte approx. 5150.

XXX **Chester,** Rua Rodrigo da Fonseca 87 D, ⊠ 1250, ☎ 385 73 47, Fax 388 78 11, Meat specialities – ▤. AE ⓓ E VISA JCB. ✻ FS **w**
closed Sunday – **Meals** a la carte 5150/6980.

XX **Saraiva's,** Rua Eng. Canto Resende 3, ⊠ 1050, ☎ 54 06 09, Fax 353 19 87, Modern decor – ▤. AE ⓓ E VISA JCB. ✻ FR **v**
closed Saturday and Bank Holidays – **Meals** a la carte approx. 5500.

XX **Espelho d'Água,** Av. de Brasilia, ⊠ 1400, ☎ 301 73 73, Fax 363 26 92, ≤, 🍽, Lakeside setting. Modern decor – ▤. AE ⓓ E VISA. ✻ W : by Av. 24 de Julho EU
closed Saturday lunch and Sunday – **Meals** a la carte approx. 6200.

XX **Adega Tía Matilde,** Rua da Beneficência 77, ⊠ 1600, ☎ 797 21 72, Fax 793 90 00 – ▤. AE ⓓ E VISA. ✻ FR **h**
closed Saturday dinner and Sunday – **Meals** a la carte 4035/6750.

XX **O Nobre,** Rua das Mercês 71, ⊠ 1300, ☎ 363 38 27, Fax 364 91 07 – ▤. AE E VISA
closed Saturday lunch and Sunday – **Meals** a la carte 4440/5740. W: by Av. 24 de Julho EU

XX **O Polícia,** Rua Marquês Sá da Bandeira 112, ⊠ 1050, ☎ 796 35 05, Fax 796 02 19 – ▤. E VISA. ✻ FR **c**
closed Saturday dinner and Sunday – **Meals** a la carte approx. 4500.

X **Xêlê Bananas,** Praça das Flores 29, ⊠ 1200, ☎ 395 25 15, Tropical style decor – ▤. AE ⓓ E VISA – **Meals** a la carte 3500/5350. FT **n**

X **Sua Excelência,** Rua do Conde 34, ⊠ 1200, ☎ 60 36 14, Fax 60 36 14 – ▤. AE ⓓ E VISA
closed Saturday lunch, Sunday lunch, Wednesday and September – **Meals** a la carte 3650/6600. EU **t**

Typical atmosphere :

XX **O Faia,** Rua da Barroca 56, ⊠ 1200, ☎ 342 67 42, Fax 342 19 23, Fado cabaret – ▤. AE ⓓ E VISA. ✻ JY **f**
closed Sunday – **Meals** (dinner only) a la carte 5150/6400.

XX **Sr. Vinho,** Rua do Meio-à-Lapa 18, ⊠ 1200, ☎ 397 74 56, Fax 395 20 72, Fado cabaret – ▤. AE ⓓ E VISA JCB. ✻ FU **r**
closed Sunday – **Meals** (dinner only) a la carte approx. 7500.

XX **A Severa,** Rua das Gáveas 51, ⊠ 1200, ☎ 342 83 14, Fax 346 40 06, Fados at dinner – ▤. AE ⓓ E VISA JCB. ✻ JY **b**
closed Thursday – **Meals** a la carte 5500/7600.

X **Adega Machado,** Rua do Norte 91, ⊠ 1200, ☎ 342 87 13, Fax 346 75 07, Fado cabaret – ▤. AE ⓓ E VISA JCB. ✻ JY **k**
closed Monday – **Meals** (dinner only) a la carte 6000/7500.

X **D'Avis,** Rua do Grilo 98, ⊠ 1900, ☎ 868 13 54, Fax 868 13 54, Alentejo rest., « Typical decor » – ▤. ⓓ E VISA JCB E : Av. Infante D. Henrique MX
closed Sunday and August – **Meals** a la carte 2800/3500.

Spain

España

MADRID - BARCELONA - MÁLAGA
MARBELLA - SEVILLA - VALENCIA

PRACTICAL INFORMATION

LOCAL CURRENCY

Peseta: 100 ESP = 0,82 USD ($) (Jan. 96)

TOURIST INFORMATION

The telephone number and address of the Tourist Information offices is given in the text of the towns under ☒.

FOREIGN EXCHANGE

Banks are usually open fron 9am to 2pm (12.30pm on Saturdays).
Exchange offices in Sevilla and Valencia airports open from 9am to 2pm, in Barcelona airport from 9am to 2pm and 7 to 11pm. In Madrid and Málaga airports, offices operate a 24-hour service.

TRANSPORT

Taxis may be hailed when showing the green light or sign "Libre" on the windscreen.
Madrid, Barcelona and Valencia have a Metro (subway) network. In each station complete information and plans will be found.

SHOPPING

In the index of street names, those printed in red are where the principal shops are found.
The big stores are easy to find in town centres; they are open from 10am to 8pm.
Exclusive shops and boutiques are open from 10am to 2pm and 5 to 8pm - In Madrid they will be found in Serrano, Princesa and the Centre; in Barcelona, Passeig de Gracia, Diagonal and the Rambla de Catalunya.
Second-hand goods and antiques: El Rastro (Flea Market), Las Cortes, Serrano in Madrid; in Barcelona, Les Encantes (Flea Market), Barrio Gótico.

TIPPING

Hotel, restaurant and café bills always include service in the total charge. Nevertheless it is usual to leave the staff a small gratuity which may vary depending upon the district and the service given. Doormen, porters and taxi-drivers are used to being tipped.

SPEED LIMITS

The maximum permitted speed on motorways is 120 km/h - 74 mph, and 90 km/h - 56 mph on other roads.

SEAT BELTS

The wearing of seat belts is compulsory for drivers and passengers.

"TAPAS"

Bars serving "tapas" (typical spanish food to be eaten with a glass of wine or an aperitif) will usually be found in central, busy or old quarters of towns. In Madrid, search out the Calle de Cuchilleros (Plaza Mayor) or to the Calle Cardenal Cisneros (Glorieta de Bilbao).

Madrid

Madrid 28000 P 444 K 19 - Pop. 3 084 673 - alt. 646 - 91.

See : The Prado Museum★★★ (Museo del Prado) NY - Casón del Buen Retiro★ NY - The Old Madrid★ : Plaza Mayor★★ KY, Plaza de la Villa★ KY, Vistillas Gardens KYZ. (✻★), San Francisco El Grande Church (chairs★, sacristy chair★) KZ - Oriente Quarter★★ : Royal Palace (Palacio Real)★★ KX (Palace★ : throne room★, Real Armería★★, Royal Carriage Museum★ DY **M1**, Campo del Moro★), Descalzas Reales Convent★★ KLX (Convento de las Descalzas Reales), Encarnación Royal Monastery★ KX (Real Monasterio de la Encarnación) From España Building ⋟★ KV, University City★ (Ciudad Universitaria) DV, Moncloa lighthouse (✻★★) (Faro de la Moncloa) DV, West Park★ (Parque del Oeste) DV, Country House★ (Casa de Campo) DX, Zoo★★ W by Casa de Campo DX - El Madrid de los Borbones★★ : Plaza de la Cibeles★ MNX, Paseo del Prado★ MNXZ, Thyssen-Bornemisza Museum★★★ MY **M6**, Reina Sofia Art Center National Museum★ (El Guernica★★) MZ - Army Museum★ (Museo del Ejército) NY, Puerta de Alcalá★ NX, Parque del Buen Retiro★★ NYZ.

Other Curiosities : Archeological National Museum★★ (Dama de Elche★★★) NV - Lázaro Galdiano Museum★★ (enamels and ivories collection★★★) HV **M4** - América Museum★ (Museo de América : Quimbayas tresor★, Trocortesiano Codex★★★) DV - Real Academia de Bellas Artes de San Fernando★ LX **M2** - San Antonio de la Florida (frescos★★) DX - Cerralbo Museum★ KV **M** - Wax Museum★ (Museo de Cera) NV - Sorolla Museum★ GV **M5** - Plaza Monumental de las Ventas★ JV **B** - City Museum (Museo de la Ciudad : maquettes★) HU.

Envir. : El Pardo (Royal Palace★ : tapestries★) - Capuchins Convent : lying Christ★ NW : 13 km by Av. Arco de la Victoria.

Racecourse of the Zarzuela NW : by Av. Arco de la Victoria - 18, 18 Puerta de Hierro ✆ 316 17 45 NW : by Av. Arco de la Victoria - 9, 18 Club de Campo ✆ 357 21 32 NW : by Av. Arco de la Victoria - 18 La Moraleja N : 11 km ✆ 650 07 00 - 9 Club Barberán SW : 10 km ✆ 509 11 40 - 18 Las Lomas - El Bosque SW : 18 km ✆ 616 75 00 - 18 Real Automóvil Club de España N : 28 km ✆ 657 00 11 - 18 Nuevo Club de Madrid, Las Matas W : 26 km ✆ 630 08 20 - 9 Somosaguas W : 10 km by Casa de Campo ✆ 352 16 47.

✈ Madrid-Barajas E : 13 km ✆ 305 83 44 - Iberia : Velázquez 130, ✉ 28006, ✆ 329 57 67 HV, and Aviaco, Maudes 51, ✉ 28003, ✉ 534 42 00 FV.

🚗 Chamartín ✆ 733 11 22.

Shipping Companies : Cia. Trasmediterránea, Pedro Muñoz Seca 2 NX, ✉ 28001, ✆ 431 07 00, Fax 431 08 04.

ℹ Princesa 1, ✉ 28008, ✆ 541 23 25, Duque de Medinaceli 2, ✉ 28014, ✆ 429 49 51 Pl. Mayor 3, ✉ 28012, ✆ 366 54 77, Chamartín Station, ✉ 28036, ✆ 315 99 76 and Barajas airport ✆ 305 86 56 - R.A.C.E. José Abascal 10, ✉ 28003, ✆ 447 32 00, Fax 593 20 64.

Paris (by Irún) 1310 - Barcelona 627 - Bilbao/Bilbo 397 - La Coruña/A Coruña 603 - Lisboa 653 - Málaga 548 - Porto 599 - Sevilla 550 - Valencia 351 - Zaragoza 322.

Centre : Paseo del Prado, Puerta del Sol, Gran Vía, Alcalá, Paseo de Recoletos, Plaza Mayor (plan pp. 6 and 7)

Palace, pl. de las Cortes 7, ✉ 28014, ✆ 429 75 51, Telex 23903, Fax 429 82 66 – ☎ – 25/600. AE E VISA JCB. rest MY **e**
Meals 4500 - ***La Cupola*** *(Italian rest, closed Saturday lunch and Sunday lunch)* **Meals** a la carte 5800/6400 – 2950 – **436 rm** 31000/40000, 20 suites.

Princesa, Princesa 40, ✉ 28008, ✆ 542 21 00, Telex 44378, Fax 542 73 28, – ☎ – 25/825. AE E VISA JCB. plan p. 4 DEV **z**
Meals 2700 – 1950 – **263 rm** 24900/31200, 12 suites.

Plaza, pl. de España, ✉ 28013, ✆ 547 12 00, Telex 27383, Fax 548 23 89, ← – ☎ – 25/350. AE E VISA JCB. KV **s**
Meals 3500 – 1450 – **294 rm** 17500/21900, 12 suites.

Tryp Ambassador, Cuesta de Santo Domingo 5, ✉ 28013, ✆ 541 67 00, Telex 49538, Fax 559 10 40 – ☎ – 25/280. AE E VISA JCB. KX **k**
Meals 2200 – 1200 – **163 rm** 17475/21900, 18 suites.

Liabeny, Salud 3, ✉ 28013, ✆ 531 90 00, Telex 49024, Fax 532 74 21 – ☎ – 25/125. AE E VISA. LX **c**
Meals 2800 – 950 – **224 rm** 11500/17000, 5 suites.

Moncloa Garden without rest, Serrano Jover 1, ✉ 28015, ✆ 542 45 82, Fax 542 71 69 – ☎. AE E VISA JCB. EV **c**
800 – **102 rm** 14600, 19 suites.

Emperador without rest, Gran Vía 53, ✉ 28013, ✆ 547 28 00, Telex 46261, Fax 547 28 17, – ☎ – 25/150. AE E VISA. KX **n**
1500 – **232 rm** 14800/18500.

Arosa coffee shop only, Salud 21, ✉ 28013, ✆ 532 16 00, Telex 43618, Fax 531 31 27 – ☎ – 25/60. AE E VISA JCB LX **q**
1100 – **139 rm** 11550/17850.

G.H. Reina Victoria, pl. de Santa Ana 14, ✉ 28012, ✆ 531 45 00, Telex 47547, Fax 522 03 07 – ☎ – 25/350. AE E VISA. LY **s**
Meals a la carte approx. 5400 – 1200 – **195 rm** 17475/21900, 6 suites.

Santo Domingo, pl. de Santo Domingo 13, ✉ 28013, ✆ 547 98 00, Fax 547 59 95 – ☎ – 25/60. AE E VISA JCB. rest KX **a**
Meals 3250 – 1275 – **120 rm** 14225/19950.

Mayorazgo, Flor Baja 3, ✉ 28013, ✆ 547 26 00, Telex 45647, Fax 541 24 85 – ☎ – 25/250. AE E VISA JCB. KV **c**
Meals 2200 – 1200 – **200 rm** 12000/16000.

El Coloso, Leganitos 13, ✉ 28013, ✆ 559 76 00, Telex 47017, Fax 547 49 68 – ☎ – 25/200. AE E VISA JCB. KX **y**
Meals 2900 – 1300 – **84 rm** 12100/13650.

Suecia, Marqués de Casa Riera 4, ✉ 28014, ✆ 531 69 00, Telex 22313, Fax 521 71 41 – ☎ – 25/150. AE E VISA JCB. MX **r**
Meals 4000 - ***Bellman*** *(Scandinavian rest)* **Meals** a la carte 3675/4275 – 1375 – **119 rm** 17900/21000, 9 suites.

Gaudí, Gran Vía 9, ✉ 28013, ✆ 531 22 22, Fax 531 54 69, – ☎ – 25/120. AE E VISA JCB. LX **s**
Meals 1650 – 1250 – **88 rm** 15500/18000.

Tryp Menfis, Gran Vía 74, ✉ 28013, ✆ 547 09 00, Telex 48773, Fax 547 51 99 – ☎. AE E VISA. KV **u**
Meals 1500 – 925 – **115 rm** 13875/17400.

Regina without rest, Alcalá 19, ✉ 28014, ✆ 521 47 25, Telex 27500, Fax 521 47 25 – ☎. AE E VISA. LX **v**
750 – **142 rm** 9050/11900.

Casón del Tormes without rest, Río 7, ✉ 28013, ✆ 541 97 46, Fax 541 18 52 – ☎. E VISA. KV **v**
650 – **63 rm** 8100/12000.

El Prado, Prado 11, ✉ 28014, ✆ 369 02 34, Fax 429 28 29 – ☎ – 25/50. AE E VISA. LY **a**
Meals *(closed Sunday)* 1600 – 650 – **47 rm** 14000/17500.

Mercator coffee shop only, Atocha 123, ✉ 28012, ✆ 429 05 00, Telex 46129, Fax 369 12 52 – ☎ P. AE E VISA NZ **b**
800 – **89 rm** 8150/11350.

Carlos V without rest, Maestro Vitoria 5, ✉ 28013, ✆ 531 41 00, Telex 48547, Fax 531 37 61 – ☎. AE E VISA JCB. LX **f**
67 rm 9345/11760.

Atlántico without rest, Gran Vía 38 - 3°, ✉ 28013, ✆ 522 64 80, Telex 43142, Fax 531 02 10 – ☎. AE E VISA JCB. LX **e**
700 – **80 rm** 9310/12305.

MADRID

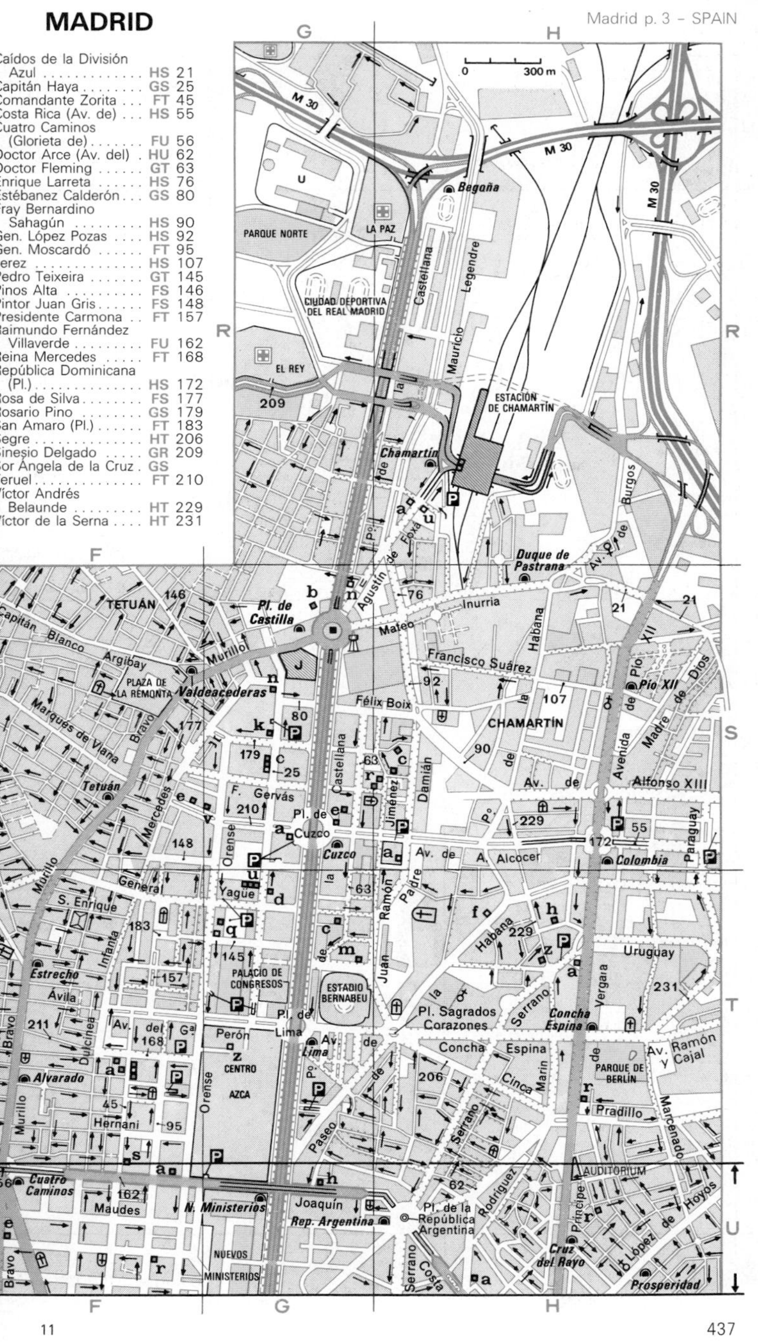

Caídos de la División Azul . . . . HS 21
Capitán Haya . . . . GS 25
Comandante Zorita . . . FT 45
Costa Rica (Av. de) . . . HS 55
Cuatro Caminos (Glorieta de) . . . . FU 56
Doctor Arce (Av. del) . HU 62
Doctor Fleming . . . . . . GT 63
Enrique Larreta . . . . . . HS 76
Estébanez Calderón . . . GS 80
Fray Bernardino Sahagún . . . . HS 90
Gen. López Pozas . . . . HS 92
Gen. Moscardó . . . . . . FT 95
Jerez . . . . HS 107
Pedro Teixeira . . . . GT 145
Pinos Alta . . . . FS 146
Pintor Juan Gris . . . . . . FS 148
Presidente Carmona . . FT 157
Raimundo Fernández Villaverde . . . . FU 162
Reina Mercedes . . . . . FT 168
República Dominicana (Pl.) . . . . HS 172
Rosa de Silva . . . . FS 177
Rosario Pino . . . . GS 179
San Amaro (Pl.) . . . . . . FT 183
Segre . . . . HT 206
Sinesio Delgado . . . . . GR 209
Sor Ángela de la Cruz . GS
Teruel . . . . FT 210
Víctor Andrés Belaunde . . . . HT 229
Víctor de la Serna . . . . HT 231
M 30
0 300 m
Begoña
PARQUE NORTE
LA PAZ
CIUDAD DEPORTIVA DEL REAL MADRID
Castellana
Legendre
Mauricio
EL REY
ESTACIÓN DE CHAMARTÍN
Chamartín
Agustín de Foxá
Duque de Pastrana
Burgos
TETUÁN
Pl. de Castilla
Mateo Inurria
Francisco Suárez
Habana
Pío XII
Madre de Dios
Capitán Blanco Argibay
Murillo
PLAZA DE LA REMONTA
Valdeacederas
Marqués de Viana
Bravo Murillo
Félix Boix
CHAMARTÍN
Tetuán
Mercedes
F. Gervás
Pl. de Cuzco
Cuzco
Orense
Jiménez
Damián
Av. de Alfonso XIII
Paraguay
Colombia
Av. de A. Alcocer
General Yagüe
S. Enrique
Infanta
Juan Ramón
Padre
Uruguay
Vergara
Estrecho
PALACIO DE CONGRESOS
ESTADIO BERNABEU
Ávila
Dulcinea
Pl. de Lima
Av. de Lima
Pl. Sagrados Corazones
Serrano
Concha Espina
Av. Ramón y Cajal
Perón
CENTRO AZCA
Alvarado
Cinca
Marín
PARQUE DE BERLÍN
Hernani
Paseo
Pradillo
Marcenado
Cuatro Caminos
Maudes
N. Ministerios
Joaquín
Rep. Argentina
Pl. de la República Argentina
Rodríguez
AUDITORIUM
Príncipe
López de Hoyos
NUEVOS MINISTERIOS
Costa
Cruz del Rayo
Prosperidad

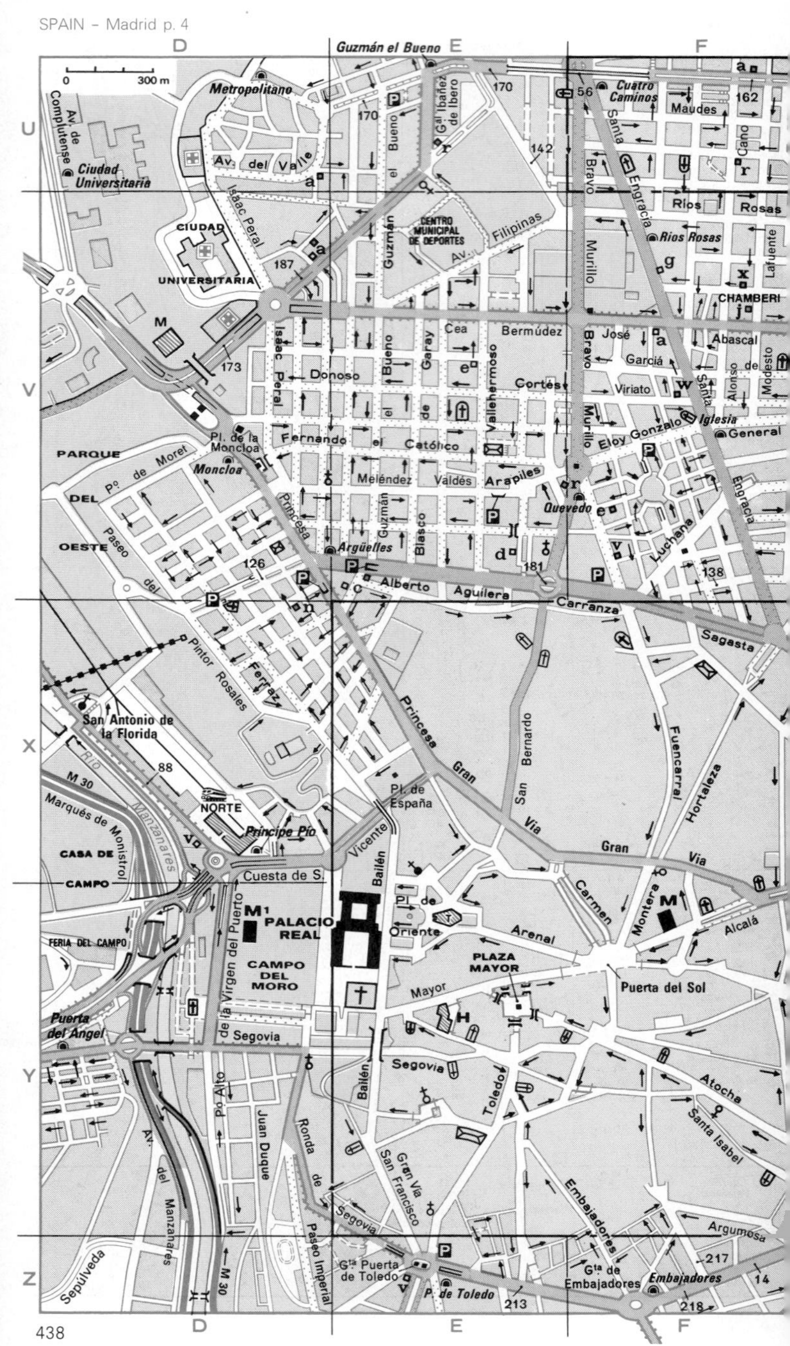
D
E
F
U
V
X
Y
Z
0
300 m
Guzmán el Bueno
Metropolitano
Cuatro Caminos
Av. de Complutense
Ciudad Universitaria
Av. del Valle
Isaac Peral
Gal Ibañez de Ibero
Bueno
el
Guzmán
Maudes
Cano
Ríos
Rosas
Ríos Rosas
Santa Engracia
Bravo
Murillo
Lafuente
CENTRO MUNICIPAL DE DEPORTES
Av. Filipinas
CIUDAD
UNIVERSITARIA
M
CHAMBERI
Cea
Bermúdez
José
Abascal
García
Alonso
Modesto
Donoso
Garay
Vallehermoso
Cortés
Viriato
Iglesia
General
Eloy Gonzalo
Fernando
el
Católico
Pl. de la Moncloa
Moncloa
PARQUE
DEL
OESTE
Pº de Moret
Paseo
del
Meléndez
Valdés
Arapiles
Quevedo
Luchana
Princesa
Blasco
de
Argüelles
Alberto
Aguilera
Carranza
Sagasta
Pintor
Rosales
Ferraz
San Antonio de la Florida
Río Manzanares
M 30
Marqués de Monistrol
CASA DE
CAMPO
NORTE
Príncipe Pío
Pl. de España
Gran Vía
San Bernardo
Fuencarral
Hortaleza
Vicente
Cuesta de S.
Bailén
M1
PALACIO
REAL
CAMPO
DEL
MORO
Pl. de Oriente
Arenal
Carmen
Montera
Alcalá
PLAZA
MAYOR
Puerta del Sol
Mayor
H
FERIA DEL CAMPO
Puerta del Angel
Segovia
de la Virgen del Puerto
Pº Alto
Juan Duque
Ronda de Segovia
Gran Vía San Francisco
Toledo
Atocha
Santa Isabel
Embajadores
Argumosa
Av. del Manzanares
Sepúlveda
Paseo Imperial
Gta Puerta de Toledo
P. de Toledo
Gta de Embajadores
170
142
56
162
187
173
126
181
138
88
213
217
218
14

MADRID

Atocha (Ronda de) . . FZ 14
Florida
(Paseo de la) . . . . . DX 88
Lagasca . . . . HVX 116
Marqués de
Salamanca (Pl.) . . . HV 125
Marqués de Urquijo . DV 126
Miguel Ángel . . . . . . GV 136
Reina Cristina
(Paseo) . . . . HZ 166
Reina Victoria (Av.) . . EU 170
Reyes Católicos (Av.) . DV 173
Ruiz Jiménez
(Glorieta) . . . . EV 181
San Francisco
de Sales (Pas.) . . . DV 187
Toledo
(Ronda de) . . . . . . EZ 213
Valencia . . . . FZ 217
Valencia
(Ronda de) . . . . . . FZ 218

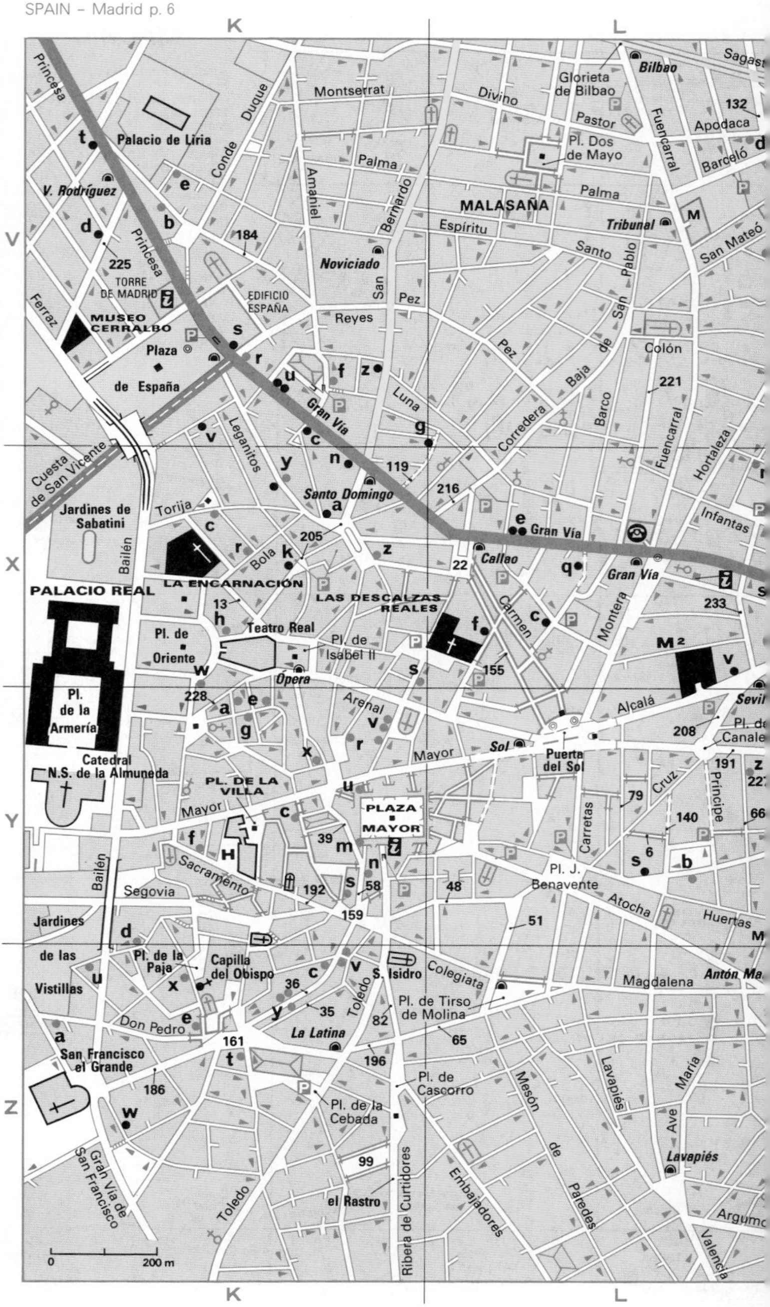

K
L
Princesa
Palacio de Liria
Conde Duque
Montserrat
Divino
Glorieta de Bilbao
Bilbao
Sagasta
Pastor
Fuencarral
132
Apodaca
Barceló
Pl. Dos de Mayo
Palma
Amaniel
San Bernardo
V. Rodríguez
MALASAÑA
Tribunal
Espíritu
Santo
San Pablo
San Mateo
184
225
Noviciado
TORRE DE MADRID
EDIFICIO ESPAÑA
Pez
Ferraz
MUSEO CERRALBO
Reyes
Baja de San Pablo
Colón
Plaza de España
Luna
Corredera
Barco
221
Gran Vía
Cuesta de San Vicente
Leganitos
119
Fuencarral
Hortaleza
Santo Domingo
216
Jardines de Sabatini
Torija
205
Gran Vía
Infantas
Bailén
Bola
Callao
22
Gran Vía
LA ENCARNACIÓN
PALACIO REAL
LAS DESCALZAS REALES
13
Carmen
Montera
233
Teatro Real
Pl. de Oriente
Pl. de Isabel II
Ópera
155
M²
228
Arenal
Alcalá
Sevilla
Pl. de la Armería
208
Pl. de Canalejas
Catedral N.S. de la Almuneda
Mayor
Sol
Puerta del Sol
191
PL. DE LA VILLA
Cruz
Príncipe
Mayor
PLAZA MAYOR
79
39
Carretas
140
Sacramento
192
58
6
Bailén
Segovia
48
Pl. J. Benavente
Atocha
Huertas
Jardines de las Vistillas
159
51
Pl. de la Paja
Capilla del Obispo
S. Isidro
Colegiata
Magdalena
Antón Martín
36
35
Toledo
82
Pl. de Tirso de Molina
Don Pedro
La Latina
65
161
San Francisco el Grande
196
Lavapiés
María
186
Pl. de Cascorro
Mesón de Paredes
Pl. de la Cebada
Ave
99
Lavapiés
Gran Vía de San Francisco
Toledo
el Rastro
Ribera de Curtidores
Embajadores
Argumosa
Valencia
0
200 m
V
X
Y
Z

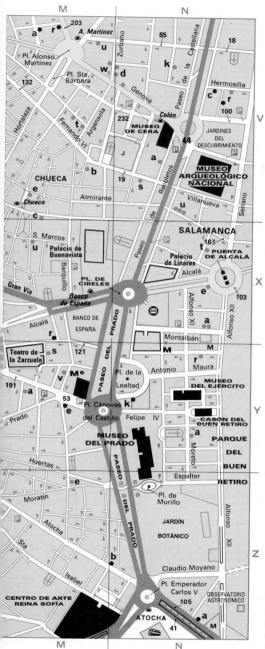

MADRID

The names of main shopping streets are indicated in red at the beginning of the list of streets.

Tryp Washington, Gran Vía 72, ⊠ 28013, ℘ 541 72 27, Telex 48773, Fax 547 51 99 – ▤ TV ☎. AE ◑ E VISA. ✈ KV **u**
Meals (at hotel *Tryp Menfis* above) – ☐ 925 – **120 rm** 11800/14800.

Los Condes without rest, Los Libreros 7, ⊠ 28004, ℘ 521 54 55, Telex 42730, Fax 521 78 82 – ▤ TV ☎. AE ◑ E VISA JCB. ✈ KLV **g**
☐ 660 – **68 rm** 7700/10450.

California without rest, Gran Vía 38, ⊠ 28013, ℘ 522 47 03, Fax 531 61 01 – ▤ TV ☎. AE ◑ VISA. ✈ LX **e**
☐ 350 – **25 rm** 6300/8375.

Paradis Madrid, Marqués de Cubas 14, ⊠ 28014, ℘ 429 73 03, Fax 429 32 95 – ▤. AE ◑ E VISA. ✈ MY **v**
closed Saturday lunch, Sunday, Bank Holidays and August – **Meals** a la carte 3550/5450.

El Landó, pl. Gabriel Miró 8, ⊠ 28005, ℘ 366 76 81, Tasteful decor – ▤. AE ◑ E VISA. ✈ KZ **a**
closed Sunday, Bank Holidays and August – **Meals** a la carte 3300/6300.

Moaña, Hileras 4, ⊠ 28013, ℘ 548 29 14, Fax 541 65 98, Galician rest – ▤ 🚗. AE ◑ E VISA JCB. ✈ KY **r**
closed Sunday – **Meals** a la carte 3440/5600.

Bajamar, Gran Vía 78, ⊠ 28013, ℘ 548 48 18, Fax 559 13 26, Seafood – ▤. AE ◑ E VISA JCB. ✈ KV **r**
Meals a la carte 4400/7100.

El Espejo, paseo de Recoletos 31, ⊠ 28004, ℘ 308 23 47, Fax 593 22 23, « Old Parisian style café » – ▤. AE ◑ E VISA. ✈ NV **a**
closed Saturday lunch – **Meals** a la carte 3800/4600.

Errota-Zar, Jovellanos 3-1°, ⊠ 28014, ℘ 531 25 64, Fax 531 25 64 – ▤. AE ◑ E VISA MY **s**
closed Sunday, Holy Week and August – **Meals** a la carte 3000/3950.

Ainhoa, Bárbara de Braganza 12, ⊠ 28004, ℘ 308 27 26, Basque rest – ▤. AE E VISA. ✈ NV **s**
closed Sunday and August – **Meals** a la carte approx. 4600.

Horno de Santa Teresa, Santa Teresa 12, ⊠ 28004, ℘ 308 66 98 – ▤. AE ◑ E VISA. ✈ MV **t**
closed Sunday, Bank Holidays, Holy Week and August – **Meals** a la carte approx. 4500.

Café de Oriente, pl. de Oriente 2, ⊠ 28013, ℘ 541 39 74, Fax 547 77 07, In a cellar – ▤. AE ◑ E VISA. ✈ KXY **w**
Meals a la carte 4350/6400.

La Gastroteca, pl. de Chueca 8, ⊠ 28004, ℘ 532 25 64, French rest – ▤. AE ◑ E VISA MV **e**
closed Saturday lunch, Sunday, Bank Holidays and August – **Meals** a la carte 4060/5100.

Platerías, pl. de Santa Ana 11, ⊠ 28012, ℘ 429 70 48, Early 20C style café – ▤. AE ◑ E VISA. ✈ LY **b**
closed Saturday lunch, Sunday, Holy Week and August – **Meals** a la carte approx. 4500.

El Asador de Aranda, Preciados 44, ⊠ 28013, ℘ 547 21 56, Roast lamb, « Castilian decor » – ▤. AE ◑ E VISA. ✈ KX **z**
closed Monday dinner and July – **Meals** a la carte approx. 4000.

Arce, Augusto Figueroa 32, ⊠ 28004, ℘ 522 04 40, Fax 522 59 13 – ▤. AE ◑ E VISA. ✈ MV **c**
closed Saturday lunch, Sunday and 15 to 31 August – **Meals** a la carte 5270/6390.

El Mentidero de la Villa, Santo Tomé 6, ⊠ 28004, ℘ 308 12 85, Fax 319 87 92, « Original decor » – ▤. AE ◑ E VISA JCB MV **b**
closed Saturday lunch and 15 to 31 August – **Meals** a la carte 3800/5050.

Julián de Tolosa, Cava Baja 18, ⊠ 28005, ℘ 365 82 10, Neorustic decor. Braised meat specialities – ▤. AE ◑ VISA JCB. ✈ KZ **c**
closed Sunday – **Meals** a la carte 4600/5100.

La Taberna de Liria, Duque de Liria 9, ⊠ 28015, ℘ 541 45 19 – ▤. AE ◑ E VISA. ✈
closed Saturday lunch, Sunday, Bank Holidays and last three weeks in August – **Meals** a la carte 4300/5200. KV **b**

Casa Gallega, pl. de San Miguel 8, ⊠ 28005, ℘ 547 30 55, Galician rest – ▤. AE ◑ E VISA JCB KY **c**
Meals a la carte 3650/5600.

La Ópera de Madrid, Amnistía 5, ⊠ 28013, ℘ 559 50 92 – ▤. AE ◑ E VISA. ✈ KY **g**
closed Sunday and August – **Meals** a la carte 3250/3750.

Casa Vallejo, San Lorenzo 9 ℘ 308 61 58 – ▤. AE E VISA LV **f**
closed Sunday, Monday lunch, Bank Holidays, Holy Week and August – **Meals** a la carte approx. 3500.

La Vaca Verónica, Jesús 7, ⊠ 28014, ℘ 429 78 27 – ▤. AE ◑ E VISA MZ **e**
closed Saturday lunch, Sunday, August and Christmas – **Meals** a la carte 3450/4050.

Ciao Madrid, Argensola 7, ⊠ 28004, ℘ 308 25 19, Italian rest – ▤. AE ◑ E VISA. ✈
closed Saturday lunch, Sunday and August – **Meals** a la carte 3100/4300. MV **t**

La Bola, Bola 5, ⊠ 28013, ℘ 547 69 30, Fax 547 04 63, Madrid style stew – ▤. ✈
closed Saturday dinner July-August and Sunday – **Meals** a la carte approx. 3400. KX **r**

Taberna Carmencita, Libertad 16, ✉ 28004, ☎ 531 66 12, Typical taverna - ▤. AE ⓓ E VISA. ✻ MX u
Meals a la carte approx. 3500.

Donzoko, Echegaray 3, ✉ 28014, ☎ 429 57 20, Fax 429 57 20, Japanese rest - ▤. AE ⓓ E VISA JCB. ✻ LY z
closed Sunday and 24 to 31 December - **Meals** a la carte 2850/5000.

La Esquina del Real, Amnistía 2, ✉ 28013, ☎ 559 43 09 - ▤. AE VISA. ✻ KY e
closed Saturday lunch and Sunday - **Meals** a la carte 4300/4600.

Ciao Madrid, Apodaca 20, ✉ 28004, ☎ 447 00 36, Italian rest - ▤. AE ⓓ E VISA. ✻
closed Saturday lunch, Sunday and September - Meals a la carte 3000/4200. LV d

El Ingenio, Leganitos 10, ✉ 28013, ☎ 541 91 33, Fax 547 35 34 - ▤. AE ⓓ E VISA. ✻
closed Sunday and Bank Holidays July-August - Meals a la carte 2245/3105. KX y

Typical atmosphere :

Posada de la Villa, Cava Baja 9, ✉ 28005, ☎ 366 18 80, Fax 366 18 80, « Castilian decor » - ▤. AE ⓓ E VISA. ✻ KZ v
closed Sunday dinner and August - **Meals** a la carte 3275/5125.

Botín, Cuchilleros 17, ✉ 28005, ☎ 366 42 17, Fax 366 84 94, Old Madrid decor. Typical cellar - ▤. AE ⓓ E VISA JCB. ✻ KY n
Meals a la carte 2730/5690.

Casa Lucio, Cava Baja 35, ✉ 28005, ☎ 365 32 52, Fax 366 48 66, Castilian decor - ▤. AE ⓓ VISA. ✻ KZ y
closed Saturday lunch and August - **Meals** a la carte 4000/5500.

Las Cuevas de Luis Candelas, Cuchilleros 1, ✉ 28005, ☎ 366 54 28, Fax 366 18 80, Old Madrid decor. Staff in bandit costumes - ▤. AE ⓓ E VISA KY m
Meals a la carte 3275/5125.

Taberna del Alabardero, Felipe V - 6, ✉ 28013, ☎ 547 25 77, Fax 547 77 07, Typical taverna - ▤. AE ⓓ E VISA. ✻ KX h
Meals a la carte 3600/5150.

Retiro, Salamanca, Ciudad Lineal : Paseo de la Castellana, Velázquez, Serrano, Goya, Príncipe de Vergara, Narváez (plan p.5 except where otherwise stated)

Ritz, pl. de la Lealtad 5, ✉ 28014, ☎ 521 28 57, Telex 43986, Fax 532 87 76, ☂, ⛹ - |‡| ▤ TV ☎ - 🏛 25/280. AE ⓓ E VISA JCB. ✻ rest plan p. 7 NY k
Meals a la carte 6100/7450 - ☕ 2750 - **127 rm** 37000/49500, 29 suites.

Villa Magna, paseo de la Castellana 22, ✉ 28046, ☎ 576 75 00, Telex 22914, Fax 575 31 58 - |‡| ▤ TV ☎ 🚗 - 🏛 25/250. AE ⓓ E VISA JCB. ✻ rest GV y
Meals 5800 - ***Berceo :*** **Meals** a la carte 5800/8350 - ☕ 2750 - **164 rm** 37000/40000, 18 suites.

Wellington, Velázquez 8, ✉ 28001, ☎ 575 44 00, Telex 22700, Fax 576 41 64, 🏊 - |‡| ▤ TV ☎ 🚗 - 🏛 25/300. AE ⓓ E VISA. ✻ HX t
Meals (see rest. ***El Fogón*** below) - ☕ 2250 - **198 rm** 20750/33250, 25 suites.

Sol Galgos, Claudio Coello 139, ✉ 28006, ☎ 562 66 00, Telex 43957, Fax 561 76 62 - |‡| ▤ TV ☎ 🚗 - 🏛 25/300. AE ⓓ E VISA JCB. ✻ HV a
Diábolo *(closed August)* **Meals** a la carte 3475/5150 - ☕ 1400 - **358 rm** 21000/26000.

Tryp Fénix, Hermosilla 2, ✉ 28001, ☎ 431 67 00, Telex 45639, Fax 576 06 61 - |‡| ▤ TV ☎ 🚗 - 🏛 25/100. AE ⓓ E VISA JCB. ✻ plan p. 7 NV c
Meals 2400 - ☕ 1550 - **213 rm** 21850/27350, 13 suites.

Meliá Avenida América, Juan Ignacio Luca de Tena 36, ✉ 28027, ☎ 320 30 30, Fax 320 14 40, 🏊 - |‡| ▤ TV ☎ ♿ 🚗 - 🏛 25/1200. AE ⓓ E VISA JCB. ✻
Meals 3550 - ☕ 1275 - **210 rm** 19500/24375, 18 suites. NE : by Av. de América HV

Sofitel Madrid-Aeropuerto, Campo de las Naciones, ✉ 28042, ☎ 721 00 70, Telex 45008, Fax 721 05 15, 🏊 - |‡| ▤ TV ☎ ♿ 🚗 - 🏛 50/120. AE ⓓ E VISA JCB
Meals a la carte 4600/5500 - ☕ 1800 - **175 rm** 22000/25000, 3 suites.
NE : by Av. de América HV

NH Príncipe de Vergara, Príncipe de Vergara 92, ✉ 28006, ☎ 563 26 95, Fax 563 72 53 - |‡| ▤ TV ☎ 🚗 - 🏛 25/300. AE ⓓ E VISA JCB. ✻ HV c
Meals 3000 - ☕ 1800 - **167 rm** 18600/26000, 3 suites.

NH Sanvy, Goya 3, ✉ 28001, ☎ 576 08 00, Fax 575 24 43 - |‡| ▤ TV ☎ - 🏛 25/150. AE ⓓ E VISA JCB. ✻ plan p. 7 NV r
Meals (see rest. ***Sorolla*** below) - ☕ 1900 - **131 rm** 20750/28440, 10 suites.

Agumar coffee shop only, paseo Reina Cristina 7, ✉ 28014, ☎ 552 69 00, Telex 22814, Fax 433 60 95 - |‡| ▤ TV ☎ 🚗 - 🏛 25/150. AE ⓓ E VISA. ✻ HZ a
☕ 1200 - **246 rm** 13500/16800, 6 suites.

Novotel Madrid, Albacete 1, ✉ 28027, ☎ 405 46 00, Telex 41862, Fax 404 11 05, ☂, 🏊 - |‡| ▤ TV ☎ ♿ 🚗 Ⓟ - 🏛 25/250. AE ⓓ E VISA E : by M 30 JY
Meals 2375 - ☕ 1390 - **236 rm** 17280/18725.

Pintor, Goya 79, ✉ 28001, ☎ 435 75 45, Telex 23281, Fax 576 81 57 - |‡| ▤ TV ☎ 🚗 - 🏛 25/350. AE ⓓ E VISA. ✻ HX c
Meals a la carte 3100/5100 - ☕ 1500 - **174 rm** 15460/20500, 2 suites.

Conde de Orgaz, av. Moscatelar 24, ✉ 28043, ☎ 388 40 99, Fax 388 00 09 – ▤ TV ☎ – 25/100. AE ⓘ E VISA. NE : by López de Hoyos HU
Meals 2500 – ☕ 1100 – **89 rm** 13600/17000, 1 suite.

NH Parque Avenidas, Biarritz 2, ✉ 28028, ☎ 361 02 88, Fax 361 21 38 – ▤ TV ☎ ♿ – 25/400. AE ⓘ E VISA JCB. JV **a**
Meals a la carte 3100/4050 – ☕ 1500 – **198 rm** 18000/22000, 1 suite.

NH Lagasca, Lagasca 64, ✉ 28001, ☎ 575 46 06, Fax 575 16 94 – ▤ TV ☎ – 25/60. AE ⓘ E VISA. HX **k**
Meals 1600 – ☕ 1500 – **100 rm** 17500.

Rafael Ventas, Alcalá 269, ✉ 28027, ☎ 326 16 20, Fax 326 18 19, – ▤ TV ☎ ♿ – 25/80. AE ⓘ E VISA. E : by Alcalá JV
Meals 1800 – ☕ 975 – **110 rm** 10275/15975, 1 suite.

Alcalá, Alcalá 66, ✉ 28009, ☎ 435 10 60, Telex 48094, Fax 435 11 05 – ▤ TV ☎ – 25/100. AE ⓘ E VISA. HX **w**
Meals *(closed August)* a la carte approx. 4200 – ☕ 950 – **153 rm** 12200/17900.

G. H. Colón, Pez Volador 11, ✉ 28007, ☎ 573 59 00, Telex 22984, Fax 573 08 09, – ▤ TV ☎ – 25/250. AE ⓘ E VISA JCB. JY **x**
Meals a la carte approx. 4900 – ☕ 1100 – **389 rm** 12100/17600.

Novotel Madrid-Campo de las Naciones, Campo de las Naciones, ✉ 28042, ☎ 721 18 18, Fax 721 11 22, – ▤ TV ☎ ♿ – 25/400. AE ⓘ E VISA JCB
Meals 2200 – ☕ 1375 – **240 rm** 16000/17000, 5 suites. NE : by Av. de América HV

Convención coffee shop only, O'Donnell 53, ✉ 28009, ☎ 574 84 00, Telex 23944, Fax 574 56 01 – ▤ TV ☎ – 25/800. AE ⓘ E VISA JCB. JX **a**
☕ 1250 – **739 rm** 14400/18000, 51 suites.

Serrano without rest, Marqués de Villamejor 8, ✉ 28006, ☎ 435 52 00, Fax 435 48 49 – ▤ TV ☎. AE ⓘ E VISA JCB. GHV **k**
☕ 950 – **30 rm** 12000/15000, 4 suites.

NH Balboa, Núñez de Balboa 112, ✉ 28006, ☎ 563 03 24, Fax 562 69 80 – ▤ TV ☎ – 25/30. AE ⓘ E VISA JCB. HV **n**
Meals 2000 – ☕ 1500 – **122 rm** 16400/22800.

NH Sur, paseo Infanta Isabel 9, ✉ 28014, ☎ 539 94 00, Fax 467 09 96 – ▤ TV ☎ – 25/30. AE ⓘ E VISA JCB. plan p. 7 NZ **a**
Meals *(closed Saturday, Sunday and August)* 1600 – ☕ 1200 – **68 rm** 12500/14500.

Abeba without rest, Alcántara 63, ✉ 28006, ☎ 401 16 50, Fax 402 75 91 – ▤ TV ☎. AE ⓘ E VISA. HV **r**
☕ 600 – **90 rm** 8500/10500.

XXX **Club 31,** Alcalá 58, ✉ 28014, ☎ 531 00 92 – ▤. AE ⓘ E VISA JCB plan p. 7 NX **e**
closed Sunday, Bank Holidays and August – **Meals** a la carte approx. 6900.

XXX ✿ **El Amparo,** Puigcerdá 8, ✉ 28001, ☎ 431 64 56, Fax 575 54 91, « Original decor » – ▤. AE E VISA JCB. HX **h**
closed Saturday lunch, Sunday and August – **Meals** a la carte approx. 6750
Spec. Mousse de ventresca de bonito con bogavante, aceite de perejil y trufa. Rabo de buey guisado al vino tinto. Soufflé caliente de giardenja.

XXX **El Fogón,** Villanueva 34, ✉ 28001, ☎ 575 44 00, Telex 22700, Fax 576 41 64 – ▤. AE ⓘ E VISA. HX **t**
closed August – **Meals** a la carte 5950/7100.

XXX **Sorolla,** Hermosilla 4, ✉ 28001, ☎ 431 27 15, Telex 44994, Fax 575 24 43 – ▤. AE ⓘ E VISA JCB. plan p. 7 NV **r**
Meals a la carte 4400/5000.

XXX **Suntory,** paseo de la Castellana 36, ✉ 28046, ☎ 577 37 34, Fax 577 44 55, Japanese rest – ▤. AE ⓘ E VISA JCB. GV **d**
closed Sunday and Bank Holidays – **Meals** a la carte 5550/8880.

XXX **Villa y Corte de Madrid,** Serrano 110, ✉ 28006, ☎ 564 50 19, Fax 564 50 19, Tasteful decor – ▤. AE ⓘ E VISA. HV **a**
closed Sunday and August – **Meals** a la carte 3575/4875.

XXX **El Gran Chambelán,** Ayala 46, ✉ 28001, ☎ 431 77 45 – ▤. AE ⓘ VISA. HX **r**
closed Sunday – **Meals** a la carte approx. 4500.

XXX **Balzac,** Moreto 7, ✉ 28014, ☎ 420 01 77, Fax 429 83 70 – ▤. AE ⓘ E VISA.
closed Sunday and August – **Meals** a la carte 4500/5700. plan p. 7 NY **a**

XXX **El Comedor,** Montalbán 9, ✉ 28014, ☎ 531 69 68, Fax 531 61 91, – ▤. AE ⓘ E VISA. plan p. 7 NX **a**
closed Saturday lunch and Sunday – **Meals** a la carte 3350/4800.

XXX **Ponteareas,** Claudio Coello 96, ✉ 28006, ☎ 575 58 73, Fax 541 65 98, Galician rest – ▤. AE ⓘ E VISA JCB. HV **w**
closed Sunday, Bank Holidays and August – **Meals** a la carte 3440/5795.

XXX **Castelló 9,** Castelló 9, ✉ 28001, ☎ 435 00 67, Fax 435 91 34 – ▤. AE ⓘ E VISA. HX **e**
closed Sunday and Bank Holidays – **Meals** a la carte 4925/5775.

XX ✿ **La Paloma,** Jorge Juan 39, ✉ 28001, ☎ 576 86 92 – ▤. AE E VISA. ✈ HX **g**
closed Sunday, Bank Holidays, Holy Week and August – **Meals** a la carte 4800/5100
Spec. Ensalada de carabineros y alcachofas (season). Rollitos crujientes de langosta con salsa de soja. Degustación de cabeza de ternera con lengua carrillada.

XX ✿ **Viridiana,** Juan de Mena 14, ✉ 28014, ☎ 523 44 78, Fax 532 42 74 – ▤. AE VISA. ✈
closed Sunday and August – **Meals** a la carte 4900/7250 plan p. 7 NY **r**
Spec. Foie de pato sobre brioche al Pedro Ximénez. Calamarcitos salteados con Curry y arroces. Tocinillo de flores de naranjo en salsa de maracuyá.

XX **Al Mounia,** Recoletos 5, ✉ 28001, ☎ 435 08 28, North African rest, « Oriental atmosphere » – ▤. AE ⊕ E VISA. ✈ plan p. 7 NV **u**
closed Sunday, Monday and August – **Meals** a la carte 4200/4600.

XX **La Fonda,** Lagasca 11, ✉ 28001, ☎ 577 79 24, Catalonian rest – ▤. AE ⊕ E VISA. ✈
Meals a la carte approx. 4400. HX **f**

XX **Rafa,** Narváez 68, ✉ 28009, ☎ 573 10 87, ⛱ – ▤. AE ⊕ E VISA. ✈ HY **a**
Meals a la carte 4200/5100.

XX ✿ **Casa d'a Troya,** Emiliano Barral 14, ✉ 28043, ☎ 416 44 55, Galician rest – ▤. E VISA. ✈
closed Sunday, Bank Holidays and 15 July-1 September – **Meals** (booking essential) a la carte 2700/4850 E : by M 30 JY
Spec. Pulpo a la gallega. Merluza a la gallega. Tarta de Santiago.

XX **El Asador de Aranda,** Diego de León 9, ✉ 28006, ☎ 563 02 46, Roast lamb – ▤. AE ⊕ E VISA. ✈ HV **s**
closed Sunday dinner and August – **Meals** a la carte approx. 4000.

XX **St. James,** Juan Bravo 26, ✉ 28006, ☎ 575 00 69, ⛱, Rice dishes – ▤. AE VISA. ✈
closed Sunday – **Meals** a la carte 4000/5600. HV **t**

XX **Nicolás,** Villalar 4, ✉ 28001, ☎ 431 77 37, Fax 431 77 37 – ▤. AE ⊕ E VISA. ✈ NX **t**
closed Sunday, Monday and August – **Meals** a la carte 3500/4300.

XX **El Chiscón de Castelló,** Castelló 3, ✉ 28001, ☎ 575 56 62, « Hospitable atmosphere » – ▤. E VISA. ✈ HX **e**
closed Sunday, Monday dinner, Bank Holidays and August – **Meals** a la carte 3375/4825.

X **La Giralda IV,** Claudio Coello 24, ✉ 28001, ☎ 576 40 69, Andalusian rest – ▤. AE ⊕ E VISA. ✈ HX **h**
closed Sunday in summer and 15 to 31 August – **Meals** a la carte 4000/5050.

X **Asador Velate,** Jorge Juan 91, ✉ 28009, ☎ 435 10 24, Basque rest – ▤. AE ⊕ E VISA. ✈ HJX **x**
closed Sunday, Bank Holidays, Holy Week and August – **Meals** a la carte approx. 5000.

X **Pelotari,** Recoletos 3, ✉ 28001, ☎ 578 24 97, Fax 431 60 04 – ▤. AE ⊕ E VISA NV **u**
closed Sunday and 15 days in August – **Meals** a la carte approx. 4900.

X ✿ **La Trainera,** Lagasca 60, ✉ 28001, ☎ 576 05 75, Fax 575 06 31, Seafood – ▤. AE E VISA. ✈
closed Sunday and August – **Meals** a la carte 4150/5600 HX **k**
Spec. Sopa bullabesa. Bonito fresco (season). Langosta a la americana.

X ✿ **El Pescador,** José Ortega y Gasset 75, ✉ 28006, ☎ 402 12 90, Seafood – ▤. E VISA. ✈
closed Sunday, Holy Week and August – **Meals** a la carte 4250/5750 JV **t**
Spec. Angulas de Aguinaga. Lenguado Evaristo. Bogavante a la americana.

Arganzuela, Carabanchel Villaverde : Antonio López, Paseo de Las Delicias, Paseo de Santa María de la Cabeza (plan p. 4 to 6 except where otherwise stated)

🏨 **Rafael Pirámides,** paseo de las Acacias 40, ✉ 28005, ☎ 517 18 28, Fax 517 00 90 – |♦| ▤ TV ☎ ♿ 🚗. AE ⊕ E VISA S : by Gta. Puerta de Toledo EZ
Meals *(closed Saturday, Sunday and August)* a la carte 3600/4500 – ☕ 925 – **84 rm** 10475/12875, 9 suites.

🏨 **Carlton,** paseo de las Delicias 26, ✉ 28045, ☎ 539 71 00, Telex 44571, Fax 527 85 10 – |♦| ▤ TV ☎. AE ⊕ E VISA. ✈ plan p. 5 GZ **n**
Meals 3000 – ☕ 1300 – **112 rm** 12500/15625.

🏨 **Praga** coffee shop only, Antonio López 65, ✉ 28019, ☎ 469 06 00, Telex 22823, Fax 469 83 25 – |♦| ▤ TV ☎ 🚗 – 🏛 25/350. AE ⊕ E VISA. ✈
☕ 790 – **428 rm** 8950/11900. S : by Gta. Puerta de Toledo EZ

🏨 **Aramo,** paseo Santa María de la Cabeza 73, ✉ 28045, ☎ 473 91 11, Telex 45885, Fax 473 92 14 – |♦| ▤ TV ☎ 🚗. AE ⊕ E VISA. ✈ rest
Meals 1500 – ☕ 1000 – **105 rm** 9600/12000. S : by pl. Emperador Carlos V NZ

🏨 **Puerta de Toledo,** glorieta Puerta de Toledo 4, ✉ 28005, ☎ 474 71 00, Telex 22291, Fax 474 07 47 – |♦| ▤ TV ☎ 🚗 – 🏛 25/30. AE ⊕ E VISA JCB. ✈ EZ **v**
Meals (see rest. ***Puerta de Toledo*** below) – ☕ 850 – **152 rm** 7200/10950.

XX ✿ **Hontoria,** pl. del General Maroto 2, ✉ 28045, ☎ 473 04 25, Rustic decor – ▤. AE E VISA. ✈
closed Sunday, Bank Holidays and August – **Meals** a la carte 3500/5225
Spec. Terrina de hígado de pato hecha en casa. Escalopines de solomillo a los ajos tiernos. Hojas de chocolate blanco rellenas de fruta roja. S : by Gta. de Embajadores FZ

XX **Puerta de Toledo,** glorieta Puerta de Toledo 4, ✉ 28005, ☎ 474 76 75, Fax 474 30 35 – ▤. AE ⊕ E VISA EZ **v**
Meals a la carte approx. 3600.

Moncloa : Princesa, Paseo del Pintor Rosales, Paseo de la Florida, Casa de Campo (plan p. 4 except where otherwise stated)

Meliá Madrid, Princesa 27, ✉ 28008, ✆ 541 82 00, Telex 22537, Fax 541 19 88, Fö – |‡| ▤ TV ☎ – 25/200. AE ⓘ E VISA JCB. ✗ plan p. 6 KV t
Meals 4000 – ☐ 2000 – **253 rm** 18250/21200, 23 suites.

Tryp Monte Real ⛰, Arroyofresno 17, ✉ 28035, ✆ 316 21 40, Telex 22089, Fax 316 39 34, « Garden », ⛱ – |‡| ▤ TV ☎ ⇔ P – 25/250. AE ⓘ E VISA. ✗
Meals a la carte 4000/4500 – ☐ 1500 – **76 rm** 17475/21900, 4 suites.
NW : 8 km by Av. A. de la Victoria DV

Florida Norte, paseo de la Florida 5, ✉ 28008, ✆ 542 83 00, Telex 23675, Fax 547 78 33 – |‡| ▤ TV ☎ ⇔. AE ⓘ E VISA JCB. ✗ plan p. 4 DX v
Meals 2600 – ☐ 900 – **399 rm** 12000/17000.

Sofitel-Plaza de España without rest, Tutor 1, ✉ 28008, ✆ 541 98 80, Telex 43190, Fax 542 57 36 – |‡| ▤ TV ☎. AE ⓘ E VISA. ✗ plan p. 6 KV d
☐ 1400 – **99 rm** 19750/23500.

Currito, Casa de Campo - Pabellón de Vizcaya, ✉ 28011, ✆ 464 57 04, Fax 479 72 54, ☂, Basque rest – ▤ P. AE ⓘ E VISA W : by Feria del Campo DY
closed Sunday dinner – **Meals** a la carte 4600/5600.

Chamberí : San Bernardo, Fuencarral, Alberto Aguilera, Santa Engracia (plan p. 4 to 7)

NH Santo Mauro, Zurbano 36, ✉ 28010, ✆ 319 69 00, Fax 308 54 77, ☂, « Elegant palace with garden », ⛱ – |‡| ▤ TV ☎ ⇔ – 25/70. AE ⓘ E VISA JCB. ✗ GV e
Belagua (closed Sunday, Bank Holidays and August) **Meals** a la carte 5175/6700 – ☐ 2000 – **33 rm** 29160/40500, 4 suites.

Miguel Ángel, Miguel Ángel 31, ✉ 28010, ✆ 442 00 22, Telex 44235, Fax 442 53 20, ☂, Fö, ⛱ – |‡| ▤ TV ☎ ⇔ – 25/300. AE ⓘ E VISA JCB. ✗ GV c
Meals 5500 – ☐ 2000 – **251 rm** 28500/35700, 20 suites.

Castellana Inter-Continental, paseo de la Castellana 49, ✉ 28046, ✆ 310 02 00, Telex 27686, Fax 319 58 53, ☂, « Garden », Fö – |‡| ▤ TV ☎ ⇔ – 25/550. AE ⓘ E VISA JCB. ✗ GV a
Meals a la carte 3200/6200 – ☐ 2100 – **278 rm** 31000/38000, 27 suites.

Mindanao, San Francisco de Sales 15, ✉ 28003, ✆ 549 55 00, Telex 22631, Fax 544 55 96, ⛱, ⛱ – |‡| ▤ TV ☎ ⇔ – 25/200. AE ⓘ E VISA JCB. ✗ DV a
Meals *(closed August)* 3750 – ☐ 1600 – **272 rm** 16500/21000, 9 suites.

G.H. Conde Duque coffee shop only, pl. Conde Valle de Suchil 5, ✉ 28015, ✆ 447 70 00, Telex 22058, Fax 448 35 69 – |‡| ▤ TV ☎ – 25/100. AE ⓘ E VISA JCB. ✗ EV d
☐ 1500 – **142 rm** 15250/22850, 1 suite.

Gran Versalles without rest, Covarrubias 4, ✉ 28010, ✆ 447 57 00, Telex 49150, Fax 446 39 87 – |‡| ▤ TV ☎ – 25/120. AE ⓘ E VISA. ✗ MV a
☐ 975 – **143 rm** 15250/21600, 2 suites.

NH Zurbano, Zurbano 79, ✉ 28003, ✆ 441 45 00, Telex 27578, Fax 441 32 24 – |‡| ▤ TV ☎ ⇔ – 25/100. AE ⓘ E VISA JCB. ✗ GV x
Meals 4500 – ☐ 1400 – **263 rm** 18200/22800, 1 suite.

NH Embajada, Santa Engracia 5, ✉ 28010, ✆ 594 02 13, Fax 447 33 12, Spanish style building – |‡| ▤ TV ☎ – 25/45. AE ⓘ E VISA JCB. ✗ MV r
Meals 1700 – ☐ 1300 – **101 rm** 16000.

NH Prisma, Santa Engracia 120, ✉ 28003, ✆ 441 93 77, Fax 442 58 51 – |‡| ▤ TV ☎ – 25/70. AE ⓘ E VISA JCB. ✗ FV g
Meals a la carte 3100/3600 – ☐ 1900 – **103 suites** 22000/27500.

NH Argüelles coffee shop only, Vallehermoso 65, ✉ 28015, ✆ 593 97 77, Fax 594 27 39 – ▤ TV ☎ ⇔. AE ⓘ E VISA. ✗ EV e
☐ 1100 – **75 rm** 13200.

Escultor, Miguel Ángel 3, ✉ 28010, ✆ 310 42 03, Telex 44285, Fax 319 25 84 – |‡| ▤ TV ☎ – 25/150. AE ⓘ E VISA JCB. ✗ GV s
Meals (see rest. ***Señorío de Errazu*** below) – ☐ 1300 – **79 rm** 17000/21000, 3 suites.

Sol Alondras coffee shop only, José Abascal 8, ✉ 28003, ✆ 447 40 00, Telex 49454, Fax 593 88 00 – |‡| ▤ TV ☎. AE ⓘ E VISA JCB. ✗ FV a
☐ 1000 – **72 rm** 15200/19100.

XXXX ✿ **Jockey,** Amador de los Ríos 6, ✉ 28010, ✆ 319 24 35, Fax 319 24 35 – ▤. AE ⓘ E VISA JCB. ✗ NV k
closed Saturday lunch, Sunday and August – **Meals** a la carte 6250/9400
Spec. Langostinos de Huelva crudos con crema fresca al caviar. Lomo de rodaballo al aceite de oliva virgen y verduras fritas. Pato de corral braseado con higos.

XXXX **Lúculo,** Génova 19, ✉ 28004, ✆ 319 40 29, ☂, « Garden-terrace in summer » – ▤. AE ⓘ E VISA. ✗ NV d
closed Saturday lunch and Sunday – **Meals** a la carte 5400/7500.

XXXX ✿ **Las Cuatro Estaciones,** General Ibáñez de Íbero 5, ✉ 28003, ☎ 553 63 05, Fax 553 32 98, Modern decor – ▤. AE ⓓ VISA JCB EU **r**
closed Saturday lunch, Sunday, Bank Holidays, Holy Week and August – **Meals** a la carte 4630/5680
Spec. Gazpacho de bogavante. Lomo de merluza Las Cuatro Estaciones. Foie caliente a las uvas y Pedro Ximénez.

XXX **Lur Maitea,** Fernando el Santo 4, ✉ 28010, ☎ 308 03 50, Fax 308 03 93, Basque rest – ▤. AE ⓓ E VISA. ✽ MV **u**
closed Saturday lunch, Sunday, Bank Holidays and August – **Meals** a la carte 4450/5250.

XXX **Annapurna,** Zurbano 5, ✉ 28010, ☎ 308 32 49, Indian rest – ▤. AE ⓓ VISA MV **w**
closed Saturday lunch and Sunday – **Meals** a la carte 2750/3300.

XXX **Señorío de Errazu,** Miguel Ángel 3, ✉ 28010, ☎ 308 24 25 – ▤. AE ⓓ E VISA JCB. ✽ GV **s**
closed Sunday and August – **Meals** a la carte approx. 4500.

XX **Polizón,** Viriato 39, ✉ 28010, ☎ 593 39 19, Seafood – ▤. AE ⓓ E VISA JCB. ✽ FV **w**
closed Sunday dinner and 16 to 31 August – **Meals** a la carte 3300/4250.

XX **La Plaza de Chamberí,** pl. de Chamberí 10, ✉ 28010, ☎ 446 06 97 – ▤. AE ⓓ E VISA JCB. ✽ FV **k**
closed Sunday – **Meals** a la carte 3475/4675.

XX **La Fuente Quince,** Modesto Lafuente 15, ✉ 28003, ☎ 442 34 53, Fax 441 90 24 – ▤. AE ⓓ VISA. ✽ FV **j**
closed Saturday lunch, Sunday, Holy Week and August – **Meals** a la carte 2825/3200.

XX **O'Xeito,** paseo de la Castellana 49, ✉ 28046, ☎ 308 23 83, Galician style decor. Seafood – ▤. AE E VISA GV **a**
closed Sunday, Holy Week and August – **Meals** a la carte approx. 4700.

XX **Vatel,** Rafael Calvo 40, ✉ 28010, ☎ 310 00 74 – ▤. AE E VISA. ✽ GV **n**
closed Sunday, Monday dinner and August – **Meals** a la carte 3150/4130.

X **Pinocchio,** Orfila 2, ✉ 28010, ☎ 308 16 47, Fax 766 98 04, Italian rest – ▤. AE ⓓ E VISA. ✽ NV **d**
closed Saturday lunch, Bank Holidays and August – **Meals** a la carte 2635/3605.

X **La Gran Tasca,** Santa Engracia 24, ✉ 28010, ☎ 448 77 79, Castilian decor – ▤. AE ⓓ E VISA. ✽ FV **c**
closed Sunday and August – **Meals** a la carte 3300/4750.

X **La Despensa,** Cardenal Cisneros 6, ✉ 28010, ☎ 446 17 94 – ▤. AE ⓓ E VISA. ✽
closed Sunday in summer, Sunday dinner and Monday the rest of the year and September – **Meals** a la carte 2350/2850. FV **p**

Chamartín, Tetuán : Paseo de la Castellana, Capitán Haya, Orense, Alberto Alcocer, Paseo de la Habana (plan p. 3 except where otherwise stated)

Meliá Castilla, Capitán Haya 43, ✉ 28020, ☎ 567 50 00, Telex 23142, Fax 567 50 51, ⛱ – |‡| ▤ TV ☎ ♿ 🚗 – 🏛 25/800. AE ⓓ E VISA JCB. ✽ GS **c**
Meals (see rest. ***L'Albufera*** and rest. ***La Fragata*** below) – ☕ 2200 – **896 rm** 25935/29925, 14 suites.

Holiday Inn, pl. Carlos Trías Beltrán 4 (entrance by Orense 22-24), ✉ 28020, ☎ 597 01 02, Telex 44709, Fax 597 02 92, 🏋, ⛱ – |‡| ▤ TV ☎ ♿ – 🏛 25/400. AE ⓓ E VISA JCB. ✽ rest GT **z**
La Terraza : **Meals** a la carte 3800/6730 - ***La Tasca*** *(buffet lunch only, closed Saturday, Sunday, Bank Holidays and August)* **Meals** 1500 – ☕ 1950 – **282 rm** 25650/28650, 31 suites.

Eurobuilding, Padre Damián 23, ✉ 28036, ☎ 345 45 00, Telex 22548, Fax 345 45 76, ⛱, « Garden and terrace with ⛱ », 🏋 – |‡| ▤ TV ☎ 🚗 – 🏛 25/900. AE ⓓ E VISA JCB. ✽ HS **a**
La Taberna *(closed Saturday and Sunday)* **Meals** a la carte approx. 4500 - ***Le Relais*** *(buffet lunch only)* **Meals** 3200 – ☕ 1975 – **416 rm** 23900/29200, 84 suites.

Cuzco coffee shop only, paseo de la Castellana 133, ✉ 28046, ☎ 556 06 00, Telex 22464, Fax 556 03 72, 🏋 – |‡| ▤ TV ☎ 🚗 Ⓟ – 🏛 25/450. AE ⓓ E VISA. ✽ GS **a**
☕ 1190 – **320 rm** 16200/20550, 8 suites.

Chamartín without rest, Chamartín railway station, ✉ 28036, ☎ 323 18 33, Telex 49201, Fax 733 02 14 – |‡| ▤ TV ☎ – 🏛 25/500. AE ⓓ E VISA JCB. ✽ HR
☕ 1160 – **360 rm** 11910/13790, 18 suites.

NH La Habana, paseo de la Habana 73, ✉ 28036, ☎ 345 82 84, Telex 41869, Fax 457 75 79 – |‡| ▤ TV ☎ 🚗 – 🏛 25/250. AE ⓓ E VISA JCB. ✽ HT **f**
Meals 2000 – ☕ 1800 – **157 rm** 14000/20000.

Orense 38, Pedro Teixeira 5, ✉ 28020, ☎ 597 15 68, Fax 597 12 95, 🏋 – |‡| ▤ TV ☎ 🚗. AE ⓓ E VISA. ✽ GT **q**
Meals a la carte approx. 4800 – ☕ 1100 – **140 rm** 18700/22500.

Foxá 32, Agustín de Foxá 32, ✉ 28036, ☎ 733 10 60, Fax 314 11 65 – |‡| ▤ TV ☎ 🚗 – 🏛 25/250. AE ⓓ E VISA. ✽ HR **u**
Meals 1500 – ☕ 1575 – **63 rm** 19110/23885, 98 suites.

Foxá 25, Agustín de Foxá 25, ✉ 28036, ☎ 323 11 19, Fax 314 53 11 - AE E VISA. HR a
Meals 1500 - 1575 - **121 suites** 19110/23885.

Castilla Plaza, paseo de la Castellana 220, ✉ 28046, ☎ 323 11 86, Fax 315 54 06 - 25/150. AE E VISA. GS n
Meals 1900 - 1250 - **147 rm** 18725/21293.

El Gran Atlanta without rest, Comandante Zorita 34, ✉ 28020, ☎ 553 59 00, Fax 533 08 58, - 25/120. AE E VISA. FT p
1150 - **180 rm** 13825/17280.

El Jardín without rest, carret. N I km 5'7 (entrance by M 40 service road), ✉ 28050, ☎ 302 83 36, Fax 766 86 91, AE E VISA
41 suites 11000/12500. N : by M 30 HR

XXXXX ✿✿ **Zalacaín,** Álvarez de Baena 4, ✉ 28006, ☎ 561 48 40, Fax 561 47 32, - AE E VISA JCB. plan p. 5 GV b
closed Saturday lunch, Sunday, Bank Holidays, Holy Week and August - **Meals** a la carte 7500/8500
Spec. Crema de espárragos en gelatina. Rodaballo sobre soubise de hongos a la mantequilla con hierbas. Pastel ruso con frambuesas y crema de anís.

XXXXX **Príncipe y Serrano,** Serrano 240, ✉ 28016, ☎ 458 62 31, Fax 458 86 76 - AE E VISA. HT a
closed Saturday lunch, Sunday, Bank Holidays, Holy Week and August - **Meals** a la carte 5200/7300.

XXXX **La Máquina,** Sor Ángela de la Cruz 22, ✉ 28020, ☎ 572 33 18, Fax 570 13 04 - AE E VISA. FS e
closed Sunday and 15 to 31 August - **Meals** a la carte 4100/4925.

XXXX **Nicolasa,** Velázquez 150, ✉ 28002, ☎ 563 17 35, Fax 564 32 75 - AE E VISA.
closed Sunday and August - **Meals** a la carte 4650/5800. HU a

XXXX **El Bodegón,** Pinar 15, ✉ 28006, ☎ 562 88 44 - AE E VISA JCB plan p. 5 GV q
closed Saturday lunch, Sunday, Bank Holidays and August - **Meals** a la carte 5450/6450.

XXXX ✿ **Príncipe de Viana,** Manuel de Falla 5, ✉ 28036, ☎ 457 15 49, Fax 457 52 83, Basque rest - AE E VISA JCB. GT c
closed Saturday lunch, Sunday, Bank Holidays, Holy Week and August - **Meals** a la carte 4950/5625
Spec. Crema de lentejas con pato y cuscurros. Menestra de verduras. Salmonetes con vinagreta de vino de Jerez.

XXX **O'Pazo,** Reina Mercedes 20, ✉ 28020, ☎ 553 23 33, Fax 554 90 72, Seafood - E VISA. FT p
closed Sunday, Holy Week and August - **Meals** a la carte 4250/5650.

XXX **L'Albufera,** Capitán Haya 43, ✉ 28020, ☎ 567 51 97, Fax 567 50 51, Rice dishes - AE E VISA JCB. GS c
Meals a la carte 4300/5700.

XXX **La Fragata,** Capitán Haya 43, ✉ 28020, ☎ 567 51 96 - AE E VISA JCB.
closed August - **Meals** a la carte 3900/5200. GS c

XXX **José Luis,** Rafael Salgado 11, ✉ 28036, ☎ 457 50 36, Fax 344 18 37 - AE E VISA.
closed Sunday and August - **Meals** a la carte approx. 6500. GT m

XXX **Señorío de Bertiz,** Comandante Zorita 6, ✉ 28020, ☎ 533 27 57, Fax 534 50 90 - AE E VISA JCB FTU s
closed Saturday lunch, Sunday, Bank Holidays and August - **Meals** a la carte 4500/4900.

XXX **Bogavante,** Capitán Haya 20, ✉ 28020, ☎ 556 21 14, Fax 597 00 79, Seafood - AE E VISA JCB. GT d
closed Sunday dinner - **Meals** a la carte 2800/6600.

XXX **Señorío de Alcocer,** Alberto Alcocer 1, ✉ 28036, ☎ 345 16 96 - AE E VISA. GS e
closed Saturday lunch, Sunday, Bank Holidays and August - **Meals** a la carte 4600/6100.

XXX ✿ **El Olivo,** General Gallegos 1, ✉ 28036, ☎ 359 15 35, Fax 345 91 83 - AE E VISA JCB. HS c
closed Sunday, Monday and 15 to 30 August - **Meals** a la carte 4800/5700
Spec. Surtido de bacalaos. Lamprea al vino de la Ribera del Duero (spring). Merluza cocida al caldo corto.

XXX ✿ **Goizeko Kabi,** Comandante Zorita 37, ✉ 28020, ☎ 533 01 85, Fax 533 02 14, Basque rest - AE E VISA. FT a
closed Saturday lunch July-August and Sunday - **Meals** a la carte 5400/8500
Spec. Ensalada templada de bogavante. Raviolis de bacalao en porrusalda de cigalitas. Tatin de manzanas en compota.

XXX ✿ **Cabo Mayor,** Juan Ramón Jiménez 37, ✉ 28036, ☎ 350 87 76, Fax 359 16 21 - AE E VISA JCB GHS r
closed Sunday and Holy Week - **Meals** a la carte 4275/6075
Spec. Ensalada de jamón de Jabugo y foie-gras con piñones. Rape a la barquereña con setas de primavera. Entrecot de cebón al vino tinto con puré de almendras.

XXX **Blanca de Navarra,** av. de Brasil 13, ✉ 28020, ☎ 555 10 29 - AE E VISA JCB GT q
closed Sunday and August - **Meals** a la carte 4500/6500.

XXX **Lutecia,** Corazón de María 78, ✉ 28002, ☎ 519 34 15 – ▤. AE ⓓ E VISA. ✂
closed Saturday lunch, Sunday and August – **Meals** a la carte 2700/3500.
NE : by López de Hoyos HU

XXX **Aldaba,** Alberto Alcocer 5, ✉ 28036, ☎ 345 21 93 – ▤. AE ⓓ E VISA. ✂ GS **e**
closed Saturday lunch, Sunday, Holy Week and August – **Meals** a la carte 3650/5795.

XXX **El Foque,** Suero de Quiñones 22, ✉ 28002, ☎ 519 25 72, Cod dishes – ▤. AE ⓓ E VISA. ✂
closed Sunday – **Meals** a la carte 4150/4950. HU **r**

XX **Combarro,** Reina Mercedes 12, ✉ 28020, ☎ 554 77 84, Fax 534 25 01, Seafood – ▤. AE ⓓ E VISA JCB FT **a**
closed Sunday dinner and August – **Meals** a la carte 4000/5675.

XX **La Tahona,** Capitán Haya 21 (side), ✉ 28020, ☎ 555 04 41, Roast lamb, « Castilian medieval decor » – ▤. AE ⓓ E VISA. ✂ GT **u**
closed Sunday dinner and August – **Meals** a la carte approx. 4100.

XX **De Funy,** Serrano 213, ✉ 28016, ☎ 457 95 22, Fax 458 85 84, 余, Lebanese rest – ▤. AE ⓓ E VISA HT **z**
Meals a la carte approx. 4100.

XX **Gaztelupe,** Comandante Zorita 32, ✉ 28020, ☎ 534 90 28, Basque rest – ▤. AE ⓓ E VISA. ✂
closed Sunday July-August and Sunday dinner the rest of the year – **Meals** a la carte 4300/5350. FT **p**

XX **Asador Errota-Zar,** Corazón de María 32, ✉ 28002, ☎ 413 52 24, Fax 519 30 84 – ▤. AE ⓓ E VISA. ✂ NE : by Cartagena HV
closed Sunday, Holy Week and August – **Meals** a la carte 3950/4700.

XX **Serramar,** Rosario Pino 12, ✉ 28020, ☎ 570 07 90, Fax 570 48 09, Seafood – ▤. AE ⓓ E VISA. ✂ GS **k**
closed Sunday – **Meals** a la carte 3900/4850.

XX **Inés Villanueva,** López de Hoyos 42, ✉ 28006, ☎ 563 14 85, Fax 563 15 44 – ▤. AE ⓓ E VISA
closed Sunday and August – **Meals** a la carte approx. 5500. HV **v**

XX **Sacha,** Juan Hurtado de Mendoza 11 (back), ✉ 28036, ☎ 345 59 52, 余 – ▤. AE ⓓ E VISA. ✂ GHS **r**
closed Sunday, Bank Holidays, Holy Week and 10 to 31 August – **Meals** a la carte approx. 5000.

XX **Rianxo,** Oruro 11, ✉ 28016, ☎ 457 10 06, Galician rest – ▤. AE ⓓ E VISA. ✂ HT **h**
closed Sunday and August – **Meals** a la carte approx. 6500.

XX **House of Ming,** paseo de la Castellana 74, ✉ 28046, ☎ 561 10 13, Fax 561 98 27, Chinese rest – ▤. AE ⓓ E VISA. ✂ plan p. 5 GV **f**
Meals a la carte 2535/3740.

X **La Ancha,** Príncipe de Vergara 204, ✉ 28002, ☎ 563 89 77, 余 – ▤. AE ⓓ E VISA. ✂ HT **r**
closed Sunday, Bank Holidays, Holy Week and Christmas – **Meals** a la carte approx. 4700.

X **El Asador de Aranda,** pl. de Castilla 3, ✉ 28046, ☎ 733 87 02, Roast lamb. Castilian decor – ▤. AE ⓓ E VISA. ✂ GS **b**
closed Sunday dinner and 13 August-12 September – **Meals** a la carte approx. 4000.

Environs

on the road to the airport E : 12,5 km – ✉ 28042 Madrid – ☎ 91 :

Tryp Diana, Galeón 27 (Alameda de Osuna) ☎ 747 13 55, Telex 45688, Fax 747 97 97, ⛱ – |$| ▤ TV ☎ – 🏛 25/220. AE ⓓ E VISA. ✂ rest
Meals 1800 - ***Asador Duque de Osuna*** *(closed Sunday)* **Meals** a la carte 3100/4400 – ☐ 800 – **220 rm** 12800/16000, 40 suites.

by motorway N VI – ✉ 28023 Madrid – ☎ 91 :

XXX **Gaztelubide,** Sopelana 13 - La Florida : 12,8 km ☎ 372 85 44, Fax 372 84 19, 余, Basque rest – |$| ▤ P. AE ⓓ E VISA. ✂
closed Sunday dinner – **Meals** a la carte approx. 6500.

XX **Los Remos,** La Florida : 13 km ☎ 307 72 30, Fax 372 84 35, Seafood – ▤ P. AE E VISA
closed Sunday dinner and Bank Holidays dinner – **Meals** a la carte 4500/5400.

by motorway N I N : 13 km – ✉ 28100 Alcobendas – ☎ 91 :

La Moraleja, av. de Europa 17 - parque empresarial La Moraleja ☎ 661 80 55, Fax 661 21 88, Fō, ⛱ – |$| ▤ TV ☎ 🚗 P. AE ⓓ E VISA. ✂
Meals 2500 – ☐ 1350 – **37 suites** 22000.

at Barajas E : 14 km – ✉ 28042 Madrid – ☎ 91 :

Barajas, av. de Logroño 305 ☎ 747 77 00, Telex 22255, Fax 747 87 17, 余, Fō, ⛱, 🌳 – |$| ▤ TV ☎ P – 🏛 25/675. AE ⓓ E VISA
Meals 4750 – **218 rm** ☐ 24650/32200, 12 suites.

Alameda, av. de Logroño 100 ☎ 747 48 00, Telex 43809, Fax 747 89 28, ⛱ – |$| ▤ TV ☎ P – 🏛 25/280. AE ⓓ E VISA JCB. ✂ rest
Meals 3950 – ☐ 1300 – **136 rm** 18000/22500, 9 suites.

at San Sebastián de los Reyes N : 17 km – ✉ 28700 San Sebastián de los Reyes – ☎ 91 :

XXX **Mesón Tejas Verdes,** ☎ 652 73 07 , 余, Castilian decor, 🌳 – ▤ P. AE ⓓ E VISA. ✂
closed Sunday dinner, Bank Holidays dinner and August – **Meals** a la carte 3500/4100.

Moralzarzal 28411 Madrid 444 J 18 - pop. 2 248 - alt. 979 - ☎ 91.
◆Madrid 42.

XXX ✿ **El Cenador de Salvador,** av. de España 30 ☎ 857 77 22, Fax 857 77 80, ☂, « Garden terrace » - ▤ 🅟. AE ⓞ E VISA JCB. ✗
closed Sunday dinner and Monday except Bank Holidays and summer and 15 to 30 October - **Meals** a la carte 5575/7875
Spec. Lasagna de bogavante y berenjenas. Lomos de conejo asado con trufas. Espuma de chocolate amargo con cerezas.

BARCELONA 08000 P 443 H 36 - pop. 1 681 132 - ☎ 93.

See : Gothic Quarter★★ (Barrio Gótico) : Cathedral★★ MX, Plaça del Rei★ MX **149,** Frederic Marés **Museum★★ (Museo F. Marés)** MX - La Rambla★ LX, MY : Atarazanas and Maritim Museum★★ MY, Plaça Reial★ MY, Güell Palace★ LY - Montcada st.★ (carrer de Montcada) NX **121** : Picasso Museum★ NV, Santa María del Mar Church★ NX - Montjuich★ ≤★ (Montjuïc) : Catalonian Art Museum★★★ (romanic and gothic collections★★★), Spanish Village★ (Poble espanyol), Joan Miró Foundation★ - Archeological Museum★ (Museo Arqueológico) S : by Av. Reina María Cristina GY - El Eixample : Holy Family★★ (Sagrada Familia) JU, Passeig de Gràcia★★ HV : (Casa Batlló★ HV **B,** La Pedrera or Casa Milà★ HV **P)** - Güell Park★★ (Parque Güell) N : by Pl. de Lesseps GU - Catalonian Music Palace★ (Palau de la Mìsica Catalana) MV **Y,** Antoni Tàpies Foundation★ HV **S.**

Other curiosities : Tibidabo (✳ ★★) NW : by Balmes FU, Pedralbes Monastery★ (Thyssen Bornemisza collection★) W : by Av. de Pedralbes EV. Pedralbes Palace (Palau de Pedralbes : ceramic collection★) EX Zoo★ (Parque zoológico) KX.

18, 18 of Prat SW : 16 km ☎ 379 02 78 - 18 of Sant Cugat NW : 20 km ☎ 674 39 08, Fax 675 51 52.

✈ Barcelona SW : 12 km ☎ 478 50 00 - Iberia : Passeig de Gràcia 30, ✉ 08007, ☎ 412 56 67 HV - and Aviaco : Airport ☎ 478 24 11.

🚗 Sants ☎ 490 75 91.

⛴. to the Balearic Islands : Cía. Trasmediterránea, Moll de Barcelona - Estació Marítima, ✉ 08039, ☎ 443 25 32, Fax 442 63 45.

ℹ Gran Vía de les Corts Catalanes 658, ✉ 08010, ☎ 301 74 43 Fax 412 25 70, Sants Estació, ☎ 491 44 31 and at Airport 478 47 04 - **R.A.C.C.** Santaló 8, ✉ 08021, ☎ 200 33 11, Fax 209 47 14.

Madrid 627 - Bilbao/Bilbo 607 - Lérida/Lleida 169 - Perpignan 187 - Tarragona 109 - Toulouse 388 - Valencia 361 - Zaragoza 307.

Plans on following pages

Old Town and the Gothic Quarter : Ramblas, Pl. S. Jaume, Via Laietana, Passeig Nacional, Passeig de Colom

Le Meridien Barcelona, La Rambla 111, ✉ 08002, ☎ 318 62 00, Telex 54634, Fax 301 77 76 - |⇕| ▤ TV ☎ ♿ 🚗 - 🏛 25/200. AE ⓞ E VISA JCB. ✗ LX **b**
Meals a la carte 3000/4400 - ☕ 2000 - **198 rm** 23000/29000, 7 suites.

Colón, av. de la Catedral 7, ✉ 08002, ☎ 301 14 04, Telex 52654, Fax 317 29 15 - |⇕| ▤ TV ☎ ♿ - 🏛 25/120. AE ⓞ E VISA JCB. ✗ rest MV **e**
Meals 3300 - ☕ 1500 - **138 rm** 13750/20500, 9 suites.

Rivoli Rambla, La Rambla 128, ✉ 08002, ☎ 302 66 43, Telex 99222, Fax 317 20 38, 🏋 - |⇕| ▤ TV ☎ ♿ - 🏛 25/180. AE ⓞ E VISA JCB. ✗ LX **r**
Meals 3000 - ☕ 1900 - **81 rm** 19000/24000, 9 suites.

Royal coffee shop only, La Rambla 117, ✉ 08002, ☎ 301 94 00, Telex 97565, Fax 317 31 79 - |⇕| ▤ TV ☎ 🚗 - 🏛 25/100. AE ⓞ E VISA JCB LX **e**
☕ 1500 - **107 rm** 12500/16000, 1 suite.

Ambassador, Pintor Fortuny 13, ✉ 08001, ☎ 412 05 30, Telex 99222, Fax 317 20 38, 🏋, 🏊 - |⇕| ▤ TV ☎ ♿ 🚗 - 🏛 25/200. AE ⓞ E VISA JCB. ✗ rest LX **v**
Meals a la carte approx. 3250 - ☕ 1600 - **96 rm** 15900/19900, 9 suites.

Almirante, Via Laietana 42, ✉ 08003, ☎ 268 30 20, Fax 268 31 92 - |⇕| ▤ TV ☎ 🚗 - 🏛 25/40. AE ⓞ E VISA JCB. ✗ MV **d**
Meals 2500 - ☕ 1300 - **73 rm** 15000/20000, 3 suites.

Gravina coffee shop only, Gravina 12, ✉ 08001, ☎ 301 68 68, Telex 99370, Fax 317 28 38 - |⇕| ▤ TV ☎ - 🏛 25/50. AE ⓞ E VISA. ✗ HX **d**
☕ 700 - **60 rm** 9900/14900.

Montecarlo without rest, La Rambla 124, ✉ 08002, ☎ 412 04 04, Fax 318 73 23 - |⇕| ▤ TV ☎ ♿ 🚗. AE ⓞ E VISA. ✗ LX **r**
☕ 1000 - **80 rm** 8500/12000.

Reding, Gravina 5, ✉ 08001, ☎ 412 10 97, Fax 268 34 82 - |⇕| ▤ TV ☎ 🚗. AE ⓞ E VISA. ✗ rest HX **d**
Meals *(closed Sunday and Bank Holidays)* 1900 - ☕ 1200 - **44 rm** 13400/16100.

Atlantis without rest, Pelai 20, ✉ 08001, ☎ 318 90 12, Fax 412 09 14 - |⇕| ▤ TV ☎. AE ⓞ E VISA. ✗ HX **a**
☕ 900 - **42 rm** 8000/10000.

Metropol without rest, Ample 31, ✉ 08002, ☎ 310 51 00, Fax 319 12 76 – AE VISA JCB.
950 – **68 rm** 8925/11800. NY r

Lleó coffee shop only, Pelai 22, ✉ 08001, ☎ 318 13 12, Fax 412 26 57 – AE VISA JCB
925 – **75 rm** 8500/10500. HX a

Turín, Pintor Fortuny 9, ✉ 08001, ☎ 302 48 12, Fax 302 10 05 – AE VISA. rest
Meals 1000 – 800 – **60 rm** 8500/12900. LX v

Ramblas H. without rest, Rambles 33, ✉ 08002, ☎ 301 57 00, Fax 412 25 07 – 25. AE VISA.
975 – **70 rm** 10225/12750. MY z

Rialto coffee shop only, Ferran 42, ✉ 08002, ☎ 318 52 12, Telex 97206, Fax 318 53 12 – 25/50. AE VISA JCB
700 – **141 rm** 8850/11550. MX s

Park H., av. Marquès de l'Argentera 11, ✉ 08003, ☎ 319 60 00, Telex 99883, Fax 319 45 19 – AE VISA JCB.
Meals 2500 – 950 – **87 rm** 8000/11000. NX e

Regencia Colón without rest, Sagristans 13, ✉ 08002, ☎ 318 98 58, Telex 98175, Fax 317 28 22 – AE VISA
1000 – **55 rm** 7900/13500. MV r

Continental without rest, Rambles 138-2º, ✉ 08002, ☎ 301 25 70, Fax 302 73 60 – AE VISA JCB
35 rm 6950/8650. LV b

Agut d'Avignon, Trinitat 3, ✉ 08002, ☎ 302 60 34, Fax 302 53 18 – AE VISA JCB.
Meals a la carte 3975/6250. MY n

Quo Vadis, Carme 7, ✉ 08001, ☎ 302 40 72, Fax 301 04 35 – AE VISA JCB
closed Sunday – **Meals** a la carte 4065/6050. LX k

Aitor, Carbonell 5, ✉ 08003, ☎ 319 94 88, Basque rest – VISA. KY m
closed Sunday dinner, Monday, Holy Week, 15 August-15 September and Christmas – **Meals** a la carte 4500/5500.

Brasserie Flo, Junqueres 10, ✉ 08003, ☎ 319 31 02, Fax 268 23 95 – AE VISA
Meals a la carte 3200/4300. LV a

Reial Club Marítim, Moll d'Espanya, ✉ 08039, ☎ 221 71 43, Fax 221 44 12, ≤, – VISA
Meals a la carte 3400/4300. NY a

Senyor Parellada, Argenteria 37, ✉ 08003, ☎ 310 50 94 – AE VISA JCB.
closed Sunday and Bank Holidays – **Meals** a la carte 2600/3350. NX t

7 Portes, passeig d'Isabel II - 14, ✉ 08003, ☎ 319 30 33, Fax 319 46 62 – AE VISA.
Meals a la carte 2870/4470. NX s

Can Ramonet, Maquinista 17, ✉ 08003, ☎ 319 30 64, Fax 319 70 14, Seafood – AE VISA JCB
closed 8 August-9 September – **Meals** a la carte 3575/5275. KY e

Pitarra, Avinyó 56, ✉ 08002, ☎ 301 16 47, Fax 301 16 47 – AE VISA JCB NY e
closed Sunday and August – **Meals** a la carte 1975/3250.

Can Solé, Sant Carles 4, ✉ 08003, ☎ 221 58 15, Seafood – AE VISA KY a
closed Saturday dinner, Sunday, 15 days in February and 15 days in August – **Meals** a la carte approx. 3275.

Ca la María, Tallers 76 bis, ✉ 08001, ☎ 318 89 93 – AE VISA JCB HX d
closed Sunday dinner, Monday and August – **Meals** a la carte 2550/2925.

South of Av. Diagonal : Pl. de Catalunya, Gran Via de les Corts Catalanes, Passeig de Gràcia, Balmes, Muntaner, Aragó

Rey Juan Carlos I, av. Diagonal 661, ✉ 08028, ☎ 448 08 08, Fax 448 06 07, ≤ city, « Modern facilities. Park with lake and », – 25/1000. AE VISA JCB.
W : by Av. Diagonal EX
Chez Vous *(closed Saturday lunch, Sunday and August)* **Meals** a la carte 3900/5850 - ***Café Polo :*** **Meals** a la carte 3850/4900 – 2100 – **375 rm** 27000/36000, 37 suites.

Arts, de la Marina 19, ✉ 08005, ☎ 221 10 00, Fax 221 10 70, ≤, – 25/900. AE VISA JCB.
E : by Av. d'Icària KX
Newport *(dinner only, closed Sunday and August)* **Meals** a la carte approx. 4500 – 2400 – **397 rm** 27500/50000, 58 suites.

Ritz, Gran Via de les Corts Catalanes 668, ✉ 08010, ☎ 318 52 00, Telex 52739, Fax 318 01 48, – 25/350. AE VISA JCB. JV p
Meals a la carte 4350/6600 – 2300 – **148 rm** 32800/43000, 13 suites.

Princesa Sofía, pl. Pius XII-4, ✉ 08028, ☎ 330 71 11, Telex 51032, Fax 330 76 21, ≤, – 25/1200. AE VISA. EX x
Meals 3600 - ***L'Empordà*** *(closed Saturday, Sunday and 15 July-15 August)* **Meals** a la carte approx. 5600 – 1800 – **481 rm** 17000/25000, 24 suites.

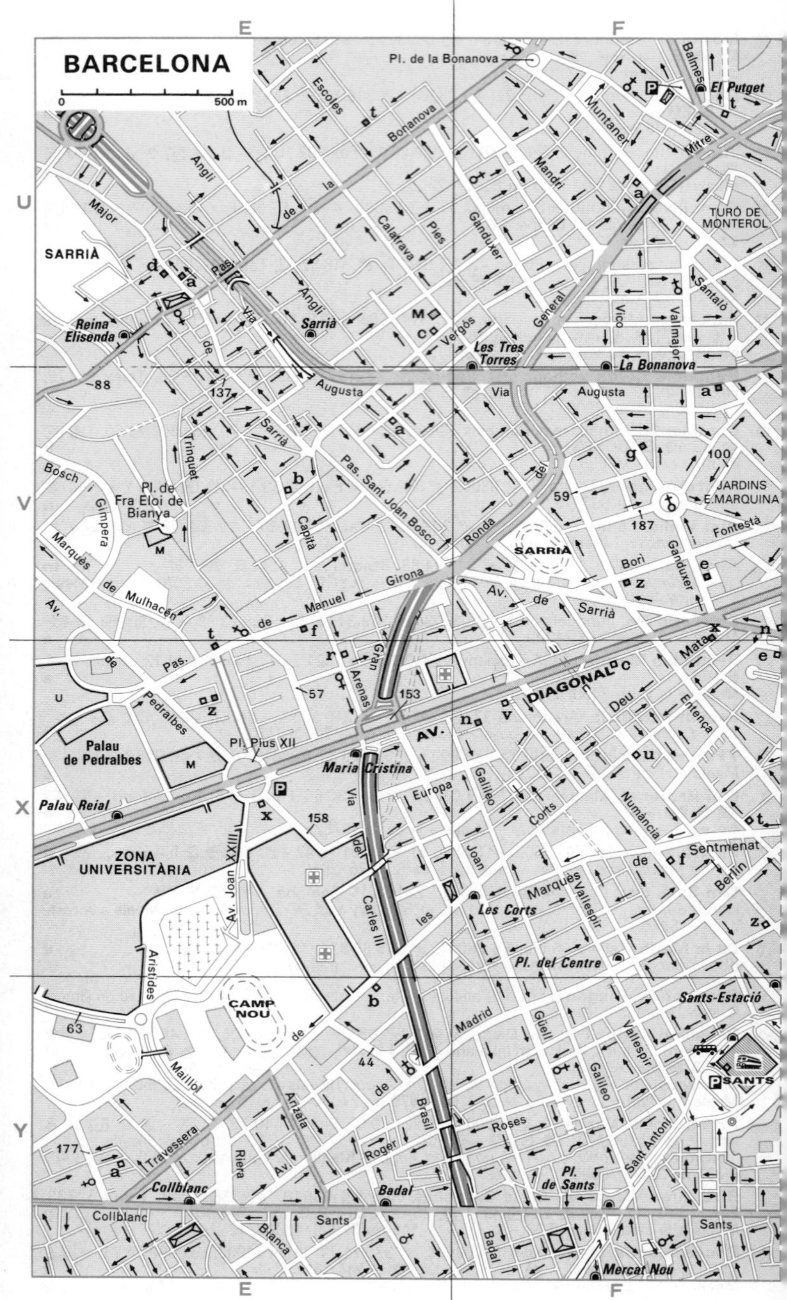
BARCELONA
0
500 m
E
F
U
V
X
Y
SARRIÀ
Reina Elisenda
Sarrià
Les Tres Torres
La Bonanova
El Putget
TURÓ DE MONTEROL
Pl. de la Bonanova
Pl. de Fra Eloi de Bianya
JARDINS E. MARQUINA
Palau de Pedralbes
Palau Reial
Pl. Pius XII
Maria Cristina
DIAGONAL
AV.
ZONA UNIVERSITÀRIA
CAMP NOU
Les Corts
Pl. del Centre
Sants-Estació
SANTS
Collblanc
Badal
Pl. de Sants
Mercat Nou
Via Augusta
Ronda del General Mitre
Pas. Sant Joan Bosco
Av. de Sarrià
Manuel Girona
Av. de Pedralbes
Gran Via de Carles III
Travessera de les Corts
Av. Joan XXIII
Madrid
Brasil
Roses
Sants
Numància
Entença
Galileo
Vallespir
Güell
Sant Antoni
Arizala
Riera Blanca
Maillol
Aristides
Europa
Sentmenat
Berlín
Muntaner
Balmes
Ganduxer
Calatrava
Anglí
Escoles Pies
Capità Arenas
Trinquet
Bosch i Gimpera
Marquès de Mulhacén
88
137
57
153
158
63
44
177
59
187
100

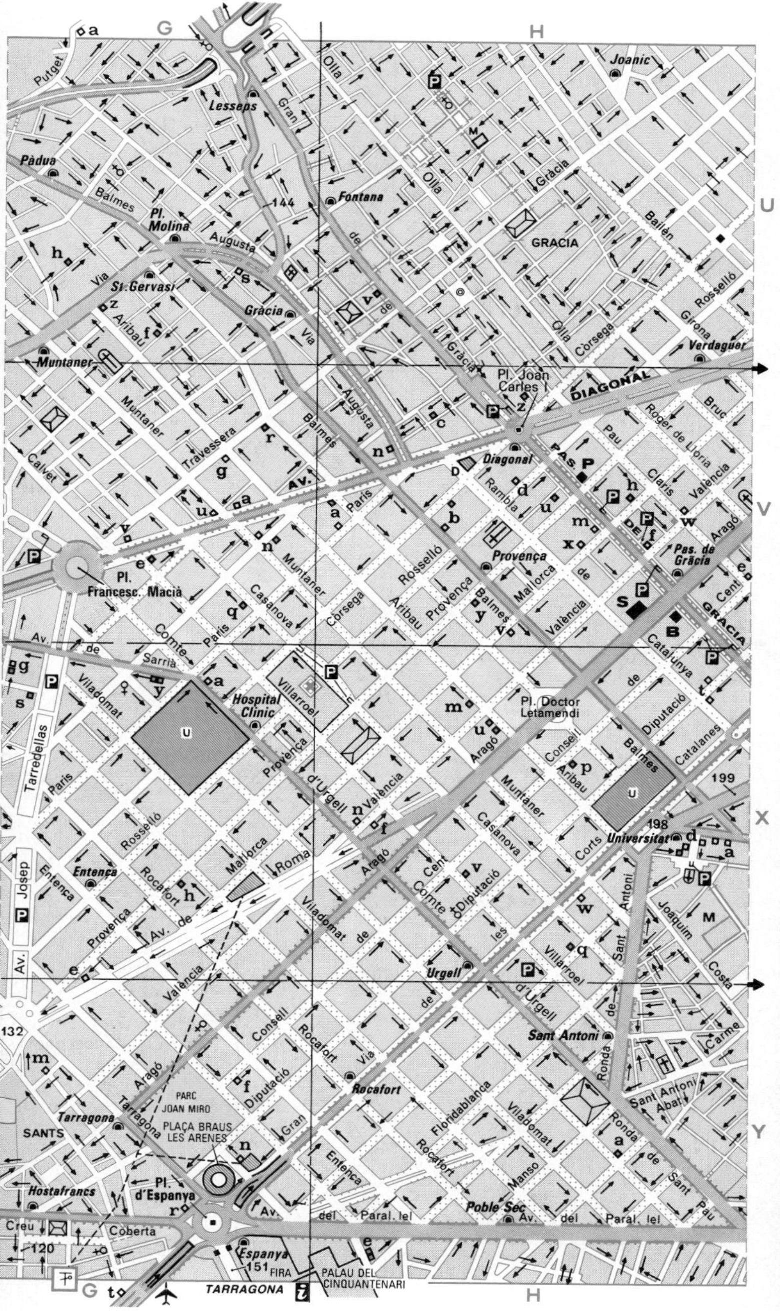
G
H
U
V
X
Y
Lesseps
Pàdua
Pl. Molina
Fontana
St. Gervasi
Gràcia
GRACIA
Joanic
Verdaguer
Muntaner
DIAGONAL
Pl. Joan Carles I
Diagonal
Provença
Pas. de Gràcia
Pl. Francesc. Macià
Hospital Clinic
Pl. Doctor Letamendi
Universitat
Entença
Urgell
Sant Antoni
Rocafort
Tarragona
SANTS
Hostafrancs
Pl. d'Espanya
Poble Sec
Espanya
PARC JOAN MIRO
PLAÇA BRAUS LES ARENES
FIRA
PALAU DEL CINQUANTENARI
TARRAGONA
144
132
120
151
198
199
Balmes
Augusta
Via
Aribau
Muntaner
Travessera
Calvet
Casanova
Còrsega
Rosselló
Mallorca
València
Aragó
Consell
Diputació
Corts
Catalanes
Viladomat
Villarroel
Comte d'Urgell
Roma
Paral.lel
Tarradellas
Josep
Sarrià
Olla
Bailèn
Girona
Bruc
Pau
Claris
Roger de Llúria
Rambla
Catalunya
Cent
Joaquim Costa
Carme
Sant Antoni Abat
Ronda de Sant Antoni
Ronda de Sant Pau
Floridablanca
Manso
Creu
Coberta
Putget
Gran de Gràcia
Gran Via
Comte de Sarrià
Av. de Roma
Av. Diagonal
Pas. de Gràcia

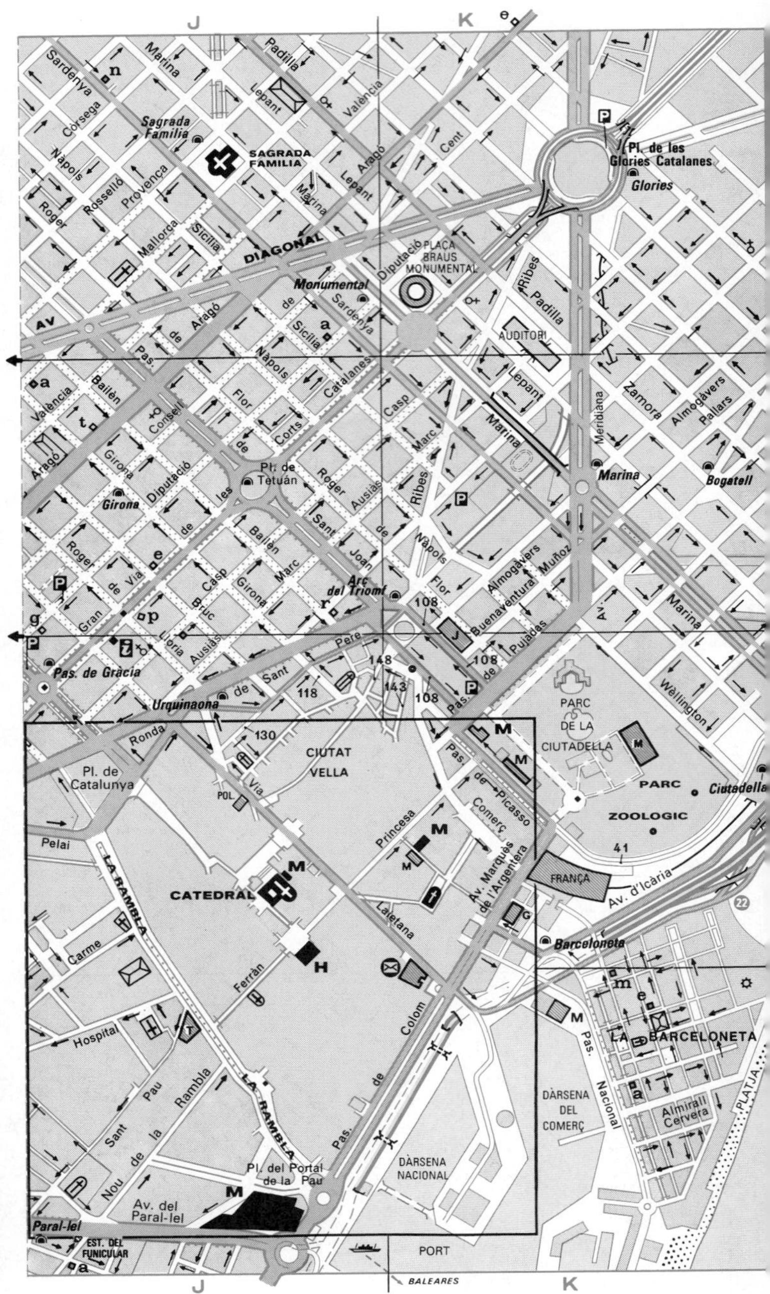
J
K
SAGRADA FAMILIA
Sagrada Familia
Pl. de les Glories Catalanes
Glories
DIAGONAL
PLAÇA BRAUS MONUMENTAL
Monumental
AUDITORI
Pl. de Tetuán
Girona
Marina
Bogatell
Arc del Triomf
Pas. de Gràcia
Urquinaona
PARC DE LA CIUTADELLA
PARC ZOOLOGIC
Ciutadella
CIUTAT VELLA
Pl. de Catalunya
CATEDRAL
LA RAMBLA
FRANÇA
Barceloneta
LA BARCELONETA
DÀRSENA DEL COMERÇ
DÀRSENA NACIONAL
Pl. del Portal de la Pau
Av. del Paral-lel
Paral-lel
EST. DEL FUNICULAR
PORT
BALEARES
PLATJA

STREET INDEX TO BARCELONA TOWN PLAN

BARCELONA

Street	Grid	No.
Capútxins (Rambla dels)	MY	35
Catalunya (Pl. de)	LV	
Estudis (Rambla dels)	LX	
Sant Josep (Rambla de)	LX	168
Santa Mònica (Rambla de)	MY	
Universitat (Ronda de la)	LV	199
Banys Nous	MX	7
Bergara	LV	10
Bisbe Irurita	MX	15
Bòria	MV	18
Born (Pas. del)	NX	20
Boters	MX	23
Canaletes (Rambla de)	LV	27
Canonge Colom (Pl.)	LY	28
Canvis Vells	NX	32
Cardenal Casañas	LX	36
Catedral (Av.)	MV	40
Ciutat	MX	43
Comercial (Pl.)	NV	45
Cucurella	LX	55
Doctor Joaquim Pou	MV	61
Escudellers	MY	72
Francesc Cambó (Av.)	MV	79
Isabel II (Pas. d')	NX	98
Montcada	NX	121
Montjuïc del Bisbe	MX	123
Nou de Sant Francesc	MY	126
Nova (Pl.)	MX	128
Paradís	MX	135
Pintor Fortuny	LX	140
Portal de Santa Madrona	MY	142
Ramon Berenguer el Gran (Pl.)	MX	147
Rei (Plaça del)	MX	149
Sant Felip Neri (Pl.)	MX	163
Sant Miquel (Pl. de)	MX	173
Sant Sever	MX	181
Santa Anna	LV	182
Santa Maria (Pl.)	NX	189

We suggest:

For a successful tour, that you prepare it in advance.

***Michelin maps** and **guides** will give you much useful information on route planning, places of interest, accommodation, prices etc.*

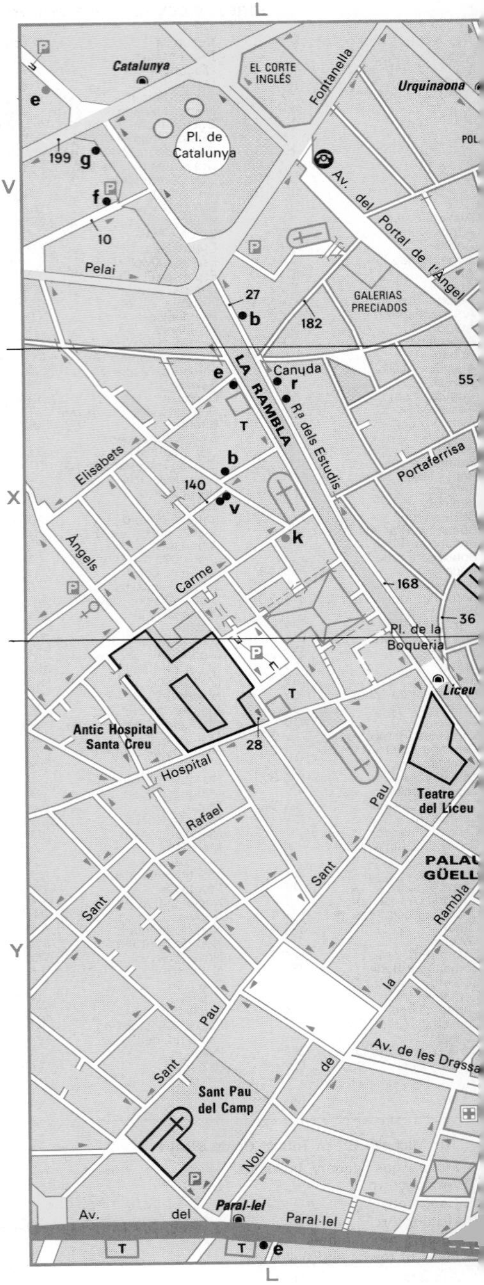

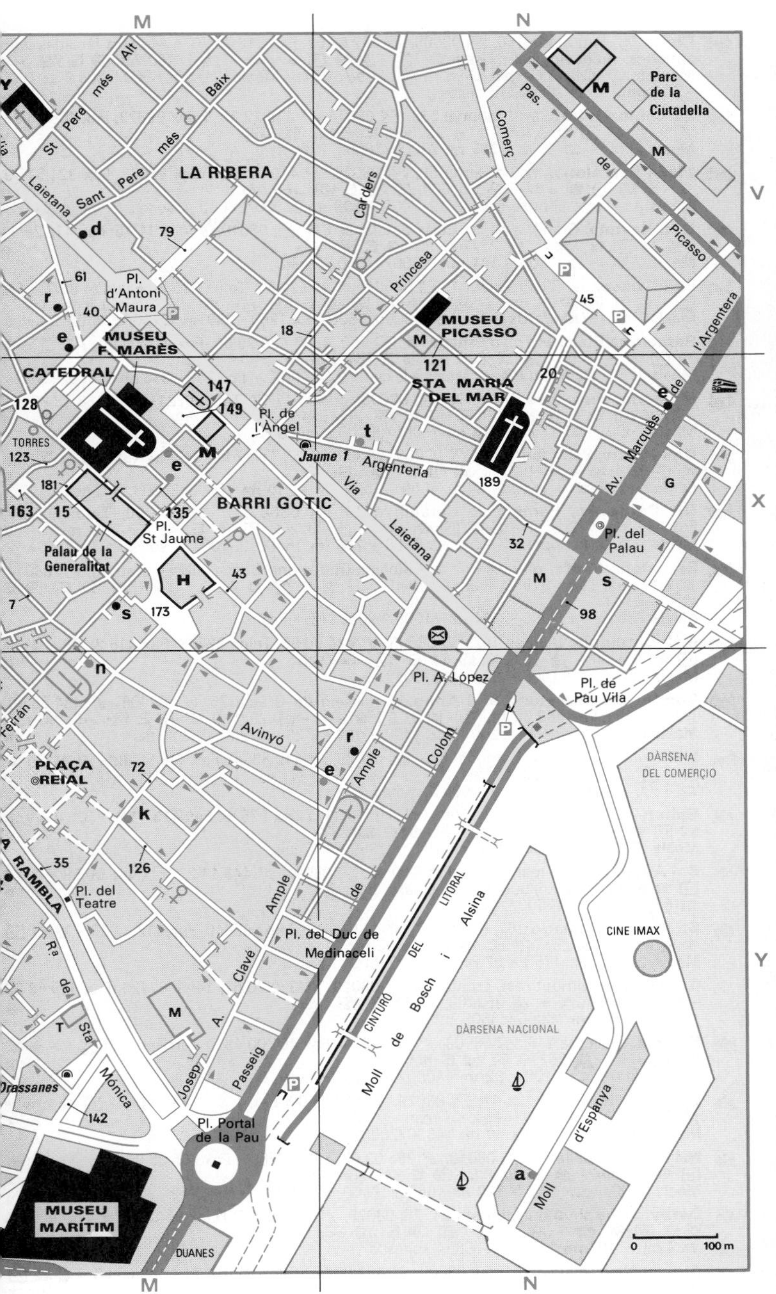
M
N
LA RIBERA
Parc de la Ciutadella
Pas. de Picasso
Comerç
Carders
Princesa
St Pere més Alt
St Pere més Baix
Sant Pere
Laietana
79
61
Pl. d'Antoni Maura
40
MUSEU F. MARÈS
18
MUSEU PICASSO
121
45
STA MARIA DEL MAR
20
CATEDRAL
147
149
Pl. de l'Àngel
128
TORRES
123
181
163
15
135
Jaume 1
Argenteria
189
BARRI GOTIC
Via Laietana
Av. Marquès de l'Argentera
Pl. del Palau
32
Pl. St Jaume
Palau de la Generalitat
43
173
7
98
V
X
Pl. A. López
Pl. de Pau Vila
Avinyó
Ample
Colom
PLAÇA REIAL
72
126
35
LA RAMBLA
Pl. del Teatre
Pl. del Duc de Medinaceli
DÀRSENA DEL COMERÇIO
CINE IMAX
Y
CINTURÓ DEL LITORAL
Moll de Bosch i Alsina
DÀRSENA NACIONAL
Moll d'Espanya
Rª de Sta Mónica
Drassanes
142
A. Josep Clavé
Passeig de Colom
Pl. Portal de la Pau
MUSEU MARÍTIM
DUANES
0 100 m

Claris, Pau Claris 150, 08009, 487 62 62, Fax 215 79 70, « Modern facilities with antiques. Archaeological museum », - 25/60. AE E VISA JCB
Meals 5000 - ***Caviar Caspio*** *(dinner only, closed Sunday)* **Meals** a la carte 5800/7800 - 1900 - **106 rm** 23600/29500, 18 suites. HV **w**

Barcelona Hilton, av. Diagonal 589, 08014, 419 22 33, Telex 99623, Fax 405 25 73, - 25/800. AE E VISA JCB FX **v**
Meals 2800 - 2000 - **285 rm** 23000/28000, 2 suites.

Meliá Barcelona, av. de Sarrià 50, 08029, 410 60 60, Telex 51638, Fax 321 51 79, - 25/500. AE E VISA JCB. FV **n**
Meals a la carte approx. 4500 - 2000 - **308 rm** 22000/28000, 4 suites.

G.H. Havana, Gran Via de les Corts Catalanes 647, 08010, 412 11 15, Fax 412 26 11 - 25/200. AE E VISA JCB. JV **e**
Meals 2800 - 1300 - **141 rm** 15800/17800, 4 suites.

Fira Palace, av. Rius i Taulet 1, 08004, 426 22 23, Telex 97588, Fax 424 86 79, - 25/1300. AE E VISA JCB. S : by Lleida HY
Meals 2800 - ***El Mall :*** **Meals** a la carte 3000/3500 - 1250 - **260 rm** 16260/20330, 16 suites.

Barcelona Plaza H., pl. d'Espanya 6, 08014, 426 26 00, Fax 426 04 00, - 25/600. AE E VISA JCB. GY **r**
Meals 2750 - ***Gourmet Plaza :*** **Meals** a la carte 3000/4000 - 1250 - **338 rm** 15800, 9 suites.

Majestic, passeig de Gràcia 70, 08008, 488 17 17, Telex 52211, Fax 488 18 80, - 25/600. AE E VISA JCB. HV **f**
Meals 2400 - 1700 - **328 rm** 19000/23000, 1 suite.

Diplomatic, Pau Claris 122, 08009, 488 02 00, Telex 54701, Fax 488 12 22, - 25/250. AE E VISA JCB. HV **e**
La Salsa : **Meals** a la carte 3400/4550 - 1500 - **210 rm** 16000/20000, 7 suites.

NH Calderón, Rambla de Catalunya 26, 08007, 301 00 00, Telex 99529, Fax 317 31 57, - 25/200. AE E VISA JCB. rest HX **t**
Meals a la carte approx. 3700 - 1600 - **245 rm** 18500/23100, 17 suites.

Barcelona Sants, pl. dels Països Catalans (Barcelona Sants railway station), 08014, 90 95 95, Telex 97568, Fax 490 60 45, - - 25/1500. AE E VISA JCB. FY
Meals 3350 - 1650 - **364 rm** 11000/22000, 13 suites.

G.H. Catalonia, Balmes 142, 08008, 415 90 90, Telex 98718, Fax 415 22 09 - - 50/260. AE E VISA JCB. HV **b**
Meals 2400 - 1500 - **82 rm** 15750, 2 suites.

Condes de Barcelona and Annexe, passeig de Gràcia 75, 08008, 484 86 00, Telex 51531, Fax 488 06 14, - - 25/180. AE E VISA JCB. rest
Meals a la carte approx. 6200 - 1700 - **180 rm** 23000/29000, 2 suites. HV **m**

L'Illa without rest, av. Diagonal 555, 08029, 410 33 00, Fax 410 88 92 - - 25/100. AE E VISA. FX **c**
1300 - **103 rm** 19200/24000, 10 suites.

Gallery H., Roselló 249, 08008, 415 99 11, Telex 97518, Fax 415 91 84, - - 25/200. AE E VISA. HV **d**
Meals 3500 - 1600 - **110 rm** 19400/23500, 5 suites.

Sol Apolo without rest, av. del Paral·lel 57, 08011, 443 11 22, Fax 443 00 59 - - 25/500. AE E VISA JCB. LY **e**
850 - **303 rm** 12600/15750.

St. Moritz, Diputació 262, 08007, 412 15 00, Telex 97340, Fax 412 12 36 - - 25/140. AE E VISA JCB JV **g**
Meals 2400 - 1750 - **92 rm** 20400/25500.

Gran Derby without rest, Loreto 28, 08029, 322 20 62, Telex 97429, Fax 419 68 20 - - 25/100. AE E VISA JCB GX **g**
1250 - **31 rm** 15000/16500, 12 suites.

Balmes, Mallorca 216, 08008, 451 19 14, Fax 451 00 49, « Terrace with » - - 25/70. AE E VISA JCB HV **v**
Meals 1500 - 1100 - **92 rm** 15000/16500, 8 suites.

City Park H., Nicaragua 47, 08029, 419 95 00, Fax 419 71 63 - - 25/40. AE E VISA JCB. rest FX **z**
Meals 1600 - 1000 - **80 rm** 14500/20500.

NH Podium, Bailén 4, 08010, 265 02 02, Telex 97007, Fax 265 05 06, - - 25/240. AE E VISA JCB. JV **r**
Meals 2500 - 1500 - **140 rm** 15600/19500, 5 suites.

Derby coffee shop only, Loreto 21, 08029, 322 32 15, Telex 97429, Fax 410 08 62 - - 25/100. AE E VISA JCB FX **e**
1250 - **107 rm** 14750/16500, 4 suites.

Alexandra, Mallorca 251, 08008, 487 05 05, Telex 81107, Fax 488 02 58 - - 25/100. AE E VISA. HV **x**
Meals 2300 - 1600 - **73 rm** 15000/19000, 2 suites.

Astoria without rest, París 203, ✉ 08036, ☎ 209 83 11, Telex 81129, Fax 202 30 08 – |‡| ▤ TV ☎ – 🏛 25/30. AE ⓓ E VISA JCB HV **a**
☕ 975 – **114 rm** 13500/15400, 3 suites.

NH Master, València 105, ✉ 08011, ☎ 323 62 15, Telex 81258, Fax 323 43 89 – |‡| ▤ TV ☎ 🚗 – 🏛 25/170. AE ⓓ E VISA JCB. ✳ rest HX **n**
Meals 2400 – ☕ 1100 – **80 rm** 11880/16500, 1 suite.

Cristal, Diputació 257, ✉ 08007, ☎ 487 87 78, Telex 54560, Fax 487 90 30 – |‡| ▤ TV ☎ 🚗 – 🏛 25/70. AE ⓓ E VISA JCB. ✳ HX **t**
Meals 1400 – ☕ 1125 – **148 rm** 12250/18500.

NH Numància, Numància 74, ✉ 08029, ☎ 322 44 51, Fax 410 76 42 – |‡| ▤ TV ☎ 🚗 – 🏛 25/70. AE ⓓ E VISA JCB. ✳ FX **f**
Meals a la carte approx. 2865 – ☕ 1100 – **140 rm** 11000.

NH Sant Angelo without rest, Consell de Cent 74, ✉ 08015, ☎ 423 46 47, Fax 423 88 40 – |‡| ▤ TV ☎ ♿ 🚗 – 🏛 25. AE ⓓ E VISA JCB GY **f**
☕ 1100 – **50 rm** 11880/16500.

Guitart Grand Passage, Muntaner 212, ✉ 08036, ☎ 201 03 06, Telex 98311, Fax 201 00 04 – |‡| ▤ TV ☎ – 🏛 25/80. AE ⓓ E VISA. ✳ rest GV **n**
Meals 2500 – ☕ 1300 – **40 suites** 14000/20000.

Núñez Urgel without rest, Comte d'Urgell 232, ✉ 08036, ☎ 322 41 53, Fax 419 01 06 – |‡| ▤ TV ☎ 🚗 – 🏛 25/100. AE ⓓ E VISA JCB GX **a**
☕ 1250 – **120 rm** 9000/11500, 2 suites.

Expo H., Mallorca 1, ✉ 08014, ☎ 325 12 12, Telex 54147, Fax 325 11 44, 🏊 – |‡| ▤ TV ☎ 🚗 – 🏛 25/900. AE ⓓ E VISA JCB. ✳ GY **m**
Meals 1900 – ☕ 950 – **435 rm** 12000/15000.

Duques de Bergara, Bergara 11, ✉ 08002, ☎ 301 51 51, Fax 317 34 42 – |‡| ▤ TV ☎ – 🏛 25/80. AE ⓓ E VISA JCB. ✳ LV **f**
Meals 1800 – ☕ 1200 – **51 rm** 15300.

Caledonian without rest, Gran Via de les Corts Catalanes 574, ✉ 08011, ☎ 453 02 00, Fax 451 77 03 – |‡| ▤ TV ☎ ♿ 🚗. AE ⓓ E VISA JCB HX **w**
44 rm ☕ 8500/13000.

Abbot without rest, av. de Roma 23, ✉ 08029, ☎ 430 04 05, Fax 419 57 41 – |‡| ▤ TV ☎ 🚗 – 🏛 25/100. AE ⓓ E VISA. ✳ GXY **e**
☕ 1100 – **39 rm** 10750/13750.

NH Forum, Ecuador 20, ✉ 08029, ☎ 419 36 36, Fax 419 89 10 – |‡| ▤ TV ☎ 🚗 – 🏛 25/50. AE ⓓ E VISA JCB. ✳ FX **t**
Meals 1500 – ☕ 1000 – **47 rm** 11000, 1 suite.

NH Rallye, Travessera de les Corts 150, ✉ 08028, ☎ 339 90 50, Fax 411 07 90, 🏊 – |‡| ▤ TV ☎ ♿ 🚗 – 🏛 25/200. AE ⓓ E VISA JCB. ✳ EY **b**
Meals 1750 – ☕ 1100 – **106 rm** 11880/16500.

NH Les Corts, Travessera de les Corts 292, ✉ 08029, ☎ 322 08 11, Fax 322 09 08 – |‡| ▤ TV ☎ 🚗 – 🏛 25/80. AE ⓓ E VISA JCB. ✳ FX **u**
Meals 1750 – ☕ 1100 – **80 rm** 11880/16500, 1 suite.

Catalunya Plaza without rest, pl. de Catalunya 7, ✉ 08002, ☎ 317 71 71, Fax 317 78 55 – |‡| ▤ TV ☎ ♿ – 🏛 25. AE ⓓ E VISA. ✳ LV **g**
☕ 975 – **46 rm** 12000/14000.

Onix without rest, Llansà 30, ✉ 08015, ☎ 426 00 87, Fax 426 19 81, 🏊 – |‡| ▤ TV ☎ 🚗 – 🏛 25/150. AE ⓓ VISA. ✳ GY **n**
☕ 1000 – **80 rm** 11200/14000.

XXXXX **Beltxenea,** Mallorca 275, ✉ 08008, ☎ 215 30 24, Fax 487 00 81, 🌂, « Garden-terrace » – ▤. AE ⓓ E VISA. ✳ HV **h**
closed Saturday lunch, Sunday, Bank Holidays, Holy Week, 15 days in August and Christmas
Meals a la carte 7500/8500.

XXXX ✿ **La Dama,** av. Diagonal 423, ✉ 08036, ☎ 202 06 86, Fax 200 72 99 – ▤. AE ⓓ E VISA. ✳
Meals a la carte 4750/6475 HV **a**
Spec. Ensalada tibia de cigalas al vinagre de naranja. Rodaballo asado con ajo y bacon. Carro de repostería.

XXXX **Finisterre,** av. Diagonal 469, ✉ 08036, ☎ 439 55 76, Fax 439 99 41 – ▤. AE ⓓ E VISA. ✳ GV **e**
Meals a la carte 4650/6750.

XXX **Oliver y Hardy,** av. Diagonal 593, ✉ 08014, ☎ 419 31 81, Fax 419 18 99, 🌂 – ▤. AE ⓓ E VISA JCB. ✳ FX **n**
closed Sunday – **Meals** a la carte 3650/5700.

XXX **Casa Calvet,** Casp 48, ✉ 08010, ☎ 412 40 12, Fax 412 43 36 – ▤. AE ⓓ E VISA. ✳ JVX **r**
closed Sunday, Bank Holidays and 15 to 31 August – **Meals** a la carte 4140/5200.

XXX ✿ **Jaume de Provença,** Provença 88, ✉ 08029, ☎ 430 00 29, Fax 439 29 50 – ▤. AE ⓓ E VISA JCB. ✳ GX **h**
closed Sunday dinner, Monday, Holy Week and August – **Meals** a la carte 4300/5500
Spec. Pastel de esqueixada de bacalao. Crustáceos y pescados en jugo de bouillabaisse. Muslito de conejo relleno y lacado con miel de romero.

XXX **Talaia Mar,** Marina 16, ✉ 08005, ℘ 221 90 90, Fax 221 89 89 – ▤ ⇔. AE ⓓ E VISA. ✗ E : by Av. d'Icària KX
closed Sunday dinner and Monday lunch – **Meals** a la carte 4700/5900.

XXX **Bel Air,** Córsega 286, ✉ 08008, ℘ 237 75 88, Fax 237 95 26, Rice dishes – ▤. AE ⓓ E VISA JCB HV **b**
closed Sunday – **Meals** a la carte 3200/5220.

XXX **El Tragaluz,** passatge de la Concepció 5 - 1°, ✉ 08008, ℘ 487 01 96, Fax 217 01 19, « Original decor with glass roof » – ▤. AE ⓓ E VISA JCB. ✗ HV **u**
closed Saturday lunch, Sunday and Bank Holidays – **Meals** a la carte 4350/5775.

XXX **Tikal,** Rambla de Catalunya 5, ✉ 08007, ℘ 302 22 21 – ▤. AE ⓓ E VISA JCB. ✗ LV **e**
closed Saturday lunch, Sunday, Bank Holidays and 7 to 27 August – **Meals** a la carte approx. 3470.

XX **El Asador de Aranda,** Londres 94, ✉ 08036, ℘ 414 67 90, Roast lamb – ▤. AE ⓓ E VISA. ✗ GV **n**
closed August – **Meals** a la carte approx. 4100.

XX **Els Pescadors,** pl. Prim 1, ✉ 08005, ℘ 309 20 18, Fax 485 40 42, 🍴, Seafood – ▤. AE ⓓ E VISA JCB E : by Av. d'Icària KX
closed Holy Week and Christmas – **Meals** a la carte 3100/4675.

XX **Rías de Galicia,** Lleida 7, ✉ 08004, ℘ 424 81 52, Fax 426 13 07, Seafood – ▤. AE ⓓ E VISA JCB. ✗ HY **e**
Meals a la carte 3900/5700.

XX **Vinya Rosa-Magí,** av. de Sarrià 17, ✉ 08029, ℘ 430 00 03, Fax 430 00 41 – ▤. AE ⓓ E VISA GX **y**
closed Saturday lunch and Sunday – **Meals** a la carte 3500/4500.

XX **Gorría,** Diputació 421, ✉ 08013, ℘ 245 11 64, Fax 232 78 57, Basque rest – ▤. AE ⓓ E VISA JCB. ✗ JU **a**
closed Sunday, Bank Holidays dinner and August – **Meals** a la carte 4515/5270.

XX **La Provença,** Provença 242, ✉ 08008, ℘ 323 23 67, Fax 451 23 89 – ▤. ⓓ E VISA
Meals a la carte 2470/3070. HV **y**

XX **Sibarit,** Aribau 65, ✉ 08011, ℘ 453 93 03 – ▤. AE ⓓ E VISA. ✗ HX **u**
closed Saturday lunch, Sunday, Bank Holidays, Holy Week and 15 to 31 August – **Meals** a la carte approx. 5500.

XX **Casa Darío,** Consell de Cent 256, ✉ 08011, ℘ 453 31 35, Fax 451 33 95 – ▤. AE ⓓ E VISA. ✗ HX **p**
closed Sunday and August – **Meals** a la carte 3900/6100.

XX **El Túnel del Port,** moll de Gregalt (Port Olímpic), ✉ 08005, ℘ 221 03 21, Fax 221 35 86, ⩤, 🍴 – ▤. AE E VISA E : by Av. d'Icària KX
closed Sunday dinner – **Meals** a la carte 3300/4500.

X **El Celler de Casa Jordi,** Rita Bonnat 3, ✉ 08029, ℘ 430 10 45 – ▤. AE ⓓ E VISA. ✗ GX **s**
closed Sunday and August – **Meals** a la carte approx. 2850.

X **Rosamar,** Sepúlveda 159, ✉ 08011, ℘ 453 31 92 – ▤. AE ⓓ E VISA HX **q**
closed Sunday dinner, Monday, Holy Week and August – **Meals** a la carte 2750/3500.

X **El Pescador,** Mallorca 314, ✉ 08037, ℘ 207 10 24, Seafood – ▤. AE ⓓ E VISA. ✗ JV **a**
closed Sunday dinner and Bank Holidays dinner – **Meals** a la carte 2550/4800.

X **Elche,** Vila i Vilà 71, ✉ 08004, ℘ 329 68 46, Fax 329 40 12, Rice dishes – ▤. AE ⓓ E VISA JY **a**
closed Sunday dinner – **Meals** a la carte 2580/3320.

X **Chicoa,** Aribau 73, ✉ 08036, ℘ 453 11 23 – ▤. AE E VISA HX **m**
closed Sunday, Bank Holidays and August – **Meals** a la carte 3500/4575.

X **Els Perols de l'Empordà,** Villarroel 88, ✉ 08011, ℘ 323 10 33, Ampurdan rest – ▤. ⓓ E VISA. ✗ HX **v**
Meals a la carte 1800/3200.

X **Azpiolea,** Casanova 167, ✉ 08036, ℘ 430 90 30, Basque rest – ▤. AE ⓓ E VISA. ✗ GV **q**
closed Sunday and 31 July-30 August – **Meals** a la carte 3325/4150.

X **Cañota,** Lleida 7, ✉ 08004, ℘ 325 91 71, Fax 426 13 07, Braised meat specialities – ▤. AE ⓓ E VISA JCB. ✗ HY **e**
Meals a la carte 2100/3100.

North of Av. Diagonal : Via Augusta, Capità Arenas, Ronda General Mitre, Passeig de la Bonanova, Av. de Pedralbes

🏨 **Tryp Presidente,** av. Diagonal 570, ✉ 08021, ℘ 200 21 11, Fax 209 51 06 – |‡| ▤ 📺 ☎ – 🅰 25/420. AE ⓓ E VISA JCB. ✗ GV **u**
Meals 2500 – ☕ 1350 – **155 rm** 14500/18500.

Hesperia coffee shop only, Vergós 20, 08017, 204 55 51, Telex 98403, Fax 204 43 92 - 25/150. AE E VISA EU **c**
1200 - **139 rm** 15900/17900.

Suite H., Muntaner 505, 08022, 212 80 12, Telex 99077, Fax 211 23 17 - 25/90. AE E VISA JCB. FU **a**
Meals 2000 - 1200 - **77 suites** 12700.

Balmoral without rest, Via Augusta 5, 08006, 217 87 00, Telex 54087, Fax 415 14 21 - 25/250. AE E VISA. HV **n**
1050 - **94 rm** 11100/13600.

NH Cóndor, Via Augusta 127, 08006, 209 45 11, Telex 52925, Fax 202 27 13 - 25/50. AE E VISA JCB. GU **z**
Meals 1750 - 1000 - **78 rm** 11880/16500, 12 suites.

Arenas coffee shop only, Capità Arenas 20, 08034, 280 03 03, Fax 280 33 92 - 25/50. AE E VISA EX **r**
1000 - **58 rm** 12000/15000, 1 suite.

Victoria, av. de Pedralbes 16 bis, 08034, 280 15 15, Fax 280 52 67, , - . AE E VISA JCB. rest EX **z**
Meals 1575 - 1350 - **74 suites** 13125/16400.

Park Putxet, Putxet 68, 08023, 212 51 58, Telex 98718, Fax 418 58 17 - 25/200. AE E VISA JCB. GU **a**
Meals 1700 - 950 - **141 rm** 8700.

NH Belagua, Via Augusta 89, 08006, 237 39 40, Telex 99643, Fax 415 30 62 - 25/90. AE E VISA. GU **s**
Meals 1800 - 1000 - **72 rm** 11880/16500.

Mitre without rest, Bertràn 9, 08023, 212 11 04, Fax 418 94 81 - . AE E VISA FU **t**
750 - **57 rm** 9800/13000.

Condado without rest, Aribau 201, 08021, 200 23 11, Fax 200 25 86 - . AE VISA GV **g**
1000 - **88 rm** 10440/13050.

NH Pedralbes coffee shop dinner only, Fontcuberta 4, 08034, 203 71 12, Fax 205 70 65 - 25. AE E VISA JCB. EV **b**
1100 - **30 rm** 11880/16500.

Covadonga without rest, av. Diagonal 596, 08021, 209 55 11, Fax 209 58 33 - . AE E VISA JCB GV **v**
600 - **85 rm** 8300/13100.

Albéniz without rest, Aragó 591, 08026, 265 26 26, Fax 265 40 07 - 25/50. AE E VISA JCB. NE : by Aragó HV
950 - **47 rm** 8500.

Via Veneto, Ganduxer 10, 08021, 200 72 44, Fax 201 60 95, « Early 20C style » - . AE E VISA JCB. FV **e**
closed Saturday lunch, Sunday and 1 to 20 August - **Meals** a la carte 5270/5900
Spec. Conejo con hígado de pato, verduras y aceite de nueces. Rodaballo asado y raviolis de setas. Crestas de gallo y riñones de ternera con mostaza y verduras.

Reno, Tuset 27, 08006, 200 91 29, Fax 414 41 14 - . AE E VISA JCB. GV **r**
closed Saturday in August and Saturday lunch the rest of the year - **Meals** a la carte 5200/7100.

Neichel, Beltran i Rózpide 16 bis, 08034, 203 84 08, Fax 205 63 69 - . AE E VISA EX **z**
closed Saturday lunch, Sunday, Holy Week, August and Christmas - **Meals** a la carte 5700/6900
Spec. Casoleta de vieiras y gambas al jugo de erizo e hinojo (winter). Remo con suquet de espardenyes. Tournedos de cordero relleno de olivada y albahaca.

Jean Luc Figueras, Santa Teresa 10, 08012, 415 28 77, Fax 415 28 77, Tasteful decor - . AE E VISA. HV **z**
closed Saturday lunch, Sunday, Holy Week and 12 to 27 August - **Meals** a la carte 5250/6700
Spec. Canelones de cigala con provenzal de tomate y olivas negras. Dorada con julivertada de caracoles y ceps (season). Canetón asado con cardamomo y citronela.

Botafumeiro, Gran de Gràcia 81, 08012, 218 42 30, Fax 415 58 48, Seafood - . AE E VISA JCB. HU **v**
Meals a la carte 4400/6600
Spec. Cocochas de bacalao. Salpicón de bogavante y marisco. Sepia con albóndigas.

Roncesvalles, Via Augusta 201, 08021, 209 01 25, Fax 209 12 95 - . AE E VISA JCB. FV **a**
closed Saturday lunch and Sunday dinner - **Meals** a la carte approx. 3900.

El Trapío, Esperanza 25, 08017, 211 58 17, Fax 417 10 37, , « Terrace » - . AE VISA. EU **t**
closed Sunday dinner - **Meals** a la carte 3000/4500.

La Petite Marmite, Madrazo 68, 08006, 201 48 79 - . AE E VISA. GU **f**
closed Sunday, Bank Holidays, Holy Week and August - **Meals** a la carte 2900/3700.

XX **El Asador de Aranda,** av. del Tibidabo 31, ✉ 08022, ☎ 417 01 15, Fax 212 24 82, Roast lamb, « Former palace » – AE ⓓ E VISA. NW : by Balmes FU
closed Sunday dinner – **Meals** a la carte approx. 4000.

XX ✿ **El Racó d'en Freixa,** Sant Elíes 22, ✉ 08006, ☎ 209 75 59, Fax 209 79 18 – ▤. AE ⓓ E VISA. GU **h**
closed Bank Holidays dinner, Monday, Holy Week and August – **Meals** a la carte 4400/6175
Spec. Ravioli de gambas y setas (season). Lomo de conejo relleno de ciruelas con teja de piñones. Crema de chocolate con pimientos morrones a la miel de lavanda.

XX ✿ **Gaig,** passeig de Maragall 402, ✉ 08031, ☎ 429 10 17, Fax 429 70 02, – ▤. AE ⓓ E VISA N : by Travessera de Gràcia HU
closed Monday, Bank Holidays dinner, Holy Week, 27 July-26 August and Christmas – **Meals** a la carte 4525/5350
Spec. Foie estofado con guisantes (Jan-May). Rapito de playa asado a la catalana. Canetón asado con salsa de piel de naranja.

XX **Roig Robí,** Séneca 20, ✉ 08006, ☎ 218 92 22, Fax 415 78 42, « Garden-terrace » – ▤. AE ⓓ E VISA JCB HV **c**
closed Sunday, 1st week in January and 3rd week in August – **Meals** a la carte 3700/5650.

XX **Tram-Tram,** Major de Sarrià 121, ✉ 08017, ☎ 204 85 18, – ▤. AE ⓓ VISA. EU **d**
closed Saturday lunch, Sunday, Holy Week, 2nd week in August and 23 to 31 December – **Meals** a la carte 3950/4050.

X **Vivanda,** Major de Sarrià 134, ✉ 08017, ☎ 205 47 17, Fax 203 19 18, – ▤. AE E VISA.
closed Sunday and Monday lunch – **Meals** a la carte 2900/4500. EU **a**

X **Sal i Pebre,** Alfambra 14, ✉ 08034, ☎ 205 36 58, Fax 205 56 72 – ▤. AE ⓓ E VISA JCB. W : by Pas. de Manuel Girona EX
Meals a la carte 1900/3300.

X **La Yaya Amelia,** Sardenya 364, ✉ 08025, ☎ 456 45 73 – ▤. AE E VISA JCB. JU **n**
closed Sunday and Holy Week – **Meals** a la carte 2650/3750.

Typical atmosphere :

XX **Font del Gat,** passeig Santa Madrona (Montjuic), ✉ 08004, ☎ 424 02 24, Fax 207 10 26, Regional decor – Ⓟ. AE ⓓ E VISA. S : by Av. Reina María Cristina GY
closed Monday except Bank Holidays or day before – **Meals** a la carte 2700/4200.

X **La Cuineta,** Paradís 4, ✉ 08002, ☎ 315 01 11, Fax 315 07 98, Typical rest, « In a 17C cellar » – ▤. AE ⓓ E VISA JCB. MX **e**
Meals a la carte 3675/6450.

X **Can Culleretes,** Quintana 5, ✉ 08002, ☎ 317 64 85, Fax 317 64 85, Typical rest – ▤. AE ⓓ E VISA MY **c**
closed Sunday dinner, Monday and 1 to 22 July – **Meals** a la carte 1950/3000.

X **Los Caracoles,** Escudellers 14, ✉ 08002, ☎ 302 31 85, Fax 302 07 43, Typical rest. Rustic regional decor – ▤. AE ⓓ E VISA JCB. MY **k**
Meals a la carte 2775/4775.

X **Pá i Trago,** Parlament 41, ✉ 08015, ☎ 441 13 20, Fax 441 13 20, Typical rest – ▤. E VISA HY **a**
closed Monday except Bank Holidays and 22 June-10 July – **Meals** a la carte 2400/3700.

X **A la Menta,** passeig Manuel Girona 50, ✉ 08034, ☎ 204 15 49, Typical taverna – ▤. AE ⓓ E VISA. EV **f**
closed Sunday June-September and Sunday dinner the rest of the year – **Meals** a la carte approx. 4300.

Environs

at Esplugues de Llobregat W : 5 km – ✉ 08950 Esplugues de Llobregat – ☎ 93 :

XXX **La Masía,** av. Països Catalans 58 ☎ 371 00 09, Fax 372 84 00, « Terrace under pine trees » – ▤ Ⓟ. AE ⓓ E VISA JCB.
closed Sunday dinner and Holy Week – **Meals** a la carte 3450/5150.

X **Quirze,** Laureá Miró 202 ☎ 371 10 84, Fax 371 65 12, – ▤ Ⓟ. AE E VISA.
closed Saturday dinner and Sunday June-September and Sunday dinner the rest of the year – **Meals** a la carte 3400/4400.

at Sant Just Desvern W : 6 km – ✉ 08960 Sant Just Desvern – ☎ 93 :

Sant Just, Frederic Mompou 1 ☎ 473 25 17, Fax 473 24 50, – ▤ TV ☎ – 25/450. AE ⓓ E VISA JCB.
Alambí : **Meals** a la carte 3640/5400 – ☐ 1200 – **138 rm** 13550/14600, 12 suites.

at Valldoreix NW : 14,5 km – ✉ 08190 Valldoreix – ☎ 93 :

La Reserva, rambla Mossèn Jacint Verdaguer 41 ☎ 674 21 00, Fax 674 21 00, ←, « Former manor house », – ▤ TV ☎. AE ⓓ E VISA JCB
closed 1 to 29 August – **Meals** a la carte 3000/5250 – **16 rm** ☐ 10000/12000.

at Sant Cugat del Vallés NW : 18 km – ✉ 08190 Sant Cugat del Vallés – ☎ 93 :

Novotel Barcelona-Sant Cugat, pl. Xavier Cugat, ✉ apartado 122, ☎ 589 41 41, Fax 589 30 31, ←, – ▤ TV ☎ Ⓟ – 25/300. AE ⓓ E VISA
Meals 2750 – ☐ 1400 – **146 rm** 12150/15200, 4 suites.

San Celoni o **Sant Celoni** 08470 Barcelona 443 G37 - pop. 11 937 alt. 152 - ☎ 93.
Envir. : NO : Sierra de Montseny★ : itinerary★★ from San Celoni to Santa Fé del Montseny - Road★ from San Celoni to Tona by Montseny.

Madrid 662 - Barcelona 49 - Gerona/Girona 57.

XXX ✿✿✿ **El Racó de Can Fabes,** Sant Joan 6 ☎ 867 28 51, Fax 867 38 61, Rustic decor - ▤ ⇔. AE ⓓ E VISA
closed Sunday dinner, Monday, 30 January- 12 February and 25 June-8 July - **Meals** a la carte 8000/8650
Spec. Almejas imperiales a la vinagreta. Merluza del Mediterráneo al hinojo. Pichón en crapaudine al cardamomo.

GREEN TOURIST GUIDES
Picturesque scenery, buildings
Attractive routes
Touring programmes
Plans of towns and buildings

MÁLAGA - MARBELLA

Málaga 29000 446 V 16 - pop. 534 683 - ☎ 95 - Seaside resort.
See : Gibralfaro : ≤★★ DY - Alcazaba★ (museum ★) DY.
Envir. : Finca de la Concepción★ N : 7 km.
Club de Campo of Málaga SW : 9 km ☎ 238 11 20, Fax 238 21 41 - of El Candado E : 5 km ☎ 229 93 40, Fax 229 08 45.
✈ Málaga SW : 9 km ☎ 224 00 00 - Iberia : Molina Larios 13, ✉ 29015, ☎ 213 61 67 CY and - Aviaco : Airport ☎ 223 08 63.
☎ 231 13 96.
. to Melilla : Cía Trasmediterránea, Estación Marítima, ✉ 29016 CZ, ☎ 222 43 93, Fax 222 48 83.
ℹ Pasaje de Chinitas 4, ✉ 29015, ☎ 221 34 45, Fax 222 94 21 and International Airport, ✉ 29004, ☎ 221 34 45, Fax 224 54 66 - R.A.C.E. Calderería 1, ✉ 29008, ☎ 221 42 60, Fax 221 20 32.

Madrid 548 - Algeciras 133 - Córdoba 175 - Sevilla 217 - Valencia 651.

Plan on next page

Parador de Málaga-Gibralfaro ⛰, Castillo de Gibralfaro, ✉ 29016, ☎ 222 19 02, Fax 222 19 04, « Magnificent setting with ≤ Málaga and sea », ⛱ - |♦| ▤ TV ☎ ♿ P - 🏛 25/60. AE ⓓ E VISA. ✗ DY
Meals 3500 - ☐ 1200 - **38 rm** 16500.

Málaga Palacio without rest, av. Cortina del Muelle 1, ✉ 29015, ☎ 221 51 85, Fax 221 51 85, ≤, ⛱ - |♦| ▤ TV ☎ - 🏛 25/300. AE ⓓ E VISA. ✗ CZ **b**
☐ 1000 - **221 rm** 12500/18000.

Larios coffee shop only, Marqués de Larios 2, ✉ 29005, ☎ 222 22 00, Fax 222 24 07 - |♦| ▤ TV ☎ - 🏛 25/40. AE E VISA. ✗ CY **s**
☐ 950 - **40 rm** 11500/16500.

Don Curro coffee shop only, Sancha de Lara 7, ✉ 29015, ☎ 222 72 00, Telex 77366, Fax 221 59 46 - |♦| ▤ TV ☎. AE ⓓ E VISA JCB CZ **e**
☐ 625 - **100 rm** 8650/12675.

Los Naranjos without rest, paseo de Sancha 35, ✉ 29016, ☎ 222 43 19, Fax 222 59 75 - |♦| ▤ TV ☎ ⇔. AE ⓓ E VISA. ✗ E : by Pas. Cánovas del Castillo DZ
☐ 900 - **40 rm** 10800/14800, 1 suite.

XXX **Café de París,** Vélez Málaga 8, ✉ 29016, ☎ 222 50 43, Fax 260 38 64 - ▤. AE ⓓ E VISA JCB. ✗ E : by Pas. Cánovas del Castillo DZ
closed Sunday and 15 to 31 July - **Meals** a la carte 3900/5800.

XX **Adolfo,** paseo Marítimo Pablo Ruiz Picasso 12, ✉ 29016, ☎ 260 19 14 - ▤. AE E VISA. ✗ E : by Pas. Cánovas del Castillo DZ
closed Sunday - **Meals** a la carte 2450/4150.

X **Refectorium,** Cervantes 8, ✉ 29016, ☎ 221 89 90 - ▤. AE ⓓ E VISA. ✗
closed Sunday and 15 to 30 June - **Meals** a la carte approx. 4200.
E : by Pas. Cánovas del Castillo DZ

at Club de Campo SW : 9 km - ✉ 29000 Málaga - ☎ 95 :

Parador de Málaga del Golf, at the golf course, ✉ 29080 apartado 324 Málaga, ☎ 238 12 55, Fax 238 21 41, ≤, 🌴, « Overlooking the golf course », ⛱, 🎾, 18 - ▤ TV ☎ P - 🏛 25/70. AE ⓓ E VISA. ✗
Meals 3500 - ☐ 1200 - **56 rm** 16500, 4 suites.

MÁLAGA

Constitución . . . . CY 40
Granada . . . . CDY
Marqués de Larios . . . . . CYZ 84
Nueva . . . . CYZ
Santa Lucía . . . . CY 123

Aduana (Pl. de la) . . . . . . DY 2
Arriola (Pl. de la) . . . . CZ 5
Atocha (Pasillo) . . . . CZ 8
Calderería . . . . CY 13
Cánovas del Castillo (Pas.) . DZ 18
Cárcer . . . . CY 27
Casapalma . . . . CY 30
Colón (Alameda de) . . . . . . CZ 32
Comandante Benítez (Av. del) . . . . CZ 35
Compañía . . . . CY 37
Cortina del Muelle . . . . CZ 42
Especerías . . . . CY 56
Frailes . . . . CDY 61
Huerto del Conde . . . . DY 67
Mariblanca . . . . CY 77
Martínez . . . . CZ 86
Molina Larios . . . . CYZ 95
Postigo de los Abades . . CDZ 106
Reding (Paseo de) . . . . . . DY 110
Santa Isabel (Pasillo de) . CYZ 120
Santa María . . . . CY 125
Sebastián Souvirón . . . . . CZ 130
Strachan . . . . CZ 133
Teatro (Pl. del) . . . . CY 135
Tejón y Rodríguez . . . . . . CY 138
Tetuán (Puente de) . . . . . CZ 140

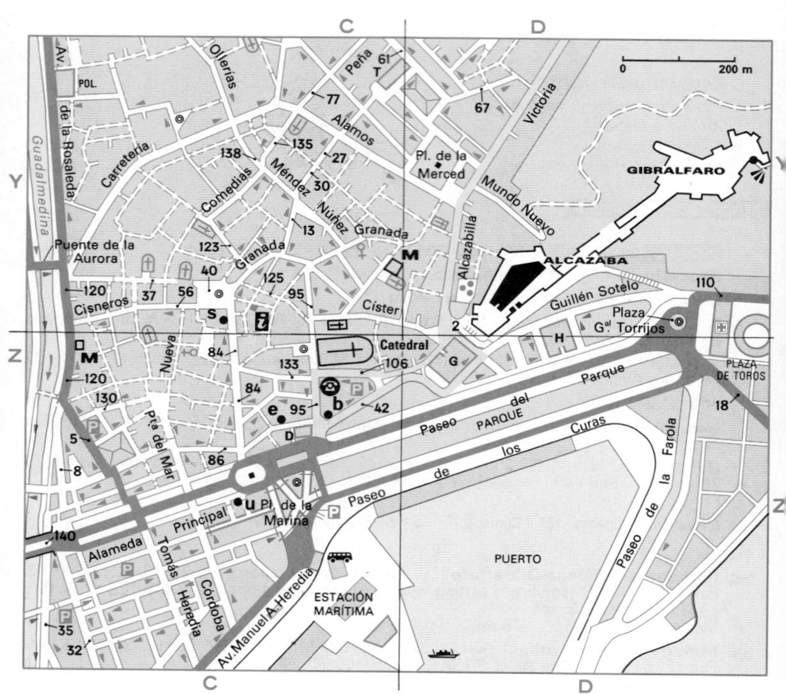

at Urbanización Mijas Golf by N 340 SW : 30 km – ✉ 29640 Fuengirola – ☎ 95 :

Byblos Andaluz ⛳, ☎ 247 30 50, Telex 79713, Fax 247 67 83, ≤ golf course and mountains, ☂, Thalassotherapy facilities, « Tasteful Andalusian style situated between two golf courses », 🏋, 🏊, 🏊, 🌳, 🎾, ⛳18 ⛳18 – 🛗 ▤ 📺 ☎ 🅿 – 🏛 20/200. AE ⓓ E VISA. ✈ rest
Meals 5800 - ***Le Nailhac*** *(dinner only, closed Wednesday)* **Meals** a la carte approx. 5700 - ***El Andaluz*** *(dinner only)* **Meals** a la carte approx. 4200 – ☕ 2100 – **108 rm** 29000/35000, 36 suites.

Marbella **29600** Málaga 446 W 15 – pop. 84 410 – ☎ 95 – Beach.

Envir. : Puerto Banús (Pleasure harbour★) by ② : 8 km.

⛳18 Río Real-Los Monteros by ① : 5 km ☎ 277 37 76, Fax 277 21 40 – ⛳18 Nueva Andalucía by ② : 5 km ☎ 278 72 00 – ⛳18 Aloha Golf, urb. Aloha by ② : 8 km ☎ 281 23 88 – ⛳18 Golf Las Brisas, Nueva Andalucía by ② : 11 km, ☎ 281 08 75.

ℹ Glorieta de la Fontanilla ☎ 277 14 42, Fax 277 94 57.

Madrid 602 ① – Algeciras 77 ② – Cádiz 201 ② – Málaga 56 ①.

Plan opposite

Meliá Don Pepe ⛳, José Meliá ☎ 277 03 00, Telex 77055, Fax 277 99 54, ≤ sea and mountains, ☂, « Subtropical plants », 🏋, 🏊, 🏊, 🌳, 🎾 – 🛗 ▤ 📺 ☎ ♿ 🅿 – 🏛 25/400. AE ⓓ E VISA JCB. ✈ by ②
Meals 5400 - ***Grill La Farola*** *(dinner only)* **Meals** a la carte 6300/ 7800 – ☕ 2200 – **182 rm** 23000/34500, 18 suites.

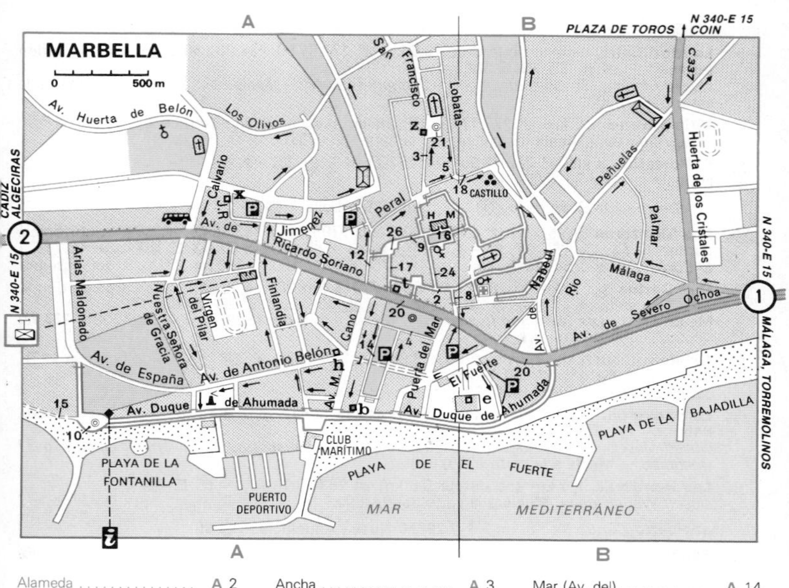

El Fuerte, av. del Fuerte ℘ 286 15 00, Telex 77523, Fax 282 44 11, ≤, « Terraces with garden and palm trees », heated, – TV – 25/600. AE E VISA. rest — AB **e**
Meals 3600 – 1400 – **244 rm** 10300/18000, 19 suites.

Marbella Inn coffee shop only, Jacinto Benavente - bloque 6 ℘ 282 54 87, Fax 282 54 87, heated – TV. AE E VISA JCB. — A **x**
650 – **40 suites** 8700/10800.

San Cristóbal, Ramón y Cajal 3 ℘ 277 12 50, Telex 77712, Fax 286 20 44 – TV. AE E VISA. — A **t**
Meals 1700 – 550 – **97 rm** 7200/9975.

Lima without rest, av. Antonio Belón 2 ℘ 277 05 00, Fax 286 30 91 – AE E VISA JCB. — A **h**
495 – **64 rm** 7160/8950.

La Fonda, pl. Santo Cristo 10 ℘ 277 25 12, « Andalusian patio » – AE E VISA. — A **z**
closed Sunday – **Meals** (dinner only) a la carte 4650/6325.

Santiago, av. Duque de Ahumada 5 ℘ 277 43 39, Fax 282 45 03, Seafood – AE E VISA JCB. — A **b**
closed November – **Meals** a la carte 3800/4650.

Cenicienta, av. Cánovas del Castillo 52 (by pass) ℘ 277 43 18, – AE E VISA — by ②
closed February – **Meals** (dinner only) a la carte approx. 4350.

on the road to Cádiz by ② – ✉ 29600 Marbella – 95 :

Marbella Club, 3 km ℘ 282 22 11, Telex 77319, Fax 282 98 84, heated, – TV – 25/180. AE E VISA.
Meals 6000 – 2200 – **83 rm** 31000/43000, 36 suites.

Puente Romano, 3,5 km ℘ 277 01 00, Telex 77399, Fax 277 57 66, « Elegant Andalusian complex in attractive garden », heated, – TV – 25/170. AE E VISA. rest
Meals a la carte 4515/6560 – 1785 – **217 rm** 29800/37200.

Coral Beach, 5 km ℘ 282 45 00, Telex 79816, Fax 282 62 57, – TV – 25/300. AE E VISA.
15 March-October – **Meals** 4200 - ***Florencia*** *(dinner only)* **Meals** a la carte approx. 6400 – 1750 – **148 rm** 24000/29000, 22 suites.

Tryp Marbella Dinamar, 6 km, ✉ 29660 Nueva Andalucía, ℘ 281 05 00, Fax 281 23 46, ≤, « Garden with », – TV – 25/150. AE E VISA.
Meals 2900 – **106 rm** 16550/21580, 10 suites.

XXXX **La Meridiana,** camino de la Cruz - 3,5 km ✆ 277 61 90, Fax 282 60 24, ←, 🍴, « Garden terrace » - ▤ P. AE ⓓ E VISA
closed Monday, Tuesday lunch and 9 January-February - **Meals** (dinner only in summer) a la carte 5350/6900.

XXX **Villa Tiberio,** 2,5 km ✆ 277 17 99, 🍴, Italian rest, « Garden Terrace » - P
closed Sunday - **Meals** (dinner only) a la carte 4200/5700.

XX **El Portalón,** 3 km ✆ 282 78 80, Fax 277 71 04 - P. AE ⓓ VISA
Meals a la carte 3300/5100.

on the road to Málaga by ① - ✉ 29600 Marbella - ☎ 95 :

Los Monteros ⑤, 5,5 km ✆ 277 17 00, Telex 77059, Fax 282 58 46, ←, 🍴, « Subtropical garden », Ƒ₺, ⛱, ⛱, ℅, 🏌18 - |₺| ▤ TV ☎ P - 🏊 25/80. AE ⓓ E VISA JCB. ℅
El Corzo (dinner only) **Meals** a la carte 4900/6700 - ☕ 1500 - **160 rm** 25000/31400, 9 suites.

Don Carlos ⑤, 10 km ✆ 283 11 40, Telex 77015, Fax 283 34 29, ←, 🍴, « Large garden », Ƒ₺, ⛱ heated, ⛱, ℅ - |₺| ▤ TV ☎ P - 🏊 25/1200. AE ⓓ E VISA. ℅
Meals 4700 - ***Los Naranjos*** *(dinner only)* **Meals** a la carte 4800/8250 - ☕ 1200 - **223 rm** 19500/26000, 15 suites.

Artola without rest, 12,5 km ✆ 283 13 90, Fax 283 04 50, ←, 🍴, « On a golf course », ⛱, ⛱, 🏌9 - |₺| TV 🚗 P. AE E VISA
☕ 900 - **29 rm** 7000/11000, 2 suites.

XXX **La Hacienda,** 11,5 km and detour 1,5 km ✆ 283 12 67, Fax 283 33 28, 🍴, « Rustic decor. Patio » - P. AE ⓓ E VISA JCB. ℅
closed Monday except August, Tuesday except July-August, 1 to 15 November and 15 to 31 December - **Meals** a la carte 5385/6295.

XX **Las Banderas,** 9,5 km and detour 0,5 km ✆ 283 18 19, 🍴 - AE E VISA
closed Wednesday - **Meals** a la carte 2500/3800.

at Puerto Banús W : 8 km - ✉ 29660 Nueva Andalucía - ☎ 95 :

XXX **Taberna del Alabardero,** muelle Benabola ✆ 281 27 94, Fax 281 86 30, 🍴 - ▤. AE ⓓ E VISA. ℅
closed January and February - **Meals** a la carte 4775/6375.

XX **Cipriano,** edificio Levante - local 4 y 5 ✆ 281 10 77, Fax 281 10 77, 🍴, Seafood - ▤. AE ⓓ E VISA
Meals a la carte 4400/6700.

SEVILLA 41000 P 446 T 11 y 12 - pop. 704 857 alt. 12 - ☎ 95.

See : La Giralda★★★ (✻★★) BX - Cathedral★★★ (Capilla Mayor altarpiece★★★, Capilla Real★★) BX - Reales Alcázares★★★ BXY (Admiral Apartment : Virgin of the Mareantes altarpiece★ ; Pedro el Cruel Palace★★★ : Ambassadors room - vault★★ ; - Carlos V Palace : tapestries★★, gardens★) - Santa Cruz Quarter★★ BCX (Venerables Hospital★) - Fine Arts Museum★★ (room V★★★, room X★★) AV - Pilate's House★★ (Azulejos★★, staircase★ : cupule★) CX - María Luisa Park★★ (España Square★, - Archeological Museum : Carambolo tresor★) S : by Paseo de las Delicias BY Charity Hospital★ BY Santa Paula Convent★ CV (front★ church) - Salvador Church★ BX (baroque altarpieces★★) - Sant Josep Chappel★ BX - Town Hall (Ayuntamiento) : east front★ BX.

🏌18 and Racecourse Club Pineda SE : 3 km ✆ 461 14 00.

✈ Sevilla - San Pablo NE : 14 km ✆ 451 61 11 - Iberia : Almirante Lobo 2, ✉ 41001, ✆ 422 89 01 BX.

🚗 Santa Justa ✆ 453 86 86.

ℹ av. de la Constitución 21 B ✉ 41004, ✆ 422 14 04, Fax 422 97 53 and paseo de las Delicias ✉ 41012, ✆ 423 44 65 - R.A.C.E. av. Eduardo Dato 22, ✉ 41002, ✆ 463 13 50.

Madrid 550 - La Coruña/A Coruña 950 - Lisboa 417 - Málaga 217 - Valencia 682.

Plans on following pages

Alfonso XIII, San Fernando 2, ✉ 41004, ✆ 422 28 50, Telex 72725, Fax 421 60 33, 🍴, « Magnificent Andalusian building », ⛱, ⛱ - |₺| ▤ TV ☎ 🚗 P - 🏊 25/500. AE ⓓ E VISA JCB. ℅ rest — BY c
Meals 7350 - ☕ 2400 - **129 rm** 45000/56000, 19 suites.

Príncipe de Asturias Radisson H. Sevilla ⑤, Isla de La Cartuja, ✉ 41092, ✆ 446 22 22, Fax 446 04 28, ⛱ - |₺| ▤ TV ☎ ♿ 🚗 - 🏊 25/900. AE ⓓ E VISA. ℅
Meals 3000 - **288 rm** ☕ 16800/25000, 7 suites. — N : by Torneo AV

Tryp Colón, Canalejas 1, ✉ 41001, ✆ 422 29 00, Telex 72726, Fax 422 09 38, Ƒ₺ - |₺| ▤ TV ☎ ♿ 🚗 - 🏊 25/240. AE ⓓ E VISA JCB. ℅ — AX s
Meals (see rest. ***El Burladero*** below) - ☕ 1600 - **211 rm** 17000/21000, 7 suites.

Occidental Porta Coeli, av. Eduardo Dato 49, ✉ 41018, ✆ 453 35 00, Telex 72913, Fax 453 23 42, ⛱ - |₺| ▤ TV ☎ - 🏊 25/600. AE ⓓ E VISA. ℅
Meals (see rest. ***Florencia*** below) - ☕ 1400 - **241 rm** 14000/18000, 3 suites. — E : by Demetrio de los Ríos CXY

Meliá Lebreros, Luis Morales 2, ✉ 41005, ✆ 457 94 00, Telex 72772, Fax 458 27 26, 🍴, Ƒ₺, ⛱ - |₺| ▤ TV ☎ ♿ 🚗 - 🏊 25/500. AE ⓓ E VISA JCB. ℅ — E : by Luis Montoto CX
Meals (see rest. ***La Dehesa*** below) - ☕ 1500 - **431 rm** 14000/17500, 6 suites.

Meliá Sevilla, Doctor Pedro de Castro 1, ✉ 41004, ✆ 442 15 11, Telex 73094, Fax 442 16 08, - - 25/1000. AE VISA JCB. *closed July and August* - **Meals** 3850 - 1650 - **361 rm** 15950/19525, 5 suites. SE : by Av. de Portugal CY

Sol Macarena, San Juan de Ribera 2, ✉ 41009, ✆ 437 58 00, Fax 438 18 03, - - 25/700. AE VISA JCB. N : by María Auxiliadora CV **Meals** 3500 - 1500 - **317 rm** 11200/14200, 10 suites.

Occidental Sevilla coffee shop only, av. Kansas City, ✉ 41018, ✆ 458 20 00, Fax 458 46 15, - - 25/320. AE VISA JCB. 1400 - **228 rm** 22000/250000, 14 suites. E : by Luis Montoto CX

Inglaterra, pl. Nueva 7, ✉ 41001, ✆ 422 49 70, Fax 456 13 36 - - 25/200. AE VISA JCB. rest AX **r** **Meals** 3000 - 1200 - **109 rm** 16500/21000, 4 suites.

Los Seises, Segovias 6, ✉ 41004, ✆ 422 94 95, Fax 422 43 34, « On the 3rd patio of the Archbishop's Palace », - - 25/100. AE VISA. BX **f** **Meals** *(closed August)* a la carte 3125/4475 - 1500 - **43 rm** 20000/25000.

Al-Andalus Palace, av. de la Palmera, ✉ 41012, ✆ 423 06 00, Fax 423 02 00, - - 25/1100. AE VISA. SE : by Paseo de las Delicias BY **Meals** 3000 - ***El Patio :*** **Meals** a la carte 2350/4100 - 1500 - **327 rm** 13200/16500, 1 suite.

NH Ciudad de Sevilla, av. Manuel Siurot 25, ✉ 41013, ✆ 423 05 05, Fax 423 85 39, - - 25/300. AE VISA JCB. rest **Meals** 3500 - 1400 - **90 rm** 13500/16000, 3 suites. SE : by Paseo de las Delicias BY

Pasarela without rest, av. de la Borbolla 11, ✉ 41004, ✆ 441 55 11, Fax 442 07 27, - - 25. AE VISA SE : by Av. de Portugal CY 1000 - **77 rm** 11000/18000, 5 suites.

G. H. Lar, pl. Carmen Benítez 3, ✉ 41003, ✆ 441 03 61, Telex 72816, Fax 441 04 52 - - 25/300. AE VISA. CX **f** **Meals** 2600 - 1000 - **129 rm** 11000/16000, 8 suites.

Husa Sevilla, Pagés del Corro 90, ✉ 41010, ✆ 434 24 12, Fax 434 27 07 - - 25/220. AE VISA. AY **a** **Meals** a la carte 3175/3900 - 1000 - **114 rm** 18000/24000, 14 suites.

NH Plaza de Armas, av. Marqués de Paradas, ✉ 41001, ✆ 490 19 92, Fax 490 12 32, heated - - 25/250. AE VISA JCB. AV **c** **Meals** 3500 - 1200 - **260 rm** 11200/14000, 2 suites.

Sevilla Congresos, Alcalde Luis Uruñuela, ✉ 41020, ✆ 425 90 00, Fax 425 95 00, - - 25/270. AE VISA. rest **Meals** a la carte approx. 4350 - **202 rm** 9900/11550, 16 suites. NE : by Luis Montoto CX

Emperador Trajano, José Laguillo 8, ✉ 41003, ✆ 441 11 11, Fax 453 57 02 - - 25/150. AE VISA JCB. CV **a** **Meals** 1700 - 1000 - **77 rm** 13800.

San Gil without rest, Parras 28, ✉ 41002, ✆ 490 68 11, Fax 490 69 39, « Early 20C partially converted typical Sevilian building. Patio with garden », - . AE VISA JCB. N : by María Auxiliadora CV 800 - **4 rm** 9200/10900, 35 suites.

Álvarez Quintero coffee shop only, Álvarez Quintero 9, ✉ 41004, ✆ 422 12 98, Fax 456 41 41 - . AE VISA. BX **c** 750 - **43 rm** 9500/14000.

Bécquer coffee shop only, Reyes Católicos 4, ✉ 41001, ✆ 422 89 00, Telex 72884, Fax 421 44 00 - - 25/45. AE VISA. AX **v** 850 - **120 rm** 7000/11000.

Giralda, Sierra Nevada 3, ✉ 41003, ✆ 441 66 61, Telex 72417, Fax 441 93 52 - - 25/250. AE VISA JCB. CX **e** **Meals** 1800 - 950 - **98 rm** 12650.

Derby without rest, pl. del Duque 13, ✉ 41002, ✆ 456 10 88, Telex 72709, Fax 421 33 91, Terrace with - . AE VISA. BV **r** 650 - **75 rm** 8000/10000.

Doña María without rest, Don Remondo 19, ✉ 41004, ✆ 422 49 90, Fax 421 95 46, « Elegant classic decor. Terrace with and » - - 25/40. AE VISA. BX **u** 1300 - **59 rm** 10500/17000, 2 suites.

Monte Triana without rest, Clara de Jesús Montero 24, ✉ 41010, ✆ 434 31 11, Fax 434 33 28 - - 25/50. AE VISA. 700 - **117 rm** 9200/11500. W : by Puente Isabel II AX

Alcázar without rest, Menéndez Pelayo 10, ✉ 41004, ✆ 441 20 11, Telex 72360, Fax 442 16 59 - . AE VISA. CY **u** 500 - **93 rm** 11000/14000.

América coffee shop only, Jesús del Gran Poder 2, ✉ 41002, ✆ 422 09 51, Telex 72709, Fax 421 06 26 - . AE VISA. BV **h** 650 - **100 rm** 8000/10000.

SEVILLA

Francos . . . . BX
Sierpes . . . . BVX
Tetuán . . . . BX

Alemanes . . . . BX 12
Alfaro (Pl.) . . . . CXY 15
Almirante Apodaca . . . . CV 20
Almirante Lobo . . . . BY 22
Álvarez Quintero . . . . . . BX 23
Amparo . . . . BV 25
Aposentadores . . . . BV 28
Argote de Molina . . . . . . BX 30
Armas (Pl. de) . . . . AX 31
Banderas (Patio de) . . . BXY 35
Capitán Vigueras . . . . . . CY 42
Cardenal Spínola . . . . . . AV 47
Castelar . . . . AX 55
Chapina (Puente) . . . . . . AX 59
Cruces . . . . CX 75
Doña Elvira . . . . BX 95
Doña Guiomar . . . . AX 97
Escuelas Pías . . . . CV 112
Farmaceútico E.
Murillo Herrera . . . . . . AY 115
Feria . . . . BV 123
Francisco Carrión
Mejías . . . . CV 126
Fray Ceferino
González . . . . BX 127
García de Vinuesa . . . . . BX 130
General Polavieja . . . . . . BX 135
Jesús de la Vera Cruz . . AV 147
José María Martínez
Sánchez Arjona . . . . . AY 150
Julio César . . . . AX 152
Luis Montoto . . . . CX 160
Marcelino Champagnat . AY 172
Martín Villa . . . . BV 190
Mateos Gago . . . . BX 192
Murillo . . . . AV 202
Museo (Pl.) . . . . AV 205
Navarros . . . . CVX 207
O'Donnell . . . . BV 210
Pascual de Gayangos . . . AV 220
Pastor y Landero . . . . . . AX 222
Pedro del Toro . . . . AV 227
Ponce de León (Pl.) . . . . CV 234
Puente y Pellón . . . . BV 239
Puerta de Jerez . . . . BY 242
República Argentina
(Av.) . . . . AY 255
Reyes Católicos . . . . AX 260
San Gregorio . . . . BY 272
San Juan
de la Palma . . . . BV 277
San Pedro (Pl.) . . . . BV 286
San Sebastián (Pl.) . . . . . CY 287
Santa María
La Blanca . . . . CX 297
Santander . . . . BY 300
Saturno . . . . CV 302
Triunfo (Pl.) . . . . BX 307
Velázquez . . . . BV 310
Venerables (Pl.) . . . . BX 312
Viriato . . . . BV 329

Inclusion in the
Michelin Guide
cannot be achieved
by pulling strings
or by offering favours.

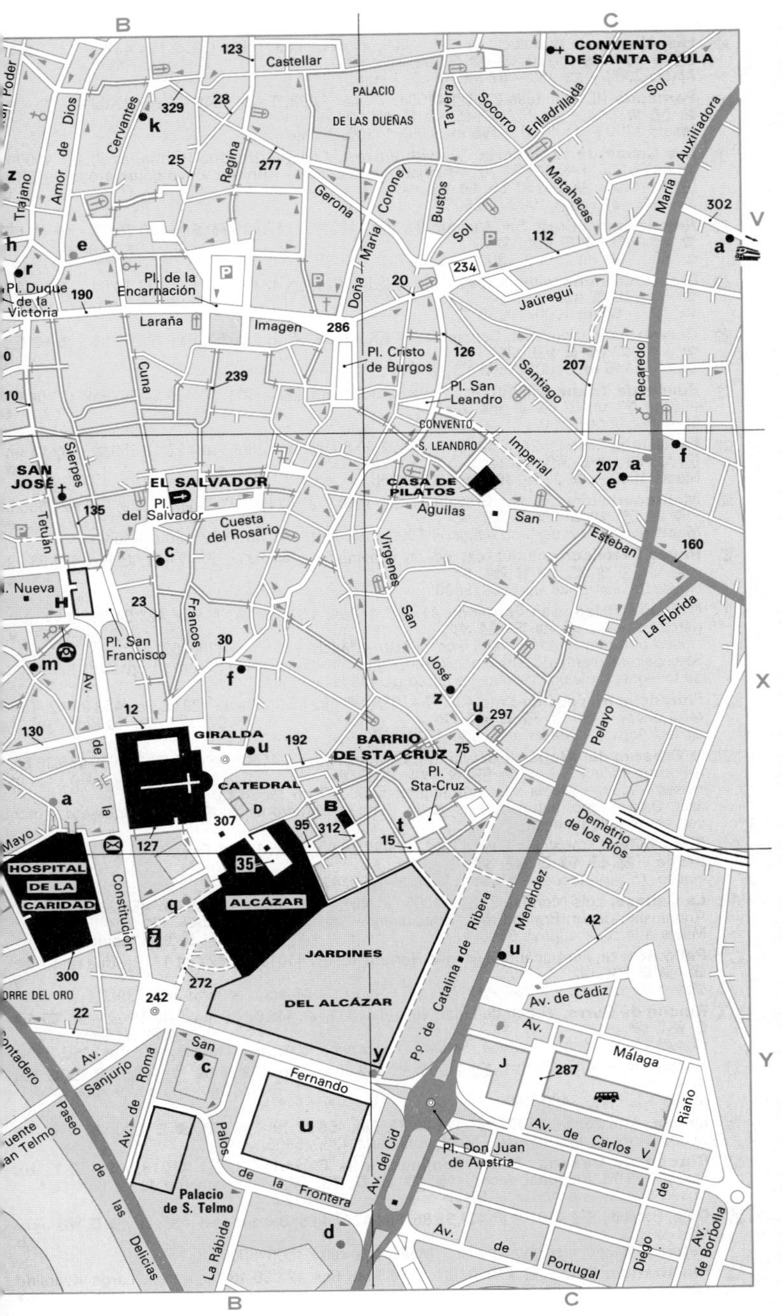
B
C
CONVENTO DE SANTA PAULA
PALACIO DE LAS DUEÑAS
Castellar
Cervantes
Regina
Amor de Dios
Trajano
Gerona
Doña María Coronel
Bustos Tavera
Socorro
Enladrillada
Sol
María Auxiliadora
Matahacas
Jaúregui
Pl. de la Encarnación
Pl. Duque de la Victoria
Laraña
Imagen
Pl. Cristo de Burgos
Pl. San Leandro
Santiago
Recaredo
Cuna
CONVENTO S. LEANDRO
Imperial
SAN JOSÉ
Sierpes
EL SALVADOR
Pl. del Salvador
CASA DE PILATOS
Aguilas
San Esteban
Tetuán
Cuesta del Rosario
Vírgenes
San José
La Florida
Pl. San Francisco
Francos
Pelayo
GIRALDA
BARRIO DE STA CRUZ
CATEDRAL
Pl. Sta-Cruz
Av. de la Constitución
Mayo
Demetrio de los Ríos
HOSPITAL DE LA CARIDAD
ALCÁZAR
JARDINES DEL ALCÁZAR
Menéndez
Pº de Catalina de Ribera
Av. de Cádiz
TORRE DEL ORO
Av. Sanjurjo
Av. de Roma
Málaga
Fernando
San
Palos de la Frontera
Av. del Cid
Pl. Don Juan de Austria
Av. de Carlos V
Riaño
Palacio de S. Telmo
Paseo de las Delicias
La Rábida
Av. de Portugal
Diego
Av. de Borbolla
Contadero
Puente San Telmo
V
X
Y

Hispalis, av. de Andalucía 52, ✉ 41006, ☎ 452 94 33, Telex 73208, Fax 467 53 13 - |♦| ▤ TV ☎ P - 🏛 25/70. AE ① E VISA JCB. ✈ E : by Luis Montoto CX
Meals 2000 - ☕ 950 - **67 rm** 10900, 1 suite.

Fernando III, San José 21, ✉ 41004, ☎ 421 77 08, Telex 72491, Fax 422 02 46, 🏊 - |♦| ▤ TV ☎ 🚗 - 🏛 25/250. AE ① E VISA. ✈ rest CX z
Meals 2300 - ☕ 1100 - **156 rm** 8960/11200, 1 suite.

Las Casas de la Judería 🐉 without rest, Callejón de Dos Hermanas 7, ✉ 41004, ☎ 441 51 50, Fax 442 21 70, « Ancient stately home with attractive courtyards » - |♦| ▤ TV ☎ 🚗 - 🏛 25/50. AE ① VISA. ✈ CX u
☕ 950 - **31 suites** 10000/12500.

Regina without rest, San Vicente 97, ✉ 41002, ☎ 490 75 75, Fax 490 75 62 - |♦| ▤ TV ☎ 🚗. AE ① E VISA. ✈ N : by San Vicente AV
☕ 850 - **68 rm** 11000/18000, 4 suites.

Monte Carmelo without rest, Turia 7, ✉ 41011, ☎ 427 90 00, Fax 427 10 04 - |♦| ▤ TV ☎ 🚗. AE E VISA S : by Pl. de Cuba AY
☕ 700 - **68 rm** 7000/10000.

Cervantes without rest, Cervantes 10, ✉ 41003, ☎ 490 05 52, Fax 490 05 36 - |♦| ▤ TV ☎ 🚗. AE ① E VISA. ✈ BV k
☕ 550 - **46 rm** 9200/11500.

Puerta de Triana without rest, Reyes Católicos 5, ✉ 41001, ☎ 421 54 04, Fax 421 54 01 - |♦| ▤ TV ☎. AE ① E VISA JCB. ✈ AX t
65 rm ☕ 6500/9500.

La Rábida, Castelar 24, ✉ 41001, ☎ 422 09 60, Telex 73062, Fax 422 43 75, 🌳 - |♦| ▤ rm TV ☎. AE ① E VISA. ✈ rest AX d
Meals 1850 - ☕ 375 - **100 rm** 5200/8250.

Montecarlo (annexe 🏨), Gravina 51, ✉ 41001, ☎ 421 75 03, Telex 72729, Fax 421 68 25 - |♦| ▤ TV ☎. AE ① E VISA. ✈ AX e
Meals *(closed Sunday and January)* 1900 - ☕ 550 - **47 rm** 6500/9500, 4 suites.

Reyes Católicos without rest. no ☕, Gravina 57, ✉ 41001, ☎ 421 12 00, Fax 421 63 12 - |♦| ▤ TV ☎. AE ① E VISA. ✈ AX z
closed January - **26 rm** 6500/9500.

XXX ✿ **Egaña Oriza,** San Fernando 41, ✉ 41004, ☎ 422 72 11, Fax 421 04 29, « Winter garden » - ▤. AE ① E VISA. ✈ BY y
closed Saturday lunch, Sunday and August - **Meals** a la carte 5200/6200
Spec. Salmón marinado con almejas crudas y pochas en ensalada (summer). Ensalada templada de foie-gras y melón. Manitas de cerdo gratinadas con ali-oli.

XXX **Florencia,** av. Eduardo Dato 49, ✉ 41018, ☎ 453 35 00, Telex 72913, Fax 453 23 42, Tasteful decor - ▤. AE ① E VISA. ✈ E : by Demetrio de los Ríos CXY
closed August - **Meals** a la carte 4600/6000.

XXX ✿ **Taberna del Alabardero** with rm, Zaragoza 20, ✉ 41001, ☎ 456 06 37, Fax 456 36 66, « Former palace » - |♦| ▤ TV ☎ 🚗. AE E VISA. ✈ AX n
closed August - **Meals** a la carte approx. 5500 - **7 rm** ☕ 28000
Spec. Urta al vapor con cangrejos de río. Cuna de cordero lechal al tomillo. Mousse de limón con sorbete de naranja.

XXX **El Burladero,** Canalejas 1, ✉ 41001, ☎ 422 29 00, Telex 72726, Fax 422 09 38, Bullfighting theme - ▤. AE ① E VISA. ✈ AX a
closed 15 July-August - **Meals** a la carte 4000/4900.

XXX **La Dehesa,** Luis Morales 2, ✉ 41005, ☎ 457 94 00, Telex 72772, Fax 458 23 09, Typical Andalusian decor. Braised meat specialities - ▤. AE ① E VISA JCB. ✈
Meals a la carte approx. 3900. E : by Luis Montoto CX

XXX **Pello Roteta,** Farmacéutico Murillo Herrera 10, ✉ 41010, ☎ 427 84 17, Basque rest - ▤. AE ① E VISA. ✈ AY y
closed Sunday, Holy Week, and 11 to 31 August - **Meals** a la carte 3600/3900.

XXX **Rincón de Curro,** Virgen de Luján 45, ✉ 41011, ☎ 445 02 38, Fax 445 58 22 - ▤. AE ① E VISA. ✈ S : by Pl. de Cuba AY
closed Sunday dinner in winter, Sunday in summer and August - **Meals** a la carte 3150/3950.

XX **Al-Mutamid,** Alfonso XI-1, ✉ 41005, ☎ 492 55 04, Fax 492 25 02, 🌳 - ▤. AE ① E VISA JCB. ✈ E : by Demetrio de los Ríos CXY
Meals a la carte 3400/4600.

XX **La Isla,** Arfe 25, ✉ 41001, ☎ 421 26 31, Fax 456 22 19 - ▤. AE ① E VISA. ✈ BX a
closed Monday and August - **Meals** a la carte 4200/5600.

XX **Rincón de Casana,** Santo Domingo de la Calzada 13, ✉ 41018, ☎ 453 17 10, Fax 464 49 74, Regional decor - ▤. AE ① E VISA. ✈ E : by Demetrio de los Ríos CXY
closed Sunday July-August - **Meals** a la carte 3150/5125.

XX **Ox's,** Betis 61, ✉ 41010, ☎ 427 95 85, Fax 427 84 65, Basque rest - ▤. AE ① E VISA JCB. ✈ AY b
closed Sunday dinner and August - **Meals** a la carte 4000/5000.

XX **Río Grande,** Betis, ✉ 41010, ☎ 427 39 56, Fax 427 98 46, <, 🌳, « Large riverside terrace » - ▤. AE ① E VISA JCB. ✈ AY r
Meals a la carte 3100/4600.

XX **La Albahaca,** pl. Santa Cruz 12, ✉ 41004, ℘ 422 07 14, Fax 456 12 04, « Former manor house » – ▤. AE ⓞ E VISA JCB. ✻ CX **t**
closed Sunday – **Meals** a la carte 4500/5500.

XX **Horacio,** Javier Lasso de la Vega 6, ✉ 41002, ℘ 490 61 04, Fax 490 61 36 – ▤. AE ⓞ E VISA. ✻ BV **e**
closed Saturday and Sunday in August and 15 to 25 August – **Meals** a la carte 3100/4400.

X **El Cantábrico,** Jesús del Gran Poder 20, ✉ 41002, ℘ 438 73 03 – ▤. AE ⓞ E VISA. ✻ BV **z**
closed Sunday, Bank Holidays dinner and August – **Meals** a la carte 3150/3900.

X **Los Alcázares,** Miguel de Mañara 10, ✉ 41004, ℘ 421 31 03, Fax 456 18 29, Regional decor – ▤. AE E VISA. ✻ BY **q**
Meals a la carte 3325/4250.

at San Juan de Aznalfarache W : 4 km – ✉ 41920 San Juan de Aznalfarache – ☎ 95 :

Alcora ⚲, carret. de Tomares ℘ 476 94 00, Fax 476 94 98, ≤, « Patio with plants », – ▤ ▤ TV ☎ ♿ P – 25/1200. AE ⓞ E VISA. ✻
Meals 1950 - ***Don Aníbal :*** **Meals** a la carte 2500/3900 – ☕ 1200 – **331 rm** 12800/16000, 68 suites.

at Castilleja de la Cuesta W : 5 km Sevilla – ✉ 41950 Castilleja de la Cuesta – ☎ 95 :

Hacienda San Ygnacio, Real 194 ℘ 416 04 30, Fax 416 14 37, « In an old rustic inn », – ▤ TV ☎ P – 25/200. AE ⓞ E VISA JCB. ✻
Meals 2500 - ***Almazara*** *(closed Sunday dinner, Monday and August)* **Meals** a la carte approx. 4500 – ☕ 1100 – **16 rm** 14000/19000.

at Benacazón W : 23 km – ✉ 41805 Benacazón – ☎ 95 :

Andalusi Park H., autopista A 49 salida 6 ℘ 570 56 00, Fax 570 50 79, « Arabian style building. Garden », – ▤ ▤ TV ☎ ♿ P – 25/500. AE ⓞ E VISA. ✻
Meals 4000 - ***Los Olivos :*** **Meals** a la carte approx. 4000 - ***Al'Mutamid :*** **Meals** a la carte approx. 5500 – ☕ 1500 – **189 rm** 12800/16000, 11 suites.

at Sanlúcar la Mayor W : 27 km – ✉ 41800 Sanlúcar la Mayor – ☎ 95 :

Hacienda Benazuza ⚲, Virgen de las Nieves ℘ 570 33 44, Fax 570 34 10, ≤, « In a 10C Arabian farmhouse », – ▤ ▤ TV ☎ P – 25/300. AE ⓞ E VISA. ✻ rest
closed 15 July-August – **Meals** 4500 - ***La Alquería :*** **Meals** a la carte 4300/6250 – ☕ 1500 – **26 rm** 32000/40000, 18 suites.

at Carmona E : 33 km – ✉ 41410 Carmona – ☎ 95 :

Parador de Carmona ⚲, ℘ 414 10 10, Telex 72992, Fax 414 17 12, ≤ Corbones fertile plain, « Mudéjar style », – ▤ ▤ TV ☎ P – 25/250. AE ⓞ E VISA. ✻
Meals 3500 – ☕ 1200 – **63 rm** 18000.

Casa de Carmona, pl. de Lasso 1 ℘ 414 33 00, Fax 414 37 52, « In a 16C palace. Grand style furniture » – ▤ ▤ TV ☎ P – 25/70. AE ⓞ E VISA. ✻ rest
Meals a la carte 3400/4600 – ☕ 1500 – **29 rm** 29000/34000, 1 suite.

If you would like a more complete selection of hotels and restaurants, consult the MICHELIN Red Guides for the following countries :

Benelux, Deutschland, España Portugal, France, Great Britain and Ireland, Italia, Suisse

all in annual editions.

VALENCIA 46000 445 N 28 y 29 – pop. 777 427 alt. 13 – ☎ 96.

See : The Old town★ : Cathedral★ (El Miguelete★) EX – Palacio de la Generalidad★ (golden room : ceiling★) EX **D** – Lonja★ (silkhall★★, Maritime consulate hall : ceiling★) DY – **Other curiosities :** Ceramic Museum★★ (Palacio del Marqués de Dos Aguas★) EY **M1** – San Pío V Museum★ (valencian primitifs★★) FX – Patriarc College or of the Corpus Christi★ (Passion triptych★) EY **N** – Serranos Towers★ EX.

Manises E : 12 km, ℘ 152 38 04 – Club Escorpión NW : 19 km ℘ 160 12 11 – El Saler (Parador Luis Vives) SE : 15 km ℘ 161 11 86.

Valencia - Manises Airport E : 9,5 km ℘ 370 95 00 – Iberia : Paz 14, ✉ 46003, ℘ 352 75 52 EFY.

. To the Balearic Islands : Estación Marítima-Puerto de Valencia, ✉ 46024, ℘ 367 65 12, Fax 367 33 45.

Pl. del Ayuntamiento 1, ✉ 46002, ℘ 351 04 17 Av. Cataluña 1, ✉ 46010, ℘ 369 79 32, Paz 48 ✉ 46003, ℘ 394 22 22 – **R.A.C.E.** (R.A.C. de Valencia), Antic Regne de València 64, ✉ 46005, ℘ 374 94 05.

Madrid 351 – Albacete 183 – Alicante/Alacant (by coast) 174 – Barcelona 361 – Bilbao/Bilbo 606 – Castellón de la Plana/Castelló de la Plana 75 – Málaga 651 – Sevilla 682 – Zaragoza 330.

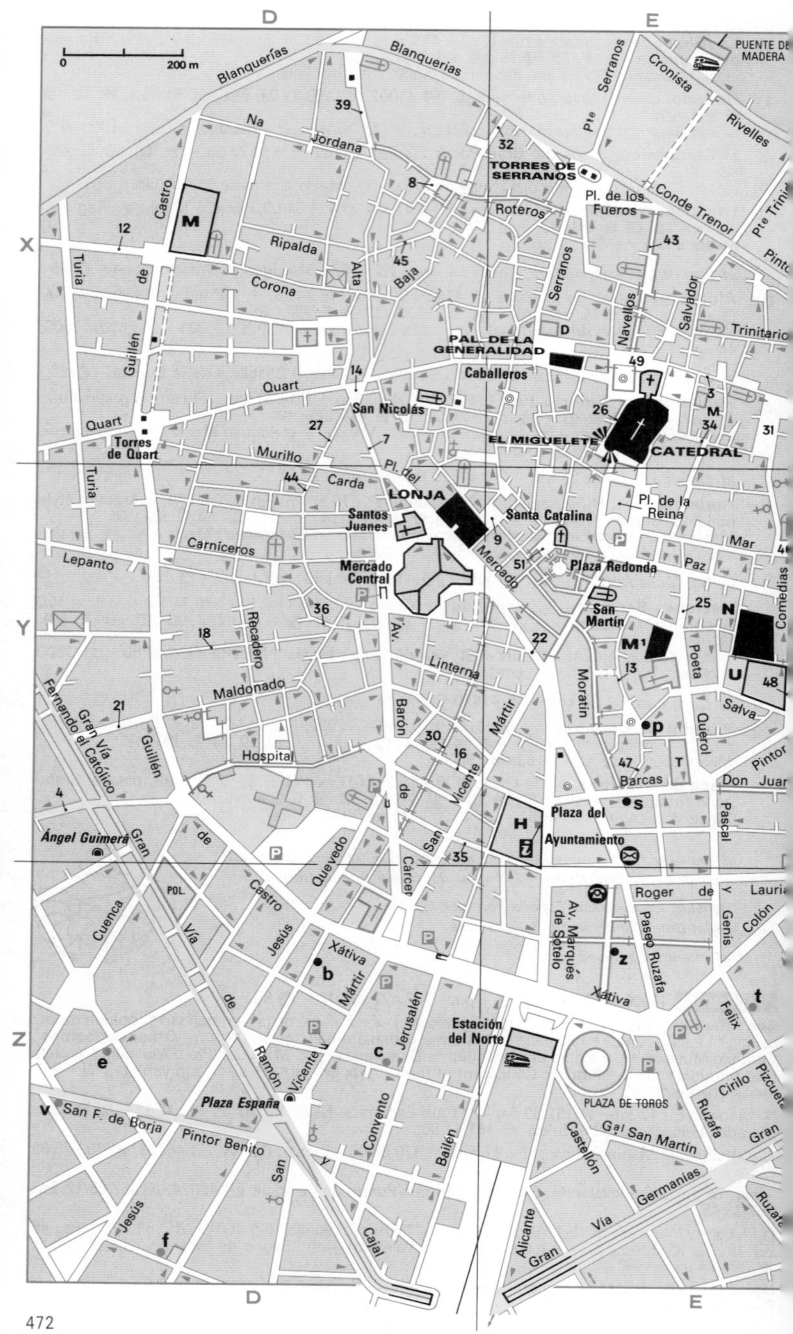
D
E
X
Y
Z
0
200 m
Blanquerías
PUENTE DE MADERA
Serranos
Cronista
Rivelles
Na Jordana
39
32
TORRES DE SERRANOS
8
Pl. de los Fueros
Conde Trenor
Roteros
Castro
M
12
Ripalda
45
Baja
Alta
43
Turia
de
Corona
Serranos
Navellos
Salvador
Trinitarios
Guillén
D
PAL. DE LA GENERALIDAD
49
Caballeros
14
Quart
San Nicolás
26
3
M
34
31
27
7
EL MIGUELETE
CATEDRAL
Torres de Quart
Murillo
Pl. del
44
Carda
LONJA
Pl. de la Reina
Santos Juanes
Santa Catalina
9
Mar
Carniceros
Lepanto
Mercado Central
51
Plaza Redonda
Mercado
Paz
Comedias
San Martín
25
N
36
Recadero
18
Av.
Linterna
22
M¹
Poeta
13
Moratín
U
48
Salva
Maldonado
Barón
Mártir
21
Gran Vía
Fernando el Católico
p
Querol
30
16
Hospital
Vicente
47
Barcas
T
Pintor
Don Juan
4
s
Pascal
Ángel Guimerá
Gran
H
Plaza del Ayuntamiento
de
San
35
Quevedo
Cárcel
POL.
Castro
Roger de Lauria
Cuenca
Vía
Jesús
Av. Marqués de Sotelo
Paseo Ruzafa
Genís
Colón
Xátiva
b
Mártir
z
Xátiva
de
Jerusalén
t
Félix
Estación del Norte
e
Ramón
c
Vicente
Plaza España
PLAZA DE TOROS
Cirilo
Pizcueta
V
San F. de Borja
Convento
Ruzafa
Pintor Benito
Bailén
Castellón
Gal San Martín
Gran
San
Germanías
Ruzafa
y
Jesús
Cajal
Vía
Alicante
Gran
f

VALENCIA

Ayuntamiento (Pl. del) . EY
Marqués de Sotelo (Av.). EZ
Pascual y Genís . . . . . . EYZ
Paz . . . . EFY
San Vicente Mártir . . . . DY

Almirante . . . . EX 2
Almudin . . . . EX 3
Ángel Guimerá . . . . DY 4
Bolsería . . . . DX 7
Carmen (Pl. del) . . . . . . DX 8
Dr. Collado (Pl.). . . . . . . EY 9
Dr. Sanchís
Bergón . . . . DX 12
Embajador Vich . . . . . . EY 13
Esparto (Pl. del) . . . . . . DX 14
Garrigues . . . . DY 16
General Palanca . . . . . . FY 17
Guillém Sorolla . . . . DY 18
Maestres . . . . FX 20
Maestro Palau . . . . DY 21
María Cristina (Av.) . . . . EY 22
Marqués de
Dos Aguas . . . . EY 25
Micalet . . . . EX 26
Moro Zeit . . . . DX 27
Músico Peydro . . . . DY 30
Nápoles y
Sicilia (Pl.) . . . . EX 31
Padre Huérfanos . . . . . . EX 32
Palau . . . . EX 34
Periodista Azzati . . . . . . DY 35
Pie de la Cruz . . . . DY 36
Poeta Quintana . . . . FY 38
Salvador Giner . . . . DX 39
San Vicente
Ferrer (Pl.) . . . . EY 40
Santa Ana (Muro) . . . . . EX 43
Santa Teresa . . . . DY 44
Santo Tomás . . . . DX 45
Transits . . . . EY 47
Universidad . . . . EY 48
Virgen (Pl. de la) . . . . . . EX 49
Virgen de
la Paz (Pl.) . . . . EY 51

We suggest:

For a successful tour, that you prepare it in advance.

***Michelin maps** and **guides** will give you much useful information on route planning, places of interest, accommodation, prices, etc.*

Meliá Valencia Palace, paseo de la Alameda 32, ✉ 46023, ☎ 337 50 37, Fax 337 55 32, ←, Fb, 🏊 - |‡| ▤ TV ☎ ♿ 🚗 - 25/800. AE ⓓ E VISA JCB. ✻
Meals 4000 - ☕ 1500 - **183 rm** 22600/28000, 16 suites. E : by Puente de Aragón FZ

Meliá Rey Don Jaime, av. Baleares 2, ✉ 46023, ☎ 337 50 30, Telex 64252, Fax 337 15 72, 🏊 - |‡| ▤ TV ☎ P - 25/250. AE ⓓ E VISA. ✻ E : by Puente de Aragón FZ
Meals 4000 - ☕ 1425 - **312 rm** 17430/21900, 2 suites.

Astoria Palace, pl. Rodrigo Botet 5, ✉ 46002, ☎ 352 67 37, Telex 62733, Fax 352 80 78 - |‡| ▤ TV ☎ ♿ - 25/500. AE ⓓ E VISA JCB. ✻ EY **p**
Meals 3800 - ***Vinatea :* Meals** a la carte 3550/4100 - ☕ 1500 - **196 rm** 17700/22000, 7 suites.

Turia, Profesor Beltrán Baguena 2, ✉ 46009, ☎ 347 00 00, Fax 347 32 44 - |‡| ▤ TV ☎ 🚗 - 25/300. E VISA. ✻ NW : by G.V. Fernando el Católico DY
Meals *(closed Sunday)* 3000 - ☕ 600 - **160 rm** 12000/15000, 10 suites.

Conqueridor, Cervantes 9, ✉ 46007, ☎ 352 29 10, Fax 352 28 83 - |‡| ▤ TV ☎ 🚗. AE ⓓ E VISA. ✻ DZ **b**
Meals 2700 - ☕ 1300 - **55 rm** 13250/20800, 4 suites.

Dimar coffee shop only, Gran Vía Marqués del Turia 80, ✉ 46005, ☎ 395 10 30, Fax 395 19 26 - |‡| ▤ TV ☎ - 25/60. AE ⓓ E VISA JCB FZ **q**
☕ 1200 - **107 rm** 12400/20500, 1 suite.

Reina Victoria, Barcas 4, ✉ 46002, ☎ 352 04 87, Telex 64755, Fax 352 04 87 - |‡| ▤ TV ☎ - 25/50. AE ⓓ E VISA. ✻ EY **s**
Meals 3800 - ☕ 1100 - **94 rm** 11900/19100, 3 suites.

NH Ciudad de Valencia, av. del Puerto 214, ✉ 46023, ☎ 330 75 00, Telex 63069, Fax 330 98 64 - |‡| ▤ TV ☎ 🚗 - 30/80. AE ⓓ E VISA. ✻
Meals 3900 - ☕ 1100 - **145 rm** 12500/17500, 2 suites. E : by Puente de Aragón FZ

NH Abashiri, av. Ausias March 59, ✉ 46013, ☎ 373 28 52, Telex 63017, Fax 373 49 66 - |‡| ▤ TV ☎ 🚗 - 30/250. AE ⓓ E VISA JCB. ✻
Meals 2300 - ☕ 1100 - **105 rm** 12000/17000. S : by Av. Antic Regne de València FZ

NH Villacarlos without rest, av. del Puerto 60, ✉ 46023, ☎ 337 50 25, Fax 337 50 74 - |‡| ▤ TV ☎ 🚗. AE ⓓ E VISA. ✻ E : by Puente de Aragón FZ
51 rm ☕ 15500/17500.

Ad-Hoc, Boix 4, ✉ 46003, ☎ 391 91 40, Fax 391 36 67, « Attractive 19C building » - |‡| ▤ TV ☎. AE E VISA FX **a**
Meals (see rest. ***Chust Godoy*** below) - ☕ 750 - **28 rm** 10900/15500.

Renasa coffee shop only, av. de Cataluña 5, ✉ 46010, ☎ 369 24 50, Fax 393 18 24 - |‡| ▤ TV ☎ - 25/75. AE ⓓ E VISA E : by Puente del Real FX
☕ 600 - **69 rm** 7000/11400, 4 suites.

Llar without rest, Colón 46, ✉ 46004, ☎ 352 84 60, Fax 351 90 00 - |‡| ▤ TV ☎ - 25/30. AE ⓓ E VISA. ✻ FZ **u**
☕ 750 - **50 rm** 9070/11340.

Sorolla without rest, no ☕, Convento de Santa Clara 5, ✉ 46002, ☎ 352 33 92, Fax 352 14 65 - |‡| ▤ TV ☎. AE ⓓ E VISA. ✻ EZ **z**
50 rm 5800/10500.

XXX **Chambelán,** Chile 4, ✉ 46021, ☎ 393 37 74, Fax 393 37 72 - ▤. AE ⓓ E VISA. ✻
closed Saturday lunch and Sunday - **Meals** a la carte 5200/6400.
E : by Puente de Aragón FZ

XXX **Eladio,** Chiva 40, ✉ 46018, ☎ 384 22 44, Fax 384 22 44 - ▤. AE ⓓ E VISA. ✻
closed Sunday and August - **Meals** a la carte 4050/4750. W : by Ángel Guimerá DY

XXX ✿ **Óscar Torrijos,** Dr. Sumsi 4, ✉ 46005, ☎ 373 29 49 - ▤. AE ⓓ E VISA. ✻ FZ **h**
closed Sunday and 15 August-15 September - **Meals** a la carte 4500/5900
Spec. Ensalada templada de bacalao ligeramente ahumado. Lomo de cordero con molleja y salsa de tomillo. Tarta de manzana con hojaldre.

XXX ✿ **Rías Gallegas,** Matemático Marzal 11, ✉ 46007, ☎ 357 20 07, Fax 351 99 10, Galician rest - ▤. AE ⓓ E VISA DZ **c**
closed Sunday and August - **Meals** a la carte 3550/5550
Spec. Pulpo a la gallega. Caldeirada de pescado. Turnedó Rías.

XXX **Albacar,** Sorní 35, ✉ 46004, ☎ 395 10 05 - ▤. AE ⓓ E VISA. ✻ FY **s**
closed Saturday lunch, Sunday, Holy Week and 7 August-7 September - **Meals** a la carte approx. 4400.

XXX **Galbis,** Marvá 28, ✉ 46007, ☎ 380 94 73, Fax 380 06 54 - ▤. AE VISA. ✻ DZ **f**
closed Saturday lunch, Sunday and 15 days in August - **Meals** a la carte 3425/3850.

XX **El Ángel Azul,** Conde de Altea 33, ✉ 46005, ☎ 374 56 56 - ▤. AE ⓓ E VISA. ✻ FZ **e**
closed Sunday - **Meals** a la carte 2950/4500.

XX **Kailuze,** Gregorio Mayáns 5, ✉ 46005, ☎ 374 39 99, Basque rest - ▤. AE VISA. ✻ FZ **d**
closed August - **Meals** a la carte 3350/4100.

XX **El Gastrónomo,** av. Primado Reig 149, ✉ 46020, ☎ 369 70 36 - ▤. AE E VISA. ✻
closed Sunday, Holy Week and August - **Meals** a la carte 3150/4300.
NE : by Puente del Real FX

XX **Joaquín Schmidt,** Visitación 7 ✆ 340 17 10, Fax 340 17 10, ☂ - ▤. AE ⓓ E VISA. ✻ N : by Cronista Rivelles EX
closed Saturday lunch, Sunday, 25 March-4 April and 19 August-5 September - **Meals** a la carte 3625/5650.

XX **El Gourmet,** Taquígrafo Martí 3, ✉ 46005, ✆ 395 25 09 - ▤. AE E VISA. ✻ FZ **b**
closed Sunday, Holy Week and August - **Meals** a la carte 2650/3750.

XX **Civera,** Lérida 11, ✉ 46009, ✆ 347 59 17, Fax 348 46 38, Seafood - ▤. AE ⓓ E VISA. ✻ N : by Cronista Rivelles EX
closed Sunday dinner, Monday and August - **Meals** a la carte 3400/4800.

XX **José Mari,** Estación Marítima 1°, ✉ 46024, ✆ 367 20 15, ≤, Basque rest - ▤. AE ⓓ E VISA. ✻ SE : by Puente de Aragón FZ
closed Sunday and August - **Meals** a la carte approx. 4300.

XX **Mey Mey,** Historiador Diago 19, ✉ 46007, ✆ 384 07 47, Chinese rest - ▤. AE VISA
closed Holy Week and last three weeks in August - **Meals** a la carte 1745/2500. DZ **e**

XX **El Asador de Aranda,** Félix Pizcueta 9, ✉ 46004, ✆ 352 97 91, Roast lamb - ▤. AE ⓓ E VISA. ✻ EZ **t**
closed Sunday dinner - **Meals** a la carte approx. 4000.

X **Alghero,** Burriana 52, ✉ 46005, ✆ 333 35 79 - ▤. VISA. ✻ FZ **m**
closed Saturday lunch and Sunday - **Meals** a la carte 3250/3750.

X **Chust Godoy,** Boix 4, ✉ 46003, ✆ 391 38 15, Fax 391 36 67 - ▤. AE E VISA. ✻ FX **a**
Meals a la carte 2800/3600.

X **Montes,** pl. Obispo Amigó 5, ✉ 46007, ✆ 385 50 25 - ▤. AE ⓓ E VISA. ✻ DZ **v**
closed Sunday dinner, Monday and 6 August-6 September - **Meals** a la carte 2775/4475.

X **El Plat II,** Císcar 3, ✉ 46005, ✆ 374 12 54 - ▤. AE ⓓ E VISA FZ **w**
closed Sunday dinner, Monday and Holy Week - **Meals** a la carte 3000/4150.

X **Eguzki,** av. Baleares 1, ✉ 46023, ✆ 337 50 33, Basque rest - ▤. E VISA. ✻
closed Sunday, Bank Holidays and August - **Meals** a la carte 3400/4900.
E : by Puente de Aragón FZ

X **Palace Fesol,** Hernán Cortés 7, ✉ 46004, ✆ 352 93 23, Fax 352 93 23, « Regional decor » - ▤. AE ⓓ E VISA. ✻ FZ **s**
Meals a la carte 2850/3400.

X **Bazterretxe,** Maestro Gozalbo 25, ✉ 46005, ✆ 395 18 94, Basque rest - ▤. AE VISA. ✻ FZ **a**
closed Sunday dinner, and 15 August-14 September - **Meals** a la carte 2000/3500.

X **El Romeral,** Gran Vía Marqués del Turia 62, ✉ 46005, ✆ 395 15 17 - ▤. AE ⓓ E VISA. ✻ FZ **z**
closed Monday, Holy Week and August - **Meals** a la carte 3400/4300.

X **Olabarrieta,** Barraca 35, ✉ 46011, ✆ 367 07 79 - ▤. VISA. ✻
closed Sunday and August - **Meals** a la carte 1250/2500. E : by Puente de Aragón FZ

by road C 234 NW : 8,5 km - ✉ 46035 Valencia - ☎ 96 :

Feria, av. de las Ferias 2 ✆ 364 44 11, Telex 61079, Fax 364 54 83 - |‡| ▤ TV ☎ ⇔ - 🏊 25/60. AE ⓓ E VISA. ✻ rest NW : by G.V. Fernando el Católico DY
Meals a la carte 3400/5100 - **136 suites** ☕ 15875/25500.

at El Saler S : 8 km - ✉ 46012 Valencia - ☎ 96 :

Sidi Saler ⛰, playa - 3 km ✆ 161 04 11, Telex 64208, Fax 161 08 38, ≤, 🏊, 🏊, 🌳, 🎾 - |‡| ▤ TV ☎ P - 🏊 25/300. AE ⓓ E VISA. ✻ rest
Meals 3450 - ***Grill Bendinat :*** **Meals** a la carte 3200/4900 - ☕ 1500 - **260 rm** 16000/22600, 16 suites.

Parador de El Saler ⛰, 7 km ✆ 161 11 86, Fax 162 70 16, ≤, « In the middle of the golf course », 🏊, 🎾, 18 - |‡| ▤ TV ☎ P - 🏊 25/60. AE ⓓ E VISA. ✻
Meals 3500 - ☕ 1200 - **58 rm** 18000.

at Manises on the airport road E : 9,5 km - ✉ 46940 Manises - ☎ 96 :

Sol Azafata, autopista del aeropuerto ✆ 154 61 00, Telex 61451, Fax 153 20 19 - |‡| ▤ TV ☎ ⇔ P - 🏊 25/300. AE ⓓ E VISA. ✻ rest
Meals 2700 - ☕ 1100 - **126 rm** 11500/14300, 4 suites.

at Puçol N : 25 km by motorway A 7 - ✉ 46760 Puçol - ☎ 96 :

Monte Picayo ⛰, urb. Monte Picayo ✆ 142 01 00, Telex 62087, Fax 142 21 68, ☂, « On a hillside with ≤ », 🏊, 🌳, 🎾 - |‡| ▤ TV ☎ P - 🏊 25/800. AE ⓓ VISA. ✻
Meals a la carte 3500/3800 - ☕ 1350 - **79 rm** 18350/22950, 4 suites.

Sweden

Sverige

STOCKHOLM – GOTHENBURG

PRACTICAL INFORMATION

LOCAL CURRENCY

Swedish Kronor: 100 SEK = 15.11 US $ (Jan. 96).

TOURIST INFORMATION

In Stockholm, the Tourist Centre is situated in Sweden House, entrance from Kungsträdgården at Hamngatan. Open Mon-Fri 9am-7pm. Sat. and Sun. 9am-5pm. Telephone weekdays 08/789 24 00, weekends to Excursion Shop and Tourist Centre. For Gothenburg, see information in the text of the town under ℹ.

FOREIGN EXCHANGE

Banks are open between 9.00am and 3.00pm on weekdays only. Some banks in the centre of the city are usually open weekdays 9am to 5.30pm. Most large hotels have exchange facilities, and Arlanda airport has banking facilities between 7am to 10pm seven days a week.

MEALS

At lunchtime, follow the custom of the country and try the typical buffets of Scandinavian specialities.
At dinner, the a la carte and set menus will offer you more conventional cooking.

SHOPPING

In the index of street names, those printed in red are where the principal shops are found.
The main shopping streets in the centre of Stockholm are: Hamngatan, Biblioteksgatan, Drottninggatan.
In the Old Town mainly Västerlånggatan.

THEATRE BOOKINGS

Your hotel porter will be able to make your arrangements or direct you to Theatre Booking Agents.

CAR HIRE

The international car hire companies have branches in Stockholm, Gothenburg, Arlanda and Landvetter airports. Your hotel porter should be able to give details and help you with your arrangements.

TIPPING

Hotels and restaurants normally include a service charge of 15 per cent.
Doormen, baggage porters etc. are generally given a gratuity.
Taxis include 10 % tip in the amount shown on the meter.

SPEED LIMITS - SEAT BELTS

The maximum permitted speed on motorways and dual carriageways is 110 km/h - 68 mph and 90 km/h - 56 mph on other roads except where a lower speed limit is indicated.
The wearing of seat belts is compulsory for drivers and passengers.

Stockholm

Sverige 985 M 15 - pop. 674 459 Greater Stockholm 1 491 726 - ☎ 08.

See : Old Town*** (Gamla Stan) : Stortorget**, AZ, Köpmangatan** AZ **35**, Österlånggatan** AZ ; Vasa Museum*** (Vasamuseet) DY, Skansen Open-Air Museum*** DY.
Royal Palace** (Kungliga Slottet) AZ ; Changing of the Guard** ; Apartments**, Royal Armoury**, Treasury* ; Museum* ; Stockholm Cathedral** (Storkyrkan) AZ ; Riddarholmen Church** (Riddarholmskyrkan) AZ ; City Hall** (Stadshuset) BY H : ✳***, Djurgården DYZ ; Prins Eugens Waldemarsudde** (house and gallery), Rosendal Palace*, Thiel Gallery* ; Gröna Lunds Tivoli* DZ.
Kaknäs TV Tower* (Kaknästornet) ✳*** DY ; Gustav Adolf Square* (Gustav Adolfs Torg) CY **16** ; Kings Gardens* (Kungsträdgården) CY ; House of the Nobility* (Riddarhuset) AZ ; German Church* (Tyska Kyrkan) AZ ; Fjällgatan* DZ ; Sergels Torg CY **54** - Hötorget* CY **20**.

Museums : Museum of National Antiquities*** (Historiska Museet) DY ; National Art Gallery** (Nationalmuseum) DY **M1** ; Nordic Museum** (Nordiska Museet) DY **M2** ; Museum of Far Eastern Antiquities** (Ostasiatiska Museet) DY **M3** ; Museum of Modern Art (Moderna Museet) CX **M4** ; National Maritime Museum** (Sjöhistoriska Museet) DY ; Hallwyl Collection* (Hallwylska Museet) CY **M5** ; City Museum* (Stads Museet) CZ **M6** ; Strindberg Museum* BX **M7** ; Museum of Medieval Stockholm* (Stockholms Medeltidsmuseum) CY **M8** ; Swedish Museum of Natural History (Naturhistoriska Riksmuseet : Cosmonova*) CX.

Outskirts : Drottningholm Palace** (Drottningholms Slott) W : 12 km BY ; Apartments**, Gardens**, Court Theatre*, Chinese Pavilion* ; Tours by boat** (in summer) : Under the Bridges** ; Archipelago** (Vaxholm, Möja, Sandhamn, Utö), Mälarenlake* (Gripsholm, Skokloster) ; Haga Park and Pavilion of Gustav III* (Hagapartien) (N : 4 km) BX ; Millesgården* (E : 4 km) DX.

Svenska Golfförbundet (Swedish Golf Federation) ☎ 622 15 00.

Stockholm-Arlanda N : 41 km ☎ 797 61 00 - SAS : Flygcity, Stureplan 8 ☎ 797 41 75, Reservations 020/727 727 - Air-Terminal : opposite main railway station.

Motorail for Southern Europe : Ticket Travel-Agency, Kungsgatan 60 ☎ 24 00 90.

To Finland : contact Silja Line ☎ 22 21 40 or Viking Line ☎ 714 57 70 - Excursions by boat : contact Stockholm Information Service (see below).

Stockholm Information Service, Tourist Centre, Sverigehuset, Hamngatan 27 ☎ 789 24 00 - Motormännens Riksförbund ☎ 690 38 00 - Kungliga. Automobilklubben (Royal Automobile Club) Gyllenstiernsgatan 4 ☎ 660 00 55.

Hamburg 935 - Copenhagen 630 - Oslo 522.

STOCKHOLM

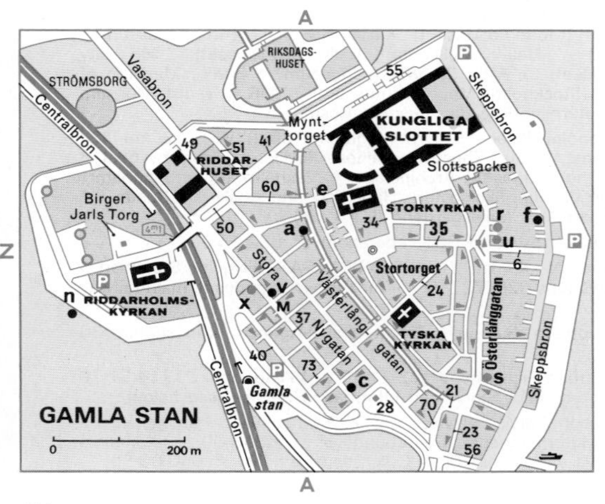

RIKSDAGSHUSET
STRÖMSBORG
Vasabron
Centralbron
Skeppsbron
KUNGLIGA SLOTTET
Mynttorget
Slottsbacken
RIDDARHUSET
Birger Jarls Torg
STORKYRKAN
Stortorget
RIDDARHOLMSKYRKAN
Stora Nygatan
Västerlånggatan
TYSKA KYRKAN
Österlånggatan
Gamla stan
GAMLA STAN
0
200 m
RIDDARFJÄRDEN
Söder Mälarstrand
Torkel Knutssonsgatan
Brännkyrkagatan
Hornsgatan
Mariatorget
Ringvägen
SÖDERTÄLJE

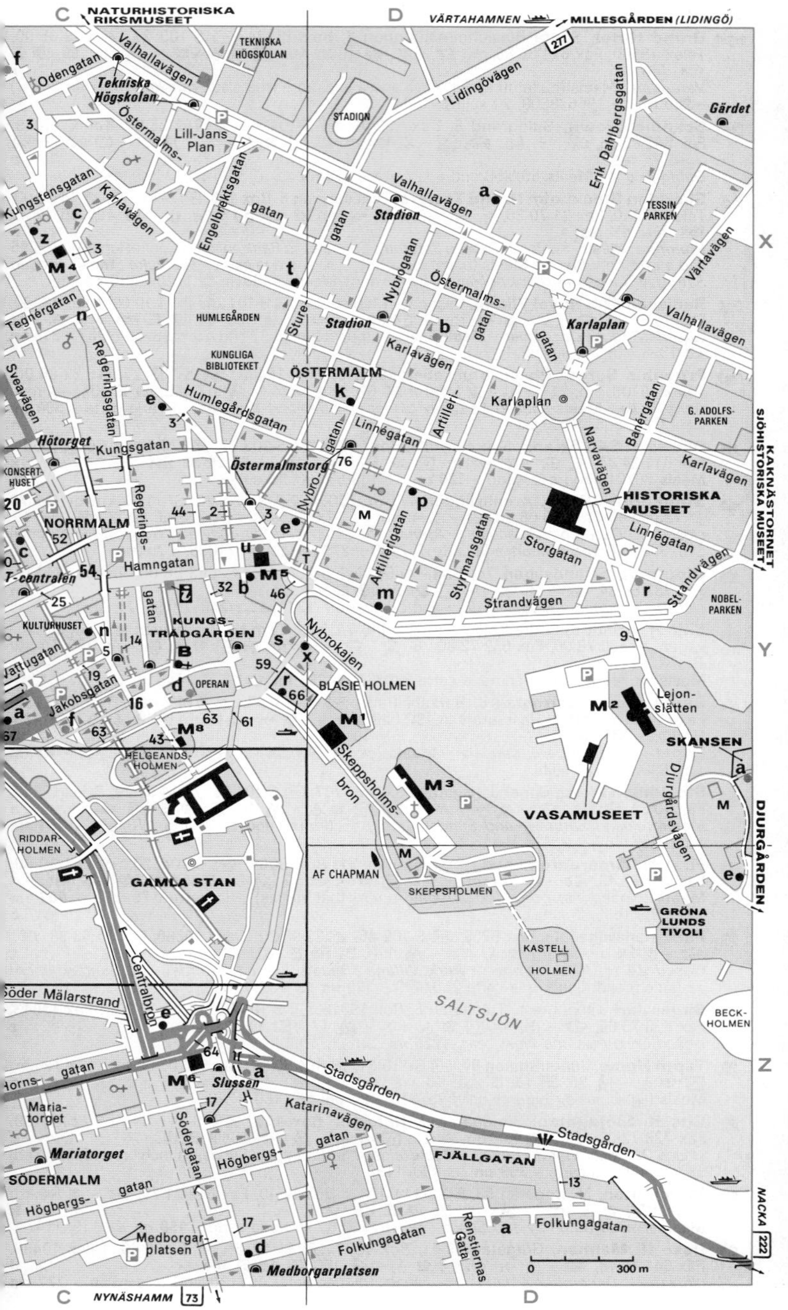
NATURHISTORISKA RIKSMUSEET
VÄRTAHAMNEN
MILLESGÅRDEN (LIDINGÖ)
TEKNISKA HÖGSKOLAN
Valhallavägen
Odengatan
Tekniska Högskolan
Östermalms-
Lill-Jans Plan
STADION
Lidingövägen
Erik Dahlbergsgatan
Gärdet
Kungstensgatan
Karlavägen
Engelbrektsgatan
gatan
Stadion
TESSIN PARKEN
Värtavägen
Tegnérgatan
HUMLEGÅRDEN
Sture-
Nybrogatan
Östermalms-
Karlaplan
KUNGLIGA BIBLIOTEKET
ÖSTERMALM
Regeringsgatan
Sveavägen
Humlegårdsgatan
Linnégatan
Artilleri-
Narvavägen
Banérgatan
G. ADOLFS-PARKEN
Hötorget
Kungsgatan
Östermalmstorg
KONSERT-HUSET
NORRMALM
Regerings-
HISTORISKA MUSEET
Artillerigatan
Styrmansgatan
Storgatan
T-centralen
Hamngatan
KULTURHUSET
KUNGSTRÄDGÅRDEN
Strandvägen
NOBEL-PARKEN
KAKNÄSTORNET
SJÖHISTORISKA MUSEET
Nybrokajen
Vattugatan
Jakobsgatan
OPERAN
BLASIE HOLMEN
Lejon-slätten
SKANSEN
HELGEANDS-HOLMEN
Skeppsholmsbron
VASAMUSEET
Djurgårdsvägen
DJURGÅRDEN
RIDDAR-HOLMEN
AF CHAPMAN
SKEPPSHOLMEN
GAMLA STAN
GRÖNA LUNDS TIVOLI
KASTELL HOLMEN
SALTSJÖN
Söder Mälarstrand
Centralbron
BECK-HOLMEN
Hornsgatan
Slussen
Stadsgården
Maria-torget
Katarinavägen
Södergatan
Högbergs-gatan
Mariatorget
FJÄLLGATAN
SÖDERMALM
Högbergs-gatan
Medborgarplatsen
Folkungagatan
Renstiernas Gata
Medborgarplatsen
NACKA
0
300 m
NYNÄSHAMM
73
222
277

Grand Hotel, Södra Blasieholmshamnen 8, Box 16424, ✉ S-103 27, ☎ 679 35 00, Telex 19500, Fax 611 86 86, <, – rm rest ☎ & – 600. AE ① E VISA JCB. CY **r**
Verandan :* Meals** (buffet lunch) 85/275 and a la carte – (see also ***Franska Matsalen below) – **280 rm** 1955/3000, 20 suites.

Scandic Crown, Guldgränd 8, Box 15270, ✉ S-104 65, ☎ 702 25 00, Telex 11019, Fax 642 83 58, <, – rm ☎ & – 285. AE ① E VISA JCB. rest CZ **e**
***Guldgränd 4 :* Meals** 50/250 and a la carte – **253 rm** 1320/1870, 11 suites.

Sheraton Stockholm H. and Towers, Tegelbacken 6, Box 195, ✉ S-101 23, ☎ 14 26 00, Telex 17750, Fax 21 70 26, <, – rm rest ☎ & – 420. AE ① E VISA JCB. rest CY **a**
***Premiere :* Meals** - Seafood - *(closed Saturday, Sunday and Bank holidays)* (buffet lunch) 110/295 and a la carte – ***Bistro :* Meals** (buffet lunch) 85/290 and a la carte – ***Die Ecke :* Meals** *(closed Saturday, Sunday and Bank holidays)* 75/175 and a la carte – **453 rm** 1720/2450, 6 suites.

Radisson SAS Royal Viking, Vasagatan 1, Box 234, ✉ S-101 24, ☎ 14 10 00, Telex 13900, Fax 10 81 80, – rm & – 130. AE ① E VISA JCB. rest
closed 23 to 27 December – **Meals** - Italian - (buffet lunch) 97 and a la carte 301/367 – **315 rm** 1395/2095, 4 suites. BY **f**

Provobis Sergel Plaza, Brunkebergstorg 9, Box 16411, ✉ S-103 27, ☎ 22 66 00, Telex 16700, Fax 21 50 70 – rm ☎ & – 200. AE ① E VISA. rest
***Anna Rella :* Meals** *(closed Saturday dinner and Sunday)* 195/445 and a la carte – **394 rm** 1230/1665, 12 suites. CY **n**

Radisson SAS Strand, Nybrokajen 9, Box 16396, ✉ S-103 27, ☎ 678 78 00, Telex 10504, Fax 611 24 36, <, – rm ☎ & – 70. AE ① E VISA. CDY **x**
Meals 70/210 and a la carte – **120 rm** 1690/2390, 18 suites.

Stockholm Globe, Arenaslingan 7, Box 10004, ✉ S-121 26, S : 1 ½ km by Rd 73 ☎ 725 90 00, Fax 649 08 80, – rm ☎ & – 220. AE ① E VISA JCB.
closed 20 December-2 January – ***Arena :* Meals** *(closed Saturday and Sunday)* (lunch only) 260/398 – ***Tabac :* Meals** a la carte 75/180 – **279 rm** 945/1095, 8 suites.

Diplomat, Strandvägen 7c, Box 14059, ✉ S-104 40, ☎ 663 58 00, Telex 171119, Fax 783 66 34, – rm ☎. AE ① E VISA. DY **m**
closed Christmas – **Meals** 75/295 and a la carte – **131 rm** 1465/2195, 2 suites.

Silja H. Ariadne, Sodra Kajen 37, ✉ S-115 74, NE : 3 km by Värtavägen and Tegeludds-vägen ☎ 665 78 00, Fax 662 72 80, <, – rm ☎ & – 250. AE ① E VISA. rest
Meals (buffet lunch) 73 and a la carte 280/330 – **283 rm** 1220/1445.

Berns, Näckströmsgatan 8, Berzelii Park, ✉ S-111 47, ☎ 614 07 00, Telex 12132, Fax 611 51 75, « Restaurant in 19C ballroom » – rm rm ☎ & – 180. AE ① E VISA. CY **b**
closed 23 December-2 January – **Meals** *(closed Sunday)* 70/290 and a la carte – **62 rm** 1690/2390, 1 suite.

Stockholm Plaza, Birger Jarlsgatan 29, Box 7707, ✉ S-103 95, ☎ 14 51 20, Telex 13982, Fax 10 34 92, – rm rest ☎ & – 45. AE ① E VISA. CX **e**
Meals *(closed Saturday and Sunday lunch)* 65 (lunch) and a la carte 178/294 – **151 rm** 1225/1450.

First H. Amaranten, Kungsholmsgatan 31, Box 8054, ✉ S-104 20, ☎ 654 10 60, Fax 662 62 48, – rm rest ☎ & – 85. AE ① E VISA. rest
Meals *(closed Saturday and Sunday lunch)* (bar meals) a la carte 170/285 – **407 rm** 1195/1595, 3 suites. BY **c**

Park, Karlavägen 43, Box 5255, ✉ S-102 46, ☎ 22 96 20, Telex 10666, Fax 21 62 68, – rm ☎ & – 120. AE ① E VISA. CX **t**
closed 24 to 30 December – ***Park Village :* Meals** *(closed Saturday and Sunday lunch)* 72 (lunch) and dinner a la carte 250/400 – **199 rm** 1325/1860, 3 suites.

Birger Jarl without rest., Tulegatan 8, Box 19016, ✉ S-104 32, ☎ 15 10 20, Telex 11843, Fax 673 73 66, – ☎ & – 175. AE ① E VISA CX **z**
closed Christmas and New Year – **225 rm** 625/1390.

Tapto Home, Jungfrugatan 57, ✉ S-115 31, ☎ 664 50 00, Fax 664 07 00, – rm ☎ & – 25. AE ① E VISA. DX **a**
Meals (light meals residents only) 75/250 – **86 rm** 1150/1290.

City H. Slöjdgatan, Slöjdgatan 7, Hötorget, Box 1132, ✉ S-111 81, ☎ 723 72 00, Fax 723 72 09, – rm rest ☎ & – 90. AE ① E VISA. CY **c**
closed 22 December-3 January – **Meals** *(closed Saturday and Sunday)* (lunch only) (unlicensed) 58/65 and a la carte – **293 rm** 990/1190.

Mornington, Nybrogatan 53, ✉ S-114 40, ☎ 663 12 40, Fax 662 21 79, – rm rest ☎ & – 100. AE ① E VISA. DX **k**
Meals *(closed Saturday and Sunday lunch)* 70/180 and a la carte – **139 rm** 1195/1470.

Reso H. Malmen, Götgatan 49-51, Box 4274, ✉ S-102 66, ☎ 22 60 80, Telex 19489, Fax 641 11 48, – rm ☎ & – 100. AE ① E VISA. CZ **d**
closed 22 December-2 January – **Meals** (dinner only) 40/130 and a la carte – **277 rm** 895/1295, 6 suites.

Wellington, Storgatan 6, ✉ S-114 51, ☎ 667 09 10, Fax 667 12 54, – rm AE E VISA. DY **p**
closed 23 to 26 December – **Meals** *(closed Saturday and Sunday lunch)* 175 (lunch) and dinner a la carte 135/345 – **49 rm** 995/1295.

Castle, Riddargatan 14, ✉ S-114 35, ☎ 679 57 00, Fax 611 20 22, – rest – 120 CY **e**
48 rm, 2 suites.

Freys, Bryggargatan 12b, Box 594, ✉ S-101 31, ☎ 20 13 00, Fax 24 22 24 – rm rm AE E VISA. rest BY **u**
closed Christmas – **Meals** 60/240 and dinner a la carte – **107 rm** 985/1160.

XXXX **Franska Matsalen** (at Grand Hotel), Södra Blasieholmshamnen 8, Box 16424, ✉ S-103 27, ☎ 679 35 84, Telex 19500, Fax 611 86 86, ≤ – AE E VISA CY **r**
closed Saturday, Sunday, Easter, July and Christmas – **Meals** (dinner only) 625/825 and a la carte.

XXX **Operakällaren** (at Opera House), Operahuset, Box 1616, ✉ S-111 86, ☎ 676 58 00, Fax 20 95 92, ≤, « Opulent classical decor » – AE E VISA JCB CY **d**
closed Sunday lunch and July – **Meals** 172/595 and a la carte.

XXX **Videgård,** Regeringsgatan 111, ✉ S-111 39, ☎ 411 61 53, Fax 10 76 35 – AE E VISA JCB CX **n**
closed Saturday lunch, Sunday and 24 June-15 August – **Meals** 215/595 and a la carte.

XX ❀ **Paul and Norbert** (Lang), Strandvägen 9, ✉ S-114 56, ☎ 663 81 83, Fax 667 72 36 – AE E VISA DY **m**
closed Saturday, Sunday, July and 24 December-6 January – **Meals** (booking essential) 240/980 and a la carte 525/770
Spec. Le romsteck de renne farcie aux baies de genièvre sauce vin rouge à la genièvre, Le suprême rôti de gelinotte blanche sauce petit lait au poivre vert, Le canard sauvage croustillant sauce caramelisée au vinaigre de pousses de pin.

XX **Gondolen,** Stadsgården 6, Box 15155, ✉ S-104 56, ☎ 641 70 90, Fax 641 11 40, ≤ Saltsjön – AE E VISA JCB CZ **a**
closed 1 to 27 July lunch, Sunday, 5, 7 and 8 April, 22 June, 24 to 26 December and 1 January – **Meals** 200/530 and a la carte.

XX **Nils Emil,** Folkungagatan 122, ✉ S-116 30, ☎ 640 72 09, Fax 640 37 25 – AE E VISA
closed Saturday and Sunday lunch, July and Bank Holidays – **Meals** (booking essential) a la carte 215/350. DZ **a**

XX **Clas På Hörnet** with rm, Surbrunnsgatan 20, ✉ S-113 48, ☎ 16 51 30, Fax 612 53 15, « 18C atmosphere » – AE E VISA. CX **f**
closed lunch Saturday and Sunday, midsummer eve, Christmas, 31 December and 1 January – **Meals** (buffet lunch) 175/385 and a la carte – **10 rm** 940/1140.

XX Stallmästaregården, Norrtull, ✉ S-113 47, N : 2 km by Sveavägen (at beginning of E 4) ☎ 610 13 00, Fax 32 27 40, ≤, , « 17C inn, waterside setting », – Ⓟ.

XX ❀ **Wedholms Fisk** (Wedholm), Nybrokajen 17, ✉ S-111 48, ☎ 611 78 74 – AE E VISA CY **s**
closed Saturday lunch, Sunday, July and Bank Holidays – **Meals** - Seafood - 150/585 and a la carte 330/620
Spec. Tartar of salmon and salmon roe with crème fraîche, Boiled turbot with melted butter and horseradish, Fricassee of sole, turbot, lobster and scallops with a Champagne sauce.

XX **Player's Inn,** Karlavägen 73, ✉ S-114 49, ☎ 662 22 62, Fax 662 22 63 – AE E VISA
closed Saturday lunch, Sunday, Christmas-New Year and Bank Holidays – **Meals** 135/425 and dinner a la carte. DX **b**

XX **Wedholms Kött,** Kungstensgatan 9, ✉ S-114 25, ☎ 21 61 69, Fax 20 34 46 – AE E VISA JCB CX **c**
closed Saturday lunch and Sunday – **Meals** 75/230 and a la carte.

X ❀ **KB** (Klein), Smålandsgatan 7, ✉ S-111 46, ☎ 679 60 32, Fax 611 82 83 – AE E VISA
closed Saturday lunch, Sunday, 20 June-5 August and Bank Holidays – **Meals** (booking essential) 125/425 and a la carte 240/512 CY **u**
Spec. Assorted marinated herring and Baltic herring, Steak and rack of lamb with rosemary, aubergine caviar and courgette timbale, Capon as "Osso Bucco".

X **Gässlingen,** Brännkyrkagatan 93, ✉ S-117 26, ☎ 669 54 95, Fax 84 89 90 – AE E VISA
closed 22 June-6 August and 23 December-7 January – **Meals** (booking essential) (dinner only except December) 395/495 and a la carte. BZ

X **Eriks Bakficka,** Frederikshovgatan 4, ✉ S-115 23, ☎ 660 15 99, Fax 663 25 67, – . AE E VISA DY **r**
closed Saturday, Sunday, 23 to 25 June and 22 December-2 January – **Meals** - Bistro - 65/210 and a la carte.

X **Greitz,** Vasagatan 50, ✉ S-111 20, ☎ 23 48 20, Fax 24 20 93 – AE E VISA JCB BY **a**
closed Saturday lunch, Sunday, July and Bank Holidays – **Meals** 88/245 and a la carte.

X **Fredsgatan 12,** Fredsgatan 12, ✉ S-111 52, ☎ 24 80 52, Fax 20 23 00 – AE E VISA
closed Sunday, July and 22 December-2 January – **Meals** (booking essential) (light lunch) 65/625 and dinner a la carte. CY **f**

Gamla Stan (Old Stockholm) :

First H. Reisen, Skeppsbron 12-14, ✉ S-111 30, ☎ 22 32 60, Telex 17494, Fax 20 15 59, ≤, « Original maritime decor », – rm rest – 60. AE ⓓ E VISA JCB. rest AZ **f**
Meals *(closed Sunday and Bank holidays)* 195/500 and a la carte – **111 rm** 1260/1895, 3 suites.

Victory, Lilla Nygatan 5, ✉ S-111 28, ☎ 14 30 90, Telex 14050, Fax 20 21 77, « Swedish rural furnishings, maritime antiques », – rm – 90. AE ⓓ E VISA JCB. AZ **v**
closed 20 December-6 January – **Meals** – (see ***Leijontornet*** below) – **45 rm** 1680/2180, 3 suites.

Gamla Stan without rest., Lilla Nygatan 25, ✉ S-111 28, ☎ 24 44 50, Fax 21 64 83 – – 35. AE ⓓ E VISA JCB AZ **c**
closed 23 December-2 January – **50 rm** 990/1190, 1 suite.

Lady Hamilton without rest., Storkyrkobrinken 5, ✉ S-111 28, ☎ 23 46 80, Fax 411 11 48, « Swedish rural antiques », – . AE ⓓ E VISA JCB. AZ **e**
34 rm 1380/1810.

Lord Nelson without rest., Västerlånggatan 22, ✉ S-111 29, ☎ 23 23 90, Fax 10 10 89, « Ship style installation, maritime antiques », – . AE ⓓ E VISA JCB. AZ **a**
closed Christmas and New Year – **31 rm** 1100/1550.

Mälardrottningen, Riddarholmen, ✉ S-111 28, ☎ 24 36 00, Telex 15864, Fax 24 36 76, « Formerly Barbara Hutton's yacht », – rm . AE ⓓ E VISA JCB. rest
closed Christmas – **Meals** *(closed Saturday and Sunday lunch and Bank Holidays)* 55/385 and a la carte **58 rm (cabins)** 690/950, 1 suite. AZ **n**

✿ **Eriks** (Lallerstedt), Österlånggatan 17, ✉ S-111 31, ☎ 23 85 00, Fax 796 60 69 – rest. AE ⓓ E VISA JCB AZ **u**
closed Sunday, July, Christmas, New Year and Bank Holidays – **Meals** - Seafood - (booking essential) 75/660 and a la carte 570/671
Spec. Fried duck liver with spinach and port sauce, Fish and shellfish, Fried duckling in two servings.

✿ **Leijontornet** (at Victory H.), Lilla Nygatan 5, ✉ S-111 28, ☎ 14 23 55, Telex 14050, Fax 406 08 14, , « Remains of a 14C fortification tower in the dining room » – . AE ⓓ E VISA JCB AZ **v**
closed Saturday lunch, Sunday, July, 23 December-7 January and Bank Holidays – **Meals** (booking essential) (restricted lunch) 180/520 and a la carte 385/535
Spec. Duck stew with beans and grilled duck liver, Baked salmon and langoustines with ginger and a butter sauce with yoghurt, Mandarin mousse with chocolate and a coffee sauce.

Den Gyldene Freden, Österlånggatan 51, Box 2269, ✉ S-103 17, ☎ 24 97 60, Fax 21 38 70 – . AE ⓓ E VISA AZ **s**
closed Sunday and July – **Meals** 75/325 and a la carte.

Källaren Aurora, Munkbron 11, ✉ S-111 28, ☎ 21 93 59, Fax 411 16 22, « In the cellars of a 17C house » – AE ⓓ E VISA JCB AZ **x**
closed 24 and 25 December – **Meals** (dinner only) 325/485 and a la carte.

Fem Små Hus, Nygränd 10, ✉ S-111 30, ☎ 10 87 75, Fax 14 96 95, « 17C cellars, antiques » – . AE ⓓ E VISA JCB AZ **r**
Meals 84/360 and a la carte.

to the E :

at Djurgården – ✪ 08 Stockholm :

Arctia H. Hasselbacken, Hazeliusbacken 20, Box 10274, ✉ S-100 55, ☎ 670 50 00, Telex 10320, Fax 663 84 10, , – rm – 300. AE ⓓ E VISA. rest DZ **e**
Meals (booking essential) 68/295 and a la carte – **110 rm** 1190/1590, 2 suites.

Källhagens Wärdshus , Djurgårdsbrunnsvägen 10, ✉ S-115 27, E : 3 km by Strandvägen ☎ 665 03 00, Fax 665 03 99, ≤, , « Waterside setting, garden », – rm – 60. AE ⓓ E VISA JCB. rest
closed 23 December-7 January – **Meals** 215/315 and a la carte – **18 rm** 1350/1550, 2 suites.

Ulla Winbladh, Rosendalsvägen 8, ✉ S-115 21, ☎ 663 05 71, Fax 663 05 73, – AE ⓓ E VISA DY **a**
Meals (booking essential) 85/235 and a la carte.

at Fjäderholmarna Island 25 mn by boat, departure every hour from Nybroplan – CY – ✪ 08 Stockholm :

Fjäderholmarnas Krog, Box 14046, ✉ S-104 40, ☎ 718 33 55, Fax 716 39 89, , « Waterside setting on Archipelago Island with ≤ neighbouring islands and sea » – AE ⓓ E VISA
closed 1 October-30 November and 22 December-30 April – **Meals** a la carte 285/445.

to the W :

at Bromma W : 6 ½ m. by Norr Mälarstrand - BY - and Drottningholmsvägen - 08 Stockholm :

XXX **Sjöpaviljongen,** Tranebergs Strand 4, ✉ 161 32, E : 1 ½ km ✆ 704 04 24, Fax 704 82 40, « Waterside setting » - P. AE ⓓ E VISA JCB
closed Sunday dinner and 23 December-6 January - **Meals** 90/350 and a la carte.

to the NW :

at Solna NW : 5 km by Sveavägen - BX - and E 4 - 08 Stockholm :

Radisson SAS Royal Park, Frösundaviks Allé 15, Box 3005, ✉ S-171 03, Exit Frösunda by E 4 and Frösundavik rd ✆ 624 55 00, Fax 85 85 66, <, park - rm P - 200. AE ⓓ E VISA. rest
Meals 130/600 and a la carte - **190 rm** 1330/1770, 9 suites.

XXX **Ulriksdals Wärdshus,** , ✉ 170 71, Exit E 18/E 3 from E 4 ✆ 85 08 15, Fax 85 08 58, <, « Former inn in Royal Park », - P. AE ⓓ E VISA
closed dinner Sunday and Bank Holidays and 24 to 26 December - **Meals** (booking essential) (buffet lunch) 75/595 and a la carte.

XX **Finsmakaren,** Råsundavägen 9, ✉ 171 52, ✆ 27 67 71 - AE ⓓ E VISA JCB
closed Saturday and Sunday - **Meals** 90/275 and a la carte.

at Sollentuna NW : 15 km by Sveavägen - BX - and E 4 - 08 Stockholm :

XX ✿ **Edsbacka Krog** (Lingström), Sollentunavägen 220, ✉ 191 47, ✆ 96 33 00, Fax 96 40 19, « 17C inn » - P. AE ⓓ E VISA JCB
closed Saturday lunch, Monday dinner, Sunday, Easter, Whitsun, midsummer and 4 weeks July-August - **Meals** 145/635 and a la carte 313/629
Spec. Edsbacka's classical Bagarby soup, Scandinavian halibut with a mustard grain cream and various kinds of roasted onions, Cupola of bitter chocolate and passion fruit.

at Upplands Väsby NW : 29 km by Sveavägen - BX - and E 4 - 08 Stockholm :

Scandic Crown, Kanalvägen 10, ✉ S-194 61, E 4 - Bredden Exit ✆ 590 955 00, Telex 10565, Fax 590 955 80, - rm - 350. AE ⓓ E VISA
Meals 55/450 and a la carte - **228 rm** 1165/1428, 8 suites.

at Arlanda Airport NW : 40 km by Sveavägen - BX - and E 4 - ✉ Arlanda - 08 Stockholm :

Radisson SAS Sky City, Box 82, ✉ 190 45 Stockholm-Arlanda, between Terminal 4 and 5 ✆ 590 773 00, Fax 593 781 00, - rm - 350. AE ⓓ E VISA JCB.
Meals (buffet lunch) 68/350 and a la carte - **230 rm** 1555/1695.

Radisson SAS Arlandia, Box 103, ✉ 190 45 Stockholm-Arlanda, SE : 1 km ✆ 593 618 00, Fax 593 619 70, - rm rest P - 245. AE ⓓ E VISA.
Meals 149/295 and a la carte - **335 rm** 1250/1450, 2 suites.

*Ask your bookseller for the catalogue of **Michelin publications**.*

GOTHENBURG *(Göteborg)* Sverige 985 O 8 - pop. 437 313 - 031.

See : Art Gallery★★★ (Konstmuseum) CX **M1** - Castle Park★★★ (Slottsskogen) AX - Botanical Gardens★★ (Botaniska Trädgården) AX - East India House★★ (Ostindiska Huset) BU **M2** - Liseberg Amusement Park★★ (Lisebergs Nöjespark) DX - Natural History Museum★★ (Naturhistoriska Museet) AX - Röhss Museum of Arts and Crafts★★ (Röhsska Konstslöjdmuseet) BV **M3** - Älvsborg Bridge★ (Älvsborgsbron) AV - Kungsportsavenyn★ CVX **22** - Maritima Centre★ (Maritime Centrum) (Viking★) BT - Maritime Museum★ (Sjöfartsmuseet) AV - New Älvsborg Fortress★ (Nya Älvsborgs Fästning) AU - Götaplatsen (Carl Milles Poseidon★★) CX - Seaman's Tower (Sjömanstornet) (✱★★) AV - Masthugg Church (Masthuggskyrkran) (inside★) AV.

Envir. : Northern and southern archipelago★ (Hönö, Öckerö, Vrängö) - Kungsbacka : Tjolöholms Castle★, S : 40 km by E6.

18 Albatross, Lillhagsvägen Hisings Backa ✆ 55 19 01 - 18 Delsjö, Kallebäck ✆ 40 69 59 - 18 Göteborgs, Golfbanevägen, Hovås ✆ 28 24 44.

Scandinavian Airlines System : Svenska Mässan (vid Korsvägen) ✆ 94 20 00 Landvetter Airport : ✆ 94 10 00.

To Denmark : contact Stena Line A/B ✆ 775 00 00, Fax 85 85 95 - To Continent : contact Scandinavian Seaways ✆ 65 06 50, Fax 53 23 09.

Kungsportplatsen 2 ✆ 10 07 40.

Copenhagen 279 - Oslo 322 - Stockholm 500.

Plans on following pages

Sheraton Göteborg H. and Towers, Södra Hamngatan 59-65, Box 288, ✉ S-401 24, ✆ 80 60 00, Telex 28250, Fax 15 98 88, - rm - 450. AE ⓓ E VISA JCB. BU **b**
closed 19 December-2 January - ***Frascati :*** **Meals** *(closed lunch Saturday and Sunday)* (buffet lunch) 90/625 and a la carte - **300 rm** 1680/2080, 11 suites.

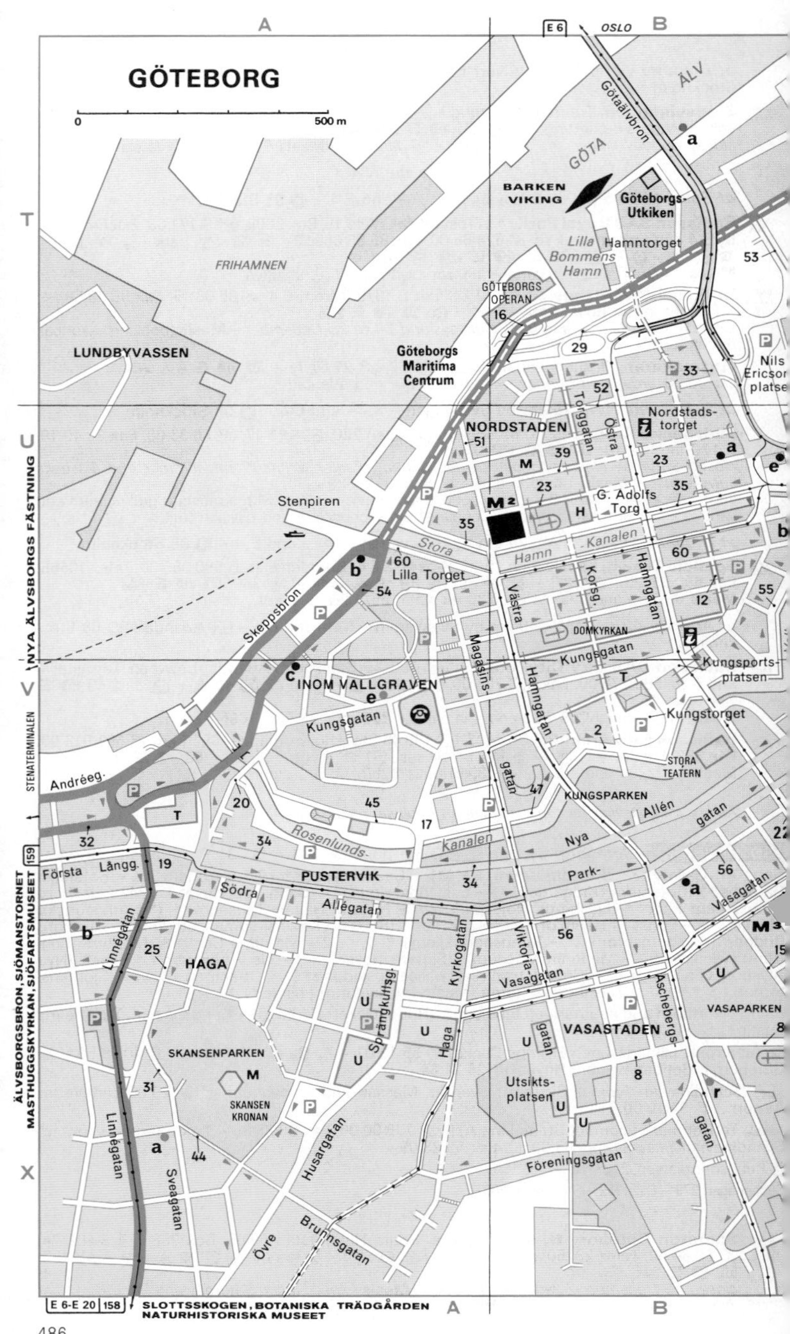
GÖTEBORG
0
500 m
E 6
OSLO
GÖTA ÄLV
Götaälvbron
BARKEN VIKING
Göteborgs-Utkiken
Lilla Bommens Hamn
Hamntorget
FRIHAMNEN
GÖTEBORGS OPERAN
LUNDBYVASSEN
Göteborgs Maritima Centrum
Nils Ericson platsen
NORDSTADEN
Nordstads-torget
Torggatan
Östra
Stenpiren
G. Adolfs Torg
Stora Hamn Kanalen
Lilla Torget
Västra
Korsg.
Hamngatan
DOMKYRKAN
Kungsgatan
Kungsports-platsen
Skeppsbron
INOM VALLGRAVEN
Magasinsgatan
Kungstorget
STORA TEATERN
KUNGSPARKEN
Andréeg.
Rosenlunds-Kanalen
Nya Allén
Park-gatan
Första Långg.
PUSTERVIK
Södra Allégatan
Vasagatan
Viktoria-
Linnégatan
HAGA
Sprängkullsg.
Kyrkogatan
Aschebergsgatan
VASAPARKEN
VASASTADEN
SKANSENPARKEN
SKANSEN KRONAN
Utsikts-platsen
Husargatan
Föreningsgatan
Sveagatan
Övre Brunnsgatan
NYA ÄLVSBORGS FÄSTNING
STENATERMINALEN
ÄLVSBORGSBRON, SJÖMANSTORNET
MASTHUGGSKYRKAN, SJÖFARTSMUSEET
E 6-E 20
158
159
SLOTTSSKOGEN, BOTANISKA TRÄDGÅRDEN
NATURHISTORISKA MUSEET

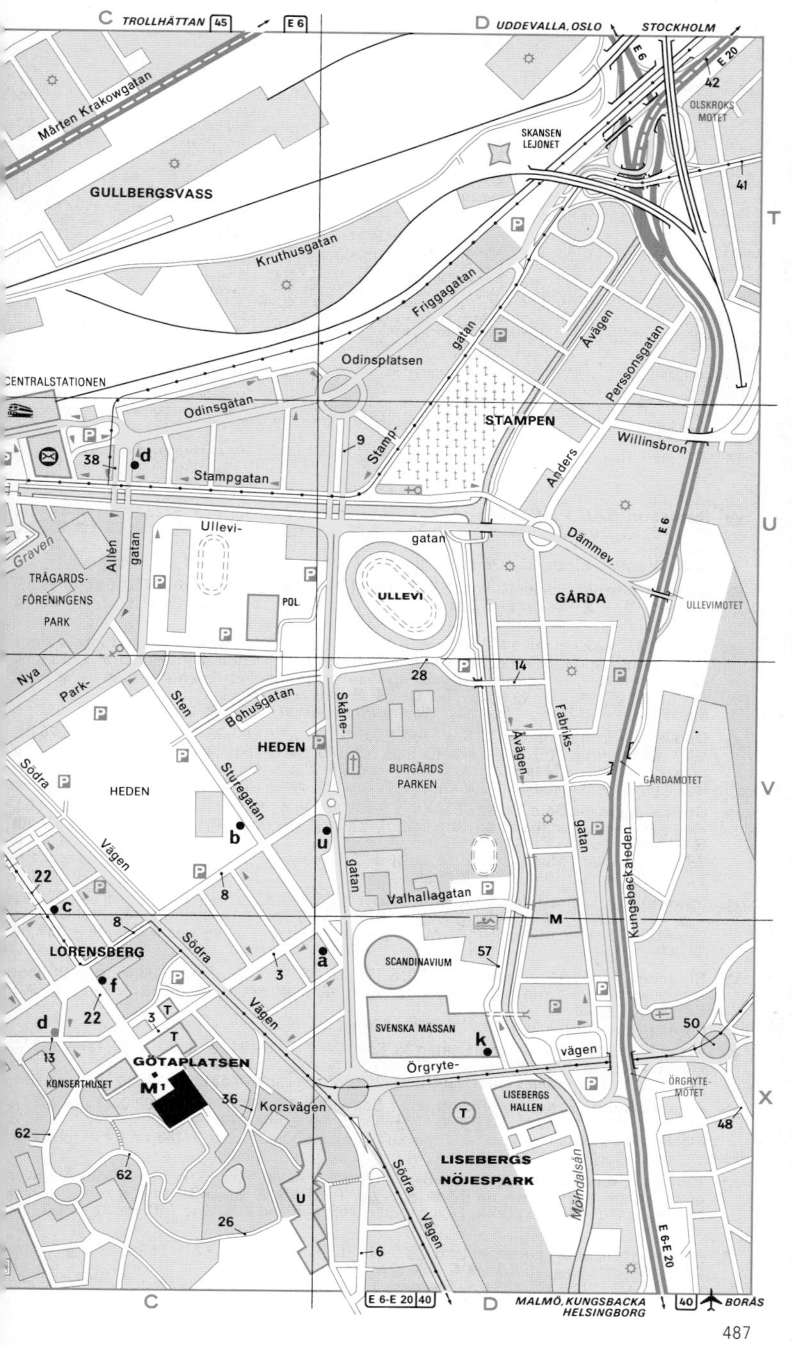

C
TROLLHÄTTAN
45
E 6
D
UDDEVALLA, OSLO
STOCKHOLM
E 6
E 20
42
OLSKROKS MOTET
Mårten Krakowgatan
GULLBERGSVASS
SKANSEN LEJONET
41
T
Kruthusgatan
Friggagatan
gatan
Åvägen
Perssonsgatan
Odinsplatsen
CENTRALSTATIONEN
Odinsgatan
STAMPEN
Willinsbron
9
Stamp-
Anders
38
d
Stampgatan
Ullevi-
gatan
Dämmev.
E 6
U
Graven
Allén
gatan
TRÄGARDS-FÖRENINGENS PARK
POL.
ULLEVI
GÅRDA
ULLEVIMOTET
Nya
Park-
Sten
Bohusgatan
28
14
Skåne-
Fabriks-
HEDEN
Åvägen
BURGÅRDS PARKEN
GÅRDAMOTET
Södra
HEDEN
Sturegatan
V
b
u
gatan
Vägen
gatan
Kungsbackaleden
22
8
Valhallagatan
c
M
8
Södra
LORENSBERG
a
SCANDINAVIUM
57
3
f
22
Vägen
d
3
T
T
SVENSKA MÄSSAN
k
50
13
vägen
GÖTAPLATSEN
Örgryte-
ÖRGRYTE-MOTET
KONSERTHUSET
M1
36
Korsvägen
LISEBERGS HALLEN
X
62
T
48
62
Södra
LISEBERGS NÖJESPARK
U
Vägen
Mölndalsån
E 6-E 20
26
6
C
E 6-E 20
40
D
MALMÖ, KUNGSBACKA HELSINGBORG
40
BORÅS

STREET INDEX TO GÖTEBORG TOWN PLAN

Radisson SAS Park Avenue, Kungsportsavenyn 36-38, Box 53233, ✉ S-400 16, ☎ 17 65 20, Fax 16 95 68, – rm rest – 550. AE E VISA. rest — CX f
***Belle Avenue* : Meals** 85/225 and a la carte – **301 rm** 1449/2015, 17 suites.

Scandic Crown, Polhemsplatsen 3, ✉ S-411 11, ☎ 80 09 00, Telex 28750, Fax 15 45 88, – rm – 300. AE E VISA. rest — CU d
Meals 58/200 and a la carte – **310 rm** 1135/1528, 10 suites.

Hotel 11, Maskingatan 11, Eriksberg, ✉ S-417 64, W : 6 km by Götaälvbron follow signs for Torslanda and turn left at Shell garage, or boat from Lilla Bommens Hamn ☎ 779 11 11, Fax 779 11 10, ≤, « Former shipbuilding warehouse, modern interior design », – rm – 200. AE E VISA JCB. rest
Meals (in bar) 134/450 – (see also ***Westra Piren*** below) – **133 rm** 990/1100.

Opalen, Engelbrektsgatan 73, Box 5106, ✉ S-402 23, ☎ 81 03 00, Telex 2215, Fax 18 76 02, – rm – 180. AE E VISA. — DV u
closed Christmas – **Meals** *(closed Sunday lunch)* (buffet lunch) (dancing Tuesday to Saturday evenings except in summer) 80/335 and dinner a la carte – **238 rm** 995/1490, 4 suites.

Gothia, Mässans Gata 24, Box 5184, ✉ S-402 26, ☎ 40 93 00, Telex 21941, Fax 18 98 04, ≤, « Panoramic restaurant on 18th floor », – rm – 1500. AE E VISA JCB. rest — DX k
***18 : E Våningen* : Meals** *(closed Saturday and Sunday lunch)* (buffet lunch) 89/189 and a la carte – **288 rm** 1050/1550, 2 suites.

Panorama, Eklandagatan 51-53, Box 24037, ✉ S-400 22, ☎ 81 08 80, Fax 81 42 37, – rm – 120. AE E VISA. rest — DX s
closed 20 December-7 January – **Meals** *(closed Sunday)* 78/229 and a la carte – **339 rm** 875/1290.

Riverton, Stora Badhusgatan 26, ✉ S-411 21, ☎ 10 12 00, Fax 13 08 66, « 12th floor restaurant with ≤ Göta Älv river and docks », – rm – 340. AE E VISA. — AV c
Meals (dinner only) a la carte 250/425 – **190 rm** 995/1295, 4 suites.

Provobis H. Europa, Köpmansgatan 38, Box 11444, ✉ S-404 29, ☎ 80 12 80, Telex 21374, Fax 15 47 55, – rm – 60. AE E VISA. rest — BU a
closed Christmas – **Meals** (buffet lunch) 58/250 and a la carte – **453 rm** 1090/1490, 7 suites.

Reso H. Rubinen, Kungsportsavenyn 24, Box 53097, ✉ S-400 14, ☎ 81 08 00, Telex 20837, Fax 16 75 86 – rm – 60. AE E VISA JCB. rest — CV c
Meals *(closed Saturday lunch and Sunday)* 75/495 and a la carte – **189 rm** 1055/1745, 1 suite.

Victors, Skeppsbroplatsen 1, ✉ S-411 18, ☎ 17 41 80, Fax 13 96 10, ≤ Göta Älv river and harbour, – rm – 40. AE E VISA JCB. rest — AU b
Meals *(closed Friday to Sunday)* (dinner only) 150/285 and a la carte – **31 rm** 950/1150, 13 suites.

Mornington, Kungsportsavenyn 6, ✉ S-411 36, ☎ 17 65 40, Fax 711 34 39, – rm – 35. AE E VISA JCB. — CV e
closed 20 December-6 January – ***Brasserie Lipp* : Meals** *(closed Sunday in winter)* 59/350 and dinner a la carte – **91 rm** 920/1395.

Novotel, Klippan 1, ✉ S-414 51, SW : 3 ½ km by Andréeg or boat from Lilla Bommens Hamn ☎ 14 90 00, Telex 28181, Fax 42 22 32, ≤, « Converted brewery on waterfront », – rm TV ☎ P – 150. AE E VISA. rest
Meals (buffet lunch) 70/225 and a la carte – **144 rm** 940/1070, 4 suites.

Tidbloms, Olskroksgatan 23, ✉ S-416 66, NE : 2 ½ km by E 20 ☎ 19 20 70, Fax 19 78 35, – rm TV ☎ P – 80. AE E VISA.
Meals *(closed Sunday and July)* 75/400 and a la carte – **42 rm** 895/1050.

Eggers, Drottningtorget, Box 323, ✉ S-401 25, ☎ 80 60 70, Fax 15 42 43 – rm TV ☎ – 30. AE E VISA JCB. BU **e**
closed 23 to 27 December – **Meals** *(closed Saturday lunch and Sunday)* 64/275 and a la carte – **67 rm** 985/1465.

Liseberg Heden, Sten Sturegatan, ✉ S-411 38, ☎ 20 02 80, Fax 16 52 83, – rm TV ☎ P – 70. AE E VISA JCB. CV **b**
closed 22 December-2 January – **Meals** *(closed Sunday lunch)* 55/180 and a la carte – **156 rm** 930/1280, 3 suites.

Onyxen, Sten Sturegatan 23, ✉ S-412 52, ☎ 81 08 45, Fax 16 56 72 – rm TV ☎ P. AE E VISA. rest DX **a**
Meals *(closed Saturday and Sunday)* 80/250 and a la carte – **34 rm** 845/990.

Poseidon without rest., Storgatan 33, ✉ S-411 38, ☎ 10 05 50, Telex 27663, Fax 13 83 91, – rm TV ☎. AE E VISA JCB BV **a**
closed Christmas – **49 rm** 840/1100.

XXX ✿ **Westra Piren** (Öster), Eriksberg, Dockepiren, (on Pier No. 4) Box 8335, ✉ S-417 64, W : 6 km by Götaälvbron, follow signs for Torslanda and turn left at Shell garage, or boat from Lilla Bommens Hamn ☎ 51 95 55, Fax 23 99 40, « Dockside setting, overlooking Göta Älv river and harbour » – P. AE E VISA JCB
closed Sunday, 7 July-5 August, 23 December-7 January and Bank Holidays – **Meals** (booking essential) (dinner only) 375/640 and a la carte 420/570
Spec. Lasagne aux champignons des bois de la saison, jus aux truffes, Ragoût de lotte et homard à l'Armagnac, tagliolini à l'encre de supion, Pommes d'automne sautées à la canelle et caramelisé à la cassonade.

X **Brasserie,**
closed 21 to 24 June, 23 to 27 December and 31 December-1 January – **Meals** 70/375 and a la carte.

XXX **The Place,** Arkivgatan 7, ✉ S-411 34, ☎ 16 03 33, Fax 16 78 54 – AE E VISA CX **d**
closed 24 June and 24 to 26 December – **Meals** (booking essential) (dinner only) 249/455 and a la carte.

XX ✿ **28 +** (Lyxell), Götabergsgatan 28, ✉ S-411 34, ☎ 20 21 61, Fax 81 97 57, « Cellar » – AE E VISA JCB BX **n**
closed Saturday lunch, Sunday, 23 June-4 August and 22 December-6 January – **Meals** 235/525 and a la carte 293/491
Spec. Basil gratinated crayfish with a tomato timbale and fennel cream, Breast of duck with duck confit sausage, cider sauce and apple rösti, Plum and Armagnac parfait with plum caramel.

XX **Sjömagasinet,** Klippans Kulturreservat, ✉ S-414 51, SW : 3 ½ km by Andréeg or boat from Lilla Bommens Hamn ☎ 24 65 10, Fax 24 55 39, ≤, « Former East India company warehouse » – P. AE E VISA
closed 23 December-3 January – **Meals** - Seafood - (buffet lunch) 95/395 and a la carte.

XX **Le Village,** Tredje Långgatan 13, ✉ S-413 03, ☎ 20 20 03, Fax 24 20 69, « Antiques shop in the cellar » – AE E VISA JCB AX **b**
closed Sunday and 5 to 30 July – **Meals** 195/425 and a la carte.

XX **Le Chablis,** Aschebergsgatan 22, ✉ S-411 27, ☎ 20 35 45, Fax 20 82 01 – AE E VISA JCB BX **r**
closed 1 July-1 August – **Meals** - Seafood - (dinner only) 269/575 and a la carte.

X **Hos Pelle,** Djupedalsgatan 2, ✉ S-413 07, ☎ 12 10 31, Fax 775 38 32 – AE E VISA JCB AX **a**
closed Sunday and Monday – **Meals** (dinner only) 465 and a la carte.

X **Eriksbergs Färjan,** Gullbergskajen Plats 212, ✉ S-411 04, ☎ 15 35 05, « Converted boat » – AE E VISA BT **a**
closed Sunday except October-April and 23 December-13 January – **Meals** (lunch only) 50/169 and a la carte.

X **Bröderna Dahlbom,** Kungsgatan 12, ✉ S-411 19, ☎ 701 77 84, Fax 701 77 85, « Bistro restaurant in original decor » – AE E VISA JCB AV **e**
closed Saturday lunch, Sunday and July – **Meals** 230 (lunch) and a la carte 323/409.

at Landvetter Airport E : 30 km by Rd 40 – DX – ✉ S-438 02 Landvetter :

Landvetter Airport H., Box 2103, ✉ S-438 13, ☎ 94 64 10, Fax 94 64 70, – rm TV ☎ P – 25. AE E VISA.
Meals *(closed Saturday and Sunday)* a la carte 210/320 – **41 rm** 995/1190, 3 suites.

Switzerland

Suisse
Schweiz
Svizzera

BERNE - BASLE - GENEVA - ZÜRICH

PRACTICAL INFORMATION

LOCAL CURRENCY - PRICES

Swiss Franc: 100 CHF = 86.87 USD ($) (Jan. 96).

LANGUAGES SPOKEN

German, French and Italian are usually spoken in all administrative departments, shops, hotels and restaurants.

AIRLINES

SWISSAIR: P.O. Box 316, 1215 Genève 15, ✆ 022/799 59 99, Fax 022/799 31 38. Hirschengraben 84, 8058 Zürich, ✆ 01/258 34 34, Fax 01/258 34 40.

AIR FRANCE: IBC, 24 Pré-Bois, 1201 Genève, ✆ 022/798 05 05, Fax 022/788 50 40. Talstr. 70, 8001 Zürich, ✆ 01/211 13 77, Fax 01/212 01 35.

ALITALIA: rue Lausanne 36, 1201 Genève, ✆ 022/731 66 50, Fax 022/732 40 29. Thurgauerstr. 39, 8050 Zürich, ✆ 01/306 93 33, Fax 01/306 91 44.

AMERICAN AIRLINES: Lintheschergasse 15, 8001 Zürich, ✆ 01/225 16 16, Fax 01/212 04 21.

BRITISH AIRWAYS: Chantepoulet 13, 1201 Genève, ✆ 022/788 10 10, Talacker 42, 8023 Zürich, ✆ 01/211 40 90, Fax 01/212 06 35.

LUFTHANSA: Chantepoulet 1-3, 1201 Genève, ✆ 022/731 95 50, Fax 022/738 96 55. Gutenbergstr. 10, 8027 Zürich, ✆ 01/286 70 00, Fax 01/286 72 07.

POSTAL SERVICES

In large towns, post offices are open from 7.30am to noon and 1.45pm to 6pm, and Saturdays until 11am. The telephone system is fully automatic.
Many public phones are equipped with phone card facilities. Prepaid phone cards are available from post offices, railway stations and tobacconist's shops.

SHOPPING

Department stores are generally open from 8.30am to 6pm, except on Saturdays when they close at 4 or 5pm. They close on Monday mornings. In the index of street names, those printed in red are where the principal shops are found.

TIPPING

In hotels, restaurants and cafés the service charge is generally included in the prices.

SPEED LIMITS - MOTORWAYS

The speed limit on motorways is 120 km/h - 74 mph, on other roads 80 km/h - 50 mph, and in built up areas 50 km/h - 31 mph.
Driving on Swiss motorways is subject to the purchase of a single rate annual road tax (vignette) obtainable from frontier posts, tourist offices and post offices.

SEAT BELTS

The wearing of seat belts is compulsory in all Swiss cantons for drivers and all passengers.

Town plans of Berne, Basle, Geneva and Zürich : with the permission of Federal directorate for cadastral surveys.

Berne

3000 Bern 427 ⑬, 217 ⑥ - pop. 130 069 - alt. 548 - ☎ 031.

See : Old Berne★★ : Marktgasse★ DZ ; Clock Tower★ EZ **C** ; Kramgasse★ EZ ; views★ from the Nydegg Bridge FY ; Bear Pit★ FZ ; Cathedral of St Vincent★ EZ : tympanum★★, panorama★★ from the tower EZ - Rosengarden FY : view★ of the Old Berne - Botanical Garden★ DY - Dählhölzli Zoo★ - Church of St Nicholas★.

Museums : Fine Arts Museum★★ DY - Natural History Museum★★ EZ - Bernese Historical Museum★★ EZ - Alpine Museum★★ EZ - Swiss Postal Museum★ EZ.

Excursions : The Gurten★★.

18 Blumisberg, ✉ 3184 Wünnewil, (18 March-13 November), ☎ (037) 36 34 38, Fax (037) 36 35 23, SW : 18 km.

✈ Bern-Belp, ☎ 960 21 11, Fax 960 21 12.

ℹ Tourist Office, Im Bahnhof ☎ 311 66 11, Fax 312 12 33 - T.C.S., Thunstr. 63, ☎ 352 22 22, Fax 352 22 29 - A.C.S., Theaterplatz 13, ☎ 311 38 13, Fax 311 26 37.

Basle 100 - Lyons 315 - Munich 435 - Paris 556 - Strasbourg 235 - Turin 311.

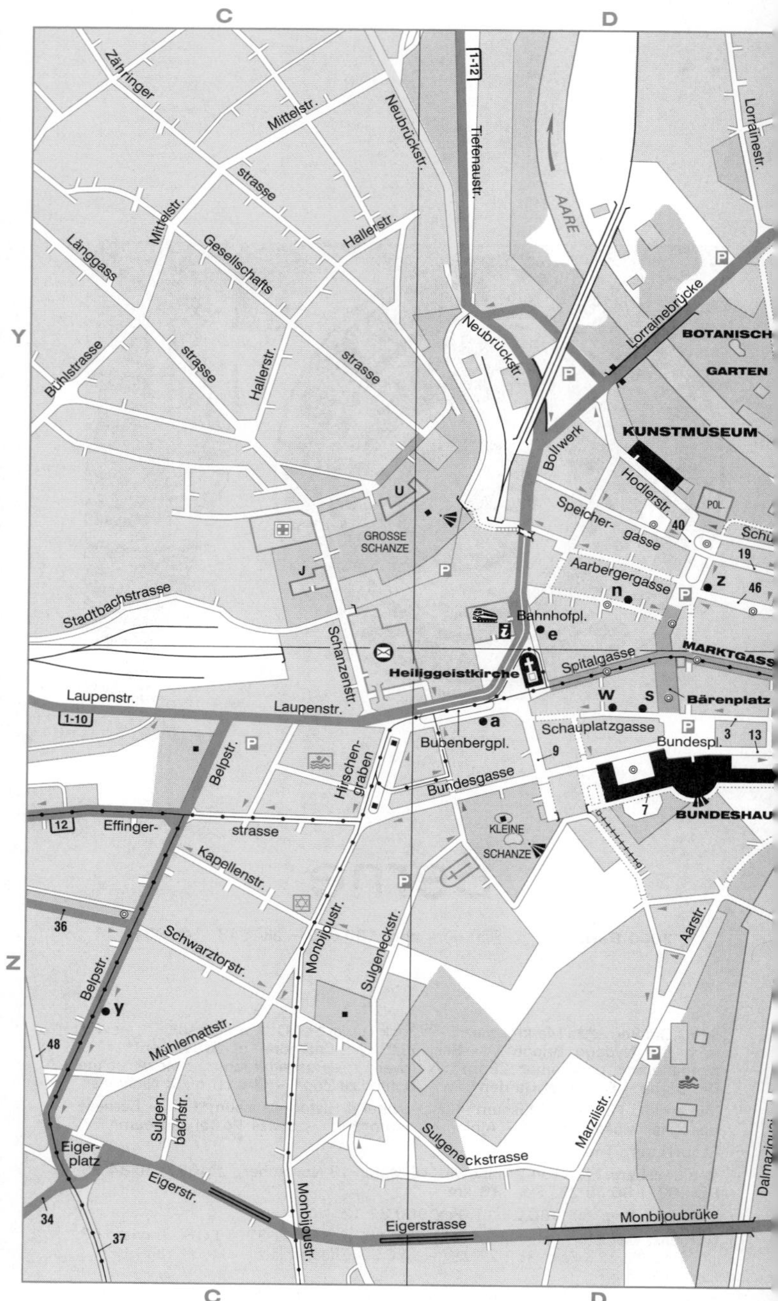
C
D
Y
Z
Zähringer
Mittelstr.
strasse
Neubrückstr.
Tiefenaustr.
1-12
AARE
Lorrainestr.
Mittelstr.
Hallerstr.
Länggass
Gesellschafts
strasse
Lorrainebrücke
BOTANISCH
GARTEN
Bühlstrasse
strasse
Hallerstr.
Neubrückstr.
KUNSTMUSEUM
Bollwerk
Hodlerstr.
POL.
Speicher-
gasse
40
Schü
19
GROSSE
SCHANZE
Aarbergergasse
Z
46
Stadtbachstrasse
Bahnhofpl.
Schanzenstr.
MARKTGASS
Heiliggeistkirche
Spitalgasse
Laupenstr.
Laupenstr.
1-10
W
S
Bärenplatz
Schauplatzgasse
Bundespl.
3
13
Bubenbergpl.
Belpstr.
Hirschen-
graben
9
Bundesgasse
7
BUNDESHAU
12
Effinger-
strasse
KLEINE
SCHANZE
Kapellenstr.
36
Monbijoustr.
Sulgeneckstr.
Aarstr.
Schwarztorstr.
Belpstr.
y
48
Mühlemattstr.
Sulgen-
bachstr.
Marzilistr.
Eiger-
platz
Sulgeneckstrasse
Dalmaziquai
Eigerstr.
Monbijoustr.
34
Eigerstrasse
Monbijoubrüke
37

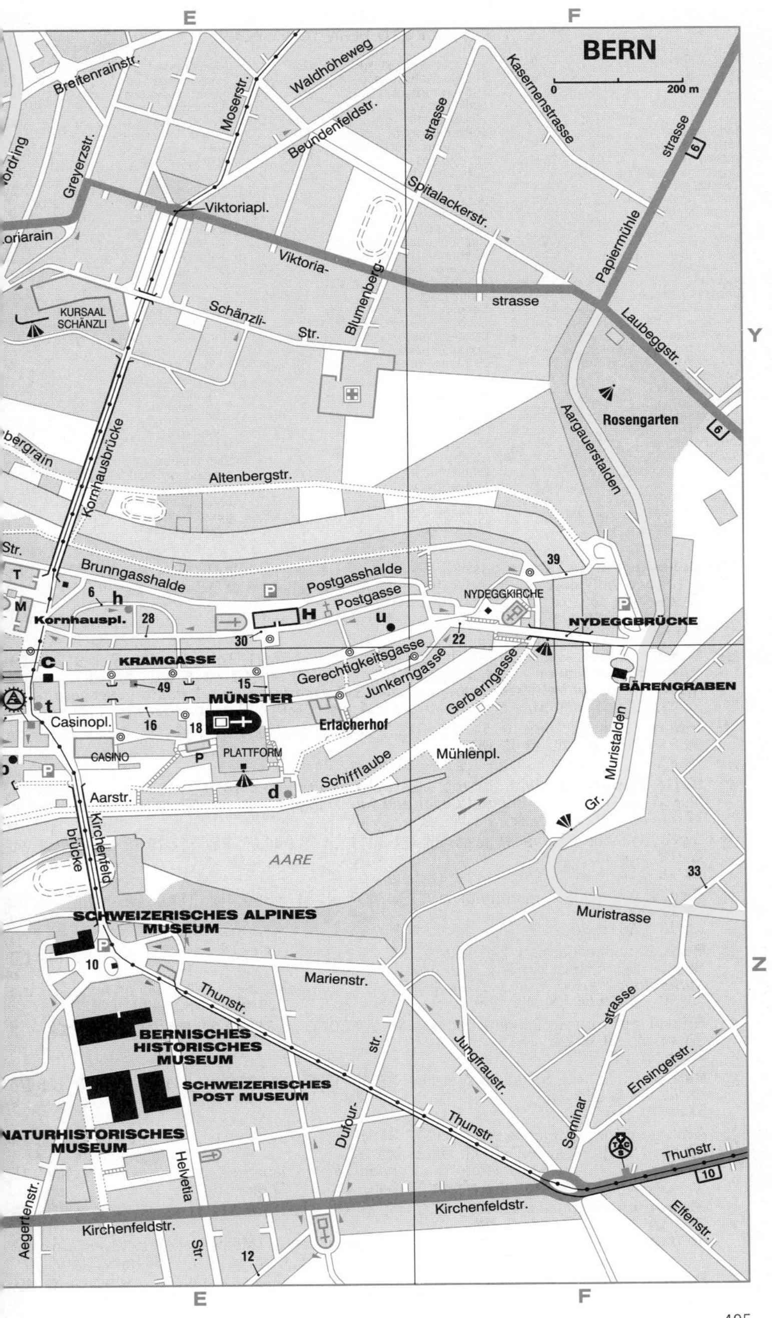
BERN
0
200 m
E
F
Y
Z
Breitenrainstr.
Moserstr.
Waldhöheweg
Beundenfeldstr.
Kasernenstrasse
strasse
Greyerzstr.
Viktoriapl.
Viktoria-
strasse
Spitalackerstr.
Papiermühle
strasse
6
Blumenberg-
Schänzli-
Str.
KURSAAL
SCHÄNZLI
Laubeggstr.
Rosengarten
Aargauerstalden
Kornhausbrücke
Altenbergstr.
Brunngasshalde
Postgasshalde
Postgasse
NYDEGGKIRCHE
NYDEGGBRÜCKE
39
Kornhauspl.
28
30
22
KRAMGASSE
Gerechtigkeitsgasse
Junkerngasse
Gerberngasse
BÄRENGRABEN
49
15
MÜNSTER
Erlacherhof
Casinopl.
16
18
CASINO
PLATTFORM
Mühlenpl.
Muristalden
Schifflaube
Aarstr.
Gr.
Kirchenfeldbrücke
AARE
33
Muristrasse
SCHWEIZERISCHES ALPINES MUSEUM
10
Marienstr.
Thunstr.
BERNISCHES HISTORISCHES MUSEUM
SCHWEIZERISCHES POST MUSEUM
NATURHISTORISCHES MUSEUM
Jungfraustr.
Dufour-str.
Seminar
Ensingerstr.
Helvetia Str.
Aegertenstr.
Kirchenfeldstr.
Elfenstr.
12

STREET INDEX TO BERN TOWN PLAN

Street	Grid	No.
Bärenplatz	DZ	
Kramgasse	EZ	
Marktgasse	DZ	
Spitalgasse	DYZ	
Aarbergergasse	DY	
Aargauerstalden	FY	
Aarstrasse	DEZ	
Aegertenstrasse	EZ	
Altenbergrain	DEY	
Altenbergstrasse	EFY	
Amthausgasse	DEZ	3
Bahnhofplatz	DY	
Belpstrasse	CZ	
Beundenfeldstrasse	EFY	
Blumenbergstrasse	EFY	
Bollwerk	DY	
Breitenrainstrasse	EY	
Brunngasse	EY	6
Brunngasshalde	EY	
Bubenbergplatz	DZ	
Bühlstrasse	CY	
Bundesgasse	DZ	
Bundesplatz	DZ	
Bundesterrasse	DZ	7
Casinoplatz	EZ	
Christoffelgasse	DZ	9
Dalmaziquai	DZ	
Dufourstrasse	EZ	
Effingerstrasse	CZ	
Eigerplatz	CZ	
Eigerstrasse	CDZ	
Elfenstrasse	FZ	
Ensingerstrasse	FZ	
Gerberngasse	FZ	
Gerechtigkeitsgasse	EYZ	
Gesellschaftsstrasse	CY	
Greyerstrasse	EY	
Hallerstrasse	CY	
Helvetiaplatz	EZ	10
Helvetiastrasse	EZ	
Hirschengraben	CZ	
Holderstrasse	DY	
Jubiläumsstrasse	EZ	12
Jungfraustrasse	FZ	
Junkerngasse	EFZ	
Kapellenstrasse	CZ	
Kasernenstrasse	FY	
Kirchenfeldbrücke	EZ	
Kirchenfeldstrasse	EFZ	
Kochergasse	DEZ	13
Kornhausbrücke	EY	
Kreuzgasse	EZ	15
Langassstrasse	CY	
Laubeggstrasse	FY	
Laupenstrasse	CZ	
Lorrainebrücke	DY	
Lorrainestrasse	DY	
Luisenstrasse	EZ	
Marienstrasse	EZ	
Marzilistrasse	DZ	
Mittelstrasse	CY	
Monbijoubrücke	DZ	
Monbijoustrasse	CZ	
Moserstrasse	EY	
Mühlemattstrasse	CZ	
Mühlenplatz	FZ	
Münstergasse	EZ	16
Münsterplatz	EZ	18
Muristalden	FZ	
Muristrasse	FZ	
Nägeligasse	DY	19
Neubrückstrasse	CDY	
Nordring	EY	
Nydeggasse	FY	22
Papiermühlestrasse	FY	
Postgasse	EY	
Postgasshalde	EY	
Rathausgasse	EY	28
Rathausplatz	EY	30
Schanzenstrasse	CYZ	
Schänzlistrasse	EY	
Schauplatzgasse	DZ	
Schifflaube	EY	
Schosshaldenstrasse	FZ	33
Schüttestrasse	DEY	
Schwarztorstrasse	CZ	36
Seftigenstrasse	CZ	37
Seminarstrasse	FZ	
Speichergasse	DY	
Spitalackerstrasse	EFY	
Stadtbachstrasse	CY	
Sulgenbachstrasse	CZ	
Sulgeneckstrasse	CDZ	
Thunstrasse	EFZ	
Tiefenaustrasse	DY	
Untertorbrücke	FY	39
Viktoriaplatz	EY	
Viktoriarain	EY	
Viktoriastrasse	EFY	
Waisenhausplatz	DY	40
Waldhöheweg	EY	
Zähringerstrasse	CY	
Zeughausgasse	DY	46
Zieglerstrasse	CZ	48

Bellevue Palace, Kochergasse 3, ✉ 3001, ☏ 320 45 45, Telex 911524, Fax 311 47 43, « Terrace with views over the Aare » – rest video ☎ – 25/150. AE E VISA JCB. rest EZ **p**
Meals see ***Bellevue-Grill/La Terrasse*** below – ***Zur Münz :*** **Meals** *20* and a la carte 53/105 – **131 rm** 290/450, 14 suites.

Schweizerhof, Bahnhofplatz 11, ✉ 3001, ☏ 311 45 01, Telex 911782, Fax 312 21 79, « Tasteful installation » – ☎ – 25/140. AE E VISA. rest DY **e**
Meals see ***Schultenheissenstube*** and ***Jack's Brasserie*** below – ***Yamato*** - Japanese rest. - *(closed Sunday and Monday) (dinner only)* **Meals** 60/80 – **87 rm** 260/430, 4 suites.

Innere Enge, Engestr. 54, ✉ 3012, ☏ 309 61 11, Fax 309 61 12, park – rm rm ☎ P. AE E VISA by Tiefenaustrasse DY
Meals *17* - 29 and a la carte 30/76 – **26 rm** 185/260.

Belle Epoque M without rest, Gerechtigkeitsgasse 18, ✉ 3011, ☏ 311 43 36, Fax 311 39 36, « Belle Epoque decor and furnishings » – ☎. AE E VISA EY **u**
17 rm 220/300.

Savoy without rest, Neuengasse 26, ✉ 3011, ☏ 311 44 05, Fax 312 19 78 – ☎. AE E VISA JCB DY **n**
18 – **56 rm** 157/244.

City M without rest, Bahnhofplatz 7, ✉ 3007, ☏ 311 53 77, Fax 311 06 36 – ☎. AE E VISA JCB DZ **a**
16 – **58 rm** 105/175.

Bern, Zeughausgasse 9, ✉ 3011, ☏ 312 10 21, Fax 312 11 47, – rm rest ☎ – 25/160. AE E VISA JCB EY **b**
Kurierstube *(closed July - mid August and Sunday)* **Meals** *26.50* - 60/80 (dinner) and a la carte 43/90 – ***7 Stube :*** **Meals** *19.50* and a la carte 30/77 – **100 rm** 180/280.

Bristol without rest, Schauplatzgasse 10, ✉ 3011, ☏ 311 01 01, Fax 311 94 79, – ☎. AE E VISA JCB DZ **w**
92 rm 165/265.

Bären without rest, Schauplatzgasse 4, ✉ 3011, ☏ 311 33 67, Fax 311 69 83, – ☎. AE E VISA JCB DZ **s**
57 rm 165/265.

Ambassador, Seftigenstr. 99, ✉ 3007, ☏ 370 99 99, Fax 371 41 17, – rest ☎ P – 25/150. AE E VISA JCB by Seftigenstrasse CZ
Meals a la carte 34/74, children 10 – ***Teppan Taishi*** - Japanese rest. - *(closed 15 July - 15 August, Sunday and Monday)* **Meals** 24/84 – 16 – **97 rm** 130/190.

Metropole, Zeughausgasse 28, ✉ 3011, ☏ 311 50 21, Fax 312 11 53, – rm ☎ – 25/100. AE E VISA DY **z**
Rôtisserie Vieux Moulin *(closed Saturday lunch and Sunday)* **Meals** 26.50 (lunch) and a la carte 41/91 – ***Brasserie :*** **Meals** *16.50* and a la carte 34/65, children 21.50 – **58 rm** 150/220.

Pergola without rest, Belpstr. 43, ✉ 3007, ☏ 381 91 46, Fax 381 50 54 – ☎. E VISA CZ **y**
closed 23 December - 1 January – **55 rm** 132/180.

XXXX **Bellevue Grill / Bellevue Terrasse** - Hotel Bellevue Palace, Kochergasse 3, ✉ 3001, ☎ 320 45 45, Telex 911524, Fax 311 47 43, 宗, « Terrace with views over the Aare » – ▤. AE ⓓ E VISA JCB. ✻ EZ **p**
Grill : closed June - September and lunch ; Terrasse : closed dinner from November - May – **Meals** 95/114 and a la carte 76/120.

XXX **Schultenheissenstube** - Hotel Schweizerhof, Bahnhofplatz 11 (1st floor), ✉ 3001, ☎ 311 45 01, Telex 911782, Fax 312 21 79 – ▤. AE ⓓ E VISA. ✻ DY **e**
closed Sunday – **Meals** 48 - 75/120 and a la carte 68/128.

XX **Jack's Brasserie** - Hotel Schweizerhof, Bahnhofplatz 11, ✉ 3001, ☎ 311 45 01, Telex 911782, Fax 312 21 79, 宗 – ▤. AE ⓓ E VISA DY **e**
Meals *29* and a la carte 49/108.

XX **du Théâtre,** Theaterplatz 7, ✉ 3011, ☎ 312 30 31, Fax 311 71 77, 宗 – AE ⓓ E VISA EZ **t**
closed 15 July - 5 August and Sunday – **Meals** *24* - 36/55 (lunch) and a la carte 52/116.

XX **Ermitage,** Marktgasse 15, ✉ 3011, ☎ 311 35 41, Fax 311 35 42 – AE E VISA EZ **g**
closed Sunday – ***Bonbonnière*** (1st floor) **Meals** 59/125 and a la carte 30/112 – ***Carnozet :*** **Meals** *17.50* - 27 and a la carte 30/78.

X **Zum Zähringer,** Badgasse 1, ✉ 3013, ☎ 311 32 70, 宗 – AE ⓓ E VISA EZ **d**
closed Sunday – **Meals** *17.50* - 26 (lunch) and a la carte 48/79.

X **Zimmermania,** Brunngasse 19, ✉ 3011, ☎ 311 15 42, Fax 312 28 22, Old Bernese bistro – E VISA EY **h**
closed 4 weeks beginning of July, Sunday, Monday and Bank Holidays – **Meals** (booking essential) *17.50* - 35 (lunch) and a la carte 38/88.

at Muri SE : 3,5 km by Thunstrasse – ✉ 3074 Muri bei Bern – ✪ 031 :

Sternen, Thunstr. 80, ☎ 950 71 71, Fax 950 71 00, 宗 – |‡| ⇔ TV ☎ ⇔ – 🏛 25/120. AE ⓓ E VISA
Läubli : **Meals** 39 (lunch)/60 and a la carte 40/93 – ***Da Pietro*** - Italian rest. - *(closed 8 July - 4 August and lunch Saturday, Sunday and Bank Holidays)* **Meals** *17.50* and a la carte 32/70 - **44 rm** ☕ 170/250.

at Wabern S : 5 km direction Belp – ✉ 3084 Wabern – ✪ 031 :

XX **Maygut** with rm, Seftigenstr. 370, ☎ 961 39 81, 宗 – **P**. AE ⓓ E VISA JCB
closed Sunday and Monday – ***Kreidolfstube :*** **Meals** 65/85 and a la carte 73/106 – ***Gaststube :*** **Meals** *15.50* and a la carte 40/89 – ☕ 9 – **3 rm** 105/120.

at Liebefeld SW : 3 km direction Schwarzenburg – ✉ 3097 Liebefeld – ✪ 031 :

XX **Landhaus,** Schwarzenburgstr. 134, ☎ 971 07 58, Fax 972 02 49, 宗 – **P**. AE ⓓ E VISA
closed Easter, Christmas and Sunday – ***Rôtisserie :*** **Meals** 54 (lunch)/108 and a la carte 62/111 – ***Taverne Alsacienne :*** **Meals** *15.50* and a la carte 25/63.

BASLE (BASEL)

4000 Basel-Stadt 427 ④, 216 ④, 66 ⑩ – 175 510 – alt. 273 – ✪ Basle and environs ; from France 19-41-61 from Switzerland 061.

See : Old town★ : Cathedral★★ (Münster) : ≤★ CY – Fish Market Fountain★ (Fischmarktbrunnen) BY – Old Streets★ BY – Zoological Garden★★★ AZ – The Port (Hafen) ✵★, "From Basle to the high Seas"★ Exhibition.

Museums : Fine Arts★★★ (Kunstmuseum) CY – Historical★ (Historisches Museum) BY – Ethnographic★ (Museum für Völkerkunde) BY **M¹** – Antiquities★ (Antikenmuseum) CY – Paper Museum★ (Basler Papiermühle) DY **M⁶** – Haus zum Kirschgarten★ BZ.

Envir : ✵★ from Bruderholz Water Tower S : 3,5 km – Chapel of St.-Chrischona★ NE : 8 km – Augst Roman Ruins★★ SE : 11 km.

18 at Hagenthal-le-Bas, ✉ F-68220 (March - November), SW : 10 km, ☎ (0033) 89 68 50 91, Fax (0033) 89 68 55 66.

✈ Euro-Airport, ☎ 325 31 11, Basle (Switzerland) by Flughafenstrasse 8 km and – at Saint-Louis (France), ☎ (0033) 89 90 31 11.

i Tourist Office, Schifflände 5, ☎ 261 50 50, Fax 261 59 44 – T.C.S., Steinentorstr. 13, ☎ 272 19 55, Fax 272 93 54 – A.C.S., Birsigstr. 4, ☎ 272 39 33, Fax 281 36 57.

Berne 100 – Freiburg im Breisgau 72 – Lyons 401 – Mulhouse 35 – Paris 554 – Strasbourg 145.

Plans on following pages

Drei Könige, Blumenrain 8, ✉ 4001, ☎ 261 52 52, Fax 261 21 53, ≤, 宗 – |‡| ⇔ rm ▤ TV ☎ **P** – 🏛 25/80. AE ⓓ E VISA JCB BY **a**
Rôtisserie des Rois : **Meals** 52 (lunch)/105 and a la carte 69/116, children 10 – ***Königsbrasserie :*** **Meals** *21* and a la carte 31/79, children 10 – ☕ 29 – **82 rm** 320/590, 6 suites.

Plaza M, Messeplatz 25, ✉ 4021, ☎ 690 33 33, Fax 690 39 70, ≘, ▣ – |‡| ⇔ rm ▤ TV ☎ ♿ ⇔ – 🏛 35. AE ⓓ E VISA JCB. ✻ rest DX **r**
Le Monet *(closed beginning of July - mid August)* **Meals** *29* - 49 (lunch)/64 and a la carte 55/95 – ***Le Provence :*** **Meals** *19* - 23 (lunch) and a la carte 32/80 – **218 rm** ☕ 370/525, 20 suites.

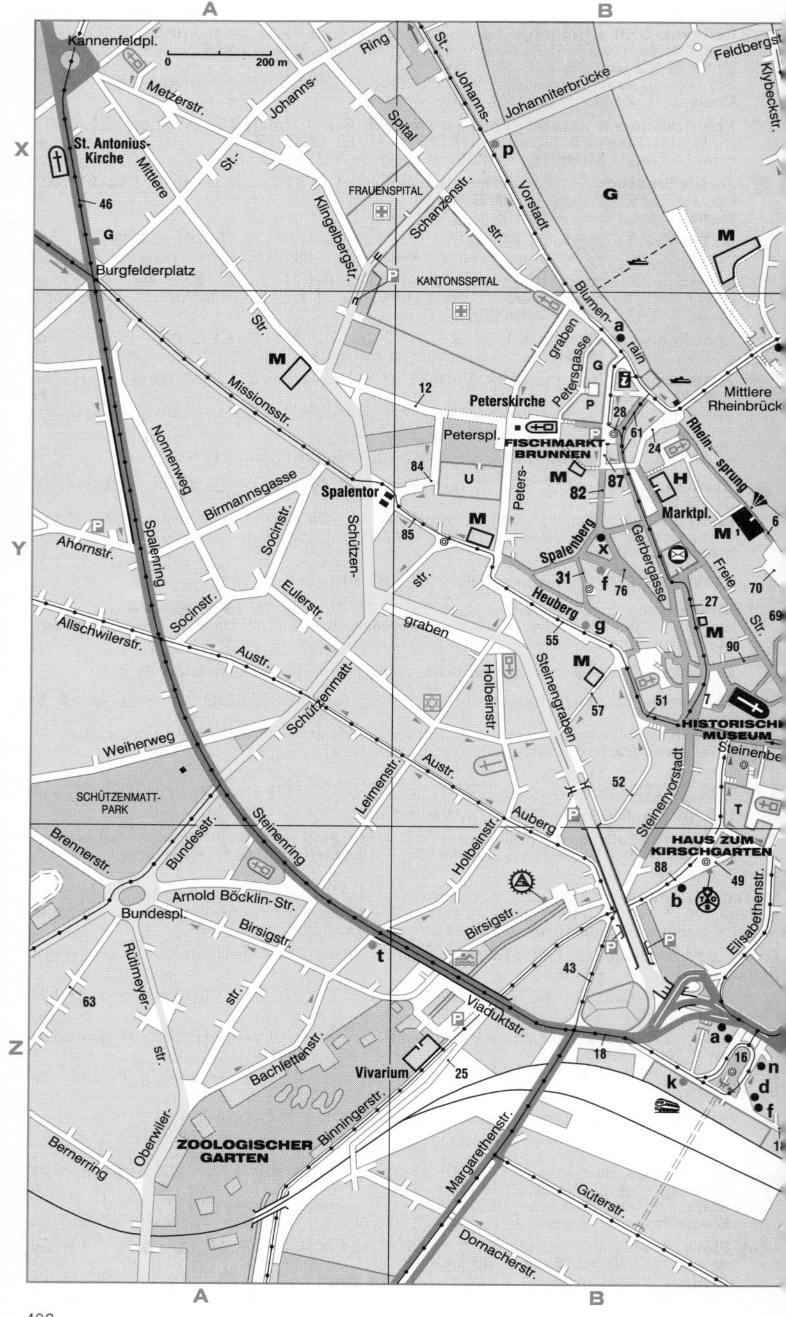
A
B
X
Y
Z
Kannenfeldpl.
0
200 m
St. Antonius-Kirche
Metzerstr.
Mittlere
St.-
Johanns-
Ring
Spital
St.-
Johanns-
Vorstadt
Johanniterbrücke
Feldbergstr.
Klybeckstr.
Klingelbergstr.
FRAUENSPITAL
Schanzenstr.
KANTONSSPITAL
Burgfelderplatz
Missionsstr.
Nonnenweg
Birmannsgasse
Spalenring
Socinstr.
Ahornstr.
Allschwilerstr.
Austr.
Eulerstr.
Schützen-
graben
Spalentor
Peterskirche
Peterspl.
Petersgraben
Petersgasse
Blumenrain
Mittlere Rheinbrück
Rheinsprung
FISCHMARKT-BRUNNEN
Marktpl.
Spalenberg
Heuberg
Gerbergasse
Freie Str.
Steinengraben
Holbeinstr.
Schützenmattstr.
Weiherweg
SCHÜTZENMATT-PARK
Leimenstr.
Auberg
Steinenvorstadt
HISTORISCHES MUSEUM
Steinenberg
HAUS ZUM KIRSCHGARTEN
Elisabethenstr.
Brennerstr.
Bundesstr.
Steinenring
Arnold Böcklin-Str.
Bundespl.
Birsigstr.
Rütimeyerstr.
Viaduktstr.
Bachlettenstr.
Vivarium
Binningerstr.
Oberwiler-str.
ZOOLOGISCHER GARTEN
Bernerring
Margarethenstr.
Güterstr.
Dornacherstr.

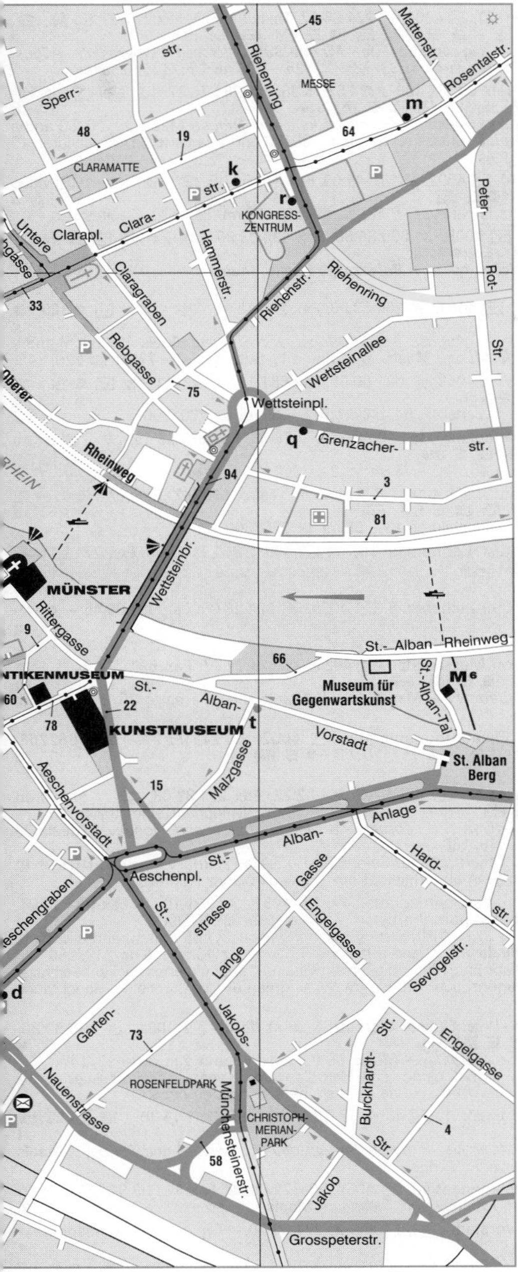

BASEL

Street	Grid	No.
Aeschenvorstadt	CYZ	
Barfüsserplatz	BY	7
Centralbahnplatz	BZ	16
Claraplatz	CX	
Eisengasse	BY	24
Falknerstrasse	BY	27
Freie Strasse	BY	
Gerbergasse	BY	
Greifengasse	BCY	33
Marktplatz	BY	
Steinenvorstadt	BYZ	
Alemannengasse	DY	3
Andreas Heusler-Strasse	DZ	4
Augustinergasse	BY	6
Bäumleingasse	CY	9
Bernoullistrasse	ABY	12
Brunngässlein	CYZ	15
Centralbahnstrasse	BZ	18
Drahtzugstrasse	CX	19
Dufourstrasse	CY	22
Erdbeergraben	BZ	25
Fischmarkt	BY	28
Gemsberg	BY	31
Innere Margarethenstrasse	BZ	43
Isteinerstrasse	DX	45
Kannenfeldstrasse	AX	46
Klingentalstrasse	CX	48
Klosterberg	BZ	49
Kohlenberg	BY	51
Kohlenberggasse	BY	52
Leonhardsgraben	BY	55
Leonhardsstrasse	BY	57
Lindenhofstrasse	CZ	58
Luftgässlein	CY	60
Marktgasse	BY	61
Marschalkenstrasse	AZ	63
Messeplatz	DX	64
Mühlenberg	CDY	66
Münsterberg	BY	69
Münsterplatz	BY	70
Peter Merian-Strasse	CZ	73
Riehentorstrasse	CY	75
Rümelingsplatz	BY	76
St.Alban-Graben	CY	78
Schaffhauserrheinweg	DY	81
Schneidergasse	BY	82
Spalengraben	BY	84
Spalenvorstadt	BY	85
Stadthausgasse	BY	87
Steinentorstrasse	BZ	88
Streitgasse	BY	90
Wettsteinstrasse	CY	94

The names of main shopping streets are printed in red at the beginning of the list of streets.

Hilton [M], Aeschengraben 31, ✉ 4002, ☏ 271 66 22, Telex 965555, Fax 271 52 20, Fitness, sauna, pool – lift, no smoking rm, air-conditioned, TV, ☏, disabled access – 25/300. AE, DC, E, VISA, JCB. rest CZ **d**
Le Wettstein : **Meals** 39 and a la carte 52/105 – ***Marine Suisse*** *(closed 4 weeks July - August and Sunday)* **Meals** *17.50* and a la carte 33/78 – ☐ 25 – **205 rm** 295/435, 9 suites.

International, Steinentorstr. 25, ✉ 4001, ☏ 281 75 85, Fax 281 76 27, Fitness, sauna, pool – lift, no smoking, air-conditioned rm, TV, ☏, disabled access, garage – 25/180. AE, DC, E, VISA, JCB. rest BZ **b**
Rôtisserie Charolaise *(closed weekends from late June-mid August)* **Meals** *29* - 50/80 and a la carte 41/110 – ***Steinenpick*** (Brasserie) **Meals** *23* -30/50 and a la carte 31/92, children 10 – **200 rm** ☐ 270/480, 7 suites.

Euler, Centralbahnplatz 14, ✉ 4002, ☏ 272 45 00, Fax 271 50 00, terrace – lift, no smoking rest, TV video ☏, garage – 25/100. AE, DC, E, VISA BZ **a**
Meals *39* - 49 (lunch) and a la carte 64/118 – ☐ 28.50 – **58 rm** 295/520, 6 suites.

Europe [M], Clarastr. 43, ✉ 4005, ☏ 690 80 80, Fax 690 88 80 – lift, no smoking, air-conditioned, TV, ☏, garage – 25/100. AE, DC, E, VISA, JCB. rest CX **k**
Meals see ***Les Quatre Saisons*** below – ***Bajazzo*** (Brasserie) **Meals** *19* and a la carte 30/72 – **166 rm** ☐ 290/390.

Basel [M], Münzgasse 12, ✉ 4051, ☏ 264 68 00, Fax 264 68 11 – lift, air-conditioned rest, TV, ☏. AE, DC, E, VISA. rest BY **x**
Basler Keller *(closed 6 July - 5 August, Saturday lunch and Sunday)* **Meals** 45 (lunch) and a la carte 47/112 – ***Brasserie Münz*** : **Meals** *19.50* and a la carte 31/57 – **72 rm** ☐ 220/345.

Mérian [M], Rheingasse 2, ✉ 4058, ☏ 681 00 00, Fax 681 11 01, ←, terrace – lift, TV, ☏, disabled access, garage – 25/100. AE, DC, E, VISA, JCB BY **b**
Meals *17.50* - 46/70 and a la carte 47/84, children 12 – **65 rm** ☐ 220/300.

Schweizerhof, Centralbahnplatz 1, ✉ 4002, ☏ 271 28 33, Fax 271 29 19, terrace – lift, air-conditioned rm, TV, ☏, parking – 25/100. AE, DC, E, VISA BZ **n**
Meals *27* - 90 and a la carte 48/106 – **75 rm** ☐ 210/350.

Victoria, Centralbahnplatz 3, ✉ 4002, ☏ 271 55 66, Telex 962362, Fax 271 55 01 – lift, air-conditioned rest, TV, ☏ – 25/80. AE, DC, E, VISA, JCB BZ **d**
Meals *24* and a la carte 41/79, children 13 – **95 rm** ☐ 220/300.

St. Gotthard [M] without rest, Centralbahnstr. 13, ✉ 4051, ☏ 271 52 50, Fax 271 52 14 – lift, no smoking, TV, ☏. AE, DC, E, VISA, JCB BZ **f**
64 rm ☐ 220/320.

Wettstein without rest., Grenzacherstr. 8, ✉ 4058, ☏ 691 28 00, Fax 691 05 45 – lift, no smoking, TV, ☏. AE, DC, E, VISA DY **q**
closed 22 December - 3 January – **40 rm** ☐ 200/330.

Admiral, Rosentalstr. 5 (on Messeplatz), ✉ 4021, ☏ 691 77 77, Fax 691 77 89, outdoor pool – lift, no smoking rm, TV, ☏ – 25. AE, DC, E, VISA, JCB DX **m**
closed 23 December - 2 January – **Meals** *16.50* - 30/60 and a la carte 30/86 – **140 rm** ☐ 200/350.

Metropol without rest, Elisabethenanlage 5, ✉ 4002, ☏ 271 77 21, Telex 962268, Fax 271 78 82 – lift, TV video, ☏ – 25/120. AE, DC, E, VISA BZ **a**
46 rm ☐ 260/400.

XXXX ✿✿ **Stucki,** Bruderholzallee 42, ✉ 4059, ☏ 361 82 22, Fax 361 82 03, terrace, « Flowered garden », terrace – parking. AE, E, VISA by Münchensteinerstrasse CDZ
closed 24 December - 8 January, 26 February - 6 March, Sunday and Monday – **Meals** 85 (lunch)/185 and a la carte 118/160
Spec. Escalope de foie de canard chaud, Saint-Pierre grillé au citron vert, huile d'olives et gingembre, Chausson de pigeon aux truffes et aux poireaux blancs (winter).

XXX ✿ **Der Teufelhof** with rm, Leonhardsgraben 47, ✉ 4051, ☏ 261 10 10, Fax 261 10 04, « Rooms decorated by contemporary artists » – no smoking rest, ☏. AE, E, VISA BY **g**
Meals (1st floor) *(closed 8 July - 10 August, Sunday and Monday)* 65 (lunch) and a la carte 114/163 – ***Weinstube*** : **Meals** *45* - 70 and a la carte 58/97 – ☐ 13.50 – **8 rm** 210/280
Spec. Variation von der Challans Ente mit Honig-Sesam Vinaigrette, Gratiniertes Zackenbarschfilet mit Krustentieren auf Estragonsauce, Grouse im Wirsingmantel mit Wacholder-Specksauce (Autumn - Winter).

XXX ✿ **Les Quatre Saisons** - Hotel Europe, Clarastr. 43 (1st floor), ✉ 4005, ☏ 690 80 80, Fax 690 88 80 – air-conditioned. AE, DC, E, VISA, JCB. CX **k**
closed 15 July - 4 August and Sunday – **Meals** 55 (lunch)/165 and a la carte 92/145
Spec. Saint-Pierre rôti au romarin et jus de veau, Filet d'épaule de veau à l'huile d'olives et aux artichauts, Mousseline de citron vert chaude et la soupe à la noix de coco.

XXX **Le Bourguignon,** Bachlettenstr. 1, ✉ 4054, ☏ 281 14 10, Fax 281 14 20 – air-conditioned, parking. AE, DC, E, VISA. AZ **t**
closed 22 July - 12 August, Carnival, Saturday (except dinner in winter) and Sunday – **Meals** 38 (lunch)/125 and a la carte 56/126.

XX **Chez Donati,** St. Johanns-Vorstadt 48, ✉ 4056, ☏ 322 09 19, Fax 322 09 81, terrace BX **p**
closed 15 July - 14 August, Monday and Tuesday – **Meals** - Italian rest. - a la carte 58/112.

XX **St. Alban-Eck,** St. Alban-Vorstadt 60, ✉ 4052, ☏ 271 03 20, « Typical local atmosphere » – AE, E, VISA. CDY **t**
closed 13 July - 11 August, Saturday except mid September - June, Sunday and Bank Holidays – **Meals** *28* - 75 and a la carte 67/103.

Sakura, Centralbahnstr. 14, ✉ 4051, ℘ 272 05 05, Fax 295 39 88, Japanese rest. – ▤. AE ⓓ E VISA JCB BZ k
closed 15 July - 12 August and Sunday – ***Teppanyaki :*** **Meals** *29* - 48/99 – ***Yakitori*** (Grill) **Meals** *17.50* and a la carte 30/70.

Zum Schnabel, Trillengässlein 2, ✉ 4051, ℘ 261 49 09, ⛱, « Typical bistro » – AE ⓓ E VISA BY f
closed Sunday and Bank Holidays – **Meals** *17* and a la carte 36/72.

at Birsfelden E : 3 km by St. Alban-Anlage CDZ – ✉ 4127 Birsfelden – ☎ 061 :

Alfa, Hauptstr. 15, ℘ 311 80 15, Fax 311 05 77 – 🛗 TV ☎ P – 🏛 25/100. AE ⓓ E VISA
Meals *18.50* and a la carte 43/78 – **52 rm** ☕ 170/210.

Waldhaus with rm, E : 2 km direction Rheinfelden, ℘ 313 00 11, ⛱, « Beautiful cottage in a park beside the Rhein » – TV ☎ P – 🏛 30. AE ⓓ E VISA. ✗
closed 23 December - 15 January, Sunday dinner and Monday – **Meals** 60 and a la carte 35/103, children 15.50 – **8 rm** ☕ 112/176.

at Binningen S : 2 km by Oberwilerstrasse AZ – ✉ 4102 Binningen – ☎ 061 :

Schlüssel, Schlüsselgasse 1, ℘ 421 25 66, Fax 421 66 62, ⛱ – 🛗 TV ☎ P. AE ⓓ E VISA
Meals *(closed Sunday dinner and Saturday)* *19* and a la carte 31/80, children 20 – **29 rm** ☕ 108/190.

Schloss Binningen, Schlossgasse 5, ℘ 421 20 55, Fax 421 06 35, ⛱, « Old mansion, antique furniture, park » – P. AE ⓓ E VISA JCB
closed 2 weeks at Carnival, Sunday and Monday – **Meals** *22.50* - 45 (lunch)/95 and a la carte 46/103, children 15.

Gasthof Neubad with rm, Neubadrain 4, ℘ 302 07 05, Fax 302 81 16, ⛱, 🚗 – TV ☎ P. E VISA
closed 16 February - 6 March and Wednesday – **Meals** *21* - 50 (lunch)/85 and a la carte 40/110 – **6 rm** ☕ 110/170.

Leimbach, Hasenrainstr. 59, ℘ 421 24 30, Fax 421 24 90, ⛱ – P. E VISA
closed 2 weeks late September, 2 weeks late February and Wednesday – **Meals** 49/110 and a la carte 49/99.

at Euro-Airport NW : 8 km by Kannenfeldstrasse AX :

Euroairport, 5th floor of the airport, ✉ 4030 Basel, ℘ 325 32 32, Fax 325 32 65, ← – ▤. AE ⓓ E VISA
Grill : **Meals** 55 and a la carte 38/70, children 8.50 – ***Brasserie :*** **Meals** 24 and a la carte 31/47, children 8.50.

GENEVA **1200** Genève 427 ⑪, 217 ⑪, 74 ⑥ – 170 189 – alt. 375 – ☎ Geneva, environs : from France 19-41-22, from Switzerland 022.

See : The Shores of the lake★★ : ←★★★ FGY – Parks★★ : Mon Repos GX, La Perle du Lac and Villa Barton CTU – Botanical Garden★ : alpine rock-garden★★ CT **E** – Cathedral St-Pierre★ : north Tower ✻★★ FZ – Old Town★ : Reformation Monument★ FZ **D** ; Archaeological Site★ – Palais des Nations★★ CT – Parc de la Grange★ CU – Parc des Eaux-Vives★ CU – Nave★ of Church of Christ the King BV **N** – Woodwork★ in the Historical Museum of the Swiss Abroad CT **M4** – Baur Collection★ (in 19C mansion) GZ – Maison Tavel★ FZ.

Museums : Ariana★★ CT **M2** – Art and History★★ GZ – Natural History★★ GZ – Old Musical Instruments★ GZ **M1** – Petit Palais : Modern Art★★ GZ – International Red Cross and Red Crescent Museum★ CT **M3**.

Excursions : by boat on the lake, Information : Cie Gén. de Nav., Jardin Anglais ℘ 311 25 21- Mouettes genevoises, 8 quai du Mont-Blanc, ℘ 732 29 44 - Swiss Boat, 4 quai du Mont-Blanc, ℘ 736 79 35.

18 at Cologny DU ✉ 1223 (March - December), ℘ 735 75 40, Fax 735 71 05 ; 18 at Bossey ✉ F-74160 (March - December), ℘ (0033) 50 43 75 25, Fax (0033) 50 95 32 57 by road to Troinex ; 18 at Esery ✉ F-74930 Reignier (March - December), ℘ (0033) 50 36 58 70, Fax (0033) 50 36 57 62,. SE : 15 km ; 18 Maison Blanche at Echenevex-Gex ✉ F-01170 (March - mid December), ℘ (0033) 50 42 44 42, Fax (0033) 50 42 44 43, NW : 17 km.

✈ Genève-Cointrin, ℘ 717 71 11.

ℹ Tourist Office, Place du Molard, ℘ 311 98 27, Fax 311 80 52 and under Gare Cornavin, ℘ 738 52 00, Fax 731 90 56 – T.C.S., 9 r. Pierre-Fatio, ℘ 737 12 01, Fax 737 13 10 – A.C.S., 21 r. de la Fontenette ✉ 1227 Carouge, ℘ 342 22 33, Fax 301 37 11.

Berne 164 – Bourg-en-B. 101 – Lausanne 60 – Lyons 151 – Paris 538 – Turin 252.

Plans on following pages

Right Bank (Cornavin Railway Station - Les Quais) :

Richemond, Jardin Brunswick, ✉ 1201, ℘ 731 14 00, Telex 412560, Fax 731 67 09, ←, ⛱ – 🛗 ▤ TV video ☎ 🚗 – 🏛 25/230. AE ⓓ E VISA JCB. ✗ rest FY u
Meals see ***Le Gentilhomme*** below – ***Le Jardin :*** **Meals** *24* and a la carte 60/116 – ☕ 32 – **86 rm** 370/720, 12 suites.

Rhône, 1 quai Turrettini, ✉ 1201, ℘ 731 98 31, Telex 412559, Fax 732 45 58, ←, ⛱ – 🛗 ⇔ rm ▤ TV video ☎ 🚗 – 🏛 25/150. AE ⓓ E VISA JCB. ✗ rest FY r
Meals see ***Le Neptune*** below – ***Café Rafael :*** **Meals** *29* - 44 (lunch) and a la carte 52/95 – ☕ 30 – **194 rm** 350/760, 20 suites.

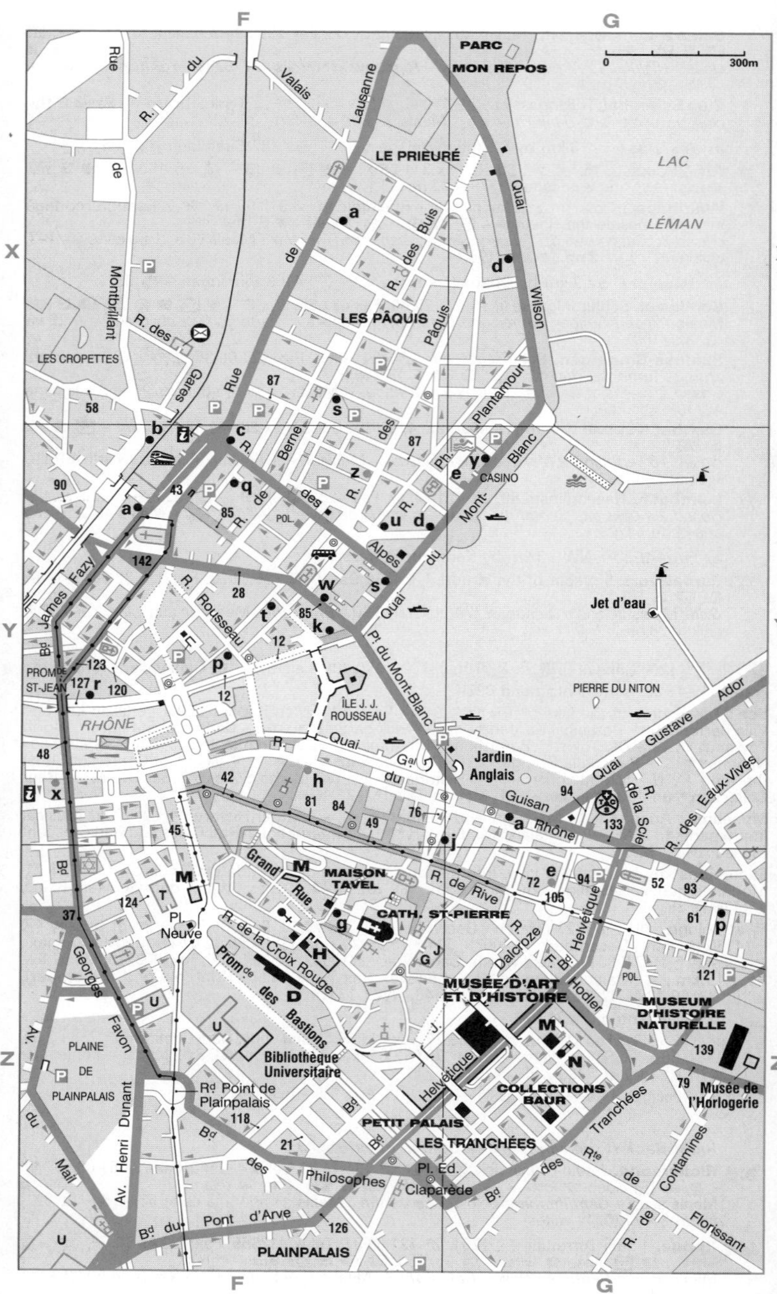
PARC
MON REPOS
LE PRIEURÉ
LAC
LÉMAN
LES PÂQUIS
LES CROPETTES
CASINO
Jet d'eau
PIERRE DU NITON
ÎLE J. J. ROUSSEAU
RHÔNE
Jardin Anglais
MAISON TAVEL
CATH. ST-PIERRE
MUSÉE D'ART ET D'HISTOIRE
MUSEUM D'HISTOIRE NATURELLE
Musée de l'Horlogerie
COLLECTIONS BAUR
PETIT PALAIS
LES TRANCHÉES
Bibliothèque Universitaire
PLAINE DE PLAINPALAIS
PLAINPALAIS
Quai Wilson
Quai du Mont-Blanc
Pt du Mont-Blanc
Quai Gustave Ador
Quai du Général Guisan
Rue de Lausanne
Rue de Montbrillant
Bd James Fazy
Bd Georges Favon
Av. Henri Dunant
Rd Point de Plainpalais
Bd des Philosophes
Bd du Pont d'Arve
Pl. Ed. Claparède
Pl. Neuve
Prom. des Bastions
R. de la Croix Rouge
Grand'Rue
R. de Rive
R. de la Scie
R. des Eaux-Vives
Rte de Florissant
R. de Contamines
Bd Helvétique
Prom. de St-Jean
0
300m

STREET INDEX TO GENEVE TOWN PLAN

Confédération (R. de la) . . . . . FY 42
Marché (R. du) . . . . . FY 81
Mont-Blanc (R. du) . . . . . FY 85
Rhône (R. du) . . . . . FGY
Rive (R. de) . . . . . FGZ

Alpes (R. des) . . . . . FY
Bastions (Prom. des) . . . . . FZ
Bel-Air (Pl.) . . . . . FY 10
Bergues (Quai des) . . . . . FY 12
Berne (R. de) . . . . . FY
Buis (R. des) . . . . . FX
Candolle (R. de) . . . . . FZ 21
Chantepoulet (R. de) . . . . . FY 28
Cirque (Pl. du) . . . . . FZ 37
Contamines (R. de) . . . . . GZ
Cornavin (Pl. de) . . . . . FY 43
Corraterie (R. de la) . . . . . FY 45
Coulouvrenière (Pont de la) . . . . . FY 48
Croix-d'Or (R. de la) . . . . . FY 49
Croix-Rouge (R. de la) . . . . . FZ
Eaux-Vives (Pl. des) . . . . . GZ 52
Eaux-Vives (R. des) . . . . . GY

Edouard-Claparède (Pl.) . . . FGZ
Ferdinand-Hodler (R.) . . . . GZ
Fort-Barreau (R. du) . . . . . FX 58
Frontenex (Av. de) . . . . . GZ 61
Gares (R. des) . . . . . FX
Général-Guisan (Quai) . . . . FGY
Georges-Favon (Bd) . . . . . FZ
Grand'Rue . . . . . FZ
Gustave-Ador (Quai) . . . . . GY
Helvétique (Bd) . . . . . FGZ
Henri-Dunant (Av.) . . . . . FZ
Italie (R. d') . . . . . GZ 72
Jacques-Dalcroze (Bd) . . . . FGZ
James-Fazy (Bd) . . . . . FY
Lausanne (R. de) . . . . . FX
Longemalle (Pl.) . . . . . FY 76
Mail (Av. du) . . . . . FZ
Malagnou (Rte de) . . . . . GZ 79
Molard (Pl. du) . . . . . FY 84
Mont-Blanc (Pont du) . . . . FY
Mont-Blanc (Quai du) . . . . . FGY
Montbrillant (R. de) . . . . . FX
Monthoux (R. de) . . . . . FXY 87
Neuve (Pl.) . . . . . FZ
Pâquis (R. des) . . . . . FXY

Pépinière (R. de la) . . . . . FY 90
Philippe-Plantamour (R.) . GX
Philosophes (Bd des) . . . FZ
Pictet-de-Rochemont (Av.) . . . . . GZ 93
Pierre-Fatio (R.) . . . . . GYZ 94
Plainpalais (Rond-Point de) . . . . . FZ
Pont-d'Arve (Bd du) . . . . FZ
Rive (Rond-Point de) . . . . GZ 105
Rousseau (R.) . . . . . FY
Scie (R. de la) . . . . . GY
St-Léger (R.) . . . . . FZ 118
Temple (R. du) . . . . . FY 120
Terrassière (R. de la) . . . . GZ 121
Terreaux-du-Temple (R. des) . . . . . FY 123
Théâtre (Bd du) . . . . . FZ 124
Tour (Bd de la) . . . . . FZ 126
Tranchées (Bd des) . . . . . GZ
Turrettini (Quai) . . . . . FY 127
Valais (R. du) . . . . . FX
Versonnex (R.) . . . . . GY 133
Villereuse (R. de) . . . . . GZ 139
Wilson (Quai) . . . . . GX
22-Cantons (Pl. des) . . . . FY 142

Des Bergues, 33 quai des Bergues, ⊠ 1201, ℰ 731 50 50, Telex 412540, Fax 732 19 89, ≤ – |‡| ▤ rm 📺 video ☎ ♿ – 🏛 25/350. AE ⓓ E VISA JCB FY **k**
Meals see ***Amphitryon*** below – ***Le Pavillon :*** **Meals** *25* - 40 and a la carte 45/88 – ☕ 32 – **113 rm** 390/660, 10 suites.

Noga Hilton, 19 quai du Mont-Blanc, ⊠ 1201, ℰ 908 90 81, Telex 412337, Fax 908 90 90, ≤, 🌳, Fö, ≘s, 🏊 – |‡| ⇹ rm ▤ 📺 video ☎ ♿ – 🏛 25/850. AE ⓓ E VISA JCB GY **y**
Meals see ***Le Cygne*** below – ***La Grignotière :*** **Meals** *21* and a la carte 42/91, children 9 – ☕ 32 – **375 rm** 340/530, 36 suites.

Président Wilson Ⓜ, 47 quai Wilson, ⊠ 1201, ℰ 731 10 00, Telex 412328, Fax 731 22 06, ≤ lake, 🌳, ≘s, 🏊 – |‡| ⇹ rm ▤ 📺 ☎ ♿ 🚗 – 🏛 25/1100. AE ⓓ E VISA JCB. ✻ rest GX **d**
Le Cirque : **Meals** *28* - 45 (lunch)/88 and a la carte 58/116 – ***L'Arabesque*** - Oriental rest. - *(closed for lunch from October - May)* **Meals** a la carte 42/86 – ☕ 29 – **222 rm** 530/800, 28 suites.

Beau-Rivage, 13 quai du Mont-Blanc, ⊠ 1201, ℰ 731 02 21, Telex 412539, Fax 738 98 47, ≤, 🌳 – |‡| ⇹ rm ▤ rm 📺 video ☎ 🚗 – 🏛 25/300. AE ⓓ E VISA JCB. ✻ FY **d**
Meals see ***Le Chat Botté*** below – ***Le Quai 13,*** ℰ 731 31 82 **Meals** a la carte 34/90 – ☕ 34 – **89 rm** 375/570, 8 suites.

Paix, 11 quai du Mont-Blanc, ⊠ 1201, ℰ 732 61 50, Telex 412554, Fax 738 87 94, ≤ – |‡| ▤ rest 📺 video ☎ – 🏛 25/70. AE ⓓ E VISA FY **s**
Meals *24* - 40 (lunch)/87 and a la carte 57/114 – ☕ 30 – **91 rm** 410/525, 10 suites.

Forum, 19 r. de Zurich, ⊠ 1201, ℰ 731 02 41, Telex 412557, Fax 738 75 14 – |‡| ⇹ rm ▤ 📺 video ☎ 🚗 – 🏛 25/120. AE ⓓ E VISA JCB FX **s**
The Taj - Indian rest. - **Meals** *19*-62 and a la carte 40/79 – ***Le Refuge*** - "fondues" speciality - **Meals** 38 and a la carte 40/77 – ☕ 27 – **196 rm** 290/395, 11 suites.

Warwick, 14 r. de Lausanne, ⊠ 1201, ℰ 731 62 50, Telex 412731, Fax 738 99 35 – |‡| ⇹ rm ▤ 📺 ☎ – 🏛 25/300. AE ⓓ E VISA JCB. ✻ FY **c**
Les 4 Saisons *(closed 15 July - 10 August, 24 to 30 December, Saturday lunch and Sunday)* **Meals** 43 (lunch)/70 and a la carte 51/99 – ***La Bonne Brasserie :*** **Meals** *15* - 32 and a la carte 35/79, children 13 – ☕ 26 – **169 rm** 300/442.

Sofitel Genève, 18 r. du Cendrier, ⊠ 1201, ℰ 731 52 00, Telex 412704, Fax 731 91 69, 🌳, « Fine antique furniture » – |‡| ⇹ rm ▤ rm 📺 ☎. AE ⓓ E VISA JCB. ✻ rest FY **t**
Meals *(closed 23 December - 7 January, Saturday and Sunday)* *20* - 41 and a la carte 57/106 – ☕ 28 – **84 rm** 310/350, 10 suites.

Bristol, 10 r. du Mont-Blanc, ⊠ 1201, ℰ 732 38 00, Telex 412544, Fax 738 90 39, Fö, ≘s – |‡| ▤ 📺 video ☎ – 🏛 25/100. AE ⓓ E VISA JCB. ✻ rest FY **w**
Meals *19* - 41/62 and a la carte 38/87 – ☕ 27 – **92 rm** 275/450, 5 suites.

Cornavin without rest, 23 bd James-Fazy, ⊠ 1201, ℰ 732 21 00, Fax 732 88 43 – |‡| ▤ 📺 ☎. AE ⓓ E VISA FY **a**
☕ 16 – **118 rm** 139/273.

Ambassador, 21 quai des Bergues, ⊠ 1201, ℰ 731 72 00, Telex 412533, Fax 738 90 80 – |‡| ▤ rm 📺 ☎ – 🏛 40. AE ⓓ E VISA FY **p**
Meals 40/58 and a la carte 44/95 – ☕ 15 – **86 rm** 150/315.

Carlton, 22 r. Amat, ⊠ 1202, ℰ 731 68 50, Telex 412546, Fax 732 82 47 – |‡| ▤ rm 📺 ☎. AE ⓓ E VISA JCB FX **a**
Meals *(closed 1 to 7 January, Sunday lunch and Saturday)* *13* and a la carte 31/64 – **123 rm** ☕ 182/326.

Grand Pré Ⓜ without rest, 35 r. du Grand-Pré, ⊠ 1202, ℰ 918 11 11, Telex 414210, Fax 734 76 91 – |‡| ⇹ 📺 ☎ – 🏛 25. AE ⓓ E VISA by rue du Fort-Barreau FX
89 rm ☕ 208/298.

Le Montbrillant, 2 r. de Montbrillant, ✉ 1201, ☎ 733 77 84, Fax 733 25 11, – TV ☎ P. AE ① E VISA FY b
Meals *15* - 34 and a la carte 33/73, children 12.50 – **58 rm** ☐ 160/240.

Strasbourg - Univers M, 10 r. Pradier, ✉ 1201, ☎ 732 25 62, Telex 412773, Fax 738 42 08 – TV ☎ – 25. AE ① E VISA. FY q
Meals *14* - 23/44 and a la carte 38/54 – **51 rm** ☐ 150/200.

XXXX ✿ **Le Cygne** - Hotel Noga Hilton, 19 quai du Mont-Blanc, ✉ 1201, ☎ 908 90 81, Telex 412337, Fax 908 90 90, ← – ▤. AE ① E VISA JCB. GY y
Meals 61 (lunch)/110 and a la carte 82/141
Spec. Bar de ligne cuit à la fumée de bois et vinaigrette aux truffes, Pigeon du Haut-Anjou aux pignons et foie gras grillé (summer), Chariots de desserts.

XXXX ✿ **Le Chat Botté** - Hotel Beau-Rivage, 13 quai du Mont-Blanc, ✉ 1201, ☎ 731 65 32, Telex 412539, Fax 738 98 47, – . AE ① E VISA JCB. FY d
closed Easter, Christmas - New Year, Saturday, Sunday and Bank Holidays – **Meals** 60 (lunch)/135 and a la carte 78/140
Spec. Filets de perche à la vinaigrette aux appétits (summer), Volaille de Bresse aux légumes du jardin, Eventail de truffes glacées en coffret de nougatine.

XXXX ✿✿ **Le Neptune** - Hotel du Rhône, quai Turrettini, ✉ 1201, ☎ 738 74 89, Fax 732 45 58, – ▤. AE ① E VISA JCB. FY r
closed 22 July - 11 August, Saturday, Sunday and Bank Holidays – **Meals** 65 (lunch)/185 and a la carte 82/127
Spec. Assiette royale de l'Atlantique (winter), Blanc de turbot poêlé aux supions et piments doux (summer), Grouse d'Ecosse rôtie en casserole, confit d'endives (autumn).

XXXX **Le Gentilhomme** - Hotel Richemond, Jardin Brunswick, ✉ 1201, ☎ 731 14 00, Telex 412560, Fax 731 67 09, « Elegant decor » – ▤. AE ① E VISA JCB FY u
closed 15 June - 15 September, Saturday lunch and Sunday – **Meals** a la carte 71/138.

XXXX **Amphitryon** - Hotel Les Bergues, 33 quai des Bergues, ✉ 1201, ☎ 731 50 50, Telex 412540, Fax 732 19 89, – ▤. AE ① E VISA FY k
closed 7 July - 25 August, 24 December - 7 January, Saturday lunch and Sunday – **Meals** 62 (lunch)/120 and a la carte 68/134.

XXX **Tsé Yang,** 19 quai du Mont-Blanc, ✉ 1201, ☎ 732 50 81, Fax 908 90 90, ←, « Elegant installation » – ▤. AE ① E VISA JCB GY e
Meals - Chinese rest. - 38 (lunch)/125 and a la carte 57/123.

X **Boeuf Rouge,** 17 r. Alfred-Vincent, ✉ 1201, ☎ 732 75 37 – AE E VISA FY z
closed 21 July - 21 August, Saturday and Sunday – **Meals** - Specialities of Lyons - *16* - 30 (lunch) and a la carte 47/81.

Left Bank (Commercial Centre) :

Métropole, 34 quai Général-Guisan, ✉ 1204, ☎ 311 13 44, Telex 421550, Fax 311 13 50, – ▤ TV video ☎ – 25/200. AE E VISA. rest GY a
Meals see *L'Arlequin* below – ***Le Grand Quai :*** **Meals** *24.50* and a la carte 47/87 – ☐ 18 – **121 rm** 295/620, 6 suites.

La Cigogne, 17 pl. Longemalle, ✉ 1204, ☎ 311 42 42, Telex 421748, Fax 311 40 65, « Tastefully decorated and furnished » – ▤ TV video ☎ – 25. AE ① E VISA. rest
Meals *36* - 52 (lunch) and a la carte 82/114 – **42 rm** ☐ 325/430, 8 suites. FGY j

Les Armures , 1 r. du Puits-Saint-Pierre, ✉ 1204, ☎ 310 91 72, Fax 310 98 46, , « Attractive rustic furnishings in a 17C house » – ▤ rm TV video ☎ – 25. AE ① E VISA
Meals 45 and a la carte 35/73, children 15 – **28 rm** ☐ 278/434. FZ g

Century without rest, 24 av. de Frontenex, ✉ 1207, ☎ 736 80 95, Telex 413246, Fax 786 52 74 – TV ☎ P – 35. AE ① E VISA JCB GZ p
119 rm ☐ 165/350, 14 suites.

XXXX ✿ **Parc des Eaux-Vives,** 82 quai G.-Ador, ✉ 1207, ☎ 735 41 40, Fax 786 87 65, ←, , « Pleasant setting in extensive park » – P. AE E VISA by quai G. Ador GY
closed 8 to 15 April, 28 October - 4 November, January, Sunday except lunch May - September and Monday – **Meals** 98/145 and a la carte 80/165
Spec. Dos de loup sur peau croustillante aux olives noires et tomates confites, Coussinet d'omble du lac Léman aux échalotes grises, Côte de veau rôtie en cocotte aux légumes confits et romarin.

XXXX **L'Arlequin** - Hotel Métropole, 34 quai Général-Guisan, ✉ 1204, ☎ 311 13 44, Telex 421550, Fax 311 13 50 – ▤. AE E VISA. GY a
closed 15 July - 28 August, Saturday, Sunday and Bank Holidays – **Meals** *38* - 58 (lunch)/110 and a la carte 53/133.

XXX ✿✿ **Le Béarn** (Goddard), 4 quai de la Poste, ✉ 1204, ☎ 321 00 28, Fax 781 31 15 – ▤. AE ① E VISA FY x
closed 15 July - 19 August, 19 to 25 February, Saturday except dinner October - May and Sunday – **Meals** 58 (lunch)/155 and a la carte 92/143
Spec. Oursin de Bretagne fourré de coquilles St-Jacques (autumn - winter), Soufflé glacé de crabes, tomate confite et caviar (Summer), Coralline de homard printanier.

XXX **Baron de la Mouette (Mövenpick Fusterie),** 40 r. du Rhône, ✉ 1204, ☎ 311 88 55, Fax 310 93 22 – ▤. AE ① E VISA JCB FY h
closed Tuesday dinner and Monday – **Meals** 65 and a la carte 46/101.

XX **Roberto,** 10 r. Pierre-Fatio, ✉ 1204, ☎ 311 80 33 – ▤. AE E VISA GZ e
closed Saturday dinner and Sunday – **Meals** - Italian rest. - a la carte 55/102.

Environs

to the N :

Palais des Nations : by quai Wilson FGX :

Intercontinental M, 7 chemin du Petit-Saconnex, ✉ 1209, ☎ 919 39 39, Telex 412921, Fax 919 38 38, <, ☂, ₣₆, ⛱ - |‡| ▤ TV ☎ ⇔ Ⓟ - 🏛 25/600. AE ⓘ E VISA JCB. ✂ rest
Meals see ***Les Continents*** below - ***La Pergola* : Meals** *26* and a la carte 64/96 - ☕ 26 - **271 rm** 420/500, 60 suites.

XXXX ✿ **Les Continents** - Hotel Intercontinental, 7 chemin du Petit-Saconnex, ✉ 1209, ☎ 919 33 50, Telex 412921, Fax 919 38 38 - ▤ Ⓟ. AE ⓘ E VISA. ✂
closed 24 December - 2 January, Saturday and Sunday - **Meals** 55 (lunch)/92 and a la carte 89/141
Spec. Foie gras poêlé au jus d'agrumes, fricassée de champignons, Homard sauté aux artichauts et son fumet au curry et coriandre, Pigeon rôti en cocotte au rameau de laurier.

XXX **La Perle du Lac,** 128 r. de Lausanne, ✉ 1202, ☎ 731 79 35, Fax 731 49 79, < lake, ☂, Chalet on lakeside - Ⓟ. AE ⓘ E VISA JCB. ✂
closed 22 December - 1 February and Monday - **Meals** 58 (lunch)/145 and a la carte 72/131.

at Palais des Expositions : by quai Wilson FGX : 5 km - ✉ 1218 Le Grand-Saconnex - ✆ 022 :

Holiday Inn Crowne Plaza M, 26 voie de Moëns, ☎ 791 00 11, Telex 415695, Fax 789 92 73, ₣₆, ≘s, ▣ - |‡| ✂ rm ▤ TV ☎ ♿ ⇔ - 🏛 25/140. AE ⓘ E VISA JCB
Meals *22* and a la carte 43/104, children 8 - ☕ 25 - **305 rm** 340/395.

at Bellevue : by road to Lausanne FX : 6 km - ✉ 1293 Bellevue - ✆ 022 :

La Réserve ⛭, 301 rte de Lausanne, ☎ 774 17 41, Fax 774 25 71, <, ☂, « Park setting near lake, marina », ₣₆, ≘s, ⛱, ▣, ✂ - ▤ TV video ☎ ⇔ Ⓟ - 🏛 25/80. AE ⓘ E VISA JCB
Meals see ***Tsé Fung*** below - ***La Closerie* : Meals** 48/120 and a la carte 72/114 - ***Chez Gianni*** - Italian rest. - *(dinner only)* **Meals** a la carte 54/124 - ***Mikado*** - Japanese rest. - *(closed Saturday lunch and Sunday lunch)* **Meals** *38* - 65/95 and a la carte 39/89 - ☕ 28 - **108 rm** 295/495, 6 suites.

XXX **Tsé Fung** - Hotel La Réserve, 301 rte de Lausanne, ☎ 774 17 41, Fax 774 25 71, ☂ - ▤ Ⓟ. AE ⓘ E VISA
Meals - Chinese rest. - 50 (lunch)/125 and a la carte 62/109.

to the E by road to Evian :

at Cologny : by Quai Gustave Ador GY : 3,5 km - ✉ 1223 Cologny - ✆ 022 :

XXXX ✿ **Aub. du Lion d'Or,** 5 pl. Pierre-Gautier, ☎ 736 44 32, Fax 786 74 62, <, ☂, « Overlooking the lake and Geneva » - Ⓟ. AE ⓘ E VISA
closed 22 December - 23 January, Saturday, Sunday and Bank Holidays - **Meals** 70 (lunch)/165 and a la carte 82/135
Spec. Bouillabaisse (September - May), Soupe de langoustines aux légumes croquants, Mignons de lotte poêlés aux épices.

to the E by road to Annemasse :

at Thônex : by rte de Chêne GZ : 5 km - ✉ 1226 Thônex - ✆ 022 :

XX **Chez Cigalon,** 39 rte d'Ambilly, at the customs border of Pierre-à-Bochet, ☎ 349 97 33, ☂ - AE ⓘ VISA. ✂
closed Saturday lunch, Sunday dinner and Monday - **Meals** 42 (lunch)/78 and a la carte 55/116.

to the S :

at Conches : by rte de Florissant GZ : 5 km - ✉ 1234 Conches - ✆ 022 :

X **Le Vallon,** 182 rte de Florissant, ☎ 347 11 04, Fax 347 63 81, ☂, Bistro-style decor
closed 11 to 22 April, 28 June - 26 July, 23 December - 8 January, Saturday and Sunday - **Meals** *29* and a la carte 48/82.

at Vessy : by road to Veyrier : 4 km - ✉ 1234 Vessy - ✆ 022 :

XX **Alain Lavergnat,** 130 rte de Veyrier, ☎ 784 26 26, Fax 784 13 34, ☂ - Ⓟ. AE E VISA. ✂
closed 21 July - 5 August, 23 December - 8 January, Sunday and Monday - **Meals** *20* - 48 (lunch)/96 and a la carte 74/119.

at Carouge : by Av. Henri-Dunant FZ : 3 km - ✉ 1227 Carouge - ✆ 022 :

XXX **Aub. de Pinchat** with rm, 33 chemin de Pinchat, ☎ 342 30 77, Fax 300 22 19, ☂ - TV ☎ Ⓟ. E VISA
closed 1 to 8 April, 20 October - 5 November, 23 December - 8 January, Sunday and Monday - **Meals** 40 (lunch)/94 and a la carte 74/120 - **5 rm** ☕ 120/145.

XX **La Cassolette,** 31 r. J. Dalphin, ☎ 342 03 18, Fax 342 02 05 - AE E VISA
closed 5 to 14 April, 27 July - 19 August, 30 December - 7 January, Saturday except dinner 1 September - 4 April and Sunday - **Meals** 48 (lunch)/80 and a la carte 70/112.

at Petit-Lancy : by Av. Henri-Dunant FZ : 3 km – ✉ 1213 Petit-Lancy – ☎ 022 :

Host. de la Vendée, 28 chemin de la Vendée, ☎ 792 04 11, Fax 792 05 46, Wintergarden – |‡| ▤ TV ☎ ⇔ P – 40. AE ① E VISA
closed Easter and 23 December - 3 January – **Meals** *(closed Saturday lunch and Sunday)* 50 (lunch)/120 and a la carte 72/124 – ***Bistro*** *(closed Saturday and Sunday)* **Meals** *18*-34 and a la carte 43/74 – **33 rm** ⊒ 160/270
Spec. Crème mousseuse aux orties, Ris de veau aux artichauts barigoule (spring), Crème de mascarpone au Cointreau.

to the W :

at Peney-Dessus : by road to Satigny and private lane : 10 km – ✉ 1242 Satigny – ☎ 022 :

XXX ✿✿ **Domaine de Châteauvieux** (Chevrier) with rm, ☎ 753 15 11, Fax 753 19 24, ≤, « Beautiful country inn, in a former farm » – TV ☎ P. AE VISA
closed 1 to 15 August, 24 December - 8 January – **Meals** *(closed Sunday and Monday)* 62 (lunch)/150 and a la carte 96/162 – **20 rm** ⊒ 145/235
Spec. Queue de boeuf mijotée et foie gras de canard en gelées d'herbettes, Carré d'agneau d'Ecosse rôti au foin et aux herbes aromatiques, Salmis de perdreau gris à l'embeurrée de chou vert et pommes reinettes au foie gras (autumn - winter).

at Cointrin : by road to Lyons : 4 km – ✉ 1216 Cointrin – ☎ 022 :

Mövenpick Genève M, 20 rte Pré-Bois, ✉ 1215, ☎ 798 75 75, Telex 415701, Fax 791 02 84 – |‡| ⇍ ▤ TV ☎ & ⇔ – 25/400. AE ① E VISA JCB
La Brasserie : **Meals** *17*-65 and a la carte 41/80 – ***Kikkoman,*** ☎ 788 18 80 - Japanese rest. - *(closed Sunday and Monday)* **Meals** *27*-48 (lunch)/98 and a la carte 42/90 – ⊒ 24 – **344 rm** 275/400, 6 suites.

Penta, 75 av. Louis-Casaï, ☎ 798 47 00, Telex 415571, Fax 798 77 58, Fб, ≘s – |‡| ⇍ rm ▤ rm TV ☎ & ⇔ P – 25/700. AE ① E VISA JCB. ⚘ rest
La Récolte : **Meals** *16*-29 and a la carte 40/85 – ⊒ 25 – **302 rm** 270/540, 6 suites.

XX **Canonica,** at the airport, ☎ 717 76 76, Fax 798 77 68, ≤, Restaurants arranged around an aircraft cabin – ▤. AE ① E VISA
Plein Ciel *(closed Saturday and Sunday except Bank Holidays)* **Meals** *39*-48 (lunch)/80 and a la carte 68/124 – ***L'Avion*** (Brasserie) **Meals** *14.50* and a la carte 36/77, children 12.50.

Lausanne

1000 Vaud 427 ⑪, 217 ③ ⑬ – 117 571 – alt. 455 – ☎ 021.
Genève 60.

at Crissier : NW by road to Vallorbe : 5 km – ✉ 1023 Crissier – ☎ 021 :

XXXX ✿✿✿ **Girardet,** 1 r. d'Yverdon, ☎ 634 05 05, « Elegant decor » – ▤
closed 27 July - 19 August, 23 December - 16 January, Sunday and Monday – **Meals** 180/195 and a la carte 125/195
Spec. Rognon de veau Bolo, Volaille fermière "pattes noires" au coulis de poireaux et truffes (winter), Tarte vaudoise à la raisinée.

Montreux

1820 Vaud 427 ⑫, 217 ⑭ – 21 362 – alt. 398 – ☎ 021.
Genève 91.

at Brent : NW : 7 km – ✉ 1817 Brent – ☎ 021 :

XXXX ✿✿ **Le Pont de Brent** (Rabaey), ☎ 964 52 30, Fax 964 55 30, « Elegant decor » – ▤ P. E VISA
closed 21 July - 5 August, 24 December - 9 January, Sunday and Monday – **Meals** 70 (lunch)/165 and a la carte 102/158
Spec. Morilles farcies sur un coulis de poireaux (April - June), Noix de ris de veau braisée aux légumes glacés, Arlette aux petits fruits rouges (May - September).

at Clarens : W : 1,5 km – ✉ 1815 Clarens – ☎ 021 :

XXX ✿ **L'Ermitage** (Krebs) with rm, 75 r. du Lac, ☎ 964 44 11, Fax 964 70 02, ≤ lake, « Garden on the lakeside », ⚓ – TV ☎ P. AE ① E VISA
closed 23 December - 20 January – **Meals** *(closed Sunday and Monday October - May)* 52 (lunch)/140 and a la carte 87/123 – **7 rm** ⊒ 220/360
Spec. Saucisson de ris de veau au foie gras et pistaches (winter), Parmentier de truite du lac aux deux persils, Bouchons vaudois aux fraises des bois et crème de pralin (June - July).

Vufflens-le-Château

1134 Vaud 427 ⑪, 217 ② – 554 – alt. 471 – ☎ 021.
Genève 51.

XXXX ✿✿ **L'Ermitage** (Ravet) with rm, ☎ 802 21 91, Fax 802 22 40, « Beautiful residence in a garden, pond » – TV ☎ P. ① E VISA
closed 29 July - 22 August, 23 December - 12 January, Sunday and Monday – **Meals** 78 (lunch)/170 and a la carte 124/180 – **9 rm** ⊒ 280/400
Spec. Pêche du lac Léman, Pigeon de grains en saveurs de laurier, Jarret de veau à l'os rôti à la broche.

ZÜRICH 8000 Zürich 427 ⑥, 216 ⑱ – 345 235 – alt. 409 – 01.

See: The Quays★★ : ≤★ FZ; Mythenquai : ≤★ CX – Fraumünster cloisters★ (Alter Kreuzgang des Fraumünsters), windows★ EZ – Church of SS. Felix and Regula★ AT **E** – Cathedral★ (Grossmünster) – Fine Arts Museum★★ (Kunsthaus) FZ – Zoological Gardens★ (Zoo Dolder) BT – Bührle Collection★★ (Sammlung Bührle) BU **M³**.

Museums: Swiss National Museum★★★ (Schweizerisches Landesmuseum) EY – Rietberg Museum★★ CX **M²**.

Envir: Uetliberg★★ SW : by rail – Albis Pass Road★ SW by the Bederstrasse – Former Abbey of Kappel★ SW : 22 km – Eglisau : site★ N : 27 km.

Excursions: Boat Trips, Information : Zürichsee-Schiffahrtsgesellschaft, Bürkliplatz 10, 482 10 33.

9 Dolder (April - 15 November), 261 50 45, Fax 261 53 02 ; 18 at Zumikon, ✉ 8126 (April - October), 918 00 50, Fax 918 00 37, SE : 9 km ; 18 at Hittnau, ✉ 8335 (April - November), 950 24 42, Fax 951 01 66 E : 33 km, 18 at Breitenloo, ✉ 8309 Nürensdorf (April - October), 836 40 80, Fax 837 10 85, N : 22 km.

Zürich-Kloten, 816 22 11.

Tourist Office, Bahnhofplatz 15, 211 40 00, Fax 211 39 81 – T.C.S., Alfred Escher-Str. 38, 286 86 86, Fax 286 86 87 – A.C.S., Forchstr. 95, 422 15 00, Fax 422 15 37.

Berne 125 – Basle 109 – Geneva 278 – Innsbruck 288 – Milan 304.

Plans on following pages

On the right bank of river Limmat (University, Fine Arts Museum) :

Dolder Grand Hotel, Kurhausstr. 65, ✉ 8032, 251 62 31, Telex 816416, Fax 251 88 29, 9, « In a beautiful park ≤ lake and mountains », – 25/200. AE E VISA JCB. rest — by Gloriastrasse DV
La Rotonde : **Meals** 48 (lunch)/80 and a la carte 67/154 – **174 rm** 390/540, 11 suites.

Zürich and La Résidence, Neumühlequai 42, ✉ 8001, 363 63 63, Telex 817587, Fax 363 60 15, ≤, – rm video – 25/250. AE E VISA. rest — EY **c**
Scala : **Meals** *37* - 48 (lunch)/88 and a la carte 57/111 – ***White Elephant*** - Thaï rest. - *(closed 17 December - 16 January, Sunday and Monday)* **Meals** 36 (lunch)/85 and a la carte 50/79 – ***La Brasserie :*** **Meals** *16.50* - 32 (lunch) and a la carte 38/87 – **265 rm** 380/430, 10 suites.

Eden au Lac, Utoquai 45, ✉ 8023, 261 94 04, Fax 261 94 09, ≤, – AE E VISA. rest — DX **a**
Meals *42* - 62/110 and a la carte 66/134 – **52 rm** 330/630, 3 suites.

Waldhaus Dolder, Kurhausstr. 20, ✉ 8032, 251 93 60, Telex 816460, Fax 251 00 29, ≤ Zürich and lake, 9, – rest – 35. AE E VISA — by Gloriastrasse DV
Meals *22* and a la carte 51/90, children 15 – 16 – **97 rm** 250/500, 3 suites.

Central Plaza M, Central 1, ✉ 8001, 251 55 55, Telex 817152, Fax 251 85 35 – video – 35. AE E VISA JCB — FY **z**
Cascade *(closed Saturday and Sunday)* **Meals** 42 and a la carte 48/100, children 8 – ***Entrecôte :*** **Meals** a la carte 48/76, children 8 – 24 – **94 rm** 270/362, 6 suites.

Sofitel, Stampfenbachstr. 60, ✉ 8035, 363 33 63, Fax 363 33 18 – rm – 25/70. AE E VISA JCB. rest — FY **b**
Diff : **Meals** *20* - 42 and a la carte 57/125 – 16 – **176 rm** 270/320.

Europe without rest, Dufourstr. 4, ✉ 8008, 261 10 30, Fax 251 03 67 – . AE E VISA JCB — FZ **u**
40 rm 240/340.

Florhof M, Florhofgasse 4, ✉ 8001, 261 44 70, Fax 261 46 11, « Tasteful installation » – rm . AE E VISA — FZ **k**
Meals *(closed 23 December - 15 January, Saturday and Sunday)* *27* - 44 (lunch)/63 and a la carte 60/96 – **33 rm** 200/330.

Opera without rest, Dufourstr. 5, ✉ 8008, 251 90 90, Telex 816480, Fax 251 90 01 – video . AE E VISA JCB — FZ **b**
closed 23 December - 3 January – **67 rm** 195/430.

Ambassador, Falkenstr. 6, ✉ 8008, 261 76 00, Fax 251 23 94 – video . AE E VISA JCB — FZ **a**
Meals *23* and a la carte 44/109 – **46 rm** 195/340.

Tiefenau, Steinwiesstr. 8, ✉ 8032, 251 24 09, Fax 251 24 76, – video – 30. AE E VISA JCB — FZ **h**
closed 22 December - 7 January – ***Züri-Stube :*** **Meals** *30* and a la carte 40/96 – **27 rm** 240/400, 3 suites.

Krone Unterstrass, Schaffhauserstr. 1, ✉ 8006, 361 16 88, Fax 361 19 67 – – 25/90. AE E VISA — CV **b**
Kronen-Grill : **Meals** *25.50* - 58 (dinner) and a la carte 37/83 – **57 rm** 145/215.

Wellenberg without rest, Niederdorfstr. 10, ✉ 8001, 262 43 00, Fax 251 31 30 – . AE E VISA — FZ **s**
45 rm 240/330.

ZÜRICH

Street	Grid	No.
Bahnhofstrasse	EYZ	
Bellevueplatz	FZ	
Limmatquai	FYZ	
Löwenstrasse	EY	
Paradeplatz	EZ	
Poststrasse	EZ	58
Rennweg	EYZ	63
Storchengasse	EZ	85
Strehlgasse	EZ	87
Uraniastrasse	EYZ	
Allmendstrasse	CX	6
Augustinergasse	EZ	9
Bärengasse	EZ	10
Beethovenstrasse	EZ	12
Birmensdorferstrasse	CX	15
Claridenstrasse	EZ	18
Clausiusstrasse	FY	19
Culmannstrasse	FY	21
Dufourstrasse	DX	24
Feldstrasse	CV	27
Fraumünsterstrasse	EZ	28
Freiestrasse	DVX	30
Gablerstrasse	CX	31
General Wille-Strasse	CX	33
Hafnerstrasse	EY	36
Kantonsschulstrasse	FZ	39
Konradstrasse	EY	40
Kreuzstrasse	DX	42
Manessestrasse	CX	45
Marktgasse	FZ	46
Münsterhof	EZ	48
Museumstrasse	EY	49
Nelkenstrasse	FY	52
Neumarkt	FZ	54
Nordstrasse	DV	55
Rathausbrücke	EFZ	60
Rindermarkt	FZ	64
Schimmelstrasse	CX	69
Seebahnstrasse	CX	72
Selnaustrasse	CX	75
Sihlhölzlistrasse	CX	76
Stadelhoferstrasse	FZ	78
Stampfenbachplatz	FY	79
Stampfenbachstrasse	EFY	81
Stauffacherplatz	CX	82
Stauffacherstrasse	CVX	84
Sumatrastrasse	FY	88
Talacker	EZ	90
Tannenstrasse	FY	91
Theaterstrasse	FZ	93
Toblerstrasse	DV	96
Tunnelstrasse	CX	97
Usteristrasse	EY	100
Waffenplatzstrasse	CX	102
Weinbergfussweg	FY	103
Zollikerstrasse	DX	108

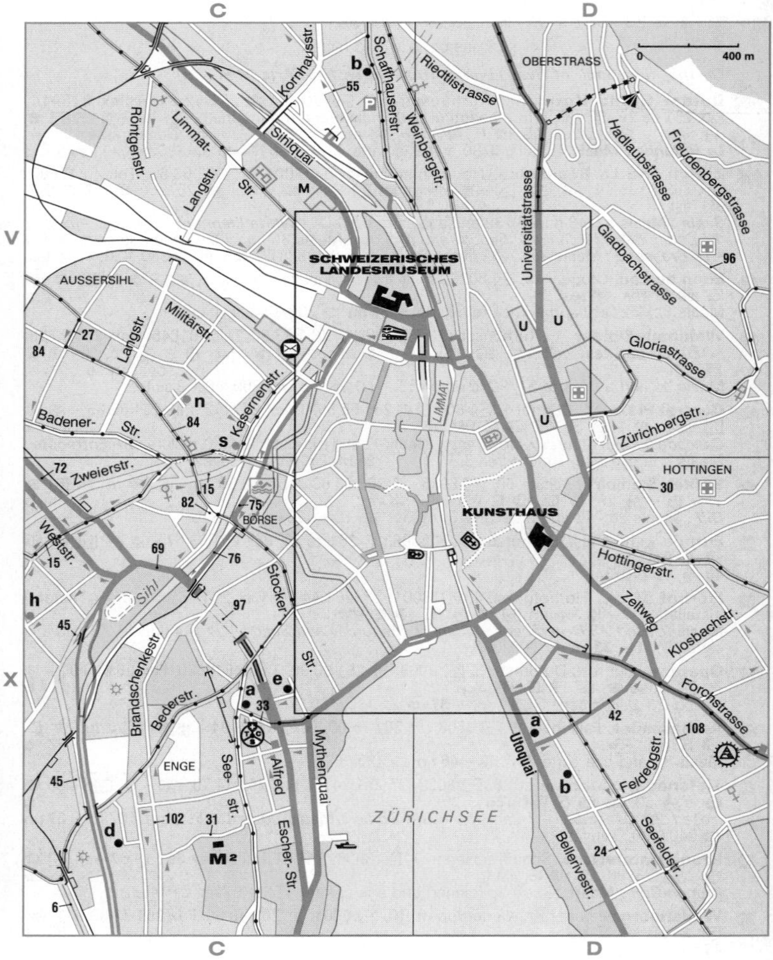

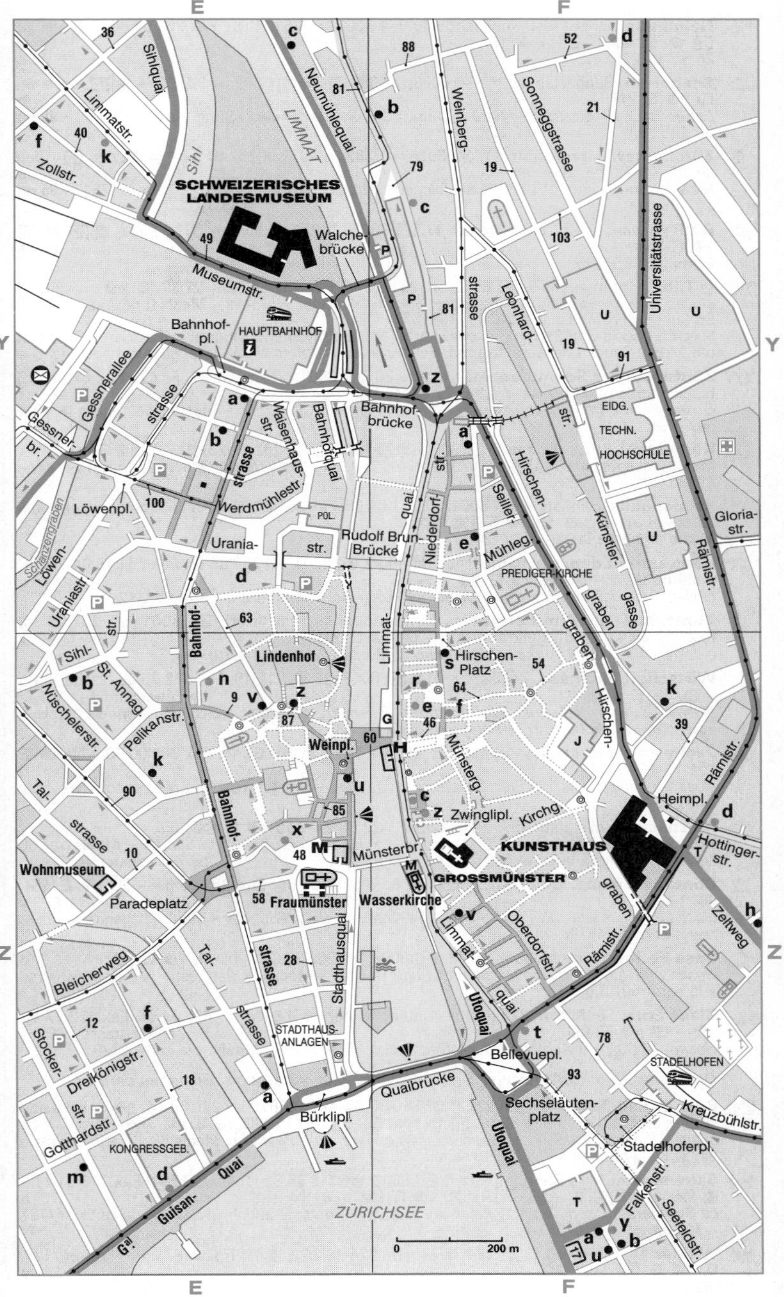
SCHWEIZERISCHES LANDESMUSEUM
HAUPTBAHNHOF
KUNSTHAUS
GROSSMÜNSTER
Fraumünster
Wasserkirche
Lindenhof
EIDG. TECHN. HOCHSCHULE
PREDIGER-KIRCHE
STADELHOFEN
KONGRESSGEB.
STADTHAUS-ANLAGEN
Wohnmuseum
ZÜRICHSEE
LIMMAT
Sihl
Bahnhofstrasse
Limmatquai
Utoquai
Quaibrücke
Paradeplatz
Bellevuepl.
Sechseläutenplatz
Stadelhoferpl.
Bürklipl.
Münsterbr.
Rudolf Brun-Brücke
Bahnhofbrücke
Walchebrücke
Weinpl.
Zwinglipl.
Heimpl.
Hirschen-Platz
Löwenpl.
Bahnhof-pl.
Gen. Guisan-Quai
200 m

Helmhaus without rest, Schifflände 30, ✉ 8001, ✆ 251 88 10, Fax 251 04 30 – 🛗 ✈ ▤ 📺 ☎. AE ⓓ E VISA JCB FZ **v**
25 rm ☕ 205/315.

Seegarten, Seegartenstr. 14, ✉ 8008, ✆ 383 37 37, Fax 383 37 38, 🌂 – 🛗 📺 video ☎. AE ⓓ E VISA DX **b**
Latino - Italian rest. - *(closed Saturday lunch and Sunday)* **Meals** *25* and a la carte 38/85 – **28 rm** ☕ 165/269.

Zürcherhof, Zähringerstr. 21, ✉ 8025, ✆ 262 10 40, Fax 262 04 84 – 🛗 ▤ rest 📺 video ☎. AE ⓓ E VISA JCB FY **e**
Meals - Specialities of Le Valais - *(closed Saturday and Sunday)* a la carte 40/81 – **35 rm** ☕ 185/260.

Rütli Ⓜ without rest, Zähringerstr. 43, ✉ 8001, ✆ 251 54 26, Fax 261 21 53 – 🛗 📺 ☎. AE ⓓ E VISA FY **a**
62 rm ☕ 180/260.

XXX ✿ **Tübli,** Hottingerstr. 5, ✉ 8032, ✆ 251 26 26, Fax 252 50 62 – AE ⓓ E VISA FZ **d**
closed 2 weeks in February, Saturday, Sunday and Bank Holidays – **Meals** (booking essential) 56 (lunch)/170 and a la carte 77/138
Spec. Carpaccio vom Stör mit Fenchel-Kartoffelstock, Kaviar und Sauerrahm, Pochiertes Rindsfilet mit Merlot-Sauce und Kartoffelstroh, Schokoladen Millefeuille mit Mirabellenkompott.

XXX **Zunfthaus zur Schmiden,** Marktgasse 20, ✉ 8001, ✆ 251 52 87, Fax 261 12 67, « 15C blacksmith's guild house » – ▤. AE ⓓ E VISA JCB FZ **f**
closed Easter, Pentecost, mid July - mid August and Christmas – **Meals** *24.50* and a la carte 55/107.

XXX **Königstuhl,** Stüssihofstatt 3, ✉ 8001, ✆ 261 76 18, Fax 262 71 23, 🌂 – AE ⓓ E VISA FZ **r**
Meals (1st floor) *28.50* - 45 (lunch)/95 and a la carte 58/109 – ***Bistro :*** **Meals** *18.50* and a la carte 49/95.

XX **Kronenhalle,** Rämistr. 4, ✉ 8001, ✆ 251 66 69, Fax 251 66 81, « Collection of exceptional works of art » – ▤. AE ⓓ E VISA. ✻ FZ **t**
Meals *30* and a la carte 52/126.

XX **Haus zum Rüden,** Limmatquai 42 (1st floor), ✉ 8001, ✆ 261 95 66, Fax 261 18 04, « 13C guild house » – ▤. AE ⓓ E VISA JCB FZ **c**
closed Saturday and Sunday – **Meals** *45* - 52 (lunch)/92 and a la carte 60/112.

XX **Zunfthaus zur Zimmerleuten,** Limmatquai 40 (1st floor), ✉ 8001, ✆ 252 08 34, Fax 252 08 48, « 18C guild house » – AE ⓓ E VISA FZ **z**
closed 14 July - 11 August and Sunday – **Meals** *22* and a la carte 42/98.

XX **Wirtschaft Flühgass,** Zollikerstr. 214, ✉ 8008, ✆ 381 12 15, Fax 422 75 32, « 16C inn » – Ⓟ. AE E VISA by Zollikerstrasse DX
closed 13 July - 11 August, 23 December - 2 January, Saturday and Sunday – **Meals** (booking essential) *19* - 56 (lunch)/120 and a la carte 51/111.

XX **Jacky's Stapferstube,** Culmannstr. 45, ✉ 8006, ✆ 361 37 48, Fax 364 00 60 – AE ⓓ E VISA FY **d**
closed mid July - mid August, Sunday and Monday – **Meals** - veal and beef specialities - a la carte 65/149.

XX **Riesbächli,** Zollikerstr. 157, ✉ 8008, ✆ 422 23 24 – AE ⓓ E VISA JCB
closed 20 July - 10 August, 25 December - 3 January, Saturday and Sunday – **Meals** *38* - 50 (lunch)/130 and a la carte 59/131. by Zollikerstrasse DX

XX **Conti-da Bianca,** Dufourstr. 1, ✉ 8008, ✆ 251 06 66, Fax 251 06 67 – AE ⓓ E VISA. ✻ FZ **y**
closed 2 weeks late July - early August, Saturday lunch and Sunday – **Meals** - Italian rest. - *22.50* and a la carte 48/98.

XX **Casa Ferlin,** Stampfenbachstr. 38, ✉ 8006, ✆ 362 35 09 – ▤. AE ⓓ E VISA FY **c**
closed mid July - mid August, Saturday and Sunday – **Meals** - Italian rest. - *27* - 48 (lunch) and a la carte 60/108.

X **Blaue Ente,** Seefeldstr. 223 (Mühle Tiefenbrunnen), ✉ 8008, ✆ 422 77 06, Fax 422 77 41, 🌂 – AE ⓓ E VISA by Zollikerstrasse DX
closed 14 July - 6 August and 24 December - 5 January – **Meals** a la carte 57/92.

On the left bank of the river Limmat (Main railway station, Business centre) :

Baur au Lac, Talstr. 1, ✉ 8022, ✆ 220 50 20, Telex 813567, Fax 220 50 44, 🌂, « Lakeside setting and garden » – 🛗 ▤ rm 📺 ☎ 🚗 Ⓟ – 🏛 25/150. AE ⓓ E VISA JCB. ✻ EZ **a**
Limited availability, due to alterations being carried out – ***Pavillon :*** **Meals** 68/84 and a la carte 64/121 – **37 rm** ☕ 430/630, 16 suites.

Schweizerhof Ⓜ, Bahnhofplatz 7, ✉ 8023, ✆ 218 88 88, Telex 813754, Fax 218 81 81 – 🛗 ✈ rm ▤ 📺 ☎ – 🏛 25/45. AE ⓓ E VISA JCB. ✻ rest EY **a**
La Soupière *(closed Saturday lunch and Sunday)* **Meals** 62 (lunch)/125 and a la carte 67/122 – **115 rm** ☕ 340/470.

Widder Ⓜ, Rennweg 7, ✆ 224 25 26, Fax 224 24 24 – 🛗 ▤ 📺 ☎ ♿ 🚗 – 🏛 25/170. AE ⓓ E VISA JCB. ✻ rest EZ **v**
Meals *38* - 58 (lunch)/88 and a la carte 58/103 – **42 rm** ☕ 330/630, 7 suites.

Atlantis Sheraton, Döltschiweg 234, ✉ 8055, ☎ 454 54 54, Fax 454 54 00, ≤, park, ≘s, – |♦| ⇋ rm ▤ TV ☎ ⇔ P – 25/200. AE ⓓ E VISA JCB. ✗ rest — by Zweierstrasse CX
Les Quatre Saisons *(closed Saturday lunch)* **Meals** *39* - 54 (lunch)/62 and a la carte 60/116, children 16 – ***Döltschi Stube*: Meals** *23.50* and a la carte 39/94, children 11 – **157 rm** ☐ 370/435, 3 suites

Annexe Sheraton Inn without rest, ☎ 454 54 54, Fax 454 54 00 – |♦| ⇋ TV ☎. AE ⓓ E VISA JCB
64 rm ☐ 200/250.

St. Gotthard, Bahnhofstr. 87, ✉ 8023, ☎ 211 55 00, Fax 211 24 19, ≘s – |♦| ⇋ rm ▤ TV video ☎ – 25/45. AE ⓓ E VISA — EY **b**
La Bouillabaisse* : Meals** *33* - 52 (lunch) and a la carte 52/140 – ***Hummer- und Austernbar* : Meals** a la carte 70/141 – ***Prime Grill *(July - August closed Saturday and Sunday)* **Meals** a la carte 44/108 – ☐ 27 – **135 rm** 260/490.

Ascot M, Tessinerplatz 9, ✉ 8002, ☎ 201 18 00, Telex 815454, Fax 202 72 10 – |♦| ▤ rest TV ☎ ⇔ – 25/50. AE ⓓ E VISA JCB — CX **a**
Lawrence* : Meals** 48 (lunch)/75 and a la carte 57/89 – ***Fujiya of Japan ☎ 201 11 55 *(closed Sunday and Monday)* **Meals** 48 (lunch)/85 and a la carte 58/82 – **73 rm** ☐ 290/510.

Splügenschloss, Splügenstr. 2 / Genferstrasse, ✉ 8002, ☎ 201 08 00, Telex 815553, Fax 201 42 86 – |♦| ⇋ rm ▤ rm TV ☎ P. AE ⓓ E VISA JCB — CX **e**
Meals *34* - 59/120 and a la carte 68/130 – **52 rm** ☐ 290/530.

Neues Schloss, Stockerstr. 17, ✉ 8022, ☎ 201 65 50, Telex 815560, Fax 201 64 18 – |♦| TV ☎. AE ⓓ E VISA JCB. ✗ rest — EZ **m**
Le Jardin *(Sunday and Bank Holidays dinner only for residents)* **Meals** *36.50* - 58 (lunch)/100 and a la carte 65/112 – **58 rm** ☐ 215/400.

Nova-Park M, Badenerstr. 420, ✉ 8040, ☎ 404 44 44, Telex 822822, Fax 404 44 40, ≘s, – |♦| ⇋ rm ▤ TV ☎ ⇔ – 25/400. AE ⓓ E VISA JCB
Meals a la carte 45/93 – ☐ 21 – **363 rm** 245/335. — by Badenerstrasse CV

Stoller, Badenerstr. 357, ✉ 8040, ☎ 492 65 00, Fax 492 65 01, – |♦| ⇋ rm TV ☎ P – 35. AE ⓓ E VISA JCB — by Badenerstrasse CV
Meals *18.50* - 38 (lunch)/63 and a la carte 53/98 – **79 rm** ☐ 220/340.

Zum Storchen, Weinplatz 2, ✉ 8001, ☎ 211 55 10, Fax 211 64 51, ≤ River Limmat and City, « Riverside setting », – |♦| ⇋ rm TV ☎ – 30. AE ⓓ E VISA JCB. ✗ rest — EZ **u**
Meals *44* and a la carte 64/95 – **78 rm** ☐ 240/530.

Glockenhof, Sihlstr. 31, ✉ 8023, ☎ 211 56 50, Fax 211 56 60, – |♦| ▤ rest TV ☎. AE ⓓ E VISA JCB — EZ **b**
Meals *19* and a la carte 41/83 – **108 rm** ☐ 240/350.

Carlton Elite, Bahnhofstr. 41, ✉ 8001, ☎ 211 65 60, Telex 812781, Fax 211 30 19, – |♦| TV ☎ – 25/240. AE ⓓ E VISA JCB. ✗ rest — EZ **k**
Locanda - Italian rest. - **Meals** *36* and a la carte 41/103 – ☐ 26 – **73 rm** 225/445.

Senator M, Heinrichstr. 254, ✉ 8005, ☎ 272 20 21, Fax 272 25 85, – |♦| ⇋ rm TV ☎ ⇔ – 25/90. AE ⓓ E VISA JCB — by Limmatstrasse CV
Meals *19* and a la carte 34/76 – ☐ 15 – **102 rm** 185/210.

Glärnischhof, Claridenstr. 30, ✉ 8022, ☎ 202 47 47, Fax 201 01 64 – |♦| ▤ rest TV ☎ – 30. AE ⓓ E VISA JCB — EZ **f**
Meals *24* - 48 and a la carte 52/98 – **63 rm** ☐ 260/420.

Engematthof, Engimattstr. 14, ✉ 8002, ☎ 284 16 16, Fax 201 25 16, – |♦| TV ☎ ⇔ – 25. AE ⓓ E VISA JCB — CX **d**
Meals *19* and a la carte 42/90, children 11.50 – **80 rm** ☐ 180/290.

Kindli, Pfalzgasse 1, ✉ 8001, ☎ 211 59 17, Fax 211 65 28, « English country house style installation » – |♦| TV ☎. AE ⓓ E VISA — EZ **z**
Opus *(closed Sunday)* **Meals** *19.50* and a la carte 46/88 – **21 rm** ☐ 160/260.

Montana, Konradstr. 39, ✉ 8005, ☎ 271 69 00, Telex 822640, Fax 272 30 70 – |♦| TV ☎ ♿ ⇔. AE ⓓ E VISA JCB — EY **f**
Bistrot le Lyonnais *(closed Saturday lunch and Sunday)* **Meals** *19* - 40 (dinner) and a la carte 41/95 – **74 rm** ☐ 210/290.

XX **Sukhothai,** Erlachstr. 46, ✉ 8003, ☎ 462 66 22, Fax 462 66 54 – ▤. AE E VISA. ✗ — CX **h**
closed Easter, 22 July - 14 August, Saturday except September - May and Sunday – **Meals** - Thai rest. - *32* - 110/130 and a la carte 69/127.

XX ✿ **Giangrossi** (Rosa Tschudi), Rebgasse 8, ☎ 241 20 64, Fax 241 20 84, – ⇔. AE ⓓ E VISA — CV **s**
closed Sunday and Monday – **Meals** (booking essential) 55 (lunch)/140 and a la carte 80/125
Spec. Schwartenmagen mit Balsamicovinaigrette, Eglifilets Sauce Mousseline, Coq-au-vin in Chambertinsauce mit Kartoffelpuree.

XX **L'Hexagone,** Kuttelgasse 15, ✉ 8001, ☎ 211 94 11, Fax 212 70 38, Bistro – AE E VISA — EZ **n**
closed 20 July - 12 August, 24 December - 7 January, Saturday and Sunday – **Meals** (booking essential) *38* - 65 (lunch)/110 and a la carte 60/102.

XX **Intermezzo** - Kongresshaus Zürich, Gotthardstr. 5, ✉ 8022, ℘ 206 36 36, Fax 206 36 59 – AE ◑ E VISA. ✻ EZ **d**
closed 13 July - 4 August, Saturday and Sunday – **Meals** 43 (lunch) and a la carte 52/89.

XX **Accademia Piccoli,** Rotwandstr. 48, ✉ 8004, ℘ 241 42 02, Fax 241 62 43 – ▤. AE E VISA CV **n**
closed Saturday except dinner September - April and Sunday – **Meals** - Italian rest. - a la carte 58/113.

XX **Sala of Tokyo,** Limmatstr. 29, ✉ 8031, ℘ 271 52 90, Fax 271 78 07 – AE ◑ E VISA JCB EY **k**
closed 21 July - 12 August, 24 December - 15 January, Sunday and Monday – **Meals** - Japanese rest. - 58/115 and a la carte 48/98.

XX **Zunfthaus zur Waag,** Münsterhof 8 (1st floor), ✉ 8001, ℘ 211 07 30, Fax 212 01 69, « 17C weavers' guild house » – AE ◑ VISA JCB EZ **x**
Meals *24* and a la carte 48/120.

X **Brasserie Lipp,** Uraniastr. 9, ✉ 8001, ℘ 211 11 55, Fax 212 17 26 – AE ◑ E VISA EY **d**
closed Sunday July - August – **Meals** *26* and a la carte 37/94.

at Zürich-Oerlikon : N : by Universitätstrasse DV : 5 km – ✉ 8050 Zürich-Oerlikon – ☎ 01 :

Swissôtel Zürich M, Am Marktplatz, ℘ 311 43 41, Telex 823251, Fax 312 44 68, Fb, ≘s, ▣ – |♦| ⇔ rm ▤ TV video ☎ ⇔ – 🔺 25/650. AE ◑ E VISA JCB
Szenario : **Meals** *23* - 30/45 (lunch) and a la carte 36/76, children 9 – ☕ 25 – **334 rm** 270/400, 11 suites.

at Glattbrugg : N : by Universitätstrasse DV : 8 km – ✉ 8152 Glattbrugg – ☎ 01 :

Renaissance M, Talackerstr. 1, ℘ 810 85 00, Telex 825003, Fax 810 87 55, Fb, ≘s, ▣ – |♦| ⇔ rm ▤ TV ☎ ♿ ⇔ – 🔺 25/600. AE ◑ E VISA JCB. ✻ rest
Asian Place - Asian rest. - *(closed mid July - mid August, Saturday lunch and Sunday lunch)* **Meals** a la carte 49/124 – ***Brasserie La Noblesse*** *(closed Saturday and Sunday)* **Meals** 44 (lunch) and a la carte 48/119, children 10 – ***The Bostonian*** - Spanish rest. - **Meals** 44 (lunch) and a la carte 46/85 – ☕ 29 – **196 rm** 245/304, 8 suites.

Hilton, Hohenbühlstr. 10, ℘ 810 31 31, Telex 825428, Fax 810 93 66, 🏔, ≘s – |♦| ⇔ rm ▤ TV ☎ ♿ P – 🔺 25/280. AE ◑ E VISA JCB
Harvest Grill *(closed mid July - mid August, Saturday dinner from September - June and Sunday lunch)* **Meals** 46 (lunch)/79 and a la carte 60/121 – ***Taverne*** *(closed Saturday lunch from July - August and Sunday)* **Meals** *21* and a la carte 40/96 – ☕ 30 – **276 rm** 265/365, 10 suites.

Mövenpick M, Walter Mittelholzerstr. 8, ℘ 808 88 88, Fax 808 88 77 – |♦| ⇔ rm ▤ TV ☎ ♿ P – 🔺 25/250. AE ◑ E VISA JCB
Mövenpick Rest. : **Meals** *19.50* and a la carte 29/70 – ***Appenzeller Stube*** *(closed mid July - mid August)* **Meals** a la carte 52/103 – ***Dim Sum*** - Chinese rest. - *(closed 3 weeks beginning of July, Saturday lunch and Sunday lunch)* **Meals** 60 and a la carte 37/76 – ☕ 23 – **335 rm** 290/330.

Novotel Zürich Airport, Talackerstr. 21, ℘ 810 31 11, Telex 828770, Fax 810 81 85, 🏔 – |♦| ⇔ rm ▤ TV ☎ ♿ P – 🔺 25/150. AE ◑ E VISA
Meals *22* and a la carte 33/67, children 16 – ☕ 19 – **257 rm** 150/203.

Airport, Oberhauserstr. 30, ℘ 810 44 44, Fax 810 97 08, 🏔 – |♦| ⇔ rm TV ☎ P. AE ◑ E VISA JCB
Edo Garden : **Meals** *28* - 62/78 and a la carte 47/85 – ***Fujiya of Japan :*** **Meals** 65/85 and a la carte 57/92 – **44 rm** ☕ 180/235.

at Kloten : N : by Universitätstrasse DV : 12 km – ✉ 8302 Kloten – ☎ 01 :

Fly Away, Marktgasse 19, ℘ 813 66 13, Fax 813 51 25 – |♦| TV video ☎ ♿ ⇔ P. AE ◑ E VISA
Mercato - Italian rest. - **Meals** *17* and a la carte 33/65 – ☕ 9.50 – **42 rm** 150/185.

Welcome Inn, Holbergstr. 1, ℘ 814 07 27, Fax 813 56 16, 🏔 – |♦| TV ☎ ⇔ P. AE ◑ E VISA
Meals *20* and a la carte 38/72, children 13 – ☕ 12 – **96 rm** 128/158.

XX **Top-Air,** at the airport (Terminal A), ℘ 816 60 60, Fax 816 41 91, ← – ▤. AE ◑ E VISA
Meals *34* - 52 and a la carte 41/116, children 18.50.

at Zollikon : SE : by Bellerivestrasse DX : 4 km – ✉ 8702 Zollikon – ☎ 01 :

XX **Wirtschaft zur Höhe,** Höhestr. 73, ℘ 391 59 59, Fax 392 00 02, 🏔, « Former farmhouse » – P. AE ◑ E VISA
Meals *32* - 47 (lunch)/85 and a la carte 67/122.

at Küsnacht : SE : by Bellerivestrasse DX : 8 km – ✉ 8700 Küsnacht – ☎ 01 :

🏨 ✿ **Ermitage am See,** Seestr. 80, ✆ 910 52 22, Fax 910 52 44, ≤ Lake, 🍽, « Lakeside setting, terrace and garden », ⛱, ⚓ – |♦| TV ☎ P. AE ⓓ E VISA. ✂ rest
Meals 59 (lunch)/144 and a la carte 76/132 – ☕ 17 – **20 rm** 200/270, 6 suites
Spec. Salade de langoustines à l'orange, tête de veau et cébettes, Saint-Pierre rôti à la peau au romarin et pâte d'olives, Tarte au vin de Muscat du Valais.

XXX ✿✿ **Petermann's Kunststuben,** Seestr. 160, ✆ 910 07 15, Fax 910 04 95, 🍽 – ▤ P. AE ⓓ E VISA
closed 18 August - 10 September, 10 to 24 February, Sunday and Monday – **Meals** (booking essential) 76 (lunch)/185 and a la carte 96/190
Spec. Cabillaud de ligne poêlé au lard cru, purée de haricots à l'huile d'olives et romarin, Poulette "pattes noires" farcie à l'ancienne, Canneloni au chocolat à la crème d'ananas et cardamone.

at Gattikon : S : by motorway N3 CX : 11 km – ✉ 8136 Gattikon – ☎ 01 :

XXX ✿ **Sihlhalde** (Smolinsky), Sihlhaldenstr. 70, ✆ 720 09 27, Fax 720 09 25, 🍽 – P. E VISA
closed 20 July - 12 August, 20 December - 2 January, Sunday and Monday – **Meals** *35* - 55 (lunch) and a la carte 74/108
Spec. Ravioli mit schwarzen Trüffeln, Zander gebraten in einer Kartoffelkruste, Rehrücken aus der Sommerjagd mit Saisonpilzen.

at Unterengstringen : NW : by Sihlquai CV : 10 km – ✉ 8103 Unterengstringen – ☎ 01 :

XXX ✿ **Witschi's,** Zürcherstr. 55, ✆ 750 44 60, Fax 750 19 68, 🍽, « Elegant installation » – 🚗. AE ⓓ E VISA
closed 14 July - 5 August, 24 December - 8 January, Sunday and Monday – **Meals** *48* - 69 (lunch) and a la carte 99/156
Spec. Cappucino de lentilles vertes au blanc de poularde et truffe noire (winter - spring), Millefeuille de langoustines au jus de bouillabaisse (summer - winter), Crépinette de chevreuil au feuilleté de pommes (summer - winter).

United Kingdom

LONDON - BIRMINGHAM - EDINBURGH
GLASGOW - LEEDS - LIVERPOOL
MANCHESTER

PRACTICAL INFORMATION

LOCAL CURRENCY

Pound Sterling: 1 GBP = 1.55 US $ (Jan. 96).

TOURIST INFORMATION

Tourist information offices exist in each city included in the Guide. The telephone number and address is given in each text under ℹ

FOREIGN EXCHANGE

Banks are open between 9.30am and 3pm on weekdays only and some open on Saturdays. Most large hotels have exchange facilities, and Heathrow and Gatwick Airports have 24-hour banking facilities.

SHOPPING

In London: Oxford St./Regent St. (department stores, exclusive shops)
Bond St. (exclusive shops, antiques)
Knightsbridge area (department stores, exclusive shops, boutiques)
For other towns see the index of street names: those printed in red are where the principal shops are found.

THEATRE BOOKINGS IN LONDON

Your hotel porter will be able to make your arrangements or direct you to Theatre Booking Agents.
In addition there is a kiosk in Leicester Square selling tickets for the same day's performances at half price plus a booking fee. It is open 12 noon-6.30pm.

CAR HIRE

The international car hire companies have branches in each major city. Your hotel porter should be able to give details and help you with your arrangements.

TIPPING

Many hotels and restaurants include a service charge but where this is not the case an amount equivalent to between 10 and 15 per cent of the bill is customary. Additionally doormen, baggage porters and cloakroom attendants are generally given a gratuity.
Taxi drivers are customarily tipped between 10 and 15 per cent of the amount shown on the meter in addition to the fare.

SPEED LIMITS

The maximum permitted speed on motorways and dual carriageways is 70 mph (113 km/h.) and 60 mph (97 km/h.) on other roads except where a lower speed limit is indicated.

SEAT BELTS

The wearing of seat belts in the United Kingdom is compulsory for drivers, front seat passengers and rear seat passengers where seat belts are fitted. It is illegal for front seat passengers to carry children on their lap.

ANIMALS

It is forbidden to bring domestic animals (dogs, cats...) into the United Kingdom.

London

404 folds 42 to 44 – pop. 6 679 699 – ☎ 0171 or 0181 : see heading of each area.

✈ Heathrow, ☎ (0181) 759 4321 – **Terminal** : Airbus (A1) from Victoria, Airbus (A2) from Paddington – Underground (Piccadilly line) frequent service daily.

✈ Gatwick, ☎ (01293) 535353, and ☎ (0181) 763 2020, by A 23 and M 23 – **Terminal** : Coach service from Victoria Coach Station (Flightline 777, hourly service) – Railink (Gatwick Express) from Victoria (24 h service).

✈ London City Airport, ☎ (0171) 474 5555.

✈ Stansted, at Bishop's Stortford, ☎ (01279) 680500, Fax 66 20 66, NE : 34 m. off M 11 and A 120.

British Airways, Victoria Air Terminal : 115 Buckingham Palace Rd., SW1, ☎ (0171) 834 9411, Fax 828 7142, p. 16.

🚘 Euston ☎ (0345) 090700.

ℹ British Travel Centre, 12 Regent St. Piccadilly Circus, SW1Y 4 PQ, ☎ (0171) 971 0026.
Victoria Station Forecourt, SW1, ☎ (0171) 730 3488.

Sights

HISTORIC BUILDINGS AND MONUMENTS

Palace of Westminster*** p. 10 LY – Tower of London*** p. 11 PVX – Banqueting House** p. 10 LX – Buckingham Palace** p. 16 BVX – Kensington Palace** p. 8 FX – Lincoln's Inn** p. 17 EV – Lloyds Building** p. 7 PV – London Bridge* p. 11 PVX – Royal Hospital Chelsea** p. 15 FU – St. James's Palace** p. 13 EP – South Bank Arts Centre** p. 10 MX – Spencer House** p. 13 DP – The Temple** p. 6 MV – Tower Bridge** p. 11 PX – Albert Memorial* p. 14 CQ – Apsley House* p. 12 BP – George Inn*, Southwark p. 11 PX – Guildhall* p. 7 OU – Dr Johnson's House* p. 6 NUV **A** – Leighton House* p. 8 EY – The Monument* (✳*) p. 7 PV **G** – Royal Opera Arcade* p. 13 FGN – Staple Inn* p. 6 MU **Y** – Theatre Royal* (Haymarket) p. 13 GM.

CHURCHES

The City Churches

St. Paul's Cathedral*** p. 7 NOV – St. Bartholomew the Great** p. 7 OU **K** – St. Mary-at-Hill** p. 7 PV **B** – Temple Church** p. 6 MV – All Hallows-by-the-Tower (font cover**, brasses*) p. 7 PV **Y** – St. Bride* (steeple**) p. 7 NV **J** – St. Giles Cripplegate* p. 7 OU **N** – St. Helen Bishopsgate* (monuments**) p. 7 PUV **R** – St. James Garlickhythe (tower and spire*, sword rest*) p. 7 OV **R** – St. Margaret Lothbury p. 7 PU **S** – St. Margaret Pattens (woodwork*) p. 7 PV **N** – St. Mary Abchurch* p. 7 PV **X** – St. Mary-le-Bow (tower and steeple**) p. 7 OV **G** – St. Michael Paternoster Royal (tower and spire*) p. 7 OV **D** – St. Olave* p. 7 PV **S**.

Other Churches

Westminster Abbey*** p. 10 LY – Southwark Cathedral** p. 11 PX – Queen's Chapel* p. 13 EP – St. Clement Danes* p. 17 EX – St. James's* p. 13 EM – St. Margaret's* p. 10 LY **A** – St. Martin in-the-Fields* p. 17 DY – St. Paul's* (Covent Garden) p. 17 DX – Westminster Roman Catholic Cathedral* p. 10 KY **B**.

STREETS – SQUARES – PARKS

The City*** p. 7 NV – Regent's Park*** (Terraces**, Zoo***) p. 5 HIT – Belgrave Square** p. 16 AVX – Burlington Arcade** p. 13 DM – Covent Garden* p. 17 DX – Hyde Park** p. 9 GHVX – The Mall** p. 13 FP – St. James's Park** p. 10 KXY – Trafalgar Square** p. 17 DY – Whitehall** (Horse Guards*) p. 10 LX – Barbican* p. 7 OU – Bloomsbury* p. 6 LMU – Bond Street* pp. 12-13 CK-DM – Charing Cross* p. 17 DY – Cheyne Walk* p. 9 GHZ – Jermyn Street* p. 13 EN – Piccadilly Arcade* p. 13 DEN – Piccadilly Circus* p. 13 FM – Queen Anne's Gate* p. 10 KY – Regent Street* p. 13 EM – St. James's Square* p. 13 FN – St. James's Street* p. 13 EN – Shepherd Market* p. 12 CN – Soho* p. 13 FKL – Strand* p. 17 DY – Victoria Embankment* p. 17 DEXY – Waterloo Place* p. 13 FN.

MUSEUMS

British Museum*** p. 6 LU – National Gallery*** p. 13 GM – Science Museum*** p. 14 CR – Tate Gallery*** p. 10 LZ – Victoria and Albert Museum*** p. 15 DR – Courtauld Institute Galleries** p. 6 KLU **M** – Museum of London** p. 7 OU **M** – National Portrait Gallery** p. 13 GM – Natural History Museum** p. 14 CS – Queen's Gallery** p. 16 BV – Wallace Collection** p. 12 AH – Imperial War Museum* p. 10 NY – London Transport Museum* p. 17 DX – Madame Tussaud's* p. 5 IU **M** – Sir John Soane's Museum* p. 6 MU **M** – Wellington Museum* p. 12 BP.

Alphabetical list of areas included

LONDON CENTRE

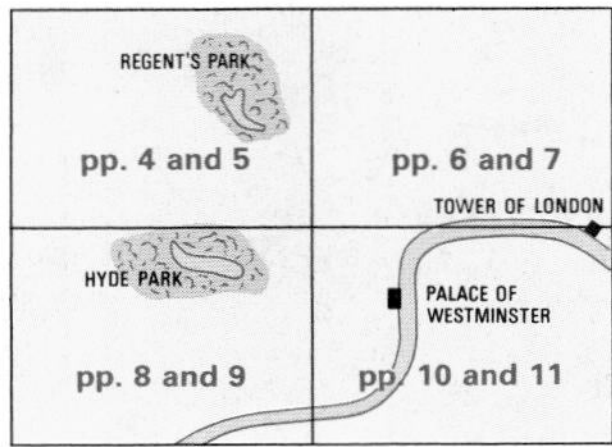

STREET INDEX TO LONDON CENTRE TOWN PLANS

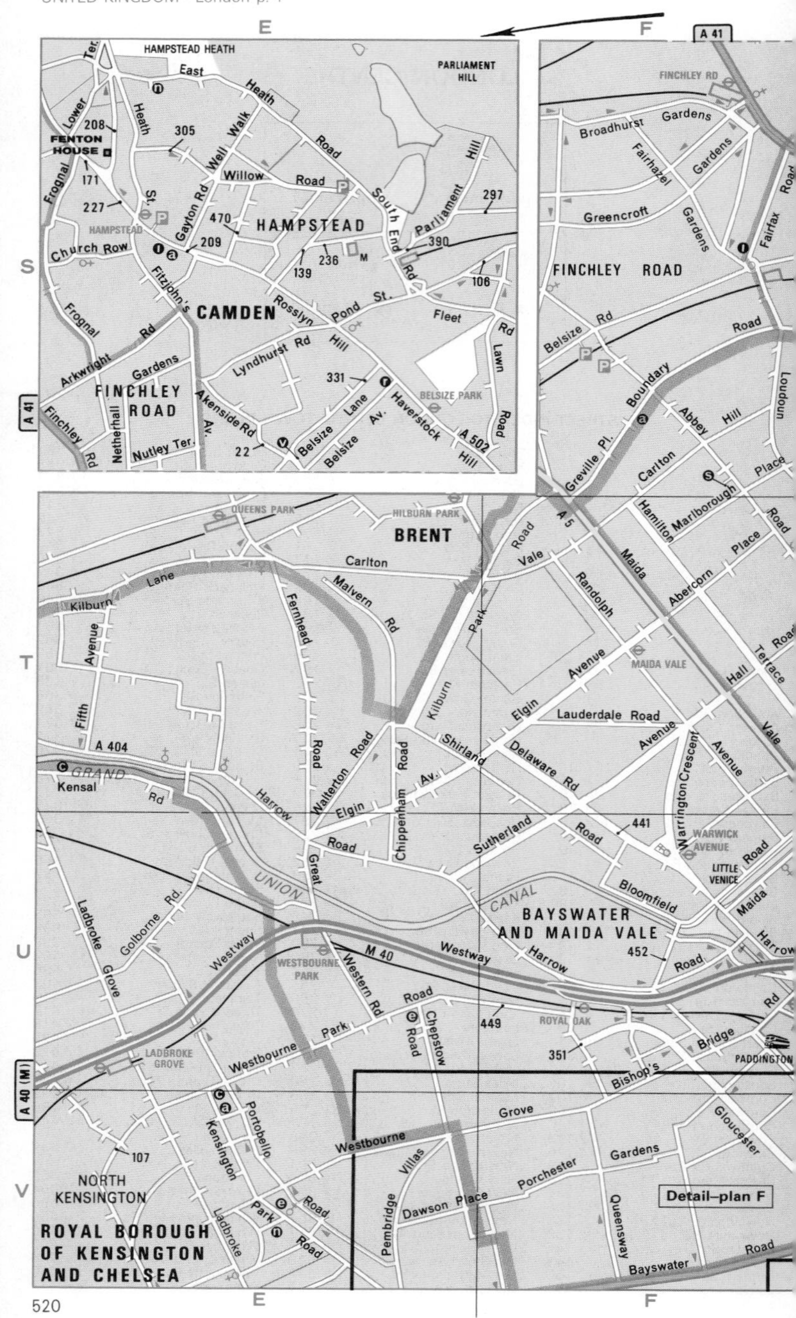

E
F
A 41
HAMPSTEAD HEATH
PARLIAMENT HILL
HAMPSTEAD
CAMDEN
FINCHLEY ROAD
FENTON HOUSE
BELSIZE PARK
FINCHLEY RD
BRENT
QUEENS PARK
KILBURN PARK
MAIDA VALE
WARWICK AVENUE
LITTLE VENICE
BAYSWATER AND MAIDA VALE
WESTBOURNE PARK
ROYAL OAK
PADDINGTON
LADBROKE GROVE
NORTH KENSINGTON
ROYAL BOROUGH OF KENSINGTON AND CHELSEA
A 40 (M)
M 40
A 404
A 502
A 5
S
T
U
V
Detail–plan F

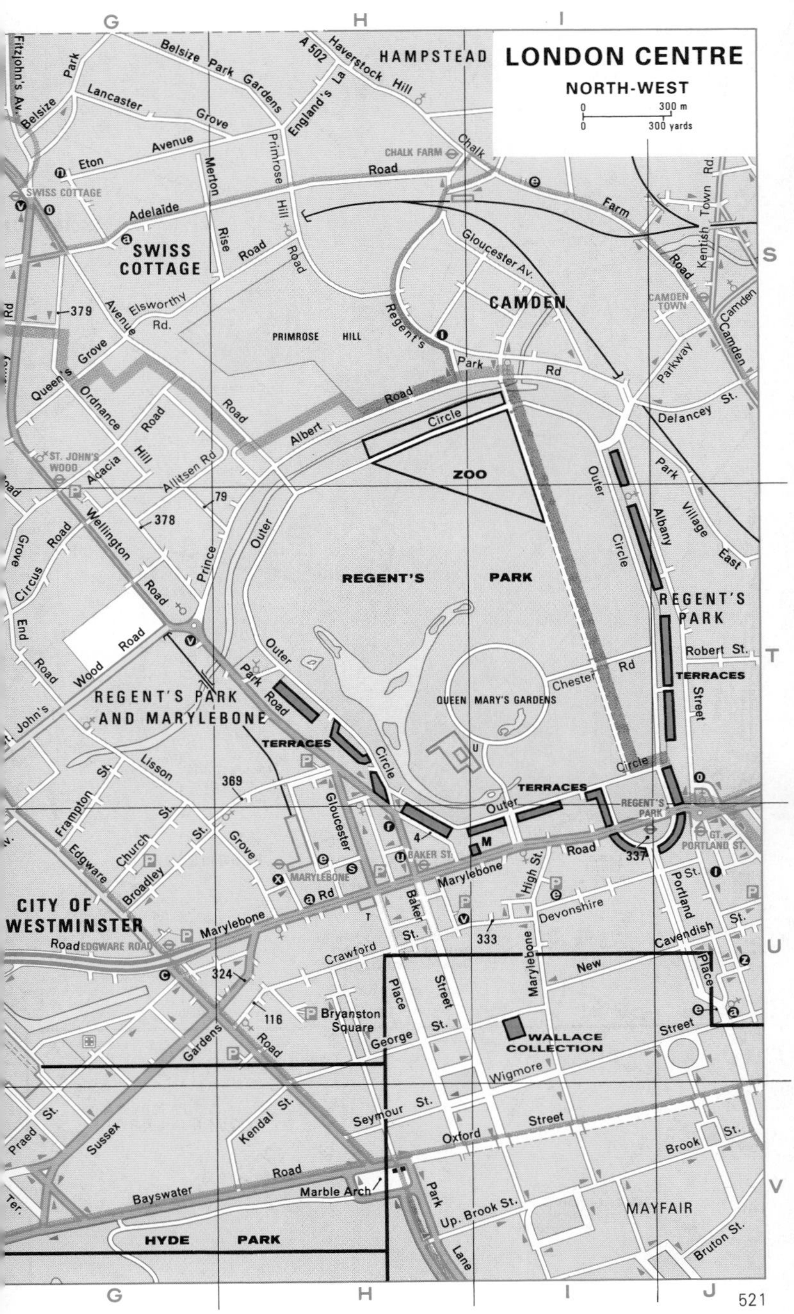

LONDON CENTRE
NORTH-WEST
0 300 m
0 300 yards
G
H
I
J
S
T
U
V
HAMPSTEAD
SWISS COTTAGE
CAMDEN
PRIMROSE HILL
ZOO
REGENT'S PARK
QUEEN MARY'S GARDENS
TERRACES
REGENT'S PARK AND MARYLEBONE
CITY OF WESTMINSTER
WALLACE COLLECTION
HYDE PARK
MAYFAIR
CHALK FARM
SWISS COTTAGE
CAMDEN TOWN
ST. JOHN'S WOOD
BAKER ST.
MARYLEBONE
REGENT'S PARK
GT. PORTLAND ST.
EDGWARE ROAD
Fitzjohn's Av.
Belsize Park Gardens
Belsize Park
Lancaster Grove
Eton Avenue
Haverstock Hill
A 502
England's La
Primrose Hill Road
Merton Rise
Adelaide Road
Chalk Farm Road
Gloucester Av.
Regent's Park Rd
Kentish Town Rd.
Camden
Parkway
Delancey St.
Elsworthy Rd.
Avenue Road
Queen's Grove
Ordnance Hill
Acacia Road
Allitsen Rd
Prince Albert Road
Outer Circle
Albany Street
Park Village East
Wellington Road
Grove End Road
Circus Road
St. John's Wood Road
Park Road
Robert St.
Chester Rd
Lisson Grove
Frampton St.
Church St.
Broadley St.
Edgware Road
Gloucester Place
Marylebone Road
Baker St.
High St.
Devonshire St.
Portland Place
Cavendish St.
New Cavendish Street
Marylebone Lane
Crawford St.
Bryanston Square
George St.
Wigmore Street
Seymour St.
Kendal St.
Sussex Gardens
Praed St.
Oxford Street
Brook St.
Bayswater Road
Marble Arch
Park Lane
Up. Brook St.
Bruton St.
Sussex Ter.
379
378
79
369
4
337
333
324
116

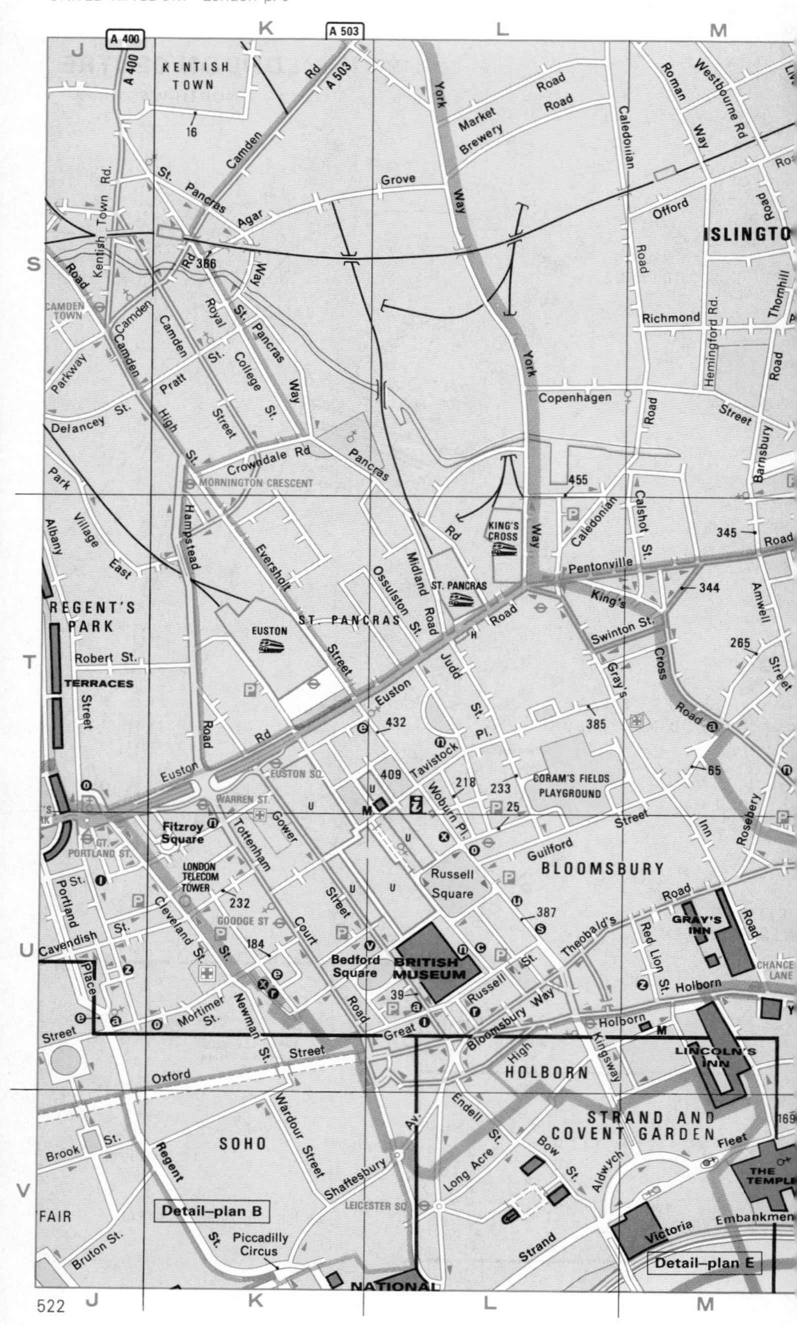
KENTISH TOWN
CAMDEN TOWN
REGENT'S PARK
TERRACES
EUSTON
ST. PANCRAS
KING'S CROSS
ISLINGTON
CORAM'S FIELDS PLAYGROUND
BLOOMSBURY
BRITISH MUSEUM
GRAY'S INN
LINCOLN'S INN
HOLBORN
STRAND AND COVENT GARDEN
SOHO
THE TEMPLE
LONDON TELECOM TOWER
Russell Square
Bedford Square
Fitzroy Square
Piccadilly Circus
Detail-plan B
Detail-plan E
MORNINGTON CRESCENT
EUSTON SQ.
WARREN ST.
GT. PORTLAND ST.
GOODGE ST
LEICESTER SQ
CHANCERY LANE
Camden Rd
Agar Grove
York Way
Caledonian Road
Pentonville Road
King's Cross Road
Euston Road
Gray's Inn Road
Guilford Street
Theobald's Road
Tottenham Court Road
Gower Street
Oxford Street
Regent St.
Shaftesbury Av.
Kingsway
Strand
Victoria Embankment
Wardour Street
Charing Cross Road

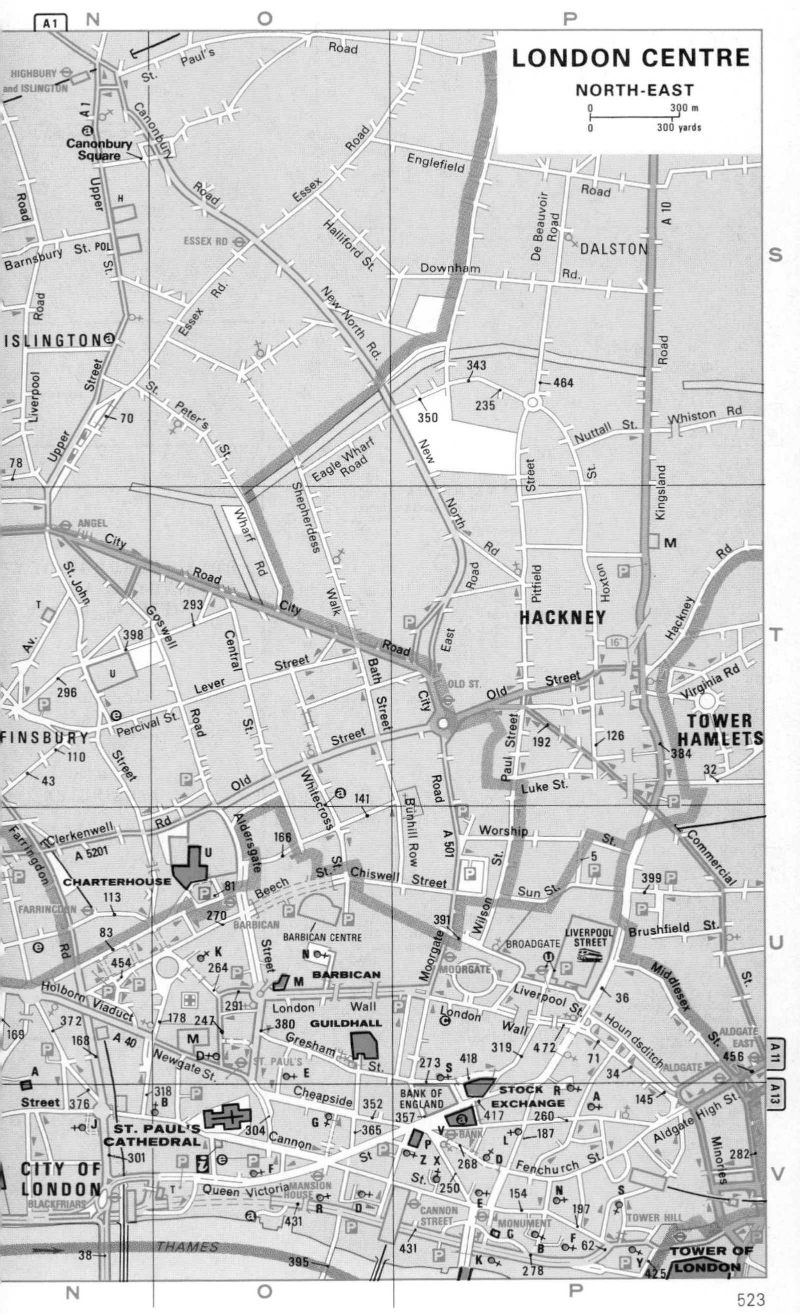
LONDON CENTRE
NORTH-EAST
0 300 m
0 300 yards
HIGHBURY and ISLINGTON
Canonbury Square
ESSEX RD
DALSTON
ISLINGTON
ANGEL
HACKNEY
OLD ST.
TOWER HAMLETS
FINSBURY
CHARTERHOUSE
FARRINGDON
BARBICAN
BARBICAN CENTRE
BROADGATE
LIVERPOOL STREET
MOORGATE
GUILDHALL
ST. PAUL'S
BANK OF ENGLAND
STOCK EXCHANGE
BANK
ALDGATE
ALDGATE EAST
ST. PAUL'S CATHEDRAL
CITY OF LONDON
BLACKFRIARS
MANSION HOUSE
CANNON STREET
MONUMENT
TOWER HILL
TOWER OF LONDON
THAMES

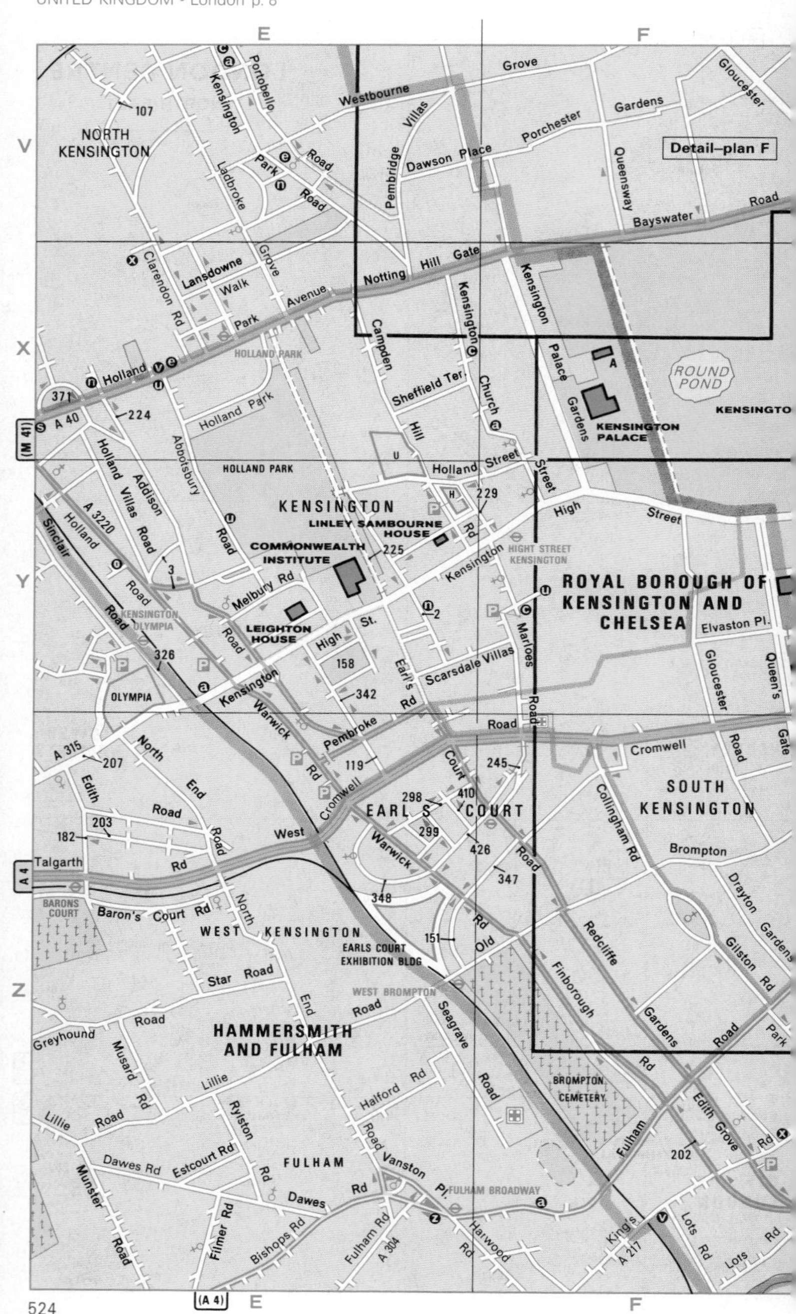
E
F
V
X
Y
Z
NORTH KENSINGTON
Detail–plan F
ROUND POND
KENSINGTON PALACE
HOLLAND PARK
KENSINGTON
LINLEY SAMBOURNE HOUSE
COMMONWEALTH INSTITUTE
LEIGHTON HOUSE
ROYAL BOROUGH OF KENSINGTON AND CHELSEA
OLYMPIA
KENSINGTON OLYMPIA
HIGHT STREET KENSINGTON
EARL'S COURT
SOUTH KENSINGTON
WEST KENSINGTON
EARLS COURT EXHIBITION BLDG
BARONS COURT
WEST BROMPTON
HAMMERSMITH AND FULHAM
BROMPTON CEMETERY
FULHAM
FULHAM BROADWAY
Westbourne Grove
Portobello Road
Kensington Park Road
Ladbroke Grove
Pembridge Villas
Dawson Place
Porchester Gardens
Queensway
Bayswater Road
Notting Hill Gate
Holland Park Avenue
Lansdowne Walk
Clarendon Rd
Campden Hill
Kensington Church Street
Kensington Palace Gardens
Sheffield Ter.
Holland Street
Kensington High Street
Abbotsbury Road
Addison Road
Holland Villas Road
Holland Road
Sinclair Road
Melbury Rd
Warwick Road
Earl's Court Road
Scarsdale Villas
Marloes Road
Pembroke Rd
Cromwell Road
Elvaston Pl.
Gloucester Road
Queen's Gate
North End Road
Edith Road
West Cromwell Rd
Talgarth Rd
Baron's Court Rd
Star Road
Old Brompton Road
Collingham Rd
Redcliffe Gardens
Finborough Rd
Drayton Gardens
Gilston Rd
Park Road
Edith Grove
Seagrave Road
Greyhound Road
Musard Rd
Lillie Road
Rylston Rd
Halford Rd
Vanston Pl.
Dawes Rd
Estcourt Rd
Munster Road
Filmer Rd
Bishops Rd
Fulham Rd
Harwood Rd
King's Rd
Lots Rd
Gloucester
KENSINGTO
A 40
A 3220
A 315
A 4
A 304
A 217
M 41
(A 4)
107
371
224
3
225
229
2
158
342
326
119
245
298
410
299
426
347
348
151
207
203
182
202
A
H
U

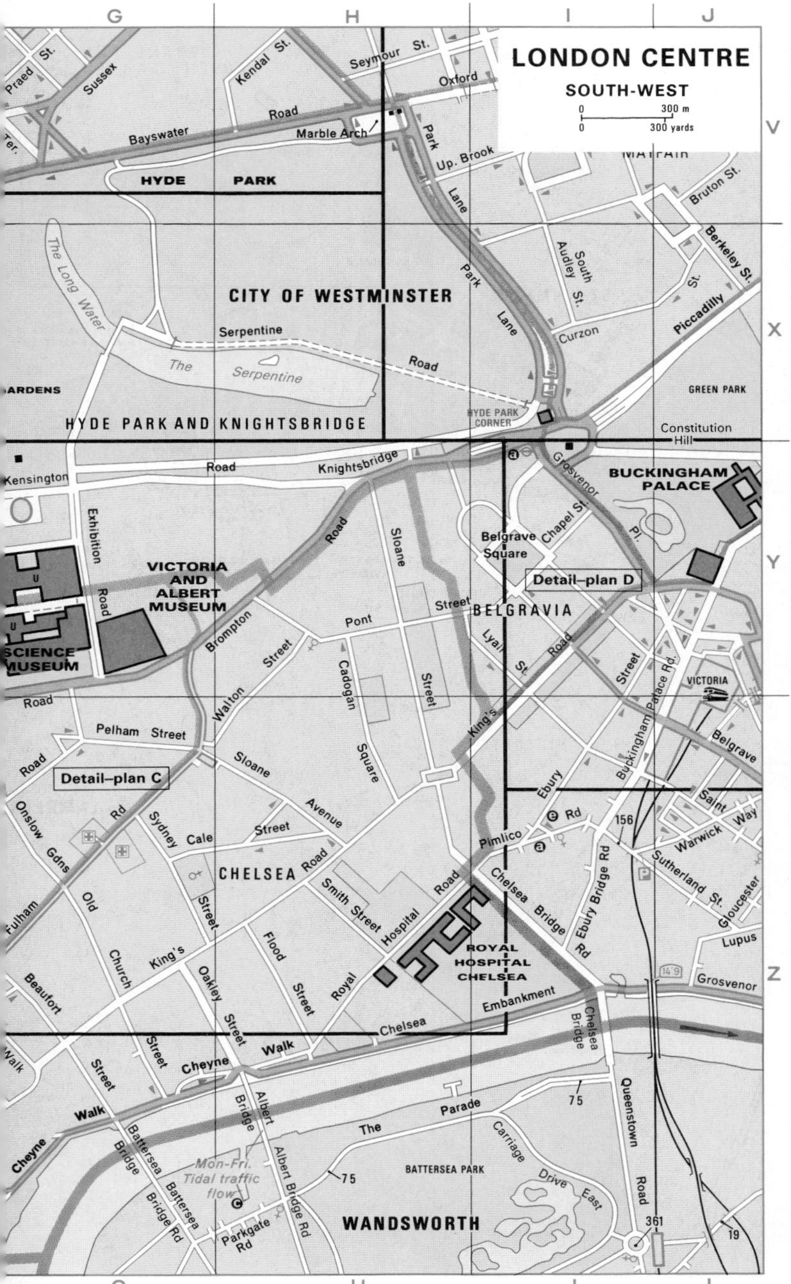

G H I J

LONDON CENTRE

SOUTH-WEST

0 300 m
0 300 yards

V
X
Y
Z

Praed St.
Sussex
Kendal St.
Seymour St.
Oxford
Bayswater Road
Marble Arch
Park Lane
Up. Brook
MAYFAIR
Bruton St.
Berkeley St.
HYDE PARK
The Long Water
CITY OF WESTMINSTER
South Audley St.
Park Lane
Piccadilly
Curzon
Serpentine Road
The Serpentine
GARDENS
GREEN PARK
HYDE PARK AND KNIGHTSBRIDGE
HYDE PARK CORNER
Constitution Hill
Kensington Road
Knightsbridge
Grosvenor Pl.
BUCKINGHAM PALACE
Exhibition Road
Brompton Road
Sloane Street
Belgrave Square
Chapel St.
VICTORIA AND ALBERT MUSEUM
Detail-plan D
BELGRAVIA
Pont Street
Lyall St.
SCIENCE MUSEUM
Cadogan Square
King's Road
Buckingham Palace Rd.
VICTORIA
Road
Walton Street
Pelham Street
Belgrave
Sloane Avenue
Detail-plan C
Ebury Rd
Saint
Way
Onslow Gdns
Rd
Sydney
Cale Street
156
Warwick
Pimlico
Sutherland St.
Gloucester
CHELSEA
Road
Smith Street
Hospital Road
Chelsea Bridge Rd
Ebury Bridge Rd
Fulham
Old Church
Street
Flood Street
ROYAL HOSPITAL CHELSEA
Lupus
King's
Oakley Street
Royal
149
Grosvenor
Beaufort
Embankment
Chelsea Bridge
Chelsea
Walk
Street
Cheyne Walk
75
Albert Bridge
Parade
Queenstown Road
The
Carriage Drive East
Battersea Bridge
Mon-Fri. Tidal traffic flow
Albert Bridge Rd
75
BATTERSEA PARK
Battersea Bridge Rd
Parkgate Rd
WANDSWORTH
361
19

G H I J

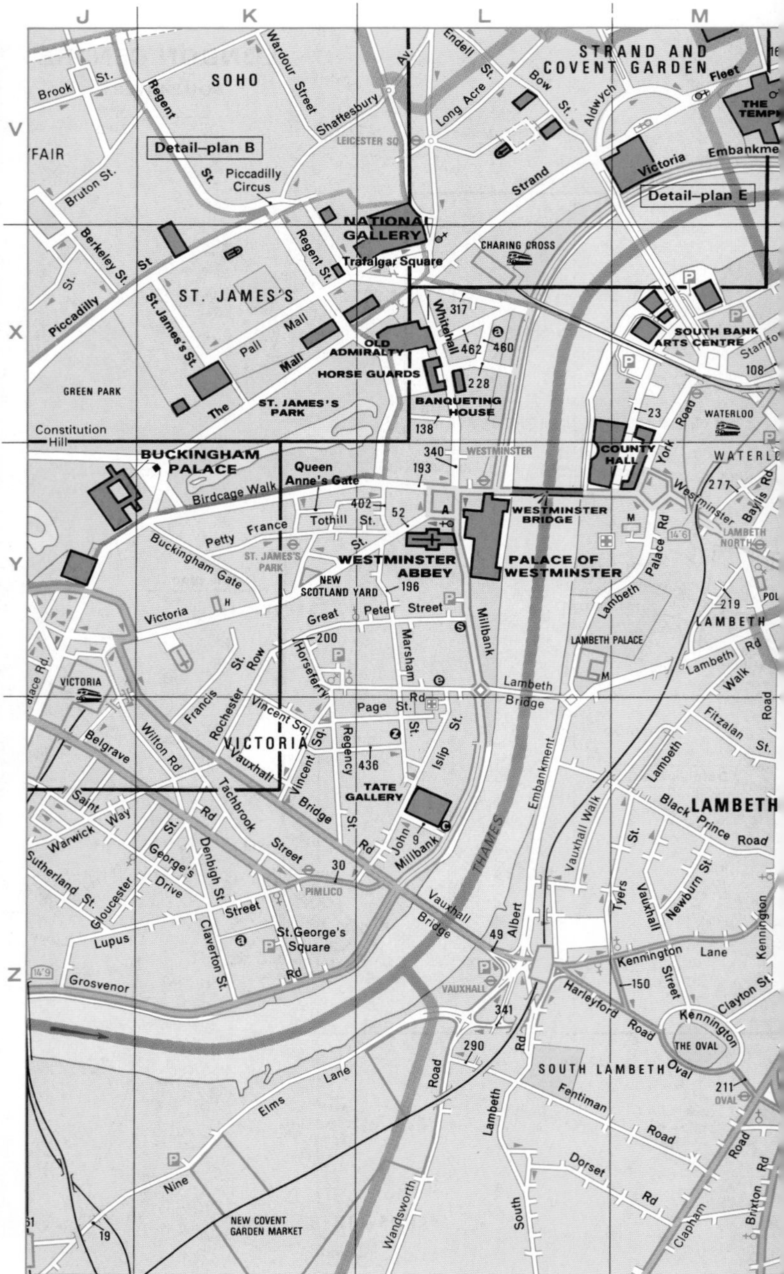

SOHO
STRAND AND COVENT GARDEN
Detail-plan B
Detail-plan E
Piccadilly Circus
NATIONAL GALLERY
Trafalgar Square
CHARING CROSS
ST. JAMES'S
OLD ADMIRALTY
HORSE GUARDS
BANQUETING HOUSE
GREEN PARK
ST. JAMES'S PARK
SOUTH BANK ARTS CENTRE
WATERLOO
COUNTY HALL
BUCKINGHAM PALACE
Queen Anne's Gate
WESTMINSTER BRIDGE
WESTMINSTER ABBEY
PALACE OF WESTMINSTER
NEW SCOTLAND YARD
LAMBETH PALACE
LAMBETH
VICTORIA
TATE GALLERY
THAMES
PIMLICO
VAUXHALL
THE OVAL
SOUTH LAMBETH
NEW COVENT GARDEN MARKET

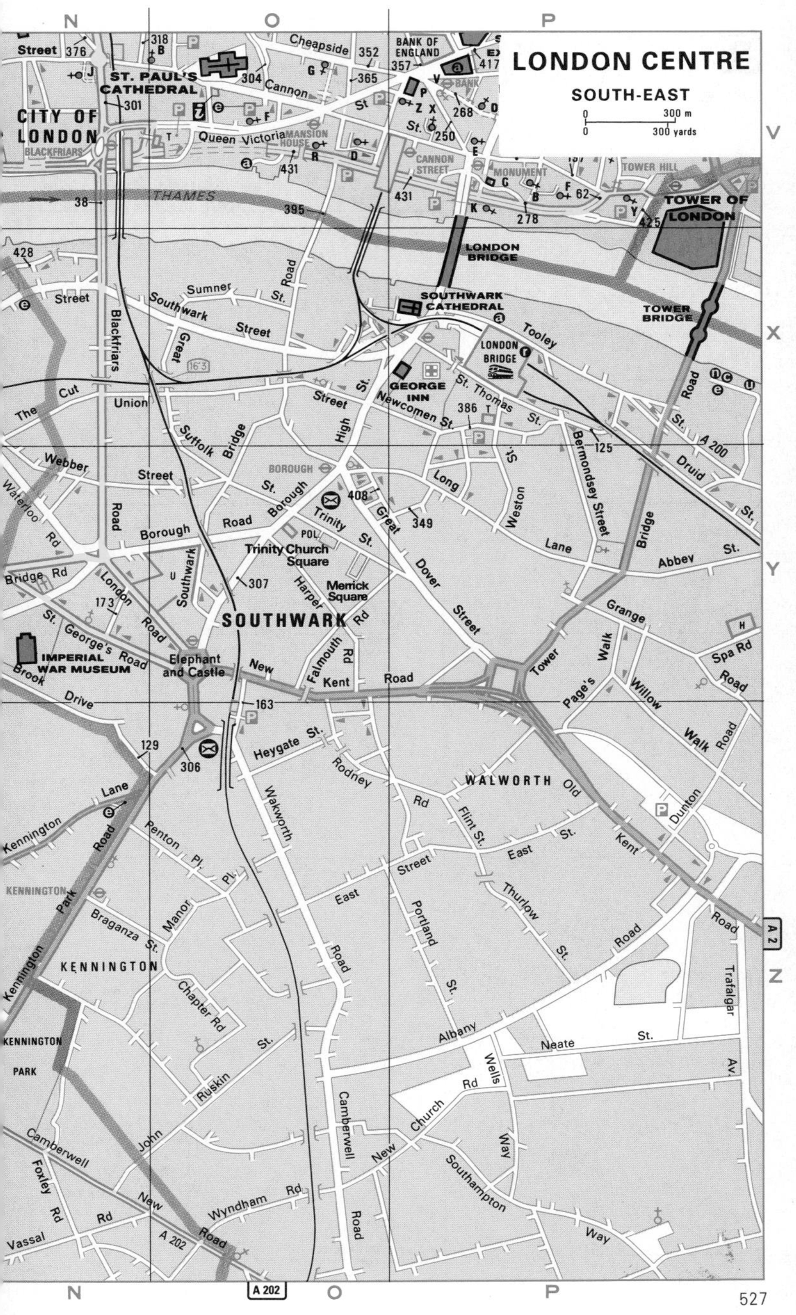
LONDON CENTRE
SOUTH-EAST
300 m
300 yards
CITY OF LONDON
ST. PAUL'S CATHEDRAL
BANK OF ENGLAND
MANSION HOUSE
CANNON STREET
MONUMENT
TOWER HILL
TOWER OF LONDON
THAMES
LONDON BRIDGE
TOWER BRIDGE
SOUTHWARK CATHEDRAL
GEORGE INN
BOROUGH
Trinity Church Square
Merrick Square
SOUTHWARK
Elephant and Castle
IMPERIAL WAR MUSEUM
WALWORTH
KENNINGTON
KENNINGTON PARK
A 200
A 2
A 202

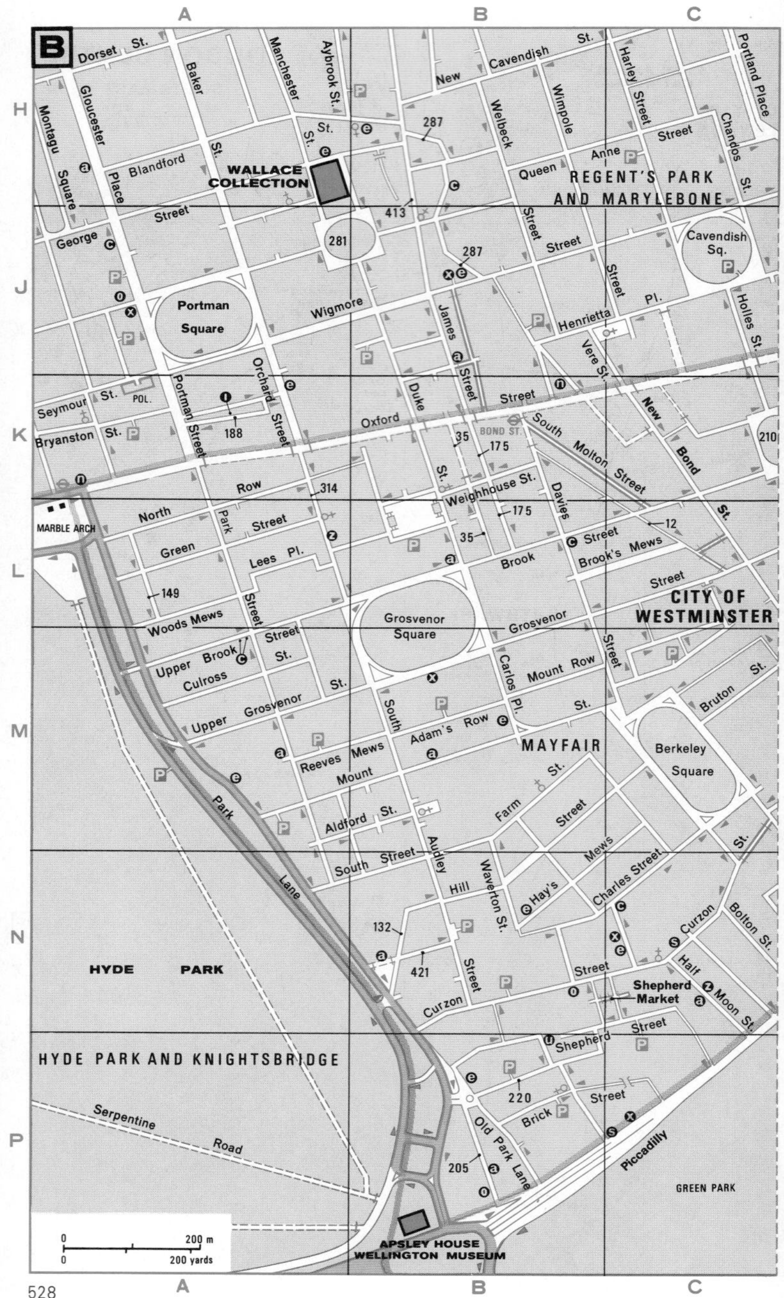
A
B
C
H
J
K
L
M
N
P
Dorset St.
Baker St.
Manchester
Aybrook St.
New Cavendish St.
Harley Street
Portland Place
Montagu Square
Gloucester Place
Blandford Street
WALLACE COLLECTION
Welbeck Street
Wimpole Street
Chandos St.
Queen Anne Street
REGENT'S PARK AND MARYLEBONE
George Street
281
287
413
Cavendish Sq.
Portman Square
Wigmore Street
James Street
Henrietta Pl.
Holles St.
Vere St.
Seymour St.
POL.
Bryanston St.
Portman Street
188
Orchard Street
Duke St.
Oxford Street
BOND ST.
South Molton Street
New Bond St.
210
MARBLE ARCH
North Row
Park Street
314
Weighhouse St.
175
35
Davies Street
12
Green Street
Lees Pl.
Brook Street
Brook's Mews
149
Woods Mews
Grosvenor Square
Grosvenor Street
CITY OF WESTMINSTER
Upper Brook Street
Culross St.
Carlos Pl.
Mount Row
Bruton St.
Upper Grosvenor St.
South Audley Street
Adam's Row
MAYFAIR
Berkeley Square
Reeves Mews
Mount St.
Farm Street
Park Lane
Aldford St.
South Street
Hill Street
Waverton St.
Hay's Mews
Charles Street
Curzon Street
Bolton St.
Half Moon St.
132
421
HYDE PARK
Shepherd Market
Shepherd Street
HYDE PARK AND KNIGHTSBRIDGE
220
Brick Street
Serpentine Road
Old Park Lane
205
Piccadilly
GREEN PARK
0
200 m
0
200 yards
APSLEY HOUSE WELLINGTON MUSEUM

Oxford Street is closed to private traffic, Mondays to Saturdays : from 7 am to 7 pm between Portman Street and St. Giles Circus

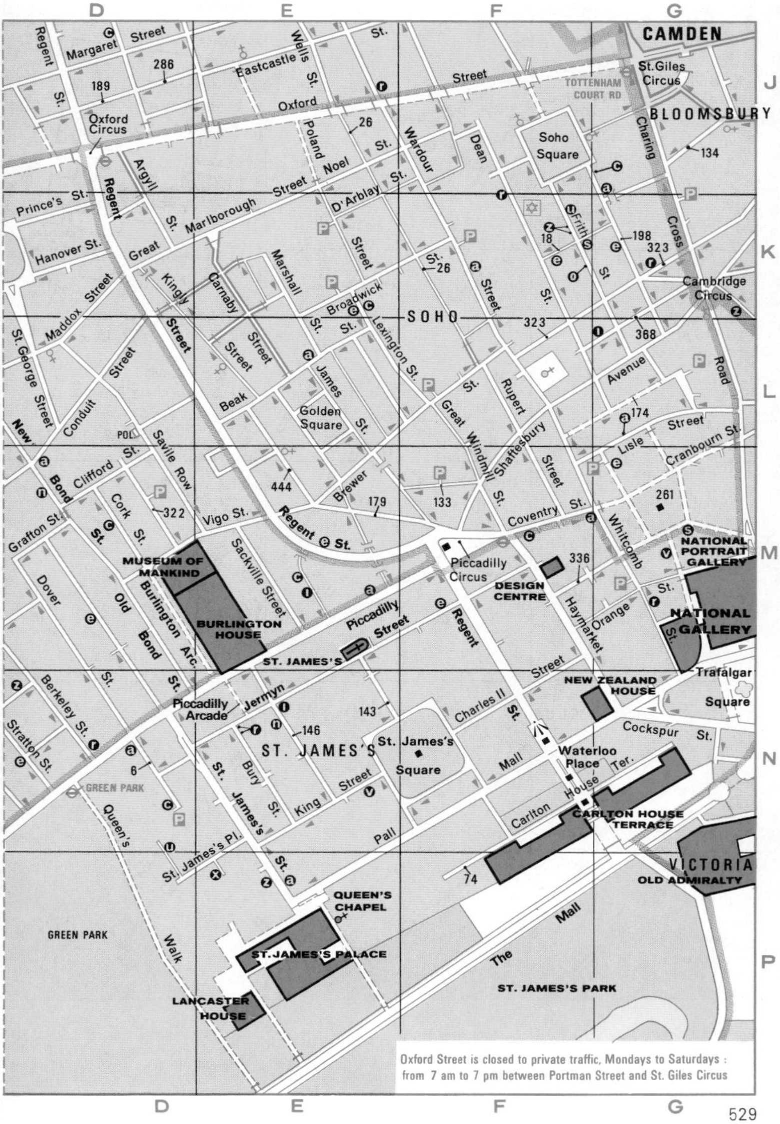

Barkston Gardens . . . . AT 14	Cromwell Place . . . . CS 120	Foulis Terrace . . . . CT 170
Bray Place . . . . ET 45	Egerton Gardens . . . . DS 160	Glendower Place . . . . CS 180
Bute Street . . . . CS 59	Egerton Terrace . . . . DR 161	Harriet Street . . . . FQ 214
Collingham Gardens . . . . . AT 99	Egerton Gardens Mews . . . . ER 162	Harrington Road . . . . CS 215
Collingham Road . . . . AT 101		Holbein Mews . . . . FT 223

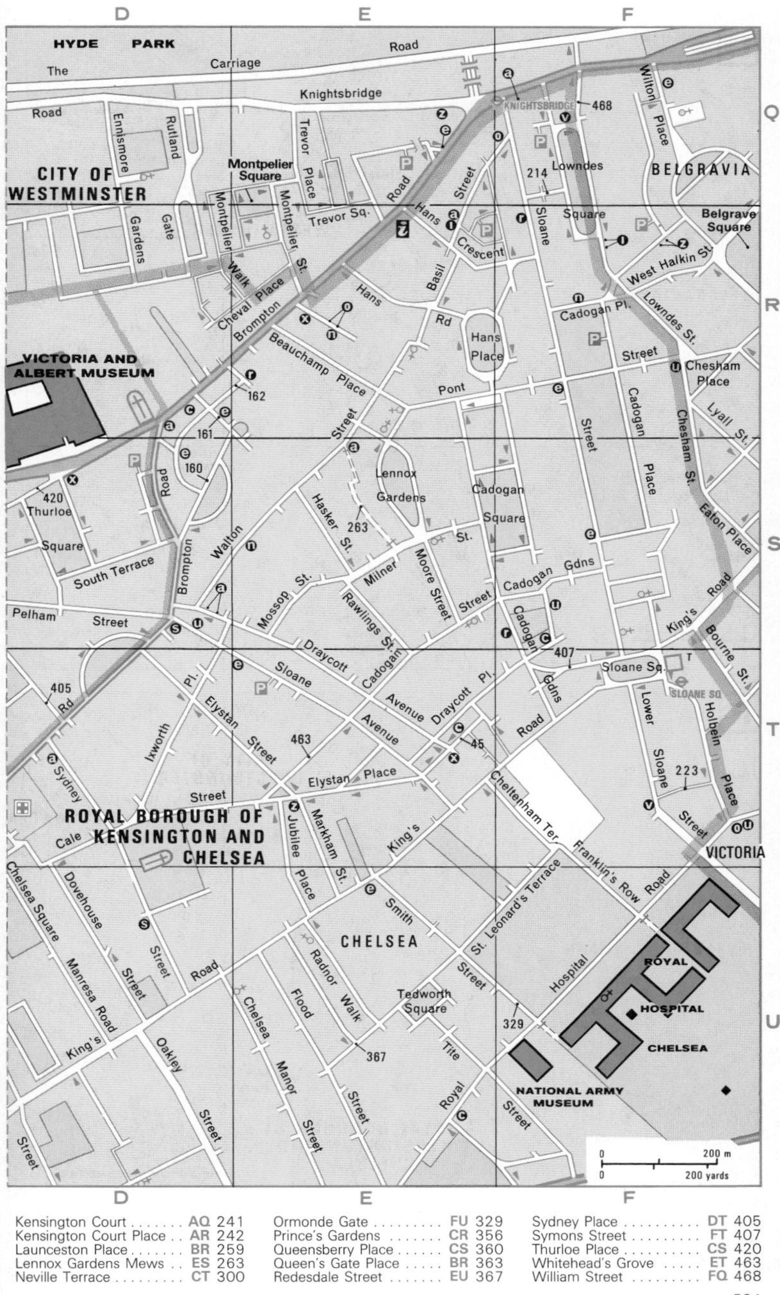

Kensington Court	AQ	241	Ormonde Gate	FU	329	Sydney Place	DT	405
Kensington Court Place	AR	242	Prince's Gardens	CR	356	Symons Street	FT	407
Launceston Place	BR	259	Queensberry Place	CS	360	Thurloe Place	CS	420
Lennox Gardens Mews	ES	263	Queen's Gate Place	BR	363	Whitehead's Grove	ET	463
Neville Terrace	CT	300	Redesdale Street	EU	367	William Street	FQ	468

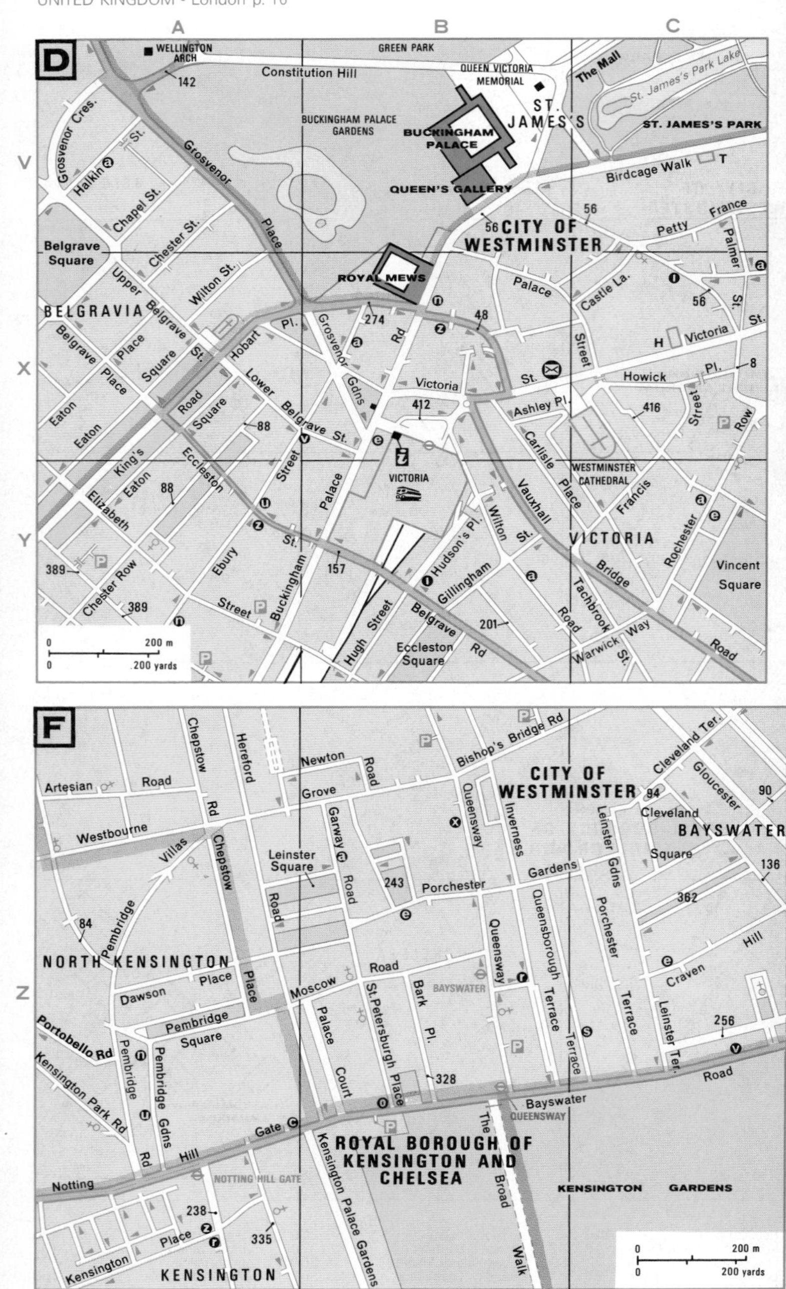
D
WELLINGTON ARCH
GREEN PARK
Constitution Hill
QUEEN VICTORIA MEMORIAL
The Mall
St. James's Park Lake
ST. JAMES'S
ST. JAMES'S PARK
BUCKINGHAM PALACE GARDENS
BUCKINGHAM PALACE
QUEEN'S GALLERY
Birdcage Walk
CITY OF WESTMINSTER
Petty France
ROYAL MEWS
BELGRAVIA
Belgrave Square
VICTORIA
WESTMINSTER CATHEDRAL
Vincent Square
Eccleston Square
Victoria
Grosvenor Place
Buckingham Palace Rd
Vauxhall Bridge Road
Eccleston St.
Ebury Street
Chester Row
Elizabeth St.
Hugh Street
Belgrave Rd
Wilton St.
Rochester Row
Tachbrook St.
Warwick Way
Howick Pl.
Ashley Pl.
Carlisle Place
Francis Street
Palmer St.
Castle La.
Palace Street
Hobart Pl.
Lower Belgrave St.
Upper Belgrave St.
Chester St.
Chapel St.
Halkin St.
Grosvenor Cres.
Eaton Place
Eaton Square
King's Road
Gillingham St.
Hudson's Pl.
0 200 m
0 200 yards
F
CITY OF WESTMINSTER
BAYSWATER
NORTH KENSINGTON
ROYAL BOROUGH OF KENSINGTON AND CHELSEA
KENSINGTON
KENSINGTON GARDENS
Bishop's Bridge Rd
Cleveland Ter.
Gloucester Ter.
Cleveland Square
Artesian Road
Westbourne Grove
Westbourne Park Villas
Chepstow Rd
Chepstow Place
Hereford Road
Newton Road
Leinster Square
Garway Road
Porchester Gardens
Queensway
Inverness Terrace
Queensborough Terrace
Porchester Terrace
Leinster Gdns
Leinster Ter.
Craven Hill
Moscow Road
St. Petersburgh Place
Palace Court
Bark Pl.
Pembridge Villas
Pembridge Place
Pembridge Square
Pembridge Rd
Pembridge Gdns
Dawson Place
Portobello Rd
Kensington Park Rd
Notting Hill Gate
NOTTING HILL GATE
Bayswater Road
BAYSWATER
QUEENSWAY
Kensington Palace Gardens
The Broad Walk
Kensington Place
0 200 m
0 200 yards

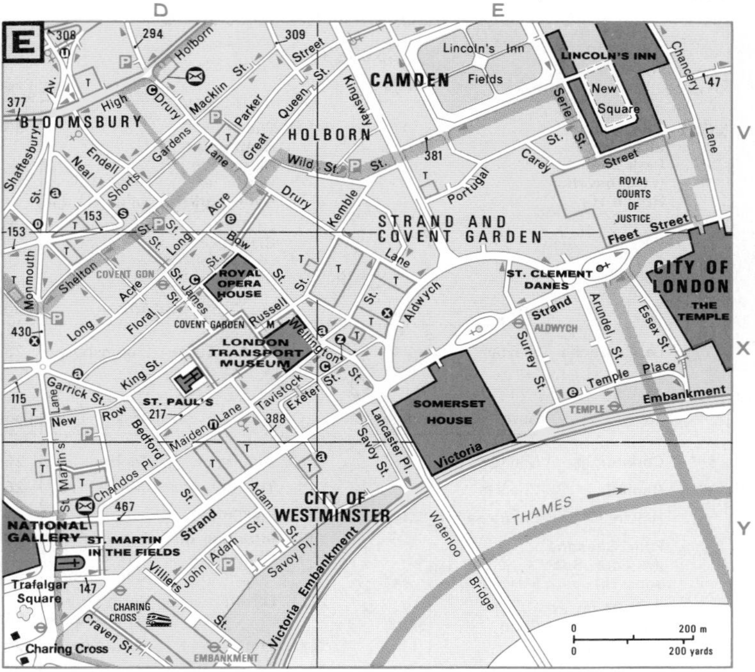

D E

E

308 294 309 Holborn Street Lincoln's Inn LINCOLN'S INN Chancery 47
Av. High Drury Macklin St. Parker Queen St. Kingsway CAMDEN Fields New Square Serle St. Lane
377 BLOOMSBURY Gardens Great HOLBORN St. V
Shaftesbury Endell Neal Lane Wild St. St. 381 Carey Street
St. Shorts Acre Drury Kemble Portugal ROYAL COURTS OF JUSTICE
153 153 St. Long Bow STRAND AND COVENT GARDEN Fleet Street
Monmouth Shelton COVENT GDN ROYAL OPERA HOUSE St. Lane Aldwych ST. CLEMENT DANES CITY OF LONDON
Acre St. James Russell Wellington St. Strand ALDWYCH Arundel St. Essex St. THE TEMPLE
430 Long Floral COVENT GARDEN LONDON TRANSPORT MUSEUM St. Surrey St. X
115 King St. Garrick St. ST. PAUL'S Tavistock Exeter St. Temple Place
Lane New Row 217 Maiden Lane 388 Lancaster Pl. Savoy St. SOMERSET HOUSE TEMPLE Embankment
St. Martin's Bedford Victoria
Chandos Pl. St. Adam CITY OF WESTMINSTER THAMES
467 Strand St. Waterloo Y
NATIONAL GALLERY ST. MARTIN IN THE FIELDS John Adam St. Savoy Pl. Embankment
Trafalgar Square 147 Villiers Bridge
CHARING CROSS Craven St. St. Victoria 0 200 m
Charing Cross EMBANKMENT 0 200 yards

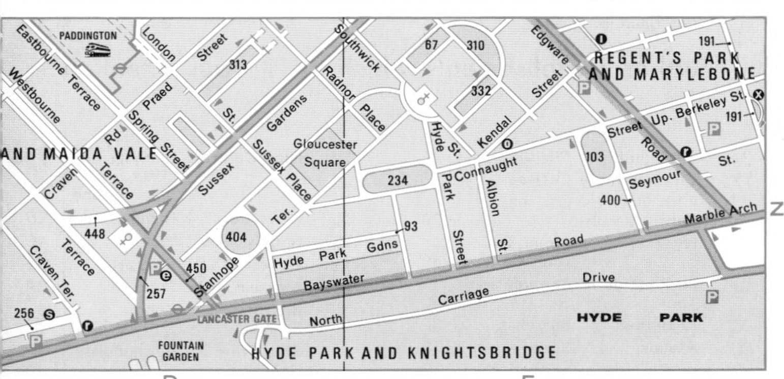

D E

Artillery Row CVX 8	Eccleston Bridge BY 157	Orme Court BZ 328
Bream's Building EV 47	Great Cumberland Place EZ 191	Oxford Square EZ 332
Bressenden Place BX 48	Guildhouse Street BY 201	Palace Gardens Terrace AZ 335
Buckingham Gate CV 56	Henrietta Street DX 217	Queen's Gardens CZ 362
Cambridge Square EZ 67	Hyde Park Square EZ 234	St. Giles High Street DV 377
Chepstow Crescent AZ 84	Kensington Church Street AZ 238	Sardinia Street EV 381
Chester Square AX 88	Kensington Gardens Square BZ 243	Southampton Street DX 388
Chilworth Street CZ 90	Lancaster Gate CDZ 256	South Eaton Place AY 389
Clarendon Place EZ 93	Lancaster Terrace DZ 257	Stanhope Place EZ 400
Cleveland Gardens CZ 94	Lower Grosvenor Place BX 274	Sussex Square DZ 404
Connaught Square EZ 103	Museum Street DV 294	Terminus Place BX 412
Cranbourn Street DX 115	New Oxford Street DV 308	Thirleby Road CX 416
Devonshire Terrace CZ 136	Newton Street DV 309	Upper St. Martin's Lane DX 430
Duke of Wellington Place AV 142	Norfolk Crescent EZ 310	Westbourne Crescent DZ 448
Duncannon Street DY 147	Norfolk Square DZ 313	Westbourne Street DZ 450
Earlham Street DV 153		William IV Street DY 467

Starred establishments in London

✿✿✿

		Area	Page
XXXXX	**Chez Nico at Ninety Park Lane (at Grosvenor House H.)**	Mayfair	34
XXXX	**The Restaurant, Marco Pierre White (at Hyde Park H.)**	Hyde Park & Knightsbridge	33
XXXX	**La Tante Claire**	Chelsea	26

✿✿

		Area	Page
XXXX	**Le Gavroche**	Mayfair	34
XX	**Pied à Terre**	Bloomsbury	23

✿

		Area	Page
	Connaught	Mayfair	33
	Capital	Chelsea	25
	Halkin	Belgravia	32
XXXX	**Four Seasons (at Four Seasons H.)**	Mayfair	34
XXXX	**Grill Room at the Café Royal**	Soho	38
XXXX	**Oriental (at Dorchester H.)**	Mayfair	34
XXXX	**Les Saveurs**	Mayfair	34
XXX	**Aubergine**	Chelsea	26
XXX	**The Canteen**	Chelsea	26
XXX	**L'Escargot**	Soho	38
XXX	**Interlude de Chavot**	Regent's Park & Marylebone	36
XXX	**Leith's**	North Kensington	28
XXX	**The Square**	St. James's	38
XX	**Fulham Road**	Chelsea	27
XX	**Greenhouse**	Mayfair	35

Further establishments which merit your attention

Meals

		Area	Page
XXX	**Bibendum**	Chelsea	26
XXX	**Chutney Mary**	Chelsea	26
XXX	**Fifth Floor (at Harvey Nichols)**	Chelsea	26
XXX	**Ivy**	Strand & Covent Garden	39
XXX	**Le Pont de la Tour**	Bermondsey	30
XX	**Al Bustan**	Belgravia	32
XX	**Atelier**	Soho	39
XX	**Le Caprice**	St. James's	38
XX	**Clarke's**	Kensington	28
XX	**Hilaire**	South Kensington	30
XX	**Nico Central**	Regent's Park & Marylebone	36
XX	**River Café**	Hammersmith	25
XX	**Simply Nico**	Victoria	40
XX	**Zafferano**	Belgravia	32
X	**Alastair Little**	Soho	39
X	**Bistrot Bruno**	Soho	39
X	**Blue Print Café**	Bermondsey	30
X	**Kensington Place**	Kensington	28
X	**Malabar**	Kensington	28

Restaurants classified acording to type

Seafood

- XXX **Overton's** (City of Westminster - *St. James's*) 38
- XXX **Scotts** (City of Westminster - *Mayfair*) 35
- XX **Bentley's** (City of Westminster - *Mayfair*) 35
- XX **Downstairs at One Ninety** (Royal Borough of Kensington & Chelsea - *South Kensington*) 30
- XX **Park Inn** (Royal Borough of Kensington & Chelsea - *North Kensington*) 28
- XX **Poissonnerie de l'Avenue** (Royal Borought of Kensington & Chelsea - *Chelsea*) 27
- XX **Sheekey's** (City of Westminster - *Strand & Covent Garden*) 39

Chinese

- XXXX ✿ **Oriental** (City of Westminster - *Mayfair*) 34
- XXX **Inn of Happiness** (City of Westminster - *Victoria*) 40
- XXX **Pearl** (City of Westminster - *Hyde Park and Knightsbridge*) 33
- XXX **Princess Garden** (City of Westminster - *Mayfair*) 35
- XXX **WestZENders** (City of Westminster - *Strand & Covent Garden*) 39
- XXX **Zen Central** (City of Westminster - *Mayfair*) 35
- XX **Good Earth** (Royal Borough of Kensington & Chelsea - *Chelsea*) 27
- XX **Hunan** (City of Westminster - *Victoria*) 41
- XX **Imperial City** (City of London) .. 24
- XX **Ken Lo's Memories of China** (City of Westminster - *Victoria*) 40
- XX **Mao Tai** (Hammersmith & Fulham - *Fulham*) 25
- XX **Ming** (City of Westminster - *Soho*) 38
- XX **Park Inn** (Royal Borough of Kensington & Chelsea - *North Kensington*) 28
- XX **Poons** (City of Westminster - *Bayswater & Maida Vale*) 32
- XX **Poons of Russell Square** (Camden - *Bloomsbury*) 23
- XX **Red** (Royal Borough of Kensington & Chelsea - *Chelsea*) 27
- XX **Sampans** (City of Westminster - *Regent's Park & Marylebone*) . 37
- XX **Shanghai** (Royal Borough of Kensington & Chelsea - *Kensington*) 28
- XX **ZeNW3** (Camden - *Hampstead*) . 24
- X **Fung Shing** (City of Westminster - *Soho*) 39
- X **Poons** (City of Westminster - *Soho*) 39

English

- XXX **Shepherds** (City of Westminster - *Victoria*) 40
- XX **English Garden** (Royal Borough of Kensington & Chelsea - *Chelsea*) . 27
- XX **Green's** (City of Westminster - *St. James's*) 38
- XX **Hudson's** (City of Westminster - *Regent's Park & Marylebone*) . 36
- XX **Rules** (City of Westminster - *Strand & Covent Garden*) 39
- XX **Tate Gallery** (City of Westminster - *Victoria*) 41
- X **Alfred** (Camden - *Bloomsbury*) .. 23

French

XXXXX ✿✿✿ **Chez Nico at Ninety Park Lane** (City of Westminster - *Mayfair*) ... 34

XXXXX **Oak Room** (City of Westminster - *Mayfair*) ... 34

XXXX ✿✿ **Gavroche (Le)** (City of Westminster - *Mayfair*) ... 34

XXXX ✿ **Saveurs (Les)** (City of Westminster - *Mayfair*) ... 34

XXXX ✿✿✿ **Tante Claire (La)** (Royal Borough of Kensington & Chelsea - *Chelsea*) ... 26

XXX **Auberge de Provence** (City of Westminster - *Victoria*) ... 40

XXX ✿ **Interlude de Chavot** (City of Westminster - *Regent's Park & Marylebone*) ... 36

XXX **Jardin des Gourmets (Au)** (City of Westminster - *Soho*) ... 38

XX **Brasserie St. Quentin** (Royal Borough of Kensington & Chelsea - *Chelsea*) ... 27

XX **Chez Moi** (Royal Borough of Kensington & Chelsea - *North Kensington*) ... 28

XX **Escargot Doré (L')** (Royal Borough of Kensington & Chelsea - *Kensington*) ... 28

XX **Estaminet (L')** (City of Westminster - *Stand and Covent Garden*) 39

XX **Mon Plaisir** (Camden - *Bloomsbury*) ... 23

XX **Poissonnerie de l'Avenue** (Royal Borough of Kensington & Chelsea - *Chelsea*) ... 27

XX **Pomme d'Amour (La)** (Royal Borough of Kensington & Chelsea - *Kensington*) ... 28

XX **Quai (Le)** (City of London) ... 24

XX **Truffe Noire (La)** (Southwark - *Southwark*) ... 31

X **Aventure (L')** (City of Westminster - *Regent's Park & Marylebone*) 37

X **Magno's Brasserie** (City of Westminster - *Strand & Covent Garden*) ... 39

X **Muscadet (Le)** (City of Westminste - *Regent's Park & Marylebone*) ... 37

X **Poule au Pot (La)** (City of Westminster - *Victoria*) ... 41

Hungarian

XX **Gay Hussar** (City of Westminster - *Soho*) ... 39

Indian & Pakistani

XXX **Bengal Clipper** (Southwark - *Bermondsey*) ... 30

XXX **Bombay Brasserie** (Royal Borough of Kensington & Chelsea - *South Kensington*) ... 30

XXX **Chutney Mary** (Anglo-Indian) (Royal Borough of Kensington & Chelsea - *Chelsea*) ... 26

XX **Café Lazeez** (Royal Borough of Kensington & Chelsea - *South Kensington*) ... 30

XX **Delhi Brasserie** (Royal Borough of Kensington & Chelsea - *South Kensington*) ... 30

XX **Gaylord** (City of Westminster - *Regent's Park & Marylebone*) ... 36

XX **Gopal's** (City of Westminster - *Soho*) ... 38

XX **Khan's of Kensington** (Royal Borough of Kensington & Chelsea - *South Kensington*) ... 30

XX **Memories of India** (Royal Borough of Kensington & Chelsea - *South Kensington*) ... 30

XX **Red Fort** (City of Westminster - *Soho*) ... 38

XX **Tabaq** (Wandsworth - *Wandsworth*) ... 31

XX **Tamarind** (City of Westminster - *Mayfair*) ... 35

XX **Tandoori Nights** (Hammersmith & Fulham - *Hammersmith*) ... 25

X **Bombay Bicycle Club** (Wandsworth - *Wandsworth*) ... 31

X **Malabar** (Royal Borough of Kensington & Chelsea - *Kensington*) 28

Irish

XX **Mulligans** (City of Westminster - *Mayfair*) ... 35

Italian

- Halkin (City of Westminster - *Belgravia*) 32
- **Incontro (L')** (City of Westminster - *Victoria*) 40
- **Santini** (City of Westminster - *Victoria*) 40
- **Amico (L')** (City of Westminster - *Victoria*) 41
- **Bertorelli's** (City of Westminster - *Strand & Covent Garden*) 39
- **Caldesi** (City of Westminster - *Regent's Park & Marylebone*) 36
- **Daphne's** (Royal Borough of Kensington & Chelsea - *Chelsea*) 27
- **Del Buongustaio** (Wandsworth - *Putney*) 31
- **Fenice (La)** (Royal Borough of Kensington & Chelsea - *Kensington*) 28
- **Finezza (La)** (Royal Borough of Kensington & Chelsea - *Chelsea*) 27
- **Gran Paradiso** (City of Westminster - *Victoria*) 41
- **Luigi's** (Southwark - *Dulwich*) .. 31
- **Orchard** (Camden - *Hampstead*) 24
- **Orsino** (Royal Borough of Kensington & Chelsea - *North Kensington*) . 28
- **Orso** (City of Westminster - *Strand & Covent Garden*) 39
- **Portico** (City of London) 24
- **River Café** (Hammersmith & Fulham - *Hammersmith*) 25
- **San Vincenzo (Al)** (City of Westminster - *Bayswater & Maida Vale*) 32
- **Toto's** (Royal Borough of Kensington & Chelsea - *Chelsea*) 27
- **Zafferano** (City of Westminster - *Belgravia*) 32
- **Accento (L')** (City of Westminster - *Bayswater & Maida Vale*) 32
- **Altro (L')** (Royal Borough of Kensington & Chelsea - *North Kensington*) 29
- **Cantina Del Ponte** (*Mediterranean*) (Southwark - *Bermondsey*) 30
- **Castelletto (IL)** (Camden - *Bloomsbury*) 23
- **Cibo** (Royal Borough of Kensington & Chelsea - *Kensington*) 28
- **Olivo** (City of Westminster - *Victoria*) 41

Japanese

- **Benihana** (Royal Borough of Kensington & Chelsea - *Chelsea* 27
- **Suntory** (City of Westminster - *St. James's*) 37
- **Tatsuso** (City of London) 24
- **Asuka** (City of Westminster - *Regent's Park & Marylebone*) 37
- **Benihana** (Camden - *Hampstead*) 24
- **Matsuri** (City of Westminster - *St. James's*) 38
- **Miyama** (City of London) 24
- **Shogun** (City of Westminster - *Mayfair*) 35
- **Nakamura** (City of Westminster - *Regent's Park & Marylabone*) 37

Lebanese

- **Al Bustan** (City of Westminster - *Belgravia*) 32
- **Maroush III** (City of Westminster - *Regent's Park & Marylebone*) 36
- **Phoenicia** (Royal Borough of Kensington & Chelsea - *Kensington)* 28

Spanish

- **Albero & Grana** (Royal Borough of Kensington & Chelsea - *Chelsea*) 27

Thai

- **Blue Elephant** (Hammersmith & Fulham - *Fulham*) 25
- **Busabong Too** (Royal Borough of Kensington & Chelsea - *Chelsea*) 27
- **Chada** (Wandsworth - *Battersea*) 31
- **Tui** (Royal Borough of Kensington & Chelsea - South Kensington) 30
- **Sri Siam** (City of Westminster - *Soho*) 39

Vietnamese

- **Saigon** (City of Westminster - *Soho*) 39

Greater London is divided, for administrative purposes, into 32 boroughs plus the City; these sub-divide naturally into minor areas, usually grouped around former villages or quarters, which often maintain a distinctive character.

of Greater London: 0171 or 0181 except special cases.

LONDON AIRPORTS

Heathrow Middx. W : 17 m. by A 4, M 4 **Underground** Piccadilly line direct – 0181.
759 4321 – **Terminal :** Airbus (A 1) from Victoria, Airbus (A 2) from Paddington.
Underground Station Concourse, Heathrow Airport, TW6 2JA (0171) 824 8844.

Radisson Edwardian, 140 Bath Rd, Hayes, UB3 5AW, 759 6311, Telex 23935, Fax 759 4559, – rm – 500. AX **e**
Henleys : **Meals** *(closed lunch Saturday and Sunday)* 19.90/28.00 **st.** and a la carte 6.50 – ***Brasserie :*** **Meals** 11.95 **st.** and a la carte – 13.00 – **442 rm** 153.00/215.00 **st.**, 17 suites.

Holiday Inn Crowne Plaza Heathrow London, Stockley Rd, West Drayton, UB7 9NA, (01895) 445555, Telex 934518, Fax 445122, – rm – 200. AV **v**
Marlowe : **Meals** *(closed Sunday)* (dinner only) 23.95 **t.** and a la carte – ***Cafe Galleria :*** **Meals** 15.95/17.50 **t.** and a la carte – 11.50 – **372 rm** 110.00/125.00 **st.**, 2 suites.

Sheraton Skyline, Bath Rd, Hayes, UB3 5BP, 759 2535, Telex 934 254, Fax 750 9150, – rm – 500. AX **u**
Colony Room : **Meals** (dinner only) 32.00 **t.** and a la carte – ***Cafe Jardin :*** **Meals** a la carte 16.50/29.00 **t.** 7.00 – 12.00 – **344 rm** 180.00/190.00 **st.**, 5 suites.

London Heathrow Hilton, Terminal 4, TW6 3AF, 759 7755, Telex 925094, Fax 759 7579, – rm – 240. AX **n**
Brasserie : **Meals** 17.95/29.00 **st.** and a la carte 7.95 – ***Zen Oriental :*** **Meals** 25.00/30.00 **st.** and a la carte – 11.95 – **392 rm** 145.00/159.00 **st.**, 4 suites – SB .

Forte Crest, Sipson Rd, West Drayton, UB7 0JU, 759 2323, Telex 934280, Fax 897 8659 – rm – 100. AV **c**
Sampans : **Meals** - Chinese - (dinner only) 15.50/21.95 **t.** and a la carte 7.50 – ***Tutto :*** **Meals** (carving rest.) 16.95 **st.** and a la carte 7.50 – 10.75 – **570 rm** 99.00/110.00, 2 suites – SB .

Excelsior Heathrow (Forte), Bath Rd, West Drayton, UB7 0DU, 759 6611, Telex 24525, Fax 759 3421, – rm – 700. AX **x**
Meals (carving rest.) 15.50/16.95 **st.** 7.25 – ***Wheeler's :*** **Meals** *(closed lunch Saturday and Sunday)* a la carte 24.95/32.95 **st.** 7.25 – 11.45 – **817 rm** 99.00/110.00 **st.**, 10 suites – SB .

Sheraton Heathrow, Colnbrook bypass, West Drayton, UB7 0HJ, 759 2424, Telex 851 934331, Fax 759 2091 – rm – 50.
Meals 18.50 **t.** and a la carte – 12.50 – **426 rm** 160.00/170.00 **t.**, 4 suites. AVX **a**

Forte Posthouse, Bath Rd, Hayes, UB3 5AJ, 759 2552, Fax 564 9265 – rm rest – 40. AX **i**
Meals a la carte approx. 15.00 **t.** 5.50 – **186 rm** 59.50/69.50 **st.**

Heathrow Park (Thistle), Bath Rd, Longford, West Drayton, UB7 0EQ, W : off A 4 759 2400, Telex 934093, Fax 759 5278 – rm – 700.
Meals (carving lunch) 12.75/15.75 **st.** and a la carte 5.50 – 8.75 – **306 rm** 75.00/160.00 **st.** – SB .

Gatwick W. Sussex S : 28 m. by A 23 and M 23 - **Train** from Victoria : Gatwick Express 404 T 30 – Crawley – 01293.
535353.
International Arrivals Concourse, South Terminal, RH6 0NP 560108.

London Gatwick Airport Hilton, South Terminal, RH6 0LL, 518080, Telex 877021, Fax 528980, – rm – 500. Y **u**
Meals 12.95/23.50 **st.** and a la carte 8.75 – 11.95 – **547 rm** 130.00/165.00 **st.**, 3 suites.

Ramada H. Gatwick, Povey Cross Rd, RH6 0BE, 820169, Telex 87440, Fax 820259, squash – rm – 180. Y **a**
Meals *(closed Saturday lunch)* 15.50/16.50 **st.** and a la carte – 10.50 – **250 rm** 80.00/90.00 **st.**, 5 suites.

Forte Crest, Gatwick Airport (North Terminal), RH6 0PH, 567070, Telex 87202, Fax 567739, – rm – 350. Y **e**
Meals 12.95/15.95 **st.** and dinner a la carte 6.95 – 9.95 – **450 rm** 99.00/110.00 **st.**, 6 suites – SB .

Forte Posthouse, Povey Cross Rd, RH6 0BA, 771621, Fax 771054, heated – rm rest – 120. Y **c**
Meals a la carte 13.00/22.85 **t.** 6.95 – 7.95 – **210 rm** 56.00 **t.** – SB .

CAMDEN Except where otherwise stated see pp. 4-7.

Bloomsbury - ✉ NW1/W1/WC1 - 0171.

34-37 Woburn Pl. WC1H 0JR ☎ 580 4599.

Holiday Inn Kings Cross, 1 Kings Cross Rd, WC1X 9HX, ☎ 833 3900, Fax 917 6163, squash - rm - 220. AE VISA JCB. MT **a**
Meals 17.95 **t.** (dinner) and a la carte 15.80/30.15 **t.** 6.00 - 9.75 - **397 rm** 99.00 **st.**, 8 suites.

Russell (Forte), Russell Sq., WC1B 5BE, ☎ 837 6470, Telex 24615, Fax 837 2857 - rm rest - 400. AE VISA JCB. LU **o**
Meals 13.50/16.50 **t.** - 10.50 - **326 rm** 120.00/160.00 **st.**, 2 suites - SB.

Grafton (Radisson Edwardian), 130 Tottenham Court Rd, W1P 9HP, ☎ 388 4131, Telex 297234, Fax 387 7394 - rm - 100. AE VISA JCB.
Meals *(closed Saturday lunch)* 18.50/35.00 **st.** and a la carte - 10.00 - **317 rm** 120.00/150.00 **st.**, 7 suites - SB. KU **n**

Marlborough (Radisson Edwardian), 9-14 Bloomsbury St., WC1B 3QD, ☎ 636 5601, Telex 298274, Fax 636 0532 - rest - 200. AE VISA JCB. LU **i**
Meals 16.95/35.00 **st.** and a la carte - 10.95 - **167 rm** 135.00/180.00 **st.**, 2 suites - SB.

Mountbatten (Radisson Edwardian), 20 Monmouth St., WC2H 9HD, ☎ 836 4300, Telex 298087, Fax 240 3540 - rm rest - 75. AE VISA JCB. p. 17 DV **o**
Meals *(closed lunch Saturday and Sunday)* 18.00/35.00 **st.** and a la carte - 13.50 - **121 rm** 160.00/210.00 **st.**, 6 suites - SB.

Kenilworth (Radisson Edwardian), 97 Great Russell St., WC1B 3LB, ☎ 637 3477, Telex 25842, Fax 631 3133 - rm rest - 100. AE VISA JCB. LU **a**
Meals (carving rest.) 16.95/35.00 **st.** and a la carte - 10.00 - **187 rm** 120.00/150.00 **st.**

Montague, 12-20 Montague St., WC1B 5BJ, ☎ 637 1001, Telex 23307, Fax 637 2506 - rm rest - 120. AE VISA JCB. LU **c**
closed 24 to 26 December - **Meals** 12.50 **t.** and dinner a la carte 6.00 - **107 rm** 99.00/170.00 **st.**, 2 suites.

Blooms, 7 Montague St., WC1B 5BP, ☎ 323 1717, Fax 636 6498 - AE VISA JCB. LU **n**
Meals (in bar) a la carte 14.00/23.50 **st.** 6.00 - **27 rm** 100.00/160.00 **st.** - SB.

Bloomsbury Park (Mount Charlotte), 126 Southampton Row, WC1B 5AD, ☎ 430 0434, Telex 25757, Fax 242 0665 - rm - 25. AE VISA JCB. LU **u**
Meals *(closed Friday to Sunday and Bank Holidays)* (dinner only) 13.95 **st.** and a la carte 4.70 - 8.50 - **95 rm** 84.00/140.00 **st.** - SB.

Bonnington, 92 Southampton Row, WC1B 4BH, ☎ 242 2828, Telex 261591, Fax 831 9170 - rm rest - 250. AE VISA JCB LU **s**
Meals *(closed lunch Saturday and Sunday)* 10.00/17.75 **st.** and a la carte 7.60 - **215 rm** 85.00/105.00 **st.**

Pied à Terre (Neat), 34 Charlotte St., W1P 1HJ, ☎ 636 1178, Fax 916 1171 - AE VISA JCB KU **e**
closed Saturday lunch, Sunday, last 2 weeks August, last week December and first week January - **Meals** 19.50/39.50 **st.** 7.00
Spec. Skate wing with poached egg, parsley sauce and potato salad, Duck breast baked in rösti potatoes with a leg and gizzard confit, Rice pudding with mango, lime purée and pineapple sorbet.

Neal Street, 26 Neal St., WC2H 9PS, ☎ 836 8368, Fax 497 1361 - AE VISA
closed Sunday and Bank Holidays - **Meals** a la carte 15.00/40.00 **t.** 6.50. p. 17 DV **s**

Mon Plaisir, 21 Monmouth St., WC2H 9DD, ☎ 836 7243, Fax 379 0121 - AE VISA JCB p. 17 DV **a**
closed Saturday lunch, Sunday, 1 week Christmas-New Year and Bank Holidays - **Meals** - French - 13.95 **st.** and a la carte 5.80.

Poons of Russell Square, 50 Woburn Pl., WC1H 0JZ, ☎ 580 1188 - AE VISA JCB LU **x**
closed 24 to 27 December - **Meals** - Chinese - 9.50/20.00 **t.** and a la carte.

Bleeding Heart, Bleeding Heart Yard, EC1N 8SJ, off Greville St., Hatton Garden ☎ 242 2056, Fax 831 1402, - AE VISA NU **e**
closed Saturday, Sunday and 24 December-4 January - **Meals** a la carte 16.85/23.70 **t.** 3.95.

Il Castelletto, 17 Bury Pl., WC1A 2IB, ☎ 405 2232 - AE VISA LU **r**
closed Saturday lunch, Sunday and Bank Holidays - **Meals** - Italian - 14.00 **t.** and a la carte 4.75.

Alfred, 245 Shaftesbury Av., WC2H 8EH, ☎ 240 2566, Fax 497 0672 - AE VISA p. 17 DV **u**
closed Sunday, Christmas-New Year and Bank Holidays - **Meals** - English - 15.90 **t.** and a la carte 15.85/22.40 **t.** 5.00.

Euston – ✉ WC1 – ☎ 0171.

Euston Plaza, 17/18 Upper Woburn Pl., WC1H 0HT, ☎ 383 4105, Fax 383 4106, – rm – 130. VISA JCB. KLT **e**
Meals 15.00 **t.** (dinner) and a la carte 12.25/26.40 **st.** – ☐ 9.50 – **150 rm** 112.00/129.00 **st.** – SB .

Hampstead – ✉ NW3 – ☎ 0171.

Winnington Rd, Hampstead ☎ 455 0203.

Swiss Cottage without rest., 4 Adamson Rd, NW3 3HP, ☎ 722 2281, Fax 483 4588, « Antique furniture » – – 50. AE VISA. GS **n**
55 rm ☐ 75.00/140.00 **st.**, 5 suites.

Forte Posthouse, 215 Haverstock Hill, NW3 4RB, ☎ 794 8121, Fax 435 5586 – rm – 30. AE VISA JCB ES **r**
Meals a la carte 15.40/23.85 **st.** 5.25 – ☐ 7.95 – **140 rm** 69.00 **st.** – SB .

Benihana, 100 Avenue Rd, NW3 3HF, ☎ 586 9508, Fax 586 6740 – . AE VISA JCB GS **o**
closed Monday lunch and 25 December – **Meals** - Japanese (Teppan-Yaki) - 8.45/13.95 **t.** and a la carte.

ZeNW3, 83-84 Hampstead High St., NW3 1RE, ☎ 794 7863, Fax 794 6956 – . AE VISA ES **a**
closed Christmas – **Meals** - Chinese - 12.00/24.50 **t.** and a la carte.

Orchard, 12a Belsize Terr., NW3 4AX, ☎ 794 4288 – . VISA ES **v**
closed Monday lunch, Sunday dinner and Bank Holidays – **Meals** - Italian - a la carte 18.90/26.50 **t.** 5.50.

Holborn – ✉ WC2 – ☎ 0171.

Drury Lane Moat House (Q.M.H.), 10 Drury Lane, High Holborn, WC2B 5RE, ☎ 208 9988, Telex 8811395, Fax 831 1548 – rm – 60. AE VISA JCB
Meals *(closed lunch Saturday, Sunday and Bank Holidays)* a la carte 14.00/20.95 **t.** 7.15 – ☐ 10.75 – **151 rm** 125.00/149.00 **st.**, 2 suites – SB . p. 17 DV **c**

Regent's Park – ✉ NW1 – ☎ 0171.

White House, Albany St., NW1 3UP, ☎ 387 1200, Telex 24111, Fax 388 0091, – rm rest – 110. AE VISA JCB. JT **o**
Meals 19.50/23.50 **t.** and a la carte 6.50 – ☐ 10.75 – **584 rm** 125.00/145.00 **st.**, 2 suites.

Odette's, 130 Regent's Park Rd, NW1 8XL, ☎ 586 5486 – AE VISA HS **i**
closed Saturday lunch, Sunday, 2 weeks Christmas and Bank Holidays – **Meals** 10.00 **t.** (lunch) and a la carte 15.50/28.50 **t.** 5.95.

Swiss Cottage – ✉ NW3 – ☎ 0171.

Regents Park Marriott, 128 King Henry's Rd, NW3 3ST, ☎ 722 7711, Fax 586 5822, – rm – 400. AE VISA JCB. GS **a**
Meals 18.95/15.95 **t.** and a la carte – ☐ 11.85 – **298 rm** 145.00/150.00 **s.**, 5 suites – SB .

Peter's Chateaubriand, 65 Fairfax Rd, NW6 4EE, ☎ 624 5804 – . AE VISA JCB FS **i**
closed Saturday lunch, 1-2 January and 26-27 December – **Meals** 10.95/12.95 **t.** and a la carte.

CITY OF LONDON – ☎ 0171 Except where otherwise stated see p. 7.

Tatsuso, 32 Broadgate Circle, EC2M 2QS, ☎ 638 5863, Fax 638 5864 – . AE VISA JCB PU **u**
closed Saturday, Sunday, and Bank Holidays – **Meals** - Japanese - (booking essential) 21.00/70.00 **t.** and a la carte.

Brasserie Rocque, 37 Broadgate Circle, EC2M 2QS, ☎ 638 7919, Fax 628 5899, – . AE VISA PU **u**
closed Saturday, Sunday and Bank Holidays – **Meals** (lunch only) 23.75 **t.** and a la carte 5.00.

Le Quai, Riverside Walkway, 1 Broken Wharf, EC4V 3QQ, off High Timber St. ☎ 236 6480, Fax 236 6479 – . AE VISA JCB OV **a**
closed Saturday, Sunday and 21 December-5 January – **Meals** - French - (dinner booking essential) 25.50/32.50 **t.**

Miyama, 17 Godliman St., EC4V 5BD, ☎ 489 1937, Fax 236 0325 – . AE VISA JCB OV **e**
closed Saturday dinner, Sunday and Bank Holidays – **Meals** - Japanese - 15.00/60.00 **t.** and a la carte 6.00.

Imperial City, Royal Exchange, Cornhill, EC3V 3LL, ☎ 626 3437, Fax 338 0125 – . AE VISA PV **a**
closed Saturday, Sunday and Bank Holidays – **Meals** - Chinese - 14.90/24.90 **t.** and a la carte.

Portico, 5 Philpot Lane, EC3M 8AQ, ☎ 929 2229, Fax 929 0924 – . AE VISA JCB PV **c**
closed Saturday, Sunday, 25-26 December and Bank Holidays – **Meals** - Italian - (lunch only) 10.95 **t.** and a la carte 21.50/24.35 **t.** 5.50.

HAMMERSMITH AND FULHAM p.8.

Fulham - SW6 - 0171.

La Reserve, 422-428 Fulham Rd, SW6 1DU, 385 8561, Fax 385 7662, « Contemporary decor » - rm FZ a
37 rm.

Blue Elephant, 4-6 Fulham Broadway, SW6 1AA, 385 6595, Fax 386 7665 - . AE VISA EZ z
closed Saturday lunch and 24 to 27 December - **Meals** - Thai - (booking essential) 29.00/34.00 **t.** and a la carte 6.25.

Mao Tai, 58 New Kings Rd., Parsons Green, SW6 4LS, 731 2520 - . AE VISA p. 12 BQ e
closed Saturday lunch and 25 to 27 December - **Meals** - Chinese (Szechuan) - 18.50 **t.** and a la carte.

Fleurie, 755 Fulham Rd, SW6 5UU, 371 0695 - AE VISA BQ n
Meals (lunch by arrangement Monday to Saturday) 14.95/16.50 **t.** and dinner a la carte.

Hammersmith - W6/W12/W14 - 0181.

River Café, Thames Wharf, Rainville Rd, W6 9HA, 381 8824, Fax 381 6217 - AE VISA
closed Sunday dinner, 25 December-1 January and Bank Holidays - **Meals** - Italian - a la carte 27.00/35.50 **t.** 7.50. DV r

Tandoori Nights, 319-321 King St., W6 9NH, 741 4328 - . AE VISA JCB p. 9 CV u
closed 25 and 26 December - **Meals** - Indian - 9.95/15.00 **st.** and a la carte 5.95.

Snows on the Green, 166 Shepherd's Bush Rd, Brook Green, W6 7PB, (0171) 603 2142, Fax 602 7553 - VISA p. 9 CV x
closed Saturday lunch, Sunday dinner, 10 days Christmas-New Year and Bank Holidays - **Meals** 12.50 **t.** (lunch) and a la carte 17.00/24.85 **t.** 5.00.

Brackenbury, 129-131 Brackenbury Rd, W6 0BQ, 748 0107, Fax 741 0905 - AE VISA p. 9 CV a
closed lunch Monday and Saturday, Sunday dinner, 10 days Christmas-New Year and Bank Holidays - **Meals** a la carte 14.50/18.25 **t.**

KENSINGTON and CHELSEA (Royal Borough of).

Chelsea - SW1/SW3/SW10 - 0171 - Except where otherwise stated see pp. 14 and 15.

Hyatt Carlton Tower, 2 Cadogan Pl., SW1X 9PY, 235 1234, Telex 21944, Fax 245 6570, <, , , , - rm - 150. AE VISA JCB. FR n
Chelsea Room* : Meals** 18.50/29.50 **t.** and a la carte - ***Rib Room (824 7053) **: Meals** 23.50/29.50 **t.** and a la carte - 15.50 - **194 rm** 225.00/270.00, 30 suites.

Sheraton Park Tower, 101 Knightsbridge, SW1X 7RN, 235 8050, Telex 917222, Fax 235 8231, < - rm - 60. AE VISA JCB. FQ v
Meals 22.50/35.00 **st.** and a la carte 7.50 - **267 rm** 220.00/285.00 **s.**, 22 suites.

Conrad London, Chelsea Harbour, SW10 0XG, 823 3000, Fax 351 6525, <, , , - rm - 200. AE VISA JCB. p. 13 CQ i
Meals 16.00/24.00 **t.** and a la carte 8.00 - 17.00, **159 suites** 150.00/280.00 - SB.

Durley House, 115 Sloane St., SW1X 9PJ, 235 5537, Fax 259 6977, « Tastefully furnished Georgian town house », , - . AE VISA. FS e
Meals (room service only) a la carte approx. 22.50 - 12.50 -, **11 suites** 195.00/300.00 **s.**

Capital, 22-24 Basil St., SW3 1AT, 589 5171, Fax 225 0011 - - 25. AE VISA. ER a
Meals 25.00/40.00 **st.** and a la carte 41.00/47.50 **st.** 7.95 - 14.00 - **48 rm** 167.00/290.00 **s.**
Spec. Grilled langoustines with ginger, lemon and cucumber, Roasted Scotch beef fillet with garlic, shallots and thyme, Assiette of vanilla.

Draycott, 24-26 Cadogan Gdns, SW3 2RP, 730 6466, Fax 730 0236, - . AE VISA JCB. FS c
Meals (room service only) - 12.95 - **25 rm** 100.00/250.00 **t.**

Cadogan, 75 Sloane St., SW1X 9SG, 235 7141, Fax 245 0994, , - rm rest - 40. AE VISA. FR e
Meals *(closed Saturday lunch)* 12.90/21.90 **t.** and a la carte 6.25 - 13.50 - **60 rm** 125.00/180.00 **st.**, 5 suites - SB.

Franklin, 28 Egerton Gdns., SW3 2DB, 584 5533, Fax 584 5449, « Tastefully furnished town house », - . AE VISA. DS e
Meals (room service only) a la carte 20.00/35.00 **st.** 7.00 - 12.50 - **35 rm** 120.00/210.00 **s.**, 1 suite.

Basil Street, 8 Basil St., SW3 1AH, ℘ 581 3311, Fax 581 3693 – 55. FQ **o**
Meals (carving lunch Saturday) 14.95/23.00 **t.** 6.00 – 12.50 – **92 rm** 125.00/185.00 **t.**, 1 suite.

Chelsea, 17-25 Sloane St., SW1X 9NU, ℘ 235 4377, Fax 235 3705 – rm – 100. FR **r**
Meals 14.95/19.50 **t.** and a la carte 7.00 – 12.50 – **219 rm** 145.00/155.00 **s.**, 5 suites.

Sydney House, 9-11 Sydney St., SW3 6PU, ℘ 376 7711, Fax 376 4233, « Tastefully furnished Victorian town house » – DT **a**
Meals (room service only) – 12.00 – **21 rm** 120.00/180.00 **s.**

Egerton House, 17-19 Egerton Terr., SW3 2BX, ℘ 589 2412, Fax 584 6540, « Tastefully furnished Victorian town house », – DR **e**
Meals (room service only) – 12.50 – **27 rm** 120.00/180.00, 1 suite.

Sloane, 29 Draycott Pl., SW3 2SH, ℘ 581 5757, Fax 584 1348, « Victorian town house, antiques » – ET **c**
Meals (room service only) a la carte 14.00/17.50 7.50 – 8.00 – **12 rm** 120.00/190.00.

Fenja without rest., 69 Cadogan Gdns, SW3 2RB, ℘ 589 7333, Fax 581 4958, – FS **r**
11.75 – **12 rm** 130.00/195.00 **t.**

Beaufort without rest., 33 Beaufort Gdns, SW3 1PP, ℘ 584 5252, Telex 929200, Fax 589 2834, « English floral watercolour collection » – ER **n**
28 rm 110.00/215.00 **s.**

Eleven Cadogan Gardens, 11 Cadogan Gdns, SW3 2RJ, ℘ 730 3426, Fax 730 5217, – FS **u**
55 rm, 5 suites.

Parkes without rest., 41 Beaufort Gdns., SW3 1PW, ℘ 581 9944, Fax 581 1999 – ER **x**
17 rm 98.00 **s.**, 16 suites 135.00/215.00 **s.**.

Knightsbridge, 12 Beaufort Gdns., SW3 1PT, ℘ 589 9271, Fax 823 9692 – ER **o**
Meals (room service only) – **44 rm** 80.00/120.00 **st.**, 6 suites.

Claverley without rest., 13-14 Beaufort Gdns, SW3 1PS, ℘ 589 8541, Fax 584 3410 – ER **o**
32 rm 65.00/180.00 **t.**

L'Hotel, 28 Basil St., SW3 1AT, ℘ 589 6286, Fax 225 0011 –
***Le Metro* : Meals** *(closed Sunday and Bank Holidays)* a la carte 12.45/18.00 **t.** – 6.50 – **12 rm** 145.00/160.00 **st.** ER **i**

XXXX ✿✿✿ **La Tante Claire** (Koffmann), 68-69 Royal Hospital Rd, SW3 4HP, ℘ 352 6045, Fax 352 3257 – EU **c**
closed Saturday, Sunday, 1 week Easter, last 3 weeks August and 1 week Christmas – **Meals** - French - (booking essential) 26.00/60.00 **st.** and a la carte 53.00/68.00 **st.**
Spec. Coquilles St.Jacques à la planche, sauce encre, Pied de cochon aux morilles, Croustade de pommes caramelisée.

XXX **Waltons,** 121 Walton St., SW3 2HP, ℘ 584 0204, Fax 581 2848 – DS **a**
closed 25 December dinner and 26 December – **Meals** 14.75/21.00 **t.** and a la carte 5.00.

XXX **Bibendum,** Michelin House, 81 Fulham Rd, SW3 6RD, ℘ 581 5817, Fax 823 7925 – DS **s**
closed 24 to 28 December – **Meals** 27.00 **t.** (lunch) and dinner a la carte 25.00/44.00 **t.** 5.95.

XXX ✿ **The Canteen,** Harbour Yard, Chelsea Harbour, SW10 0XD, ℘ 351 7330, Fax 351 6189 – p. 13 CQ **i**
Meals a la carte approx. 24.85 **t.**
Spec. Risotto of sea scallops Provençal, Pavé of halibut with fennel, watercress and a warm aioli dressing, Tarte Tatin of pears.

XXX **Fifth Floor** (at Harvey Nichols), Knightsbridge, SW1X 7RJ, ℘ 235 5250, Fax 823 2207 – FQ **a**
closed Sunday dinner and 25 and 26 December – **Meals** 21.50 **t.** and dinner a la carte 19.00/35.75 **t.** 10.00.

XXX ✿ **Aubergine** (Ramsay), 11 Park Walk, SW10 0AJ, ℘ 352 3449, Fax 351 1770 – CU **r**
closed Saturday lunch, Sunday, first 2 weeks August, 2 weeks Christmas and Bank Holidays – **Meals** (booking essential) 19.50/34.00 **t.** 9.00
Spec. Sautéed sea scallops with creamed fennel and a light ginger cream, Pot au feu of Bresse pigeon with stuffed cabbage, Three crème brûlées.

XXX **Turner's,** 87-89 Walton St., SW3 2HP, ℘ 584 6711, Fax 584 4441 –
closed Saturday lunch, 25 to 30 December and Bank Holidays – **Meals** 13.50/38.75 **st.** and a la carte 6.75. ES **n**

XXX **Chutney Mary,** 535 King's Rd, SW10 0SZ, ℘ 351 3113, Fax 351 7694 – p. 8 FZ **v**
closed 25 December dinner and 26 December – **Meals** - Anglo-Indian - a la carte 21.45/30.05 **t.**

XXX **Albero & Grana,** Chelsea Cloisters, 89 Sloane Av., SW3 3DX, ✆ 225 1048, Fax 581 3259 – ▤. AE VISA ET e
closed Sunday – **Meals** - Spanish - (dinner only) a la carte 25.50/40.00 **t.** 6.00.

XXX Benihana, 77 King's Rd, SW3 4NX, ✆ 376 7799, Fax 376 7377 – ▤ EU e
Meals - Japanese (Teppan-Yaki) rest.

XX ❀ **Fulham Road,** 257-259 Fulham Rd, SW3 6HY, ✆ 351 7823, Fax 376 4971 – AE VISA
closed Saturday lunch, Sunday, 1 week Christmas and Bank Holidays – **Meals** 19.00 **t.** (lunch) and a la carte 29.00/42.00 **t.** 7.00 CU a
Spec. Celeriac remoulade with pancetta, Assiette of duck with braised chicory, Papillotte of fruit with cinnamon ice cream.

XX **English Garden,** 10 Lincoln St., SW3 2TS, ✆ 584 7272 – ▤. AE VISA JCB ET x
closed 25 and 26 December – **Meals** - English - 14.75 **t.** (lunch) and a la carte 23.25/30.00 **t.** 5.00.

XX **Brasserie St. Quentin,** 243 Brompton Rd, SW3 2EP, ✆ 589 8005, Fax 584 6064 – ▤. AE VISA JCB DR a
Meals - French - a la carte 14.70/29.10 **t.** 4.90.

XX **Poissonnerie de l'Avenue,** 82 Sloane Av., SW3 3DZ, ✆ 589 2457, Fax 581 3360 – ▤. AE VISA JCB DS u
closed Sunday, Easter, 24 December-3 January and Bank Holidays – **Meals** - French Seafood - 16.50/26.00 **st.** and a la carte 5.50.

XX **Daphne's,** 112 Draycott Av., SW3 3AE, ✆ 589 4257, Fax 581 2232 – ▤. AE VISA
closed Christmas-New Year – **Meals** - Italian - a la carte 20.25/33.75 **t.** DS a

XX **La Finezza,** 62-64 Lower Sloane St., SW1N 8BP, ✆ 730 8639 – ▤. AE VISA FT v
closed Sunday and Bank Holidays – **Meals** - Italian - a la carte 22.50/43.00 **t.** 7.50.

XX **Grill St. Quentin,** 3 Yeoman's Row, SW3 2AL, ✆ 581 8377, Fax 584 6064 – ▤. AE VISA JCB ER r
Meals a la carte 14.30/29.80 **t.** 4.90.

XX **Busabong Too,** 1a Langton St., SW10 0JL, ✆ 352 7414 – ▤. AE VISA JCB
Meals - Thai - (dinner only) 24.95 **t.** and a la carte. p. 8 FZ x

XX **Toto's,** Walton House, Walton St., SW3 2JH, ✆ 589 0075 – AE VISA JCB ES a
closed 25 and 26 December – **Meals** - Italian - 19.50 **st.** (lunch) and a la carte approx. 35.00 **st.**

XX **Red,** 8 Egerton Garden Mews, SW3 2EH, ✆ 584 7007, Fax 589 3152 – AE VISA JCB
Meals - Chinese - 5.00/35.00 **t.** and a la carte 4.00. DR n

XX **Good Earth,** 233 Brompton Rd, SW3 2EP, ✆ 584 3658, Fax 823 8769 – ▤. AE VISA JCB
Meals - Chinese - 8.00/30.00 **t.** and a la carte 4.00. DR c

XX **Dan's,** 119 Sydney St., SW3 6NR, ✆ 352 2718, Fax 352 3265 – AE VISA DU s
closed Saturday lunch, Sunday and 1 week Christmas-New Year – **Meals** a la carte 15.50/26.00 **t.** 5.00.

Kensington – ✉ SW7/W8/W11/W14 – ☎ 0171 – Except where otherwise stated see pp. 8-11.

The Milestone without rest., 1-2 Kensington Court, W8 5DL, ✆ 917 1000, Fax 917 1010, – rm ▤ TV ☎. AE VISA. p. 14 AQ u
15.00 – **50 rm** 200.00/245.00 **st.**, 6 suites.

Halcyon, 81 Holland Park, W11 3RZ, ✆ 727 7288, Fax 229 8516 – ▤ TV ☎. AE VISA JCB. EX u
The Room : **Meals** *(closed Saturday lunch)* 21.00/32.00 **t.** – 13.80 – **40 rm** 165.00/250.00 **st.**, 3 suites.

Copthorne Tara, Scarsdale Pl., W8 5SR, ✆ 937 7211, Telex 918834, Fax 937 7100 – rm ▤ TV ☎ – 500. AE VISA JCB. FY u
Brasserie : **Meals** 17.50 **st.** and a la carte 6.90 – ***Jerome K. Jerome :*** **Meals** *(closed Sunday and Bank Holidays)* (dinner only) a la carte 25.30/43.00 **t.** 6.90 – 11.50 – **815 rm** 115.00/150.00 **st.**, 10 suites.

Kensington Park (Thistle), 16-32 De Vere Gdns, W8 5AG, ✆ 937 8080, Telex 929643, Fax 937 7616 – rm ▤ rest TV ☎ – 120. AE VISA. p. 14 BQ e
Moniques Brasserie : **Meals** 14.75 **t.** and a la carte – ***Cairngorm Grill :*** **Meals** *(closed Sunday and Monday)* (dinner only) 19.95 **t.** and a la carte 7.00 – 10.75 – **326 rm** 125.00/155.00 **t.**, 6 suites.

London Kensington Hilton, 179-199 Holland Park Av., W11 4UL, ✆ 603 3355, Fax 602 9397 – rm ▤ TV ☎ – 300. AE VISA JCB EX s
Meals 5.00/35.00 **t.** and a la carte 7.60 ***Hiroko :*** **Meals** - Japanese - *(closed Monday)* 15.00/32.00 **t.** and a la carte 7.00 – 13.00 – **602 rm** 130.00/150.00 **st.**, 1 suite.

Hilton National London Olympia, 380 Kensington High St., W14 8NL, ✆ 603 3333, Telex 22229, Fax 603 4846, – rm ▤ rest TV ☎ – 400. AE VISA JCB.
Meals (bar lunch Saturday) 12.95/30.00 **t.** and a la carte 8.95 – 11.75 – **395 rm** 115.00/125.00 **st.**, 10 suites – SB. EY a

Kensington Close (Forte), Wrights Lane, W8 5SP, ✆ 937 8170, Telex 23914, Fax 937 8289, squash – rm ▤ rest TV ☎ – 180. AE VISA. FY c
Meals 15.95 **st.** and a la carte – 10.00 – **530 rm** 105.00 – SB.

XX **Clarke's,** 124 Kensington Church St., W8 4BH, ✆ 221 9225, Fax 229 4564 – ⅔ ▤. AE VISA
closed Saturday, Sunday, 2 weeks August, 10 days Christmas and Bank Holidays – **Meals** 26.00/37.00 **st.** ₰ 6.00. EX **c**

XX **La Pomme d'Amour,** 128 Holland Park Av., W11 4UE, ✆ 229 8532, Fax 221 4096 – ▤. AE ⓓ VISA EX **e**
closed Saturday lunch and Sunday – **Meals** - French - 17.50/22.00 **t.** and a la carte.

XX **L'Escargot Doré,** 2-4 Thackeray St., W8 5ET, ✆ 937 8508, Fax 937 8508 – ▤. AE ⓓ VISA p. 14 AQR **e**
closed Saturday lunch, Sunday, 25-26 December and Bank Holidays – **Meals** - French - 15.50 **t.** and a la carte ₰ 5.80.

XX **Belvedere in Holland Park,** Holland House, off Abbotsbury Rd, W8 6LU, ✆ 602 1238, « 19C orangery in park » – ▤. AE ⓓ VISA JCB EY **u**
closed Sunday dinner, 25 December and 1 January – **Meals** a la carte 17.50/26.00 **t.**

XX **La Fenice,** 148 Holland Park Av., W11 4UE, ✆ 221 6090, Fax 221 4096 – ▤. AE ⓓ VISA EX **v**
closed Saturday lunch and Monday – **Meals** - Italian - 9.50/17.00 **t.** and a la carte ₰ 4.00.

XX **Launceston Place,** 1a Launceston Pl., W8 5RL, ✆ 937 6912, Fax 938 2412 – ▤. AE VISA p. 14 BR **a**
closed Saturday lunch, Sunday dinner and Bank Holidays – **Meals** 13.50/16.50 **t.** and a la carte.

XX **Arcadia,** Kensington Court, 35 Kensington High St., W8 5BA, ✆ 937 4294, Fax 937 4393 – ▤. AE ⓓ VISA p. 14 AQ **s**
closed lunch Saturday and Sunday, 25-26 December and 1 January – **Meals** 13.95 **t.** (lunch) and a la carte 24.00/25.00 **t.** ₰ 5.90.

XX **Boyd's,** 135 Kensington Church St., W8 7LP, ✆ 727 5452, Fax 221 0615 – ▤. AE ⓓ VISA p. 16 AZ **r**
closed Sunday, first 2 weeks January and 4 days Easter – **Meals** 15.00 **t.** (lunch) and a la carte 22.00/34.00 **t.** ₰ 6.50.

XX **Phoenicia,** 11-13 Abingdon Rd, W8 6AH, ✆ 937 0120, Fax 937 7668 – ▤. AE ⓓ VISA EY **n**
closed 24 and 25 December – **Meals** - Lebanese - (buffet lunch) a la carte 14.60/17.75 **t.** ₰ 5.00.

XX Shanghai, 38c-d Kensington Church St., W8 4BX, ✆ 938 2501 – ▤ FX **a**
Meals - Chinese rest.

X **Kensington Place,** 201 Kensington Church St., W8 7LX, ✆ 727 3184, Fax 229 2025 – ▤. VISA p. 16 AZ **z**
closed 3 days Christmas – **Meals** 13.50 **t.** (lunch) and a la carte 17.00/29.00 **t.** ₰ 4.75.

X **Cibo,** 3 Russell Gdns, W14 8EZ, ✆ 371 6271, Fax 602 1371 – AE ⓓ VISA EY **o**
closed lunch Saturday and Bank Holidays, Sunday dinner and 1 to 7 January – **Meals** - Italian - a la carte 20.00/30.00 **t.** ₰ 5.90.

X **Malabar,** 27 Uxbridge St., W8 7TQ, ✆ 727 8800 – VISA p. 16 AZ **e**
closed last week August and 4 days at Christmas – **Meals** - Indian - (booking essential) (buffet lunch Sunday) a la carte 14.15/26.80 **st.** ₰ 4.60.

North Kensington

– ✉ W2/W10/W11 – ☎ 0171 – Except where otherwise stated see pp. 4-7.

🏨 **Pembridge Court,** 34 Pembridge Gdns, W2 4DX, ✆ 229 9977, Fax 727 4982, « Collection of antique clothing » – |‡| ▤ rest TV ☎. AE ⓓ VISA p. 16 AZ **n**
Meals (residents only) (restricted menu) (dinner only) a la carte 12.95/19.40 **t.** ₰ 5.25 – **20 rm** ⊐ 100.00/160.00 **t.**

🏨 **Abbey Court** without rest., 20 Pembridge Gdns, W2 4DU, ✆ 221 7518, Fax 792 0858, « Tastefully furnished Victorian town house » – TV ☎. AE ⓓ VISA. ✻ p. 16 AZ **u**
22 rm ⊐ 80.00/160.00 **t.**

🏨 Portobello, 22 Stanley Gdns, W11 2NG, ✆ 727 2777, Fax 792 9641, « Attractive town house in Victorian terrace » – |‡| TV ☎ EV **n**
25 rm.

XXX ✻ **Leith's,** 92 Kensington Park Rd, W11 2PN, ✆ 229 4481 – ▤. AE ⓓ VISA JCB EV **e**
closed lunch Saturday to Monday, Sunday dinner, 18 August-1 September and 24 December-7 January – **Meals** 19.50 **t.** (lunch) and dinner a la carte 29.50/39.50 **t.** ₰ 7.75
Spec. Pan fried salmon fillet with cèpes, boulangère potatoes and oxtail broth, Pithivier of veal sweetbreads, crisp vegetables and hazelnut vinaigrette, Leith's traditional roast duckling with a light orange jus.

XX **Chez Moi,** 1 Addison Av., Holland Park, W11 4QS, ✆ 603 8267, Fax 603 3898 – ▤. AE ⓓ VISA p. 8 EX **n**
closed Saturday lunch, Sunday dinner and Bank Holidays – **Meals** - French - 15.00 **t.** (lunch) and a la carte 18.75/31.00 **t.** ₰ 4.80.

XX **Orsino,** 119 Portland Rd, W11 4LN, ✆ 221 3299, Fax 229 9414 – ▤ EX **x**
closed 24 and 25 December – **Meals** - Italian - 13.50 **t.** (lunch) and a la carte 21.80/26.50 **t.** ₰ 5.50.

XX **Park Inn,** 6 Wellington Terr., Bayswater Rd, W2 4LW, ✆ 229 3553, Fax 229 3553 – ▤. AE VISA p. 16 AZ **c**
Meals - Chinese Seafood (Peking) - 4.80/12.00 **t.** and a la carte ₰ 4.90.

L'Altro, 210 Kensington Park Rd, W11 1NR, ℘ 792 1066, Fax 792 1077 – ▤. AE VISA EUV **c**
closed Sunday dinner, Easter, 4 days Christmas and Bank Holidays – **Meals** - Italian - a la carte 20.25/34.50 **t.** 6.25.

192, 192 Kensington Park Rd, W11 2ES, ℘ 229 0482 – AE VISA EV **a**
closed 25 to 26 December and Bank Holidays – **Meals** a la carte 16.75/25.75 **t.**

Canal Brasserie, Canalot Studios, 222 Kensal Rd, W10 5BN, ℘ (0181) 960 2732 – VISA ET **c**
closed lunch Saturday and Sunday and dinner Monday and Tuesday – **Meals** a la carte 11.75/17.50 **t.**

South Kensington – ✉ SW5/SW7/W8 – 0171 – pp. 14 and 15.

Gloucester, 4-18 Harrington Gdns, SW7 4LH, ℘ 373 6030, Fax 373 0409 – rm ▤ TV – 400. AE VISA JCB. BS **r**
Meals a la carte 19.45/27.90 **st.** – 14.50 – **542 rm** 176.25/193.90 **st.**, 6 suites.

Harrington Hall, 5-25 Harrington Gdns, SW7 4JW, ℘ 396 9696, Group Telex 290603, Fax 396 9090, – rm ▤ TV – 250. AE VISA JCB. BT **n**
Wetherby's : **Meals** 16.00/18.50 **st.** and a la carte 7.00 – 11.00 – **200 rm** 120.00/165.00 **st.**

Pelham, 15 Cromwell Pl., SW7 2LA, ℘ 589 8288, Fax 584 8444, « Tastefully furnished Victorian town house » – ▤ TV. AE VISA. CS **z**
Kemps : **Meals** *(closed Sunday lunch and Saturday)* 12.50 **t.** (lunch) and a la carte 16.50/26.00 **t.** 6.50 – 11.50 – **34 rm** 120.00/170.00 **t.**, 3 suites.

Blakes, 33 Roland Gdns, SW7 3PF, ℘ 370 6701, Telex 8813500, Fax 373 0442, « Antique oriental furnishings » – ▤ rest TV. AE VISA. BU **n**
Meals a la carte 40.00/62.00 **st.** 9.00 – 17.50 – **45 rm** 135.00/495.00 **st.**, 6 suites.

Rembrandt, 11 Thurloe Pl., SW7 2RS, ℘ 589 8100, Telex 295828, Fax 225 3363, – rm ▤ rest TV – 250. AE VISA JCB. DS **x**
Meals 15.95 **st.** and a la carte 5.00 – 9.75 – **195 rm** 115.00/155.00 **st.** – SB.

Swallow International, Cromwell Rd, SW5 0TH, ℘ 973 1000, Telex 27260, Fax 244 8194, – rm ▤ rest TV – 200. AE VISA AS **c**
Meals 13.75/17.00 **st.** and a la carte 5.50 – 10.75 – **414 rm** 110.00/125.00 **st.**, 2 suites – SB.

Regency, 100 Queen's Gate, SW7 5AG, ℘ 370 4595, Telex 267594, Fax 370 5555, – rm ▤ rest TV – 100. AE VISA JCB. CT **e**
Meals *(closed lunch Saturday and Sunday)* 16.50/18.50 **st.** and a la carte 6.00 – 12.00 – **192 rm** 115.00 **s.**, 6 suites – SB.

Vanderbilt (Radisson Edwardian), 68-86 Cromwell Rd, SW7 5BT, ℘ 589 2424, Telex 946944, Fax 225 2293 – ▤ rest TV – 120. AE VISA JCB. BS **v**
Meals 13.50/35.00 **st.** and a la carte – 9.50 – **223 rm** 97.00/125.00 **st.** – SB.

Jury's Kensington, 109-113 Queen's Gate, SW7 5LR, ℘ 589 6300, Telex 262180, Fax 581 1492 – ▤ rest TV – 80. AE VISA. CT **i**
Meals (bar lunch)/dinner 17.95 **st.** and a la carte 5.25 – 10.50 – **171 rm** 110.00/225.00 **st.** – SB.

Forum (Inter-Con), 97 Cromwell Rd, SW7 4DN, ℘ 370 5757, Group Telex 919663, Fax 373 1448, ←, – rm ▤ rest TV – 400. AE VISA JCB. BS **x**
Meals 11.50/13.50 **st.** and a la carte 8.50 – 11.00 – **906 rm** 140.00/160.00 **st.**, 4 suites.

Gore, 189 Queen's Gate, SW7 5EX, ℘ 584 6601, Fax 589 8127, « Attractive decor » – rm TV. AE VISA JCB BR **n**
closed 25 and 26 December – ***Bistrot 190 :*** **Meals** (only members and residents may book) a la carte 14.00/23.00 **t.** 6.00 – (see also ***Downstairs at One Ninety*** below) – 9.50 – **54 rm** 112.00/218.00 **st.**

Number Sixteen without rest., 16 Sumner Pl., SW7 3EG, ℘ 589 5232, Fax 584 8615, « Attractively furnished Victorian town houses », – TV. AE VISA. CT **c**
8.00 – **36 rm** 68.00/155.00 **st.**

Cranley without rest., 10-12 Bina Gardens, SW5 0LA, ℘ 373 0123, Fax 373 9497, « Tasteful decor, antiques » – TV. AE VISA. BT **c**
12.00 – **32 rm** 120.00/140.00 **st.**, 4 suites.

John Howard, 4 Queen's Gate, SW7 5EH, ℘ 581 3011, Telex 8813397, Fax 589 8403 – ▤ TV. AE VISA JCB. BQ **i**
Meals *(closed Sunday)* (dinner only) 12.50 **t.** and a la carte – 9.50 – **43 rm** 79.00/99.00 **st.**, 9 suites.

Kensington Plaza, 61 Gloucester Rd, SW7 4PE, ℘ 584 8100, Telex 8950993, Fax 823 9175 – ▤ rest TV – 40. AE VISA. BS **e**
Mongolian Brasserie : **Meals** (dinner only) 18.00 **t.** 9.50 – 5.25 – **88 rm** 75.00/90.00 **st.**

Cranley Gardens without rest., 8 Cranley Gdns, SW7 3DB, ℘ 373 3232, Telex 894489, Fax 373 7944 – TV. AE VISA JCB BT **e**
5.50 – **85 rm** 65.00/95.00 **t.**

Five Sumner Place without rest., 5 Sumner Pl., SW7 3EE, 584 7586, Fax 823 9962 – TV. AE VISA JCB. DR **a**
13 rm 69.00/99.00 **s.**

Aster House without rest., 3 Sumner Pl., SW7 3EE, 581 5888, Fax 584 4925, – TV. VISA. CT **u**
12 rm 65.00/113.00 **st.**

Hotel 167 without rest., 167 Old Brompton Rd, SW5 0AN, 373 3221, Fax 373 3360 – TV. AE VISA JCB. BT **r**
6.50 – **19 rm** 60.00/82.00 **st.**

XXX **Bombay Brasserie,** Courtfield Close, 140 Gloucester Rd, SW7 4UH, 370 4040, Fax 835 1669, « Raj-style decor, conservatory garden » – VISA BS **a**
closed 25 and 26 December – **Meals** - Indian - (buffet lunch) 14.95 **t.** and dinner a la carte 19.50/24.00 **t.** 6.50.

XX **Hilaire,** 68 Old Brompton Rd, SW7 3LQ, 584 8993, Fax 581 2949 – AE VISA CT **n**
closed Saturday lunch, Sunday and Bank Holidays – **Meals** (booking essential) 20.50/28.50 **t.** and dinner a la carte 25.50/33.50 **t.** 8.00.

XX **Shaw's,** 119 Old Brompton Rd, SW7 3RN, 373 7774, Fax 370 5102 – AE VISA BT **v**
closed Saturday lunch, Sunday dinner, 1 week Easter, last 2 weeks August, 1 week Christmas-New Year and Bank Holidays – **Meals** 17.50/29.75 **t.** 9.50.

XX **Downstairs at One Ninety,** 190 Queen's Gate, SW7 5EU, 581 5666, Fax 581 8172 – AE VISA JCB BR **n**
closed Sunday – **Meals** - Seafood - (booking essential) (dinner only) a la carte 17.75/28.50 **t.**

XX **Khan's of Kensington,** 3 Harrington Rd, SW7 3ES, 581 2900, Fax 581 2900 – AE VISA CS **e**
closed 25 and 26 December – **Meals** - Indian - 7.50/30.00 **t.** and a la carte 3.95.

XX **Tui,** 19 Exhibition Rd, SW7 2HE, 584 8359 – AE VISA JCB CS **u**
closed 5 days at Christmas and Bank Holiday Mondays – **Meals** - Thai - 10.00 **st.** (lunch) and a la carte 13.50/20.20 4.10.

XX **Delhi Brasserie,** 134 Cromwell Rd, SW7 4HA, 370 7617, Fax 244 8639 – AE VISA AS **a**
closed 25 and 26 December – **Meals** - Indian - 15.95 **t.** and a la carte 8.95.

XX **Café Lazeez,** 93-95 Old Brompton Rd, SW7 3LD, 581 9993, Fax 581 8200 – AE VISA JCB CT **a**
Restaurant : **Meals** - North Indian - (dinner only) a la carte 11.65/22.75 **t.** 4.40.
X **Cafe : Meals** a la carte 11.65/22.75 **t.**

XX **Memories of India,** 18 Gloucester Rd, SW7 4RB, 589 6450 – AE VISA JCB BR **s**
closed 25 and 26 December – **Meals** - Indian - 14.50/20.00 **t.** and a la carte.

MERTON

Wimbledon – ✉ SW19 – 0181.

Cannizaro House (Thistle) , West Side, Wimbledon Common, SW19 4UF, 879 1464, Fax 879 7338, <, « 18C country house overlooking Cannizaro Park », – rm TV – 45. AE VISA JCB. DXY **x**
Meals 21.55/25.75 **t.** and a la carte – 9.75 – **44 rm** 115.00/175.00 **t.**, 2 suites – SB.

SOUTHWARK.

Bermondsey – ✉ SE1 – 0171.

XXX **Le Pont de la Tour,** 36d Shad Thames, Butlers Wharf, SE1 2YE, 403 8403, Fax 403 0267, <, , « Riverside setting » – AE VISA PX **c**
closed Good Friday and 4 days Christmas – **Meals** (in bar Saturday lunch) 26.50 **t.** (lunch) and dinner a la carte 27.00/37.25 **t.** 6.20.

XXX **Bengal Clipper,** Cardamom Building, Shad Thames, Butlers Wharf, SE1 2YE, 357 9001, Fax 357 9002 – AE VISA JCB PX **e**
Meals - Indian - 30.00 **t.** and a la carte.

X **Blue Print Café,** Design Museum, Shad Thames, Butlers Wharf, SE1 2YD, 378 7031, Fax 378 6540, <, « Riverside setting », – AE VISA PX **u**
closed Sunday dinner, 4 days at Christmas and 1 January – **Meals** a la carte 16.75/25.25 **t.**

X **Cantina Del Ponte,** 36c Shad Thames, Butlers Wharf, SE1 2YE, 403 5403, Fax 403 0267, <, , « Riverside setting » – AE VISA PX **c**
closed Sunday dinner, Good Friday and 5 days at Christmas – **Meals** - Italian-Mediterranean - a la carte 19.40/25.25 **t.**

X **Butlers Wharf Chop House,** 36e Shad Thames, Butlers Wharf, SE1 2YE, 403 3403, Fax 403 3414, « Riverside setting, <Tower Bridge » – AE VISA PX **n**
closed Saturday lunch, Sunday dinner, Good Friday and 1 January – **Meals** 22.75 **t.** (lunch) and dinner a la carte 17.45/27.75 **t.**

Dulwich - ✉ SE19 - ☎ 0181.

XX **Luigi's,** 129 Gipsy Hill, SE19 1QS, ☎ 670 1843 - ▤. AE ① VISA JCB FX **a**
Meals - Italian - a la carte 16.20/25.00 ⚱ 4.50.

Rotherhithe - ✉ SE16 - ☎ 0171.

Scandic Crown, 265 Rotherhithe St., Nelson Dock, SE16 1EJ, ☎ 231 1001, Telex 290295, Fax 231 0599, ←, ⅙, ≘s, ⊠, ✂ - |‡| ⇔ rm ▤ rest TV ☎ ♿ P - 🔬 350. AE ① VISA JCB. ⚘ GV **r**
closed 24 to 28 December - **Meals** 18.95 **st.** and dinner a la carte ⚱ 6.50 - ⊐ 9.50 - **384 rm** 95.00/115.00 **st.**, 2 suites.

Southwark - ✉ SE1 - ☎ 0171.

XX **La Truffe Noire,** 29 Tooley St., SE1 2QF, ☎ 378 0621, Fax 403 0689 - ▤. AE ① VISA JCB
closed Sunday, 23 December-3 January and Bank Holidays - **Meals** - French - 18.00/22.00 **t.** and a la carte ⚱ 5.00. PX **a**

X **Café dell'Ugo,** 56-58 Tooley St., SE1 2SZ, ☎ 407 6001, Fax 357 8806 - ▤. AE ① VISA
closed Sunday and Bank Holidays - **Meals** a la carte 16.15/26.85 **t.** ⚱ 4.00. PX **r**

WANDSWORTH

Battersea - ✉ SW8/SW11 - ☎ 0171.

XX **Ransome's Dock,** 35-37 Parkgate Rd, SW11 4NP, ☎ 223 1611, Fax 924 2614 - AE ① VISA p. 25 HZ **c**
closed Sunday dinner, 1 week August and Christmas - **Meals** 11.50 **t.** (lunch) and a la carte 17.50/24.75 **t.** ⚱ 5.50.

XX **Chada,** 208-210 Battersea Park Rd, SW11 4ND, ☎ 622 2209, Fax 924 2178 - ▤. AE ① VISA JCB CQ **x**
closed Saturday lunch and Bank Holidays - **Meals** - Thai - a la carte 17.25/25.90 **st.**

Putney - ✉ SW15 - ☎ 0181.

XX Royal China, 3 Chelverton Rd, SW15 1RN, ☎ 788 0907, Fax 785 2305 - ▤ AQ **a**
Meals - Chinese rest.

XX **Del Buongustaio,** 283 Putney Bridge Rd, SW15 2PT, ☎ 780 9361, Fax 789 9659 - ▤. AE VISA AQ **e**
closed Saturday lunch, Sunday June-mid September and 10 days Christmas-New Year - **Meals** - Italian - 9.50 **t.** (lunch) and a la carte 17.65/19.80 **t.** ⚱ 5.80.

Wandsworth - ✉ SW12/SW17/SW18 - ☎ 0181.

XX **Tabaq,** 47 Balham Hill, SW12 9DR, ☎ 673 7820, Fax 673 2701 - ▤. AE ① VISA JCB DR **v**
closed Sunday - **Meals** - Indian - 9.25 **t.** (lunch) and a la carte 11.70/27.50 **t.** ⚱ 4.25.

XX **Chez Bruce,** 2 Bellevue Rd, SW17 7EG, ☎ 672 0114 - ▤. AE ① VISA CR **e**
closed lunch Monday and Saturday, Sunday dinner, 1 week Christmas and Bank Holidays - **Meals** 15.00/22.00 **t.**

X **Bombay Bicycle Club,** 95 Nightingale Lane, SW12 8NX, ☎ 673 6217 - AE VISA DR **o**
Meals - Indian - (dinner only) 15.00 **t.** and a la carte ⚱ 5.75.

WESTMINSTER (City of)

Bayswater and Maida Vale - ✉ W2/W9 - ☎ 0171 - Except where otherwise stated see pp. 16 and 17.

Royal Lancaster, Lancaster Terr., W2 2TY, ☎ 262 6737, Telex 24822, Fax 724 3191, ← - |‡| ⇔ rm ▤ TV ☎ P - 🔬 1400. AE ① VISA JCB. ⚘ DZ **e**
La Rosette : **Meals** 22.50/27.50 **t.** and a la carte ⚱ 8.00 - ***Pavement Cafe :*** **Meals** a la carte 15.10/26.85 **t.** ⚱ 8.00 - ⊐ 14.50 - **398 rm** 154.00/170.00 **st.**, 20 suites - SB.

London Metropole, Edgware Rd, W2 1JU, ☎ 402 4141, Telex 23711, Fax 724 8866, ←, ⅙, ≘s, ⊠ - |‡| ⇔ rm ▤ TV ☎ - 🔬 1200. AE ① VISA JCB. ⚘ p. 5 GU **c**
Meals (buffet rest.) - (see also ***Aspects*** below) - ⊐ 14.95 - **719 rm** 145.00/210.00 **st.**, 26 suites.

Whites (Thistle), Bayswater Rd, 90-92 Lancaster Gate, W2 3NR, ☎ 262 2711, Telex 24771, Fax 262 2147 - |‡| ⇔ rm ▤ TV ☎. AE ① VISA JCB. ⚘ CZ **v**
Meals *(closed Saturday lunch)* 16.00/21.50 **t.** and a la carte ⚱ 7.15 - ⊐ 11.25 - **52 rm** 155.00/235.00 **t.**, 2 suites - SB.

London Embassy (Jarvis), 150 Bayswater Rd, W2 4RT, ☎ 229 1212, Fax 229 2623 - |‡| ⇔ rm ▤ rest TV ☎ P - 🔬 60. AE ① VISA BZ **o**
Meals (carving rest.) 15.95 **st.** and a la carte - ⊐ 9.50 - **192 rm** 99.00/119.00 **st.**, 1 suite.

Plaza on Hyde Park (Hilton), 1-7 Lancaster Gate, W2 3LG, ☎ 262 5022, Telex 8954372, Fax 724 8666 - |‡| ⇔ rm TV ☎ - 🔬 30. AE ① VISA JCB. ⚘ DZ **r**
Meals 12.75 **st.** and a la carte ⚱ 6.70 - **402 rm** ⊐ 90.00/103.00 **st.** - SB.

Stakis London Coburg, 129 Bayswater Rd, W2 4RJ, ✆ 221 2217, Group Telex 268235, Fax 229 0557 – rm rest – 100. AE VISA JCB. BZ **c**
Meals (dinner only) 15.00 **t.** and a la carte 4.75 – 8.50 – **131 rm** 88.00/99.00 **st.**, 1 suite – SB.

Hyde Park Towers, 41-51 Inverness Terr., W2 3JN, ✆ 221 8484, Fax 792 3201 – rest – 45. AE VISA BZ **r**
Meals 11.00/15.00 **st.** and a la carte – 7.50 – **115 rm** 86.00/120.00 **st.**

Queen's Park, 48 Queensborough Terr., W2 3SS, ✆ 229 8080, Fax 792 1330 – rest – 80. AE VISA JCB. CZ **s**
Meals (dinner only) 15.00 **st.** and a la carte 6.00 – 7.50 – **86 rm** 90.00/110.00 **st.**

Mornington without rest., 12 Lancaster Gate, W2 3LG, ✆ 262 7361, Fax 706 1028 – rm. AE VISA DZ **s**
68 rm 85.00/115.00 **st.**

Phoenix without rest., 1 Kensington Garden Sq., W2 4BH, ✆ 229 2494, Telex 298854, Fax 727 1419 – . AE VISA JCB. BZ **e**
5.50 – **125 rm** 69.00/89.00 **st.**

XXX **Aspects** (at London Metropole H.), Edgware Rd, W2 1JU, ✆ 402 4141, Telex 23711, Fax 724 8866, ≤ London – . AE VISA JCB p. 5 GU **c**
closed Saturday lunch, Sunday and Bank Holidays – **Meals** 19.95/29.95 **t.** and a la carte 8.75.

XX **Poons,** Unit 205, Whiteleys, Queensway, W2 4YN, ✆ 792 2884 – . AE VISA
closed 24 to 27 December – **Meals** - Chinese - 10.00/15.00 **t.** and a la carte. BZ **x**

XX **Al San Vincenzo,** 30 Connaught St., W2 2AE, ✆ 262 9623 – VISA EZ **o**
closed Saturday lunch and Sunday – **Meals** - Italian - (booking essential) a la carte 25.00/32.50 **t.** 7.50.

X **L'Accento,** 16 Garway Rd, W2 4NH, ✆ 243 2201, Fax 243 2201 – VISA JCB BZ **a**
Meals - Italian - 14.00 **t.** and a la carte 16.00/23.50 **t.** 6.50.

Belgravia – ✉ SW1 – 0171 – Except where otherwise stated see pp. 14 and 15.

Lanesborough, 1 Lanesborough Pl., SW1X 7TA, ✆ 259 5599, Telex 911866, Fax 259 5606, – rm – 90. AE VISA JCB. p. 9 IY **a**
The Conservatory : **Meals** 23.00/29.50 **st.** and a la carte – 17.00 – **86 rm** 185.00/350.00 **s.**, 9 suites.

Berkeley, Wilton Pl., SW1X 7RL, ✆ 235 6000, Telex 919252, Fax 235 4330, – – 220. AE VISA JCB. FQ **e**
Restaurant : **Meals** *(closed Saturday)* 23.00/25.50 **st.** and a la carte 8.00 – 17.00 – **132 rm** 192.00/304.00 **s.**, 27 suites.

✿ **Halkin,** 5 Halkin St., SW1X 7DJ, ✆ 333 1000, Fax 333 1100, « Contemporary interior design » – rm – 25. AE VISA JCB. AV **a**
Meals - Italian - *(closed lunch Saturday and Sunday and 25-26 December)* 36.50/45.00 **st.** and a la carte 34.00/45.00 **st.** 9.50 – 13.50 – **36 rm** 200.00/250.00 **s.**, 5 suites – SB
Spec. Pan fried foie gras with Castelluccio lentils, Ravioli with scallops and parsley purée, Roasted sea bass with cold tomato soup, sour cream and caviar.

Sheraton Belgravia, 20 Chesham Pl., SW1X 8HQ, ✆ 235 6040, Telex 919020, Fax 259 6243 – rm – 40. AE VISA JCB. FR **u**
Meals *(closed Saturday lunch)* 21.95 **st.** (lunch) and a la carte 22.00/32.00 **st.** 5.50 – 11.50 – **82 rm** 170.00/215.00 **s.**, 7 suites – SB.

Lowndes (Hyatt), 21 Lowndes St., SW1X 9ES, ✆ 823 1234, Telex 919065, Fax 235 1154, – rm – 25. AE VISA JCB. FR **i**
Brasserie 21 : **Meals** a la carte approx. 16.45 **t.** 8.25 – 12.25 – **77 rm** 190.00 **s.**, 1 suite.

XX **Zafferano,** 15 Lowndes St., SW1X 9ES, ✆ 235 5800, Fax 235 1971 – . AE VISA JCB FR **i**
closed Saturday lunch, Sunday and 2 weeks August – **Meals** - Italian - 13.50/21.50 **t.** 8.00.

XX **Al Bustan,** 27 Motcomb St., SW1X 8JU, ✆ 235 8277, Fax 235 1668 – . AE VISA FR **z**
closed 25 December and 1 January – **Meals** - Lebanese - 15.00/35.00 **t.** and a la carte 18.50/21.00 **t.** 6.00.

XX **Motcombs,** 26 Motcomb St., SW1X 8JU, ✆ 235 6382, Fax 245 6351 – . AE VISA FR **z**
closed Saturday lunch, Sunday, Easter and Bank Holidays – **Meals** 14.75 **t.** (lunch) and a la carte.

Hyde Park and Knightsbridge – ✉ SW1/SW7 – 0171 – pp. 14 and 15.

Hyde Park (Forte), 66 Knightsbridge, SW1X 7LA, ✆ 235 2000, Fax 235 4552, ≤, – rm – 250. AE VISA JCB. FQ **x**
Park Room : **Meals** - Italian - 26.00/38.00 **t.** and a la carte 10.00 – (see also ***The Restaurant, Marco Pierre White*** below) – 15.00 – **166 rm** 205.00/255.00 **s.**, 19 suites – SB.

Knightsbridge Green without rest., 159 Knightsbridge, SW1X 7PD, ✆ 584 6274, Fax 225 1635 – . AE VISA. EQ **z**
closed 4 days at Christmas – 9.50 – **12 rm** 80.00/110.00 **st.**, 12 suites 125.00 **st.**.

XXXX ⚜⚜⚜ **The Restaurant, Marco Pierre White,** (at Hyde Park H.), 66 Knightsbridge, SW1X 7LA, ✆ 259 5380, Fax 235 4552 – ▤. AE ⓓ VISA FQ **x**
closed Saturday lunch, Sunday, 2 weeks August, 2 weeks Christmas and Bank Holidays – **Meals** (booking essential) 29.50/70.00 **t.** 16.00
Spec. Ballotine of salmon with crayfish, herbs, fromage blanc and caviar, Panaché of sea scallops, sauce Nero, Soufflé of bitter chocolate with a bitter chocolate sauce.

XXX **Pearl,** 22 Brompton Rd, SW1X 7QN, ✆ 225 3888, Fax 225 0252 – ▤. AE ⓓ JCB EQ **e**
closed 24 to 26 December – **Meals** - Chinese - 20.00 **t.** and a la carte 5.00.

Mayfair – ✉ W1 – ☎ 0171 – pp. 12 and 13.

Dorchester, Park Lane, W1A 2HJ, ✆ 629 8888, Telex 887704, Fax 409 0114, – rm ▤ TV ☎ & – 500. AE ⓓ VISA JCB. BN **a**
Grill Room : **Meals** - English - 24.50/32.00 **st.** and a la carte 27.50/44.00 **st.** 12.00 – (see also ***Oriental*** below) – 16.00 – **195 rm** 210.00/265.00 **s.**, 49 suites – SB .

Claridge's, Brook St., W1A 2JQ, ✆ 629 8860, Telex 21872, Fax 499 2210 – rm ▤ TV ☎ & – 200. AE ⓓ VISA JCB. BL **c**
Restaurant : **Meals** 29.00/45.00 **st.** and a la carte 10.00 – ***Causerie :*** **Meals** *(closed Saturday, Sunday and Bank Holidays)* 19.50 **st.** (dinner) and a la carte 28.50/37.50 **st.** 10.00 – 16.50 – **142 rm** 220.00/295.00 **s.**, 63 suites – SB .

Four Seasons, Hamilton Pl., Park Lane, W1A 1AZ, ✆ 499 0888, Telex 22771, Fax 493 1895, – rm ▤ TV ☎ – 500. AE ⓓ VISA JCB. BP **a**
Lanes : **Meals** 22.75/25.00 **st.** and dinner a la carte 22.50/57.50 **st.** 7.50 – (see also ***Four Seasons*** below) – 15.50 – **201 rm** 210.00/275.00 **s.**, 26 suites.

Le Meridien Piccadilly (Forte), 21 Piccadilly, W1V 0BH, ✆ 734 8000, Telex 25795, Fax 437 3574, , squash – rm ▤ TV ☎ & – 250. AE ⓓ VISA JCB.
Terrace Garden : **Meals** 16.50/19.50 **t.** and a la carte 8.00 – (see also ***Oak Room*** below) – 14.75 – **248 rm** 215.00/255.00, 18 suites. EM **a**

Grosvenor House (Forte), Park Lane, W1A 3AA, ✆ 499 6363, Telex 24871, Fax 493 3341, – rm ▤ TV ☎ & – 1500. AE ⓓ VISA JCB. AM **a**
Café Nico : **Meals** 21.00/26.00 **st.** and a la carte – ***Pasta Vino :*** **Meals** *(closed Saturday lunch and Sunday)* a la carte 21.50/33.00 **t.** 8.00 – (see also ***Chez Nico at Ninety Park Lane*** below) – 15.50 – **383 rm** 195.00/295.00, 71 suites.

London Hilton on Park Lane, 22 Park Lane, W1Y 4BE, ✆ 493 8000, Telex 24873, Fax 493 4957, ≤ Panoramic view of London, – rm ▤ TV ☎ & – 1000. AE ⓓ VISA JCB. BP **e**
Trader Vics (✆ 208 4113) **: Meals** *(closed Saturday lunch and Sunday dinner)* 12.00 **t.** (lunch) and a la carte 24.00/33.00 **t.** – ***Park Brasserie :*** **Meals** a la carte 23.70/31.45 **t.** – (see also ***Windows*** below) – 14.95 – **395 rm** 195.00/300.00 **st.**, 52 suites.

⚜ **Connaught,** Carlos Pl., W1Y 6AL, ✆ 499 7070, Fax 495 3262 – ▤ rest TV ☎. AE ⓓ VISA. BM **e**
The Restaurant : **Meals** (booking essential) 25.00/35.00 **t.** and a la carte 24.60/72.30 **t.** 11.00 – ***Grill Room :*** **Meals** *(closed lunch Saturday and Sunday)* (booking essential) 25.00/35.00 **t.** and a la carte 24.60/72.30 **t.** 11.00 – **66 rm** 198.00/265.00 **s.**, 24 suites
Spec. Sole "Jubilee", Prelude gourmande Connaught, Sherry trifle "Wally Ladd".

47 Park Street, 47 Park St., W1Y 4EB, ✆ 491 7282, Fax 491 7281 – ▤ TV ☎. AE ⓓ VISA JCB. AM **c**
Meals (room service) – (see also ***Le Gavroche*** below) – 17.00 –, **52 suites** 245.00/550.00 **s.**

Brown's (Forte), 29-34 Albemarle St., W1X 4BP, ✆ 493 6020, Fax 493 9381 – rm TV ☎ – 70. AE ⓓ VISA JCB. DM **e**
Meals (bar lunch Saturday) 23.65/32.00 **t.** and a la carte 9.50 – 15.00 – **110 rm** 195.00/225.00, 6 suites.

Park Lane, Piccadilly, W1Y 8BX, ✆ 499 6321, Telex 21533, Fax 499 1965, – rm TV ☎ Ⓟ – 300. AE ⓓ VISA JCB. CP **x**
Brasserie on the Park : **Meals** a la carte 15.75/31.50 **st.** – (see also ***Bracewells*** below) – 14.25 – **278 rm** 152.75/246.75 **st.**, 30 suites.

Britannia (Inter-Con), Grosvenor Sq., W1A 3AN, ✆ 629 9400, Telex 23941, Fax 629 7736, – rm ▤ TV ☎ – 100. AE ⓓ VISA JCB. BM **x**
Adams : **Meals** 17.50/19.50 **t.** and a la carte 6.50 – ***Best of Both Worlds :*** **Meals** 17.95 **t.** and a la carte 6.50 – (see also ***Shogun*** below) – 13.95 – **305 rm** 145.00/230.00, 12 suites.

Westbury (Forte), Conduit St., W1A 4UH, ✆ 629 7755, Telex 24378, Fax 495 1163 – rm ▤ TV ☎ – 120. AE ⓓ VISA JCB DM **a**
La Mediterranée 22.50 **t.** and a la carte 8.00 – 14.50 – **231 rm** 145.00/185.00 **st.**, 13 suites – SB .

May Fair Inter-Continental, Stratton St., W1A 2AN, ✆ 629 7777, Telex 262526, Fax 629 1459, – rm ▤ TV ☎ & – 290. AE ⓓ VISA JCB.
Meals – (see ***The Chateau*** below) – 14.50 – **262 rm** 185.00/320.00, 25 suites. DN **z**

Inter-Continental, 1 Hamilton Pl., Hyde Park Corner, W1V 0QY, ✆ 409 3131, Telex 25853, Fax 409 7460, – rm ▤ TV ☎ & – 1000. AE ⓓ VISA JCB. BP **o**
Meals 13.00 **s.** (dinner) and a la carte 20.00/50.00 **s.** 8.75 – (see also ***Le Soufflé*** below) – 15.00 – **426 rm** 240.00 **s.**, 34 suites – SB .

Athenaeum, 116 Piccadilly, W1V 0BJ, ✆ 499 3464, Fax 493 1860, Fă, ≘ - |‡| ⇹ rm ▤ TV ☎ - 55. AE VISA. ✂ CP **s**
***Bulloch's at 116 :* Meals** *(closed lunch Saturday and Sunday)* 29.00/42.00 **t.** and a la carte 9.00 - 14.50 - **111 rm** 175.00/185.00, 33 suites.

Marriott, Duke St., Grosvenor Sq., W1A 4AW, ✆ 493 1232, Telex 268101, Fax 491 3201, Fă - |‡| ⇹ rm ▤ TV ☎ ♿ - 600. AE VISA JCB. ✂ BL **a**
***Diplomat :* Meals** *(closed Saturday lunch)* 19.50 **t.** (lunch) and a la carte 14.25/26.50 **t.** 8.25 - 12.25 - **212 rm** 200.00 **s.**, 11 suites - SB.

Chesterfield, 35 Charles St., W1X 8LX, ✆ 491 2622, Fax 491 4793 - |‡| ⇹ rm ▤ rest TV ☎ - 110. AE VISA JCB. ✂ CN **c**
***Butlers :* Meals** *(closed Saturday lunch)* 10.00/23.50 **t.** and a la carte 7.95 - 10.95 - **106 rm** 130.00/199.00 **s.**, 4 suites.

Holiday Inn, 3 Berkeley St., W1X 6NE, ✆ 493 8282, Telex 24561, Fax 629 2827 - |‡| ⇹ rm ▤ TV ☎ - 60. AE VISA JCB. ✂ DN **r**
Meals 15.75/19.50 **st.** and a la carte 9.50 - 10.95 - **183 rm** 150.00/165.00 **st.**, 2 suites.

Washington, 5-7 Curzon St., W1Y 8DT, ✆ 499 7000, Telex 24540, Fax 495 6172 - |‡| ⇹ rm ▤ TV ☎ - 80. AE VISA JCB. ✂ CN **s**
Meals *(closed lunch Saturday and Sunday)* 19.95 **st.** (dinner) and a la carte 7.95 - 10.95 - **169 rm** 175.00/195.00 **st.**, 4 suites.

Flemings, 7-12 Half Moon St., W1Y 7RA, ✆ 499 2964, Fax 629 4063 - |‡| ▤ rest TV ☎ - 45. AE VISA JCB. ✂ CN **z**
Meals 9.00/25.00 **st.** and a la carte 8.75 - 10.50 - **120 rm** 120.00/185.00 **st.**, 10 suites.

Green Park, Half Moon St., W1Y 8BP, ✆ 629 7522, Telex 28856, Fax 491 8971 - |‡| ⇹ rm TV ☎ - 70. AE VISA JCB. ✂ CN **a**
Meals *(closed lunch Saturday and Sunday)* 12.95/14.50 **st.** and a la carte 7.00 - 10.25 - **160 rm** 120.00/174.00 **st.**, 1 suite.

London Mews Hilton, 2 Stanhope Row, W1Y 7HE, ✆ 493 7222, Fax 629 9423 - |‡| ⇹ rm ▤ TV ☎ 🚗 - 50. AE VISA JCB BP **u**
Meals (restricted menu) a la carte 14.20/24.75 **st.** - 11.75 - **71 rm** 155.00/195.00 **t.**, 1 suite.

XXXXX **Oak Room** (at Le Meridien Piccadilly H.), 21 Piccadilly, W1V 0BH, ✆ 465 1640, Telex 25795, Fax 437 3574 - ▤. AE VISA JCB EM **a**
closed Saturday lunch, Sunday, 3 weeks August, 26 to 30 December and Bank Holidays - **Meals** - French - 25.00/46.00 **t.** and a la carte 40.50/48.50 **t.**

XXXXX ✿✿✿ **Chez Nico at Ninety Park Lane** (Ladenis) (at Grosvenor House H.), Park Lane, W1A 3AA, ✆ 409 1290, Fax 355 4877 - ▤. AE VISA AM **e**
closed Saturday lunch, Sunday, 4 days at Easter, 10 days at Christmas and Bank Holiday Mondays - **Meals** - French - (booking essential) 29.00/65.00 **st.**
Spec. Rosette of scallops, Sea bass with olive crust, Assiette gourmande.

XXXX ✿✿ **Le Gavroche** (Roux), 43 Upper Brook St., W1Y 1PF, ✆ 408 0881, Fax 409 0939 - ▤. AE VISA AM **c**
closed Saturday, Sunday, 23 December-2 January and Bank Holidays - **Meals** - French - (booking essential) 37.00/75.00 **st.** and a la carte 50.60/87.50 **st.** 10.00
Spec. Ragoût de langoustines et pied de cochon à la graine de moutarde, Pigeonneau en vessie aux deux céleris, Parfait au chocolat blanc et framboises.

XXXX ✿ **Oriental** (at Dorchester H.), Park Lane, W1A 2HJ, ✆ 629 8888, Telex 887704, Fax 409 0114 - ▤. AE VISA JCB BN **a**
closed Saturday lunch, Sunday and August - **Meals** - Chinese (Canton) - 22.50/32.00 **st.** and a la carte 26.80/62.50 **st.** 12.00
Spec. Shredded chicken and cucumber served cold with sesame mustard sauce, Deep fried sole with chilli bean sauce and asparagus tips "Oriental style", Stir fried beef with lemon grass and black pepper.

XXXX ✿ **Four Seasons** (at Four Seasons H.), Hamilton Pl., Park Lane, W1A 1AZ, ✆ 499 0888, Telex 22771, Fax 493 1895 - |‡| ▤ 🚗. AE VISA JCB BP **a**
Meals 19.50/45.00 **st.** and a la carte 39.25/52.25 **st.** 7.50
Spec. Cassoulet terrine with a flageolet bean vinaigrette, Cannelloni of salmon, aubergine and basil with a tomato butter sauce, Raspberry crunch with an almond and pistachio cream.

XXXX **Windows** (at London Hilton on Park Lane), 22 Park Lane, W1Y 4BE, ✆ 493 8000, ≤ London - ▤. AE VISA JCB BP **e**
closed Sunday dinner - **Meals** (buffet lunch Sunday) 35.95/44.00 **t.** and dinner a la carte.

XXXX ✿ **Les Saveurs,** 37a Curzon St., W1Y 7AF, ✆ 491 8919, Fax 491 3658 - ▤. AE VISA BN **o**
closed Saturday, Sunday, 2 weeks August, 24 December-9 January and Bank Holidays - **Meals** - French - 17.00/42.00 **t.** 9.00
Spec. Terrine of duck foie gras with marinated aubergine, Scallops smoked 'a la minute' with horseradish cream and potatoes, Warm chocolate and pistachio fondant.

XXXX **Le Soufflé** (at Inter-Continental H.), 1 Hamilton Pl., Hyde Park Corner, W1V 0QY, ✆ 409 3131, Telex 25853, Fax 409 7460 - ▤ 🚗. AE VISA JCB BP **o**
closed Saturday lunch, Sunday dinner, Monday and 2 weeks Christmas-New Year - **Meals** 27.50/43.00 **t.** and a la carte 10.00.

XXX **Princess Garden,** 8-10 North Audley St., W1Y 1WF, ☎ 493 3223, Fax 629 3130 – ▤. AE ⓓ VISA JCB AL z
closed 1 week Christmas – **Meals** - Chinese (Peking, Szechuan) - 35.00/55.00 **t.** and a la carte 🍷 8.00.

XXX **Bracewells** (at Park Lane H.), Piccadilly, W1Y 8BX, ☎ 753 6725, Fax 499 1965 – Ⓟ. AE ⓓ VISA JCB CP x
closed Saturday lunch, Sunday and August – **Meals** 19.50 **st.** (lunch) and a la carte 24.75/32.75 **st.** 🍷 7.50.

XXX **The Chateau** (at May Fair Inter-Continental H.), Stratton St., W1A 2AN, ☎ 915 2842, Fax 629 1459 – ▤. AE ⓓ VISA JCB DN z
Meals 22.00/29.50 **st.** and a la carte 🍷 8.00.

XXX **Scotts,** 20 Mount St., W1Y 6HE, ☎ 629 5248, Fax 499 8246 – ▤. AE ⓓ VISA JCB
closed Saturday lunch, Sunday and Bank Holidays – **Meals** - Seafood - 15.50 **t.** and a la carte 🍷 4.75. BM a

XXX **Zen Central,** 20 Queen St., W1X 7PJ, ☎ 629 8089, Fax 493 6181 – ▤. AE ⓓ VISA
closed 4 days at Christmas – **Meals** - Chinese - 28.00/42.00 **t.** and a la carte. CN x

XX **Tamarind,** 20 Queen St., W1X 7PJ, ☎ 629 3561, Fax 499 5034 – AE ⓓ VISA JCB
closed Saturday lunch and 25 to 29 December – **Meals** - Indian - 13.50 **t.** (lunch) and a la carte 22.75/27.75 **t.** 🍷 8.00. CN e

XX ✿ **Greenhouse,** 27a Hay's Mews, W1X 7RJ, ☎ 499 3331 – ▤. AE ⓓ VISA BN e
closed Saturday lunch, Christmas and Bank Holidays – **Meals** a la carte 23.65/34.35 **t.** 🍷 7.50
Spec. Smoked haddock with Welsh rarebit, Salmon fish cakes, Apricot sponge pudding.

XX **Bentley's,** 11-15 Swallow St., W1R 7HD, ☎ 734 4756, Fax 287 2972 – ▤. AE ⓓ VISA JCB EM i
closed Sunday, 24 December-4 January and Bank Holidays – **Meals** - Seafood - 19.50 **t.** and a la carte 🍷 7.50.

XX **Nicole's,** 158 New Bond St., W1V 9PA, ☎ 499 8408, Fax 499 7522 – ▤. AE ⓓ VISA
closed Saturday dinner and Sunday – **Meals** a la carte 23.00/27.50 **t.** DM n

XX **Langan's Brasserie,** Stratton St., W1X 5FD, ☎ 491 8822 – ▤. AE ⓓ VISA DN e
closed Saturday lunch, Sunday, 1 January, Easter, 25 December and Bank Holidays – **Meals** (booking essential) a la carte 19.30/28.15 **t.** 🍷 6.50.

XX **Gaucho Grill,** 19 Swallow St., W1R 7HD, ☎ 734 4040, Fax 287 1427 – ▤. AE ⓓ VISA
Meals - Argentinian - a la carte 12.85/21.85 **t.** 🍷 6.00. EM c

XX **Mulligans,** 13-14 Cork St., W1X 1PF, ☎ 409 1370, Fax 409 2732 – ▤. AE ⓓ VISA JCB DM c
closed Saturday lunch and Sunday – **Meals** - Irish - a la carte 18.75/25.85 **t.**

XX **Shogun** (at Britannia H.), Adams Row, W1Y 5DE, ☎ 493 1255 – ▤. AE ⓓ VISA JCB BM x
closed Monday – **Meals** - Japanese - (dinner only) 32.00 **t.** and a la carte.

Regent's Park and Marylebone

– ✉ NW1/NW6/NW8/W1 – ☎ 0171 – Except where otherwise stated see pp. 12 and 13.

ℹ Basement Services Arcade, Selfridges Store, Oxford St., W1 ☎ 824 8844.

Landmark London, 222 Marylebone Rd, NW1 6JQ, ☎ 631 8000, Fax 631 8092, « Victorian Gothic architecture, atrium and winter garden », Fб, ≘s, ▣ – |‡| ⇔ rm ▤ TV ☎ ♿ Ⓟ – 🔬 350. AE ⓓ VISA JCB. ✻ HU a
The Dining Room : **Meals** 18.00/45.00 **t.** and a la carte 🍷 10.50 – ☕ 15.50 – **307 rm** 160.00/255.00 **s.**, 2 suites – SB.

Churchill Inter-Continental, 30 Portman Sq., W1A 4ZX, ☎ 486 5800, Telex 264831, Fax 486 1255, ✂ – |‡| ⇔ rm ▤ TV ☎ Ⓟ – 🔬 200. AE ⓓ VISA JCB. ✻ AJ x
Meals *(closed Saturday lunch)* 21.50 **t.** and a la carte 🍷 6.00 – ☕ 16.00 – **406 rm** 195.00/235.00 **s.**, 37 suites.

Langham Hilton, 1 Portland Pl., W1N 4JA, ☎ 636 1000, Fax 323 2340, Fб, ≘s – |‡| ⇔ rm ▤ TV ☎ ♿ – 🔬 250. AE ⓓ VISA JCB. ✻ p. 5 JU e
Memories of the Empire : **Meals** 23.00/29.95 **st.** and a la carte 🍷 8.60 – ☕ 15.20 – **360 rm** 195.00/280.00 **s.**, 20 suites.

Selfridge (Thistle), Orchard St., W1H 0JS, ☎ 408 2080, Group Telex 22361, Fax 629 8849 – |‡| ⇔ rm ▤ TV ☎ – 🔬 220. AE ⓓ VISA JCB. ✻ AK e
Fletchers : **Meals** *(closed Saturday lunch and Sunday)* 16.95/24.00 **st.** and a la carte – ***Orchard :*** **Meals** 12.95 **st.** 🍷 5.20 – ☕ 10.75 – **293 rm** 155.00/185.00 **st.**, 2 suites – SB.

Radisson SAS Portman, 22 Portman Sq., W1H 9FL, ☎ 208 6000, Telex 261526, Fax 208 6001, ✂ – |‡| ⇔ rm ▤ TV ☎ – 🔬 350. AE ⓓ VISA JCB. ✻ AJ o
Meals 9.50 **t.** (lunch) and a la carte 15.00/31.00 **t.** 🍷 9.00 – ☕ 12.50 – **272 rm** 158.60/199.75 **st.**, 7 suites.

Berkshire (Radisson Edwardian), 350 Oxford St., W1N 0BY, ☎ 629 7474, Telex 22270, Fax 629 8156 – |‡| ⇔ rm ▤ TV ☎ – 🔬 40. AE ⓓ VISA JCB. ✻ BK n
Meals *(closed Saturday, Sunday and Bank Holiday lunch)* 23.40 **st.** and a la carte – ☕ 13.50 – **145 rm** 160.00/210.00 **st.**, 2 suites – SB.

London Regent's Park Hilton, 18 Lodge Rd, NW8 7JT, ℘ 722 7722, Telex 23101, Fax 483 2408 – rm – 150. p. 5 GT **v**
***Minsky's :* Meals** 15.95/19.95 **t.** and a la carte 9.75 – ***Kashinoki :* Meals** - Japanese - *(closed Monday, 25-26 December and 1 January)* 9.00/30.00 **t.** 8.00 – 12.50 – **374 rm** 126.00/142.00 **st.**, 3 suites.

Clifton Ford, 47 Welbeck St., W1M 8DN, ℘ 486 6600, Telex 22569, Fax 486 7492 – – 150. BH **a**
Meals 16.00/18.00 **st.** and a la carte 4.65 – 13.50 – **191 rm** 140.00/155.00 **s.**, 2 suites.

Montcalm, Great Cumberland Pl., W1A 2LF, ℘ 402 4288, Telex 28710, Fax 724 9180 – rm – 80. p. 17 EZ **x**
***Crescent :* Meals** *(closed Saturday lunch and Sunday)* 19.50/43.00 **t.** and dinner a la carte 6.50 – 14.25 – **102 rm** 165.00/185.00, 14 suites.

Marble Arch Marriott, 134 George St., W1H 6DN, ℘ 723 1277, Telex 27983, Fax 402 0666, – rm rest – 150. p. 17 EZ **i**
Meals 8.00/25.00 **st.** and a la carte 7.50 – 11.85 – **239 rm** 150.00/190.00 – SB.

Berners, 10 Berners St., W1A 3BE, ℘ 636 1629, Telex 25759, Fax 580 3972 – rm rest – 150. EJ **r**
Meals 17.20/22.15 **t.** and a la carte – 11.75 – **226 rm** 132.00/185.00 **st.**, 3 suites.

Forte Crest Regent's Park, Carburton St., W1P 8EE, ℘ 388 2300, Telex 22453, Fax 387 2806 – rm rest – 220.
Meals 15.95/25.00 **st.** and a la carte 6.60 – 11.95 – **315 rm** 125.00/140.00 **st.**, 2 suites – SB. p. 5 JU **i**

St. George's (Forte), Langham Pl., W1N 8QS, ℘ 580 0111, Fax 436 7997, ← – rm p. 5 JU **a**
Meals – (see ***The Heights*** below) – 13.95 – **83 rm** 140.00/150.00 **st.**, 3 suites.

Rathbone without rest., Rathbone St., W1P 2LB, ℘ 636 2001, Telex 28728, Fax 636 3882 – rm p. 6 KU **x**
10.00 – **72 rm** 125.00/150.00 **st.**

Dorset Square, 39-40 Dorset Sq., NW1 6QN, ℘ 723 7874, Fax 724 3328, « Attractively furnished Regency town houses », – p. 5 HU **s**
Meals *(closed Sunday lunch and Saturday)* 11.95 **t.** (lunch) and a la carte 22.00/27.00 **t.** – 10.00 – **37 rm** 85.00/160.00 **s.** – SB.

25 Dorset Square without rest., 25 Dorset Sq., NW1 6QN, ℘ 724 6031, Fax 723 0194, « Regency town houses » – HU **e**
, **12 suites** 100.00/157.00 **st.**.

Durrants, 26-32 George St., W1H 6BJ, ℘ 935 8131, Fax 487 3510, « Converted Georgian houses with Regency façade » – – 60. AH **e**
Meals 17.00 **t.** and a la carte 5.35 – 8.95 – **90 rm** 86.00/106.00 **st.**, 3 suites.

Savoy Court, Granville Pl., W1H 0EH, ℘ 408 0130, Telex 8955515, Fax 493 2070 – rest AK **i**
Meals 13.50/35.00 and a la carte – 9.00 – **95 rm** 90.00/130.00 **st.** – SB.

Langham Court, 31-35 Langham St., W1N 5RE, ℘ 436 6622, Fax 436 6622 – – 80. p. 5 JU **z**
Meals *(closed lunch Saturday and Sunday)* 16.95/18.95 **t.** and a la carte 7.95 – 9.50 – **56 rm** 85.00/99.00 **st.**

Stakis London Harewood, Harewood Row, NW1 6SE, ℘ 262 2707, Telex 297225, Fax 262 2975 – rm rest p. 5 HU **x**
Meals (dinner only) 16.00 **st.** and a la carte – 9.00 – **92 rm** 78.00/98.00 **st.**

XXX ✿ **Interlude de Chavot** (Chavot), 5 Charlotte St., W1P 1HD, ℘ 637 0222, Fax 637 0224 – KU **r**
closed Saturday lunch, Sunday and Bank Holidays – **Meals** - French - 26.50 **t.**
Spec. Pithivier of quail, Roast poulet noir, fondant potatoes, Chocolate tart.

XX **The Heights** (at St. George's H.), Langham Pl., W1N 8QS, ℘ 636 1939, Fax 753 0259, ← London – JU **a**
closed Saturday lunch, Sunday, last 2 weeks August and Bank Holidays – **Meals** 19.50 **t.** (lunch) and dinner a la carte 23.20/30.40 **t.** 9.00.

XX **Hudson's,** 221b Baker St., NW1 4XE, ℘ 935 3130, Fax 224 3005 –
closed 25 December – **Meals** - English - 14.00/16.50 **t.** and a la carte 9.25. HU **r**

XX **Nico Central,** 35 Great Portland St., W1N 5DD, ℘ 436 8846, Fax 355 4877 –
closed Saturday lunch, Sunday, 4 days Easter, 10 days Christmas and Bank Holiday Mondays – **Meals** 23.50/26.00 **st.** 9.00. DJ **c**

XX **Caldesi,** 15-17 Marylebone Lane, W1M 5FE, ℘ 935 9226, Fax 929 0924 – BJ **e**
closed Saturday lunch, Sunday and Bank Holidays – **Meals** - Italian - a la carte 15.00/26.00 **t.** 4.50.

XX **Gaylord,** 79-81 Mortimer St., W1N 7TB, ℘ 580 3615, Fax 631 5077 –
Meals - Indian - 11.95/12.95 **t.** and a la carte 4.50. p. 6 KU **o**

XX **Maroush III,** 62 Seymour St., W1H 5AF, ℘ 724 5024, Fax 706 3493 – p. 17 EZ **r**
Meals - Lebanese - 8.00/30.00 **t.** and a la carte 8.50.

XX **Stephen Bull,** 5-7 Blandford St., W1H 3AA, ☎ 486 9696, Fax 490 3128 – ▤. AE VISA BH **e**
closed Saturday lunch, Sunday, 1 week Christmas and Bank Holidays – **Meals** 13.00 **t.** (lunch) and a la carte 21.75/30.00 **t.** 6.00.

XX **Baboon,** Jason Court, 76 Wigmore St., W1H 9DQ, ☎ 224 2992, Fax 224 2992 – ▤. AE VISA JCB BJ **x**
closed Saturday lunch, Sunday, 1 week Christmas and Bank Holidays – **Meals** 12.50/17.00 **t.** and a la carte 5.25.

XX Sampan's (at Cumberland H.), Marble Arch, W1A 4RF, ☎ 262 1234 AK **n**
Meals - Chinese (Canton) rest.

XX **Asuka,** Berkeley Arcade, 209a Baker St., NW1 6AB, ☎ 486 5026, Fax 224 1741 – AE VISA JCB p. 5 HU **u**
closed Saturday lunch, Sunday and Bank Holidays – **Meals** - Japanese - 13.50/37.00 **t.** and a la carte.

X **Le Muscadet,** 25 Paddington St., W1M 3RF, ☎ 935 2883 – ▤. VISA HU **v**
closed Saturday lunch, Sunday, last 3 weeks August and 2 weeks Christmas-New Year – **Meals** - French - a la carte 20.50/24.05 **t.** 8.20.

X L'Aventure, 3 Blenheim Terr., NW8 0EH, ☎ 624 6232, Fax 625 5548 p. 4 FS **s**
Meals - French rest.

X **Nakamura,** 31 Marylebone Lane, W1M 5FH, ☎ 935 2931, Fax 935 2931 – AE VISA JCB BJ **i**
closed lunch Sunday and Bank Holidays, Saturday, 1 week late August and 24 to 26 December – **Meals** - Japanese - 12.00/29.90 **t.** and a la carte.

X **Langan's Bistro,** 26 Devonshire St., W1N 1RJ, ☎ 935 4531 – ▤. AE VISA p. 5 IU **e**
closed Saturday lunch, Sunday, Easter, Christmas and Bank Holidays – **Meals** 17.95 **t.**

X **Zoe,** 3-5 Barrett St., St. Christopher's Pl., W1M 5HH, ☎ 224 1122, Fax 935 5444 – ▤. AE VISA BJ **a**
closed Sunday and Bank Holidays – **Meals** a la carte 14.30/23.85 **t.**

X **Union Café,** 96 Marylebone Lane, W1M 5FP, ☎ 486 4860 – VISA BH **c**
closed Saturday, Sunday, last 2 weeks August, first 2 weeks January and Bank Holidays – **Meals** a la carte 15.50/21.50 **t.**

St. James's – ✉ W1/SW1/WC2 – ☎ 0171 – pp. 12 and 13.

Ritz, Piccadilly, W1V 9DG, ☎ 493 8181, Fax 493 2687, « Elegant restaurant in Louis XVI style » – rm ▤ TV ☎ – 50. AE VISA JCB. DN **a**
Louis XVI : **Meals** (dancing Friday and Saturday evenings) 28.00/49.00 **st.** and a la carte – ***Italian Garden :*** **Meals** (summer only) (lunch only) 28.00 **st.** – 16.50 – **116 rm** 200.00/275.00, 14 suites - SB.

Dukes, 35 St. James's Pl., SW1A 1NY, ☎ 491 4840, Fax 493 1264 – ▤ TV ☎ – 50. AE VISA JCB. EP **x**
Meals (residents only) a la carte 35.00/60.00 **st.** 7.50 – 12.50 – **53 rm** 125.00/160.00 **s.**, 11 suites 210.00/400.00 **s.**.

22 Jermyn Street, 22 Jermyn St., SW1Y 6HL, ☎ 734 2353, Fax 734 0750 – TV ☎. AE VISA JCB. FM **e**
Meals (restricted room service only) a la carte 16.50/27.50 **t.** 8.00 – 14.00 – **5 rm** 170.00 **s.**, **13 suites** 225.00/250.00 **s.**.

Stafford, 16-18 St. James's Pl., SW1A 1NJ, ☎ 493 0111, Fax 493 7121 – ▤ rest TV ☎ – 35. AE VISA JCB. DN **u**
closed 3 January-22 April – **Meals** *(closed Saturday lunch)* 19.50/25.00 **st.** and a la carte 7.50 – 14.00 – **69 rm** 170.00/225.00 **s.**, 4 suites.

Forte Crest Cavendish, 81 Jermyn St., SW1Y 6JF, ☎ 930 2111, Fax 839 2125 – rm ▤ rest TV ☎ – 80. AE VISA JCB. EN **i**
Meals 16.50/19.50 **t.** and a la carte 7.95 – 13.50 – **252 rm** 140.00/160.00 **st.**, 3 suites - SB.

Royal Trafalgar Thistle, Whitcomb St., WC2H 7HG, ☎ 930 4477, Fax 925 2149 – rm TV ☎. AE VISA JCB. GM **r**
Meals 14.75 **t.** and a la carte 6.40 – 10.25 – **108 rm** 109.00/135.00 **st.** - SB.

Hospitality Inn Piccadilly (Mount Charlotte) without rest., 39 Coventry St., W1V 8EL, ☎ 930 4033, Telex 8950058, Fax 925 2586 – ▤ rest TV ☎. AE VISA JCB. FGM **a**
9.75 – **92 rm** 115.00/130.00 **st.**

Pastoria, 3-6 St. Martin's St., off Leicester Sq., WC2H 7HL, ☎ 930 8641, Telex 25538, Fax 925 0551 – ▤ rest TV ☎ – 60. AE VISA JCB. GM **v**
Meals *(closed Saturday lunch and Sunday)* 15.00/35.00 **st.** and a la carte – 9.25 – **58 rm** 125.00/165.00 **st.** - SB.

XXX **Quaglino's,** 16 Bury St., SW1Y 6AL, ☎ 930 6767, Fax 839 2866 – ▤. AE VISA EN **r**
closed 2 days at Christmas – **Meals** (booking essential) 13.50 **t.** (lunch) and a la carte 21.65/30.95 **t.** 6.25.

XXX **Suntory,** 72-73 St. James's St., SW1A 1PH, ☎ 409 0201, Fax 499 0208 – ▤. AE VISA JCB EP **z**
closed Sunday and Bank Holidays – **Meals** - Japanese - 15.00/90.00 **st.** and a la carte 31.70/86.00 **st.** 12.00.

XXX **Overton's,** 5 St. James's St., SW1A 1EF, ℘ 839 3774, Fax 839 4330 – ▤. AE ⓓ VISA JCB EP **a**
closed Saturday and Sunday, 10 days Christmas-New Year and Bank Holidays – **Meals** - Seafood - 21.00/27.50 **t.** 5.75.

XXX ✿ **The Square,** 32 King St., SW1Y 6RJ, (expected move during 1996 to 10 Bruton St., Mayfair, W1) ℘ 839 8787, Fax 321 2124 – ▤. AE ⓓ VISA EN **v**
closed lunch Saturday and Sunday – **Meals** a la carte 28.00/33.00 **t.**
Spec. Seared tuna with tartare of vegetables and soy wilted greens, Peppered fillet of beef, Parmesan, meat juices and truffle oil, Warm salad of duck, deep fried vegetables and balsamic vinegar.

XX **Le Caprice,** Arlington House, Arlington St., SW1A 1RT, ℘ 629 2239, Fax 493 9040 – ▤. AE ⓓ VISA DN **c**
closed 24 December-2 January – **Meals** a la carte 22.25/35.50 **t.**

XX **Green's,** 36 Duke St., SW1Y 6DF, ℘ 930 4566, Fax 491 7463 – ▤. AE ⓓ VISA EN **n**
closed Sunday dinner, 25, 26 and 31 December and 1 January – **Meals** - English - a la carte 19.00/31.00 **t.** 5.00.

XX **Criterion Brasserie Marco Pierre White,** 224 Piccadilly, W1V 9LB, ℘ 930 0488, Fax 930 8190, « 19C Neo-Byzantine decor » – AE VISA FM **c**
closed 25-26 December and 1 January – **Meals** a la carte 19.40/22.70 **t.** 10.00.

XX **Matsuri,** 15 Bury St., SW1Y 6AL, ℘ 839 1101, Fax 930 7010 – ▤. AE ⓓ VISA JCB
closed Sunday and Bank Holidays – **Meals** - Japanese (Teppan-Yaki, Sushi) - 10.50/53.50 **t.** and a la carte. EN **r**

Soho – ✉ W1/WC2 – ☎ 0171 – pp. 12 and 13.

Hampshire (Radisson Edwardian), Leicester Sq., WC2H 7LH, ℘ 839 9399, Telex 914848, Fax 930 8122 – |‡| ⇔ rm ▤ TV ☎ – 🎪 80. AE ⓓ VISA JCB. ✂ GM **s**
Meals 19.50/15.00 **st.** and a la carte – ☕ 13.50 – **120 rm** 195.00/230.00 **st.**, 4 suites – SB.

Hazlitt's without rest., 6 Frith St., W1V 5TZ, ℘ 434 1771, Fax 439 1524 – TV ☎. AE ⓓ VISA JCB FK **u**
closed 4 days at Christmas – **22 rm** 102.00/130.00 **s.**, 1 suite.

XXXX ✿ **Grill Room at the Café Royal,** 68 Regent St., W1R 6EL, ℘ 437 9090, Fax 439 7672, « Rococo decoration » – ▤. AE ⓓ VISA JCB EM **e**
closed Saturday lunch, Sunday and Bank Holidays – **Meals** 24.00/39.00 **st.** and a la carte 35.00/51.50 **st.** 9.00
Spec. Escalopes of fresh foie gras with a ragoût of celeriac and truffle sauce, Seared fillet of sea bass with fennel, sundried tomatoes and saffron, Lemon meringue with Sauternes, raspberries and pistachio sauce.

XXX **Au Jardin des Gourmets,** 5 Greek St., W1V 6NA, ℘ 437 1816, Fax 437 0043 – ▤. AE ⓓ VISA GJ **a**
closed lunch Saturday and Bank Holidays, Sunday, Christmas and Easter – ***Restaurant :*** **Meals** - French - 17.50 **t.** and a la carte.
XX **Brasserie,** *closed lunch Saturday and Bank Holidays and Sunday* – **Meals** 10.95 **st.** and a la carte 6.25.

XXX **Lindsay House,** 21 Romilly St., W1V 5TG, ℘ 439 0450, Fax 581 2848 – ▤. AE ⓓ VISA JCB GL **i**
closed 25 and 26 December – **Meals** 10.00 **t.** (lunch) and a la carte 23.50/29.25 **t.** 5.00.

XXX ✿ **L'Escargot,** 48 Greek St., W1V 5LQ, ℘ 437 2679, Fax 437 0790 – ▤. AE ⓓ VISA GK **e**
Brasserie : **Meals** *(closed Saturday lunch and Sunday)* 21.50/23.50 **t.** – ***Dining Room :*** **Meals** *(closed Saturday lunch, Sunday, Monday and August)* 25.00/30.00 **t.**
Spec. Escabèche of salmon, Roast duck with parsley jus, Raspberry soufflé.

XX **Red Fort,** 77 Dean St., W1V 5HA, ℘ 437 2115, Fax 434 0721 – ▤. AE ⓓ VISA FJK **r**
Meals - Indian - (buffet lunch) 12.50 **t.** (lunch) and a la carte 21.85/25.85 **t.**

XX **Mezzo,** Lower ground floor, 100 Wardour St., W1V 3LE, ℘ 314 4000, Fax 314 4040 – ▤. AE ⓓ VISA FK **a**
closed 24 to 26 December – **Meals** 19.50 **t.** (lunch) and a la carte 17.50/25.50 **t.**

XX **Soho Soho** (first floor), 11-13 Frith St., W1V 5TS, ℘ 494 3491, Fax 437 3091 – ▤. AE ⓓ VISA JCB FK **s**
closed Saturday lunch, Sunday and Bank Holidays – **Meals** 15.95 **t.** (dinner) and a la carte approx. 22.00 **t.**

XX **Brasserie at the Café Royal,** 68 Regent St., W1R 6EL, ℘ 437 9090, Fax 439 7672 – ▤. AE ⓓ VISA JCB EM **e**
closed Sunday dinner – **Meals** 13.50/16.50 **st.** and a la carte 7.25.

XX **Ming,** 35-36 Greek St., W1V 5LN, ℘ 734 2721, Fax 435 0812 – ▤. AE ⓓ VISA JCB
closed Sunday, Bank Holiday lunch and 25 and 26 December – **Meals** - Chinese - 10.00/20.00 **t.** and a la carte 6.50. GK **c**

XX **Lexington,** 45 Lexington St., W1R 3LG, ℘ 434 3401, Fax 287 2997 – ▤. AE ⓓ VISA
closed Saturday lunch, Sunday, 1 week Christmas-New Year and Bank Holidays – **Meals** 10.00 **t.** (dinner) and a la carte 16.25/23.75 **t.** EK **e**

XX **Gopal's,** 12 Bateman St., W1V 5TD, ℘ 434 0840 – ▤. AE VISA FK **e**
closed 25 and 26 December – **Meals** - Indian - a la carte 12.15/14.90 **t.**

XXX **Gay Hussar,** 2 Greek St., W1V 6NB, ☎ 437 0973 – ▤. AE VISA GJ **c**
closed Sunday and Bank Holidays – **Meals** - Hungarian - 16.00 **t.** (lunch) and a la carte 18.10/26.60 **t.** 7.50.

XX **Atelier,** 41 Beak St., W1R 3LE, ☎ 287 2057 – AE VISA EL **a**
closed Saturday lunch, Sunday, 2 weeks August, 2 weeks Christmas-New Year and Bank Holidays – **Meals** 17.00 **t.** and a la carte 22.75/28.75 **t.** 7.95.

X **dell 'Ugo,** 56 Frith St., W1V 5TA, ☎ 734 8300, Fax 734 8784 – AE VISA FK **z**
closed Sunday and Bank Holidays – **Meals** a la carte 15.95/26.15 **t.**

X **Sri Siam,** 16 Old Compton St., W1V 5PE, ☎ 434 3544 – ▤. AE VISA GK **r**
closed Sunday lunch – **Meals** - Thai - 9.95 **t.** and a la carte 4.60.

X **Alastair Little,** 49 Frith St., W1V 5TE, ☎ 734 5183 – AE VISA JCB FK **o**
closed Saturday lunch, Sunday and Bank Holidays – **Meals** (booking essential) 25.00 (lunch) and a la carte 28.00/40.00 6.00.

X **Bistrot Bruno,** 63 Frith St., W1V 5TA, ☎ 734 4545, Fax 287 1027 – ▤. AE VISA
closed Saturday lunch, Sunday and Christmas – **Meals** 25.00/35.00 **t.** FK **z**

X **Poons,** 4 Leicester St., Leicester Sq., WC2 7BL, ☎ 437 1528 – ▤. AE VISA GM **e**
closed 24 to 27 December – **Meals** - Chinese - a la carte 7.50/15.00 **t.** 6.50.

X **Andrew Edmunds,** 46 Lexington St., W1R 3LH, ☎ 437 5708 – AE VISA EK **c**
closed Easter, August Bank Holiday and 23 December-2 January – **Meals** a la carte 12.00/17.00 **t.** 4.25.

X **Fung Shing,** 15 Lisle St., WC2H 7BE, ☎ 734 0284 – ▤. AE VISA GL **a**
Meals - Chinese (Canton) - 12.50/20.00 **t.** and a la carte 4.75.

X **Saigon,** 45 Frith St., W1V 5TE, ☎ 437 7109, Fax 734 1668 – ▤. AE VISA FGK **x**
closed Sunday and Bank Holidays – **Meals** - Vietnamese - 15.80/19.50 **t.** 8.50.

Strand and Covent Garden – ✉ WC2 – ☎ 0171 – p. 17.

Savoy, Strand, WC2R 0EU, ☎ 836 4343, Telex 24234, Fax 240 6040, – rm ▤ – 500. AE VISA JCB. DEY **a**
Grill: **Meals** *(closed Saturday lunch, Sunday, August and Bank Holidays)* 31.00 **st.** (dinner) and a la carte 27.40/44.25 **st.** 8.60 – *River:* **Meals** 28.00/40.00 **st.** and a la carte 45.00/61.00 **st.** 8.60 – 16.25 – **154 rm** 200.00/325.00 **s.**, 48 suites – SB.

Waldorf (Forte), Aldwych, WC2B 4DD, ☎ 836 2400, Telex 24574, Fax 836 7244 – rm ▤ rm – 450. AE VISA JCB EX **x**
Meals (in bar Sunday lunch) 23.00/35.00 **t.** and a la carte 6.75 – 13.50 – **286 rm** 165.00/190.00 **s.**, 6 suites – SB.

Howard, Temple Pl., WC2R 2PR, ☎ 836 3555, Telex 268047, Fax 379 4547 – rm ▤ – 100. AE VISA JCB. EX **e**
Meals 25.00 **st.** and a la carte 4.75 – 15.50 – **133 rm** 200.00/236.00 **st.**, 2 suites.

XXX **Ivy,** 1 West St., WC2H 9NE, ☎ 836 4751, Fax 497 3644 – ▤. AE VISA GK **z**
closed dinner 24 to 28 December and lunch Bank Holidays – **Meals** a la carte 22.25/35.50 **t.**

XXX **WestZENders,** 4a Upper St. Martin's Lane, WC2H 9EA, ☎ 497 0376, Fax 497 0378 – ▤. AE VISA DX **x**
closed 25 December – **Meals** - Chinese - a la carte 16.50/21.50 **t.**

XX **Rules,** 35 Maiden Lane, WC2E 7LB, ☎ 836 5314, Fax 497 1081, « London's oldest restaurant with collection of antique cartoons, drawings and paintings » – AE VISA
closed 23 to 26 December – **Meals** - English - 12.95 **t.** (lunch) and a la carte 20.95/23.15 **t.** 4.60. DX **n**

XX **Christopher's,** 18 Wellington St., WC2E 7DD, ☎ 240 4222, Fax 240 3357 – AE VISA
closed Saturday lunch, Sunday, 25-26 December and Bank Holidays – **Meals** a la carte 22.50/45.00 6.00. EX **z**

XX **Orso,** 27 Wellington St., WC2E 7DA, ☎ 240 5269, Fax 497 2148 – ▤ EX **z**
closed 24 and 25 December – **Meals** - Italian - (booking essential) a la carte 15.50/25.50 **t.** 5.50.

XX **L'Estaminet,** 14 Garrick St., off Floral St., WC2 9BJ, ☎ 379 1432 – AE VISA DX **a**
closed Sunday and Bank Holidays – **Meals** - French - a la carte 20.50/24.00 **t.**

XX **Sheekey's,** 28-32 St. Martin's Court, WC2N 4AL, ☎ 240 2565, Fax 240 0545 – ▤. AE VISA DX **v**
Meals - Seafood - 15.95/18.75 **t.** and a la carte.

XX **Bertorelli's,** 44a Floral St., WC2E 9DA, ☎ 836 3969, Fax 836 1868 – ▤. AE VISA JCB
closed Sunday and 25-26 December – **Meals** - Italian - a la carte 15.30/27.15 **t.** DX **c**

X **Le Café du Jardin,** 28 Wellington St., WC2E 7BD, ☎ 836 8769, Fax 836 4123 – ▤. AE VISA EX **a**
Meals 13.50 **t.** (lunch) and a la carte 16.95/26.95 **t.** 4.50.

X **Magno's Brasserie,** 65a Long Acre, WC2E 9JH, ☎ 836 6077, Fax 379 6184 – ▤. AE VISA JCB DV **e**
closed Saturday lunch, Sunday, Christmas and Bank Holidays – **Meals** - French - 13.50/16.50 **t.** and a la carte.

X **Joe Allen,** 13 Exeter St., WC2E 7DT, ☎ 836 0651, Fax 497 2148 – ▤ EX **c**
closed 24 and 25 December – **Meals** a la carte 16.50/22.00 **t.**

Victoria - ✉ SW1 - ☎ 0171 - Except where otherwise stated see p. 16.

Victoria Station Forecourt, SW1V 1JU ☎ 824 8844.

St. James Court, Buckingham Gate, SW1E 6AF, ☎ 834 6655, Telex 938075, Fax 630 7587, – rm TV ☎ – 180. AE VISA JCB CX i
Café Mediterranée :* Meals** 12.50/25.00 **st.** and a la carte – (see also ***Auberge de Provence and ***Inn of Happiness*** below) – 14.00 – **375 rm** 140.00/175.00, 18 suites.

Royal Horseguards Thistle, 2 Whitehall Court, SW1A 2EJ, ☎ 839 3400, Telex 917096, Fax 925 2263 – rest TV ☎ – 60. AE VISA JCB. p. 10 LX a
Meals (light meals Saturday and Sunday) 12.95 **t.** and a la carte – 10.25 – **373 rm** 118.00/200.00 **st.**, 3 suites.

Stakis London St. Ermin's, Caxton St., SW1H 0QW, ☎ 222 7888, Fax 222 6914 – rm rest TV ☎ – 250. AE VISA JCB. CX a
Meals *(closed Saturday and Sunday lunch)* (carving rest.) 12.75/16.50 **t.** and a la carte – ***Caxton Grill :* Meals** *(closed Saturday and Sunday)* a la carte 18.75/40.90 **t.** – 9.75 – **283 rm** 119.00/139.00 **st.**, 7 suites – SB.

Goring, 15 Beeston Pl., Grosvenor Gdns, SW1W 0JW, ☎ 396 9000, Telex 919166, Fax 834 4393 – TV ☎ – 50. AE VISA. BX a
Meals 18.00/35.00 **t.** 8.00 – 12.50 – **72 rm** 130.00/165.00 **s.**, 5 suites – SB.

Royal Westminster Thistle, 49 Buckingham Palace Rd, SW1W 0QT, ☎ 834 1821, Telex 916821, Fax 931 7542 – rm TV ☎ – 160. AE VISA JCB.
Meals *(closed Sunday)* (bar lunch)/dinner 21.95 **st.** and a la carte – 10.25 – **134 rm** 122.00/145.00 **st.** – SB. BX z

Grosvenor Thistle, 101 Buckingham Palace Rd, SW1W 0SJ, ☎ 834 9494, Telex 916006, Fax 630 1978 – rm TV ☎ – 200. AE VISA JCB. BX e
Meals (carving rest.) 14.50/16.35 **st.** and a la carte 6.00 – 8.95 – **360 rm** 99.00/145.00 **st.**, 6 suites.

Dolphin Square, Dolphin Sq., SW1V 3LX, ☎ 834 3800, Fax 798 8735, squash – rest TV ☎ – 50. AE VISA. KZ a
Meals 11.95/17.95 **st.** and dinner a la carte – 11.95 – **14 rm** 99.00/125.00 **st.**, **137 suites** 130.00/148.00 **st.**.

Rubens, 39-41 Buckingham Palace Rd, SW1W 0PS, ☎ 834 6600, Telex 916577, Fax 828 5401 – rm rest TV ☎ – 75. AE VISA JCB. BX n
Meals *(closed Saturday and Sunday lunch)* (carving rest.) 14.95 **st.** and a la carte 8.00 – 9.95 – **179 rm** 110.00/150.00 **st.**, 1 suite.

Scandic Crown, 2 Bridge Pl., SW1V 1QA, ☎ 834 8123, Telex 914973, Fax 828 1099, – rm TV ☎ – 180. AE VISA JCB. BY i
Meals 16.95/25.00 **st.** and a la carte 5.00 – 10.95 – **205 rm** 120.00/160.00 **st.**, 5 suites – SB.

Rochester, 69 Vincent Sq., SW1P 2PA, ☎ 828 6611, Fax 233 6724 – rest TV ☎ – 60. AE VISA JCB. CY e
Meals 17.95 **st.** and a la carte 6.95 – 7.50 – **70 rm** 109.00/129.00 **st.**

XXX **Auberge de Provence** (at St. James Court H.), Buckingham Gate, SW1E 6AF, ☎ 821 1899, Fax 630 7587 – AE VISA JCB CX i
closed Saturday lunch, Sunday, 1 week January, 2 weeks August and Bank Holidays – **Meals** - French - 24.50/40.00 **t.**

XXX **Inn of Happiness** (at St. James Court H.), Buckingham Gate, SW1E 6AF, ☎ 821 1931, Fax 630 7587 – AE VISA JCB CX i
closed Saturday lunch – **Meals** - Chinese - (buffet lunch Sunday) 17.50/30.00 **st.** and a la carte.

XXX **L'Incontro,** 87 Pimlico Rd, SW1W 8PH, ☎ 730 6327, Fax 730 5062 – AE VISA JCB p. 15 FT u
closed lunch Saturday and Sunday, 25-26 December and Bank Holidays – **Meals** - Italian - 18.50 **t.** (lunch) and a la carte 28.00/45.50 **t.**

XXX **Santini,** 29 Ebury St., SW1W 0NZ, ☎ 730 4094, Fax 730 0544 – AE VISA JCB
closed lunch Saturday and Sunday and 25-26 December – **Meals** - Italian - 18.30 **t.** (lunch) and a la carte 24.00/43.00 **t.** ABX v

XXX **Shepherd's,** Marsham Court, Marsham St., SW1P 4LA, ☎ 834 9552, Fax 233 6047 – AE VISA p. 10 LZ z
closed Saturday, Sunday, Christmas and Bank Holidays – **Meals** - English - (booking essential) 20.95 **t.**

XX **Simply Nico,** 48a Rochester Row, SW1P 1JU, ☎ 630 8061 – AE VISA CY a
closed Saturday lunch, Sunday, 4 days at Easter, 10 days Christmas-New Year and Bank Holidays – **Meals** (booking essential) 24.00/26.00 **st.** 9.00.

XX **Atrium,** 4 Millbank, SW1P 3JA, ☎ 233 0032, Fax 233 0010 – AE VISA LY s
closed Saturday lunch, Sunday, Christmas and Bank Holidays – 15.95/18.95 **t.**

XX **Mijanou,** 143 Ebury St., SW1W 9QN, ☎ 730 4099, Fax 823 6402 – AE VISA
closed Saturday, Sunday, 1 week Easter, 3 weeks August and 2 weeks Christmas – **Meals** 12.00/38.50 **t.** and a la carte. AY n

XX **Ken Lo's Memories of China,** 67-69 Ebury St., SW1W 0NZ, ☎ 730 7734, Fax 730 2992 – AE VISA JCB AY u
closed Sunday lunch and Bank Holidays – **Meals** - Chinese - 15.25/29.80 **t.** and a la carte.

XX **L'Amico,** 44 Horseferry Rd, SW1P 2AF, ✆ 222 4680 – AE VISA p. 10 LY **e**
closed Saturday, Sunday and Bank Holidays – **Meals** - Italian - (booking essential) 16.50/28.00 **t.** and a la carte.

XX **Hunan,** 51 Pimlico Rd, SW1W 8NE, ✆ 730 5712 – AE VISA p. 9 IZ **a**
closed Sunday lunch and 24 and 25 December – **Meals** - Chinese (Hunan) - a la carte 13.80/18.80 **t.** 4.50.

XX **Tate Gallery,** Tate Gallery, Millbank, SW1P 4RG, ✆ 887 8877, Fax 887 8007, « Rex Whistler murals » – VISA p. 10 LZ **c**
closed Sunday, 24 to 26 December and Bank Holidays – **Meals** (booking essential) (lunch only) 12.00/25.00 **t.**

XX **Gran Paradiso,** 52 Wilton Rd, SW1V 1DE, ✆ 828 5818, Fax 828 3608 – AE VISA JCB BY **a**
closed Saturday lunch, Sunday, last 2 weeks August and Bank Holidays – **Meals** - Italian - a la carte 16.50/21.60 **t.** 4.50.

X **Olivo,** 21 Eccleston St., SW1W 9LX, ✆ 730 2505 – AE VISA AY **z**
closed Saturday lunch, Sunday, 1 week Christmas and Bank Holidays – **Meals** - Italian - 15.50 **t.** (lunch) and dinner a la carte 18.05/25.30 **t.**

X **La Poule au Pot,** 231 Ebury St., SW1W 8UT, ✆ 730 7763 – AE VISA IZ **e**
Meals - French - 12.95 **t.** (lunch) and dinner a la carte 25.85/34.85 **t.** 5.00.

Bray-on-Thames Berks W : 34 m. by M 4 (junction 8-9) and A 308 404 R 29 – pop. 8 121 – ✉ Maidenhead – 01628.

XXXX ✿✿✿ **Waterside Inn** (Roux) with rm, Ferry Rd, SL6 2AT, ✆ 20691, Fax 784710, « ≤ Thames-side setting », – rest TV ☎ P. VISA JCB. X **s**
closed 26 December-26 January – **Meals** - French - *(closed Tuesday lunch, Sunday dinner from 3rd weekend October-2nd weekend April, Monday and Bank Holidays)* 29.00/65.50 **st.** and a la carte 56.10/86.00 **st.** 11.50 – **6 rm** 130.00/160.00 **st.**, 1 suite
Spec. Tronçonnettes de homard poêlées minute au Porto blanc, Filets de lapereau grillés aux marrons glacés, Soufflé chaud aux framboises.

Reading Berks. - at Shinfield - W : 43 m. by M 4 and A 329 on A 327 403 404 Q 29 – pop. 128 877 – 01734.

Town Hall, Blagrave St., RG1 1QH ✆ 566226.

XXX ✿✿ **L'Ortolan** (Burton-Race), The Old Vicarage, Church Lane, RG2 9BY, ✆ 883783, Fax 885391, – P. AE VISA
closed Sunday dinner, Monday, last 2 weeks February and last 2 weeks August – **Meals** - French - 28.00/37.00 **t.** and a la carte 52.50/74.50 **t.** 10.50
Spec. Millefeuille de rouget Niçoise en tapenade, Tournedos de chevreuil aux grains de cassis et purée Dubarry, Soufflé chaud aux abricots glace au lait d'amande.

Oxford Oxon - at Great Milton - NW : 49 m. by M 40 (junction 7) and A 329 403 404 Q 28 – pop. 110 103 – ✉ Great Milton – 01844.

The Old School, Gloucester Green, OX1 2DA ✆ 726871.

✿✿ **Le Manoir aux Quat' Saisons** (Blanc), Church Rd, OX44 7PD, ✆ 278881, Fax 278847, ≤, « Part 15C and 16C manor house, gardens », heated, park, – rest rest TV ☎ P – 35. AE VISA JCB.
Meals 29.50/65.00 **st.** and a la carte 62.00/78.00 **st.** 16.00 – 14.50 – **16 rm** 175.00/325.00 **st.**, 3 suites – SB
Spec. Trois bouchées gourmandes aux parfums d'ailleurs, Courgette en fleur farcie au crabe et jus de truffes, Pêche de vigne pochée et figues farcies de glace au porto.

BIRMINGHAM W. Mids 403 404 O 26 **Great Britain G.** – pop. 961 041 – 0121.

See : City★ – Museum and Art Gallery★★ JZ **M2** – Barber Institute of Fine Arts★★ (at Birmingham University) EX – Museum of Science and Industry★ JY **M3** – Cathedral of St. Philip (stained glass portrayals★) KYZ.

Envir. : Aston Hall★★ FV **M.**

Exc. : Black Country Museum★, Dudley, NW : 10 m. by A 456 and A 4123.

18 Edgbaston, Church Rd ✆ 454 1736 FX – 18 Hilltop, Park Lane, Handsworth ✆ 554 4463 – 18 Hatchford Brook, Coventry Rd, Sheldon ✆ 743 9821 HX – 18 Brand Hall, Heron Rd, Oldbury, Warley ✆ 552 2195.

Birmingham Airport : ✆ 767 5511, E : 6 ½ m. by A 45.

Convention Visitor Bureau, 2 City Arcade, B2 4TX ✆ 643 2514, Fax 616 1038 – Convention Visitor Bureau, National Exhibition Centre, B40 1NT ✆ 780 4321 – Birmingham Airport, Information Desk, B26 3QJ, ✆ 767 7145/7146.

London 122 – Bristol 91 – Liverpool 103 – Manchester 86 – Nottingham 50.

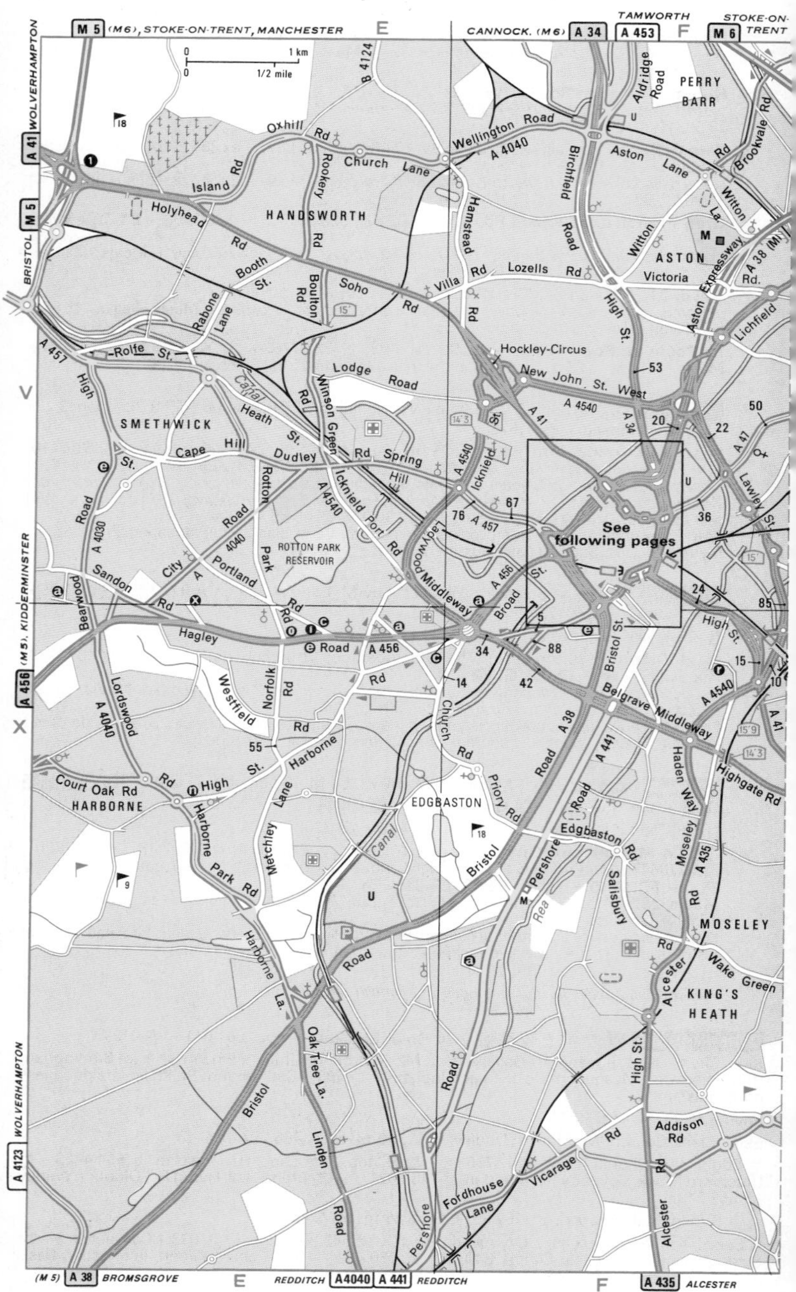
M 5 (M6), STOKE-ON-TRENT, MANCHESTER
E
CANNOCK. (M6) A 34
TAMWORTH A 453
F
STOKE-ON-TRENT M 6
A 41 WOLVERHAMPTON
BRISTOL M 5
A 456 (M5). KIDDERMINSTER
A 4123 WOLVERHAMPTON
V
X
0 1 km
0 1/2 mile
HANDSWORTH
PERRY BARR
ASTON
SMETHWICK
ROTTON PARK RESERVOIR
See following pages
HARBORNE
EDGBASTON
MOSELEY
KING'S HEATH
Oxhill Rd
Church Lane
Wellington Road
A 4040
Island Rd
Holyhead Rd
Rookery Rd
Hamstead Rd
Birchfield Road
Aldridge Road
Aston Lane
Brookvale Rd
Witton La
Witton Rd
Aston Expressway
A 38 (M)
Victoria Rd.
Lozells Rd
Villa Rd
Soho Rd
Booth St.
Boulton Rd
Rabone Lane
Rolfe St.
A 457
High St.
Hockley-Circus
New John St. West
A 4540
A 41
A 34
Lichfield
Lodge Road
Winson Green Rd
Canal
Heath St.
Cape Hill
Dudley Rd
Spring Hill
Icknield St.
Icknield Port Rd
A 4540
A 4030
Road
City Road
A 4040
Portland Rd
Rotton Park Rd
Ladywood Middleway
A 456
Broad St.
Sandon Rd
Bearwood Rd
Hagley Road
A 456
Lordswood
A 4040
Westfield Rd
Norfolk Rd
Church Rd
Bristol St.
Belgrave Middleway
A 4540
A 38
Bristol Road
A 441
Haden Way
Highgate Rd
Lawley St.
A 47
High St.
A 41
Court Oak Rd
High St.
Harborne Rd
Harborne Park Rd
Metchley Lane
Priory Rd
Pershore Road
Edgbaston Rd
Bristol Rd
Moseley Rd
A 435
Salisbury Rd
Rea
Wake Green Rd
Alcester Rd
Harborne La.
Oak Tree La.
Bristol Road
Linden Road
Pershore Road
Fordhouse Lane
Vicarage Rd
Addison Rd
High St.
Alcester Rd
53
20
22
50
36
67
76
24
85
5
88
34
42
14
15
10
55
(M 5) A 38 BROMSGROVE
E
REDDITCH A4040 A 441 REDDITCH
F
A 435 ALCESTER

BIRMINGHAM BUILT UP AREA

Bath Row	FX 5
Bordesley Middleway	FX 10
Calthorpe Rd	FX 14
Camp Hill	FX 15
Corporation St	FV 20
Darmouth Middleway	FV 22
Digbeth	FV 24
Dudley Park Rd	GX 25
High St	GV 31
Islington Row Middleway	FX 34
Jennen's Rd	FV 36
Lee Bank Middleway	FX 42
Nechell's Parkway	FV 50
New Town Row	FV 53
Nursery Rd	EX 55
Saltley Rd	GV 66
Sand Pits Parade	FV 67
Solihull Lane	GX 74
Summer Hill Rd	FV 76
Watery Lane	FV 85
Westley Rd	GX 87
Wheeley's Lane	FX 88

BIRMINGHAM
CENTRE

Albert St. . . . . KZ 2
Bull St. . . . . KY 13
Dale End . . . . KZ 21
Hall St. . . . . JY 29
Holloway Circus . . . . JZ 32
James Watt Queensway . . KY 35
Jennen's Rd . . . . KY 36
Lancaster Circus . . . . KY 39
Lancaster St. . . . . KY 41
Masshouse Circus . . . . KY 43
Moor St. Queensway . . . . . KZ 46
Navigation St. . . . . JZ 49
Newton St. . . . . KY 52
Paradise Circus . . . . JZ 56
Priory Queensway . . . . KY 57
St. Chads Circus . . . . JKY 62
St. Chads Ringway . . . . KY 63
St. Martin's Circus . . . . KZ 64
Shadwell St. . . . . KY 70
Smallbrook Queensway . . . . KZ 71
Snow Hill Queensway . . . . KY 73
Summer Row . . . . JY 77
Temple Row . . . . KZ 80
Waterloo St. . . . . JZ 84

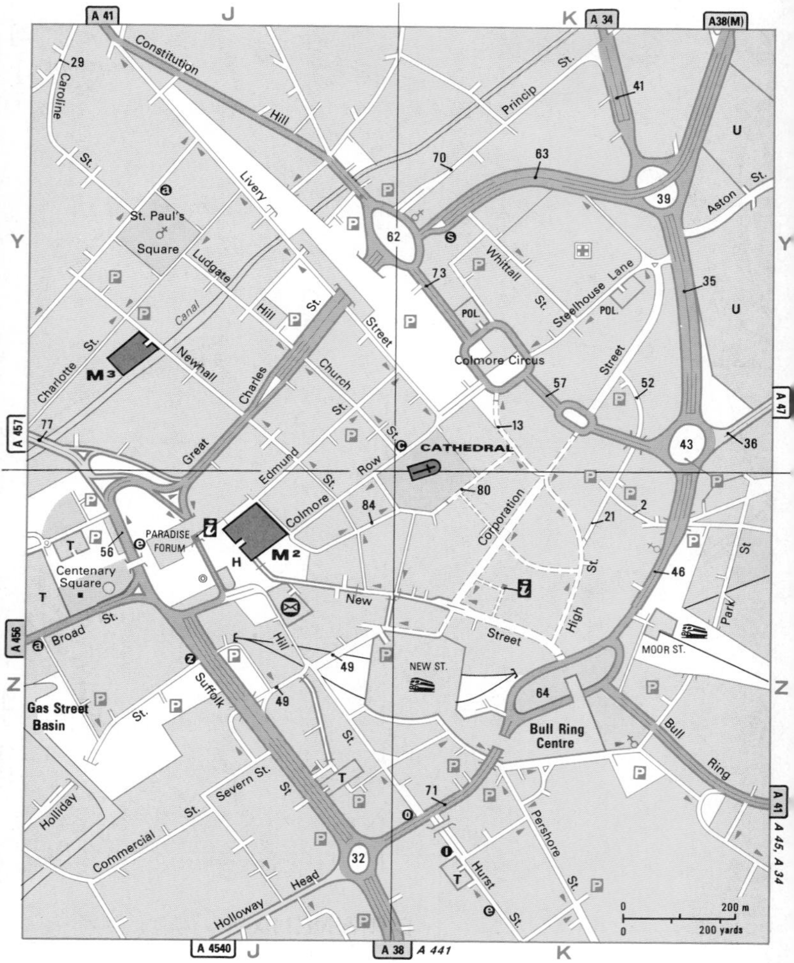

GREEN TOURIST GUIDES

Picturesque scenery, buildings
Attractive route
Touring programmes
Plans of towns and buildings.

STREET INDEX TO BIRMINGHAM TOWN PLANS

Bull Ring Centre . . . . KZ
Corporation St. . . . . KYZ
New St. . . . . JKZ
Paradise Forum
Shopping Centre . . . . . . JZ

Addison Rd . . . . FX
Albert St. . . . . KZ 2
Alcester Rd . . . . FX
Aldridge Rd . . . . FV
Alum Rock Rd . . . . GV
Aston Expressway . . . . FV
Aston Lane . . . . FV
Aston St. . . . . KY
Bath Row . . . . FX 5
Bearwood Rd . . . . EV
Belgrave Middleway . . . . . . FX
Birchfield Rd . . . . FV
Booth St. . . . . EV
Bordesley Green . . . . GV
Bordesley Green Rd . . . . . . GV
Bordesley Middleway . . . . . FX 10
Boulton Rd . . . . EV
Bowyer Rd . . . . GV
Bradford Rd . . . . HV
Bristol Rd . . . . EX
Bristol St. . . . . FX
Broad St. . . . . FV
Bromford Lane . . . . GV
Bromford Rd . . . . HV
Brook Lane . . . . GX
Brookvale Rd . . . . FV
Bull Ring . . . . KZ
Bull Ring Centre . . . . KZ
Bull St. . . . . KY 13
Calthorpe Rd . . . . FX 14
Camp Hill . . . . FX 15
Cape Hill . . . . EV
Caroline St. . . . . JY
Cattell Rd . . . . GV
Centenary Square . . . . JZ
Charlotte St. . . . . JY
Chester Rd . . . . HV
Church Lane . . . . EV
Church Rd EDGBASTON . . FX
Church Rd SHELDON . . . . . HX
Church Rd YARDLEY . . . . . HX
Church St. . . . . JY
City Rd . . . . EV
Coleshill Rd . . . . HV
College Rd . . . . GX
Colmore Circus . . . . KY
Colmore Row . . . . JZ
Commercial St. . . . . JZ
Constitution Hill . . . . JY
Corporation St. . . . . FV 20
Court Oak Rd . . . . EX
Coventry Rd . . . . GX
Dale End . . . . KZ 21
Darmouth Middleway . . . . . FV 22
Digbeth . . . . FV 24
Dudley Park Rd . . . . GX 25
Dudley Rd . . . . EV
Edgbaston Rd . . . . FX
Edmund St. . . . . JYZ
Fordhouse Lane . . . . FX
Fox Hollies Rd . . . . GX

Golden Hillock Rd . . . . GX
Gravelly Hill . . . . GV
Gravelly Hill Junction . . . . . GV
Great Charles St. . . . . JY
Hadden Way . . . . FX
Hagley Rd . . . . EX
Hall St. . . . . JY 29
Hampstead Rd . . . . FV
Harborne Lane . . . . EX
Harborne Park Rd . . . . EX
Harborne Rd . . . . EX
Heath St. . . . . EV
Highfield Rd . . . . GX
Highfield Rd SALTLEY . . . . GV
Highgate Rd . . . . FX
High St. . . . . KZ
High St. ASTON . . . . FV
High St. BORDESLEY . . . . . FX
High St. HARBORNE . . . . . EX
High St. KING'S HEATH . . . FX
High St. SALTLEY . . . . GV 31
High St. SMETHWICK . . . . EV
Hill St. . . . . JZ
Hob's Moat Rd . . . . HX
Hockley Circus . . . . FV
Hockley Hill . . . . JY
Holliday St. . . . . JZ
Holloway Circus . . . . JZ 32
Holloway Head . . . . JZ
Holyhead Rd . . . . EV
Hurst St. . . . . KZ
Icknield Port Rd . . . . EV
Icknield St. . . . . FV
Island Rd . . . . EV
Islington Row
Middleway . . . . FX 34
James Watt Queensay . . . . KY 35
Jennen's Rd . . . . FV 36
Kingsbury Rd . . . . HV
Ladywood Middleway . . . . EV
Lancaster Circus . . . . KY 39
Lancaster St. . . . . KY 41
Lawley St. . . . . FV
Lee Bank Middleway . . . . . FX 42
Lichfield Rd . . . . FV
Linden Rd . . . . EX
Livery St. . . . . JY
Lodge Rd . . . . EV
Lordswood Rd . . . . EX
Lozells Rd . . . . FV
Ludgate Hill . . . . JY
Masshouse Circus . . . . KY 43
Metchley Lane . . . . EX
Moor St. Queensway . . . . . KZ 46
Moseley Rd . . . . FX
Navigation St. . . . . JZ 49
Nechell's Parkway . . . . FV 50
Newhall St. . . . . JY
New John St. West . . . . . . FV
Newport Rd . . . . HV
New St. . . . . JZ
Newton St. . . . . KY 52
New Town Row . . . . FV 53
Norfolk Rd . . . . EX
Nursery Rd . . . . EX 55
Oak Tree Lane . . . . EX
Olton Bd East . . . . GX

Oxhill Rd . . . . EV
Paradise Circus . . . . JZ 56
Park St. . . . . KZ
Pershore Rd . . . . FX
Pershore St. . . . . KZ
Portland Rd . . . . EV
Princip St. . . . . KY
Priory Queensway . . . . KY 57
Priory Rd . . . . FX
Rabone Lane . . . . EV
Richmond Rd . . . . HX
Robin Hood Lane . . . . GX
Rolfe St. . . . . EV
Rookery Rd . . . . EV
Rotton Park Rd . . . . EV
St. Chads Circus . . . . JY 62
St. Chads Ringway . . . . KY 63
St. Martin's Circus . . . . KZ 64
St. Paul's Square . . . . JY
Salisbury Rd . . . . FX
Saltley Rd . . . . GV 66
Sandon Rd . . . . EV
Sand Pits Parade . . . . FV 67
Severn St. . . . . JZ
Shadwell St. . . . . KY 70
Shaftmoor Lane . . . . GX
Sheaf Lane . . . . HX
Sheldon Heath Rd . . . . HX
Shirley Rd . . . . GX
Smallbrook Queensway . . . KZ 71
Small Heath Highway . . . . GX
Snow Hill Queensway . . . . KY 73
Soho Rd . . . . EV
Solihull Lane . . . . GX 74
Spring Hill . . . . EV
Station Rd . . . . HV
Stechford Lane . . . . HV
Steelhouse Lane . . . . KY
Stockfield Rd . . . . GX
Stoney La MOSELEY . . . . . GX
Stoney La SHELDON . . . . . HX
Stratford Rd . . . . GX
Suffolk St. . . . . JZ
Summer Hill Rd . . . . FV 76
Summer Row . . . . JY 77
Temple Row . . . . KZ 80
Tyburn Rd . . . . GV
Vicarage Rd . . . . FX
Victoria Rd . . . . FV
Villa Rd . . . . FV
Wagon Lane . . . . HX
Wake Green Rd . . . . FX
Warwick Rd . . . . GX
Washwood Heath Rd . . . . . GV
Waterloo St. . . . . JZ 84
Watery Lane . . . . FX 85
Wellington Rd . . . . FV
Westfield Rd . . . . EX
Westley Rd . . . . GX 87
Wheeley's Lane . . . . FX 88
Whittal St. . . . . KY
Winson Green Rd . . . . EV
Witton Lane . . . . FV
Witton Rd . . . . FV
Wood End Rd . . . . GV
Yardley Rd . . . . HX
Yardley Wood Rd . . . . GX

Pleasant hotels and restaurants
are shown in the Guide by a red sign.

Please send us the names
of any where you have enjoyed your stay.

Your **Michelin Guide** will be even better.

Hyatt Regency, 2 Bridge St., B1 2JZ, ✆ 643 1234, Telex 335097, Fax 616 2323, ≤, ⅎ, ≘s, ⊡ - |◆| ⅏ rm ▤ TV ☎ ⇔ - 🏋 250. ⊠ AE ⓞ VISA. ⅏ JZ **a**
Meals - (see ***Number 282*** below) - ⊐ 12.00 - **315 rm** 99.00 **st.**, 4 suites - SB.

Swallow, 12 Hagley Rd, B16 8SJ, ✆ 452 1144, Fax 456 3442, ⅎ, ⊡ - |◆| ⅏ rm ▤ TV ☎ ♿ Ⓟ - 🏋 25. ⊠ AE ⓞ VISA FX **c**
Langtrys : **Meals** *(closed Sunday) a la carte* 19.35/32.20 **st.** 🍷 8.00 - (see also ***Sir Edward Elgar's*** below) - **94 rm** ⊐ 130.00/150.00 **st.**, 4 suites - SB.

Holiday Inn Crowne Plaza, Central Sq., Holliday St., B1 1HH, ✆ 631 2000, Fax 643 9018, ⅎ, ≘s, ⊡ - |◆| ⅏ rm ▤ TV ☎ ♿ Ⓟ - 🏋 150. ⊠ AE ⓞ VISA JZ **z**
Meals 13.95/17.95 **st.** and a la carte 🍷 8.50 - ⊐ 10.95 - **281 rm** 108.00/118.00 **st.**, 3 suites - SB.

Copthorne, Paradise Circus, B3 3HJ, ✆ 200 2727, Telex 339026, Fax 200 1197, ⅎ, ≘s, ⊡ - |◆| ⅏ rm ▤ rest TV ☎ ♿ Ⓟ - 🏋 180. ⊠ AE ⓞ VISA JCB. ⅏ JZ **e**
Meals a la carte 15.30/28.70 **st.** 🍷 6.00 - ⊐ 10.60 - **209 rm** 110.00/135.00, 3 suites.

Jonathan's, 16-24 Wolverhampton Rd, Oldbury, B68 0LH, W : 4 m. by A 456 ✆ 429 3757, Fax 434 3107, « Authentic Victorian furnishings and memorabilia » - ⅏ rest TV ☎ Ⓟ. ⊠ AE ⓞ VISA
Meals - English - *(closed Sunday dinner)* 12.90/24.50 **t.** and a la carte 🍷 6.00 - **19 rm** ⊐ 69.00/118.00 **st.**, 11 suites - SB.

Grand (Q.M.H.), Colmore Row, B3 2DA, ✆ 607 9955, Fax 233 1465 - |◆| ⅏ rm ▤ rest TV ☎ - 🏋 500. ⊠ AE ⓞ VISA JKY **c**
Meals 12.95/18.50 **st.** and a la carte. 🍷 7.00 - ⊐ 9.95 - **171 rm** 87.50/102.50 **st.**, 2 suites - SB.

Plough and Harrow (Forte), 135 Hagley Rd, Edgbaston, B16 8LS, ✆ 454 4111, Fax 454 1868, ⅏ - |◆| ⅏ TV ☎ Ⓟ - 🏋 70. ⊠ AE ⓞ VISA JCB EX **a**
Meals *(closed Saturday lunch)* 11.25/16.95 **t.** and a la carte 🍷 6.05 - ⊐ 7.95 - **42 rm** 75.00 **st.**, 2 suites - SB.

Forte Crest, Smallbrook Queensway, B5 4EW, ✆ 643 8171, Fax 631 2528, ⅎ, ≘s, ⊡, squash - |◆| ⅏ rm ▤ TV ☎ Ⓟ - 🏋 630. ⊠ AE ⓞ VISA JCB KZ **o**
Meals 12.95/14.95 **st.** and a la carte - ⊐ 10.85 - **252 rm** 89.00/119.00 **st.**, 1 suite - SB.

Strathallan Thistle, 225 Hagley Rd, Edgbaston, B16 9RY, ✆ 455 9777, Telex 336680, Fax 454 9432 - |◆| ⅏ rm ▤ rest TV ☎ Ⓟ - 🏋 170. ⊠ AE ⓞ VISA JCB EX **i**
Meals *(closed Saturday lunch)* 12.25/17.25 **st.** and a la carte 🍷 5.25 - ⊐ 9.25 - **163 rm** 79.00/89.00 **st.**, 4 suites.

Novotel, 70 Broad St., B1 2HT, ✆ 643 2000, Telex 335556, Fax 643 9796, ⅎ, ≘s - |◆| ⅏ rm ▤ rest TV ☎ ♿ Ⓟ - 🏋 250. ⊠ AE ⓞ VISA FV **a**
Meals 13.95/17.95 **st.** and a la carte 🍷 5.50 - ⊐ 8.00 - **148 rm** 71.00/81.00 **st.**

Chamberlain, Alcester St., B12 0PJ, ✆ 606 9000, Fax 606 9001 - |◆| ⅏ rest ▤ rest TV ☎ ⇔ - 🏋 400. ⊠ AE ⓞ VISA. ⅏ FX **r**
Meals *(closed Saturday lunch)* (carving rest.) 6.00/9.00 **t.** - **250 rm** ⊐ 35.00/40.00 **t.**

Royal Angus Thistle, St. Chad's, Queensway, B4 6HY, ✆ 236 4211, Fax 233 2195 - |◆| ⅏ rm TV ☎ Ⓟ - 🏋 140. ⊠ AE ⓞ VISA JCB KY **s**
Meals *(closed Saturday lunch)* 12.50/16.50 🍷 6.35 - ⊐ 9.25 - **131 rm** 79.00/99.00 **st.**, 2 suites - SB.

Apollo (Mount Charlotte), 243 Hagley Rd, Edgbaston, B16 9RA, ✆ 455 0271, Telex 336759, Fax 456 2394 - |◆| ⅏ rm ▤ rest TV ☎ Ⓟ - 🏋 150. ⊠ AE ⓞ VISA JCB EX **o**
Meals *(closed Saturday lunch and Bank Holidays)* (carving lunch) 9.95/12.80 **st.** and a la carte 🍷 5.30 - ⊐ 8.75 - **124 rm** 58.00/68.00 **st.**, 2 suites - SB.

XXXX **Sir Edward Elgar's** (at Swallow H.), 12 Hagley Rd, B16 8SJ, ✆ 452 1144, Fax 456 3442 - ▤ Ⓟ. ⊠ AE ⓞ VISA FX **c**
closed Saturday lunch - **Meals** 17.50/30.00 **st.** and a la carte 🍷 8.00.

XX **Number 282** (at Hyatt Regency H.), 2 Bridge St., B1 2JZ, ✆ 643 1234, Fax 616 2323 - ▤ ⇔. ⊠ AE ⓞ VISA JZ **a**
Meals 12.75/35.00 **t.** and a la carte 🍷 7.00.

XX **Henry's,** 27 St. Paul's Sq., B3 1RB, ✆ 200 1136, Fax 200 1190 - ▤. ⊠ AE ⓞ VISA JY **a**
closed Sunday and Bank Holidays - **Meals** - Chinese (Canton) - 13.00/20.00 **t.** and a la carte.

XX **Dynasty,** 93-103 Hurst St., B5 4TE, ✆ 622 1410 - ⊠ AE ⓞ VISA JCB KZ **e**
Meals - Chinese - (lunch by arrangement) 11.50 **st.** (dinner) and a la carte approx. 12.00/19.30 **st.**

XX Henry Wong, 283 High St., Harborne, B17 9QH, ✆ 427 9799 - ▤ EX **n**
Meals - Chinese (Canton) rest.

XX **Maharaja,** 23-25 Hurst St., B5 4AS, ✆ 622 2641 - ▤. ⊠ AE ⓞ VISA KZ **i**
closed Sunday, last week July and first week August - **Meals** - North Indian - a la carte 8.35/16.20 **t.**

XX **Franzl's,** 151 Milcote Rd, Bearwood, Smethwick, B67 5BN, ✆ 429 7920, Fax 429 1615 - ⊠ AE ⓞ VISA EV **a**
closed Sunday, Monday and first 3 weeks August - **Meals** - Austrian - (dinner only) 13.45/19.45 **st.** 🍷 4.50.

at Hall Green SE : 5 ¾ m. by A 41 on A 34 – ✉ Birmingham – ☎ 0121 :

Robin Hood (Toby), Stratford Rd, B28 9ES, ✆ 745 9900, Fax 733 1075 – rm TV ☎ P. AE VISA GX a
Meals (grill rest.) 9.25 **st.** and a la carte 5.00 – **30 rm** 59.95/69.95 **st.** – SB.

at Birmingham Airport SE : 9 m. by A 45 – HX – ✉ Birmingham – ☎ 0121 :

Novotel, Passenger Terminal, B26 3QL, ✆ 782 7000, Telex 338158, Fax 782 0445 – rm rest TV ☎ – 35. AE VISA
closed 24 and 25 December – **Meals** *(closed lunch Saturday, Sunday and Bank Holidays)* 12.00/18.00 **st.** and a la carte 6.50 – 7.50 – **195 rm** 72.50/119.00 **st.**

Forte Posthouse, Coventry Rd, B26 3QW, on A 45 ✆ 782 8141, Fax 782 2476 – rm TV ☎ P – 130. AE VISA JCB
Meals a la carte 10.70/22.15 **st.** 5.75 – 7.95 – **136 rm** 56.00 **st.** – SB.

at National Exhibition Centre SE : 9 ½ m. on A 45 – HX – ✉ Birmingham – ☎ 0121 :

Birmingham Metropole, Bickenhill, B40 1PP, ✆ 780 4242, Telex 336129, Fax 780 3923, – rm TV ☎ P – 2000. AE VISA
closed Christmas and New Year – **Meals** (carving rest.) 23.50 **st.** – ***Primavera :*** **Meals** - Italian - a la carte 28.45/35.50 **st.** – **787 rm** 145.00/220.00, 15 suites – SB.

Arden, Coventry Rd, B92 0EH, ✆ (01675) 443221, Fax 443221, – TV ☎ P – 170. AE VISA JCB
Meals (bar lunch Saturday) 12.10 **t.** and a la carte 4.85 – 8.00 – **146 rm** 69.00/79.00 **st.**

at Great Barr NW : 6 m. on A 34 – FV – ✉ Birmingham – ☎ 0121 :

Forte Posthouse, Chapel Lane, B43 7BG, ✆ 357 7444, Fax 357 7503, – rm TV ☎ P – 120. AE VISA JCB.
Meals a la carte 15.20/23.60 **t.** – 7.95 – **192 rm** 56.00 **st.** – SB.

at West Bromwich NW : 6 m. on A 41 – EV – ✉ Birmingham – ☎ 0121 :

Moat House Birmingham (Q.M.H.), Birmingham Rd, B70 6RS, ✆ 609 9988, Fax 525 7403 – rm rest TV ☎ P – 180. AE VISA JCB
Meals 6.50/14.95 **st.** and a la carte 5.95 – 8.50 – **171 rm** 65.00/90.00 **st.** – SB.

BRISTOL Avon 403 404 M 29 – pop. 376 146 – ☎ 0117.

St. Nicholas Church, St. Nicholas St., BS1 1UE ✆ 926 0767.

Manchester 121 – Birmingham 91.

XX ✿✿ **Lettonie** (Blunos), 9 Druid Hill, Stoke Bishop, BS9 1EW, ✆ 968 6456, Fax 968 6943, (probably moving during 1996) – AE VISA AV a
closed Sunday, Monday, 2 weeks August and 2 weeks Christmas – **Meals** - French - (booking essential) 17.95/34.50 **t.** 7.85
Spec. Seared scallops on a parsnip purée with reduced chicken juices, Roast skirt of beef with a rich truffle sauce, Mascarpone and peach vinegar ice cream with raspberries.

EDINBURGH Midlothian. (Lothian) 401 K 16 Scotland G. – pop. 418 914 – ☎ 0131.

See : City★★★ Edinburgh International Festival★★★ (August) – National Gallery of Scotland★★★ DY **M4** Royal Botanic Garden★★★ The Castle★★ DYZ : site★★★ – Palace Block (Honours of Scotland★★★) St. Margaret's Chapel (✻★★★) Great Hall (Hammerbeam Roof★★) ≤★★ from Argyle and Mill's Mount DZ – Abbey and Palace of Holyroodhouse★★ (Plasterwork Ceilings★★★, ✻★★ from Arthur's Seat) – Royal Mile★★ : St. Giles' Cathedral★★ (Crown Spire★★★) EYZ Gladstone's Land★ EYZ **A** – Canongate Talbooth★ EY **B** – New Town★★ (Charlotte Square★★★ CY **14** Royal Museum of Scotland (Antiquities)★★ EZ **M2** – The Georgian House ★ CY **D** National Portrait Gallery★ EY **M3** Dundas House★ EY **E**) – Victoria Street★ EZ **84** Scott Monument★ (≤★) EY **F** – Craigmillar Castle★ Calton Hill (✻★★★ from Nelson's Monument) EY.

Envir. : Edinburgh Zoo★★ – Hill End Ski Centre (✻★★), S : 5 ½ m. by A 702 – The Royal Observatory (West Tower ≤★) – Ingleston, Scottish Agricultural Museum★, W : 6 ½m. by A 8.

Exc. : Rosslyn Chapel★★ (Apprentice Pillar★★★) S : 7 ½ m. by A 701 and B 7006 – Forth Bridges★★, NW : 9 ½ m. by A 90 – Hopetoun House★★, NW : 11 ½ m. by A 90 and A 904 – Dalmeny★ (Dalmeny House★, St. Cuthbert's Church★ - Norman South Doorway★★) NW : 7 m. by A 90 – Crichton Castle (Italianate Courtyard range★), SE : 10 m. by A 7 and B 6372.

18, 18 Braid Hills, Braid Hills Rd ✆ 447 6666 – 18 Craigmillar Park, 1 Observatory Rd ✆ 667 2837 – 18 Carrick Knowe, Glendevon Park ✆ 337 1096 – 18 Duddingston Road West ✆ 661 1005 – 18 Silverknowes, Parkway ✆ 336 3843 – 18 Liberton, 297 Gilmerton Rd ✆ 664 8580 9 Portobello, Stanley St. ✆ 669 4361 – 18 (2x) Dalmahoy Hotel C.C., Kirknewton ✆ 333 4105/1845.

Edinburgh Airport : ✆ 333 1000, W : 6 m. by A 8 – **Terminal :** Waverley Bridge.

✆ 0345 090700.

Edinburgh Scotland Information Centre, 3 Princes St., EH2 2QP ✆ 557 1700 – Edinburgh Airport, Tourist Information Desk ✆ 333 2167.

Glasgow 46 – Newcastle upon Tyne 105.

EDINBURGH

Street	Grid	No.
Castle Street	DY	
Frederick Street	DY	
George Street	DY	
Hanover Street	DY	
High Street	EYZ	37
Lawnmarket	EYZ	46
Princes Street	DY	
St. James Centre	EY	
Waverley Market	EY	
Bernard Terrace	EZ	3
Bread Street	DZ	6
Bristo Place	EZ	7
Candlemaker Row	EZ	9
Castlehill	DZ	10
Chambers Street	EZ	12
Chapel Street	EZ	13
Charlotte Square	CY	14
Deanhaugh Street	CY	23
Douglas Gardens	CY	25
Drummond Street	EZ	27
Forrest Road	EZ	31
Gardner's Crescent	CZ	32
George IV Bridge	EZ	33
Gassmarket	DZ	35
Home Street	DZ	38
Hope Street	CY	39
Johnston Terrace	DZ	42
King's Bridge	DZ	44
King's Stables Road	DZ	45
Leith Street	EY	47
Leven Street	DZ	48
Lothian Street	EZ	51
Mound (The)	DY	55
North Bridge	EY	61
North St. Andrew Street	EY	66
Raeburn Place	CY	69
Randolph Crescent	CY	71
St. Andrew Square	EY	73
St. Mary's Street	EY	75
Shandwick Place	CYZ	77
South Charlotte Street	DY	78
South St. David Street	DEY	79
Spittal Street	DZ	83
Victoria Street	EZ	84
Waterloo Place	EY	87
Waverley Bridge	EY	89
West Maitland Street	CZ	92

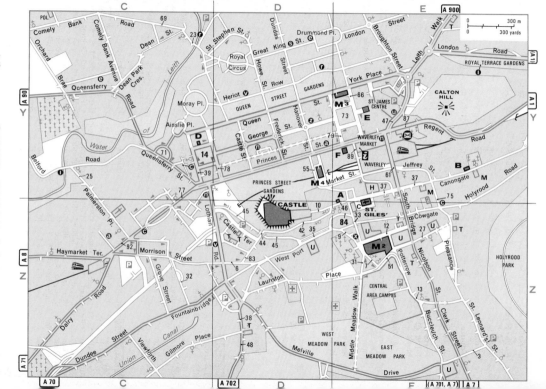

Caledonian (Q.M.H.), Princes St., EH1 2AB, ☎ 459 9988, Fax 225 6632 – |♣| ⇆ rm ▤ rest TV ☎ ♿ P – 🏛 300. AE VISA. ✂ CY **n**
Carriages : **Meals** 20.60/29.40 **st.** and a la carte 7.20 - (see also ***Pompadour*** below) – ☕ 14.50 – **223 rm** 135.50/299.00 **st.**, 11 suites – SB.

Balmoral (Forte), Princes St., EH2 2EQ, ☎ 556 2414, Telex 727282, Fax 557 8740, ⛹, ≘s, 🏊 – |♣| ⇆ rm ▤ rest TV ☎ ♿ 🚗 – 🏛 380. AE VISA JCB. ✂ EY **n**
Bridges : **Meals** 19.95/29.50 **st.** 7.50 - (see also ***Grill*** below) – ☕ 14.50 – **168 rm** 120.00/170.00 **st.**, 21 suites – SB.

Sheraton Grand, 1 Festival Sq., EH3 9SR, ☎ 229 9131, Fax 229 6254, ⛹, ≘s, 🏊 – |♣| ⇆ rm ▤ TV ☎ ♿ P – 🏛 500. AE VISA JCB. ✂ CDZ **v**
Grill : **Meals** *(closed Saturday lunch and Sunday)* 19.95/27.50 **t.** and a la carte 9.00 – *Terrace* : **Meals** 18.00 **t.** and a la carte 7.00 – ☕ 14.00 – **255 rm** 140.00/205.00 **st.**, 6 suites.

George Inter-Continental, 19-21 George St., EH2 2PB, ☎ 225 1251, Fax 226 5644 – |♣| ⇆ rm TV ☎ P – 🏛 200. AE VISA JCB. ✂ DY **z**
Meals 12.95/16.95 **st.** and a la carte 6.00 – **193 rm** ☕ 90.00/165.00 **t.**, 2 suites – SB.

Dalmahoy H. Country Club Resort (Country Club) ⛺, Kirknewton, EH27 8EB, SW : 7 m. on A 71 ☎ 333 1845, Fax 333 1433, ≤, ⛹, ≘s, 🏊, 18, park, squash – |♣| ⇆ ▤ rest TV ☎ ♿ P – 🏛 190. AE VISA. ✂
Meals *(closed Saturday lunch)* 14.50/23.50 **t.** and dinner a la carte – ☕ 9.50 – **150 rm** 109.00 **t.**, 1 suite – SB.

Howard, 32-36 Gt. King St., EH3 6QH, ☎ 557 3500, Fax 557 6515, « Georgian town houses » – |♣| ⇆ rest TV ☎ P – 🏛 40. AE VISA DY **s**
closed 24 December-2 January – **Meals** (dinner only) a la carte 18.55/27.30 **st.** 6.95 – **16 rm** ☕ 110.00/225.00 **st.** – SB.

Swallow Royal Scot, 111 Glasgow Rd, EH12 8NF, W : 4 ½ m. on A 8 ☎ 334 9191, Fax 316 4507, ⛹, ≘s, 🏊 – |♣| ⇆ rm ▤ rest TV ☎ P – 🏛 300. AE VISA
Meals 15.50/21.00 **st.** and a la carte 6.50 – **255 rm** ☕ 105.00/135.00 **st.**, 4 suites – SB.

Hilton National, 69 Belford Rd, EH4 3DG, ☎ 332 2545, Telex 727979, Fax 332 3805 – |♣| ⇆ rm TV ☎ ♿ P – 🏛 130. AE VISA JCB CY **i**
Meals (bar lunch Saturday and Sunday) 13.00/17.50 **st.** and dinner a la carte 7.00 – ☕ 11.00 – **144 rm** 90.00/250.00 **st.**

Edinburgh Capital (Q.M.H.), Clermiston Rd, EH12 6UG, ☎ 535 9988, Fax 334 9712, ⛹, ≘s, 🏊 – |♣| ⇆ rm TV ☎ ♿ P – 🏛 300. AE VISA by A 8 CZ
Meals 16.75 **st.** (dinner) and a la carte 9.00/21.00 **st.** – ☕ 10.50 – **111 rm** 90.00/120.00 **st.** – SB.

Mount Royal (Jarvis), 53 Princes St., EH2 2DZ, ☎ 225 7161, Fax 220 4671, ≤ – |♣| TV ☎ – 🏛 50. AE VISA. ✂ DY **a**
Meals 8.95/14.95 **st.** and dinner a la carte – ☕ 8.75 – **156 rm** 95.00/135.00 **st.** – SB.

Royal Terrace, 18 Royal Terrace, EH7 5AQ, ☎ 557 3222, Fax 557 5334, ⛹, ≘s, 🏊, 🌳 – |♣| TV ☎ – 🏛 80. AE VISA JCB. ✂ EY **i**
Meals *(closed lunch Saturday and Sunday)* a la carte 14.95/27.00 **t.** – ☕ 9.50 – **92 rm** 105.00/145.00 **st.**, 1 suite.

Forte Posthouse Edinburgh, Corstorphine Rd, EH12 6UA, W : 3 m. on A 8 ☎ 334 0390, Fax 334 9237 – |♣| ⇆ rm TV ☎ P – 🏛 120. AE VISA JCB. ✂
Meals a la carte 13.00/24.20 **st.** 6.95 – ☕ 7.95 – **204 rm** 69.00 **st.** – SB.

King James Thistle, 107 Leith St., EH1 3SW, ☎ 556 0111, Fax 557 5333 – |♣| ⇆ rm ▤ TV ☎ – 🏛 250. AE VISA JCB. ✂ EY **u**
Meals 12.50/19.50 **t.** and a la carte 6.10 – ☕ 9.95 – **142 rm** 110.00/135.00 **st.**, 5 suites – SB.

Stakis Edinburgh Grosvenor, Grosvenor St., EH12 5EF, ☎ 226 6001, Fax 220 2387 – |♣| TV ☎ ♿ – 🏛 300. AE VISA JCB CZ **a**
Meals *(closed lunch Saturday and Sunday)* 10.95/16.95 and a la carte 6.75 – ☕ 8.50 – **135 rm** 95.00/105.00 **st.**, 1 suite – SB.

Channings, South Learmonth Gdns, EH4 1EZ, ☎ 315 2226, Fax 332 9631 – |♣| ⇆ rest TV ☎. AE VISA. ✂ CY **e**
closed 25 to 27 December – **Meals** (light lunch Saturday) 9.95/19.50 **st.** and dinner a la carte – **48 rm** ☕ 92.00/132.00 **st.** – SB.

Malmaison, 1 Tower Pl., Leith, EH6 7DB, NE : 2 m. by A 900 ☎ 555 6868, Fax 555 6999, « Contemporary interior » – |♣| TV ☎ ♿ P – 🏛 30. AE VISA
Meals - Brasserie - a la carte 14.50/19.95 **t.** 8.50 – ☕ 10.00 – **19 rm** 75.00/85.00 **t.**, 6 suites.

Ellersly Country House (Jarvis), 4 Ellersly Rd, EH12 6HZ, ☎ 337 6888, Fax 313 2543, 🌳 – |♣| ⇆ rm TV ☎ P – 🏛 70. AE VISA by A 8 CZ
Meals *(closed Saturday lunch)* 14.95 **t.** and a la carte 6.50 – ☕ 8.50 – **57 rm** 99.00/125.00 **t.** – SB.

Holiday Inn Garden Court, 107 Queensferry Rd, EH4 3HL, ☎ 332 2442, Fax 332 3408, ≤, ⛹ – |♣| ⇆ rm ▤ rest TV ☎ ♿ P – 🏛 60. AE VISA JCB by A 90 CY
Meals (bar lunch Monday to Saturday)/dinner 14.50 **st.** and a la carte 7.95 – ☕ 8.95 – **119 rm** 79.50/89.50 **st.** – SB.

17 Abercromby Place without rest., 17 Abercromby Pl., EH3 6LB, 557 8036, Fax 558 3453, « Georgian town house » - VISA. DY r
closed Christmas - **6 rm** 35.00/70.00.

Drummond House without rest., 17 Drummond Pl., EH3 6PL, 557 9189, Fax 557 9189, « Georgian town house » - VISA. DY e
3 rm 65.00/90.00 **st.**

Sibbet House without rest., 26 Northumberland St., EH3 6LS, 556 1078, Fax 557 9445, « Georgian town house » - VISA. DY x
3 rm 55.00/70.00 **s.**

27 Heriot Row, 27 Heriot Row, EH3 6EN, 225 9474, Fax 220 1699, « Georgian town house », - VISA. DY v
Meals (by arrangement) (communal dining) 25.00/30.00 **st.** - **3 rm** 45.00/70.00 **st.**

Pompadour (at Caledonian H.), Princes St., EH1 2AB, 459 9988, Fax 225 6632 - AE VISA CY n
closed lunch Saturday and Sunday - **Meals** 23.50/42.00 **st.** and dinner a la carte 7.60.

Grill (at Balmoral H.), 1 Princes St., EH2 2EQ, 556 2414, Telex 727282, Fax 557 3747 - AE VISA JCB EY n
closed lunch Saturday and Sunday - **Meals** 21.50/35.00 **st.** and a la carte 7.00.

Vintners Room, The Vaults, 87 Giles St., Leith, EH6 6BZ, 554 6767, Fax 467 7130 - AE VISA by A 900 EY
closed Sunday and 2 weeks Christmas-New Year - **Meals** a la carte 11.50/24.75 **t.** 5.00.

Martins, 70 Rose St., North Lane, EH2 3DX, 225 3106 - AE VISA DY n
closed Saturday lunch, Sunday, Monday, 1 week May-June, 1 week September-October and 23 December-22 January - **Meals** (booking essential) 15.00 **t.** (lunch) and a la carte 24.50/30.55 **t.** 5.00.

L'Auberge, 56 St. Mary's St., EH1 1SX, 556 5888, Fax 556 2588 - AE VISA JCB EYZ c
closed 25-26 December and 1 to 3 January - **Meals** - French - 16.50/24.50 **t.** and a la carte 6.00.

Raffaelli, 10-11 Randolph Pl., EH3 7TA, 225 6060, Fax 225 8830 - AE VISA CY c
closed Saturday lunch, Sunday and Bank Holidays - **Meals** - Italian - a la carte 13.95/22.90 **t.** 4.90.

Lancer's Brasserie, 5 Hamilton Pl., Stockbridge, EH3 5BA, 332 3444 - AE VISA CY r
Meals - North Indian - 8.95 **t.** (lunch) and a la carte 10.45/15.35 **t.**

Indian Cavalry Club, 3 Atholl Pl., EH3 8HP, 228 3282, Fax 225 1911 - AE VISA CZ c
Meals - Indian - 6.95/16.95 **t.** and a la carte.

Merchants, 17 Merchant St., EH1 2QD, off Candlemaker Row, (under bridge) 225 4009, Fax 557 9318 - AE VISA JCB EZ x
closed Sunday - **Meals** (booking essential) 8.95/12.50 **t.** and a la carte 5.00.

Denzler's 121, 121 Constitution St., EH6 7AE, 554 3268, Fax 467 7239 - AE VISA JCB on A 900 EY
closed Saturday lunch, Sunday, Monday, 25 and 26 December, 1 and 2 January and last 2 weeks July - **Meals** 7.75/17.50 **st.** and a la carte 5.35.

Atrium, 10 Cambridge St., EH1 2ED, 228 8882, Fax 459 1060 - AE VISA DZ c
closed Saturday lunch, Sunday and 1 week Christmas - **Meals** a la carte 20.50/27.50 **t.** 6.50.

at Edinburgh International Airport W : 7 ½ m. by A 8 - CZ - Edinburgh - 0131 :

Stakis Edinburgh Airport, , EH28 8LL, 519 4400, Fax 519 4422 - rm rest - 220. AE VISA
Meals 5.95/25.00 **st.** and a la carte 6.50 - 8.50 - **134 rm** 89.00/99.00 **st.** - SB .

at Ingliston W : 7 ¾ m. on A 8 - CZ - Edinburgh - 0131 :

Norton House (Virgin) ,, EH28 8LX, on A 8 333 1275, Fax 333 5305, , park - rm - 250. AE VISA
Meals *(closed Saturday lunch)* 15.50/22.50 **t.** and a la carte - **46 rm** 104.00/155.00 **st.**, 1 suite - SB .

GLASGOW Lanark. (Strathclyde) 401 402 H 16 **Scotland G.** – pop. 662 853 – ☎ 0141.

See : City★★★ – Cathedral★★★ (≤★) DZ – The Burrell Collection★★★ – Hunterian Art Gallery★★ (Whistler Collection★★★ – Mackintosh Wing★★★) CY **M4** – Museum of Transport★★ (Scottish Built Cars★★★, The Clyde Room of Ship Models★★★) – Art Gallery and Museum Kelvingrove★★ CY – Pollok House★ (The Paintings★★) – Tolbooth Steeple★ DZ **A** – Hunterian Museum (Coin and Medal Collection★) CY **M1** – City Chambers★ DZ **C** – Glasgow School of Art★ CY **B** – Necropolis (≤★ of Cathedral) DYZ.

Exc. : The Trossachs★★★, N : 31 m. by A 879, A 81 and A 821 – Loch Lomond★★, NW : 19 m. by A 82.

18 Littlehill, Auchinairn Rd ℘ 772 1916 – 18 Deaconsbank, Rouken Glen Park, Stewarton Rd, Eastwood ℘ 638 7044 – 18 Linn Park, Simshill Rd ℘ 637 5871 – 18 Lethamhill, Cumbernauld Rd ℘ 770 6220 – 9 Alexandra Park, Dennistown ℘ 556 3991 – 9 King's Park, 150a Croftpark Av., Croftfoot ℘ 634 4745 – 9 Knightswood, Lincoln Av. ℘ 959 2131 9 Ruchill, Brassey St. ℘ 946 7676.

Access to Oban by helicopter.

Glasgow Airport : ℘ 887 1111, W : 8 m. by M 8 – **Terminal :** Coach service from Glasgow Central and Queen Street main line Railway Stations and from Anderston Cross and Buchanan Bus Stations Prestwick Airport : ℘ (01292) 79822 **Terminal :** Buchanan Bus Station.

℘ 0345 090700.

35 St. Vincent Pl., G1 2ER ℘ 204 4400 – Glasgow Airport, Tourist Information Desk, Paisley ℘ 848 4440.

Edinburgh 46 – Manchester 221.

Plans on following pages

Glasgow Hilton, 1 William St., G3 8HT, ℘ 204 5555, Fax 204 5004, ≤, Lo, ≘s, – |‡| ⇔ rm ▤ TV ☎ ♿ P – 🏠 1000. AE ① VISA JCB. ✻ CZ s
Minsky's **: Meals** 16.50/28.00 **t.** and a la carte 7.00 – (see also ***Camerons*** below) – ☐ 12.50 – **315 rm** 120.00/145.00 **st.**, 4 suites.

Glasgow Moat House (Q.M.H.), Congress Rd, G3 8QT, ℘ 306 9988, Fax 221 2022, ≤, Lo, ≘s, – |‡| ⇔ rm ▤ TV ☎ ♿ P – 🏠 800. AE ① VISA. ✻ CZ r
***Mariners* : Meals** 14.50/47.00 **t.** and dinner a la carte 7.50 – ***Pointhouse* : Meals** 15.95/18.95 **t.** and a la carte 7.50 – ☐ 10.95 – **267 rm** 112.00 **st.**, 16 suites – SB.

Glasgow Marriott, 500 Argyle St., Anderston, G3 8RR, ℘ 226 5577, Fax 221 7676, Lo, ≘s, , squash – |‡| ⇔ rm ▤ TV ☎ ♿ P – 🏠 720. AE ① VISA CZ a
Meals 12.95/15.95 **st.** and a la carte 7.00 – ☐ 10.25 – **293 rm** 84.00 **st.**, 5 suites – SB.

Forte Crest, Bothwell St., G2 7EN, ℘ 248 2656, Telex 77440, Fax 221 8986, ≤ – |‡| ⇔ rm ▤ TV ☎ P – 🏠 800. AE ① VISA CZ z
Meals 14.95 **st.** and a la carte – ☐ 10.95 – **248 rm** 99.00 **st.**, 3 suites – SB.

✿ **One Devonshire Gardens,** 1 Devonshire Gdns, G12 OUX, ℘ 339 2001, Fax 337 1663, « Opulent interior design » – TV ☎ – 🏠 50. AE ① VISA by A 82 CY
Meals *(closed Saturday lunch)* 25.00/40.00 **t.** 8.00 – ☐ 13.50 – **25 rm** 135.00/160.00 **t.**, 2 suites
Spec. Seared scallops with Thai sauce, Tournedos of Scottish beef fillet on a confit of shallots and sweet garlic, Creamed cold baked rice pudding with Armagnac soaked prunes.

Glasgow Thistle (Mount Charlotte), 36 Cambridge St., G2 3HN, ℘ 332 3311, Telex 777334, Fax 332 4050 – |‡| ⇔ rm TV ☎ ♿ P – 🏠 1500. AE ① VISA JCB DY z
Meals (carving rest.) 12.00/25.00 **st.** and a la carte 6.00 – ☐ 11.50 – **304 rm** 90.00/140.00 **st.**, 3 suites – SB.

Devonshire, 5 Devonshire Gdns, G12 0UX, ℘ 339 7878, Fax 339 3980 – TV ☎ – 🏠 50. AE ① VISA. ✻ by A 82 CY
Meals *(closed Saturday lunch and Sunday)* 15.00/35.00 **st.** and a la carte 7.95 – ☐ 10.75 – **14 rm** 105.00/175.00 **st.** – SB.

Copthorne Glasgow, George Sq., G2 1DS, ℘ 332 6711, Telex 778147, Fax 332 4264 – |‡| ⇔ rm TV ☎ – 🏠 100. AE ① VISA DZ n
Meals 12.95/15.95 **t.** and a la carte 5.25 – ☐ 9.25 – **136 rm** 96.50/109.00 **st.**, 4 suites.

Malmaison, 278 West George St., G2 4LL, ℘ 221 6400, Fax 221 6411, « Contemporary interior » – TV ☎. AE ① VISA. ✻ CY c
Meals - Brasserie - a la carte 15.95/19.90 **st.** – ☐ 10.00 – **17 rm** 80.00 **st.**, 4 suites.

Swallow Glasgow, 517 Paisley Rd West, G51 1RW, ℘ 427 3146, Fax 427 4059, Lo, ≘s, – |‡| ▤ rest TV ☎ P – 🏠 350. AE ① VISA by A 8 CZ
Meals *(closed Saturday lunch)* (carving lunch) 12.00/16.75 **st.** and dinner a la carte – **117 rm** ☐ 85.00/130.00 **st.** – SB.

Tinto Firs Thistle, 470 Kilmarnock Rd, G43 2BB, ℘ 637 2353, Fax 633 1340 – TV ☎ P – 🏠 50. AE ① VISA JCB by A 77 DZ
Meals (bar lunch Monday and Saturday) 12.95/19.95 **t.** and a la carte 5.50 – **25 rm** ☐ 75.00/95.00 **st.**, 2 suites – SB.

Carrick (Forte), 377 Argyle St., G2 8LL, ℘ 248 2355, Fax 221 1014 – |‡| ⇔ rm TV ☎ – 🏠 80. AE ① VISA JCB CZ x
Meals 9.50/21.00 **st.** and dinner a la carte 3.75 – ☐ 8.95 – **121 rm** 62.00 **st.** – SB.

Charing Cross Tower, Elmbank Gdns, G2 4PP, pedestrianised area off Bath St. ℘ 221 1000, Fax 248 1000, ≤ – |‡| ⇔ rm TV ☎. AE ① VISA. ✻ CY a
Meals (bar lunch)/dinner 8.95 **st.** – ☐ 4.90 – **276 rm** 38.50 **st.**

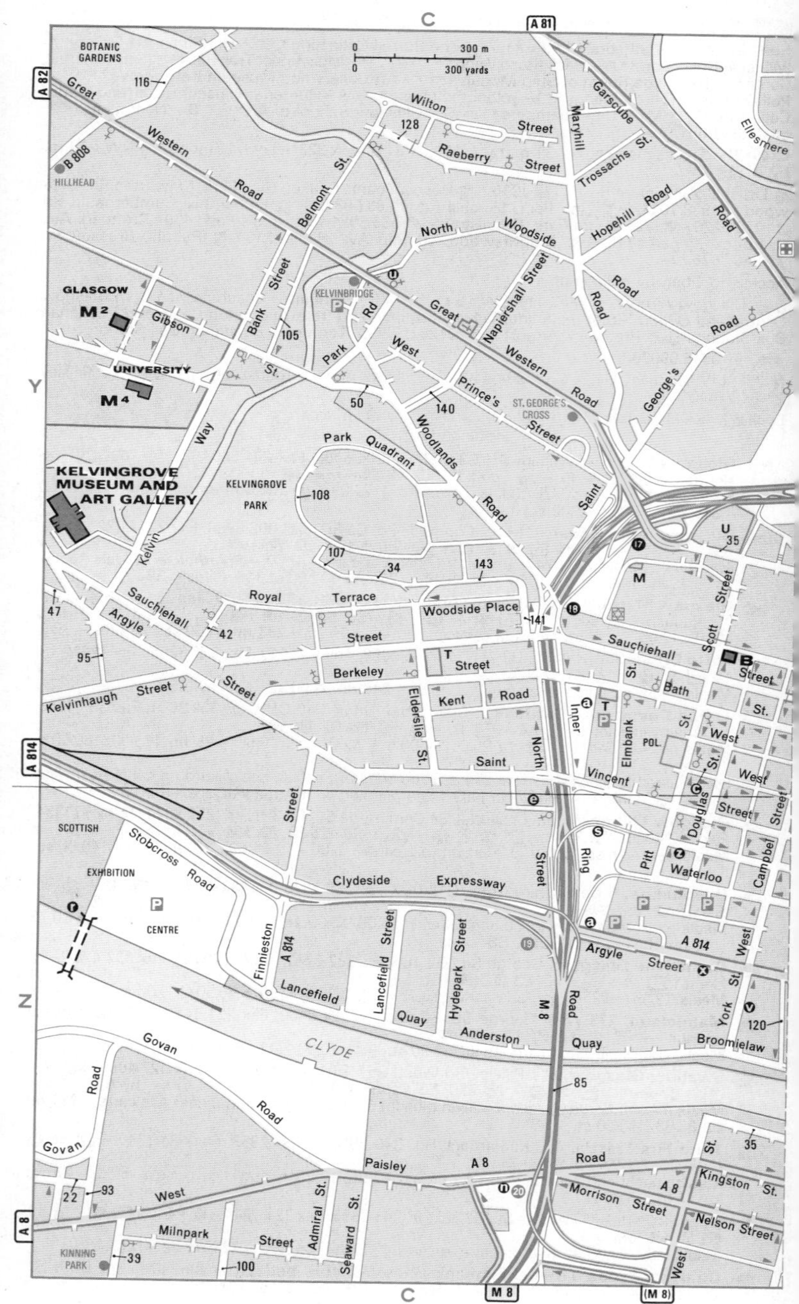

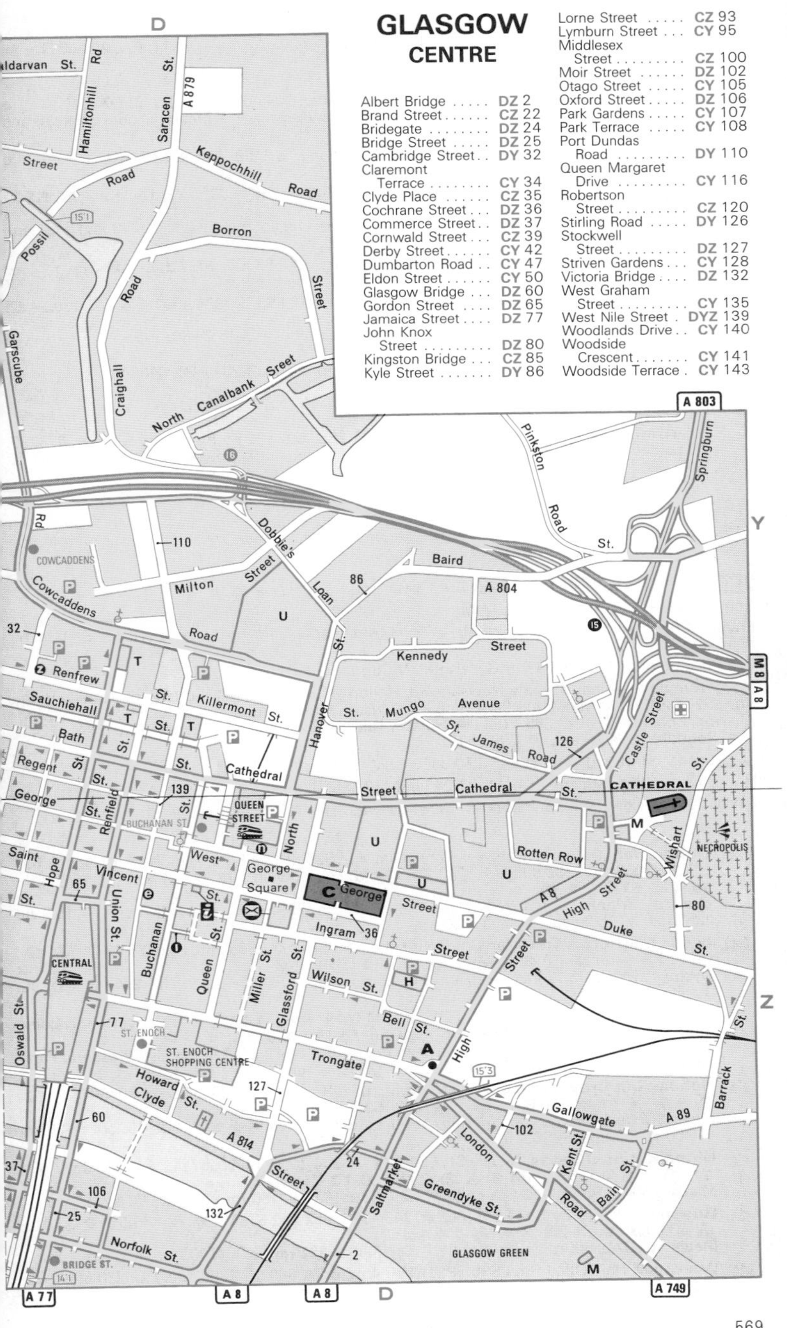
GLASGOW
CENTRE
Albert Bridge ..... DZ 2
Brand Street ...... CZ 22
Bridegate .... DZ 24
Bridge Street ..... DZ 25
Cambridge Street .. DY 32
Claremont Terrace .... CY 34
Clyde Place ...... CZ 35
Cochrane Street ... DZ 36
Commerce Street .. DZ 37
Cornwald Street ... CZ 39
Derby Street ...... CY 42
Dumbarton Road .. CY 47
Eldon Street ...... CY 50
Glasgow Bridge ... DZ 60
Gordon Street .... DZ 65
Jamaica Street .... DZ 77
John Knox Street .... DZ 80
Kingston Bridge ... CZ 85
Kyle Street .... DY 86
Lorne Street ..... CZ 93
Lymburn Street ... CY 95
Middlesex Street .... CZ 100
Moir Street ...... DZ 102
Otago Street ..... CY 105
Oxford Street ..... DZ 106
Park Gardens ..... CY 107
Park Terrace ..... CY 108
Port Dundas Road .... DY 110
Queen Margaret Drive .... CY 116
Robertson Street .... CZ 120
Stirling Road ..... DY 126
Stockwell Street .... DZ 127
Striven Gardens ... CY 128
Victoria Bridge .... DZ 132
West Graham Street .... CY 135
West Nile Street . DYZ 139
Woodlands Drive .. CY 140
Woodside Crescent .... CY 141
Woodside Terrace . CY 143
D
Y
Z
A 803
A 879
M 8
A 8
A 804
A 77
A 749
A 89
A 814
Keppochhill Road
Borron Street
Possil Road
Garscube Road
Craighall Road
North Canalbank Street
Hamiltonhill Rd
Saracen St.
Pinkston Road
Springburn
Baird St.
Dobbie's Loan
Milton Street
Cowcaddens Road
COWCADDENS
Kennedy Street
St. Mungo Avenue
St. James Road
Castle Street
Renfrew St.
Sauchiehall St.
Killermont St.
Bath St.
Regent St.
Cathedral Street
Cathedral St.
CATHEDRAL
NECROPOLIS
George St.
West George St.
George Square
QUEEN STREET
BUCHANAN ST.
Hanover St.
North
Rotten Row
Wishart
Saint Vincent St.
Hope St.
Renfield St.
Union St.
Buchanan St.
Queen St.
Ingram Street
High Street
Duke St.
Miller St.
Glassford St.
Wilson St.
Bell St.
CENTRAL
Oswald St.
ST. ENOCH
ST. ENOCH SHOPPING CENTRE
Trongate
Howard St.
Clyde Street
Gallowgate
Barrack St.
London Road
Saltmarket
Greendyke St.
Kent St.
Bain St.
Norfolk St.
BRIDGE ST.
GLASGOW GREEN

XXXX **Camerons** (at Glasgow Hilton H.), 1 William St., G3 8HT, ☎ 204 5511, Fax 204 5004 – ▤ P. AE VISA JCB CZ s
Meals *(closed Saturday lunch and Sunday)* 20.50/29.50 **t.** and a la carte 7.00.

XXX **Buttery,** 652 Argyle St., G3 8UF, ☎ 221 8188, Fax 204 4639 – P. AE VISA CZ e
closed Saturday lunch, Sunday 1 January and 25 December – **Meals** 14.85 **st.** (lunch) and a la carte 21.35/31.00 **t.**

XXX **Yes,** 22 West Nile St., G1 2PW, ☎ 221 8044, Fax 248 9159 – ▤. AE VISA DZ e
closed Sunday and Bank Holidays – **Meals** 11.95/24.95 **st.** and a la carte 10.50.

XXX **Rogano,** 11 Exchange Pl., G1 3AN, ☎ 248 4055, Fax 248 2608, « Art Deco » – ▤. AE VISA DZ i
closed 1-3 January and 25-26 December – **Meals** - Seafood - 16.50 **t.** (lunch) and a la carte 25.40/31.75.

XX **Ho Wong,** 82 York St., G2 3LE, ☎ 221 3550, Fax 248 5330 – ▤. AE VISA JCB CZ v
Meals - Chinese (Peking) - 7.50/15.00 **t.** and a la carte 5.95.

X **Ubiquitous Chip,** 12 Ashton Lane, off Byres Rd, G12 8SJ, ☎ 334 5007, Fax 337 1302 – AE VISA by A 808 CY
closed 1 January and 25 and 31 December – **Meals** a la carte 21.80/30.80 **t.**

ULLAPOOL

Ross and Cromarty. (Highland) 401 E 10 – pop. 1 231 – ☎ 01854.

West Shore St., IV26 2UR ☎ 612135 (summer only).

Edinburgh 215 – Glasgow 225 – Inverness 59 – Aberdeen 168.

✿✿ **Altnaharrie Inn** (Gunn Eriksen), IV26 2SS, SW : ½ m. by private ferry ☎ 633230, ← Loch Broom and Ullapool, **« Idyllic setting on banks of Loch Broom »**, – . AE VISA.
Easter-early November – **Meals** (booking essential) (dinner only) 55.00/65.00 **st.** 5.70 – **8 rm** (dinner included) 195.00/340.00 **st.**
Spec. Fillet of Sika deer with a mushroom and grape ravioli and two sauces, Wild salmon with asparagus, capers and ginger in a champagne aspic, Clear 'soup' of lobster with lemon grass, herbs and a small pastry.

LEEDS

W. Yorks. 402 P 22 **Great Britain G.** – pop. 680 722 – ☎ 0113.

See : City★ – City Art Gallery★ DZ **M.**

Envir. : Kirkstall Abbey★ , NW : 3 m. by A 65 – Templenewsam★ (decorative arts★) , E : 5 m. by A 64 and A 63 **D.**

Exc. : Harewood House★★ (The Gallery★) , N : 8 m. by A 61.

18, 18 Temple Newsam, Temple Newsam Rd, Halton ☎ 264 5624 – 18 Gotts Park, Armley Ridge Rd, ☎ 234 2019 – 18 Middleton Park, Ring Rd, Beeston Park, Middleton ☎ 270 9506 – 18, 9 Moor Allerton, Coal Rd, Wike ☎ 266 1154 – 18 Howley Hall, Scotchman Lane, Morley ☎ (01924) 472432 – 9 Roundhay, Park Lane ☎ 266 2695.

Leeds - Bradford Airport : ☎ 250 9696, NW : 8 m. by A 65 and A 658.

The Arcade, City Station, LS1 1PL ☎ 247 8301/247 8302.

London 204 – Liverpool 75 – Manchester 43 – Newcastle upon Tyne 95 – Nottingham 74.

Plan opposite

Oulton Hall (De Vere), Rothwell Lane, Oulton, LS26 8HN, SE : 5 ½ m. by A 61 and A 639 ☎ 282 1000, Fax 282 8066, ←, , , , 18, , squash – ▤ rest TV P – 330. AE VISA
Bronte : **Meals** *(closed Saturday lunch)* 12.95/23.45 **st.** and a la carte – **150 rm** 115.00/125.00 **st.**, 2 suites – SB .

Leeds Marriott, 4 Trevelyan Sq., Boar Lane, LS1 6ET, ☎ 236 6366, Fax 236 6367, , , – rm ▤ TV P – 350. AE VISA DZ x
Dyson's : **Meals** 15.95 **st.** (lunch) and a la carte 15.00/18.50 **st.** – 11.25 – **241 rm** 89.00 **st.**, 3 suites – SB .

42 The Calls, 42 The Calls, LS2 7EW, ☎ 244 0099, Fax 234 4100, ←, **« Converted riverside grain mill »** – rm TV – 55. AE VISA. DZ z
closed 5 days at Christmas – **Meals** – (see ***Pool Court at 42*** below) (see also ***Brasserie Forty Four*** below) – 10.00 – **38 rm** 95.00/140.00 **st.**, 3 suites – SB .

Holiday Inn Crown Plaza, Wellington St., LS1 4DL, ☎ 244 2200, Fax 244 0460, , , – rm ▤ TV P – 200. AE VISA JCB. CZ c
Meals *(closed Saturday lunch)* 9.95/17.50 **st.** and a la carte 6.00 – 11.50 – **120 rm** 115.00 **st.**, 5 suites – SB .

Hilton National Leeds, Neville St., LS1 4BX, ☎ 244 2000, Telex 557143, Fax 243 3577, , , – rm ▤ TV P – 300. AE VISA JCB DZ r
Meals 9.50/17.95 **st.** and a la carte 4.25 – 10.50 – **186 rm** 93.00 **st.**, 20 suites – SB .

Queen's (Forte), City Sq., LS1 1PL, ☎ 243 1323, Fax 242 5154 – rm TV P – 600. AE VISA JCB. DZ a
Meals 10.50/19.50 **st.** and a la carte – 11.50 – **182 rm** 75.00/100.00 **t.**, 6 suites – SB .

Weetwood Hall, Otley Rd, LS16 5PS, NW : 4 m. on A 660 ☎ 230 6000, Fax 230 6095, – ▤ rest TV P – 150
108 rm.

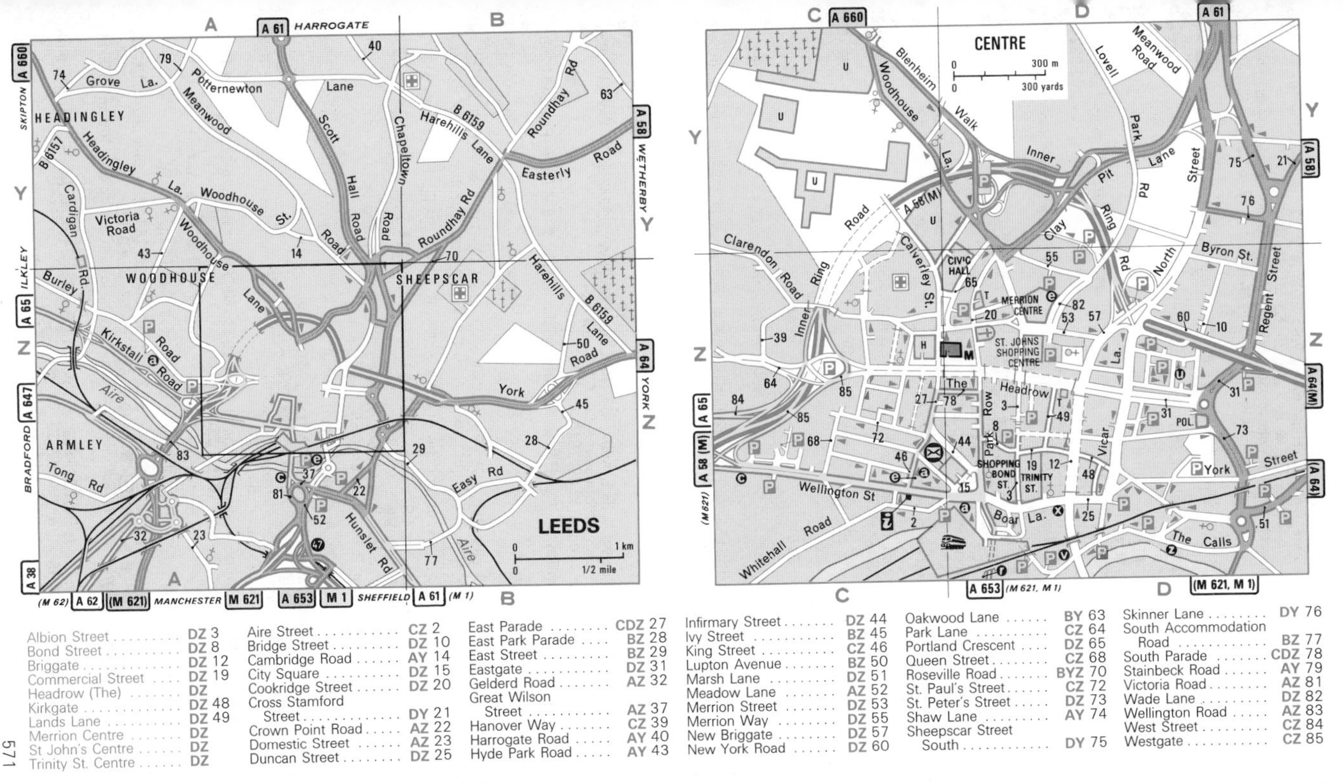

Albion Street	DZ	3
Bond Street	DZ	8
Briggate	DZ	12
Commercial Street	DZ	19
Headrow (The)	DZ	
Kirkgate	DZ	48
Lands Lane	DZ	49
Merrion Centre	DZ	
St John's Centre	DZ	
Trinity St. Centre	DZ	
Aire Street	CZ	2
Bridge Street	DZ	10
Cambridge Road	AY	14
City Square	DZ	15
Cookridge Street	DZ	20
Cross Stamford Street	DY	21
Crown Point Road	AZ	22
Domestic Street	AZ	23
Duncan Street	DZ	25
East Parade	CDZ	27
East Park Parade	BZ	28
East Street	BZ	29
Eastgate	DZ	31
Gelderd Road	AZ	32
Great Wilson Street	AZ	37
Hanover Way	CZ	39
Harrogate Road	AY	40
Hyde Park Road	AY	43
Infirmary Street	DZ	44
Ivy Street	BZ	45
King Street	CZ	46
Lupton Avenue	BZ	50
Marsh Lane	DZ	51
Meadow Lane	AZ	52
Merrion Street	DZ	53
Merrion Way	DZ	55
New Briggate	DZ	57
New York Road	DZ	60
Oakwood Lane	BY	63
Park Lane	CZ	64
Portland Crescent	DZ	65
Queen Street	CZ	68
Roseville Road	BYZ	70
St. Paul's Street	CZ	72
St. Peter's Street	DZ	73
Shaw Lane	AY	74
Sheepscar Street South	DY	75
Skinner Lane	DY	76
South Accommodation Road	BZ	77
South Parade	CDZ	78
Stainbeck Road	AY	79
Victoria Road	AZ	81
Wade Lane	DZ	82
Wellington Road	AZ	83
West Street	CZ	84
Westgate	CZ	85

Haley's (Virgin), Shire Oak Rd, Headingley, LS6 2DE, NW : 2 m. off Otley Rd (A 660) 278 4446, Fax 275 3342 – – 25. *closed 26 to 30 December* – **Meals** *(closed Sunday dinner to non-residents)* (dinner only) (Sunday lunch September-May) a la carte 18.45/23.90 **st.** 5.10 – **22 rm** 95.00/112.00 **st.** – SB.

Metropole, King St., LS1 2HQ, 245 0841, Fax 242 5156 – rm – 200. CZ **e**
Meals *(closed Saturday lunch)* 12.95/16.95 **t.** and dinner a la carte 6.50 – 8.50 – **81 rm** 78.00/120.00 **st.** – SB.

Merrion Thistle, Merrion Centre, 17 Wade Lane, LS2 8NH, 243 9191, Fax 242 3527 – rest – 80. DZ **e**
Meals 14.75 **t.** and a la carte 8.75 – 8.75 – **108 rm** 79.00/89.00 **t.**, 1 suite – SB.

Golden Lion (Mount Charlotte), 2 Lower Briggate, LS1 4AE, 243 6454, Fax 242 9327 – rm – 120. DZ **v**
Meals *(closed lunch Sunday and Bank Holidays)* 8.95/13.95 **st.** and dinner a la carte 4.60 – **89 rm** 85.00/95.00 **st.** – SB.

XXX **Pool Court at 42** (at 42 The Calls H.), 42-44 The Calls, LS2 8AQ, 244 4242, Fax 234 3332, « Riverside setting » – . DZ **z**
closed Saturday lunch, Sunday and Bank Holidays – **Meals** 22.00/26.50 **t.** 7.80
Spec. Whitby crab ravioli scented with basil, sauce vierge, Loin of venison with deep fried polenta, asparagus and balsamic dressing, Orange and ginger bavarois with passion fruit sorbet.

XX **Leodis Brasserie,** Victoria Mill, Sovereign St., LS1 4BJ, 242 1010, Fax 243 0432 – . AZ **e**
closed Saturday lunch, Sunday, 25 and 26 December and 1 January – **Meals** 11.95 **t.** and a la carte 14.55/25.55 **t.** 5.50.

XX **Rascasse,** Canal Wharf, Water Lane, LS11 5BB, 244 6611, Fax 244 0736, ← – . AZ **c**
closed Saturday lunch – **Meals** 13.00 **t.** (lunch) and a la carte 17.50/26.75 **t.** 6.00.

XX **Brasserie Forty Four** (at 42 The Calls H.), 42-44 The Calls, LS2 8AQ, 234 3232, Fax 234 3332 – . DZ **z**
closed Saturday lunch, Sunday, 5 days at Christmas and Bank Holidays – **Meals** 11.95 **t.** (lunch) and a la carte 14.15/23.15 **t.** 7.90.

XX **Maxi's,** 6 Bingley St., LS3 1LX, off Kirkstall Rd 244 0552, Fax 234 3902, « Pagoda, ornate decor » – . AZ **a**
Meals - Chinese (Canton, Peking) - 16.00 **t.**

XX **Lucky Dragon,** Templar Lane, LS2 7LP, 245 0520, Fax 245 0520 – .
closed 25 and 26 December – **Meals** - Chinese (Cantonese) - 14.00/15.00 **st.** and a la carte 4.50. DZ **u**

X **Hereford Beefstouw,** Calls Landing, 38 The Calls, LS2 7EW, 245 3870, Fax 243 9035, « Converted riverside warehouse » – . DZ **c**
Meals (grill rest.) a la carte 12.90/28.00 **st.** 5.75.

X **Sous le nez en ville,** Quebec House, Quebec St., LS1 2HA, 244 0108, Fax 245 0240 – CZ **a**
closed Saturday lunch, Sunday and Bank Holidays – **Meals** 13.95 **st.** (dinner) and a la carte 13.05/23.85 **st.**

X **La Grillade,** 31-33 East Par., LS1 5PS, 245 9707, Fax 242 6112 – . CZ **n**
closed Sunday – **Meals** - French Brasserie - 9.25 **t.** and a la carte 3.95.

at Seacroft NE : 5 ½ m. at junction of A 64 with A 6120 – BZ – ✉ Leeds – 0113 :

Stakis Leeds, Ring Rd, LS14 5QF, 273 2323, Fax 232 3018 – rm rest – 250.
Meals *(closed lunch Saturday and Bank Holidays)* 9.50/15.25 **st.** and dinner a la carte 4.50 – 8.50 – **100 rm** 75.00/85.00 **st.** – SB.

at Garforth E : 6 m. by A 63 at junction with A 642 – BZ – ✉ Leeds – 0113 :

Hilton National, Wakefield Rd, LS25 1LH, 286 6556, Fax 286 8326, , , – rm rest – 350.
Meals *(closed Saturday lunch)* (carving lunch) 10.50/17.00 **st.** and a la carte 5.35 – 10.25 – **144 rm** 82.50/105.00 **st.** – SB.

X **Paris,** Calverley Bridge, Calverley Lane, Rodley, LS13 1NP, SW : 1 m. by A 6120 258 1885, Fax 239 0651 – – 40.
closed Saturday lunch and 26 to 28 December – **Meals** 9.95 **t.** and a la carte.

at Bramhope NW : 8 m. on A 660 – AY – ✉ Leeds – 0113 :

Jarvis Parkway, Otley Rd, LS16 8AG, S : 2 m. on A 660 267 2551, Fax 267 4410, , , , , – rm – 250.
Meals *(closed Saturday lunch)* 12.95/14.95 **st.** and dinner a la carte – 8.50 – **105 rm** 95.00 **st.** – SB.

Forte Posthouse, Leeds Rd, LS16 9JJ, 284 2911, Fax 284 3451, ←, , , , , park – rm – 160.
Meals 7.95 **st.** and a la carte 6.95 – 7.95 – **123 rm** 69.00 **t.**, 1 suite – SB.

LIVERPOOL Mersey. 402 403 L 23 Great Britain G. – pop. 452 450 – ☎ 0151.

See : City★ - Walker Art Gallery★★ DY **M2** – Liverpool Cathedral★★ (Lady Chapel★) EZ – Metropolitan Cathedral of Christ the King★★ EY – Albert Dock★ CZ – (Merseyside Maritime Museum★ **M1** - Tate Gallery Liverpool★).

Exc. : Speke Hall★ , SE : 8 m. by A 561.

18, 9 Allerton Municipal, Allerton Rd ☎ 428 1046 – 18 Liverpool Municipal, Ingoe Lane, Kirkby ☎ 546 5435 – 9 Bowring, Bowring Park, Roby Rd, Huyton ☎ 489 1901.

Liverpool Airport : ☎ 486 8877, SE : 6 m. by A 561 – **Terminal** : Pier Head.

to Isle of Man (Douglas) (Isle of Man Steam Packet Co. Ltd) (4 h) – to Northern Ireland (Belfast) (Norse Irish Ferries Ltd) (11 h).

to Birkenhead (Mersey Ferries) (10 mn) – to Wallasey (Mersey Ferries) (20 mn).

Merseyside Welcome Centre, Clayton Square Shopping Centre, L1 1QR ☎ 709 3631 – Atlantic Pavilion, Albert Dock, L3 4AA ☎ 708 8854.

London 219 – Birmingham 103 – Leeds 75 – Manchester 35.

Plans on following pages

Liverpool Moat House (Q.M.H.), Paradise St., L1 8JD, ☎ 471 9988, Fax 709 2706, – rm – 400. AE VISA DZ **n**
Meals 10.95/16.25 **t.** and dinner a la carte – 9.50 – **244 rm** 97.50 **t.**, 7 suites – SB.

Atlantic Tower Thistle (Mt. Charlotte), 30 Chapel St., L3 9RE, ☎ 227 4444, Fax 236 3973, – rm – 100. AE VISA CY **r**
Meals *(closed Saturday lunch)* 7.95/19.25 and a la carte 4.95 – 8.95 – **223 rm** 78.00/98.00 **st.**, 3 suites – SB.

Campanile, Wapping and Chaloner St., L3 4AJ, ☎ 709 8104, Fax 709 8725 – rm – 30. AE VISA CZ **a**
Meals 10.35 **st.** and a la carte 4.95 – 4.50 – **80 rm** 35.75.

Travel Inn, Queens Dr., West Derby, L13 0DL, E : 4 m. on A 5058 (Ringroad) ☎ 228 4724, Fax 220 7610 – rm by A 5049 EY
Meals (grill rest.) – 4.95 – **40 rm** 34.50 **t.**

Dolby, 36-42 Chaloner St., Queens Dock, L3 4DE, ☎ 708 7272, Fax 708 7266, – rm . VISA JCB. DZ **c**
Meals (dinner only) 8.50 **t.** and a la carte 4.50 – 3.50 – **64 rm** 29.50 **st.**

Ristorante Del Secolo, 36-40 Stanley St., L1 6AL, ☎ 236 4004 – AE VISA DY **e**
closed Saturday lunch and Sunday – **Meals** - Italian - a la carte 16.85/25.15 5.95.

Est, Est, Est , Unit 5-6, Edward Pavilion, Albert Dock, L3 4AA, ☎ 708 6969, Fax 709 4912 – AE VISA CZ **e**
closed 25 December – **Meals** - Italian - 9.95/12.95 **t.** and a la carte 4.75.

at Crosby N : 5 ½ m. by A 565 – CY – ☎ 0151 :

Blundellsands, The Serpentine, Blundellsands, L23 6YB, W : 1 ¼ m. via College Rd, Mersey Rd and Agnes Rd ☎ 924 6515, Fax 931 5364 – rm – 250. AE VISA JCB.
Meals *(closed Saturday lunch)* 7.50/13.50 **t.** and a la carte – **41 rm** 59.50/78.00 **t.** – SB.

at Netherton N : 6 m. by A 5038 off A 5036 – CY – ✉ Liverpool – ☎ 0151 :

Park (Premier), Dunningsbridge Rd, L30 3SU, on A 5036 – ☎ 525 7555, Fax 525 2481 – rm – 100. AE VISA.
Meals *(closed Saturday lunch)* a la carte 7.90/17.75 **st.** 4.25 – 4.45 – **62 rm** 32.50 **st.** – SB.

at Huyton E : 8 ¼ m. by A5047 – EY – and A 5058 on B 5199 – ✉ Liverpool – ☎ 0151 :

Logwood Mill, Fallows Way, L35 1RZ, SE : 3 ¼ m. by A 5080 off Windy Arbor Rd ☎ 449 2341, Fax 449 3832, – rm – 200. AE VISA.
Meals *(closed Saturday lunch)* 10.95/25.00 **st.** and a la carte 3.45 – **62 rm** 69.50/99.50 **st.** – SB.

Derby Lodge, Roby Rd, L36 4HD, SW : 1 m. on A 5080 ☎ 480 4440, Fax 480 8132, – – 150. AE VISA.
Meals *(closed Saturday lunch)* 15.50 **st.** (dinner) and a la carte 17.90/35.75 **st.** 4.10 – **19 rm** 55.00/75.00 **st.** – SB.

Travel Inn, Wilson Rd, Tarbock, L36 6AD, SE : 2 ¼ m. on A 5080 ☎ 480 9614, Fax 480 9361 – rm . AE VISA.
Meals (grill rest.) – 4.95 – **40 rm** 34.50 **t.**

Gulshan, 544-546 Aigburth Rd, L19 3QG, on A 561 ☎ 427 2273 – . AE VISA
closed 25 December – **Meals** - Indian - (dinner only) a la carte 12.35/20.15 **t.** 5.95.

at Woolton SE : 6 m. by A 562 – EZ –A 5058 and Woolton Rd – ✉ Liverpool – ☎ 0151 :

Woolton Redbourne, Acrefield Rd, L25 5JN, ☎ 428 2152, Fax 421 1501, « Victorian house, antiques », – . AE VISA JCB
Meals (residents only) (dinner only) 22.95 **st.** 5.95 – **18 rm** 58.00/120.00 **st.** – SB.

LIVERPOOL
CENTRE

A 565
C
A 5038
A 5036
56
Pall
Vauxhall
Leeds Street
A 5053
Road
Y
Bath Street
Old Hall Street
A 565
Mall
St.
69
Tithebarn
MOORFIELDS
93
Chapel St.
Dale
135
St Nicholas Place
51
Castle St.
96
150
ISLE OF MAN
Royal Liver Building
The Strand
32
81
Pier Head
Cunard Building
Lord
WALLASEY
68
JAMES ST.
Port of Liverpool Bldg.
QUEENSWAY TUNNEL
Strand St.
23
BIRKENHEAD
Wapping
POL.
76
TATE GALLERY
M1
ALBERT DOCK
Z
Britannia Pavilion
MERSEY
0 300 m
0 300 yards
C

Great Britain and Ireland is now covered by a serie of Atlases at a scale of 1 inch to 4.75 miles.

Three easy to use versions: Paperback, Spiralbound, Hardback.

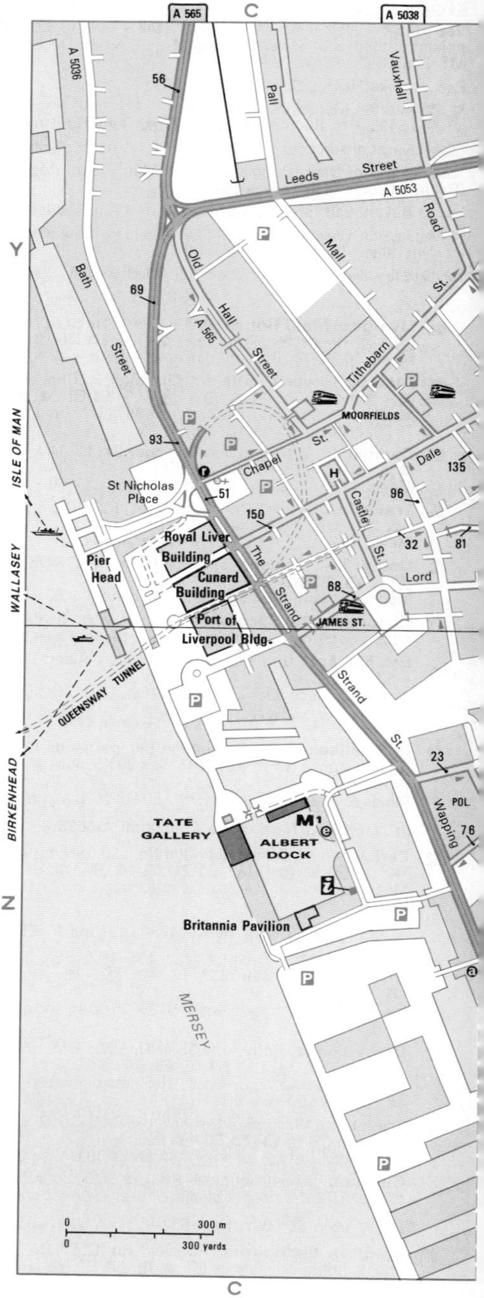

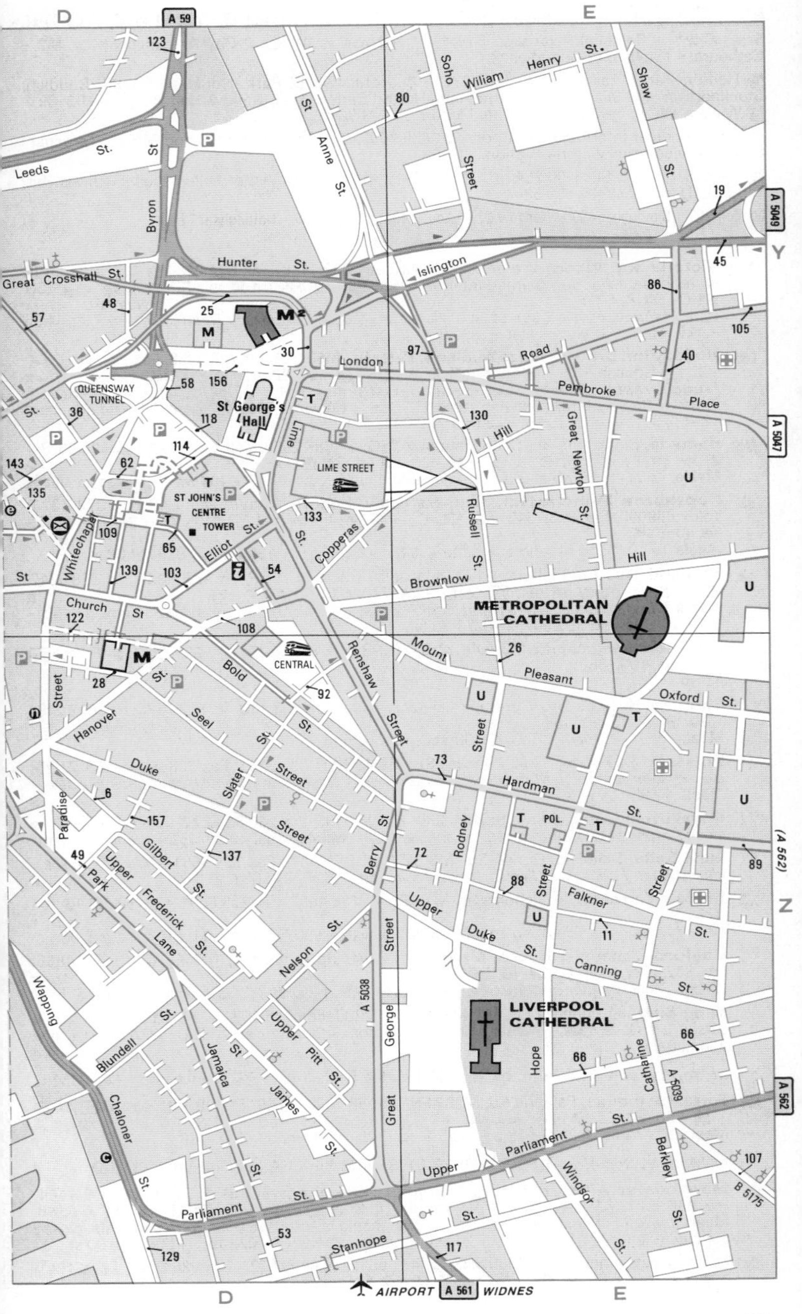
D
E
A 59
A 5049
A 5047
Y
Z
(A 562)
A 562
Leeds St.
Byron St
Great Crosshall St.
Hunter St.
Islington
London Road
Pembroke Place
Soho Street
Wiliam Henry St.
Shaw St.
Anne St.
St
QUEENSWAY TUNNEL
St George's Hall
LIME STREET
Lime St.
Copperas Hill
Hill
Great Newton St.
Russell St.
Brownlow Hill
ST JOHN'S CENTRE TOWER
Elliot St.
Whitechapel
Church St
St
METROPOLITAN CATHEDRAL
Mount Pleasant
Oxford St.
CENTRAL
Renshaw Street
Bold St.
Seel St.
Hanover St.
Slater St.
Street
Duke Street
Paradise Street
Berry St
Rodney Street
Hardman St.
POL.
Upper Duke St.
Falkner St.
Canning St.
Gilbert St.
Upper Frederick St.
Park Lane
Nelson St.
Wapping
Blundell St.
Jamaica St
Upper Pitt St.
James St.
Chaloner St.
Great George Street
A 5038
LIVERPOOL CATHEDRAL
Hope Street
Catharine Street
A 5039
Upper Parliament St.
Parliament St.
Windsor St.
Berkley St.
B 5175
Stanhope St.
AIRPORT A 561 WIDNES
123 80 19 45 86 105 48 57 25 30 97 40 58 156 36 118 130 143 62 114 135 109 65 133 139 103 54 122 108 26 28 92 73 6 157 137 49 72 88 11 89 66 66 107 53 117 129

MANCHESTER Gtr. Manchester 402 403 404 N 23 **Great Britain G.** – pop. 404 861 – 0161.

See : City★ – Castefield Heritage Park★ CZ – Town Hall★ CZ – City Art Gallery★ CZ **M2** – Cathedral★ (Stalls and Canopies★) CY.

Heaton Park, Prestwick 798 0295 – Houldsworth Park, Houldsworth St., Reddish, Stockport 442 9611 – Chorlton-cum-Hardy, Barlow Hall, Barlow Hall Rd 881 3139 – William Wroe, Pennybridge Lane, Flixton 748 8680.

Manchester International Airport : 489 3000, S : 10 m. by A 5103 and M 56 – **Terminal :** Coach service from Victoria Station.

Town Hall, Lloyd St., M60 2LA 234 3157/8 – Manchester Airport, International Arrivals Hall, Terminal 1, M90 3NY 436 3344.

London 202 – Birmingham 86 – Glasgow 221 – Leeds 43 – Liverpool 35 – Nottingham 72.

Plan opposite

Victoria and Albert, Water St., M3 4JQ, 832 1188, Fax 834 2484, « Converted 19C warehouse, television themed interior », – rm rest – 250. VISA. by Quay St. CZ
Cafe Maigret :* Meals** 14.95 **st.** and a la carte – (see also ***Sherlock Holmes below) – 11.95 – **128 rm** 132.00 **st.**, 4 suites – SB.

Holiday Inn Crowne Plaza Midland, Peter St., M60 2DS, 236 3333, Fax 932 4101, , squash – rm – 600. VISA JCB. CZ **x**
***French rest. :* Meals** *(closed Sunday)* (dinner only) 32.50 **t.** and a la carte – ***Trafford Room :* Meals** (carving rest.) 17.95 **st.** – ***Wyvern :* Meals** *(closed Sunday)* a la carte 12.40/23.40 **t.** – 10.95 – **296 rm** 120.00 **t.**, 7 suites – SB.

Ramada, Blackfriars St., Deansgate, M3 2EQ, 835 2555, Telex 669699, Fax 835 3077 – rm rest – 400. VISA JCB. CY **v**
Meals 12.50/18.50 **st.** and dinner a la carte 5.75 – 10.50 – **196 rm** 115.00 **st.**, 5 suites.

Copthorne Manchester, Clippers Quay, Salford Quays, M5 2XP, 873 7321, Telex 669090, Fax 873 7318, – rm rest – 150. VISA. by A 56 CZ
Meals 15.50/18.50 **st.** and a la carte 8.85 – 11.25 – **166 rm** 107.00/117.00 **st.**

Portland Thistle, 3-5 Portland St., Piccadilly Gdns, M1 6DP, 228 3400, Fax 228 6347, – rm rest – 270. VISA JCB CZ **a**
Meals *(closed Sunday dinner and Bank Holidays)* 16.45/18.45 **st.** and a la carte 5.50 – 9.85 – **204 rm** 102.00/124.00, 1 suite.

Castlefield, Liverpool Rd, M3 4JR, 832 7073, Fax 839 0326, – rest – 65 by Quay St. CZ
48 rm.

Sherlock Holmes (at Victoria and Albert H.), Water St., M3 4JQ, 832 1188, Fax 832 2484 – . VISA by Quay St. CZ
Meals *(closed Sunday)* 19.00/35.00 **st.** and a la carte.

Brasserie St Pierre, 57-63 Princess St., M2 4EQ, 228 0231, Fax 228 0231 – VISA
closed Saturday lunch, Monday dinner, Sunday, 24 December-2 January and Bank Holidays – **Meals** 12.95 **t.** and a la carte 6.95. CZ **s**

Royal Orchid, 36 Charlotte St., M1 4FD, 236 5183, Fax 236 8830. VISA CZ **o**
closed Monday and Saturday lunch and Sunday – **Meals** - Thai - 9.50/15.00 **t.** and a la carte.

Isola Bella, Dolefield, Crown Sq., M3 3EN, 831 7099, Fax 839 1561 – . VISA
closed Bank Holidays – **Meals** - Italian - a la carte 15.30/24.50 **st.** 5.50. CZ **e**

Giulio's Terrazza, 14 Nicholas St., M1 4EJ, 236 4033, Fax 228 6501 – . VISA JCB CZ **r**
closed Sunday and Bank Holidays – **Meals** - Italian - 8.50/14.90 **t.** and a la carte 5.80.

Gaylord, Amethyst House, Marriott's Court, Spring Gdns, M2 1EA, 832 4866, Fax 832 6037 – . VISA CZ **c**
closed 25 December and 1 January – **Meals** - Indian - 12.75/17.95 **t.** and a la carte 5.45.

Yang Sing, 34 Princess St., M1 4JY, 236 2200, Fax 236 5934 – . VISA CZ **n**
closed 25 December – **Meals** - Chinese (Canton) - (booking essential) 15.40/32.50 **t.** and a la carte.

at Northenden S : 5 ¼ m. by A 57 (M) and A 5103 – CZ – Manchester – 0161 :

Forte Posthouse, Palatine Rd, M22 4FH, 998 7090, Fax 946 0139 – rm – 150. VISA JCB.
Meals a la carte 14.35/22.15 **t.** 6.25 – 7.95 – **190 rm** 59.00 **t.** – SB.

at Manchester Airport S : 9 m. by A 5103 off M 56 – Manchester – 0161 :

Manchester Airport Hilton, Outwood Lane, Ringway, M22 5WP, 436 4404, Fax 436 1521, – rm – 250. VISA JCB.
Meals *(closed Saturday lunch)* 19.50/30.00 **st.** and a la carte 8.00 – ***Portico :* Meals** *(closed Sunday)* (dinner only) a la carte 28.00 **st.** 9.20 – 12.50 – **222 rm** 111.00/170.00 **st.**

Forte Crest, Ringway Rd, M90 3NS, 437 5811, Telex 668721, Fax 436 2340, – rm – 45. VISA.
Meals 16.00/26.00 **st.** and a la carte – 11.00 – **283 rm** 99.00/108.00 **st.**, 2 suites – SB.

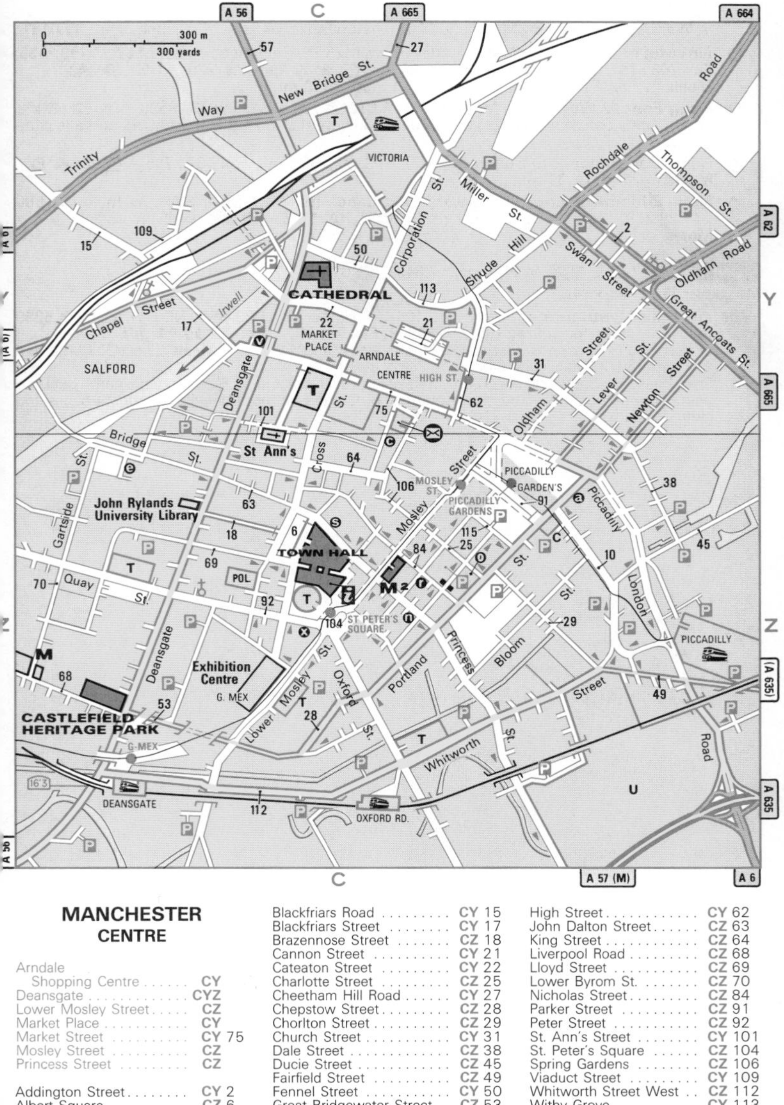

MANCHESTER
CENTRE

Street	Grid	No.
Arndale Shopping Centre	CY	
Deansgate	CYZ	
Lower Mosley Street	CZ	
Market Place	CY	
Market Street	CY	75
Mosley Street	CZ	
Princess Street	CZ	
Addington Street	CY	2
Albert Square	CZ	6
Aytoun Street	CZ	10
Blackfriars Road	CY	15
Blackfriars Street	CY	17
Brazennose Street	CZ	18
Cannon Street	CY	21
Cateaton Street	CY	22
Charlotte Street	CZ	25
Cheetham Hill Road	CY	27
Chepstow Street	CZ	28
Chorlton Street	CZ	29
Church Street	CY	31
Dale Street	CZ	38
Ducie Street	CZ	45
Fairfield Street	CZ	49
Fennel Street	CY	50
Great Bridgewater Street	CZ	53
Great Ducie Street	CY	57
High Street	CY	62
John Dalton Street	CZ	63
King Street	CZ	64
Liverpool Road	CZ	68
Lloyd Street	CZ	69
Lower Byrom St.	CZ	70
Nicholas Street	CZ	84
Parker Street	CZ	91
Peter Street	CZ	92
St. Ann's Street	CY	101
St. Peter's Square	CZ	104
Spring Gardens	CZ	106
Viaduct Street	CY	109
Whitworth Street West	CZ	112
Withy Grove	CY	113
York Street	CZ	115

Etrop Grange (Regal), Thorley Lane, M90 4EG, ☎ 499 0500, Fax 499 0790 – ⇔ rm TV ☎ ♿ P – 🏛 40. AE VISA JCB
Meals 16.50/33.50 **st.** 🍷 6.95 – ☕ 9.50 – **38 rm** 97.50/110.00 **st.**, 2 suites – SB.

Travel Inn, Finney Lane, Heald Green, SK8 2QH, E : 2 m. by B 5166 ☎ 499 1944, Fax 437 4910 – ⇔ rm TV ♿ P – 🏛 70. AE VISA. ✕ – **Meals** (grill rest.) – ☕ 4.95 – **61 rm** 34.50 **t.**

XXX **Moss Nook,** Ringway Rd, Moss Nook, M22 5WD, ☎ 437 4778, Fax 498 8089 – P. AE VISA – *closed Saturday lunch, Sunday, Monday and 2 weeks Christmas* – **Meals** 16.50/29.50 **t.** and a la carte 🍷 4.50.

at Worsley W : 7 ¼ m. by M 602 and M 62 (eastbound) on A 572 – ✉ Manchester – ☎ 0161 :

Novotel Manchester West, Worsley Brow, M28 2YA, at junction 13 of M 62 ✆ 799 3535, Fax 703 8207, heated – rm rest – 220. AE VISA
Meals 12.95/18.85 **st.** and a la carte – 7.50 – **119 rm** 52.50.

Tung Fong, 2 Worsley Rd, M28 4NL, on A 572 ✆ 794 5331, Fax 727 9598 – . AE VISA
closed lunch Saturday and Sunday – **Meals** - Chinese (Peking) - 20.50/27.50 **st.** and a la carte 5.00.

Henry Boddington, 219 Bolton Rd, M27 8TG, ✆ 736 5143, Fax 737 2786 –
Meals (grill rest.) – **31 rm**.

New Ellesmere Lodge (Premier), East Lancs Rd, M27 8AA, SW : ½ m. on A 580 ✆ 728 2791, Fax 794 8222 – rm . AE VISA.
Meals (grill rest.) 7.00/13.55 **t.** 3.95 – 4.45 – **27 rm** 39.50 **t.** – SB.

LONGRIDGE Lancs. 402 M 22 – pop. 7 349 – ☎ 01772.

Manchester 36 – Liverpool 42.

Paul Heathcote's (Heathcote), 104-106 Higher Rd, PR3 3SY, NE : ½ m. by B 5269 following signs for Jeffrey Hill ✆ 784969, Fax 785713 – . AE VISA
closed lunch Tuesday to Thursday, Saturday lunch and Monday – **Meals** 22.50/35.00 **st.** and a la carte 30.00/38.50 **t.** 8.00
Spec. Roasted lobster with dried citrus fruit, celery and lobster juice, Breast of Goosnargh duckling with caramelised apples and cider potatoes, Bread and butter pudding with apricot coulis and clotted cream.

Manufacture française des pneumatiques Michelin
Société en commandite par actions au capital de 2 000 000 000 de francs
Place des Carmes-Déchaux – 63 Clermont-Ferrand (France)
R.C.S. Clermont-Fd B 855 200 507

Michelin et Cie, propriétaires-éditeurs, 1996

Dépôt légal : mars 96 – ISBN 2.06.007059-7

Printed in the EU – 3.1996
Photocomposition : MAURY Imprimeur S.A., Malesherbes
Impression : MAURY Imprimeur S.A., Malesherbes – KAPP LAHURE JOMBART, Evreux
Reliure : S.I.R.C., Marigny-le-Châtel

Illustrations : Nathalie Benavides, Patricia Haubert, Cécile Imbert/MICHELIN

Calendar of main tradefairs and other international events in 1996

AUSTRIA

Vienna	*Wiener Festwochen*	*10 May to 16 June*
Salzburg	*Salzburg Festival (Festspiele)*	*30 March to 8 April* *27 July to 25 August*

BENELUX

Amsterdam	*Holland Festival*	*June*
Bruges	*Ascension Day Procession*	*Ascension*
Brussels	*Guild Procession (Ommegang)*	*first Thursday of July and the previous Tuesday*
	Holiday and Leisure Activities International Show	*22 to 30 March 97*
	Belgian Antique Dealers Fair	*Late January*
	Eurantica (Antiques Show)	*Late March*

CZECH REPUBLIC

Prague	*Prague's Spring International Music Festival*	*12 May to 2 June*

DENMARK

Copenhagen	*Scandinavian Furniture Fair*	*24 to 28 April*
	International Fashion Fair	*10 to 13 August*

FINLAND

Helsinki	*International Fashion Fair*	*25 to 27 August* *January 1997*
	Helsinki Festival	*Late Aug. to early Sept.*
	International Horse Show	*18 to 20 October*

FRANCE

Paris	*Paris Fair*	*26 April to 8 May*
	Motor Show	*3 to 13 October*
Cannes	*International Film Festival*	*9 to 20 May*
Lyons	*Lyons Fair*	*23 March to 1 April*
Marseilles	*Marseilles Fair*	*23 to 30 Sept.*

GERMANY

Berlin	*Berlin Fair (Grüne Woche)*	*19 to 28 January*
Frankfurt	*International Fair*	*24 to 28 February* *24 to 28 August*
	Frankfurt Book Fair	*2 to 7 October*
Hanover	*Hanover Fair*	*22 to 27 April*
Leipzig	*International Book Fair*	*28 to 31 March*
Munich	*Beer Festival (Oktoberfest)*	*21 Sept. to 6 Oct.*

GREECE

Athens	*Athens Festival*	*From June to late Sept.*

HUNGARY

Budapest	*International Motor Exibition*	*9 to 13 Oct.*
	International Boat Exibition	*20 to 23 Feb. 97*
	International Contemporary Art Fair	*20 to 23 Feb. 97*
	International Fashion Fair	*20 to 25 Feb. 97*

IRELAND

Dublin	*Dublin Horse Show*	*7 to 11 August*

ITALY

Milan	*Fashion Fair (Moda Milano)*	*1 to 5 March,* *Late Sept. to early Oct.*
Palermo	*International Trade Exibition*	*25 May to 9 June*
Turin	*International Car Exibition*	*25 April to 5 May*
Venice	*International Film Festival*	*3 to 14 September*
	The Carnival	*February*

NORWAY

Oslo	*Fashion Fair*	*10 to 12 August,* *8 to 10 February 97*
	International Book Fair	*24 to 27 October*
	International Boat Show	*14 to 19 March 97*

PORTUGAL

Lisbon	*Motorexpo*	*30 Nov. to 8 Dec.*

SPAIN

Madrid	*Fitur*	*24 to 28 Jan.*
	Madrid Motor Show	*24 May to 2 June*
Barcelona	*Expomobil*	*12 to 15 April*
Sevilla	*April Fair*	*23 to 28 April*
Valencia	*International Fair*	*26 Dec. to 3 Jan.*
	Fallas	*16 to 19 March*

SWEDEN

Stockholm	*Stockholm Water Festival*	*9 to 18 August*
	International Fashion Fair	*16 to 18 August*
	International Boat Show	*March 97*
Gothenburg	*International Horse Show*	*5 to 8 April*
	International Book & Library Fair	*24 to 27 October*
	Motor Show	*February 97*
	International Boat Show	*February 97*
	International Film Festival	*February 97*

SWITZERLAND

Berne	*BEA : Exhibition for Handicraft, Agriculture, Trade and Industry*	*27 April to 6 may*
Basle	*European Watch, Clock and Jewellery Fair*	*18 to 24 April*
Geneva	*International Motor Show*	*6 to 16 March 97*
	International exhibition of inventions, new technologies and products	*19 to 28 April*
	International fair for travel, languages and cultures	*1 to 5 May*
Zürich	*Züspa*	*19 to 29 Sept.*

UNITED KINGDOM

London	*Fine Art and Antiques Fair*	*6 to 16 June*
	London International Boat Show	*January 97*
	London International Bookfair	*March 97*
Birmingham	*International Motor Show*	*16 to 27 October*
	International Motorcycle Show	*Late Oct. to early Nov.*
Edinburgh	*Arts Festival*	*11 to 31 August*
	International Films Festival	*11 to 25 August*
Glasgow	*May Festival*	*2 to 26 May*
Leeds	*International Film Festival*	*October*

International Dialling Codes
Indicatifs Téléphoniques Internationaux
Internationale Telefon-Vorwahlnummern
国際電話国別番号

from / to	A	B	CH	CZ	D	DK	E	FIN	F	GB	GR
AUSTRIA	–	0032	05	0042	06	0045	0034	00358	0033	0044	0030
BELGIUM	0043	–	0041	0042	0049	0045	0034	00358	0033	0044	0030
CZECH REPUBLIC	0043	0032	0041	–	0049	0045	0034	00358	0033	0044	0030
DENMARK	00943	00932	00941	00942	00949	–	00934	009358	00933	00944	00930
FINLAND	99043	99032	99041	99042	99049	99045	99034	–	99033	99044	99030
FRANCE	1943	1932	1941	1942	1949	1945	1934	19358	–	1944	1930
GERMANY	0043	0032	0041	0042	–	0045	0034	00358	0033	0044	0030
GREECE	0043	0032	0041	0042	0049	0045	0034	00358	0033	0044	–
HUNGARY	0043	0032	0041	0042	0049	0045	0034	00358	0033	0044	0030
IRELAND	0043	0032	0041	0042	0049	0045	0034	00358	0033	0044	0030
ITALY	0043	0032	0041	0042	0049	0045	0034	00358	0033	0044	0030
JAPAN	00143	00132	00141	00142	00149	00145	00134	001358	00133	00144	00130
LUXEMBOURG	0043	0032	0041	0042	05	0045	0034	00358	0033	0044	0030
NORWAY	09543	09532	09541	09542	09549	09545	09534	095358	09533	09544	09530
NETHERLANDS	0043	0032	0041	0042	0049	0045	0034	00358	0033	0044	0030
PORTUGAL	0043	0032	0041	0042	0049	0045	0034	00358	0033	0044	0030
SPAIN	0743	0732	0741	0742	0749	0745	–	07358	0733	0744	0730
SWEDEN	00943	00932	00941	00942	00949	00945	00934	009358	00933	00944	00930
SWITZERLAND	0043	0032	–	0042	0049	0045	0034	00358	0033	0044	0030
UNITED KINGDOM	0043	0032	0041	0042	0049	0045	0034	00358	0033	–	0030
USA	01143	01132	01141	01142	01149	01145	01134	011358	01133	01144	01130